POLYMER SYNTHESIS

Strategies and Tactics

Braja K. Mandal

Professor of Chemistry
Illinois Institute of Technology
Chicago

Covalent Press, Inc.
Darien, IL 60561

Library of Congress Control Number: 2009907367

ISBN: 978-0-9841572-0-4

PRINTED IN THE UNITED STATES OF AMERICA

To my parents, wife Suvra and son Neil,
who provided me with consistent encouragement and enthusiasm
without which this work could not have been accomplished.

Preface

In the past two decades, there has been remarkable growth in polymer synthesis, spanning from the development of convenient synthetic protocols for complex polymer architectures to novel monomers and new polymerization reactions. These advances have provided polymer chemists unprecedented confidence to realize the potential of synthesizing polymeric materials with intended properties and well-defined structures. It is not surprising that progenitors of conducting polymers and metathesis chemistry (which led to materials with unique structural features) were awarded the Nobel Prize in Chemistry in 2000 and 2005. Kudos to those whose creative ideas and efforts have contributed to the rapid progress in polymer science and engineering in advancing existing technologies. These developments provide indispensable building blocks in coping with the myriad technological challenges of the future in all fields, from domestic, food, personal care, agricultural applications to microelectronics, automobiles, biomedical science and space research. When it comes to tell this success story in a monograph or a handy quick guide to polymer synthesis for students and mentors, it seems apparent that a comprehensive book is very much needed to describe recent achievements in this field.

Not all organic reactions are suitable for polymerization or to prepare useful monomers. This book focuses primarily on how a set of organic reactions can be manipulated or how recent synthetic reactions have been selectively adapted to prepare new polymeric materials for specific properties. The following is a brief description of the contents of this book.

Chapter-1 provides a quick introductory tour of polymers. The contents are crafted in a way that students with no prior experience can become interested in this exciting field, while those with a background in polymers can refresh their memories. Major emphasis has been placed on the types of polymerization reactions, basic polymer properties and classification of polymers. Several other important aspects, especially processing, characterization, and solution and rheological properties are beyond the scope of this book.

The next four chapters are the essence of this book. They are separated according to the application-based classification of polymers. In Chapter-2, common synthetic routes to all important general-purpose polymers are discussed. Major emphasis is placed on metallocenes, which have revolutionalized the outlook of polyolefin chemistry, because of their supremacy, in many respects, over Ziegler-Natta catalysts. A special section at the end highlights recent advances in general-purpose polymers. Important topics include controlled free-radical polymerization, common synthetic methods to metallocene catalysts, and tailor-made polymers with specifically designed architectures. Chapters-3 and 4 outline notable synthetic approaches to prepare engineering and high-performance polymers. These chapters also feature concluding sections describing the development of new monomers, catalytic systems for polymerization or synthetic methodologies to existing polymers. Chapter-5 is enriched with recent developments in polymer synthesis, leading to specialty polymers. Several informative tables and discussions relating factors affecting glass transition temperature and crystalline melting, types of initiators, and important physical parameters of noteworthy polymers have been assembled in Appendices.

The book is designed to accommodate the needs of both advanced undergraduates and graduate students who have a good background in organic chemistry, as well as a stand-alone handy polymer synthesis reference guide. For a course, several modular syllabi may be designed depending on instructor's taste and preference. I recommend that Chapter-1 be covered thoroughly, along with *selected portions* from Chapters 2-4. The course can also be planned with the inclusion of sections on specialty polymers from Chapter-5 by eliminating parts of Chapters 2-4. Problems at the end of each chapter are aimed at building skills and are strongly recommended.

Despite my strong effort to make this book free of errors, it is likely that some may exist. I welcome your comments (mandal@iit.edu) or, if you prefer to remain anonymous, through the publisher's website (www.covalentpress.com). Your critiques and suggestions will enrich the content of the next edition.

Finally, I wish to thank a number of people who made this work possible. I am most grateful to my colleague, Professor Robert Filler, who inspired me to write this book, performed a thorough review of the text, and provided useful remarks and advice during the course of its preparation. Many thanks to all publishers/organizations and individuals who have given their permissions to reproduce their copyrighted figures, which, I think, have enriched the appeal of the book. I express my appreciation to several of my students for gathering some references and drawing computer graphics. Last, but not least, my family members deserve my gratitude for their love, patience, and understanding.

May this book inspire chemists to pursue polymer chemistry and to develop new approaches to construct "out-of-the-box" materials.

August, 2009

Braja K. Mandal
Chicago, Illinois

Contents

Tapping of latex from a rubber tree. Latex is a direct source for making rubber gloves, tubing and raw material for dry rubber used in car tires.[1]

CHAPTER-1

INTRODUCTION TO POLYMERS

1.1. WHAT ARE POLYMERS?

If you imagine the linkage of individual beads to form a necklace chain, you have a rudimentary picture of polymers, which are very high molecular weight substances (as high as 10^6 Daltons), hence often called *macromolecules*. They can be organic, inorganic, or organometallic, either synthetic or natural in origin, and offer a wide range of properties that play major roles in today's better living through chemistry. The word "polymer" is derived from the Greek words *"poly"* (many) and *"meros"* (part of), due to the fact that polymers are formed by covalent linking of many small molecules.

Polymers have been with us since the beginning of time. Natural polymers, such as rubber, cellulose, cotton, wool and silk, have been used for millennia, long before their chemical structures were established. Many of them have been chemically modified since the 19th century to produce valuable materials, including vulcanized rubber (1839), celluloid (1868) and rayon (1892).

Although the first commercial synthetic polymer, *Bakelite*, named for Leo Baekeland, was developed in 1907, rapid advances in polymer science began to flourish only in the late 1930s through the 1960s. Prior to World War-II, natural substances were readily available; therefore, synthetics that were being developed were not a necessity. Once the world went to war, the natural sources of latex, wool, silk, and other materials were cut off, making the use of synthetics critical. During this time period, the world experienced the evolution of polystyrene (1937), nylon (1938), low-density polyethylene (1941), acrylonitrile-butadiene-styrene copolymer (1948), polyester (1950), acrylic (1950), fluorocarbon polymers (e.g., Teflon in 1943), high-density polyethylene (1957), polycarbonate (1957), and many more polymers. These synthetics readily replaced natural materials to meet the demand for cheaper and better alternatives.

Polymers are light materials. The density of most polymers lies between 0.9 and 1.9 g/cc, which is less than that of light metals (typically 2.7-3.0 g/cc) and steel (7.8-8.0 g/cc). Therefore, polymers are useful in those applications in which the weight-to-volume ratio is critical. The physical properties of polymers span an extremely broad range depending on the molecular structure. Consequently, the polymers are used in an amazing number of applications. Today, the polymer industry has grown to be larger than the aluminum, copper and steel industries combined, and it is difficult to find an aspect of our lives that is not affected by polymers. The applications of polymers extend from adhesives, floorings, coatings, foams, automobile tires, toys, and packaging materials to textile and industrial fibers, composites, electronic devices, biomedical and optical devices, nanofabrication and precursors/templates for many newly developed high-tech ceramics.

Synthetic polymers are prepared by a chemical process, known as *polymerization*, which is described as chemical linking of a large number of one or more kinds of small molecules, called *monomers*. When polymerization is carried out with molecules of one kind of monomer, the result is a *homopolymer,* e.g., polyethylene, polystyrene and poly(vinyl chloride) (see Appendix-I for more examples). When polymerization is performed using two or more different kinds of monomers, the resulting product is a *copolymer,* e.g., poly(ethylene terephthalate), nylon-6,6 and acrylonitrile-butadiene-styrene (ABS) copolymer. Thus, polymers with tailored properties can be obtained by the proper choice of monomers and/or chemical linking of appropriate monomers into desired polymer architectures. Indeed, synthetic polymers have a wide variety of applications and are regarded as one of the greatest accomplishments of chemistry.

In copolymers, monomers can organize into four different configurations to form a polymer chain (Figure 1.1). The structures of *random* and *alternating copolymers* are very similar, except that the former does not have any definitive sequence of monomer units, while the latter possesses a regular alternating placement of monomers. Random and alternating copolymers generally possess properties that are intermediate to those of the corresponding homopolymers.

Graft copolymers are branched polymers in which the branches are composed of different structural repeat units to that of the main chain. However, it is important to note that all graft copolymers can be called *branched polymers*, but all branched polymers are not graft copolymers (*vide infra*).

Block copolymers, which contain substantial sequences or blocks of each monomer, can be further classified into three main categories: *diblock copolymers* (sometimes referred to as AB block copolymers), *triblock copolymers* of the ABA or ABC types, and *multiblock copolymers* of the $(AB)_n$ type. Block and graft copolymers usually show properties characteristic of each of the constituent homopolymers. They also possess some unusual properties, which create strong interest by chemists to search for novel copolymers with unique properties. For example, recently developed thermoplastic elastomers, viz., polystyrene-*block*-polybutadiene-*block*-polystyrene (ABA triblock) and polyacrylonitrile-*block*-polybutadiene-*block*-polystyrene (ABC triblock), are gradually replacing natural rubber. This important advance is due to their exhibiting elastic properties of conventional rubber and the processing efficiency of plastics. These are excellent examples of creating novel properties through copolymerization. Copolymers differ from polymer blends in that the latter result from physical blending of disparate polymers without incorporating the different polymers into the chain (Figure 1.1).

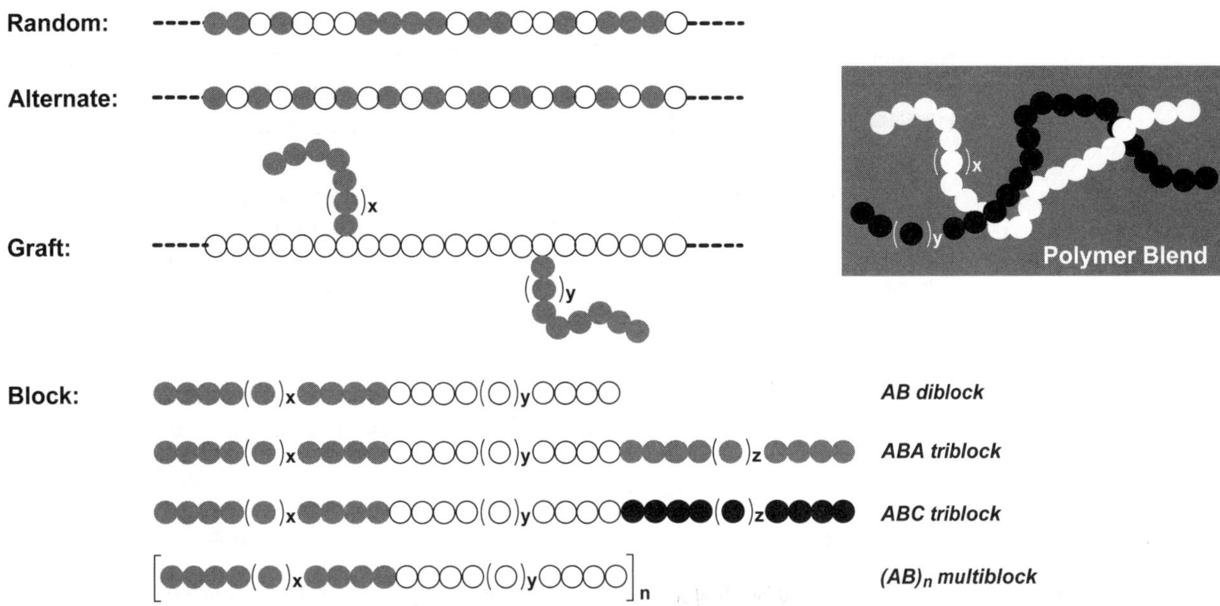

Figure 1.1. Schematic representation of different types of copolymers, including the polymer blend. *Note: Only AB, ABA, ABC and* $(AB)_n$ *block copolymers represent entire molecules, while all other copolymers represent partial structures as indicated by the dotted lines at the end.*

The chemical structure of homopolymers and copolymers is represented by a condensed formula by placing the structure of the repeating segment in parentheses with two open bonds remaining at the ends, followed by a subscript "n", called *degree of polymerization* (DP). Thus, DP represents the number of monomers linked to form the polymer, and provides a measure of molecular weight. Figure 1.2 depicts three alternative nomenclatures used to define homopolymers and copolymers. *Source-based nomenclature* places the prefix *poly* before the name of the actual or hypothetical monomer. Names of monomers having substituents or comprising at least two words are parenthesized. Otherwise, a single word, e.g., polyethylene, polystyrene, polycaprolactam, poly(methyl methacrylate), poly(vinyl chloride), is used. In *structure-based nomenclature*, the prefix *poly* is followed in parentheses by words which describe the chemical structure of the repeat unit, e.g., poly(ethylene terephthalate), poly(hexamethylene adipamide), poly(ethylene 2,6-naphthalene dicarboxylate). It is important to note that either of these nomenclatures is convenient for polymers with simple structures. Complications arise when the polymer repeat unit contains branching, sub-branching, a heteroatom, heterocyclic ring, etc. Although the Macromolecular Nomenclature Commission of the International Union of Pure and Applied Chemistry (IUPAC) has established guidelines to name polymers with complex structures[2], they are rarely used in the modern literature. *Functional group-based nomenclature* is now in common practice to define polymers with both simple and complex structures. This terminology emphasizes recognizable functional groups that are involved in the synthesis of the polymer from its monomers, although the usage is seldom exact.

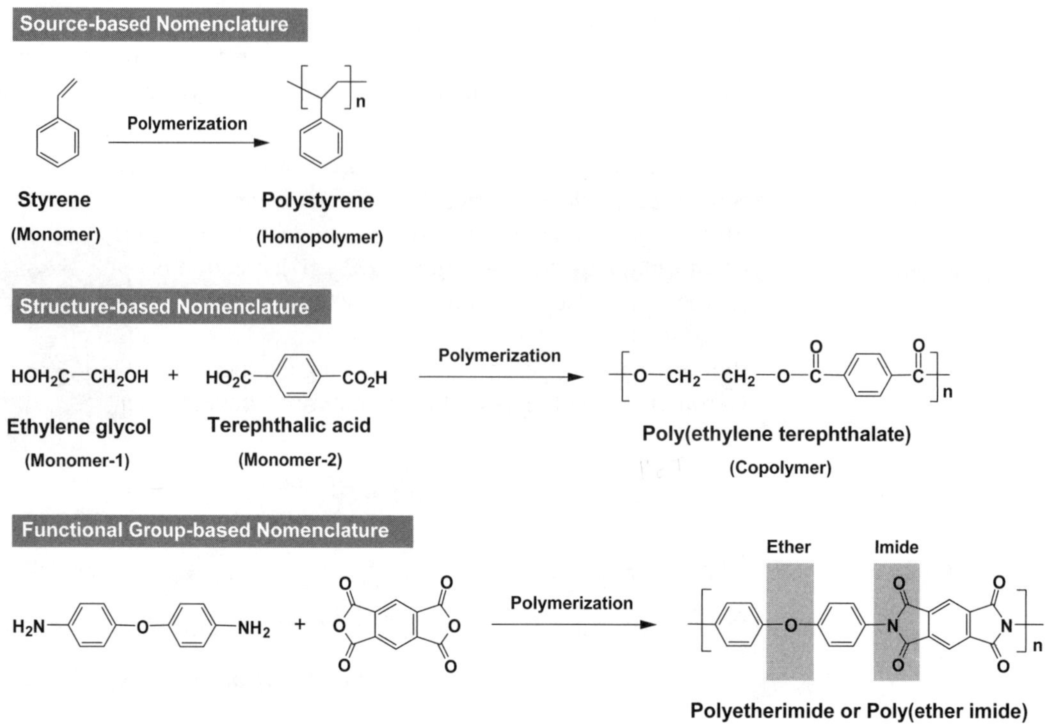

Figure 1.2. Common nomenclature for homopolymers and copolymers.

The DP has a significant effect on the physical, mechanical and chemical properties of a polymer. For example, as chain length increases, mechanical properties, such as tensile strength, ductility, and hardness rise sharply and eventually level off (Figure 1.3). As a result of these variations, the DP creates two distinct useful regions: commercial and precursor. Polymers which fall into the commercial region possess consistent properties and are independent of DP, which means the addition or subtraction of one or several repeat units does not alter the properties of the polymers. The magnitude of DP to achieve the commercial region (i.e., the minimum number of monomers required to exhibit consistent polymer properties) varies from polymer to polymer because of differences in structures and intermolecular aggregations. Thus, a typical molecular weight of a commercially used polystyrene sample starts at 300,000 (DP $\approx$ 3,000), while for poly(ethylene terephthalate) it is about 25,000 (DP $\approx$ 130). By contrast, polymers which are in the precursor regions (low DP), called *oligomers*, exhibit markedly varied properties on the addition or subtraction of one or several repeat units. The oligomers are often purposefully prepared for use as precursors or prepolymers for synthesizing block copolymers (e.g., thermoplastic elastomers) or three-dimensional template materials for microporous ceramics.

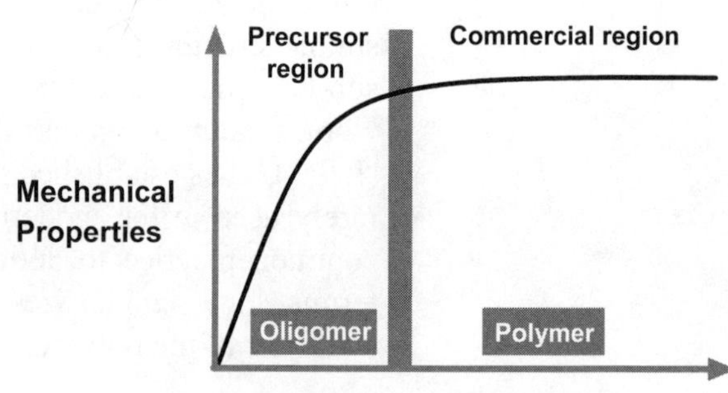

Figure 1.3. Effect on mechanical properties of DP and distinction between oligomers and polymers.

1.1.1. Supramolecular Polymers

Before the concept of macromolecules was generally accepted, the majority of scientists believed that polymer properties were the result of colloidal aggregation of small molecules or particles. It was not until 1917, when the German chemist Hermann Staudinger, who received Nobel Prize in Chemistry in 1953, concluded that polymeric properties in both solution and the solid state are the result of the macromolecular nature of the molecules.[3] In other words, a large number of repeating units are covalently linked into a long chain and the entanglements of the macromolecular chains are responsible for many typical polymer properties. Subsequently, in the early 1930s, this theory was validated by the pioneering synthetic work of the American chemist Wallace Carothers, which led to the commercial development of neoprene rubber and nylon fibers.

Supramolecular polymers form the most recent branch in the tree of "chemistry beyond the covalent bond", often called supramolecular chemistry. These polymers are commonly found in nature, especially in biological systems. Microtubules, microfilaments, and flagella are helical supramolecular polymers formed by proteins. In recent years, much attention has been focused on supramolecular polymers formed by synthetic molecules because of their unique structures and properties (especially reversibility and responsiveness to external stimuli) compared to traditional polymers. As depicted in Figure 1.4, supramolecular polymers are defined as arrays of small molecules held together *via* non-covalent bonds, such as hydrogen bonding, π-π interactions or metal-ion coordination. Despite their brief history, supramolecular polymers are already finding commercial use in applications that take advantage of the reversibility and responsiveness of non-covalent interactions (see Chapter-5 for further discussion).

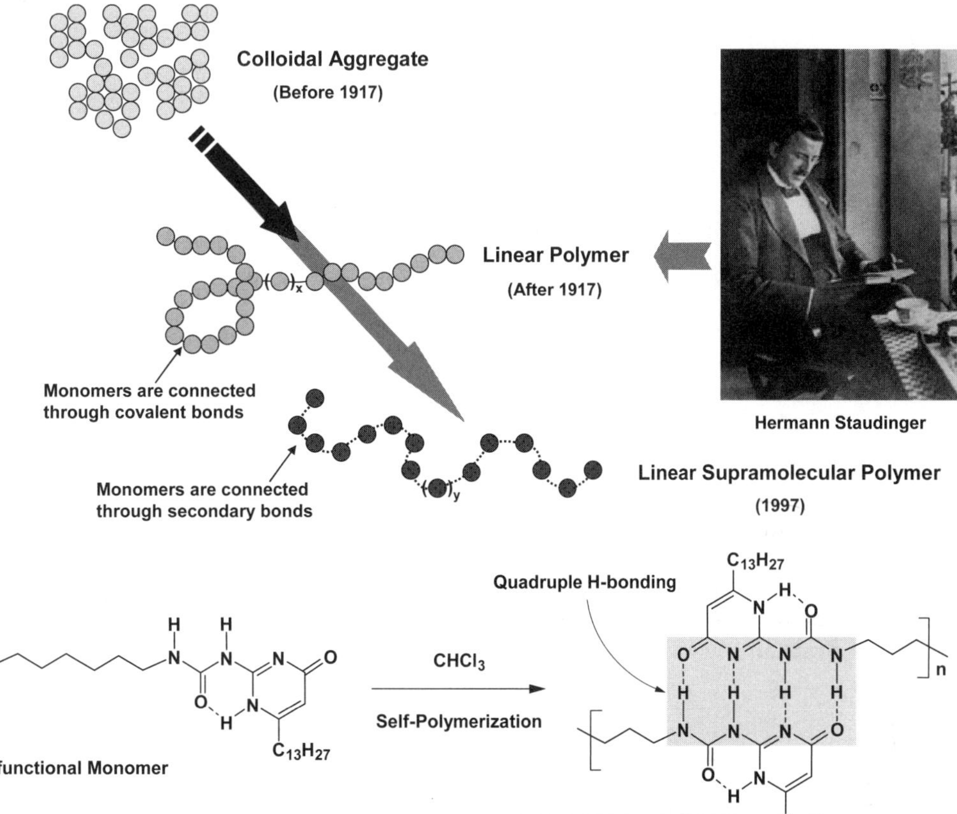

Figure 1.4. Schematic representation of the evolution of macromolecular science from colloids, via the original work of Staudinger's macromolecular theory, to supramolecular polymers. *The photo of Hermann Staudinger is courtesy of Wiley-VCH Publishers.*

1.2. POLYMER MOLECULAR WEIGHTS

Since a polymerization process involves random reactions of monomers, all synthetic polymers result in heterogeneous molecular weights, i.e., polymer chains with different values of degree of polymerization (DP). Hence, measured polymer molecular weights are only average values and a complete description of the *molecular weight distribution* (MWD) of a polymer is necessary to understand its physical, rheological and mechanical properties.

Several mathematical expressions, derived from statistical approaches, have been proposed to define the distribution of polymer lengths in a sample. The two most important are *number-average* (M_n) and *weight-average* (M_w) molecular weights. As described in the following equations, the M_n is just the sum of individual molecular weights divided by the number of polymer molecules, while the M_w is proportional to the square of the molecular weight:

$$M_n = \frac{\sum_{i=1}^{\infty} N_i M_i}{\sum_{i=1}^{\infty} N_i} \qquad M_w = \frac{\sum_{i=1}^{\infty} N_i M_i^2}{\sum_{i=1}^{\infty} N_i M_i}$$

where N_i is the number of polymer molecules of molecular weight M_i. There is another, seldom used, average molecular weight, M_v (viscosity-average), whose value is between M_n and M_w, but closer to the latter. The expression for *viscosity-average* molecular weight is:

$$M_v = \left(\frac{\sum_{i=1}^{\infty} N_i M_i^{1+a}}{\sum_{i=1}^{\infty} N_i M_i} \right)^{\frac{1}{a}}$$

where *a* is the exponent (constant) in the Mark-Houwink viscosity equation.[4,5]

When these expressions are applied to a polymer sample, M_w is always larger than M_n. The ratio of the weight-average to the number-average (M_w/M_n), termed *polydispersity index* (PDI), is a measure of MWD in a sample. Thus, a polymer with a narrow MWD will exhibit a polydispersity index close to 1, but greater than 1 (Figure 1.5). For most synthetic polymers, the polydispersity index generally varies between 1.1 and 2.8. Although the synthesis of a perfect *monodisperse polymer* (M_w/M_n = 1) is difficult, a number of naturally occurring polymers, such as certain proteins and nucleic acids, are monodisperse.

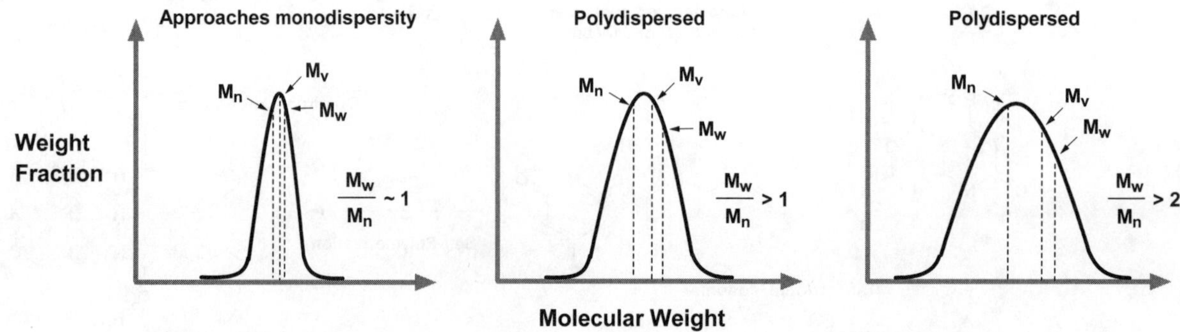

Figure 1.5. Molecular weight distribution and its effect on a sample's polydispersity.

1.3. POLYMER STRUCTURE AND CRYSTALLINITY

The details structure of a polymer chain, viz. the overall chemical composition, the sequence of monomer units (for copolymers), the stereochemistry or tacticity of the chain, and geometric isomerism in the case of diene-type polymers, has a strong influence on the macroscopic properties of polymers. For example, a polymer may be soluble or insoluble in water depends on whether it is constructed with polar monomers (e.g., ethylene oxide or acrylamide) or nonpolar monomers (e.g., ethylene or styrene). Thus, these details can be manipulated to produce materials with a range of mechanical and thermal properties, in a wide variety of colors, and/or with different optical properties. Besides their differences in chemical structures, all polymers differ in their state of macromolecular aggregation, which arises from their differences in (i) strength of intermolecular forces (ii) molecular weight and chain entanglement (iii) crystallinity and (iv) crosslinking. All these properties determine the diverse states of macromolecular aggregation that polymers show.

1.3.1. Stereoisomerism in Polymers

In *stereoisomerism*, the molecules have the same molecular formula and structural formula (the atoms are connected in the same sequence in each molecule). However, in each molecule, known as a *stereoisomer*, the atoms possess different three dimensional or spatial arrangements in space that render them non-superimposable. This means that no matter how the molecules are twisted and turned, one isomer cannot fit exactly on top of the other.

The terms configuration and conformation are often used to describe the structure of a polymer. The *configuration* of a polymer chain cannot be altered unless chemical bonds are broken and reformed. By contrast, the *conformation* of a polymer changes by the rotation (or torsion) of molecules about the single bonds without requiring bond-breaking or alteration of the chemical structure of the polymer (Figure 1.6). Conformational changes in a polymer occur during mild heating and/or mechanical stretching, but do not lead to stereoisomers. For instance, the rapid change in conformation is responsible for the sudden extension of a piece of a rubber band on stretching. There are only small energy barriers, from a few to 5 Kcal/mol, involved in these torsions. The multitude of conformations in polymers is very important for interpreting the properties of polymers.

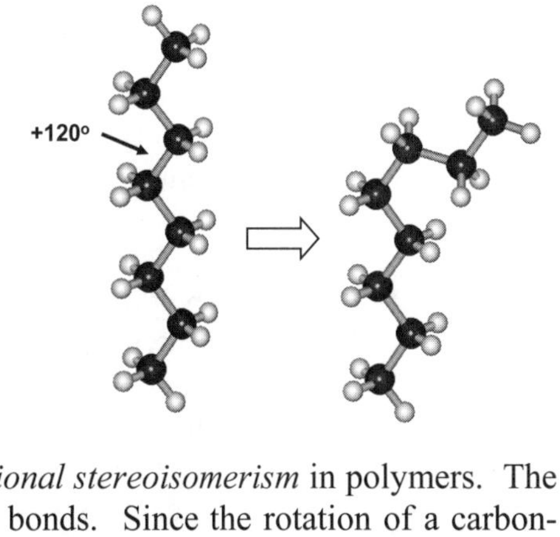

+120°

Figure 1.6. Conformational states of C_8H_{18}. The conformer on the right is generated from the left by 120° torsion about the σ bond.

There are two different types of *configurational stereoisomerism* in polymers. The first is observed in polymers containing double bonds. Since the rotation of a carbon-carbon double bond is restricted, certain polymers exist as a pair of configurational stereoisomers: *cis* and *trans*. The essential requirement for this stereoisomerism is that each carbon of the double bond must have two different substituent groups (one may be hydrogen). The *cis* configuration arises when substituent groups are on the same side of a carbon-carbon double bond. *Trans* refers to the substituents on opposite sides of the double bond. An excellent illustration of this type of stereoisomerism is the two naturally-occurring polyisoprenes. *Gutta percha*, mostly found in the *Palaquium gutta* family, is predominantly *trans*-1,4-polyisoprene, which has a regular structure that favors crystallization (Figure 1.7). As a result, *gutta percha* is hard and rigid and is extensively used in golf ball coverings, undersea cables and surgical appliances. Hevea rubber, a source of more abundant and finest quality natural rubber (*Hevea brasiliensis* of the family Euphorbiaceae), consists entirely of *cis*-1,4-polyisoprene, which has a less symmetrical structure and is not favorable for crystallization. Hence, Hevea rubber is an amorphous rubbery material and is dominant in the manufacture of automobile tires.

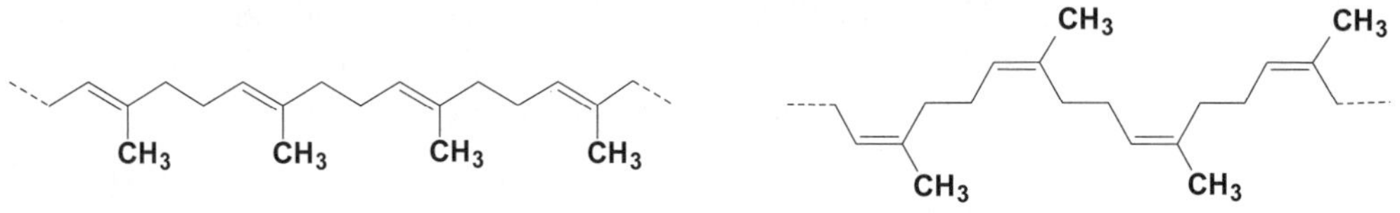

CH_3 CH_3 CH_3 CH_3

Gutta percha (trans-1,4-polyisoprene)

CH_3 CH_3 CH_3 CH_3

Hevea rubber (cis-1,4-polyisoprene)

Figure 1.7. Structures of configurational stereoisomers of polyisoprene.

The second type of configurational stereoisomerism in polymers is concerned with the relative stereochemistry of adjacent chiral centers (known as *tacticity*) within a macromolecule and is particulary significant in homopolymers of higher olefins of the type $–[H_2C–CH(R)]_n–$, where each repeat unit with a substituent R on one side of the polymer backbone is followed by the next repeating unit with the substituent on the same side as the previous one, the other side, or randomly positioned relative to the previous one. A classic example of this type of configurational stereoisomerism is polypropylene (PP). Thus far, five distinct configurational isomers of PP (isotactic, syndiotactic, heterotactic, hemiisotactic and atactic) have been synthesized (see Chapter-2). *Isotactic* is an arrangement where all stereocenters are isospecific, i.e., all methyl groups are on the same side of the polymer chain (Figure 1.8). A *syndiotactic* polymer chain is composed of alternating placement of groups and *atactic* is a random combination of the groups. *Heterotactic* arrangement is a repetition of two groups at one side followed by two groups on the opposite side. A *hemiisotactic* polymer contains isospecific stereocenters, which are separated by units of random stereochemistry.

The tacticity in these polymers is conveniently described by the Bovey formalism[6] in which an "*m*" is used for a *meso* (consecutive monomer units with the same configuration relative to the backbone) and an "*r*" for a *racemic* (consecutive monomer units with opposite configuration relative to the backbone) relationship between two adjacent stereogenic centers. The tacticity is also better described in terms of *pentads* (relative configuration between a series of five monomer units). Thus, an isotactic polymer has a high fraction of *mmmm* pentads, while syndiotactic and heterotactic polymers have a high fraction of *rrrr* and *mrmr* pentads, respectively (Figure 1.8). It should be noted that pentad contents of stereoisomeric polymers are now widely used in the literature because this gives a more accurate description of the microstructure than dyad or triad contents. An alternative and popular representation of configurational stereoisomers of stereoregular polypropylenes is *comb notation*, which is very easy to draw, yet provides the complete picture of orientations of methyl groups (Figure 1.8).

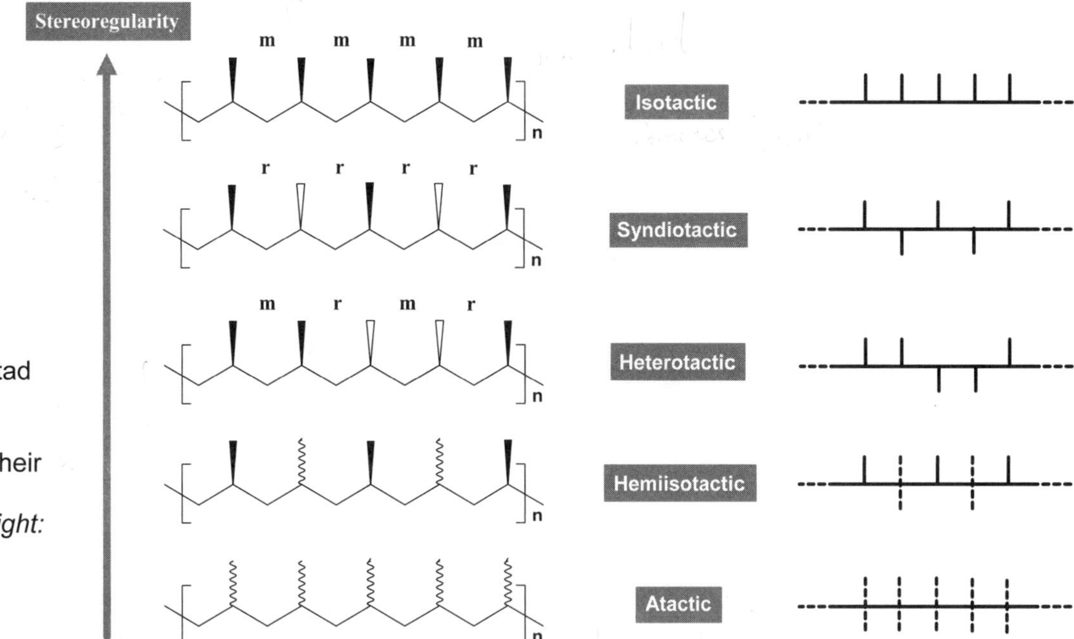

Figure 1.8. *Left:* Configurational stereoisomers of polypropylene: pentad microstructures, configurational nomenclature and their order of increasing stereoregularity. *Right:* comb notation of stereoregular polypropylenes.

Stereochemistry in polymers has an important effect on chain packing. Isotactic and syndiotactic polymers tend to crystallize readily because of their structural regularity. By contrast, an atactic polymer contains no regular sequence of monomer residues along the chain and, consequently, is not prone to crystallization. Crystallinity leads to high physical strength and increased solvent and chemical resistance. Isotactic PP has a crystalline melting point of 175°C and is highly crystalline because the regular chains can pack closely together, leading to large scale applications as both a plastic and fiber. Atactic PP, on the other hand, obtained as a by-product during the manufacture of isotactic PP, is a very soft and rubber-like material with applications in adhesives, caulks, road paints, and cable-filling compounds. Although the fundamental property of bulk polymers is the degree of polymerization, the spatial arrangements of atoms or groups in a polymer chain is also a very significant factor that determines the macroscopic properties.

1.3.2. Polymer Architecture

The *polymer architecture* (topology) describes the shape of a single polymer molecule. Size and shape of polymers are important variables because they can significantly influence many performance properties. The size of polymer molecules may be described by molecular weight, which is determined by the number of small monomer units that react to form the polymer chain. In addition to molecular weight, polymer architecture, or shape, is often controlled to produce specific end use properties. For example, highly linear (straight chain) polymers, such as high density polyethylene (HDPE), can pack together and crystallize more easily. In contrast, polymer chains with branches, such as low density polyethylene (LDPE), are typically more amorphous and may have a higher modulus due to increased entanglements. Thus, it is this architectural difference that leads to many of the observed changes in the physical properties of the two polyethylenes.

The monomers in a polymer can be arranged in a number of different ways, leading to a variety of polymer architectures. Traditionally, the polymers have been divided into three main classes: linear, branched and crosslinked. However, as shown in the tree below, dendritic polymers have recently been recognized as the fourth major class, owing to their diverse architectures, novel properties and implementation in the emerging science of nanotechnology.

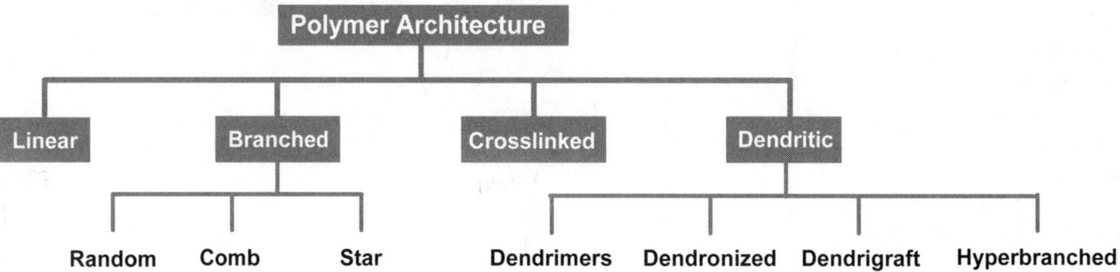

Linear polymers, which resemble "worm-like" chains with random and ordered coils, may best be described by applying a string analogy. They are equivalent to long strings, which are not tied together. Figure 1.9 depicts schematics of multiscale structural representation of linear polymers which have a strong tendency to arrange themselves in a regular, close-packed manner to form polymer crystals. They generally possess high density (arising from inter- and intra-molecular packing), higher tensile strengths, greater stiffness, and elevated softening temperature. They may be dissolved in some organic solvents and possess thermoplastic behavior. Examples of linear polymers are high density polyethylene, poly(methyl methacrylate), polystyrene, poly(ethylene terephthalate), poly(vinyl chloride), polyacrylonitrile and nylon-6,6.

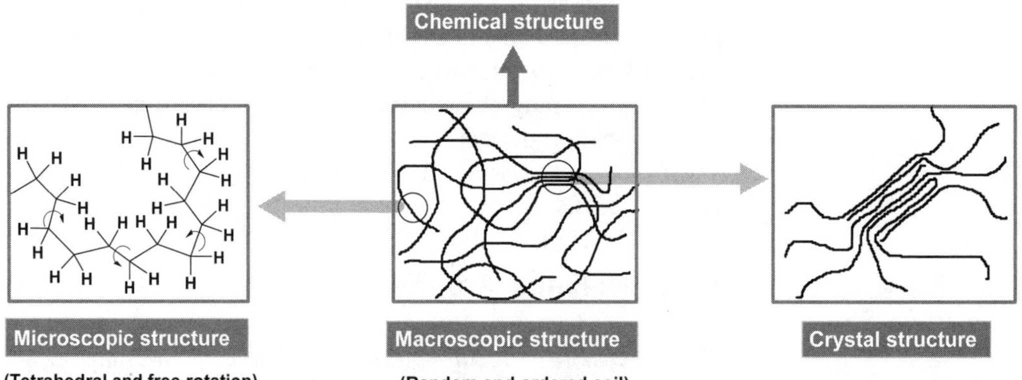

Figure 1.9. Linear polymer architecture: multiscale structural representation of high density polyethylene.

Ladder polymers are essentially linear polymers except that the main chain of the former contains highly aromatic fused-rings and possess repeat units that are always joined to each other through four atoms (two from each unit). In other words, unlike linear polymers which contain repeat units joined to each other by a single bond, the ladder polymers contain no atom-atom interactions that solely hold together the polymer backbone (Figure 1.10). Consequently, these polymers exhibit very high thermal stability because thermal cleavage of one or several single bonds may not completely degrade the main chain (see Chapter-4).

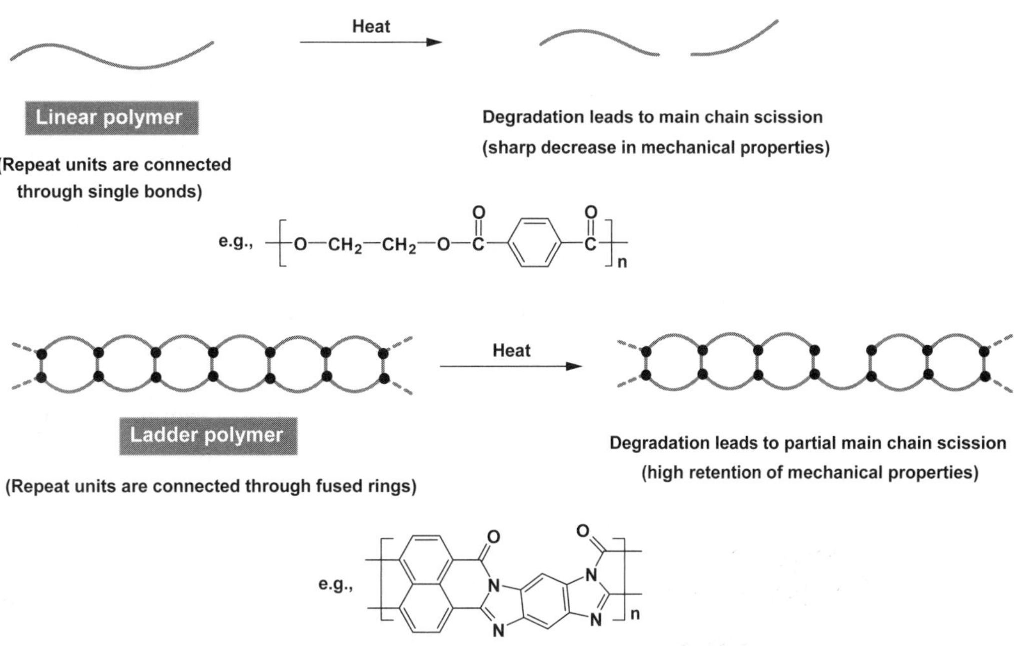

Figure 1.10. Structural differences between linear and ladder polymers.

Branched polymers consist of secondary chains extending from the main one and may be considered equivalent to tying the same pieces of string together, taking care not to tie any closed loops (Figure 1.11). Therefore, the previously mentioned graft copolymers are branched polymers, but not all branched polymers are graft polymers because branched polymers can also be a homopolymer. The branches typically differ in length, are connected to the main chain at random intervals, and often have sub-branches. Branched polymers possess more voids (free volume), lower density, higher flexibility, and are more permeable to gases and solvents than linear polymers. In fact, they resemble linear polymers in many of their properties. However, they can sometimes be distinguished from linear polymers by their lower degree of crystallinity and density or by their different solution viscosity or light scattering behavior. Low density polyethylene (LDPE) is a perfect example of this class. There are, however, many distinct forms of branched polymers, which are better known by their architectures, such as comb and star. *Comb polymers* contain linear branches which are much smaller than those of the main chain and may not have equal length, and are attached to the main chain at a regular interval. By contrast, *star polymers* possess a single branch point from which three or more linear chains (with equal or unequal length) emanate (Figure 1.11). In recent years, these polymers have been extensively studied to develop materials with special properties (see Chapter-2).

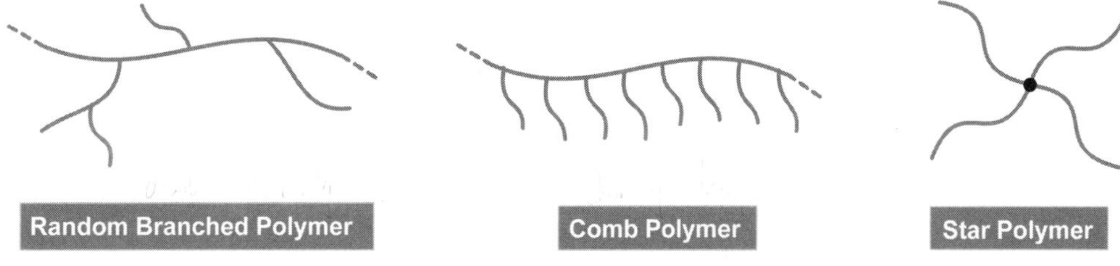

Figure 1.11. Schematic illustration of noted branched polymer architectures.

Crosslinked polymers, also called network polymers or thermosets, are produced by tying strings into closed loops, i.e., polymer molecules are covalently linked to each other at points (termed a crosslink) other than their ends. They are characterized by the molecular weight of chains between crosslinked points or the crosslink density, which is the number of junction points per unit volume. Crosslinked polymers possess a three-dimensional structure and usually swell in solvents, but they do not dissolve. The amount by which the polymer swells depends on the density of crosslinking: the more crosslinks present, the smaller the amount of swelling. Light crosslinking is used to impart good recovery (elastic) properties to polymers, such as in vulcanization of rubbers (see Chapter-2). *Vulcanization* is a process in which sulfur is added to rubber and the mixture is heated, causing light crosslinking of the polymer chains and thus, adding strength to the rubber (Figure 1.12). A high degree of crosslinking is used to impart considerable rigidity and dimensional stability (under conditions of heat and pressure) to polymers, such as epoxy, phenol-formaldehyde and urea-formaldehyde. It is noteworthy that these thermosets are often termed "resin" (e.g., phenolic resin), a usage which is strongly discouraged by the International Union of Pure and Applied Chemistry (IUPAC). The word "resin" (by analogy with natural resins) may be used for soft solids or highly viscous substances.

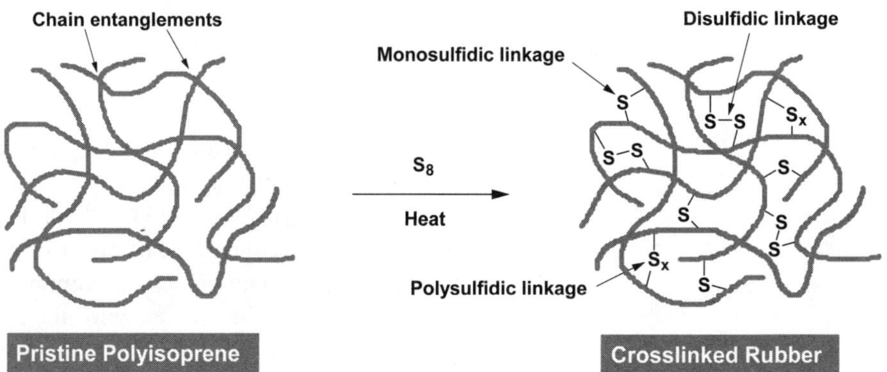

Figure 1.12. Schematic of the vulcanization of polyisoprene chains.

Dendritic polymers, a special class of highly branched macromolecules, are the most recently discovered class of polymer architecture. Depending on the degree of structural perfection, they can be grouped into four major subclasses: dendrimers, dendronized polymers, dendrigraft polymers and hyperbranched polymers (Figure 1.13, also see Chapter-5 for elaborate discussion). They are distinguished by the way in which they are branched. Dendrimers and dendronized polymers have the most ideal structure, followed by semi-perfect dendrigraft polymers, while hyperbranched polymers incorporate the largest number of defects. The word "dendrimer" is derived from the Greek words *dendri-* (tree branch-like) and *meros* (part of). *Dendrimers* typically have a branch on every repeat unit and comprise a core focal point to which several (typically two to four) "dendrons" (dendritic cone-shaped fragments) are attached. They are monodisperse (i.e., all molecules have the same molecular weights) and exhibit unique properties differing from those of conventional linear macromolecules, due to their non-entangled spherical shapes and many functional end groups. Dendrimers also possess lower viscosity, better solubility, and optical clarity due to their amorphous secondary structure. All of these properties are very useful in a number of biomedical and industrial applications, such as controlled release drugs and high quality optoelectronic films.

Dendronized polymers (often called polydendrons or "denpols") are a class of comb polymers in which dendrons with a specific number of branching layers (generations) are attached to a linear backbone at every repeat unit (Figure 1.13). Consequently, they appear almost cylindrical in shape rather than the spherical in dendrimers. *Dendrigraft polymers* are branched like dendrimers with linear polymer segments between each branch point (i.e., branches are not present on every repeat unit). They are easier to synthesize than dendrimers and bring about the properties of the linear polymer segment, such as crystallinity. *Hyperbranched polymers* are highly branched with dendritic-type branching, which do not emanate from a central core, nor is the branching necessarily regular as it is in dendrimers. Thus, hyperbranched polymers are "in between" analogs of dendrimers and linear polymers and can have a variety of shapes depending on the monomers used. Though they do not exhibit outstanding quality, they have drawn much recent attention because of their ease of synthesis (often in "one-pot") from readily available starting materials.

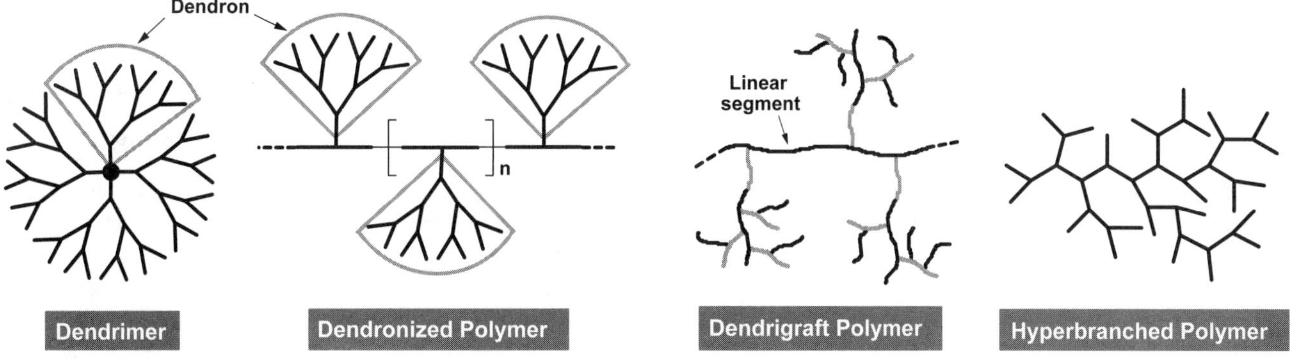

Figure 1.13. Schematics of important subclasses of dendritic polymers.

1.3.3. Crystallinity in Polymers

Crystallinity is important in polymers since it especially affects mechanical and optical properties. Unlike small organic compounds, which tend to pack themselves into perfectly crystalline three-dimensional arrays, a polymer sample can be either amorphous (totally or mostly lacking positional order on the molecular scale) or semi- to highly-crystalline (containing both crystalline and amorphous domains in the same sample). However, with the understanding that there is no commercial polymer with 100% crystallinity, polymer samples containing a high degree of crystalline domains are commonly called *crystalline polymers*. Table 1.1 lists some of the important physical and mechanical properties of crystalline and amorphous polymers.

The difference between crystalline and amorphous polymers is their behavior on heating. Crystalline polymers become liquids at a specific temperature, T_m (the melting point). At this temperature, the physical properties of the crystalline polymers change sharply. By contrast, the molecular segments in amorphous polymers or the amorphous domains of semi-crystalline polymers are randomly arranged and entangled (similar to *spaghetti noodles*). Amorphous polymers do not have sharp melting points, due to their randomness, but instead soften gradually as the temperature rises. The viscosities of these materials change when heated, but seldom are as easy flowing as semi-crystalline polymers. As a general rule, any polymer which can be produced in a clear glass form is an amorphous type. Examples of crystalline and amorphous polymers are shown in Table 1.2.

Table 1.1. Properties of Crystalline and Amorphous Polymers

Physical and Mechanical Properties	Crystalline Polymer	Amorphous Polymer
Clarity	Opaque[a]	Transparent
Density	Higher	Lower
Melting Point	Observed[b]	---[c]
Maximum Exposure Temperature	Higher	Lower
Chemical Resistance	Higher	Lower
Tensile Strength	Higher	Lower
Tensile Modulus	Higher	Lower
Elongation	Lower	Higher
Creep Resistance[d]	Higher	Lower
Melt Flow	Higher	Lower
Shrinkage (after molding)	Higher	Lower

[a]Semi-crystalline polymers, such as low density polyethylene, are translucent. [b]Melt sharply with a narrow temperature range. [c]Not observed (softens over a broad temperature range). [d]Deformation under load (slow irreversible extension).

Table 1.2. Degree of Crystallinity in Notable Commercial Polymers

Polymer	Degree of Crystallinity (%)	Comments
High density polyethylene	80-90	Crystalline
Low density polyethylene	45-55	Semi-crystalline
***Atactic* polypropylene**	35-45	Semi-crystalline
***Isotactic* polypropylene**	70-80	Crystalline
Polystyrene	0-10	Amorphous
Poly(methyl methacrylate)	0-10	Amorphous
Poly(ethylene terephthalate)	25-35	Semi-crystalline
Poly(butylene terephthalate)	50-60	Semi-crystalline
Polyoxymethylene	70-80	Crystalline
Nylon-6	35-45	Semi-crystalline
Polycarbonate	0-10	Amorphous
***Trans*-poly(1,4-butadiene)**	70-80	Crystalline
***Cis*-poly(1,4-butadiene)**	0-5	Amorphous
Polytetrafluoroethylene	85-95	Crystalline
Poly(vinyl chloride)	5-15	Amorphous
Poly(methylpentene)	50-60	Semi-crystalline
Liquid Crystalline Polyester	80-90	Crystalline

1.3.3.1. Crystallinity vs. Polymer Structure

The structure of a polymer and intermolecular forces are the most important factors that play a significant role in achieving desired polymer properties. Time for crystallization depends on structural symmetry of the repeat units in the polymer chains. The greater the symmetry, the more likely and more rapidly crystallization occurs, due to ease of packing into a crystalline order. Linear and stereoregular polymers have a strong tendency to crystallize. Polyethylene is an excellent example to demonstrate the effect of chain symmetry or branching on crystallinity. Depending on the process of manufacture, two distinctly useful polyethylenes can be made. High density polyethylene (HDPE) is highly crystalline (~90%) because of its perfect chain linearity and chemical structural simplicity that permit polymer chains to pack densely, leading to high rigidity and superior tensile strength. These properties make HDPE very suitable as containers for milk, fruit juices, water, detergents and various household and industrial liquid products. By contrast, low density polyethylene (LDPE) is highly amorphous because of the high degree of short and long branching in the polymer chains. Branching in polymers creates higher free volume, which makes LDPE more flexible. Due to its flexibility and other properties, LDPE is used predominantly to manufacture films, such as garment and produce bags, agricultural films, refuse sacks, and packaging films, foams and bubble wrap. It is noteworthy that transformation of highly amorphous polymers into highly crystalline polymers is rarely observed, because of their high melt viscosities and strong intermolecular forces.

Another example of a crystalline homopolymer is syndiotactic polystyrene, which exhibits a high melting point, high crystallization rate, and high chemical resistance compared to atactic polystyrene (see Chapter-2). Such a difference in properties arises from its ordered alternating placement of phenyl groups, making the polymer chains easy to pack into crystals. In comparison, atactic polystyrene, which does not favor crystallization, due to random placement of phenyl groups, is very amorphous. In general, all atactic polymers are highly amorphous and all stereoregular (especially, isotactic and syndiotactic) polymers are highly crystalline.

1.3.3.2. Crystallinity vs. Intermolecular Forces

Intermolecular forces can also play an important role in the crystallization of polymer chains. A great example of intermolecular force assisted crystallinity is observed in nylon-6,6. Figure 1.14 shows how inter-chain hydrogen bonding between amide groups can introduce long range order in a polymer sample.

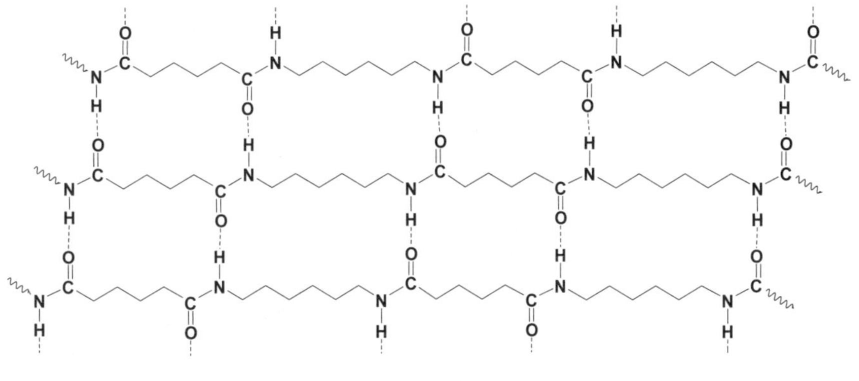

Figure 1.14. Strong intermolecular hydrogen bonding that favors crystallinity in nylon-6,6.

Another example involves isomeric aromatic polyesters, poly(ethylene terephthalate) and poly(ethylene isophthalate), where two types of intermolecular forces (weaker than hydrogen bonding) make them semi-crystalline (Figure 1.15). First, the presence of polar ester groups facilitates inter-chain dipolar interactions. Second, the aromatic rings promote intermolecular face-to-face π-π stacking. Collectively, these interactions are adequate to create crystalline domains even for poly(ethylene isophthalate), which is less symmetric.

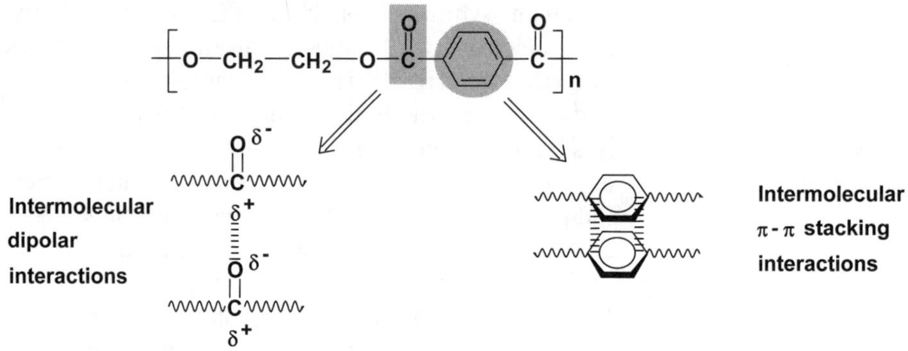

Intermolecular dipolar interactions

Intermolecular π-π stacking interactions

Figure 1.15. Intermolecular interactions in poly(ethylene terephthalate).

1.4. PHASE TRANSITIONS IN POLYMERS

A phase transition is the transformation in a thermodynamic system from one phase to another. The distinguishing characteristic of a phase transition is an abrupt sudden change in one or more physical properties, in particular, the heat capacity, with a small change in a thermodynamic variable, such as the temperature. In the modern classification scheme, phase transitions are divided into two broad categories. The *first-order phase transitions* are those that involve latent heat. During such a transition, a system either absorbs or releases a fixed (and typically large) amount of energy. The most important phase transition that falls into this category is the solid/liquid/gas transition. By contrast, continuous phase transitions, also called *second-order phase transitions*, have no associated latent heat. An excellent example of second-order phase transitions is the glass transition in polymers.

In order to develop a polymeric material with a set of physical and mechanical properties, it is important to understand the concept of the *glass transition temperature*, T_g, which is a property of the amorphous state of the polymer. The T_g is best described by the *free volume theory*.[7,8] The free volume, V_f, is defined as the unoccupied volume in the polymer material, which is the difference between the specific volume and the total volume occupied by the atoms including their van der Walls radii. It is a measure of the space available for the polymer to undergo rotation and translation.

At higher temperatures, when a polymer is in the liquid or rubber-like state, the amount of free volume is markedly increased, as is molecular motion (Figure 1.16). As temperature decreases, this free volume will contract and eventually reach a critical value where there is insufficient free space to allow large scale segmental motion to occur. The temperature at which this critical volume is reached is called the glass transition temperature. Below T_g, the free volume will remain essentially constant as the temperature decreases further, since the chains have now been immobilized and frozen in position. Thus, T_g is defined as the temperature below which molecular segmental motion is restricted. Alternatively, it is the temperature above which molecular motion begins. Highly crystalline polymers do not have a T_g because of their ordered rigid packing in the solid state, but exhibit T_m, *crystalline melting point* (Figure 1.16). Thus, polymers show both first-order (glass transition) and second-order (melting) transitions.

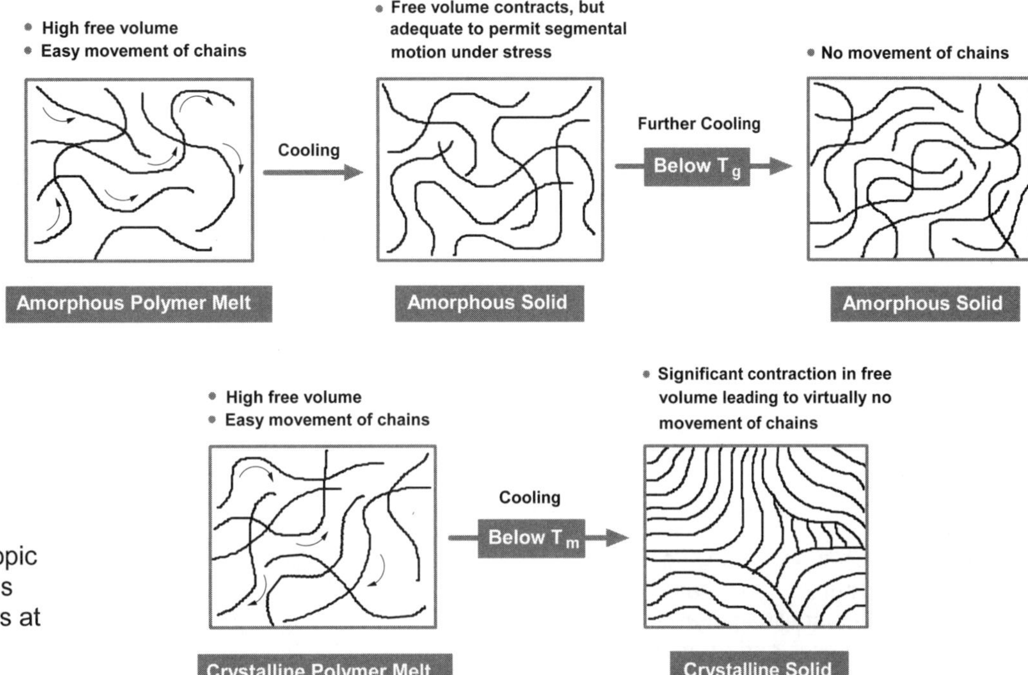

Figure 1.16. Macroscopic structures of amorphous and crystalline polymers at various states.

1.4.1. The Glass Transition vs. Melting Transition

It is tempting to think that T_g is a kind of melting of the polymer. However, there is a marked difference between the two. First, T_g of a polymer cannot be visually detected, since it entails changes in molecular motions. As shown in Figures 1.17a and b, T_m of a polymer is easily observed, as it involves phase change from solid to liquid (similar to determination of melting point of simple organic compounds).

Second, T_g is observed only in polymers in an amorphous state, while T_m is observed in polymers containing the crystalline state. Polymers with both amorphous and crystalline domains, such as semi-crystalline polymers (e.g., polyethylene terephthalate, which has 25-35% crystallinity), exhibit both T_g and T_m (however, the chains that melt are not the chains that undergo the glass transition; Figures 1.17c and d). Highly amorphous polymers, such as PMMA, do not exhibit T_m; rather, they soften over a broad temperature range, which should not be regarded as T_m. T_m is associated with polymers containing crystalline domains. There are some exceptions, typically observed in aromatic rigid-rod polymers. An example is Kevlar, an aromatic polyamide, which is a highly crystalline polymer, but does not show T_m (rather, it decomposes at high temperature) due to extensive intermolecular hydrogen bonding and rigidity of the polymer backbone. High rigidity in the polymer backbone of amorphous polymers also results in the absence of T_g.

Third, at T_g, the molecular rotation around single bonds suddenly becomes significantly easier. By contrast, at T_m, the crystalline polymer becomes a disordered melt, i.e., no short range order. Crystalline polymers do not have well-defined T_m

because of the presence of diverse molecular weight components with different T_m (lower molecular weight components melt at lower temperature) and variations in crystallite sizes (smaller and less perfect crystallites melt first). However, crystalline polymers melt completely within a narrow temperature range (10-30°C). Amorphous polymers soften into a liquid or rubber-like state over a broad temperature range (50-150°C).

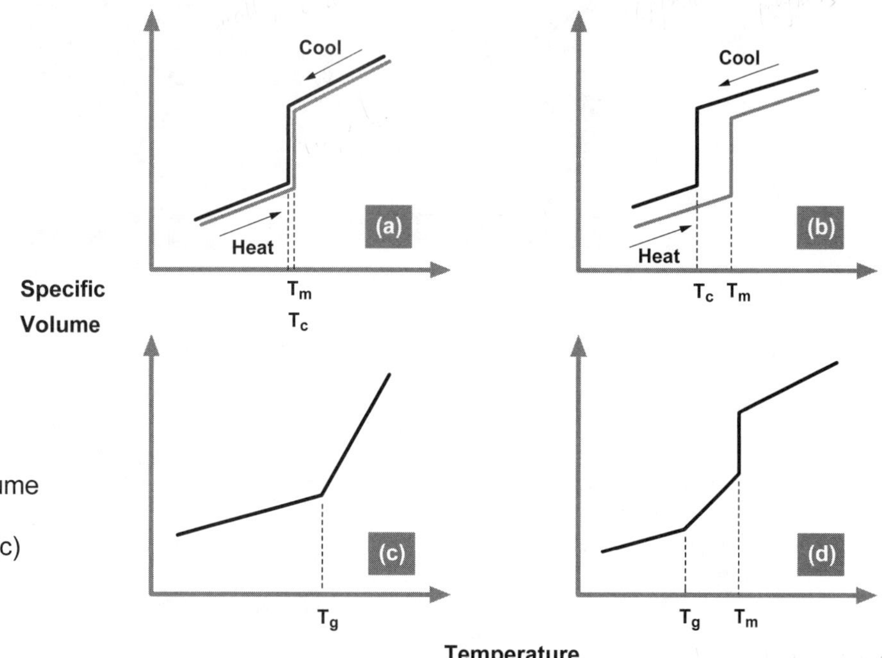

Figure 1.17. Change in specific volume versus temperature of (a) small molecules, (b) crystalline polymers, (c) amorphous polymers and (d) semi-crystalline polymers.

Fourth, in the case of a crystalline polymer, as also observed in small molecules, the temperature holds steady at T_m until all crystallites melt, i.e., the process involves *latent heat* of melting, including an abrupt change in volume. In an amorphous polymer, the temperature does not hold steady at T_g, i.e., there is no latent heat of glass transition. However, the rate of change of volume with temperature is altered at T_g (Figures 1.17a-c).

Finally, T_m is considered a *first-order* thermodynamic transition, as it involves distinct volume change, marked change in heat capacity (molten polymer has a higher heat capacity than the solid crystalline polymer) and existence of a latent heat for the phase change. By contrast, T_g is a *second-order* thermodynamic transition, since it involves a change in heat capacity, but no latent heat of glass transitioning. It is noteworthy that the T_m and the temperature for crystallization, T_c, are the same for small molecules, but the T_c is always lower than T_m in polymers (Figures 1.17a and b). Since T_c entails changes similar to T_m, including latent heat of crystallization, T_c is a first-order thermodynamic transition.

It should be noted that in an amorphous polymer, the T_g is not fixed, but depends on experimental conditions, particularly the cooling rate. As seen from Figure 1.18, a sample will show higher T_g if it is cooled faster. Slow cooling, which permits molecules to stay at equilibrium longer, results in a lower T_g.

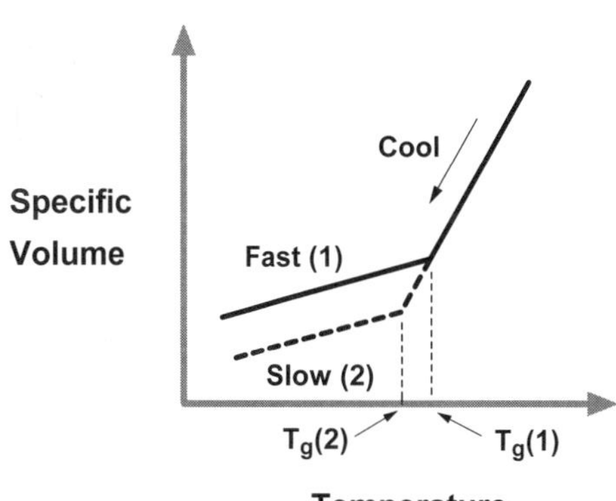

Figure 1.18. Effect of T_g on the rate of cooling.

1.4.2. Parameters Influencing T_g

As mentioned earlier, T_g is greatly dependent on the main chain flexibility and is a critical parameter in determining an application of a polymer. For instance, a polymer with a T_g well below room temperature will be suitable for applications that require high flexibility. This is because, at room temperature, the polymer will have a significant segmental motion (i.e., activation energy for conformational changes is lower). The T_g of a polymer can be tailored by placement of suitable functional groups or moieties in the main backbone or as pendants to the backbone. The T_g can also be changed by adding a plasticizer or by copolymerization with a suitable monomer. The most important structural parameters that can be used to design a polymer with specific properties are discussed below with selected examples. Further examples can be found in Appendix-II. *NOTE: Since the T_g and T_m of a polymer vary significantly with molecular weight, molecular weight distribution and crystallinity, method of measurement, precision of the instrument, and rate of heating, their values for most polymers (e.g., varieties of polyethylenes and polypropylenes) differ slightly from one literature source to the other. The numbers cited throughout the book are either an average value, the value for the highest molecular weight product, or reevaluated in the author's laboratory and should be regarded as indicative rather than definitive.*

1.4.2.1. Effect of Chain Flexing Groups

One of the best ways to decrease T_g is by increasing main chain flexibility (also called chain mobility). The flexibility of a chain can be determined by conformational analysis, which assesses the isomeric states of the polymer and the energy differences between them. The best known flexing groups are the ether linkage and methylene. The presence of these groups in the main chain markedly enhances chain mobility, thus lowering the T_g of the polymer. The effect of the ether oxygen "swivel", that permits enhanced free rotation in various polymer chains, is very prominent in high-performance polymers, such as polyimide (PIM), poly(phenylene sulfone) and poly(phenylene ketone). For example, the pyromellitimide moiety in PIM is so rigid that it does not exhibit a T_g or T_m (decomposes without melting), thus inhibiting its processing or application (Figure 1.19). One ether linkage per repeat unit in Kapton®, a poly(ether imide), is adequate to observe T_g, but not enough to melt the crystalline domains before decomposition. *m*-Phenylene linkages in a polymer chain increase chain flexibility because of the creation of more free volume, including loss of symmetry (*vide infra*). A well balanced distribution of rigid and thermostable (pyromellitimide and biphenyl) and chain flexing (ether and *m*-phenylene) units in Aurum® poly(ether imide) makes it both thermostable and melt processable. The presence of the 2,2-diphenylpropane moiety in Ultem® poly(ether imide) makes it completely amorphous, but at the cost of some thermal stability, due to the degradation of dimethyl groups at elevated temperatures. In general, the polyether version is melt-processable, quite thermostable (though slightly less than that of the non-ether counterpart) and organosoluble, making them useful for high temperature coating applications.

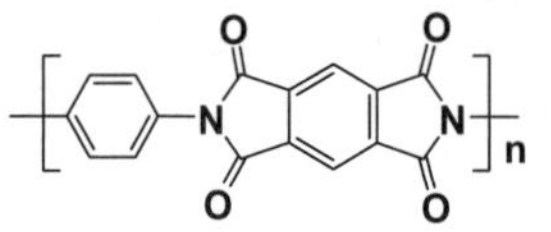

T_g = none; T_m = does not melt (dec. above 550 °C)

Polyimide (PIM)

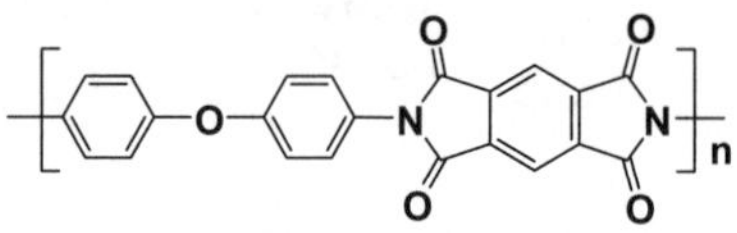

T_g = 350°C; T_m = does not melt (dec. at 520°C)

Kapton® Poly(ether imide)

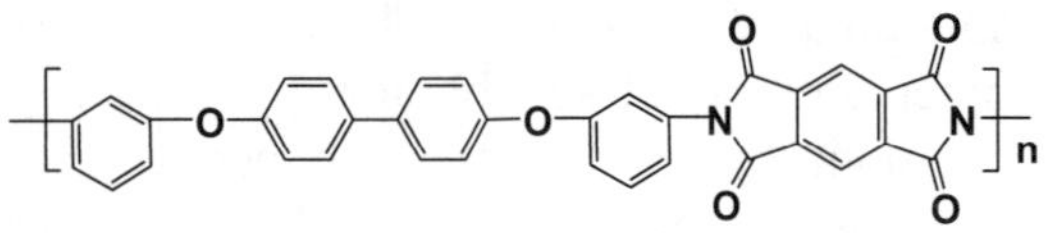

T_g = 250°C; T_m = 390°C

Aurum® Poly(ether imide)

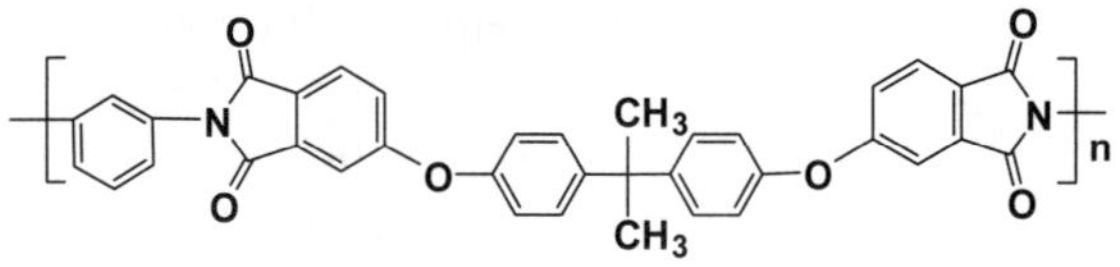

T_g = 210°C; T_m = amorphous

Ultem® Poly(ether imide)

Figure 1.19. Effect on T_g and T_m of a chain flexing group.

1.4.2.2. Effect of Chain Stiffening Groups

When chain stiffening groups or moieties are present in the polymer backbone, the flexibility of a polymer chain is severely reduced, leading to an increase in T_g. Some of the most effective chain stiffening groups that greatly restrict the mobility of the polymer chain are shown below, in the order of increasing efficiency. For example, the presence of *p*-phenylene moieties in poly(ethylene terephthalate) (PET) makes the polymer backbone much stiffer compared to poly(ethylene adipate) (PEA), which contains flexible methylene groups (Figure 1.20). The effect is even more pronounced in poly(ethylene-2,6-naphthalenedicarboxylate) (PEN) because of the presence of the 2,6-naphthalene moiety, which is more rigid than *p*-phenylene, owing to an additional fused aromatic ring and larger size.

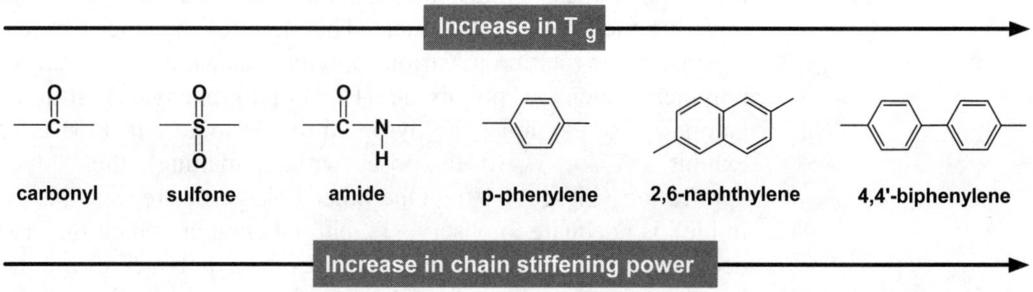

Increase in T_g

carbonyl — sulfone — amide — p-phenylene — 2,6-naphthylene — 4,4'-biphenylene

Increase in chain stiffening power

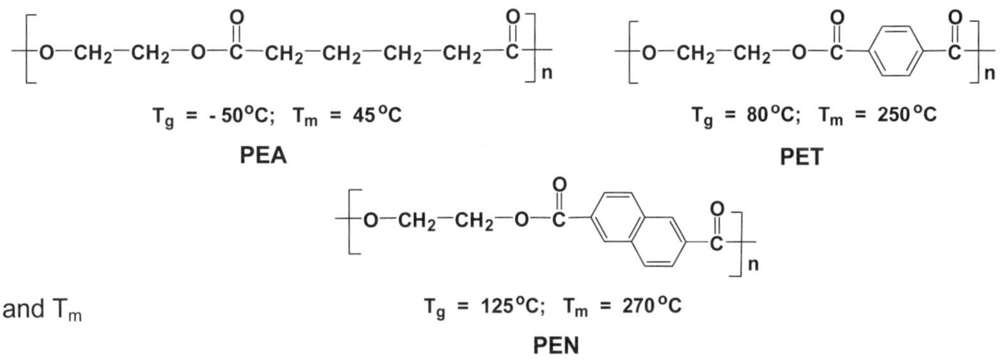

T_g = - 50°C; T_m = 45°C

PEA

T_g = 80°C; T_m = 250°C

PET

T_g = 125°C; T_m = 270°C

PEN

Figure 1.20. Effect on T_g and T_m of chain stiffening group.

1.4.2.3. Effect of Chain Symmetry

Higher chain symmetry permits polymer chains to pack better, which is favorable for forming crystalline domains, thus restricting molecular motions and leading to a higher value of T_g. Chain dissymmetry, on the other hand, creates free volume in the polymer sample, thus offering room for wiggling of polymer chains, which leads to a decrease in T_g. Superb examples to demonstrate the effect of chain symmetry include commercially available polyesters and polyamides, in which their repeat units are isomeric within their classes (Figure 1.21). Among the polyesters, PET is more symmetric because of *p*-phenylene (linear) linkages, thus making it a semicrystalline polymer. Poly(ethylene phthalate) (PEP) and poly(ethylene isophthalate) (PEIP) are highly amorphous owing to the presence of angular *o*- and *m*-phenylene linkages, which create more free volume and exhibiting comparatively lower T_g. The aforementioned analogy can be applied to a set of polyamides. Kevlar® is highly crystalline due to its higher chain symmetry (*p*-phenylene linkages) and possesses strong intermolecular hydrogen bonding through almost 100% *trans*-amide groups. Nomex® also possesses some degree of hydrogen bonding along with considerable amorphous regions, thus generating a high T_g.

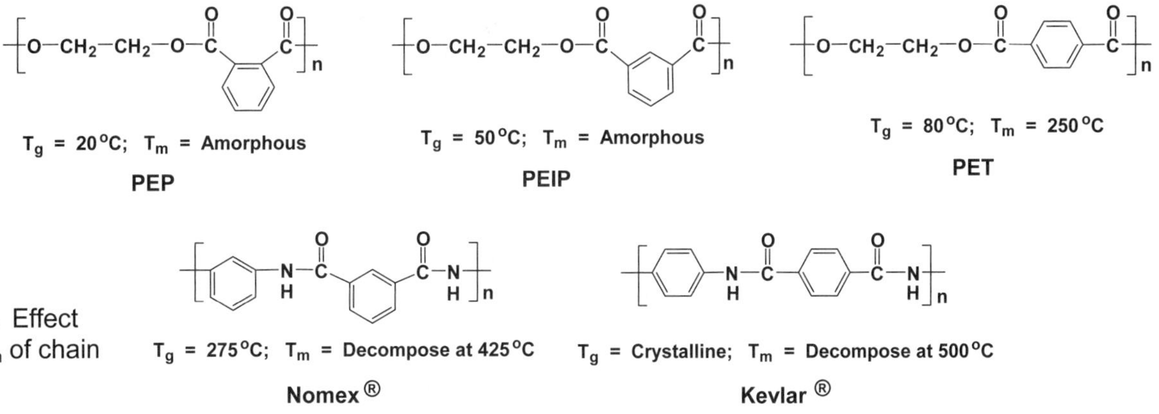

T_g = 20°C; T_m = Amorphous

PEP

T_g = 50°C; T_m = Amorphous

PEIP

T_g = 80°C; T_m = 250°C

PET

T_g = 275°C; T_m = Decompose at 425°C

Nomex®

T_g = Crystalline; T_m = Decompose at 500°C

Kevlar®

Figure 1.21. Effect on T_g and T_m of chain symmetry.

1.4.2.4. Effect of Polymer Stereoregularity

Among stereoregular polymers, such as polypropylene (PP), the isotactic variety is the most symmetric because all substituents are on the same side of the polymer chain, followed by syndiotactic (alternating pattern), followed by the least symmetric atactic (random combination). By the same free-volume analogy described above, the order of increasing T_g in stereoregular PP will be isotactic (*i*) > syndiotactic (*s*) > atactic (*a*)

(Figure 1.22). This analogy is also true for the two configurational stereoisomers of polyisoprene (PI), *cis* (*c*) and *trans* (*t*), in which the former creates more free volume than the latter because of lesser symmetry.

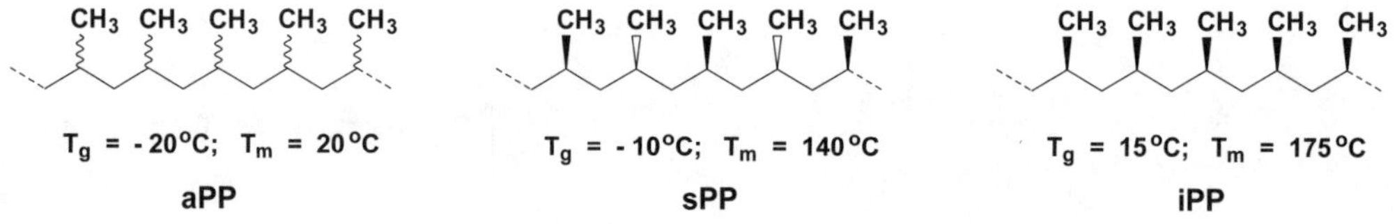

T_g = - 20°C; T_m = 20°C
aPP

T_g = - 10°C; T_m = 140°C
sPP

T_g = 15°C; T_m = 175°C
iPP

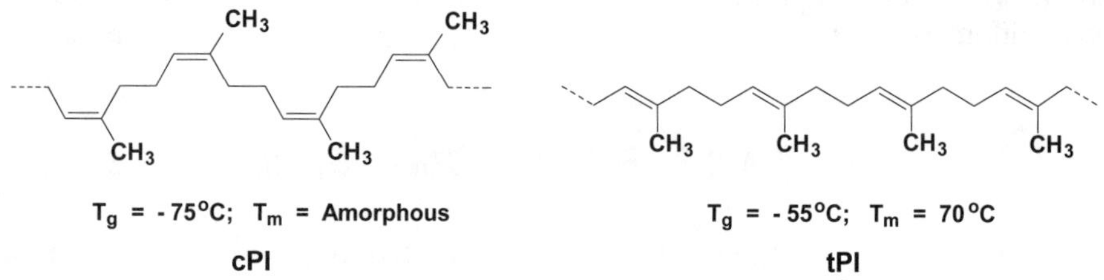

T_g = - 75°C; T_m = Amorphous
cPI

T_g = - 55°C; T_m = 70°C
tPI

Figure 1.22. Effect on T_g and T_m of polymer stereoregularity.

1.4.2.5. Effect of Pendent Groups

Since a pendent group can be bulky or flexible, the influence on T_g by these groups is somewhat complex. Similar to chain stiffening groups, the presence of bulky pendent groups hinders chain mobility. Even a small group can act as a "fish hook" that may catch any nearby molecule when the polymer chains move like a corkscrew. Pendent groups can also catch on each other when chains slither by each other. Although bulky pendants create more free volume (V_f = the difference between the specific volume of the polymer mass and the volume of the solidly packed molecules), they cause more restrictions on the rotational freedom of the polymer chains, leading to an increase in T_g. This effect is illustrated in vinyl polymers containing increasing size of pendent groups: HDPE (no substitutions), PP (methyl substitutions), PS (phenyl substitutions), poly(vinyl naphthyl) (PVN, naphthyl substitutions) and poly(vinyl biphenyl) (PVB, biphenyl substitutions) (Figure 1.23). Another example is adamantyl-substituted poly(ether ether ketone) (see Appendix-II). It is noteworthy that the direct attachment of bulky pendants to the polymer backbone results in the domination of hindrance in main chain mobility (i.e., inhibits freedom of rotation) over the creation of greater free volume.

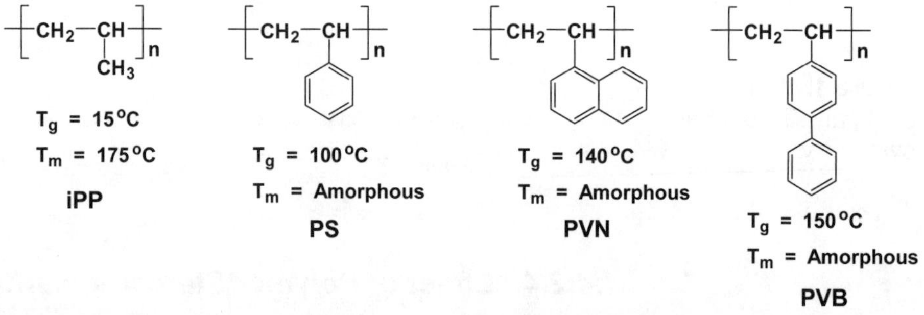

T_g = 15°C
T_m = 175°C
iPP

T_g = 100°C
T_m = Amorphous
PS

T_g = 140°C
T_m = Amorphous
PVN

T_g = 150°C
T_m = Amorphous
PVB

Figure 1.23. Effect on T_g and T_m of bulky pendent groups.

In the case of flexible pendent groups, such as aliphatic chains, the creation of free volume plays a dominant role (compared to the increase of rotational energy due to the groups pendent to the polymer backbone) in determining the mobility of the polymer chains. The higher the value of V_f, the more room the molecules will have in which to move around and to lower the T_g. This effect is well demonstrated in the series of alkyl methacrylate polymers depicted in Appendix-II.

1.4.2.6 Effect of Intermolecular Forces

Intermolecular forces increase T_g because of resistance of rotational movement of the polymer chains. The most significant is hydrogen bonding, which has a more dominant effect on T_g compared to relatively weaker intermolecular forces, such as dipole-dipole and dispersion forces. For example, intermolecular hydrogen bonding dominates in nylon homo- and copolymers (Figure 1.24). Both T_g and T_m decrease as the density of amide linkages is reduced by the increasing numbers of methylene groups. Dipole-dipole forces result from attraction between polar groups, such as those in polyesters (e.g., PET) and vinyl polymers with chlorine pendants (e.g., PVC). Dispersion forces due to instantaneous dipoles that form as charge clouds in the molecules fluctuate, are the weakest of the intermolecular forces and are present in all polymers. They are the only forces possible for nonpolar polymers, such as polyethylene.

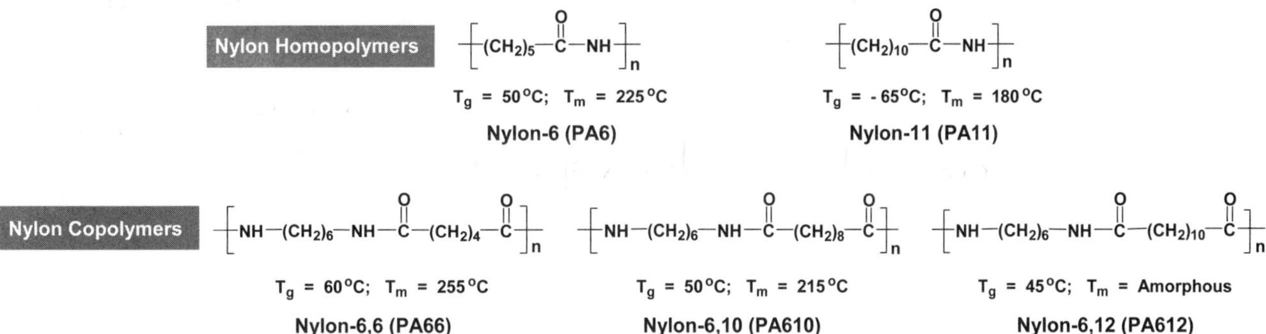

Figure 1.24. Effect on T_g and T_m of intermolecular forces.

1.4.2.7. Effect of Crosslinking

The rotational motion of polymer chains or chain mobility is gradually restricted by an increase in crosslinking. Thus, T_g will rise with an increase in crosslink density until a point is reached when it is ill-defined due to rigidity of the highly crosslinked polymer.

1.4.2.8. Effect of Plasticizers

Plasticizers are low molecular weight compounds added to plastics to increase their flexibility and processability. They weaken the intermolecular forces between the polymer chains and decrease T_g. Plasticizers are often added to semi-crystalline polymers to lower T_g below room temperature. An example is PVC, which has a T_g of 85°C in the virgin state. When PVC is plasticized with 50 wt.% of dioctyl phthalate (DOP) the T_g drops to -30°C. In this case, the amorphous phase of the polymer will be rubbery at normal temperatures, reducing the brittleness of the material.

1.4.2.9. Effect of Polymer Branching

Polymers with more branching have more chain ends, so have more free volume. This reduces T_g, but the branches also hinder rotation, like large side groups, which increases T_g. Which of these effects will predominate depends on the polymer structure. Polymers with highly flexible components result in lower values of T_g. In molecules of equal molecular weight, branched polymers have lower T_g values. A great example of this effect is LDPE (T_g = -95°C; T_m = 110°C) and HDPE (T_g = -30°C; T_m = 150°C).

1.4.2.10. Effect of Molecular Weight

The higher the molecular weight, the less ease of movement due to higher intermolecular forces and chain entanglement, resulting in greater restriction in overall molecular freedom. In general, at low molecular weights, a large increase in T_g is observed with an increase in molecular weight. As shown in Figure 1.25, the effect of molecular weight on T_g is not significant once a threshold is reached, similar to observations of many mechanical properties of polymers. For instance, a PS sample with a molecular weight of 3,000 exhibits a T_g near 40°C, while a 300,000 molecular weight sample has a T_g near 100°C.

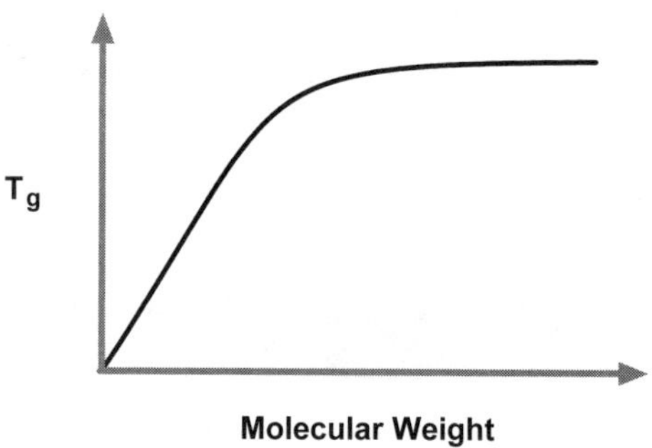

Figure 1.25. Effect on T_g of molecular weight.

1.4.2.11. Effect of Copolymerization and Polymer Blending

Random and alternate copolymers usually exhibit only one T_g, which is in between the T_gs of individual homopolymers. Block copolymers undergo phase separation into domains, which are quite regular and hence, are often referred to as "self-organizing systems". In most cases, block copolymers display multiple T_gs representing well-defined blocks (Table 1.3). Graft copolymers usually show two T_gs, one representing the main chain and the other, the branch.

Table 1.3. Effect of Copolymerization

Polymer	Homopolymer T_g (°C)	Copolymer T_g (°C)
Polystyrene	100	---
Polybutadiene	-105	---
Styrene-butadiene random copolymer	---	-35
Styrene-butadiene block copolymer	---	90 and -85

In general, an immiscible (incompatible) blend of two polymers exhibits two T_gs; each corresponding closely to the T_g of individual polymers, due to the existence of two-phase structure. In contrast, a miscible (compatible) blend of two polymers possesses one T_g somewhere in between those of the two unblended polymers. The T_g of a compatible polymer blend can be tuned by varying the composition of individual polymers (A and B) in accordance with the Fox equation shown below.[9] In fact, scientists often measure the T_g of a blend to find out if it is miscible or immiscible.

$$\frac{1}{T_g} = \frac{M_A}{(T_g)_A} + \frac{M_B}{(T_g)_B}$$

$(T_g)_A$ and $(T_g)_B$ = the glass transition temperatures (in Kelvin) of polymers A and B

M_A and M_B = weight fractions of A and B

1.4.3. Parameters Influencing T_m

Although both T_g and T_m depend on molecular structure, the variations in two transition temperatures do not always quantitatively parallel each other (compare the data in the previous section and in Appendix-II). As mentioned earlier, T_m is a property of crystalline regions of a polymer. The melting behavior of semi-crystalline polymers is intermediate between that of crystalline materials (sharp density change at T_m) and that of a pure amorphous material (slight change in the slope of density at the T_g). Since melting involves breaking the inter-chain physical bonds in the crystalline domains, T_m depends on:

- Chain stiffness/rigidity and chain symmetry (increase T_m)
- Presence of high interchain forces (increases T_m)
- Copolymerization (lowers T_m by shortening the length of crystallizable sequences)
- Plasticizer (decreases T_m due to increase in the relative mobility of polymer molecules, thus reducing the energy necessary to enter the liquid phase).

1.5. CLASSIFICATION OF POLYMERS

The coverage on synthetic polymers may be best accomplished by classifying them on the basis of their widely varied properties and applications.

1.5.1. Property-Based Classification

Using properties, polymers can be grouped into four major classes: plastics, fibers, elastomers and thermoplastic elastomers. Appendix-III defines some of the similarities and differences among these materials. There are primarily three factors that determine whether a polymer is glassy, rubbery, or fiber-forming:

- the flexibility of the macromolecules (T_g above or below room temperature)
- the magnitude of the forces between the molecules (hydrogen bonding, dipole-dipole or dispersion forces)
- the stereoregularity of the macromolecules (chain symmetry or dissymmetry)

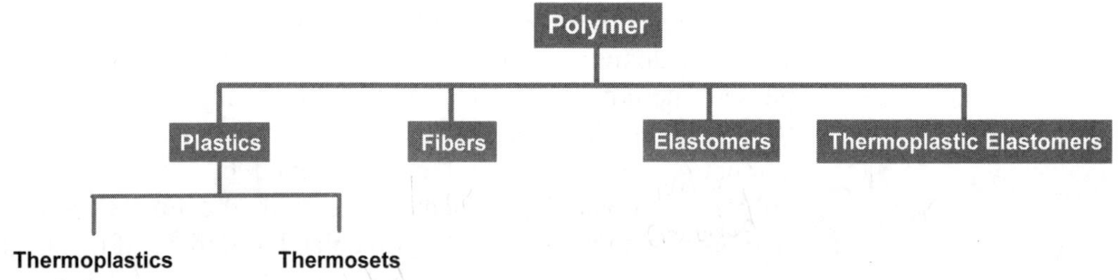

1.5.1.1. Plastics

The word "plastic" (the adjective) or "plastics" (the noun) originates from the Greek word "plastikos", which means to grow or form. The word was used first as an adjective meaning "formative = plastic" (capable of being deformed without rupture). Then it began to be used as a noun. The name "plastic" directly means the "capability to be formed", one of the features of plastics.

Plastics represent a very large group of synthetic polymers (including a few natural ones) which display unique properties when compared to other materials and have contributed greatly to the quality of everyday life. When properly applied, plastics perform functions at a low cost that other materials cannot match. They are divided into two general classes based on their behavior when exposed to heat: thermoplastics and thermosetting plastics (commonly known as *thermosets*).

1.5.1.1a. Thermoplastics

Polymers that can be repeatedly melted on heating and solidified on cooling without noticeable damage are said to be thermoplastics. They possess a linear or branched molecular structure with strong covalent bonds within the chains and weaker secondary *van der Waals* forces between the chains. They can be semi-crystalline or amorphous. *Rigid plastics* and *flexible plastics* are the result of a further classification on the basis of their stress-strain characteristics. Figure 1.26 shows typical stress-strain behavior of these materials. Rigid plastics, such as PS, PMMA and PC, require significant force to deform and/or break before any measurable elongation takes place (see Appendix-I for polymer abbreviations). By contrast, flexible plastics, such as LDPE and LLDPE, exhibit resistance to force to a certain extent and are different from rigid plastics in that they deform considerably without breaking. The serviceable temperature range for thermoplastics is much lower than that for thermosets.

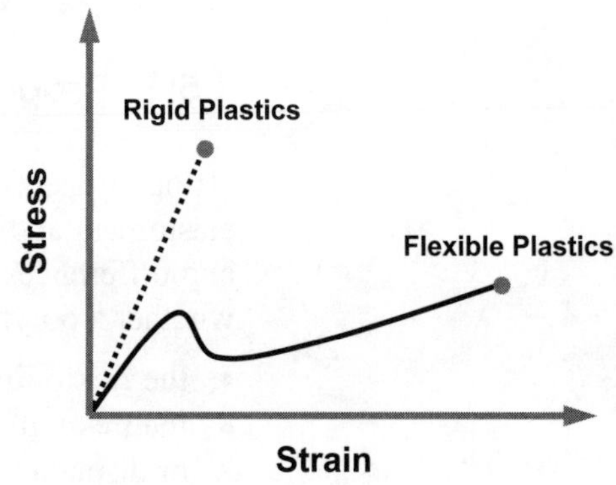

Figure 1.26. Typical stress-strain characteristics of rigid and flexible thermoplastics (● indicates occurrence of failure).

1.5.1.1b. Thermosets

A thermoset is a highly crosslinked polymer and may be viewed as a single molecule since all polymer chains are covalently connected in the form of a 3D network. Because the chains cannot rotate or slide, these polymers possess good strength, stiffness, hardness, and dimensional stability. The stress-strain behavior of thermosets resembles rigid plastics except for the failure that occurs at higher modulus (Figure 1.27). Under heat and pressure, thermoset precursors become soft for a short period of time (shaping stage) and then turn gradually into a solid material (curing stage), after which it is no longer possible to shape the material by heating (degradation rather than melting upon further heating). Further shaping may only be performed by machining. Although thermosets are difficult to reshape, they have many distinct advantages (e.g., high thermal stability and insulating properties, high rigidity and dimensional stability, excellent chemical resistance and strong resistance to creep and deformation under load) over other polymers. Most important thermosets in use are epoxies and phenolics (see Chapter-3).

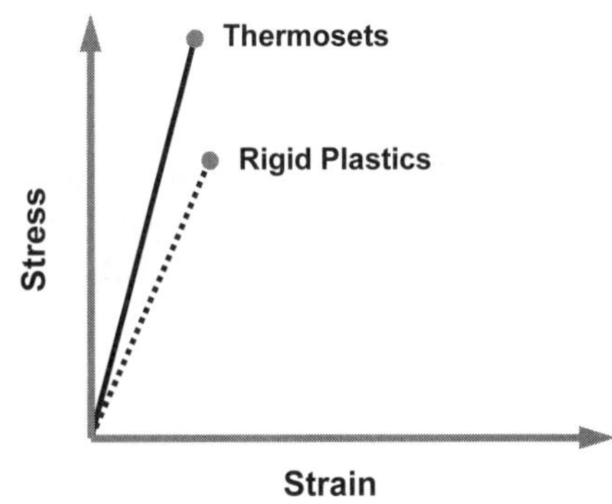

Figure 1.27. Comparison of stress-strain characteristics of rigid thermoplastics and thermosets (• indicates occurrence of failure).

Interpenetrating Polymer Networks (IPNs)

IPNs can be regarded as thermosets, in the sense that they are crosslinked and cannot be processed after curing and exhibit similar or better stress-strain characteristics than thermosets because of intermeshing of polymer chains. An IPN consists of two or more networks which are at least partially interlaced/intermeshed on a molecular scale, but not covalently bonded to each other and cannot be separated unless chemical bonds are broken.

An IPN may be further classified by the method used for its synthesis. An IPN prepared by a process in which the second component network is polymerized after completion of polymerization of the first component network, is called a *sequential IPN*. When an IPN is prepared by a process in which both component networks are polymerized concurrently, the IPN may be referred to as a *simultaneous IPN*. A *semi-IPN* results when only one of the polymer systems is crosslinked (Figure 1.28). Thus, an IPN approach can be considered a special kind of chemical blending and offers a way to combine properties of two different polymers. Other methods include copolymerization and physical mixing, such as mechanical blends (polymers are mixed at temperatures above T_g or T_m for amorphous and semi-crystalline polymers, respectively) and solution blends (polymers are dissolved in a common solvent, followed by evaporation).

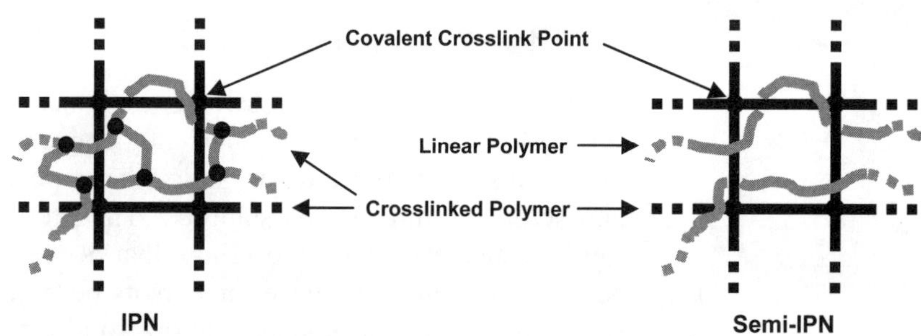

Figure 1.28. Schematic illustration of IPN systems.

1.5.1.2. Fibers

Although regarded as another form of rigid plastics, fibers possess features which merit consideration as a separate class. There is a wide variety of these materials and the polymer chains must be aligned (introduction of crystallinity) along the longitudinal direction of the fibers in order to achieve desired fiber properties, such as tensile strength. The chain alignment takes place when the polymer is spinning through a spinneret under the drawing tension. Unlike copolymerization and physical blends (most common ways to obtain unique properties using two or more different polymers), fiber properties can be tailored simply by weaving multiple fibers with appropriate properties. For example, the core (central strength member) of a string could be made of a resilient fiber for power, while the jacket (wear layer) might be a tough material for resistance to abrasion.

Several different models have been put forth in an attempt to describe the morphological texture of fibers.[10,11] Although no one model has been determined to be satisfactory, the three-phase model, shown in Figure 1.29, seems to have more support. As the name implies, the fiber consists of three distinct phases: oriented crystalline regions, amorphous regions with preferential orientation along the fiber axis which contain tie molecules connecting crystallites, and highly extended noncrystalline molecules, called the interfibrillar phase. In this model, the interfibrillar phase plays a key role in the tensile properties of the fiber. It is stated that the fiber formation process results in a morphology consisting of oriented crystalline and amorphous regions arranged in structures very different from those obtained under quiescent conditions, for the same semi-crystalline material.

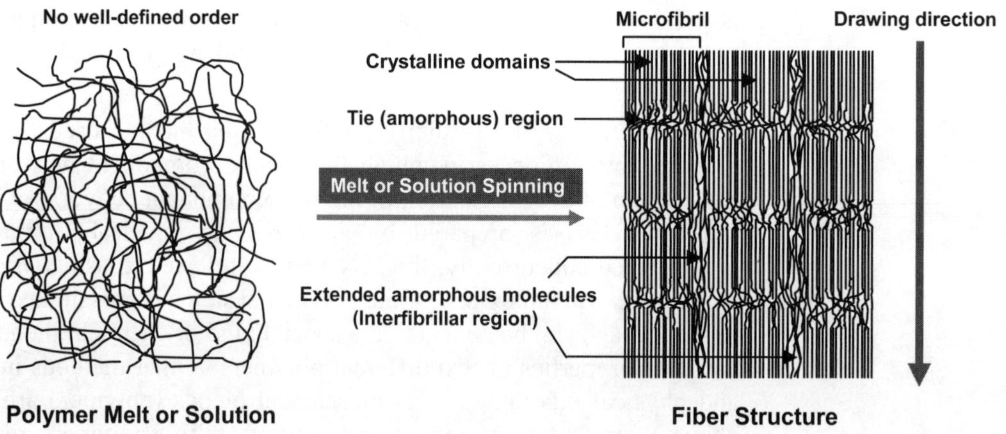

Figure 1.29. Schematic of a three-phase model of a fiber structure *(Adapted from Ref. 11)*.

Polymers which are thermoplastics and possess high stereoregularity (e.g., isotactic PP) or intermolecular hydrogen bonding (e.g., nylon-6,6 and Kevlar®) or strong polar-polar interactions (e.g., PAN and PET) are very suitable for introducing high crystallinity in fibers, thus offering high strength that in some polymers, e.g., Kevlar, exceeds the tensile strength of steel (Figure 1.30).

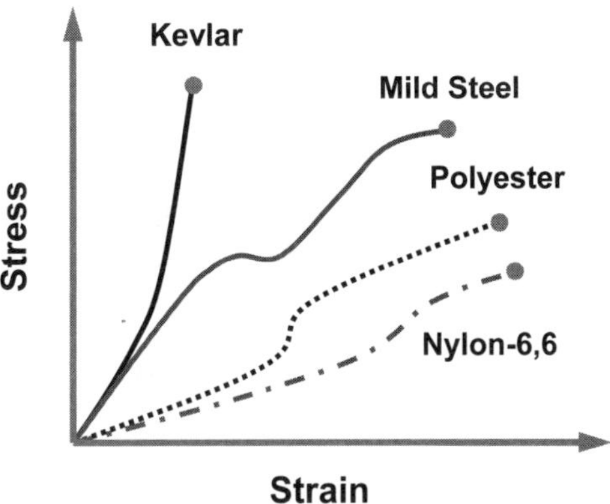

Figure 1.30. Comparison of stress-strain characteristics of important fibers.

1.5.1.3. Elastomers

Elastomers (commonly called *rubbers*) are fully amorphous polymers and exhibit completely different mechanical behavior than the other types of polymers previously discussed. Natural rubber, obtained from the sap of the *Hevea* tree, was named by the chemist Joseph Priestley, who found that a piece of solidified latex gum was good for rubbing out pencil marks on paper. In Great Britain, erasers are still called "rubbers". They are different from thermosets in that they have a fairly low crosslink density, with links at random intervals, usually between 500 and 1000 monomers. Like thermosets, once shaped, elastomers cannot be reshaped by heating. In the virgin (unvulcanized) state, an elastomer exhibits permanent viscous plastic deformation (unrestricted flow of whole molecules past neighboring ones) on the application of force (Figure 1.31). When the crosslinks are introduced (vulcanized state), the unrestricted flow is prevented, but the chain segments between crosslinks are free to move, which makes an elastomer highly elastic, i.e., when the load is removed, the material returns to its original shape. Therefore, the early part of stress-strain curves of both states corresponds to uncoiling of chains and the latter part is attributed to stretching of bonds.

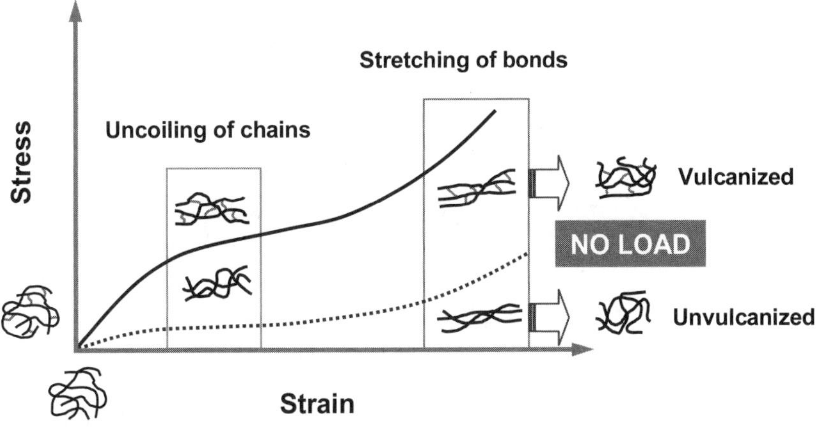

Figure 1.31. Stress-strain curves of vulcanized and unvulcanized elastomers.

1.5.1.4. Thermoplastic Elastomers

Thermoplastic elastomers (TPEs) are a unique class of synthetic copolymers which combine the look, feel and elasticity of conventional rubber, and the processing efficiency of plastics. Thus, TPEs have been called "meltable rubber". They have two big advantages over the conventional thermoset (vulcanized) types – ease of processing and speed. Other reasons for considering TPEs are recyclability of scrap, lower energy costs for processing, and the availability of standard, uniform grades, which is not accessible in thermosets. TPEs are molded or extruded on standard plastics-processing equipment in much shorter cycle times than those required for compression or transfer molding of conventional rubbers. TPEs are differntiated from elastomers by having physical crosslinks rather than chemical crosslinks.

The versatile properties of TPEs, such as SBS (styrene-butadiene-styrene) and SIS (styrene-isoprene-styrene) triblock copolymers, arise from their specific molecular architecture. In SBS, the two polystyrene end-blocks are incompatible with the butadiene mid-block due to their differences in polarities (aromatic vs. paraffinic). As a result, the polystyrene end-blocks agglomerate and form so-called polystyrene domains, which are all linked to each other by the elastic butadiene mid-blocks (Figure 1.32a). Thus, at ambient temperature, SBS forms three-dimensional networks by means of physical crosslinking, which create elastic properties that are similar to those of elastomers. However, during processing, in the presence of heat and shear forces, the network is weakened (softening of polystyrene domains) and the elastomers can be reformed; when cooled again, a new network is built, in accordance with the new form. This physical crosslinking and reinforcing effect of the polystyrene domains provide SBS with high tensile strength and elasticity (Figure 1.32b). TPEs also exhibit high impact resistance because of effective energy dissipation during impact through elastomeric domains. Major applications of TPEs are car bumpers, adhesives, the soles of shoes and toys.

The recent advent of metallocene catalyst technology provides access to a new family of TPEs, which are quickly adopting a new term, polyolefin plastomers (POPs), to distinguish them from other TPEs. POPs are normally ethylene and α-olefin copolymers, but can be homopolymers, if properly tailored. An example is aPP-iPP stereoblock homopolymer (see Chapter-2).

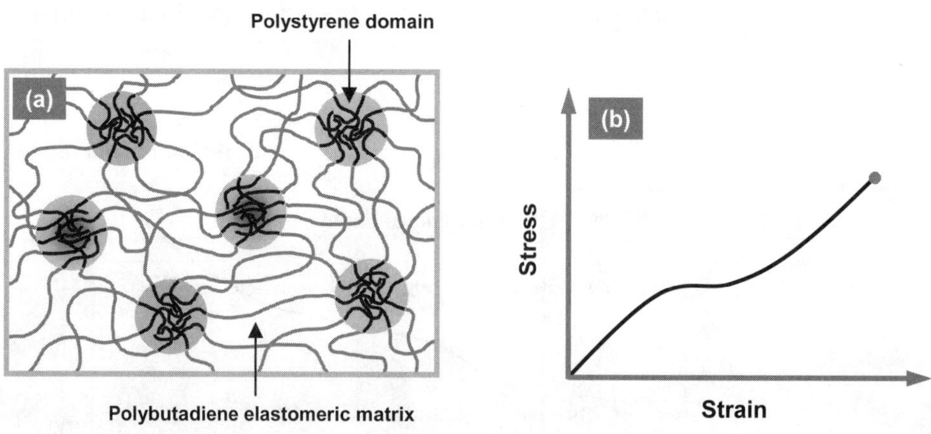

Figure 1.32. Schematic illustration of (a) domain structures in SBS network and (b) stress-strain characteristics of SBS.

Ionomers

Ionomers are another kind of thermoplastic elastomer. An ionomer is a polymer with a small number of ionic groups along its backbone chain. These groups tend to cluster, resulting in a polymer matrix as though they were crosslinked. When the ionomer is heated, the clusters break up, which permits easy processing, including molding. A good example is Surlyn®, developed by DuPont in the early 1960's, which is a family of ethylene methacrylic acid copolymers, in which part of the methacrylic acid is neutralized with metal ions, such as zinc or sodium (Figure 1.33). The resulting polymer structure has three regions: amorphous, crystalline, and ionic cluster.

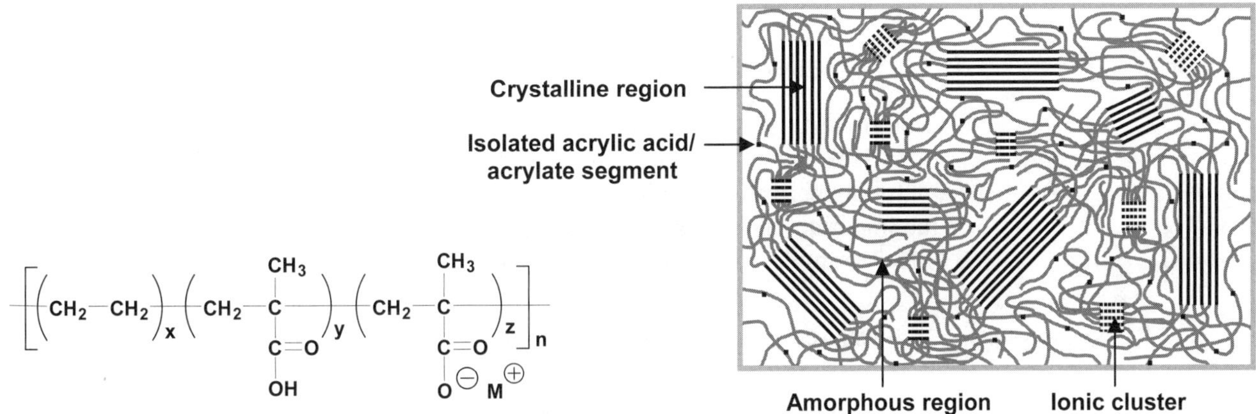

Figure 1.33. Surlyn®- poly(ethylene-*co*-methacrylic acid): chemical structure (left) and domain structure (right).

Surlyn is produced by random copolymerization of ethylene and methacrylic acid (<15 mol%) via a high pressure free-radical reaction, similar to that for the production of low density polyethylene (see Chapter-2). Neutralization of the methacrylic acid units is accomplished by addition of an appropriate base in solution, or in the melt mixing of base and copolymer. Some of the properties that make Surlyn excellent for packaging applications are its sealing performance, formability, clarity, oil/grease resistance, and high hot-draw strength. Good hot draw strength allows faster packaging line speeds and reduces packaging failures. Another well known application of Surlyn is its use in the outer covering of modern golf balls.

1.5.2. Application-Based Classification

In this classification the polymers can be separated into three groups: general-purpose (or commodity), engineering, and high-performance. As described in Table 1.4, the basis for this classification relates to stability at various temperatures for a prolonged time, mechanical performance, resistance to chemicals (e.g., aqueous alkalis and acids) and photo-degradation.

Table 1.4. Features of Application-Based Classification

Polymers	Thermal Stability	Mechanical Properties	Chemical Resistance	Photo-Degradation
General-Purpose Polymers	<100°C	Poor to good tensile strength and impact resistance	Poor to good	Poor to good
Engineering Polymers	100-150°C	Good tensile strength and impact resistance	Good	Good
High-Performance Polymers	>150°C	Very high tensile strength and dimensional stability	Excellent	Excellent

1.5.2.1. General-Purpose Polymers

These polymers serve very well in meeting the need for a variety of polymer products used in daily lives. Most are vinyl polymers (or polyolefins) which are made by chain-growth polymerization of vinyl monomers. Figure 1.34 depicts the chemical structures of the important members of this family, which are the subject of discussion in Chapter-2. More examples are cited in Appendix-I.

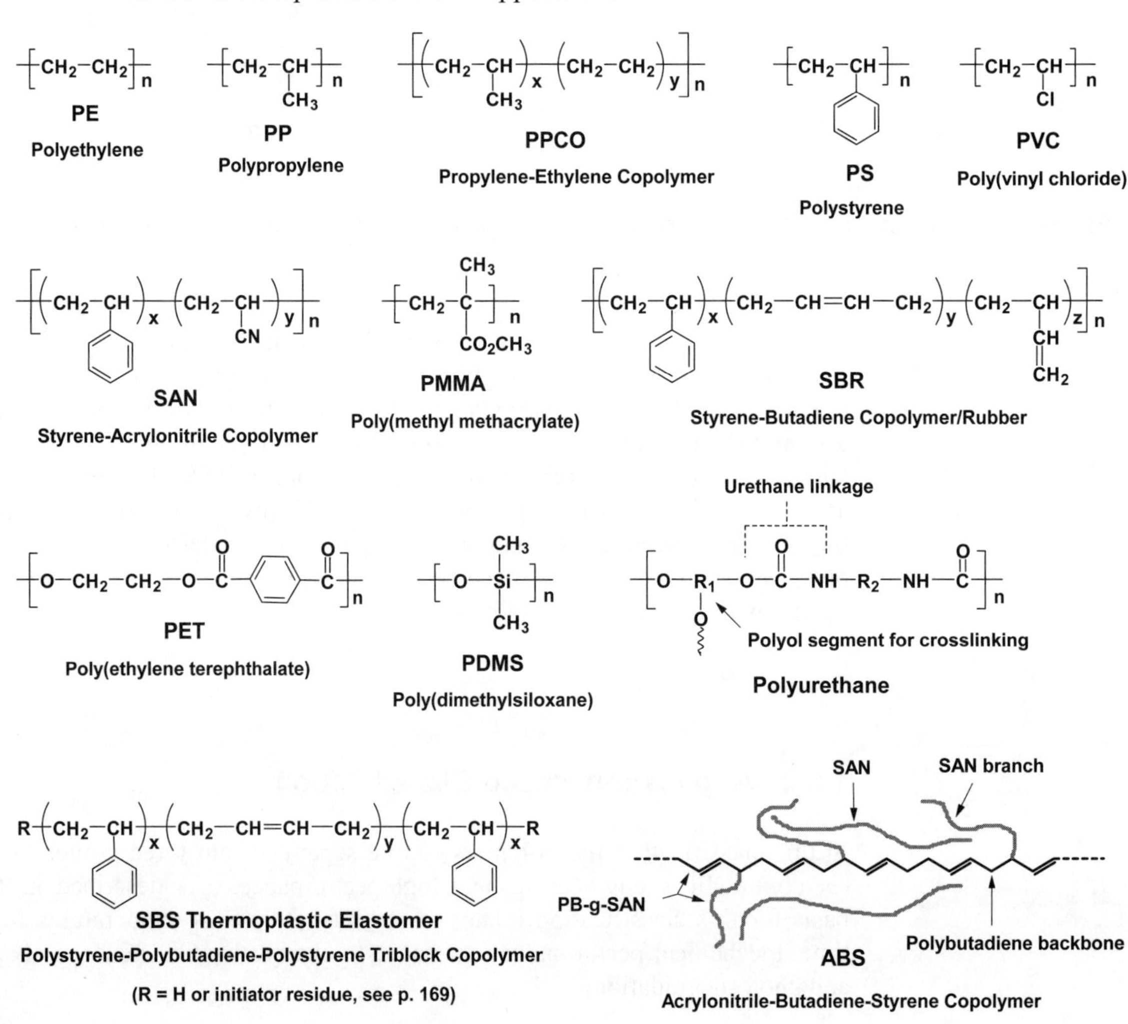

Figure 1.34. Important general-purpose polymers.

1.5.2.2. Engineering Polymers

These polymers offer good strength and durability and exhibit superior thermal stability when compared with vinyl polymers. Other criteria for engineering polymers include moldability and a good balance of mechanical properties over a long period of time and a wide range of dynamic and static conditions. The majority of engineering polymers are prepared by step-growth polymerization of monomers containing reactive functional groups. Figure 1.35 shows examples of some of the most important engineering polymers, which are covered in Chapter-3.

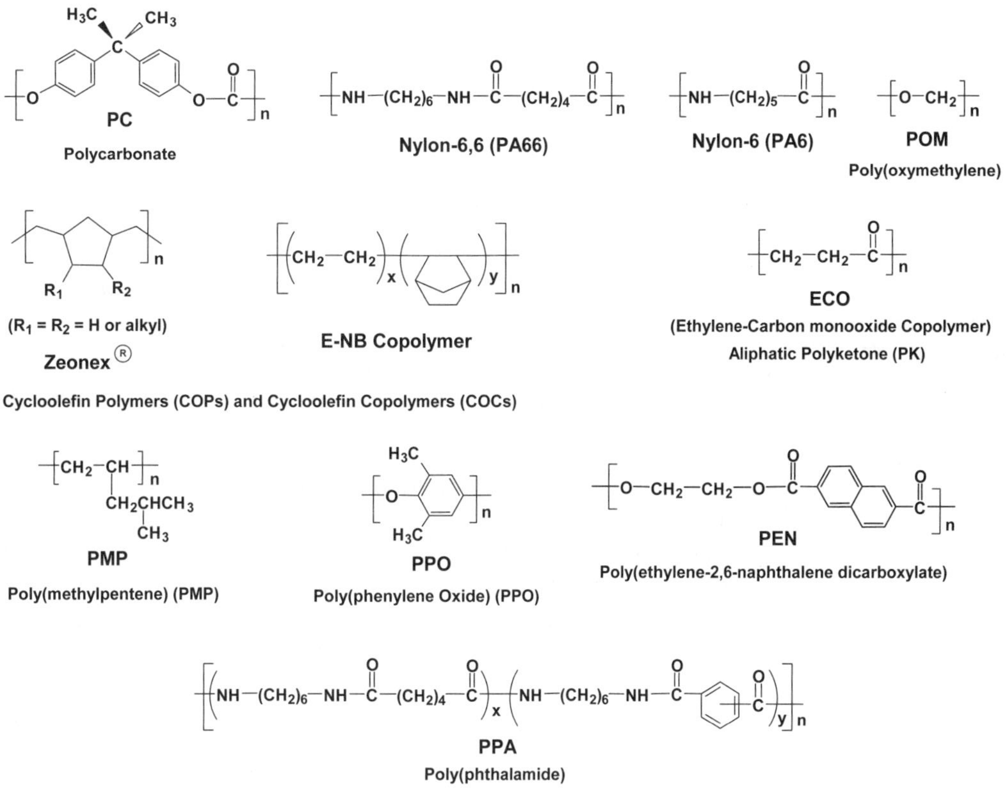

PC
Polycarbonate

Nylon-6,6 (PA66)

Nylon-6 (PA6)

POM
Poly(oxymethylene)

(R_1 = R_2 = H or alkyl)
Zeonex®

E-NB Copolymer

Cycloolefin Polymers (COPs) and Cycloolefin Copolymers (COCs)

ECO
(Ethylene-Carbon monooxide Copolymer)
Aliphatic Polyketone (PK)

PMP
Poly(methylpentene) (PMP)

PPO
Poly(phenylene Oxide) (PPO)

PEN
Poly(ethylene-2,6-naphthalene dicarboxylate)

PPA
Poly(phthalamide)

Figure 1.35. Notable engineering polymers.

1.5.2.3. High-Performance Polymers

This family of polymers is characterized by excellent dimensional stability at elevated temperatures, broad temperature-use range, outstanding hydrolytic stability, and superb dielectric properties over a wide range of frequencies and temperatures. Consequently, these polymers are suitable for structural applications or for use in mechanical and electrical components with long-term heat resistance requirements at temperatures greater than 150°C. They can be reinforced with glass, minerals, and both conductive and non-conductive graphite fibers to meet a diverse range of mechanical, physical, chemical, thermal, and electrical requirements. The major benefits of composites derived from these polymers over metals include corrosion resistance, vibration dampening, weight reduction and stealth. Composite materials directly reduce aircraft empty weights and increase fuel fractions. For the aerospace engineer, this leads directly to smaller, lower-cost aircraft that use less fuel to perform a given mission. Figure 1.36 depicts examples of some of the most important high-performance polymers, which are the subject of discussion in Chapter-4.

PPS
Poly(phenylene sulfide)

Udel®
Polysulfone (PSF)

PEEK®
Poly(ether ether ketone)

Kevlar®

Nomex®

Aramids

Kapton®
Polyetherimide (PIM)

Torlon®
Poly(amide imide) (PAI)

Vectra®
Liquid Crystal Polymers (LCPs)

Teflon®
Polytetrafluoroethylene (PTFE)

Celazole®
Polybenzimidazole (PBI)

Zylon®
Polybenzoxazole (PBO)

PBZT
Polybenzothiazole

Figure 1.36. Widely used high-performance polymers.

Finally, let's glance at all these polymers and see how they compare with each other with respect to cost vs. performance and differing molecular order (amorphous or crystalline). In general, the cost of polymers increases with improvement in all-around performance, e.g., thermal stability. As shown in Figure 1.37, these polymers are grouped into three clusters according to their cost. With few exceptions (e.g., nylons, PET and TPEs), they usually belong to either general-purpose, engineering or high-performance polymers.

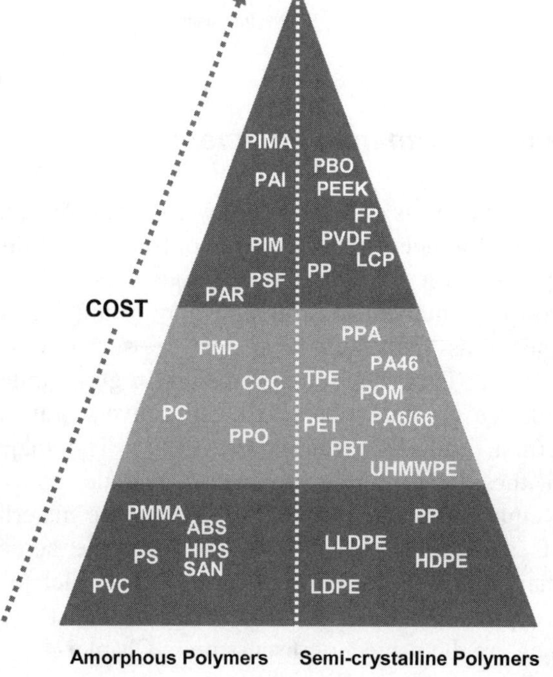

Abbreviation	
ABS	acrylonitrile-butadiene-styrene
FP	fluoropolymers
HDPE	high density polyethylene
HIPS	high impact polystyrene
LCP	liquid crystal polymers
PAI	**polyamideimide (Torlon®)**
PAR	polyarylate
PBT	poly(butylene terephthalate)
PBO	polybenzoxazole
PC	polycarbonate
UHMWPE	ultrahigh molecular weight PE
PEEK®	**polyetheretherketone**
PIM	polyetherimide
PMP	poly(4-methyl-1-pentene)
PET	poly(ethylene terephthalate)
PIMA	**polyimide (Aurum®)**
PMMA	poly(methyl methacrylate)
POM	polyoxymethylene
PP	polypropylene
PPA	polyphthalamide
PPO	poly(phenylene oxide)
PPS	poly(phenylene sulfide)
COC	cycloolefin copolymers
PS	polystyrene
PSF	polysulfone
PVC	poly(vinyl chloride)
PVDF	poly(vinylidene fluoride)
SAN	styrene-acrylonitrile
TPE	thermoplastic elastomers

Figure 1.37. The polymer pyramid: cost-property performances.

1.6. SYNTHESIS OF POLYMERS

Interest in synthetic polymers is driven by their widespread applicability, convenience of manufacture, easy recycling, superior mechanical properties, and lower cost compared to metals, alloys and ceramics. Although the chemistry of polymer synthesis has been revolutionalized by the development of a variety of novel synthetic approaches, there still exists ample opportunities to equate structure functions (e.g., functional groups, heteroatoms, hydrogen bonding, fluorine, linear, branched and crosslinked) with property functions (e.g., strength, stiffness, heat resistance, density, porosity and conductivity), leading to diverse polymers with specific properties. This section is planned to outline a concise overview of various polymerization processes as a prelude to strategies and tactics in polymer synthesis that are the subject of the subsequent chapters.

1.6.1. Polymerization Mechanisms

For polymerization to occur, the monomers (same or different type) must be reactive toward each other or to activated species generated under polymerization conditions, resulting in covalent linkages among the monomers. As shown in the polymer synthesis tree below, there are two basic polymerization mechanisms, *chain-growth* and *step-growth*, by which monomers are linked to form a polymer. The basic difference between the two mechanisms lies in their chain propagation.

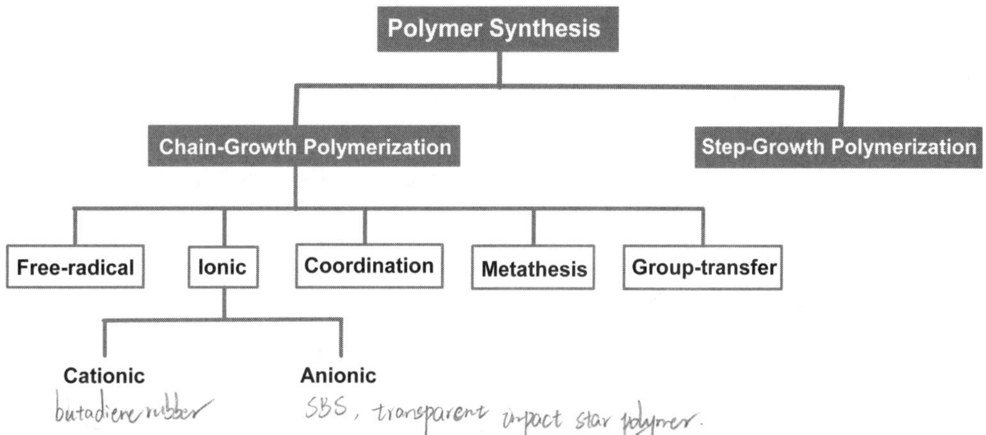

In the chain-growth mechanism, activation of a few monomers (chain initiation) is required for chain propagation. In most cases, the chain growth takes place only through one end of activated monomers. Under polymerization conditions, a monomer is unreactive to other monomers, but can react through the activated end of the propagating chains. As reaction proceeds, there will be a gradual decrease in concentration of the monomers. Thus, the existence of monomers throughout the polymerization reaction is obvious until the last monomer molecule reacts with an activated macromolecular chain (Figure 1.38). This mechanism usually involves termination of polymer chains. It is important to note that, for some specialty polymers (e.g., star polymers discussed in Chapter-2), monomers with more than one activated ends are used to perform chain propagation in multiple directions.

By contrast, step-growth mechanism involves normal reactions between functional groups of di- or multifunctional monomers and does not involve termination of polymer chains. Under polymerization conditions, monomers can react with other monomers to form dimers, which can then react with other monomers or dimers to form trimers and tetramers, and so on. In other words, monomers can react with each other or with growing polymer chains of any size. Therefore, the polymer chains propagate in both directions for difunctional monomers and multidirections for multifunctional monomers. Also, the disappearance of monomers occurs at an early stage of polymerization, leading to formation of oligomers, which through several replications, form high molecular weight polymers (Figure 1.38).

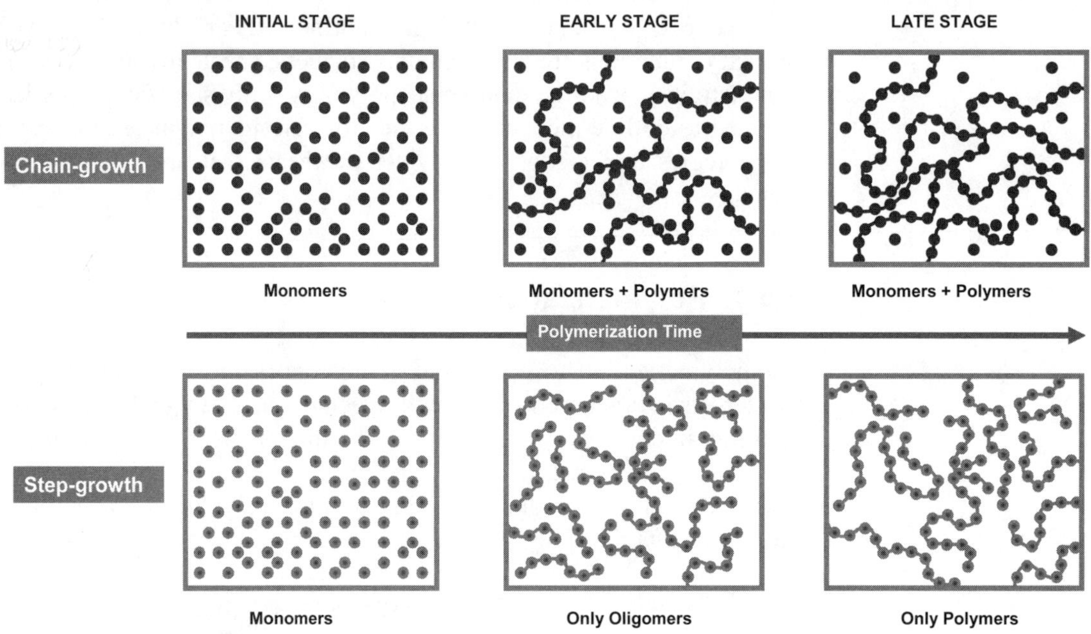

Figure 1.38. Schematic illustration of chain- and step-growth mechanisms.

Besides this fundamental difference, there are some advantages and disadvantages or unique aspects of each mode of polymerization. First, chain-growth is the best way to synthesize high molecular weight polymers composed of an all carbon backbone (e.g., HDPE, PS, PP and PMMA), but offers limited scope for the incorporation of heteroatoms or functional groups on the main chains. Poly(ethylene oxide) and nylon-6 are among the few polymers that can be made by chain-growth polymerization. By contrast, the reverse is true for step-growth polymerization, which is more convenient for the incorporation of heteroatoms, functional groups or heterocyclic rings in the main chain (e.g., PPO, PET, nylon-6,6 and PBO). Polymers containing all carbon in the backbone can also be synthesized by this method, but the opportunities are limited. Poly(phenylene vinylene) and polyphenylene are some of the polymers prepared by step-growth polymerization.

Second, in chain-growth polymerization, the polymer molecular weight rises rapidly and then increases steadily (Figure 1.39). A molecular weight in excess of 500,000 is common by this method and can be accomplished in a short reaction time, but more time is needed for high yield. In step-growth polymerization, the polymer molecular weight rises steadily, but requires long reaction times to reach a high conversion, which is a considerable disadvantage. However, as mentioned earlier, the requirement of minimum molecular weight for useful applications varies from polymer to polymer. For instance, PS must have a molecular weight in excess of a few hundred thousand for general purpose applications, while the properties of PET will be satisfactory in the molecular weight range of a few tens of thousands. Moreover, in the synthesis of step-growth copolymers, such as PET, equal stoichiometry of each monomer is extremely important for obtaining high molecular weight. Otherwise, the result will be low molecular weight polymers (oligomers) terminated with the functional groups (same as the monomer having higher concentrations) at the both ends of the polymers. Indeed, reactive oligomers, useful for the synthesis for block copolymers with the same terminal groups, are prepared by using 0.1 to 0.3 equivalent excess of the desired monomer. This situation does not exist during copolymerization by the chain-growth method.

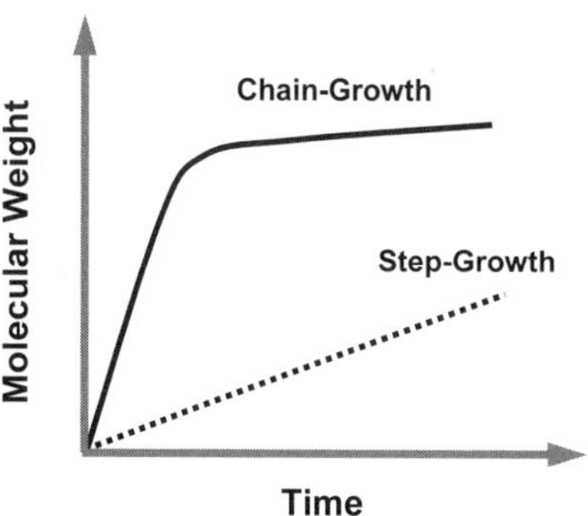

Figure 1.39. Typical relationship between molecular weight and reaction time for chain- and step-growth polymerizations.

Third, by virtue of its propagation mechanism, step-growth polymerization leads to polymers with a broad molecular weight distribution (MWD), while chain-growth polymerization produces polymers with a relatively narrow MWD.

Finally, chain-growth polymerization does not involve elimination of small molecules, while it is very common in step-growth polymerization. Chain-growth polymerization was formerly called *addition polymerization* because of the formation of polymers with repeat units having identical molecular formulae to those of the monomers. This is true for the formation of most monomers containing vinyl groups (e.g., styrene to polystyrene), but not satisfactory in certain cases, such as ring opening polymerization of caprolactam to nylon-6 (Figure 1.40). This ambiguity does not exist when the classification is based on chain-growth mechanism. Likewise, step-growth polymerization used to be called *condensation polymerization* because of chain propagation with the condensation reactions between two functional groups. Since not all step-growth syntheses are condensation reactions, such as a polyurethane by reaction of a diol and a diisocyanate, or a polyimide[12] formed by a Diels-Alder reaction between a bismaleimide and a bisbutadienyl, this confusion does not arise when called step-growth polymerization.

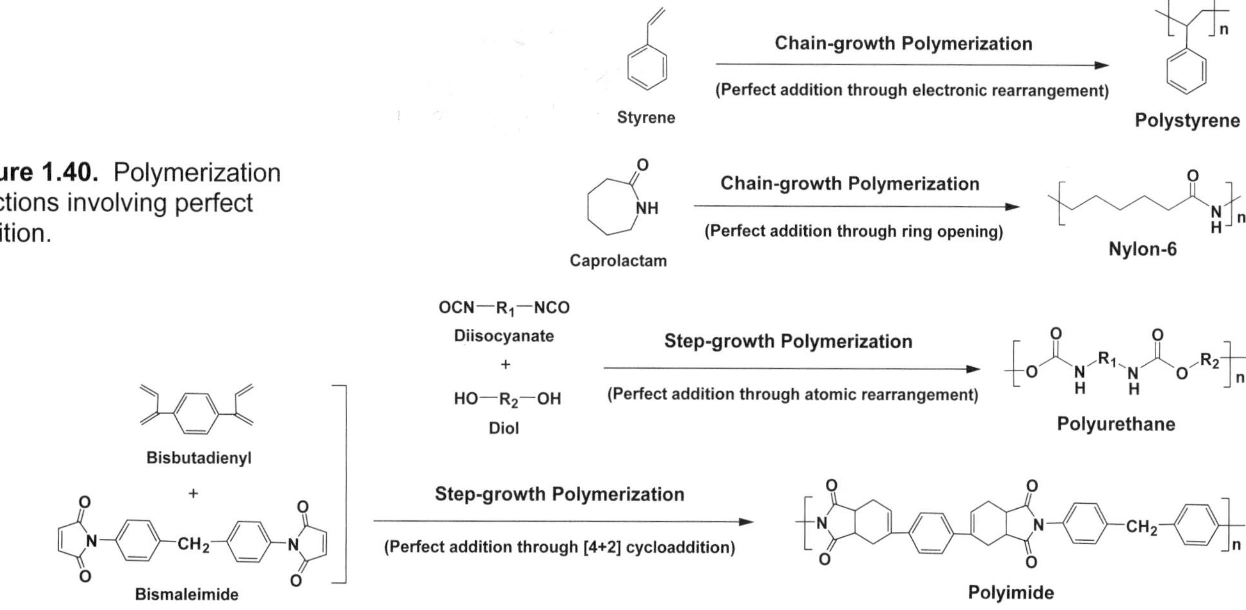

Figure 1.40. Polymerization reactions involving perfect addition.

1.6.1.1. Chain-Growth Polymerization

Chain-growth polymerization requires the activation of monomers (initiation), usually a small fraction, to start the growth of the polymer chain (chain propagation). The initiation leading to polymerization is carried out using a variety of compounds. The most important activating agents are (1) *Free-Radical Initiators* (produce free-radicals and the propagating species is a carbon free-radical), (2) *Cationic Initiators* (supply electrophiles, and the propagating species is a carbocation), (3) *Anionic Initiators* (generate nucleophiles, and the propagating species is a carbanion), (4) *Coordination Catalysts* (provide active sites in a transition metal complex, and the propagating species is a terminal catalytic complex), (5) *Metathesis Catalysts* (facilitate metathesis reaction with the monomers, and the propagating species is a terminal metal complex), and (6) *Group-transfer Catalysts* (undergo group-transfer reaction with monomers, and the propagating species is a terminal silyl ketene acetal complex). The advantages and disadvantages of these initiators, along with their chain propagation mechanism with selected monomers, are described below. More examples are discussed in the chapters which follow.

1.6.1.1a. Polymerization by Free-Radical Initiators

The chain-growth polymerization involving free-radical initiators is also called *free-radical polymerization.* Because of the tolerance of free-radicals to many functional groups and solvents (including water), free-radical polymerization is widely used in the chemical industry to produce a variety of useful *vinyl polymers*, such as PS, PMMA, PTFE and PVC. Figure 1.41 lists the structures of some vinyl compounds that are suitable for free-radical polymerization, including those which do not undergo polymerization in the presence of free-radical initiators.

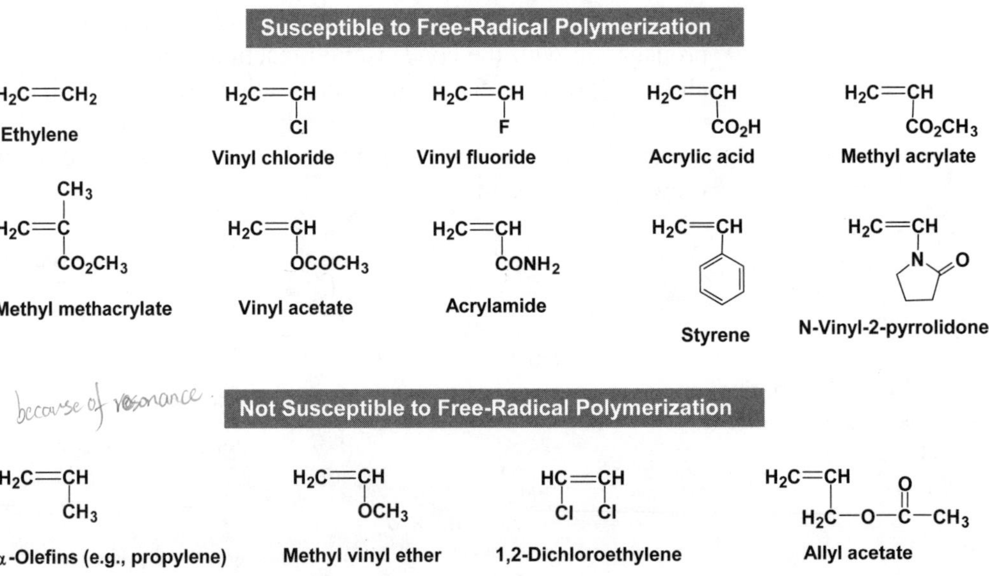

Figure 1.41. Active and inactive vinyl compounds for free-radical polymerization.

The generation of free-radicals is the starting point of the radical polymerization process (see Appendix-IV for an elaborate discussion). For instance, benzoyl peroxide (BPO) undergoes thermally induced homolysis of the peroxidic bonds to produce reactive oxy-radicals necessary to activate (initiation) vinyl monomers.

Initiation

Once the free-radicals are generated, the monomers quickly react with them to form activated monomer radical species, usually in very low concentrations (10^{-9}-10^{-7} mol/L). If the monomer is a substituted ethylene, such as styrene, there are two possible modes of reaction, α and β attacks. As shown in Figure 1.42, β-attack by the free-radical is strongly preferred because reaction occurs at the less sterically-hindered methylene carbon with formation of a resonance-stabilized free-radical (radical stability: 3°>2°>1°). The rate and orientation of the propagation also depends on the electronic effects of the monomer and the growing radical chain.

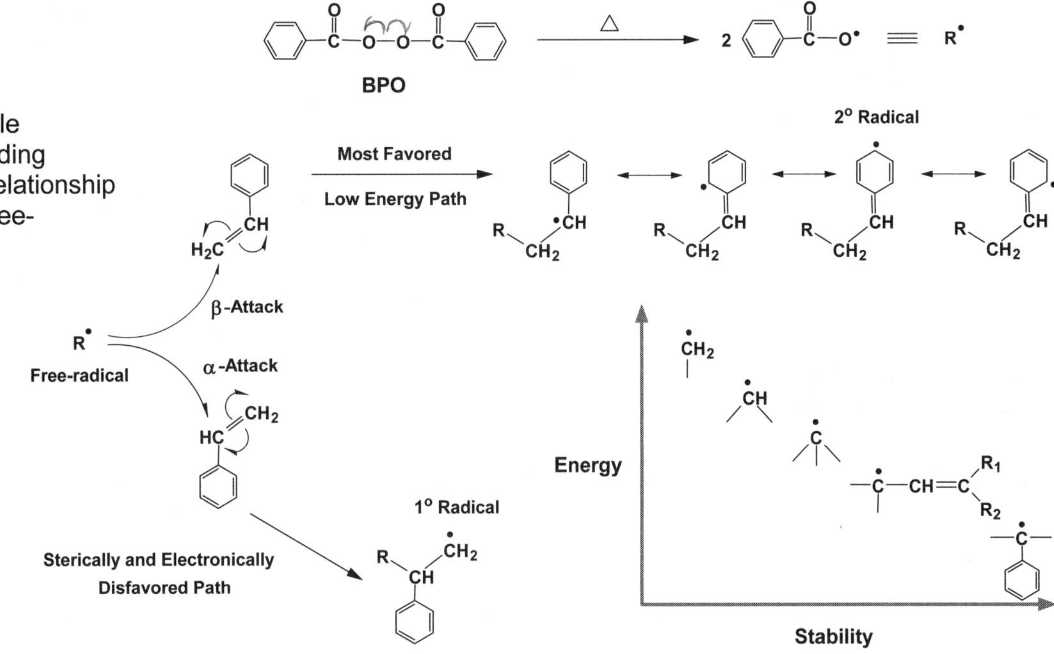

Figure 1.42. Possible initiation paths, including energy vs. stability relationship of various types of free-radicals.

Propagation

This step involves growth of the polymer chains by rapid sequential addition of monomers to the active radical centers created in the initiation step (Figure1.43). Growth rate of a chain is very high and chains with a degree of polymerization of 10^3 to 10^4 are formed in 0.1 to 10 seconds. Substituted ethylenes exhibit a marked preference for head-to-tail addition (favored for steric and electronic reasons), leading to a polymer in which every other carbon bears a substituent.

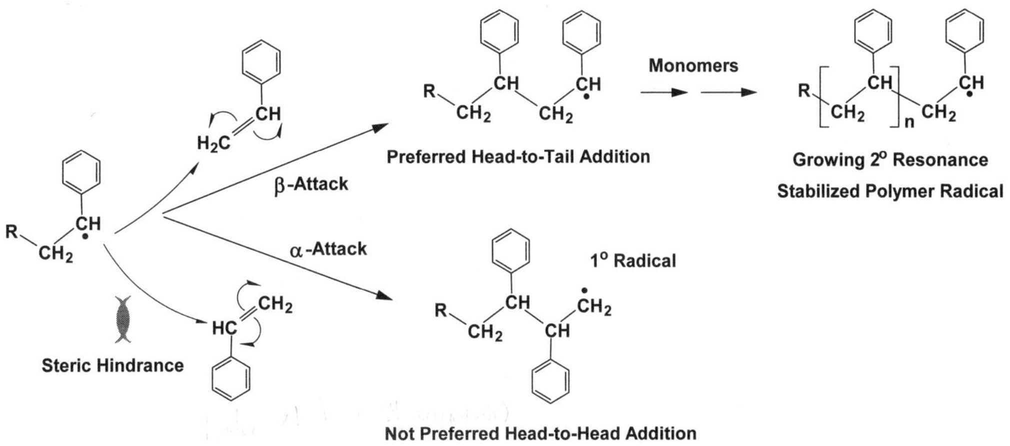

Monomers
β-Attack
Preferred Head-to-Tail Addition
Growing 2° Resonance Stabilized Polymer Radical
α-Attack
1° Radical
Steric Hindrance
Not Preferred Head-to-Head Addition

Figure 1.43. Possible propagation paths.

Chain-Transfer

This step is especially relevant to high pressure free-radical polymerization of ethylene (a method used for production of LDPE) that leads to both short and long branches. The chemistry is driven by the greater stability of the secondary radical that forms, compared to the primary one at the chain end. Since there are more short branches in LDPE (3-6 % of short branches with ≤ 6 carbons and ~ 0.2 % of long branches), it is believed that the most convenient site of attack is a hydrogen atom that is a short distance back on the same chain. Statistically, abstraction of the hydrogen from the fifth carbon atom back is favored, and the resulting branch is a butyl group. This intramolecular hydrogen abstraction reaction is termed "back-biting" (Figure 1.44). Branching makes the polymers less dense and results in low tensile strength and melting points. LDPE is much softer than HDPE, the version that is linear and made by coordination catalytic polymerization (*vide infra*).

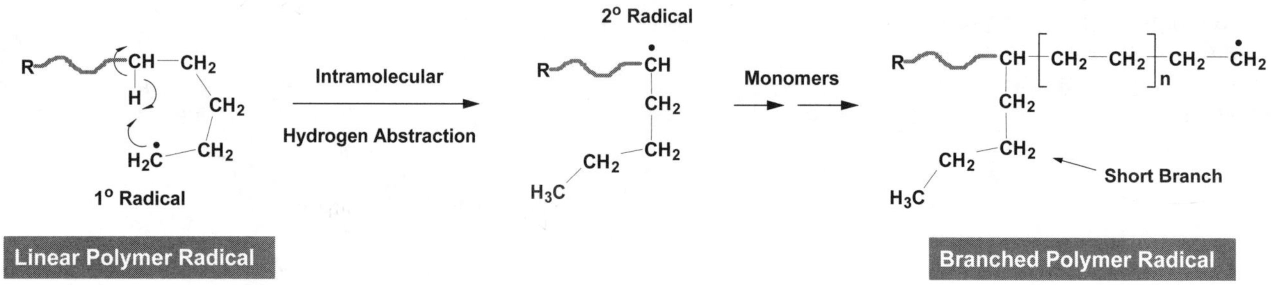

Figure 1.44. The "back-biting" mechanism responsible for short branches in LDPE.

Formation of branching by intermolecular hydrogen atom transfer, which leads to long branching in LDPE, is also a possible path in which one molecule is terminated ("dead" polymer) and the other is initiated (Figure 1.45). It is noteworthy that in the free-radical polymerizations of styrene, vinyl chloride, acrylonitrile and in most other potential monomers, the intermediate secondary radical is much more stable than a primary radical, so branching does not occur in these polymerization reactions.

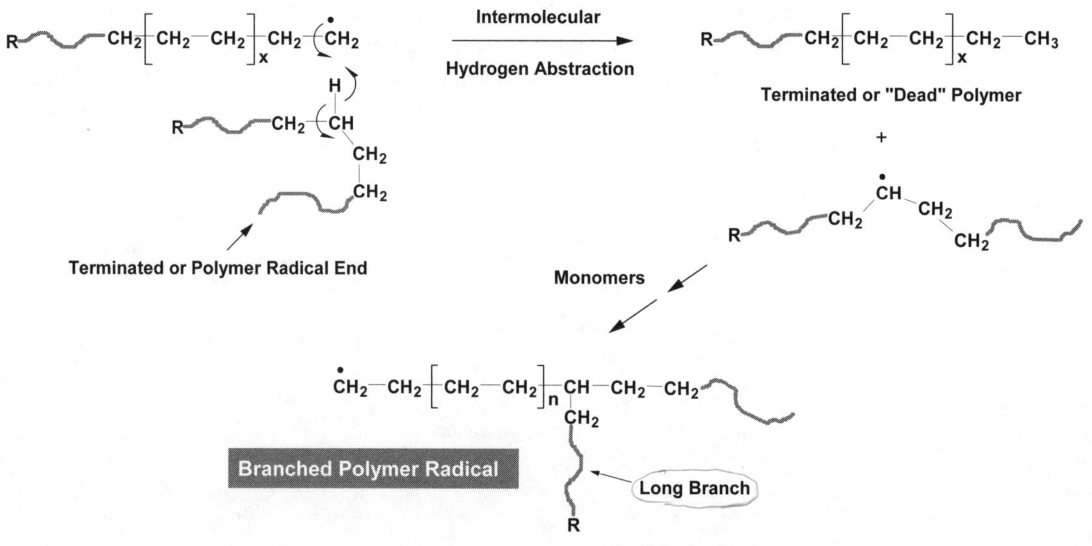

Figure 1.45. Intermolecular chain-transfer path leading to long branching in LDPE.

While the aforementioned intra- and inter-molecular events are minimal compared to that of linear chain propagation for LDPE, the chain-transfer during the polymerization of compounds possessing allylic structures, such as α-olefins (propylene, 1-butene, etc.) and allyl acetate, occurs so readily that the chain propagation path is a secondary process. Thus, the polymerization produces only low molecular weight oligomers (Figure 1.46). The driving force is the formation of a resonance-stabilized allylic radical compared to the polymer secondary radical at the chain end. This is the reason why PP is not produced by free-radical polymerization.

Propagation Path

No Propagation Path

= H, Alkyl or OAc

Stable Allyl Radical

Low Molecular Weight Product

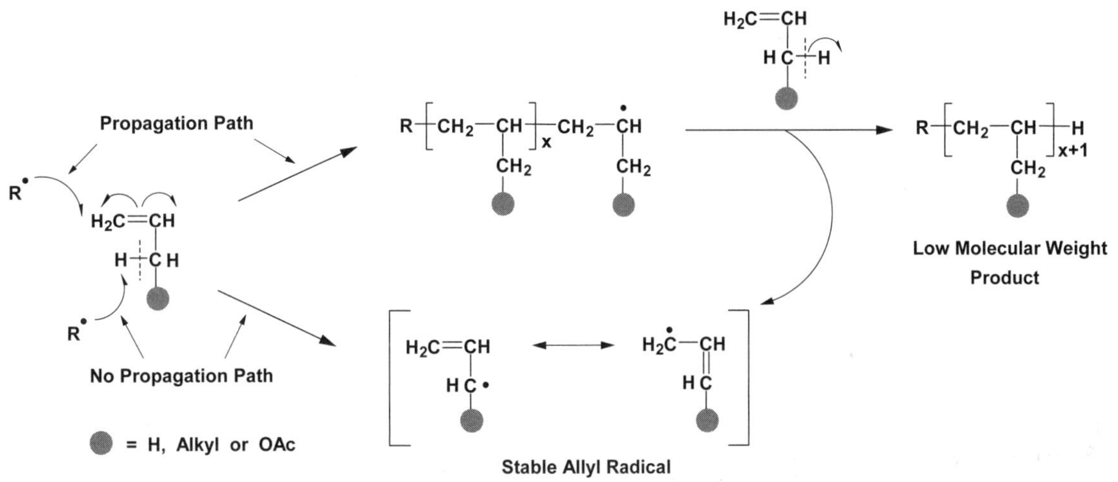

Figure 1.46: Rapid chain-transfer in α-olefin and allylic monomers render them unsuitable for free-radical polymerization (see Figure 2.12 in Chapter-2).

In many applications, the molecular weights in a polymerization reaction are controlled by deliberately adding a *chain-transfer agent*, such as butyl mercaptan, to the reaction mixture. Since the S-H bond of butyl mercaptan is weak, it is readily attacked by an active propagating chain to produce a terminated polymer and a new thiobutoxy radical, which has the ability to react with monomers very effectively, leading to regeneration of a new growing polymer radical (Figure 1.47). Thus, the process provides control of molecular weight without significantly changing the overall rate of conversion of monomer to polymer. It is important to stress that the radical polymerization reaction is exothermic, so that the use of a greater amount of initiator is not a viable path for obtaining polymers with lower molecular weights.

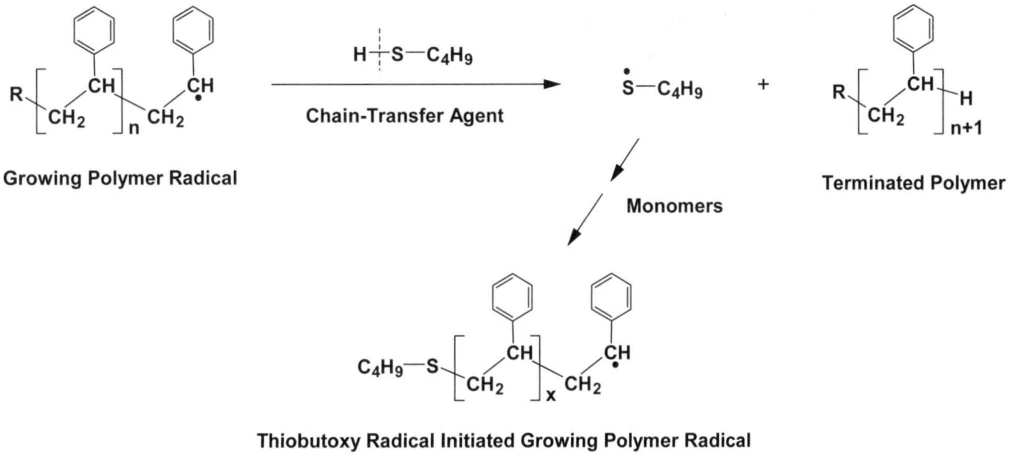

$H-S-C_4H_9$

Chain-Transfer Agent

Growing Polymer Radical

Terminated Polymer

Monomers

Thiobutoxy Radical Initiated Growing Polymer Radical

Figure 1.47. The role of a chain-transfer agent in controlling molecular weights.

Termination

In theory, the propagation reaction should continue until all the monomers are consumed to produce a few extremely long active polymer chains at the end of reaction. In practice, larger numbers of moderately sized inactive polymer chains are formed, indicating that chain-terminating reactions must be taking place between two activated propagating polymer chains, leading to one or two new inactive molecules (no radicals). As shown in Figure 1.48, the process by which two growing chains join head-to-head to form a single polymer chain with molecular weight totaling the molecular weights of two reacting chains is called *combination*. The process by which one growing chain strips a hydrogen atom from the position next to the atom bearing the radical of another growing chain, resulting in two inactive polymer chains with negligible change in molecular weights, is called *disproportionation*. The relative importance of these termination reactions varies with the nature of the monomer undergoing polymerization. For example, styrene favors the combination reaction, while methyl methacrylate disfavors combination because of steric and electrostatic repulsion between two polar groups, but instead, prefers disproportionation.

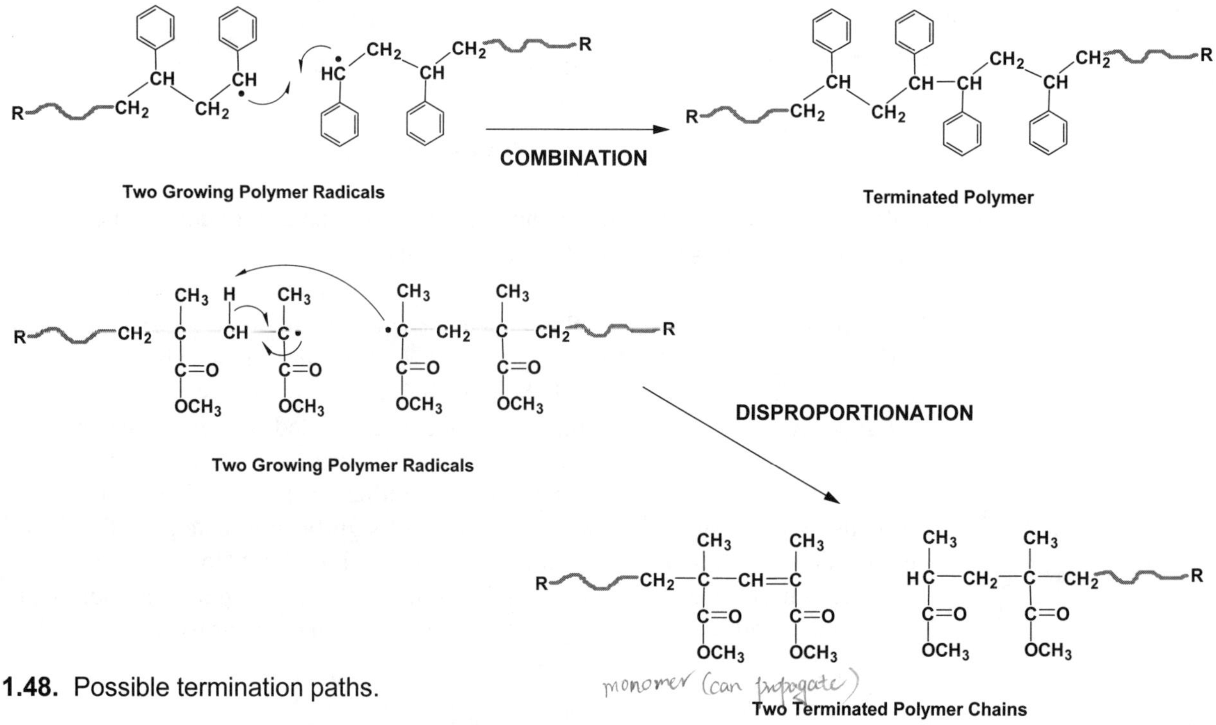

Two Growing Polymer Radicals

COMBINATION

Terminated Polymer

Two Growing Polymer Radicals

DISPROPORTIONATION

Two Terminated Polymer Chains

Figure 1.48. Possible termination paths.

1.6.1.1b. Polymerization by Cationic Initiators

Unlike free-radical polymerizations, ionic polymerizations produce active ionic (cationic or anionic) species as opposed to free-radicals, are monomer specific, and proceed with monomers that have at least one substituent capable of stabilizing the active center by inductive and/or mesomeric effects. Chain-growth polymerization involving cationic initiators is called *cationic polymerization* and will occur only if a substituent is capable of donating electrons and/or delocalizing the positive charge. For anionic polymerization, the substituent must be able to withdraw electrons and/or delocalize the negative charge. Table 1.5 describes the suitability of some monomers for ionic polymerization. Cationic and anionic mechanisms are also more ideally suited for living polymerizations (ions involved and no recombination), although free-radical living polymerizations have also been developed (see Chapter-2).

Table 1.5. Reactivity of Selected Monomers for Ionic Polymerization

Monomers	Ionic Polymerization		Comments
	Cationic	Anionic	
Ethylene	No	No	No substituent or stabilization of active center
Styrene	Yes	Yes	Stabilization of active center by delocalization
Methyl vinyl ether	Yes	No	Stabilization of active center by resonance
Iso-butylene	Yes	No	Stabilization of active center by inductive effect
Butadiene	Yes	Yes	Stabilization of active center by resonance
Acrylonitrile	No	Yes	Stabilization of active center by resonance
Methyl methacrylate	No	Yes	Stabilization of active center by resonance
N-vinyl carbazole	Yes	No	Stabilization of active center by resonance

Initiation

Cationic polymerizations are initiated by electrophilic agents, such as protonic acids (H_2SO_4, CF_3CO_2H, CF_3SO_3H and $HClO_4$) and Lewis acids (BF_3, BCl_3, $AlCl_3$, and $SnCl_4$). For the latter class, a small amount of co-initiator, typically H_2O or alkyl halide (e.g., *t*-butyl chloride) is required to initiate reaction. The active component in these cationic initiators is either a proton or a stable carbocation (e.g., *t*-butyl). The reaction between an active initiator and a monomer leads to an active monomeric species that has higher stability, as shown in Figure 1.49 for the commercially important example of isobutylene polymerization. In this case, proton addition yields the *t*-butyl ion that forms an association with a $[BF_3OH]^-$ counterion or *gegen* ion.

Vacant Electron Orbital

BF_3-H_2O Complex

Preferred Path

t-Butyl ion (3°)

Unfavored Path

Carbocation Stability: 3° > 2° > 1°

1° Carbocation

Figure 1.49. Possible initiation paths.

Propagation

Propagation also follows the path that produces the most stable carbocation (Figure 1.50). Cationic vinyl polymerizations are usually very fast and must be run at low temperatures (-70 to -100°C). Since most monomers freeze or become highly viscous at these temperatures, the polymerization is carried out in organic solvents that are stable towards acids and unable to react with electrophiles. The choice of solvent for cationic polymerizations is important, depending on the degree of association between cation and counterion. A 'firm' association will prevent monomer insertion during propagation. Typically, there is a linear increase in polymer chain-length and an exponential increase in polymerization rate as the dielectric strength of the solvent increases. Most preferred are halogenated (methylene chloride and carbon tetrachloride) or nitro (nitromethane and nitrobenzene) solvents. Since the cooling of large reactors is difficult and expensive, the industrial application of this polymerization method is limited. In addition, as this polymerization can be inhibited by water, extra precautions are necessary to have all ingredients perfectly dry (only a trace amount of water is required for Lewis acid catalysis). Nevertheless, in industry, butyl rubber, a copolymer of isobutylene and a small amount of isoprene (~2 mol%) for vulcanization, is prepared exclusively by cationic polymerization. First commercialized in 1943, the primary attributes of butyl rubber are excellent impermeability/air retention and good flex properties (T_g = -75°C), resulting from low levels of crosslinking between long polyisobutylene segments. Tire innertubes were the first major use of butyl rubber, and this continues to be a significant market today.

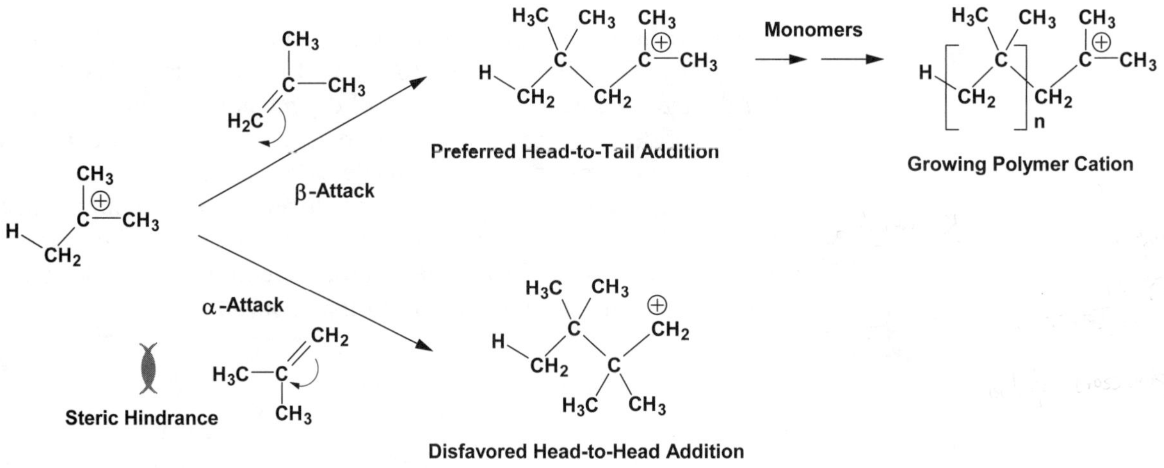

Figure 1.50. Possible propagation paths.

Termination

Unlike with free-radicals, termination of cationic polymerization cannot occur by combination of two cationic polymer chains. Consequently, most cationic polymerizations are somewhat "living". However, as shown in Figure 1.51, depending on the monomer, a variety of chain transfer reactions occur leading to termination of polymer chains. For instance, chain-transfer to a monomer by hydrogen abstraction is common to all cationic polymerizations, while termination by intramolecular ring alkylation is specific during the polymerization of styrene. The counteranions of some initiators (e.g., CF_3CO_2H) may also terminate a growing polymer cation by combination. The driving force towards combination is the formation of a stronger covalent bond.

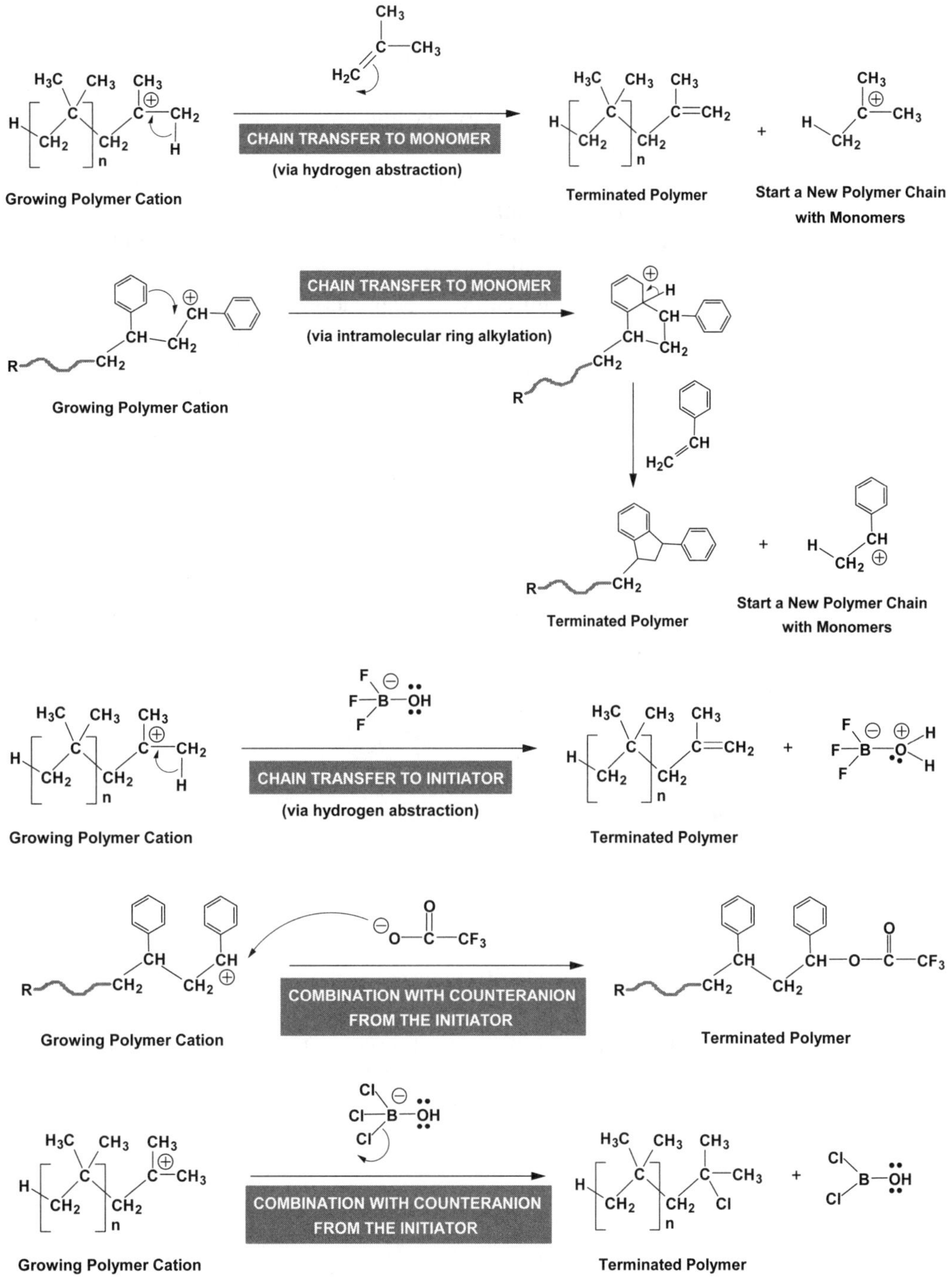

Growing Polymer Cation
CHAIN TRANSFER TO MONOMER
(via hydrogen abstraction)
Terminated Polymer
Start a New Polymer Chain with Monomers

Growing Polymer Cation
CHAIN TRANSFER TO MONOMER
(via intramolecular ring alkylation)
Terminated Polymer
Start a New Polymer Chain with Monomers

Growing Polymer Cation
CHAIN TRANSFER TO INITIATOR
(via hydrogen abstraction)
Terminated Polymer

Growing Polymer Cation
COMBINATION WITH COUNTERANION FROM THE INITIATOR
Terminated Polymer

Growing Polymer Cation
COMBINATION WITH COUNTERANION FROM THE INITIATOR
Terminated Polymer

Figure 1.51. Possible termination paths.

1.6.1.1c. Polymerization by Anionic Initiators

The chain-growth polymerization involving anionic initiators is called *anionic polymerization*. Only monomers having anion stabilizing substituents, such as phenyl, cyano or carbonyl are good substrates for this polymerization technique. Since alkyl groups are σ-donor groups, simple alkenes do not polymerize efficiently by the anionic method. In anionic polymerization, the resulting polymers are largely isotactic in configuration, and have high degrees of crystallinity.

Initiation

For a smooth anionic vinyl polymerization, it is necessary to match the monomer with the appropriate initiator so that the propagating carbanion formed after initiation is very stable. If this anion is not highly stabilized, a powerful nucleophile is required as initiator. If the anion is strongly stabilized, even a rather weak nucleophile will suffice. Typical initiators include alkyl lithium (e.g., *n*-butyl lithium and *sec*-butyl lithium, strong nucleophiles suitable for initiating styrene and isoprene monomers), Grignard reagents (e.g., PhMgBr, a medium strength nucleophile effective for polymerization of MMA) and alkali metal alkoxides (e.g., NaOMe, a weaker nucleophile especially suitable for initiation of cyanoacrylate monomer). Like other polymerization processes, anionic polymerization proceeds through the path that produces the more stable carbanion (Figure 1.52).

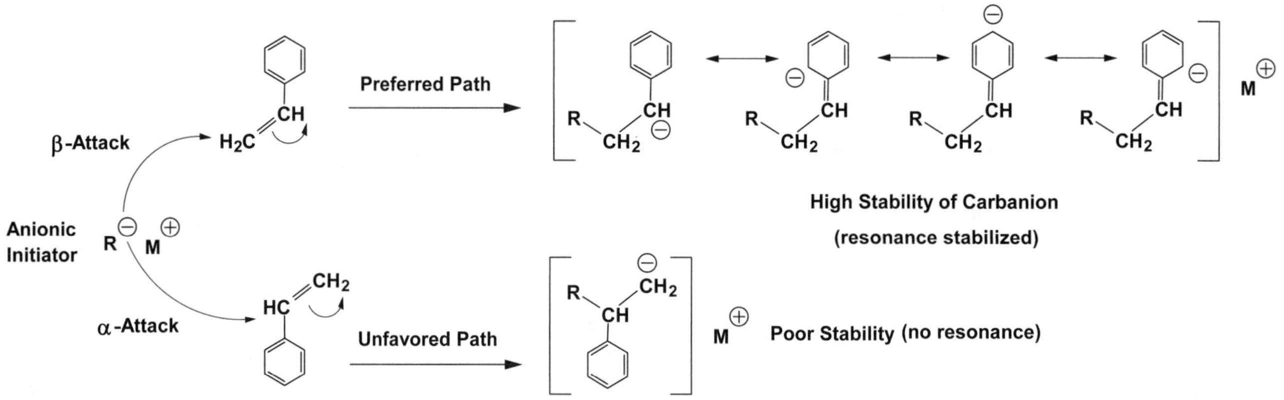

β-Attack
Anionic Initiator
α-Attack
Preferred Path
Unfavored Path
High Stability of Carbanion (resonance stabilized)
Poor Stability (no resonance)

Figure 1.52. Possible initiation paths.

Propagation

Propagation also follows the path that produces the more stable carbanion (Figure 1.53). Similar to cationic polymerization, anionic polymerization is carried out at low temperature and in the presence of aprotic solvents, such as THF. It is important to mention that, in industry, SBS and SIS triblock thermoplastic elastomers are prepared by this technique (see Chapter-2).

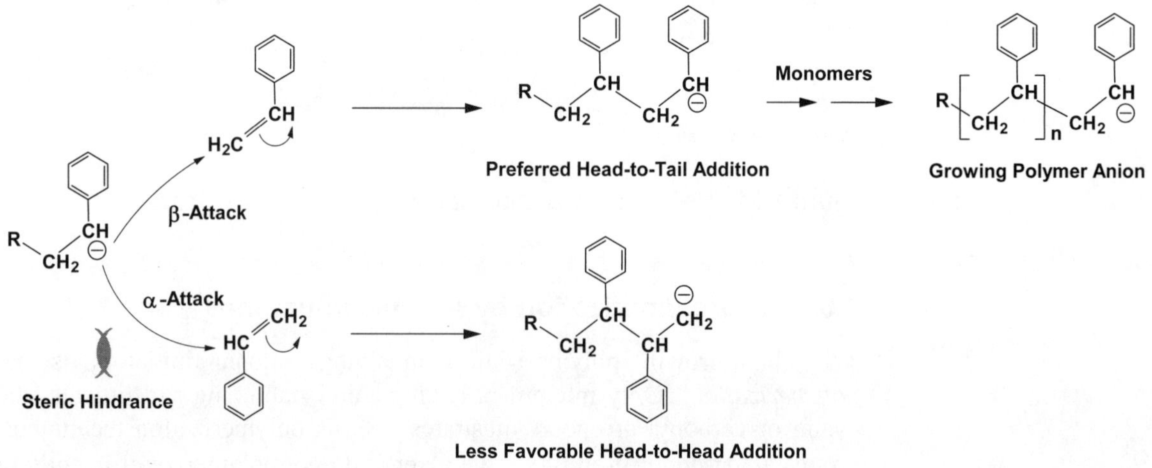

β-Attack
α-Attack
Steric Hindrance
Monomers
Preferred Head-to-Tail Addition
Growing Polymer Anion
Less Favorable Head-to-Head Addition

Figure 1.53. Possible propagation paths.

Termination

Like cationic polymerization, anionic polymerization can be considered a living system because of the presence of carbanions at the end of each propagating species. Practically, living anionic polymerization requires that levels of reactive impurities (e.g., O_2, CO_2, H_2O) be extremely low, as the concentration of propagating centers is very low. Solvents and reagents must be carefully purified. Chain growth of anionic polymerization is usually terminated by adding water or methanol (Figure 1.54).

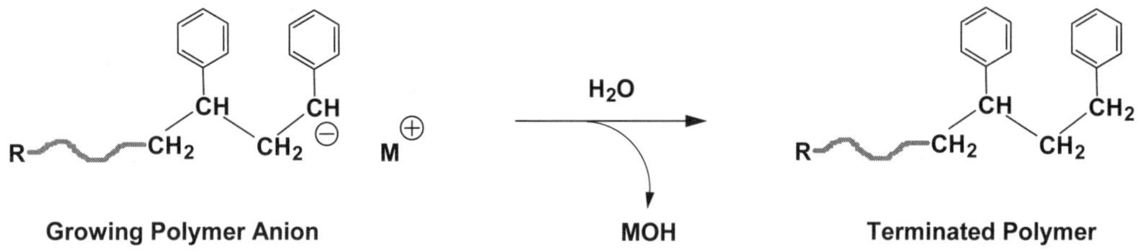

Growing Polymer Anion — H_2O → MOH — Terminated Polymer

Figure 1.54. Termination of anionic polymerization by water.

1.6.1.1d. Polymerization by Transition Metal Catalysts

Chain-growth polymerization involving transition metal catalysts is called *coordination polymerization,* since the mechanism involves repeated coordination followed by insertion of the monomers with the catalysts. There are two major types of catalysts, *Ziegler-Natta* and *metallocene*, and both can produce polymers with very high tacticity and little or no branching. In addition, the polymerization involving these catalysts is rapid and occurs at atmospheric pressure and moderate to low temperature. Further discussions on recent developments on these catalysts, including their synthesis are found in Chapter-2.

Ziegler-Natta Catalysts

These catalysts, developed by Karl Ziegler and Giulio Natta in the 1950's, are heterogeneous materials composed of a $MgCl_2$ support, a Group-IVB transition metal halide as a primary catalyst (e.g., $TiCl_4$ and VCl_4), and an alkylaluminum compound as a co-catalyst (e.g., $AlEt_3$ and $AlEt_2Cl$).[13,14] Ziegler-Natta catalysts permitted, for the first time, the synthesis of unbranched, high molecular weight polyethylene (HDPE), *cis*-polyisoprene (synthetic version of natural rubber), and configurational control of polymers from terminal alkenes (e.g., polymerization of propylene through action of the titanium catalyst gives an isotactic product; whereas, a vanadium based catalyst gives a syndiotactic product).

The mechanism of this polymerization is still unclear because it takes place on the surface of an insoluble particle, a difficult situation to probe experimentally. The Cossee-Arlman mechanism[15,16], shown in Figure 1.55, is one of several models proposed to at least partially explain the action of the catalysts, but it is only an approximation of the more complex process that actually occurs. The basic idea is that an active site contains a transition metal atom in an octahedral configuration. Five of the six coordination sites are occupied by four chlorine atoms from the crystal lattice and one alkyl group that originated from the co-catalyst. The remaining coordination site is vacant, where the double bond of an olefin monomer (e.g., ethylene) can coordinate and then insert between the alkyl group and the metal center via a four-membered-ring intermediate (or transition state), resulting in two-carbon homologation of the alkyl group. The coordination and insertion cycle continues, and the alkyl group becomes a part of the polymer chain. In the case of the titanium catalyst system ($TiCl_4/AlEt_3$), the monomers approach the catalyst active site in only one spatial orientation and add onto the chain one at a time (Figure 1.55). Therefore, if propylene is used as the monomer, the product will be isotactic PP (iPP), because each time propylene approaches the active center in one direction and insertion takes place without the shift of active center. Moreover, unlike radical polymerization, this polymerization does not have any reactive intermediates capable of undergoing side reactions, such as "backbiting". Thus, if ethylene is used as the monomer the product will be linear polyethylene, referred as high density polyethylene (HDPE). It should be emphasized that the polymerization of propylene (and other α-olefins) with Ziegler-Natta catalysts is stereoselective and takes place predominantly by a regeoselective 1,2-insertion (energetically favored) into the metal-carbon bond.

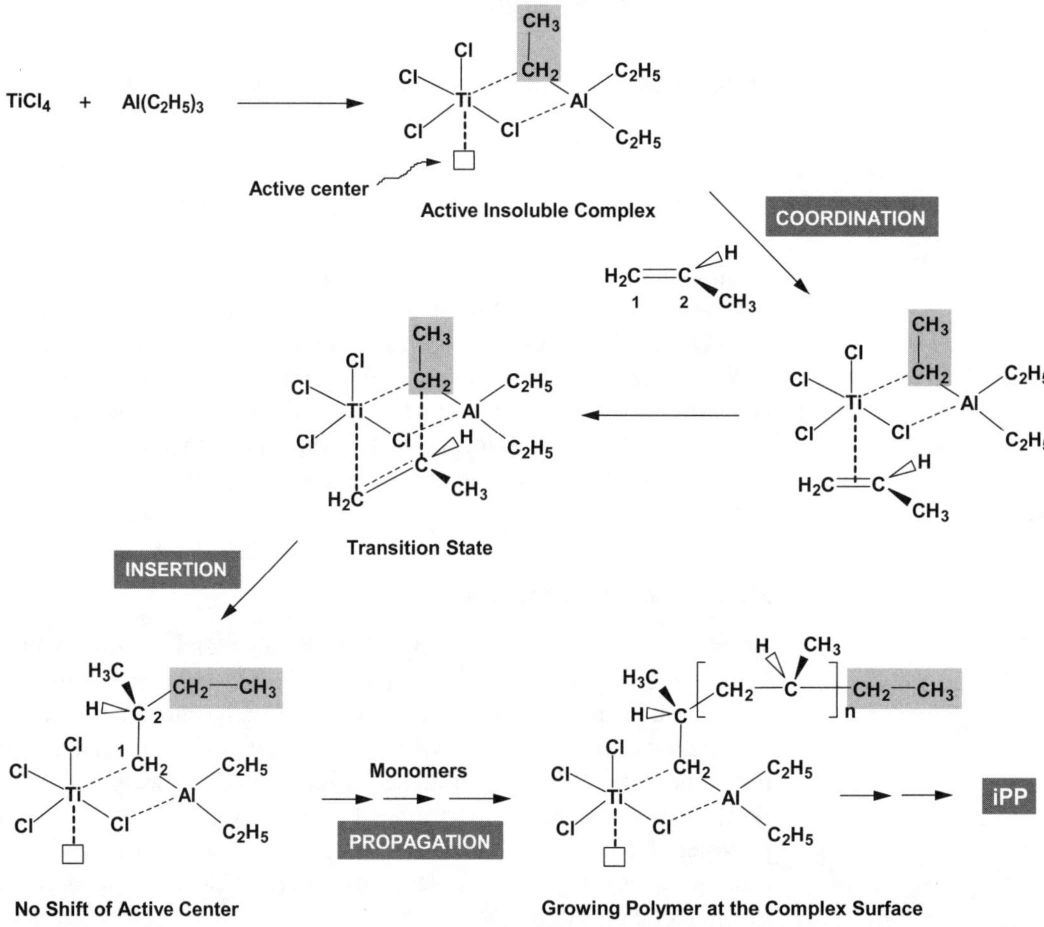

Figure 1.55. The Cossee-Arlman coordination-insertion mechanism for the isospecific polymerization of propylene.

By contrast, the vanadium catalyst system ($VCl_4/AlEt_3$) behaves differently, as propylene monomer produces syndiotactic PP (sPP) exclusively. The reason is still not clear, but it is believed that the shifting of the active center after every other insertion causes alternate placement of methyl groups in the polymer. A proposed mechanism for this syndiospecific polymerization is shown in Figure 1.56.

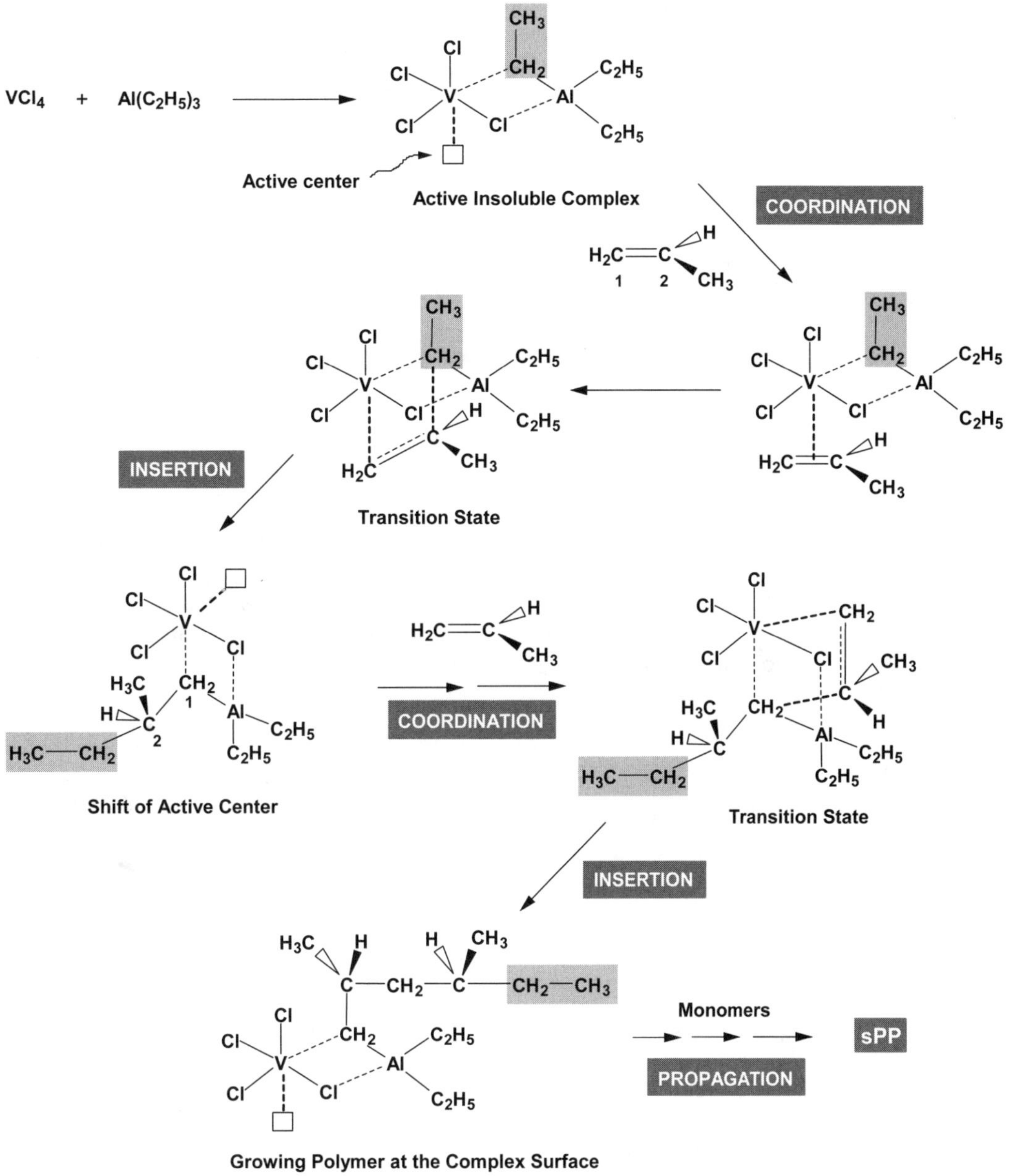

Figure 1.56. Proposed mechanism for the syndiospecific polymerization of propylene.

Chain Termination: Several reactions can separate a polymer chain from the active center, i.e., spontaneous chain transfer, chain transfer to monomer, chain transfer to aluminum, and chain transfer to hydrogen (Figure 1.57). Spontaneous chain transfer and chain transfer to monomer both include a β-hydride elimination process, in which the β-hydrogen on the polymer chain, σ-coordinated to the metal center, is extracted by the metal center. The polymer chain becomes olefin π-coordinated to the metal center through a π bond. The polymer chain can then leave the metal center to form a terminated polymer molecule, and an olefin monomer can coordinate to grow a new chain. Chain transfer to aluminum is through a four-centered metathesis mechanism, in which a metal center with a polymer chain and an Al atom in AlR_3 exchange their ligands, so the polymer chain is coordinated to the Al atom and an R group is coordinated to the metal center after metathesis. The termination of the polymerization can also be done purposefully by introduction of hydrogen, water or aromatic alcohol. Chain transfer to H_2 is also a metathesis process, which terminates the coordinated polymer chain and makes the metal center coordinate with a hydride, thereby providing a method to control the molecular weight of the polymer product.

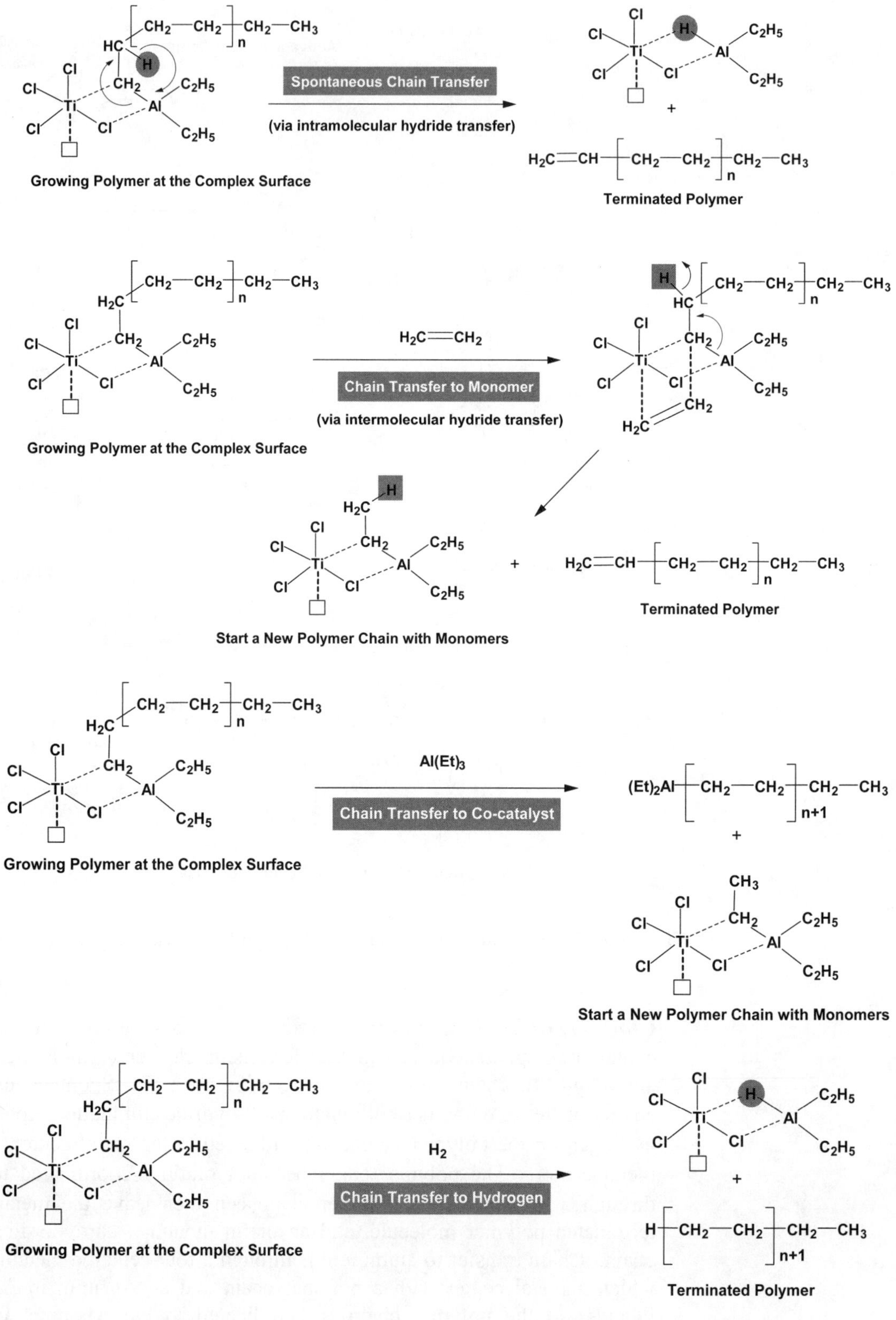

Figure 1.57. Chain termination processes in coordination polymerization of ethylene.

Metallocene Catalysts

A strict definition of "metallocene" requires that such compounds contain a metal that is sandwiched between two cyclopentadienyl (Cp) ligands. A good example is ferrocene, Cp_2Fe, in which the two Cp rings are parallel. The Cp ligand is a 6e-donor anionic ligand and the normal bonding mode for Cp is η^5 (pentahapto). In polymer chemistry, the term "metallocene catalyst" represents a broad range of metallocenes in which the metal atoms are normally Group-IVB transition metals (viz., titanium, zirconium and hafnium) and the aromatic ligands could be Cp or its alkyl, aryl, anellated or bridged (also called *ansa*) analogs (Figure 1.58). Unlike ferrocene, in these metallocenes the metal possesses two additional ligands (halide or alkyl), which make the aromatic ligands bent. Albeit not adhering to the definition of a metallocene, the half-sandwich complexes, which contain only one Cp (or its derivatives) or cyclopentadienylsilylamido ligand are also termed metallocenes (see Chapter-2 for synthesis and applications).

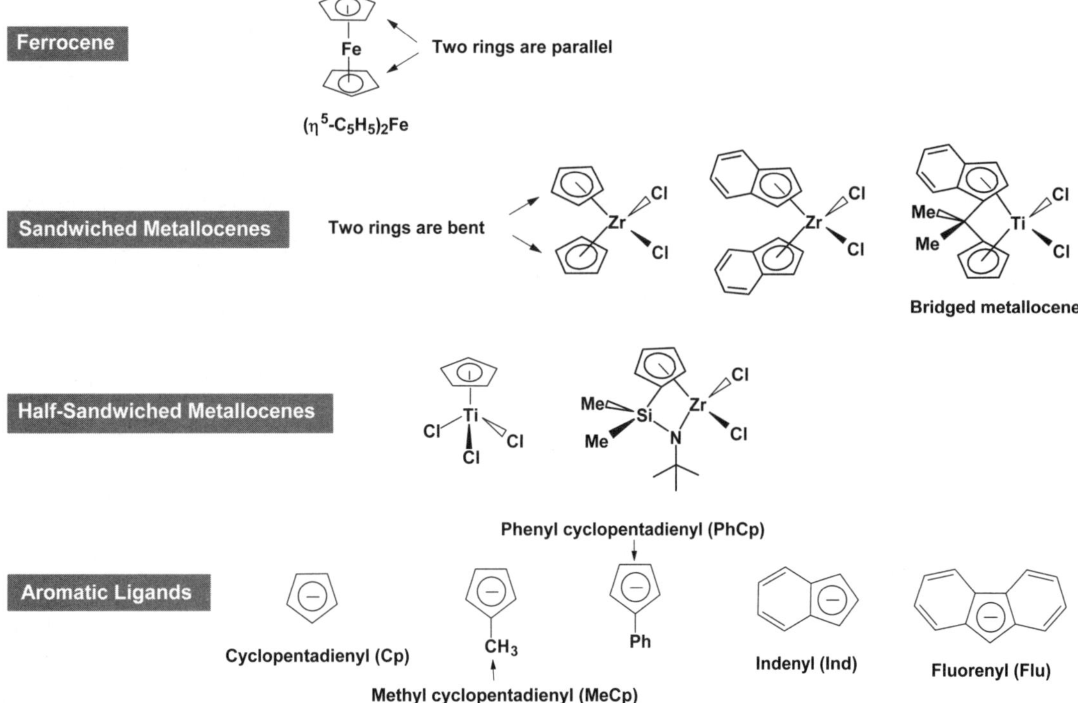

Figure 1.58. Structures of important types of metallocenes and ligands.

Metallocene catalysts have been known since the time of Ziegler-Natta catalysts, but did not receive much attention due to their very low activity. Major research activities on metallocenes reopened in 1980 when Walter Kaminsky first discovered that these catalysts become highly effective in the presence of oligomeric methylalumoxane (MAO) as a co-catalyst.[17] After a decade of further research on structure-property relationships, these catalysts began to be used in commercial production of polymers in 1991 and are now rapidly capturing the polyolefin market. The enhanced properties (such as, superior optical clarity and low-temperature ductility) coupled with reduced amounts of impurities (low catalyst metal residues) of some metallocene-catalyzed polymers open new opportunities for traditional commodity thermoplastics and in the medical area. Utilizing metallocene chemistry, nearly 100% syndiotactic polypropylene (sPP) and syndiotactic polystyrene (sPS) have been produced for the first time on a commercial scale.

Differences between Ziegler-Natta and Metallocene Catalysts

First, in the Ziegler-Natta-type catalysts, which are heterogeneous, the active metal center occupies a position on the surface of the crystal. Polymerization at the active site is influenced by the electronic and steric environment of the crystal lattice. Because the active centers can occupy a wide variety of lattice sites, Ziegler-Natta catalysts are called *multiple-site catalysts* (MSC). They tend to give products with broad molecular weight distributions (MWD) and also, for example, non-homogeneous co-monomer distribution in olefin copolymers. By contrast, metallocenes are homogeneous and possess an active center that is shielded to a large extent from the influence of its immediate surroundings and exhibit similar reactivity, hence called *single-site catalysts* (SSC). The term "single-site" means that all the active sites have the same properties, e.g., same structure, activity, selectivity, chain-transfer rate, etc. Thus, metallocenes yield a sharply defined product with narrow MWD and other molecular characteristics, as well as a minimum of undesirable byproducts [e.g., low molecular weight PE in linear low density polyethylene (LLDPE) and aPP in iPP manufacture].

Second, control of molecular weights of polymer produced by a metallocene catalyst can be easily achieved by introducing hydrogen to the polymerization system (*vide infra*) or by increasing the temperature. Unlike conventional Ziegler-Natta catalysts, metallocenes require only a trace of hydrogen to significantly reduce the molecular weights of polymer produced. By contrast, a large excess of hydrogen is required to produce oligomers using conventional Ziegler-Natta catalysts, and the oligomers produced are saturated. In addition, oligomers with unsaturated terminal vinyl or vinylidene groups can be produced by metallocene catalysts by increasing the polymerization temperature, because β-hydride elimination becomes the primary chain transfer pathway. Metallocenes can also be used to copolymerize ethylene with propylene, butene, hexene, and octane, a method by which LLDPE is prepared commercially.

Third, the modifications of metallocene catalysts by variations of the ligands surrounding the active center permit correlation of catalyst structure with catalytic activity and stereospecificity. Figure 1.59 shows a preview of selected metallocene catalysts with respect to PP microstructure (detailed discussions are in Chapter-2). So many varieties and control of polymer products are not achievable with Zieglet-Natta catalysts.

Metallocene catalysts do have some disadvantages. The activities of these metallocene catalysts for olefin polymerization are highly dependent on the MAO and catalyst ratio (commonly expressed as Al/M ratio). Metallocenes require large excesses of MAO (Al/M ratio ranging from 1,000:1 to 15,000:1) to achieve high activities. The cost of MAO is high, so the polyolefins made with metallocene catalysts are expensive, if the Al/M ratios are high. In order to compete in price with the polyolefins produced by conventional Ziegler-Natta catalysts, either the cost of MAO and/or the Al/M ratio in the polymer production processes using metallocene catalysts must be significantly reduced. Indeed, compared with Ziegler-Natta catalysts, metallocenes are more expensive, but can be much more productive (10 to 100 times) in terms of the amount of polymer produced per mole of catalyst.

The homogeneous nature of the metallocene catalysts also has some disadvantages from a practical point of view. For example, the gas-phase process for polyolefin production has many economic and technological advantages. Since this process requires solid catalyst particles, the metallocene catalysts, which are pure compounds and occur as crystalline solids, cannot be used in gas-phase processes without immobilization. The majority of Ziegler–Natta polymerization production units are designed for heterogeneous catalysis. To utilize exisiting facilities, metallocenes are now supported on a number of inorganic oxides, such as SiO_2 (silica gel), Al_2O_3, and $MgCl_2$ with or without MAO. For example, silica-supported metallocenes can be used to obtain LLDPE.

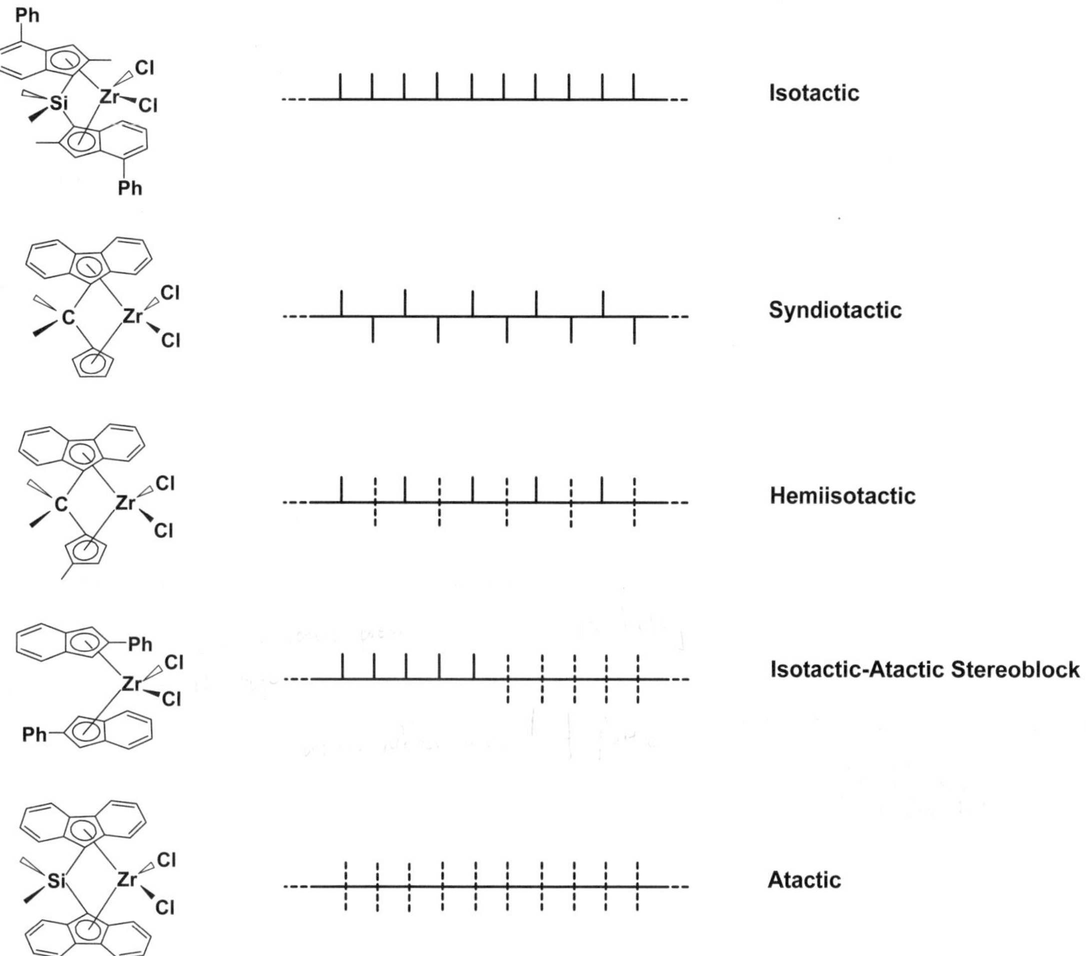

Figure 1.59. Relationship between metallocene structures and PP microstructures.

Structure and Function of MAO

As mentioned above, the co-catalyst is the key to the activity of the metallocenes. MAO is mostly used and is conventionally synthesized by the controlled hydrolysis of $AlMe_3$. The exact structure of MAO is very complex and remains the subject of significant controversy. However, it is generally accepted that MAO is a mixture of linear and cyclic oligomeric compounds with a general formula, $[Al(Me)O]_n$ (where *n* is an integer and ranging from 4 to 30) (Figure 1.60). Replacement of the methyl substituents in MAO with bulkier *tert*-butyl groups permitted the first structural (x-ray crystallography) determination of alkylalumoxanes.[18] The structure of *tert*-butylalumoxane has been characterized as a $[^tBuAlO]_6$ cage with four-coordinated aluminum atoms, leading to the suggestion (supported by molecular modeling) that some of the oligomers of MAO have three-dimensional cage structures, which contain alternating four-coordinate aluminum and three-coordinate oxygen atoms, and composed of only hexagonal and square faces.[19]

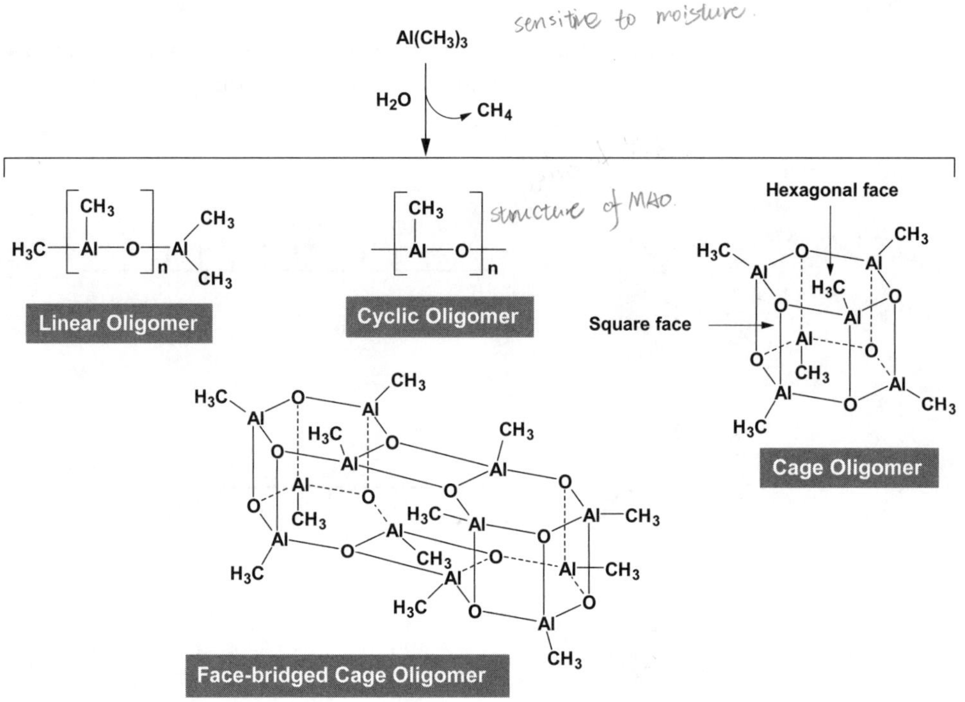

Figure 1.60. Structures of four of the several components of MAO.

The first function of MAO is the alkylation of the halogenated metallocene complex, L_2MCl_2. Monomethylation takes place within seconds, and an excess of MAO leads to dimethylated species **A** in Figure 1.61. The second function is the abstraction of a methide group to produce a metallocene monomethyl cation, $L_2M(CH_3)^{\oplus}$, which is generally regarded as the active center in olefin polymerization. Excess of MAO may be required to shift the equilibrium towards the catalyst-cocatalyst ion-pair. Other functions include reactivation of inactive complexes formed by a hydrogen transfer reaction (*vide infra*), preventing deactivation of the catalyst by bimolecular processes, and scavenging impurities, such as water and oxygen from the reaction medium.

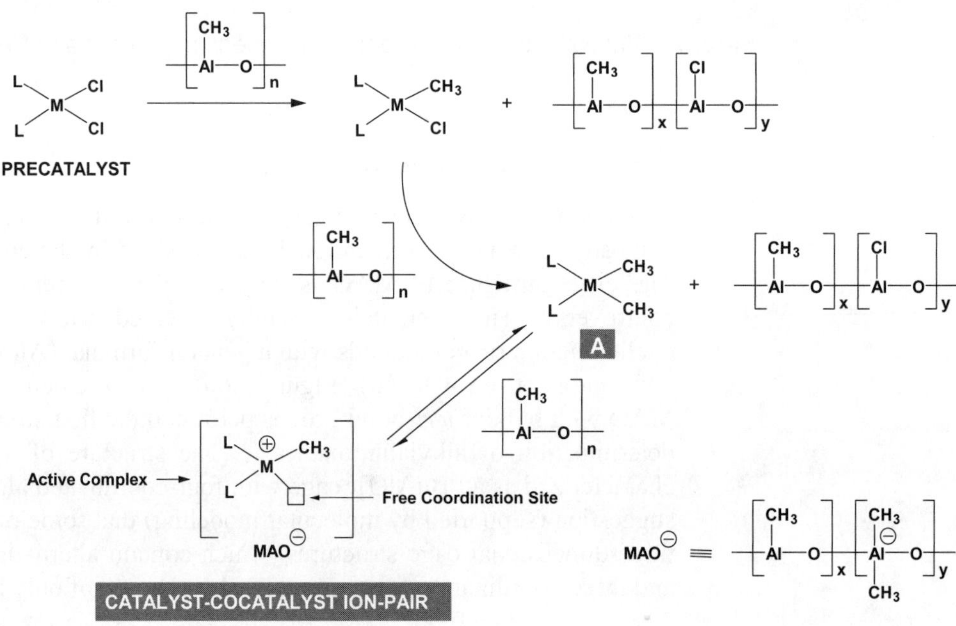

Figure 1.61. Role of cocatalyst in metallocene chemistry.

The role of MAO in methide abstraction is supported by the observation that a strong Lewis acid, such as $B(C_6F_5)_3$, can abstract one methide group from Cp_2ZrMe_2 to form a crystallographically characterizable cationic species $Cp_2ZrMe^{\oplus}$ that is the actual catalyst for the polymerization of olefins (Figure 1.62).[20] Thus, this perfluoroaryl borane and other strong Lewis acids, such as $Ph_3CB(C_6F_5)_4$, can serve as a substitute for MAO (i.e., alternate co-catalyst) in the combination with metallocene dialkyls. Unlike MAO, a relatively small amount of borane (borane/M = 1:1) is needed to form an effective catalyst for olefin polymerization. The disadvantage of this class of co-catalysts is their high cost and the incorporation of fluorine into the polymer, which can cause problems when polyolefins are thermally decomposed.

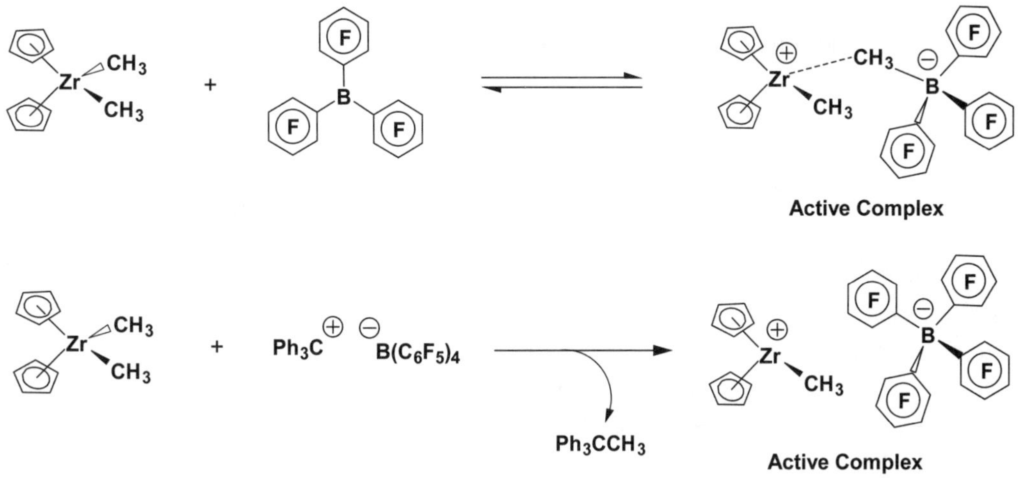

Active Complex

$Ph_3C^{\oplus}$ $^{\ominus}B(C_6F_5)_4$

Ph_3CCH_3

Active Complex

Figure 1.62. Effective, but highly expensive, co-catalysts for metallocenes and their active complexes.

The polymerization mechanism using metallocene catalysts is somewhat different from that of the conventional heterogeneous Ziegler-Natta catalysts. The Cossee-Arlman mechanism applied to explain the course of olefin polymerization with metallocene catalysts is unable to fully explain the *iso*-specificity of some metallocenes. It also fails to explain why the reaction order of the olefin monomer is higher than one.

The most accepted metallocene mechanism is the Brookhart-Green mechanism[21,22] involving an α-H agostic interaction between one of the hydrogen atoms on the α carbon atom of the alkyl (or growing polymer chain) and the metal center (Figure 1.63). The α-H agostic interaction assists the insertion of an olefin monomer and stabilizes (lowers the energy of) the transition state by relieving part of the electron deficiency of the 14-valence electron $[Cp_2ZrCH_3]^{\oplus}$ species. The insertion proceeds via an α-agostic metal-olefin π-complex and a four-center transition state (TS) to a product, which is γ-agostic. The alkyl or polymer chain may rotate from a γ-agostic to an α-agostic complex via a β-agostic conformation. Thus, the insertion step consists of an alkyl migration to the olefin ligand; at the same time, a new free coordination site is generated at the vacant position of the former alkyl ligand (*migratory insertion*). The mechanism is supported by α-H isotope effects, as well as *ab initio* calculations. The major difference between this and the Cossee-Arlman mechanism for Ziegler-Natta catalysts is that the olefin insertion is assisted by the α-H agostic interaction. The α-H interaction also accounts for stereoregularities much more effectively. Similar to Ziegler-Natta catalysts, the polymerization of propylene (and other α-olefins) with metallocene catalysts is stereoselective and takes place predominantly by a regeoselective 1,2-insertion (energetically favored) into the metal-carbon bond.

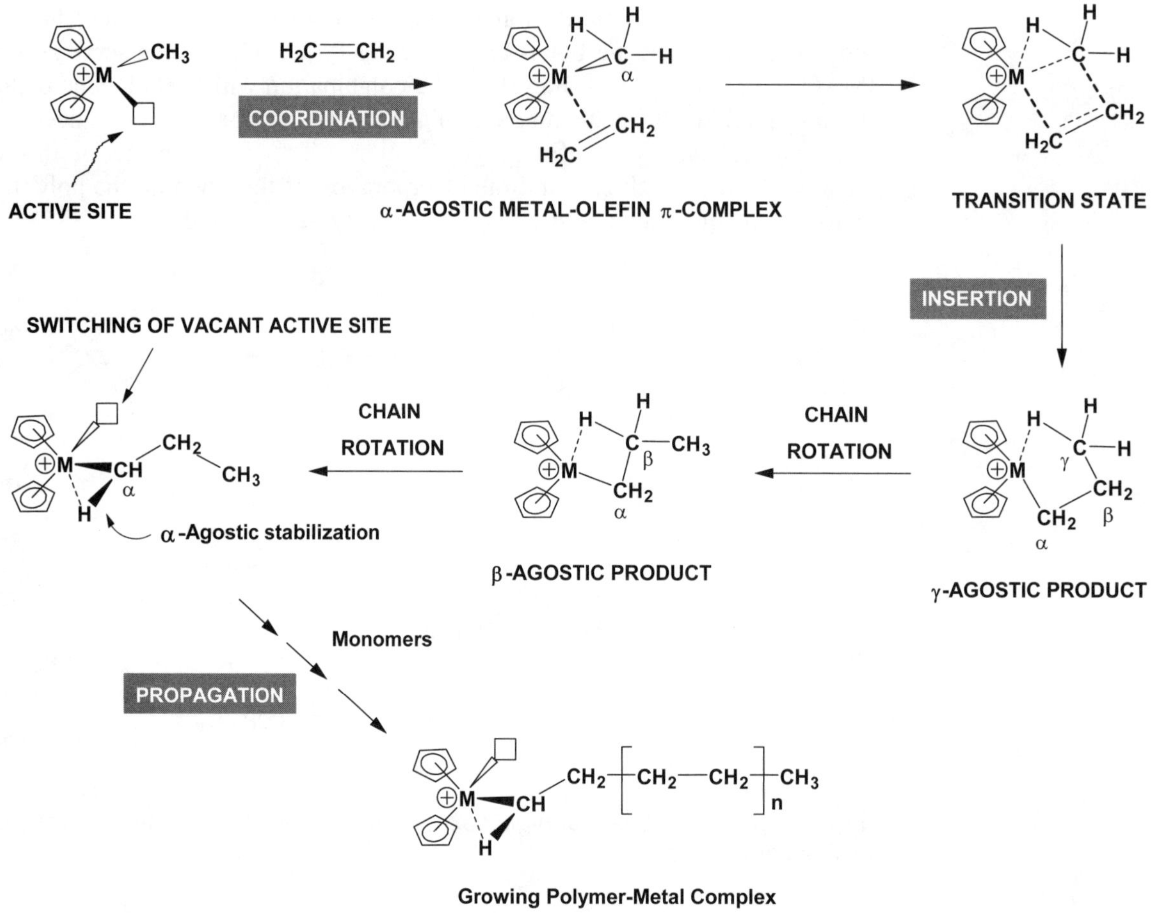

ACTIVE SITE

$H_2C{=}CH_2$

COORDINATION

α-AGOSTIC METAL-OLEFIN π-COMPLEX

TRANSITION STATE

INSERTION

SWITCHING OF VACANT ACTIVE SITE

CHAIN ROTATION

CHAIN ROTATION

α-Agostic stabilization

β-AGOSTIC PRODUCT

γ-AGOSTIC PRODUCT

Monomers

PROPAGATION

Growing Polymer-Metal Complex

Figure 1.63. Brookhart-Green mechanism for the polymerization of ethylene using metallocene catalysts. *Note that chain end and vacant site/direction of approach switch with each monomer added (migratory insertion).*

Chain termination plays a critical role in determining the fundamental property of polymer molecular weight. The most important mechanisms for chain termination start from a β-agostic structure. The termination step may take place via transfer of a β-hydrogen to a coordinated monomer (a bimolecular process) or to the metal center via a unimolecular β-hydride elimination process (Figure 1.64). Most theoretical studies suggest that the former process is dominant. Both cases result in polymers terminated with an olefin function. Depending on the catalyst, the long-chain terminal olefin can participate in further coordination steps leading to polymers with long-chain branching (see Chapter-2). In a similar manner, the addition of hydrogen to the polymerization mixture can cause a dramatic increase in catalyst activity and a decrease in the molecular weight of the polyolefin produced. Molecular hydrogen can compete with the olefin for the free coordination sites. Presumably, hydrogen coordinates to the metal center and dihydrido complexes are formed as intermediates to facilitate the elimination of a saturated alkane (polymer chain) and to produce a new coordination site. The formation of a metal-hydrogen bond allows further olefin insertion and chain growth without the loss of an active site.

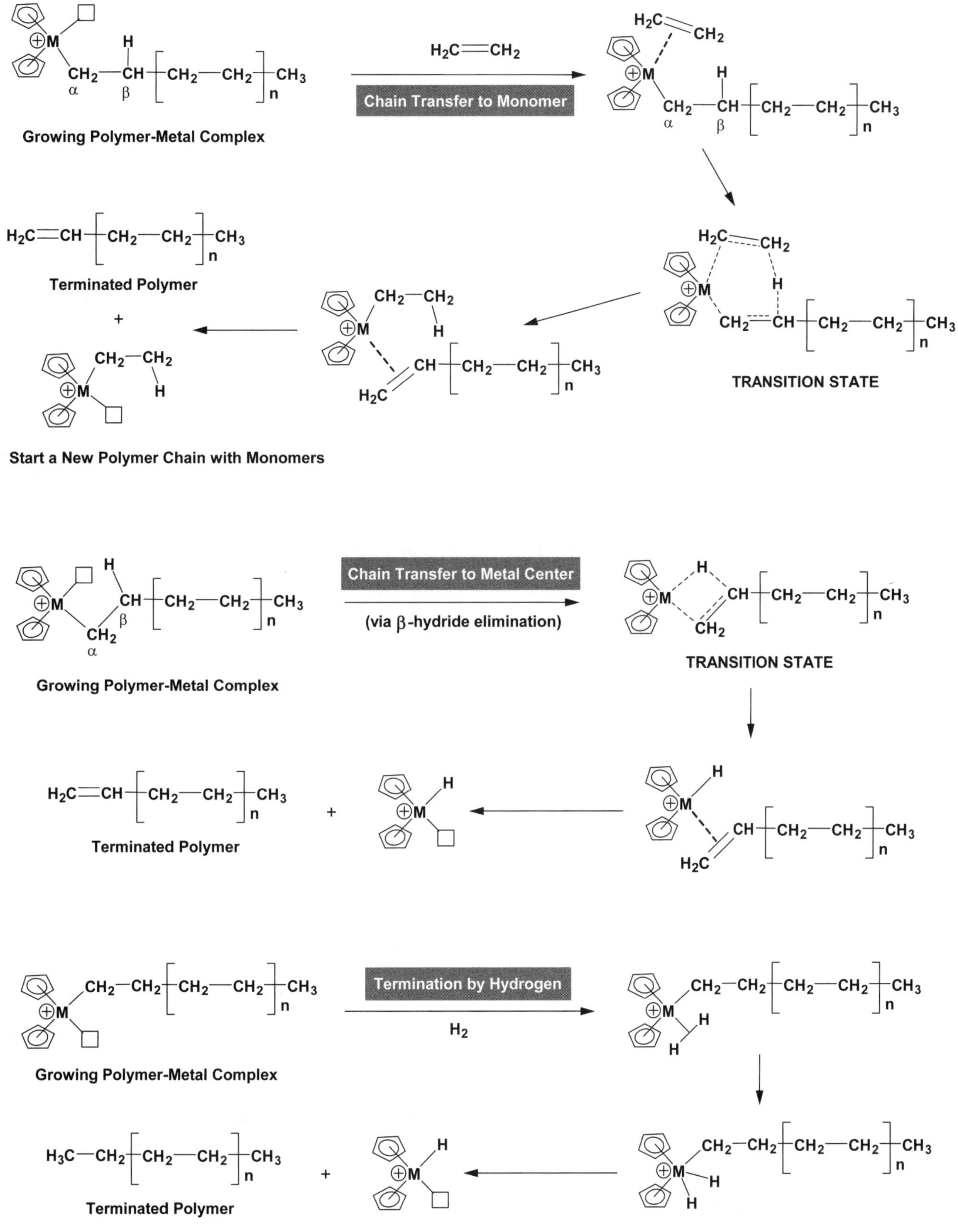

Growing Polymer-Metal Complex

$H_2C{=}CH_2$

Chain Transfer to Monomer

TRANSITION STATE

Terminated Polymer

Start a New Polymer Chain with Monomers

Growing Polymer-Metal Complex

Chain Transfer to Metal Center

(via β-hydride elimination)

TRANSITION STATE

Terminated Polymer

Growing Polymer-Metal Complex

Termination by Hydrogen

H_2

Terminated Polymer

Figure 1.64. Chain termination processes in metallocene-catalyzed polymerization of ethylene.

1.6.1.1e. Polymerization by Metathesis Catalysts

The chain-growth polymerization involving metathesis catalysts, such as metal carbene (or alkylidene), also called *metathesis polymerization*, occurs by a mechanism involving olefin metathesis type reactions. Derived from the Greek words *meta* (change) and *thesis* (position), metathesis of olefins is the formal scission of a pair of double bonds, followed by the interchange of their carbon atoms. The reaction has been known since the 1960s, but it was not until the early 1990s that this transformation became an important tool in synthetic organic chemistry, due to the development of catalysts which have high activity, enhanced selectivity, high functional group tolerance, and the ability to conduct reactions even in environmentally friendly aqueous media.

Depending on the catalysts and monomers, four important types of metathesis reactions leading to novel polymers can be conducted. The most studied is ring-opening metathesis polymerization (ROMP), a term coined by Robert Grubbs, who shared the Nobel Prize in Chemistry with Richard Schrock and Yves Chauvin in 2005 for the development of the metathesis method in organic chemistry. ROMP, a chain-growth process, is performed with strained cycloolefins to produce stereoregular and highly monodispersed unsaturated polymers and copolymers. Both acetylene metathesis polymerization (AMP) and ring-forming metathesis polymerization (RFMP) of acyclic diynes also proceed via a chain-growth mechanism and provide access to a new class of conjugated polymers. By contrast, acyclic diene metathesis polymerization (ADMP), which is discussed in the section on step-growth polymerization (*vide infra*), involves a step-growth mechanism and offers unique polymers with double bonds in the main chain.

Ring-opening Metathesis Polymerization (ROMP)

The advent of ROMP has allowed the synthesis of many polymers previously unavailable with standard synthetic techniques (see Chapter-3 for more discussion). Bicyclo[2.2.1]hept-2-ene, better known by its trivial name norbornene, is one of the most studied monomers for ROMP (Figure 1.65). Polynorbornene, commercially known as Norsorex® (Zeon Chemicals), contains >80% trans double bonds in the polymer backbone and can be vulcanized like natural rubber. The vulcanized Norsorex is used as an elastomeric material for vibration and sound damping. It has specialty applications for engine mounts, shock-proof bumpers, and flexible couplings. In addition, porous polynorbornene is a soaking material for oil spills. Polynorbornene oil spill sponges can absorb up to 400% of their own mass as oil.

Polyoctenamer (Vestenamer®, Degussa, Germany), which contains a high percentage of *trans*-1,4-polyoctenamer (TOR), is another elastomer developed by the ROMP technique (Figure 1.65). It is a semi-crystalline polymer (30% crystalline content), low melting ($T_m \sim 55^oC$) and rubbery ($T_g \sim -65^oC$). Vestenamer is compatible with almost all rubbers (irrespective of their chemical structure or polarity) and is primarily used to improve the processability of rubber compounds without the disadvantages presented by traditional processing aids. Vestenamer contains about 25% of oligomeric macrocycles, which presumably account for the high collapse resistance of Vestenamer-containing rubber compounds at temperatures well above its melting point.

Polydicyclopentadiene (PDCPD), another commercially available ROMP product (Metton®, Metton America) of the monomer *endo*-dicyclopentadiene, upon light crosslinking, produces a new class of olefinic thermoset polymer, which exhibits remarkable impact and corrosion resistance (Figure 1.65). Metton is an excellent base polymer for a variety of composite products used in areas, such as the defense/aerospace industry, golf carts and recreation, marine, ballistics, and microelectronics.

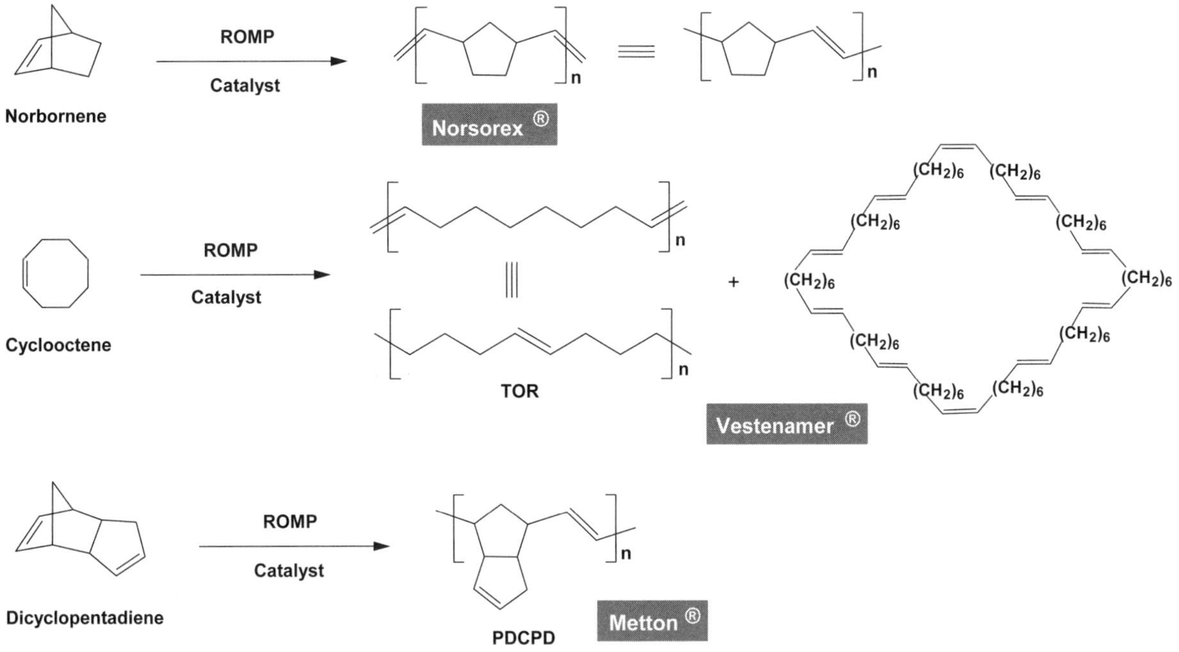

Figure 1.65. Structures of commercially available polymers prepared by ROMP.

A significant evolution in the development of olefin metathesis catalysts involves the use of ruthenium-based catalysts discovered by Robert Grubbs. These materials, better known as Grubbs catalysts, are tolerant to air, moisture and most functional groups (FGs), thus useful for producing a wide variety of terminally functionalized oligomers or polymers, commonly referred to as *telechelic polymers* (Figure 1.66). These materials are extremely difficult or impossible to prepare in high yield and selectivity by standard synthetic methods, but have several important and growing applications, including the production of multi-block copolymers and thermoplastic polyurethanes (see Chapter-2).

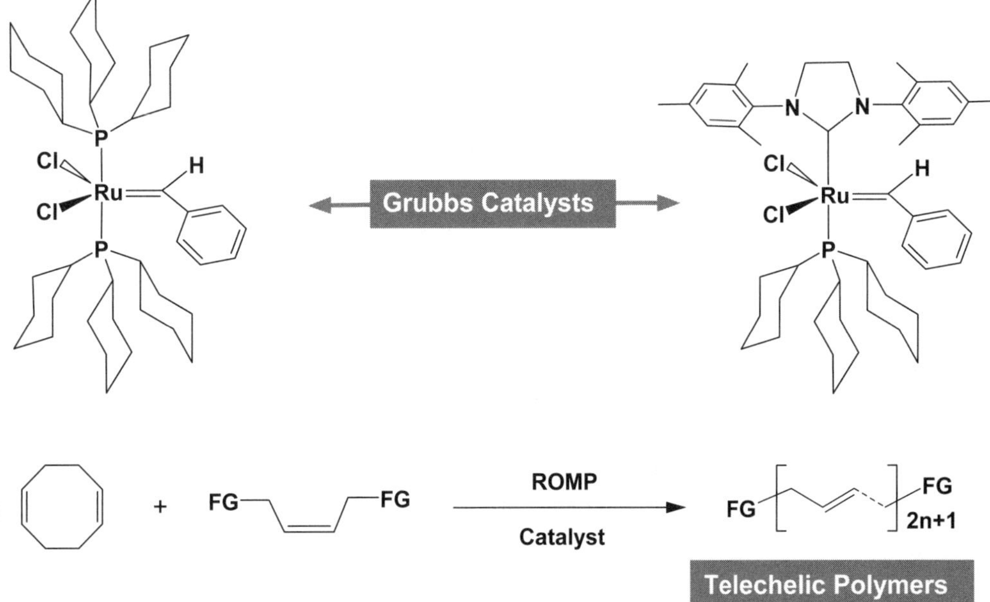

Figure 1.66. Structures of two important Grubbs Catalysts which was a significant step-forward towards commercializing metathesis products, viz., synthesis of functional polymers by ROMP.

The mechanism of ROMP is believed to be similar to the Chauvin mechanism[23] of olefin metathesis and involves the formation of a metallacyclobutane intermediate in the initiation step, resulting from [2+2] cycloaddition between the double bonds of a strained cyclic olefin (e.g., cyclobutene, cyclopentene, norbornene) and metal carbene catalyst (Figure 1.67). The driving force for the ROMP reaction (chain propagation) is the relief of ring strain, which makes the second step essentially irreversible. That is why olefins, such as cyclohexene and even benzene, have little or no ring strain and cannot be polymerized because there is no thermodynamic preference for polymer versus monomer.

When reaction is complete, the polymerization may be terminated by using a large excess (100 equiv) of an aldehyde or a vinyl ether. Most metathesis catalysts react with aldehydes in a [2+2] fashion, just as they do with olefins. The product is a metal oxo compound and an olefin (or polymer) capped with the former aldehyde functionality (Figure 1.67). The cleaved polymer can then be separated from the catalyst by precipitation with methanol. Reaction with several equivalents of diene, such as 1,4-pentadiene, is another way of cleaving the polymer chain. The advantage of this method is that the cleavage does not deactivate the catalyst, permitting additional aliquots of monomer to be polymerized. However, one does have to worry about broadening the MW distribution.

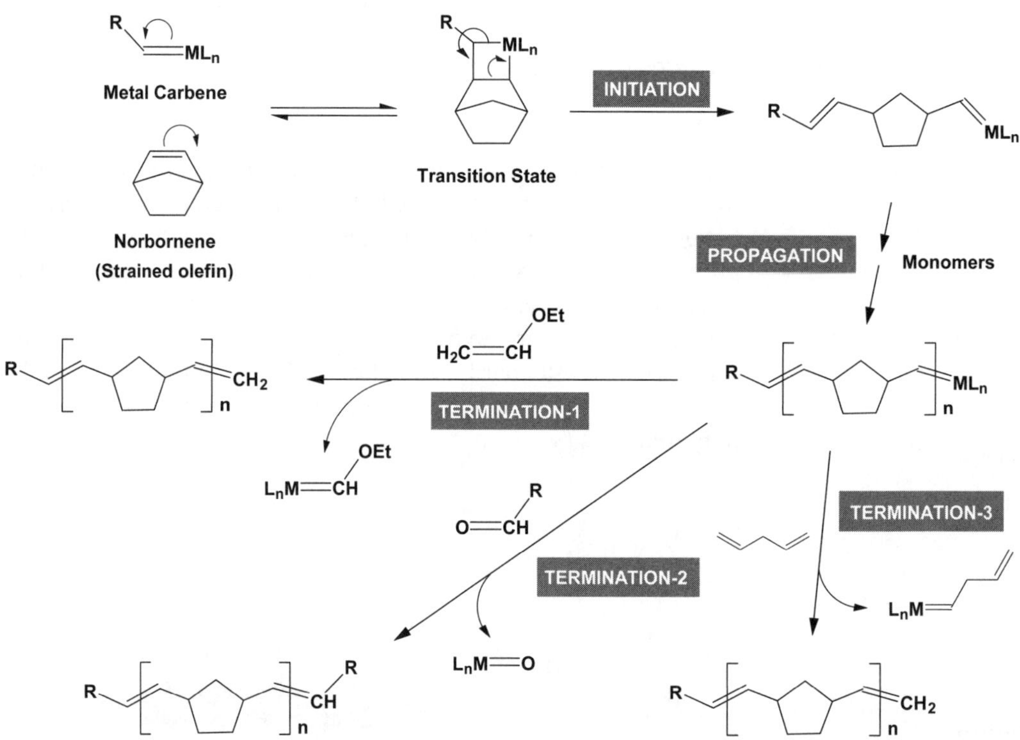

Figure 1.67. ROMP mechanism of strained olefins.

An important feature of ROMP is that, using appropriate catalyst systems, a ROMP can be made "living" and be used to produce polymers with a very narrow molecular weight distribution (polydispersities in the range of 1.03 to 1.10). For example, 100 equivalents of norbornene can be polymerized and then a second monomer added after the first is consumed (Figure 1.68). Indeed, ROMP is now a very popular method for making diblock and triblock copolymers and permits tailoring the properties of the resulting material.[24]

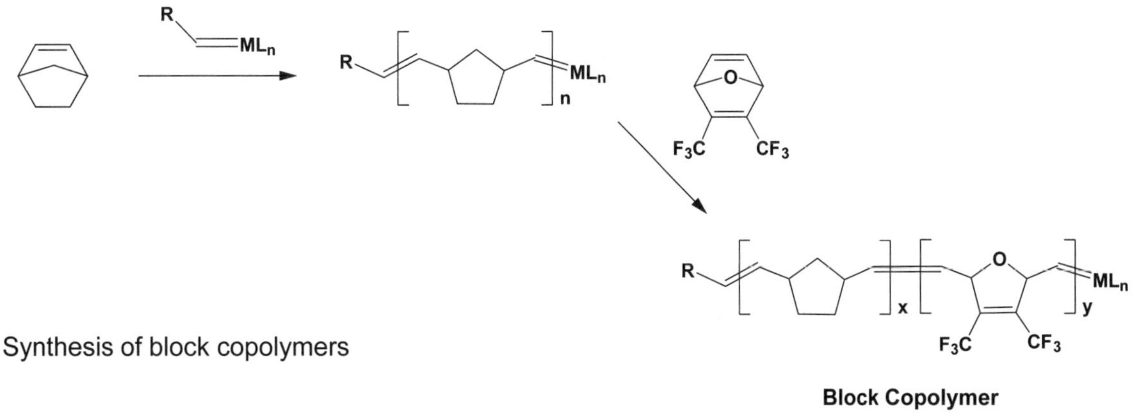

Figure 1.68. Synthesis of block copolymers by ROMP.

Acetylene Metathesis Polymerization (AMP)

AMP is an excellent method for the preparation of substituted polyacetylene (PAC) derivatives, which have strong potential for applications in organic light-emitting diodes (OLEDs), solar cells, photovoltaic devices, field-effect transistors and lasers. While PAC is electrically conductive, introduction of a pendent group, such as a mesogen, chromophore, photosensitive double bond, or naturally occurring building block, endows it with new functional properties, such as electrooptic activity, photonic responsiveness, and biological compatibility. Terminal acetylenes are polymerized preferentially by metathesis polymerization using well-defined Schrock-type metathesis catalysts to yield conjugated polyenes (see Chapter-5).[25] The degree of conjugation in these materials depends strongly on the electronic as well as steric nature of the substituents in the starting alkyne. The *effective conjugation length* (N_{eff}) describes the number of coplanar double bonds in a conjugated system. This coplanarity is required for the efficient overlap of the p_z-orbitals in the system. Highly conjugated systems show a narrow band gap between HOMO and LUMO that results in low-energy charge-transfer (CT) bands. As a consequence, these materials exhibit strong bathochromically-shifted absorption maxima. The presence of bulky groups in linear polyacetylenes often prevents high values for N_{eff} due to 1,3-steric interactions. Figure 1.69 shows a representative example of the catalyst and the synthesis of a mesogen-containing PAC. Despite significant improvements, polyacteylene-derived materials still suffer from one or more drawbacks from a technological point of view, such as insufficient stability and processability.

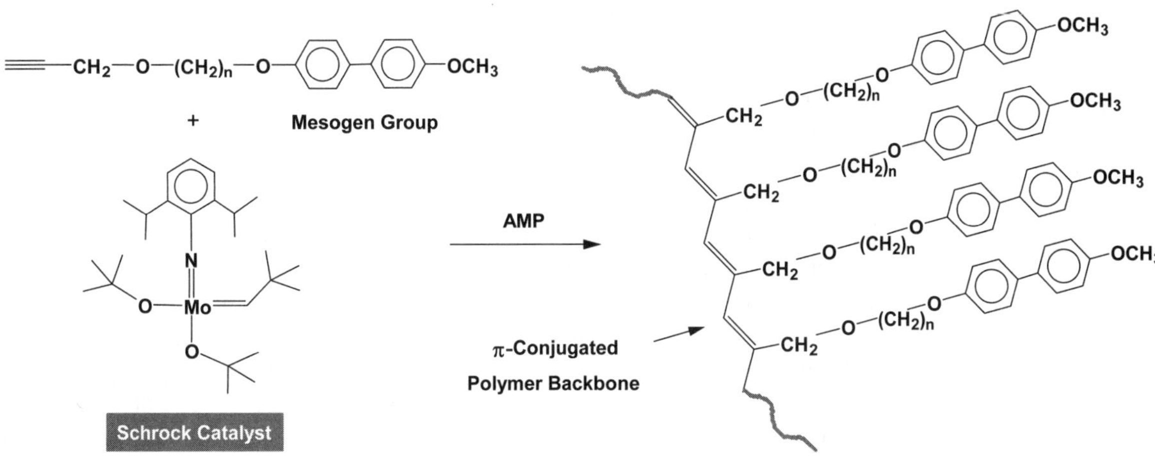

Figure 1.69. Synthesis of liquid crystalline PAC derivatives by AMP.

The mechanism of AMP is similar to ROMP, i.e., formation of a metallacyclobutene via a [2+2] cycloaddition between an acetylene monomer and the alkylidene catalyst (Figure 1.70). Further opening of the metallacycle in a productive fashion leads to a growing polymer chain. Since the alkyne is unsymmetrical, the preferred insertion (α or β) depends on the ligands on the catalyst and substituent on the alkyne. Thus, polymerization of terminal acetylenes is complicated by the potential for the R group to insert α or β with respect to the metal. It is always extremely challenging to get one type of insertion or generate a polymer with reproducible properties. However, it is anticipated that β-insertion is a preferred path as it involves the formation of a highly reactive monosubstituted alkylidene intermediate that leads to higher molecular weight products. AMP may be terminated by the protocols used for ROMP.

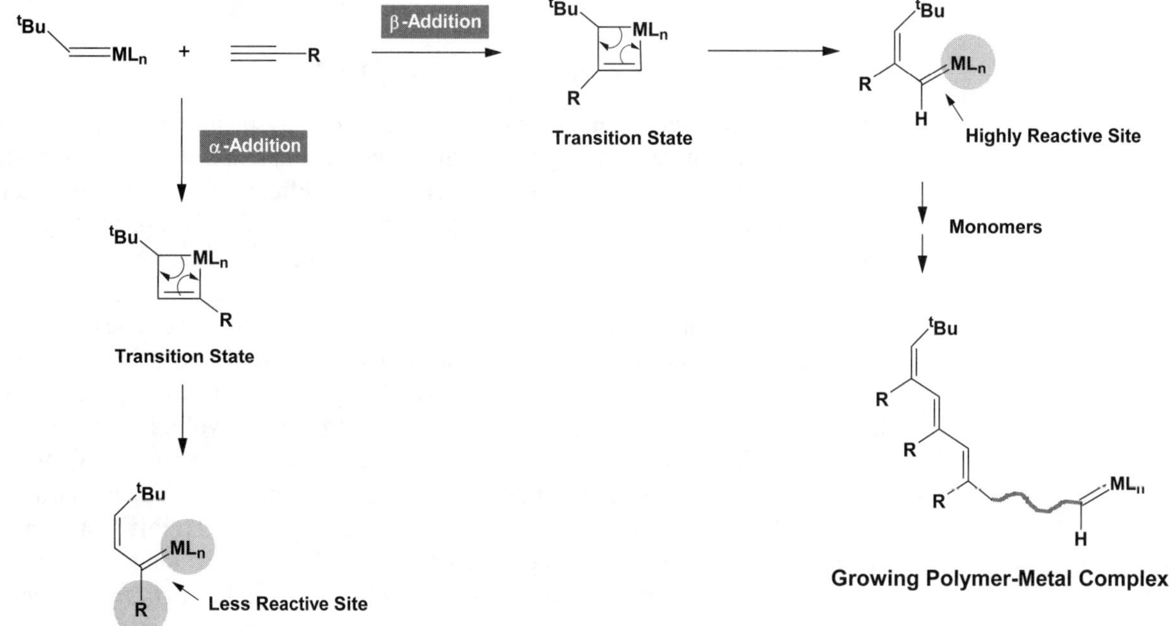

Figure 1.70. Mechanism of AMP.

Ring-forming Metathesis Polymerization (RFMP)

This technique provides access to another class of PAC derivatives, which have cyclic recurring units along the backbone that is not accessible by AMP, are soluble in common organic solvents, possess good long-term stability towards oxidation and low energy transitions between the valence and conductivity bands, and offer opportunity to incorporate pendent functional groups. However, the major limitation of this method is that, thus far, a successful cyclopolymerization only occurs with 1,6-heptadiyne derivatives. Well-defined high oxidation-state molybdenum carbenes ("Schrock catalysts") are regarded as superior initiator systems since they cyclopolymerize 1,6-heptadiynes in a living manner and can be tuned in a way that only one single repetitive unit, i.e., 1,3-(cyclopent-1-enylene)vinylenes (5-membered rings) or 1,3-(cyclohexen-1-enylene)methylidenes (6-membered rings), or both are obtained (Figure 1.71). Dipropargylmalonate esters are widely used 1,6-heptadiyne derivatives, which produce soluble polymers.

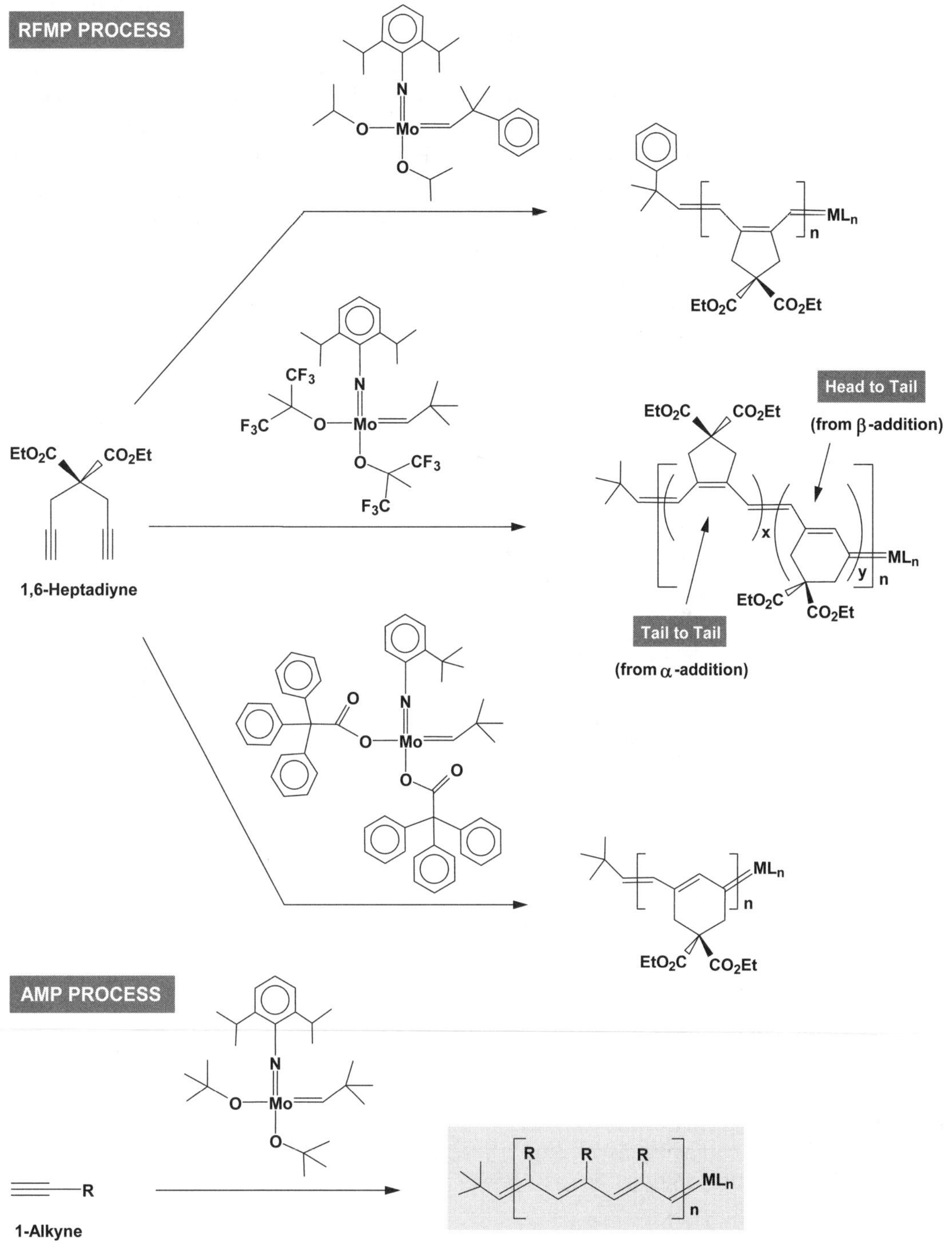

Figure 1.71. Schrock-type catalysts: structural differences between RFMP and AMP derived PAC derivatives.

As shown in Figure 1.72, the cyclopolymerization mechanism of 1,6-heptadiyne derivatives involves an “alkylidene mechanism”, in which the triple bond of the monomer reacts with a Mo=C bond to give either an α-substituted or β-substituted metallacyclobutene intermediate, which then opens to give an alkylidene complex. Subsequent reaction of the remaining triple bond of the monomer in an intramolecular cyclization step leads successively to a five- or six-membered ring predetermined by the initial α- or β- addition step. Intramolecular addition must be fast relative to intermolecular addition of the second triple bond to a Mo=C bond in order to avoid crosslinking. In accordance with the proposed mechanism, the ring size is influenced by both the substitution pattern of the monomer and the steric and electronic effects of the ligand sphere around the Mo center of a Schrock-type catalyst. As can be deduced from the mechanism shown in Figure 1.72, the use of bulky ligands (e.g., carboxylates) in the catalyst system forces the monomer to undergo selective β-addition in the first addition step. The following reaction steps result in the formation of a polyene that contains six-membered rings exclusively along the polymer backbone. To produce polyenes consisting exclusively of five-membered rings, variations in both the imido and alkoxy ligands of the catalysts are required.

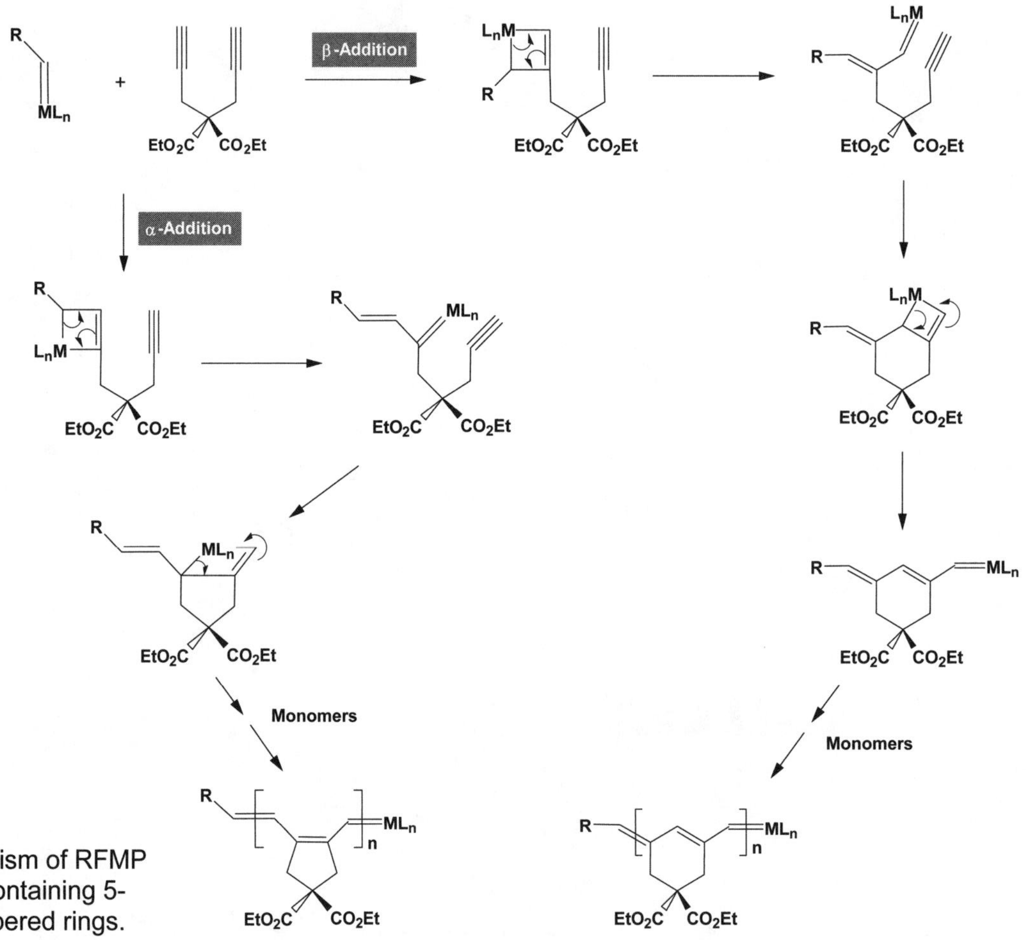

Figure 1.72. Mechanism of RFMP leading to polyenes containing 5-membered or 6-membered rings.

1.6.1.1f. Polymerization by Group-Transfer Catalysts

The chain-growth polymerization using group-transfer catalysts is also called *group-transfer polymerization* (GTP), which reflects the chain propagation mechanism involving the transfer of an active group (trimethylsilyl) of the initiator molecule to the incoming monomer after each propagation step. GTP was developed in 1983 by researchers at DuPont as an alternate method for the synthesis of acrylic block copolymers[26,27], which were synthesized at that time under living anionic conditions, an expensive process due to the requirement of maintaining reactor temperatures near -80°C and potentially hazardous because of toxicity involved with the organometallic initiators. By contrast, GTP, which can operate at ambient temperatures, uses 1-

methoxy-1-(trimethylsiloxy)-2-methylprop-1-ene (MTS) as initiator and an anionic source {e.g., $(Me_2N)_3S^+HF_2^-$, tris(dimethylamino)sulfonium bifluoride ($TASHF_2$) and tetrabutylammonium bibenzoate (TBABB)} or Lewis acid (e.g., $ZnBr_2$) as catalyst. The number of growing polymer chains corresponds to the amount of MTS used. Because of the stability of the terminal silyl ketene, GTP behaves somewhat like a living system. Indeed, chain growth stops when the monomer is depleted. Addition of a new monomer at this point starts chain growth again to produce a block copolymer (Figure 1.73). The termination of a polymer chain is usually performed either by adding aqueous acid or by addition of a dihalide, which couples two active species. GTP is also used to prepare functional polymers terminated with carboxylic acid groups by employing 1,1-bis(trimethylsiloxy)-2-methylprop-1-ene (BTS) in place of MTS.[28] Similar to the conventional anionic polymerization technique, GTP provides narrow and controllable molecular weight distributions, higher tacticity, as well as the ability to form block copolymers through the sequential addition of monomers.

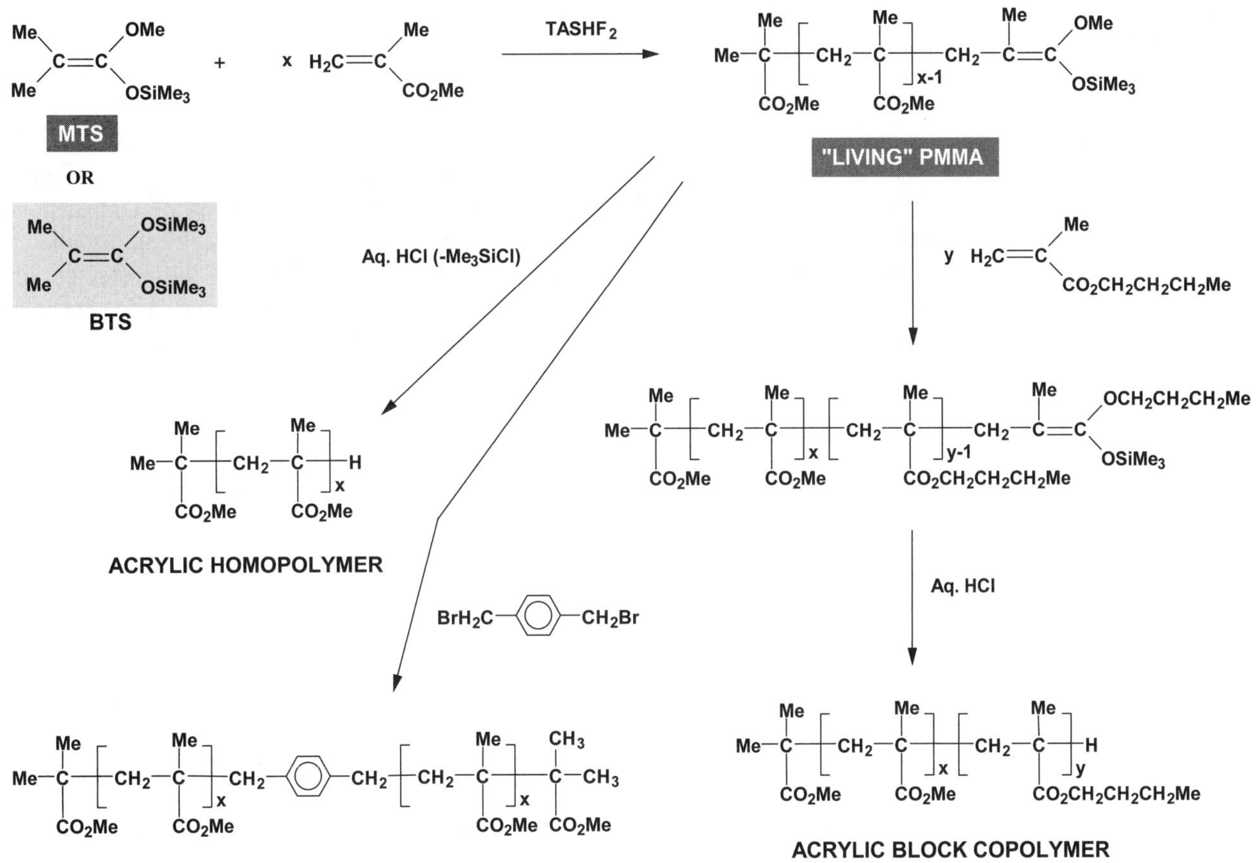

MTS

OR

BTS

$TASHF_2$

"LIVING" PMMA

Aq. HCl ($-Me_3SiCl$)

ACRYLIC HOMOPOLYMER

Aq. HCl

ACRYLIC BLOCK COPOLYMER

Figure 1.73. Synthesis of acrylate polymers by GTP.

The mechanism of GTP involves the facile Michael-type conjugate addition properties of silyl ketene acetals to α,β-unsaturated compounds. Thus, the application of GTP is limited to monomers, such as acrylate, acrylonitrile and N,N-dimethyl acrylamide. Monomers containing active hydrogen (e.g., acrylic acids and hydroxyethyl methacrylate) are not suitable for GTP because of side reactions leading to destruction of the initiator. While the detailed mechanism of GTP is still under debate, strong evidence indicates a dissociative anionic process (Figure 1.74).[29]

PMMA

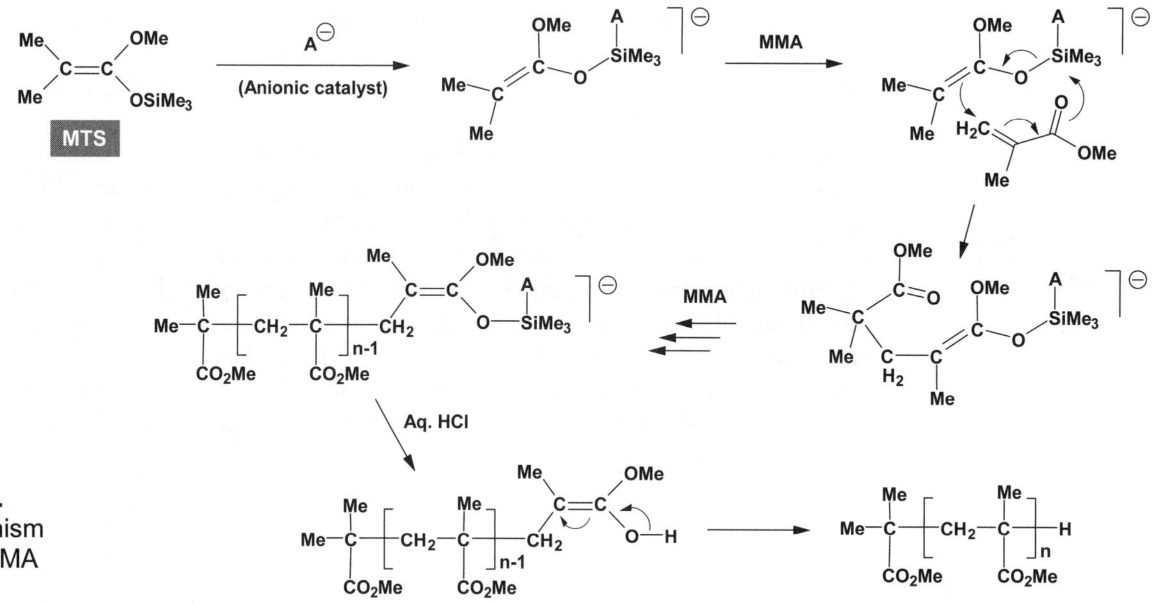

Figure 1.74. The mechanism of GTP of MMA with MTS.

In the past decade, GTP has found strong applications in the areas of synthetic hydrogels[30] (crosslinked hydrophilic polymers) and polyampholites[31,32] (linear polymers containing both acidic and basic functional groups), because of its simplicity and control of polymerization. Figure 1.75 depicts the structures of some of the protected acrylate monomers (deprotection of functional groups occurs during work-up or termination) including a difunctional initiator (MTSMC) used for these applications.

MTSMC
1,4-bis(methoxytrimethylsiloxymethylene) cyclohexane
(Bifunctional initiator)

EGDMA
Ethylene glycol dimethacrylate
(Crosslinker)

DMAEMA
N,N-dimethylaminoethyl methacrylate
(Hydrophilic monomer)

TMSEMA
Trimethylsiloxyethyl methacrylate
(Protected hydrophilic monomer: generates OH group during the termination of the polymerization)

TMSMA
Trimethylsilyl methacrylate
(Protected hydrophilic monomer: generates CO_2H group)

THPMA
Tetrahydropyranyl methacrylate
(Protected hydrophilic monomer: generates CO_2H group)

MMA
Methyl methacrylate
(Hydrophobic monomer)

BMA
Butyl methacrylate
(Hydrophobic monomer)

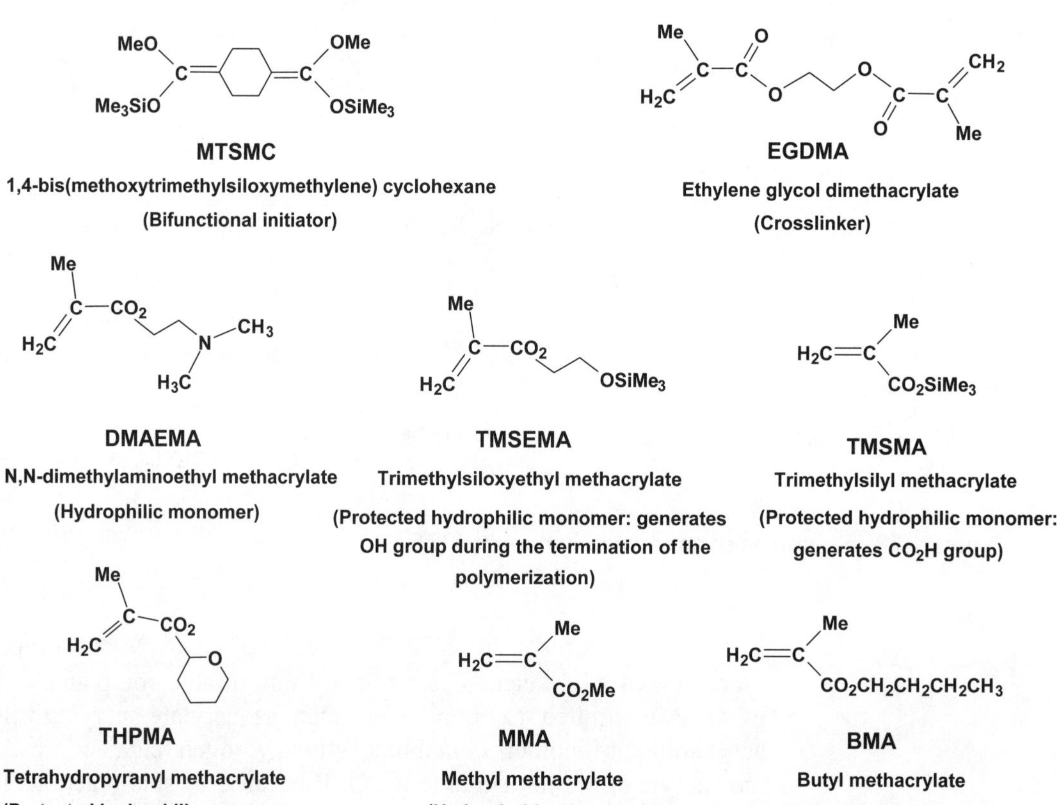

Figure 1.75. Chemical formulas and names of the monomers, crosslinker and bifunctional initiator used to prepare hydrogels and polyampholites by GTP.

Hydrogels made from these acrylate monomers, such as one shown in Figure 1.76, have attracted considerable attention due to their applications as actuators, valves, sensors, controlled release systems for drugs, artificial muscles for robotics, chemical memories, optical shutters, and molecular separation systems. Polyampholyte-mediated protein separation methods, such as ion-exchange displacement chromatography, precipitation, and aqueous two-phase partitioning are also becoming very popular because of higher efficiency. Utilization of block instead of random polyampholytes in these applications provides a dramatic improvement on the performance of these separation processes, as the properties of the block copolymers are superior (e.g., self-assembly behavior as shown in Figure 1.76) to those of the random process.

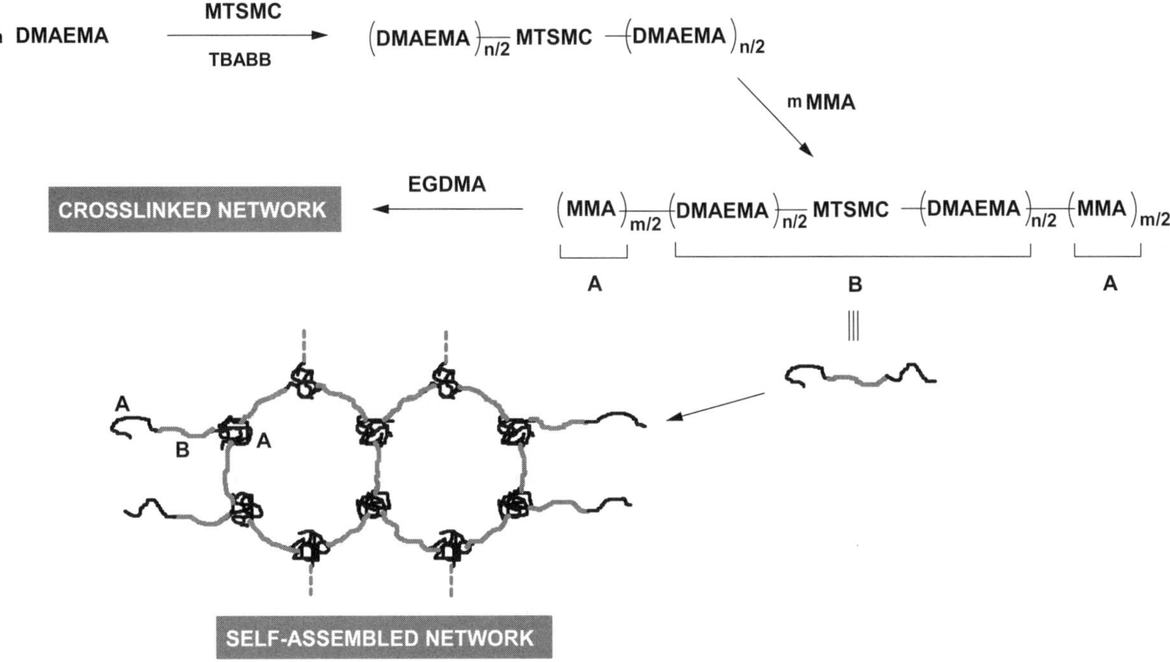

Figure 1.76. Synthesis of an ABA triblock copolymer-based model network with a DMAEMA midblock and schematics of the micellization (self-assembly) of the ABA triblock polyampholytes.

1.6.1.2. Step-Growth Polymerization

In step-growth polymerization, it is essential that the monomers be at least "bifunctional", which means that the monomer molecules must have at least two functional groups in their main structure, usually one functional group at each "end" of the molecule. Polymerization is normally carried out with two different types of bifunctional monomers in which the functional groups in one type are reactive toward those in the other type, thereby forming the polymer backbone. For example, polyamidation of adipic acid and hexamethylenediamine leads to nylon-6,6 and poly-*trans*-esterification of dimethyl terephthalate and ethylene glycol to PET (Figure 1.77). The step-growth polymerization can also be performed with only one type of bifunctional monomer, provided that the two functional groups are reactive toward each other. An example is the self-condensation of ω-hydroxycaproic acid leading to the homopolymer, polycaprolactone (PCL).

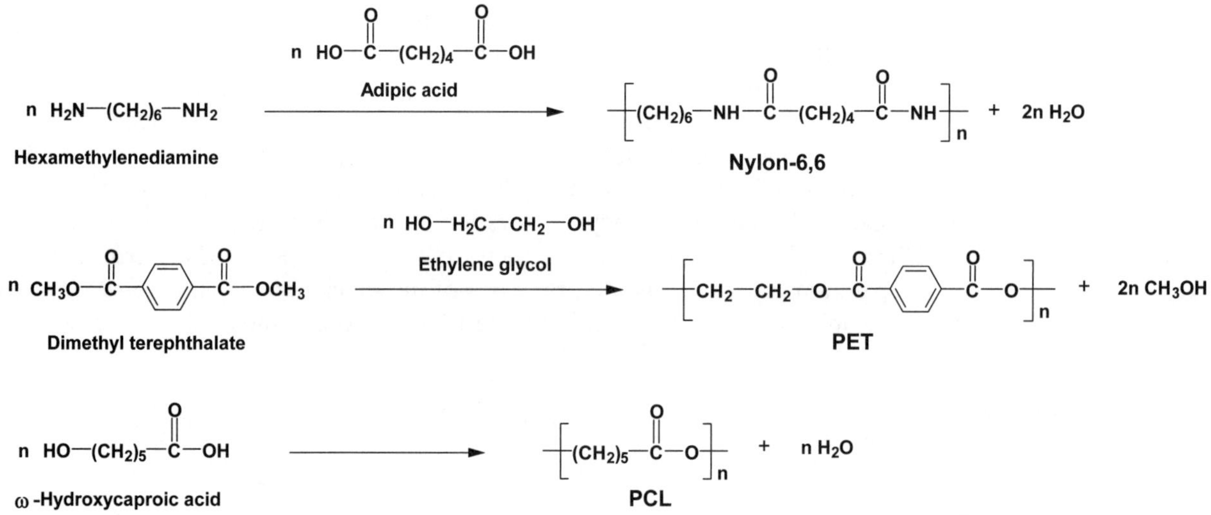

$n\ H_2N{-}(CH_2)_6{-}NH_2$ (Hexamethylenediamine) + $n\ HO{-}C(=O){-}(CH_2)_4{-}C(=O){-}OH$ (Adipic acid) $\longrightarrow$ $[{-}(CH_2)_6{-}NH{-}C(=O){-}(CH_2)_4{-}C(=O){-}NH{-}]_n$ (Nylon-6,6) + $2n\ H_2O$

$n\ CH_3O{-}C(=O){-}C_6H_4{-}C(=O){-}OCH_3$ (Dimethyl terephthalate) + $n\ HO{-}H_2C{-}CH_2{-}OH$ (Ethylene glycol) $\longrightarrow$ $[{-}CH_2{-}CH_2{-}O{-}C(=O){-}C_6H_4{-}C(=O){-}O{-}]_n$ (PET) + $2n\ CH_3OH$

$n\ HO{-}(CH_2)_5{-}C(=O){-}OH$ (ω-Hydroxycaproic acid) $\longrightarrow$ $[{-}(CH_2)_5{-}C(=O){-}O{-}]_n$ (PCL) + $n\ H_2O$

Figure 1.77. Step-growth polymerization involving condensation.

Unlike chain-growth polymerization, most monomers for step-growth polymerization are very reactive and do not require activation. Many polymerization reactions start as soon as they are mixed. For a faster process, it is often necessary to heat or cool the reaction mixture. Addition of a catalyst can reduce temperature and time of reaction. There is no real termination step in this polymerization. Once the molecular weight of the polymer chains becomes high, the reactivity of the terminal groups is significantly reduced due to a lesser number of functional groups and lower probability of finding a reactive partner, with consequent stalling of chain propagation. Usually, termination does not occur in step-growth polymerization. However, one may deliberately induce termination at any stage of the reaction (e.g., for making various grades), by adding a monofunctional monomer, such as acetic acid in the production of nylon-6,6 (Figure 1.78). The termination of growing polymer chains can also be performed by using excess stoichiometry of one monomer (typically 0.1 to 0.3 eq.), which depletes the other functional group in a short period of time, leading to an oligomeric product (often called *telechelic polymer*) terminated with the functional groups of the excess monomer.

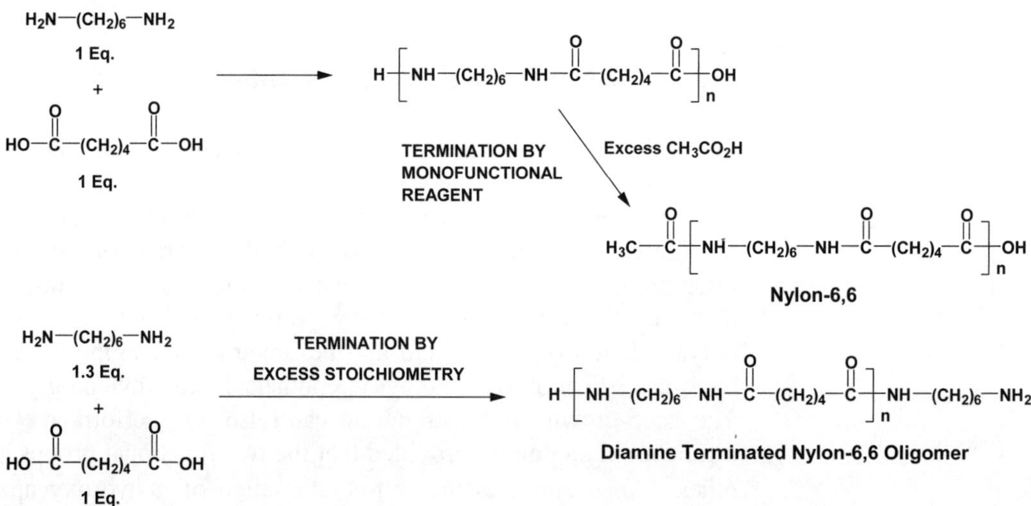

Figure 1.78. Termination methods of a step-growth polymerization process.

Oxidative Coupling of 2,6-Xylenol

This is a special type of step-growth polymerization because the reaction involves free-radical intermediates and a stepwise polycondensation (water as a condensation product) wherein the polymerization of dimer, trimer, or oligomer may be obtained without monomer (Figure 1.79). The first step of this polymerization is believed to be the formation of aryloxy radicals from oxidation of the phenol by the oxidative catalyst.[33] A dimer is formed by *p*-coupling of two aryloxy radicals via a quinone ether intermediate. The dimer can react with another aryloxy radical to form a trimer. Coupling can also occur between two dimer radicals to form a ketal intermediate, which is unstable and either dissociates to form a trimer and a monomer radical or back to two dimer radicals. Likewise, higher oligomers are converted to the next higher oligomer until a high molecular weight product, poly(2,6-dimethyl-1,4-phenyleneoxide) (PPO), is achieved (see Section 3.6. in Chapter-3 for more discussion).

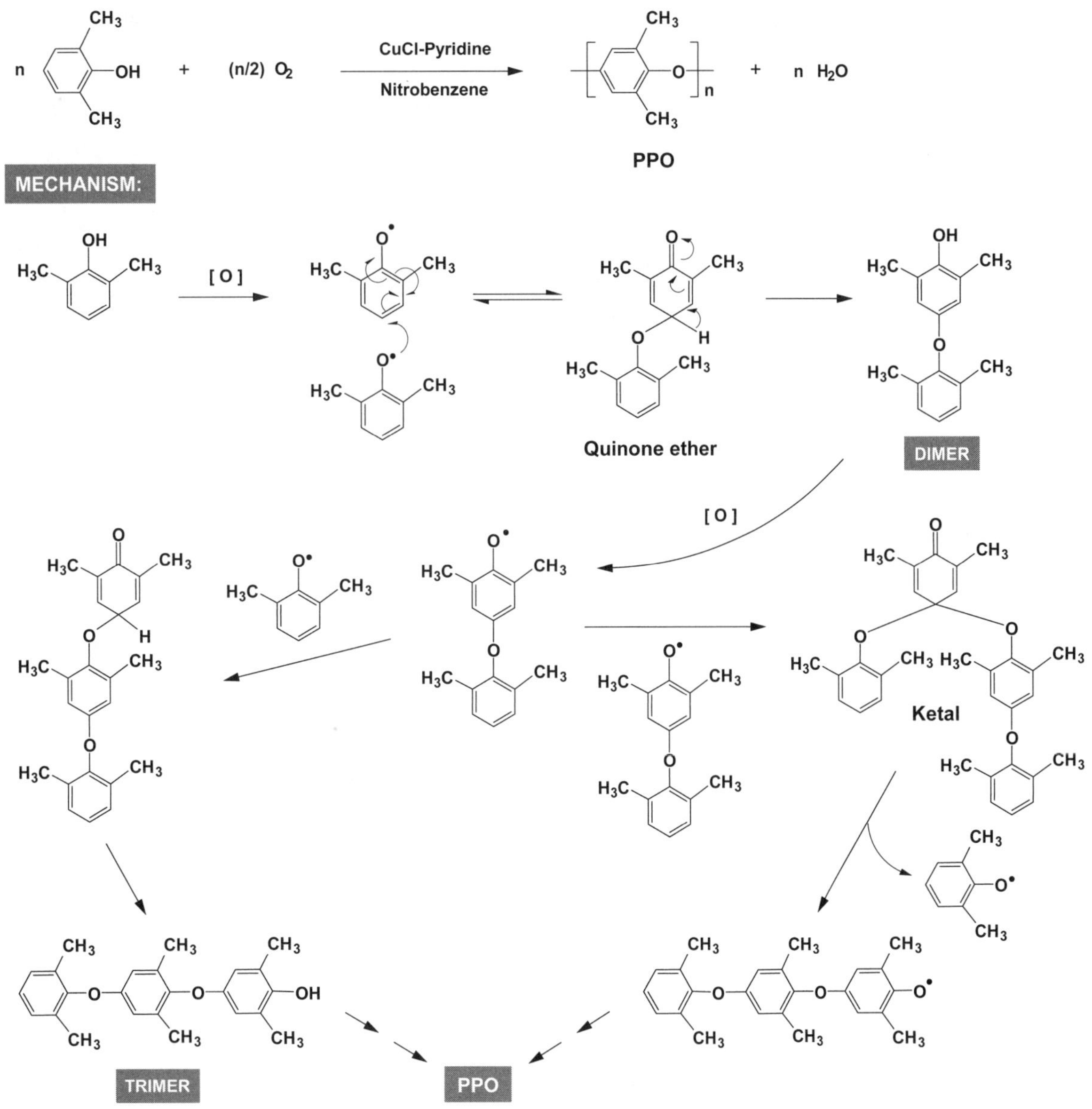

CuCl-Pyridine

Nitrobenzene

PPO

MECHANISM:

[O]

Quinone ether

DIMER

[O]

Ketal

TRIMER

PPO

Figure 1.79. Early intermediates during the synthesis of PPO, which involves a free-radical mechanism and condensation product.

Acyclic Diene Metathesis Polymerization (ADMP)

ADMP follows a step-growth mechanism involving elimination of small molecules (usually ethene) and was developed as a spin-off of a ring-closing metathesis (RCM), which has been extensively used in organic synthesis to produce 5- to 30-membered cyclic alkenes (Figure 1.80).[34] ADMP has attracted considerable attention in recent years because it provides access to a new class of unsaturated polymers that contain various functional groups in the backbone via an acyclic diene metathesis (ADMET) reaction (more discussion on Chapter-2).[35] The *E/Z*-selectivity of the product depends on the ring strain, with normally strained rings favoring *E*. The first step of both RCM and ADMET is [2+2] cycloaddition of olefin with the metal carbene catalyst to form a metallocyclobutane, which can undergo cycloreversion either towards products or back to starting materials. When the olefins of the substrate are terminal, the driving force of the reaction is the formation of catalyst-coupled olefin by elimination of ethene from the reaction mixture, usually accelerated by introducing nitrogen into the system. At this stage, whether a reaction will produce RCM or ADMET product can be controlled by adjusting the reaction conditions. Thus, high dilution, which favors intramolecular cycloaddition, is used for RCM reactions. Conditions with higher concentrations of monomers that facilitate intermolecular cycloaddition will undergo ADMP.

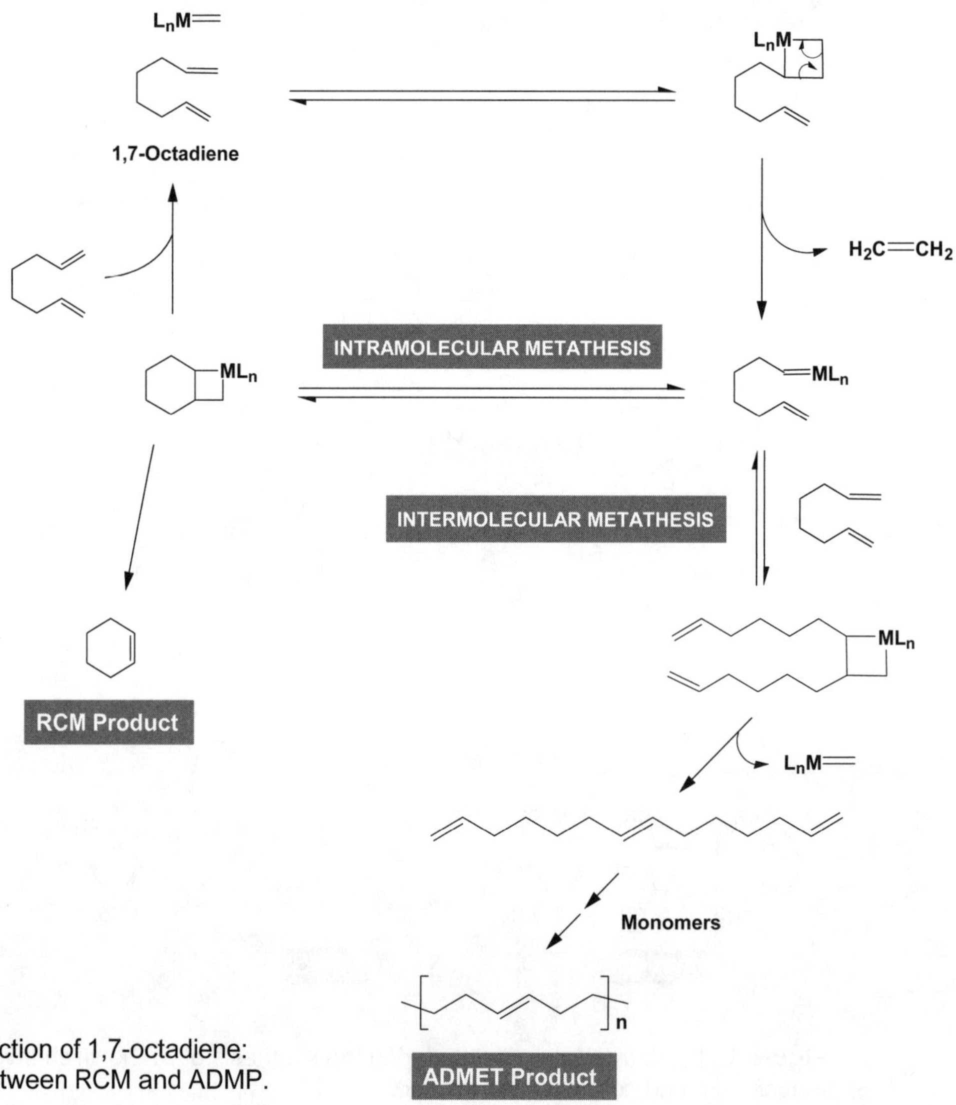

Figure 1.80. Metathesis reaction of 1,7-octadiene: differences in mechanism between RCM and ADMP.

Step-growth Polymerization Involving Perfect Addition

While most step-growth polymerization reactions involve polycondensation, i.e., elimination of small molecules, such as water and CH_3OH, there are a few step-growth reactions (e.g., formation of polyurethane from a diol and a diisocyanate, Figure 1.81), which are of the non-condensation type, i.e., do not eliminate small molecules.

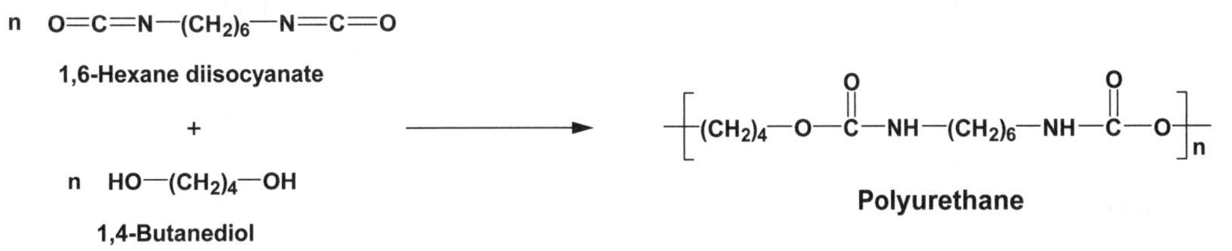

n O=C=N—$(CH_2)_6$—N=C=O

1,6-Hexane diisocyanate

\+

n HO—$(CH_2)_4$—OH

1,4-Butanediol

⟶ $[(CH_2)_4$—O—C(=O)—NH—$(CH_2)_6$—NH—C(=O)—O$]_n$

Polyurethane

Figure 1.81. Synthesis of polyurethane via a perfect addition reaction.

Thiol-Ene Photopolymerization (TEP)

This is another unique step-growth polymerization that involves vinyl monomers and radical intermediates, with no elimination of small molecules.[36,37] For linear polymers, both the thiol and ene (vinyl) monomers must be bifunctional. As shown in Figure 1.82, a monomer containing one thiol and one vinyl group at terminal positions would also be an ideal situation for the synthesis of a linear polythioether. A photoinitiator is commonly used to start the reaction (see Appendix-IV for examples and functions of photoinitiators).

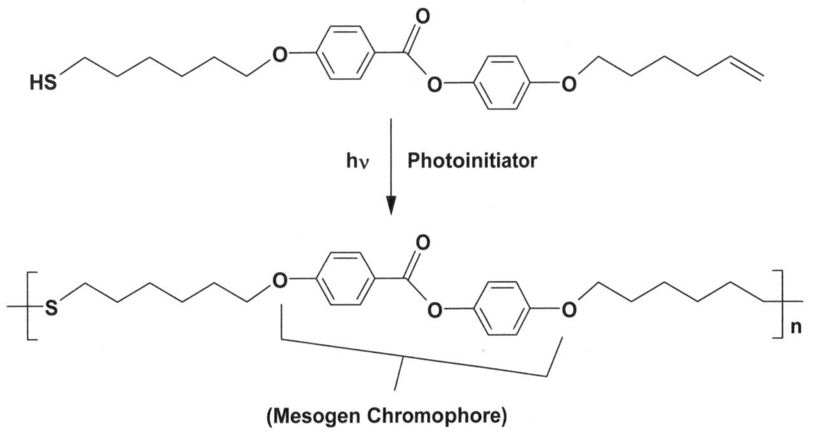

HS

hν Photoinitiator

S

(Mesogen Chromophore)

Figure 1.82. Synthesis of a liquid crystalline polymer by thiol-ene photopolymerization.

The first step of the polymerization is the abstraction of a hydrogen atom from the thiol (a very rapid process) by the photoinitiator radical to form a thiyl radical, which attacks the double bond of the vinyl monomer (Figure 1.83). This is immediately followed by chain-transfer of the radical to a thiol functional group, regenerating a thiyl radical, which then restarts the process. This successive propagation/chain transfer mechanism is the basis for step-growth thiol-ene polymerization. Termination involves free-radical coupling of at least one of the following possibilities: two thiyl radicals, two carbon radicals, and one thiyl radical and a carbon radical.

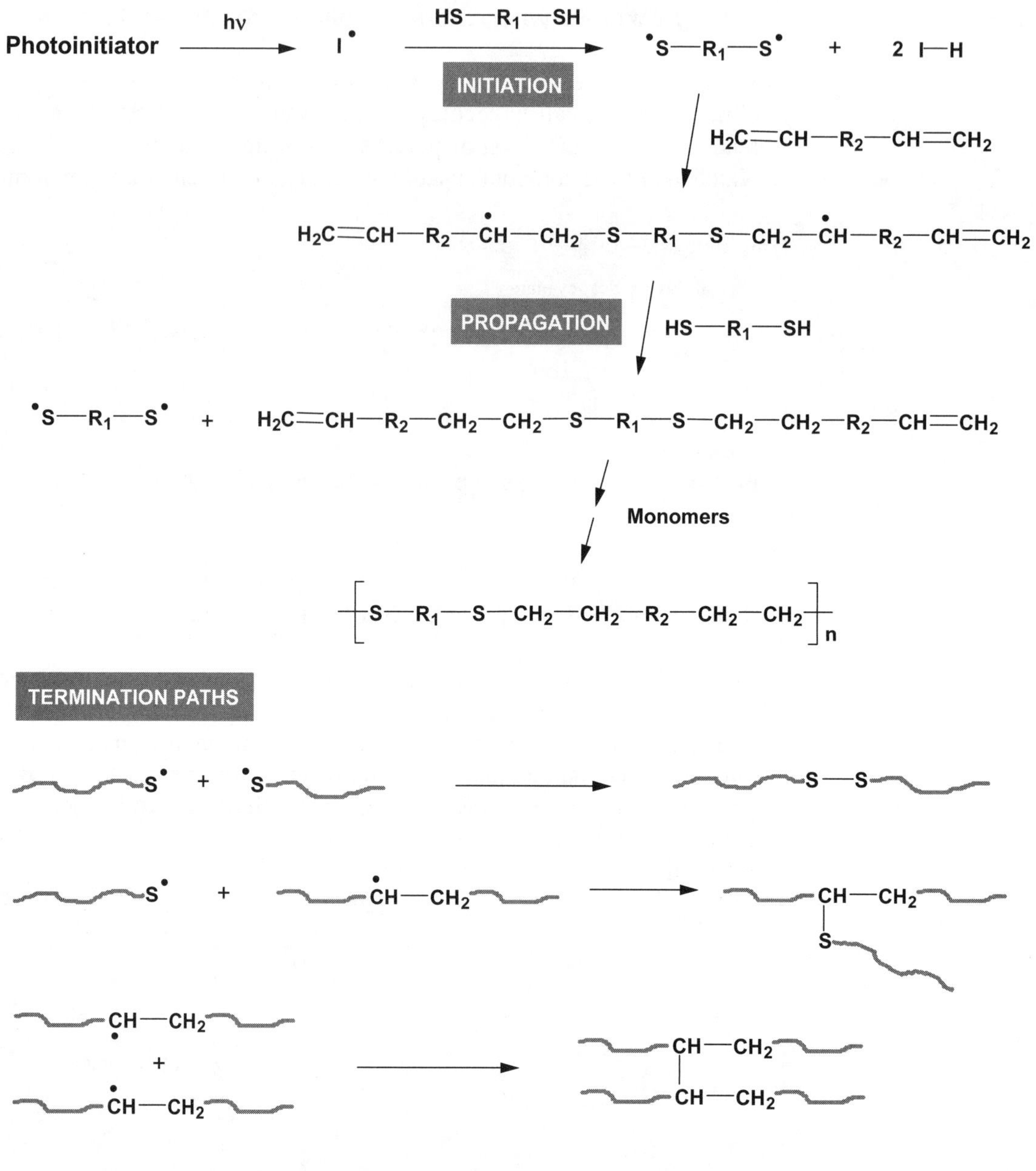

Photoinitiator $\xrightarrow{h\nu}$ $I^{\bullet}$ $\xrightarrow{HS-R_1-SH}$ $^{\bullet}S-R_1-S^{\bullet}$ + 2 I—H

INITIATION

$H_2C{=}CH-R_2-CH{=}CH_2$

$H_2C{=}CH-R_2-\dot{C}H-CH_2-S-R_1-S-CH_2-\dot{C}H-R_2-CH{=}CH_2$

PROPAGATION

$HS-R_1-SH$

$^{\bullet}S-R_1-S^{\bullet}$ + $H_2C{=}CH-R_2-CH_2-CH_2-S-R_1-S-CH_2-CH_2-R_2-CH{=}CH_2$

Monomers

$\left[S-R_1-S-CH_2-CH_2-R_2-CH_2-CH_2\right]_n$

TERMINATION PATHS

$\sim S^{\bullet} + {}^{\bullet}S\sim \longrightarrow \sim S-S\sim$

$\sim S^{\bullet} + \sim\dot{C}H-CH_2\sim \longrightarrow \sim CH(-S\sim)-CH_2\sim$

$\sim\dot{C}H-CH_2\sim + \sim\dot{C}H-CH_2\sim \longrightarrow \sim CH(-CH(\sim)-CH_2\sim)-CH_2\sim$

Figure 1.83. Mechanism of thiol-ene photopolymerization.

1.6.2. Polymerization Techniques

To summarize, polymerization of monomers takes place by either a chain-growth or step-growth mechanism. In chain-growth polymerization, monomer molecules react rapidly one at a time with the growing polymer chains to form high molecular weight molecules almost immediately, even at very low monomer conversions. By contrast, step-growth polymerization involves relatively slower random reactions between two monomer molecules, a monomer and polymer segment, or two polymer segments, and requires a longer time to obtain high molecular weights of products of commercial importance. Table 1.6 compares the important features, including advantages and disadvantages of various polymerization processes discussed in the preceding sections.

Table 1.6. Comparison of Various Polymerization Processes

Technique	General Aspects	Advantages	Disadvantages
Free-radical	• Chain-growth mechanism • Growing chain end is a radical • Termination is a part of polymerization • Produces carbon-carbon backbone • Majority of the products are homopolymers	• Very robust technique • Many monomers (sources for majority of general-purpose polymers) • Can be conducted in aqueous media • Short polymerization time • Produces very high molecular weight products	• Requires monomers with a π-bond (double bond usually) • Needs heat, often pressure
Cationic	• Chain-growth mechanism • Growing chain end is a cation • No termination by combination • Majority of the products are homopolymers	• Polymerizes olefins, cyclic ethers and cyclic amides • Can make block copolymers • Short polymerization time	• Significant chain transfer • Requires low temperature • Few monomers • Needs solvent
Anionic	• Chain-growth mechanism • Growing chain end is an anion • No termination by combination • Majority of the products are copolymers	• Gives low PDI • Can make block copolymers • Short polymerization time	• Few monomers • Requires low temperature • Needs solvent
Coordination	• Chain-growth mechanism • Growing chain end is a transition metal-insertion complex • Termination is a part of polymerization • Produces carbon-carbon backbone • Majority of the products are homopolymers	• Stereoregular polymers • Short polymerization time • High molecular weight products	• Few monomers • Removal of catalysts from polymers
Metathesis	• Chain-growth mechanism (except ADMP) • Growing chain end is a carbene complex • Termination is not a part of polymerization • Can produce both carbon-carbon and heteroatom-containing backbone • Majority of the products are homopolymers	• Unique polymers which are difficult to prepare by other techniques • Polymerizes cyclic olefins • Short polymerization time	• Few monomers • Removal of catalysts from polymers
Group-transfer	• Chain-growth mechanism • Growing chain end is a silyl ketene acetal • Termination is not a part of polymerization • Produces carbon-carbon backbone • Majority of the products are copolymers	• Narrow molecular weight range • Polymerizes at room temperature	• Limited choice monomers
Step-growth	• Step-growth mechanism • All propagation steps are one reaction • No real termination • Produces primarily carbon-heteroatom, including heterocyclic and aromatic rings in the backbone • Majority of the products are copolymers	• No initiator • Many monomers (sources for majority of engineering and high-performance polymers)	• Often provides low MW products • Equimolecular stoichiometry is required for copolymerization • Requires significant heat and time

As shown in the polymer synthesis chart below, there are primarily four general practical techniques for chain-growth and five for step-growth polymerizations. Bulk, solution, suspension and emulsion are all very popular methods for producing chain-growth polymers, using various initiation mechanisms (free-radical, cationic, anionic and catalytic). By contrast, step-growth polymers are almost exclusively prepared by bulk and solution methods. The suspension and emulsion techniques do not lend themselves to step-growth polymerization. However, interfacial and solid-state methods are now frequently used to produce special kinds of polymers. The preparation of polymers by an electrochemical route, also called *electrochemical polymerization*, is a special application of step-growth polymerization and is restricted to a few monomers (see Chapter-5). Table 1.7 shows the commercial methods used for well-known general purpose polymers. Each has advantages and disadvantages (*vide infra*). The selection of a method depends mostly on the end use of the polymer. For example, if a polymer latex is desired, the emulsion technique is the only choice, while for a glassy sheet material, bulk is a preferred method. In some cases, polymerization of monomers can only be accomplished by a specific method. Thus, polydiacetylene is prepared only by the solid-state method.

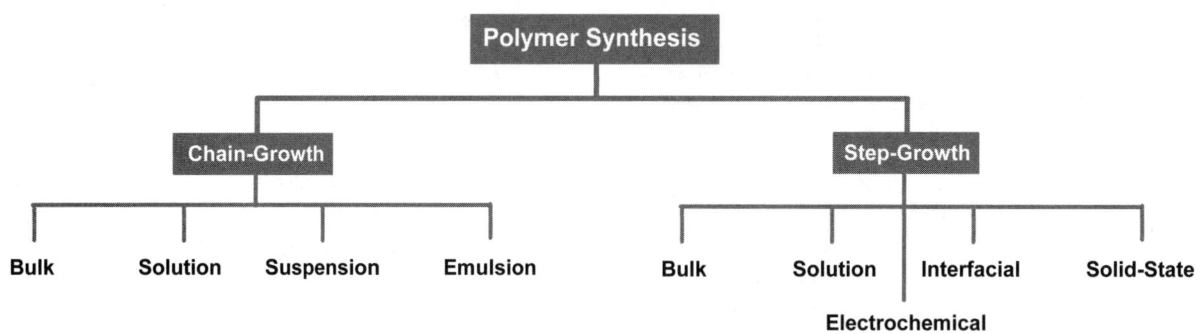

1.6.2.1. Bulk Polymerization

Bulk polymerization is a major industrial method for both chain-growth polymerization of monomers containing a double bond (vinyl monomers) and step-growth polymerization of monomers containing functional groups. This technique is termed *bulk* because it is carried out with neat monomers, i.e., in the absence of a solvent. The monomers can be solid, liquid, or gaseous or a combination.

While bulk polymerization of liquid vinyl monomers requires monomer-soluble initiators, heterogeneous conditions involving insoluble solid catalyst (e.g., Ziegler-Natta) are used for gaseous monomers, such as ethylene and tetrafluoroethylene. The catalysts are very efficient, with a gram of catalyst capable of producing as much as 1000 kg of polymer. In general, polymerization of gaseous monomers is conducted under high pressure in a reaction vessel containing an initiator. Once polymerization begins, monomer molecules diffuse to the growing polymer chains. The resulting polymer is a granular solid. Commercially, the polymerization of ethylene is carried out at temperatures near 300°C and at high pressure (1000-3000 atm) in the presence of appropriate initiators. Under these conditions, ethylene is in the supercritical state and acts as a solvent, as well as reactant. The LDPE produced by this process consists of chains of between 5,000 and 50,000 carbon atoms, with a relatively high degree of branching (up to 30 branches per 1000 carbon-atoms). Polymerization initiated by free-radicals leads to LDPE and reactions initiated by Ziegler-Natta catalysts produce HDPE. Although LLDPE has applications similar to LDPE, its manufacture is more like HDPE (i.e., by catalytic method). The same reactors can, in fact, be used for both. The main difference is that one or more co-monomers are used with ethylene in order to introduce some degree of controlled branching of the polymer chains.

Table 1.7. Commercial Methods Used for Notable General-Purpose Polymers

Polymer Family	Polymer	Polymerization Mechanism	Polymerization Method			
			Bulk	Solution	Suspension	Emulsion
Polyolefins	LDPE	Chain-Growth	Yes		Yes	
	HDPE			Yes	Yes	
	PP		Yes	Yes	Yes	
Acrylics	PMMA	Chain-Growth	Yes	Yes	Yes	Yes
	PAN			Yes	Yes	
Vinyls	PVC	Chain-Growth			Yes	Yes
	PVDC					Yes
Styrenics	PS	Chain-Growth	Yes		Yes	
	HIPS					Yes
	ABS					Yes
	SAN					Yes
Fluoropolymers	PTFE	Chain-Growth				Yes
	CTFE					Yes
	PVDF					Yes
Elastomers	Butyl Rubber	Chain-Growth		Yes		
	EPDM			Yes		
	Polyisoprene			Yes		
	SBS, SIS			Yes		
Polyesters	PET	Step-Growth	Yes			
	PBT		Yes			
Polyamides	PA66	Step-Growth	Yes			
	PA6		Yes	Yes		
Polyurethane	PU	Step-Growth	Yes	Yes		

One major application of bulk polymerization is in the manufacture of sheet-glass plastics. A good example is PMMA, sold under the trademark Lucite® (Lucite International) and Plexiglass® (Arkema Inc.). The monomer, methyl methacrylate (MMA) may be polymerized without difficulty in sheets up to 5 cm in thickness under static conditions in a two-stage process. The monomer containing monomer-soluble initiator is first partially polymerized to yield a viscous fluid, which is then poured into a sheet mold where polymerization is completed. This method produces unusually high molecular weight polymers due to very poor diffusion characteristics of macroradicals in the viscous medium, resulting in a very slow termination reaction. Since the monomers diffuse quite readily, the chain propagation continues. This autoacceleration in molecular weight, as a result of the absence of chain termination, is called the *Norris-Trommsdorff effect*.[38] The very high molecular weight product is advantageous for sheet plastics, but not for those that must be molded or extruded. As shown in Figure 1.84, autoacceleration is clearly dominant under neat conditions (used for bulk method) compared to a situation where the monomer is diluted with a solvent.

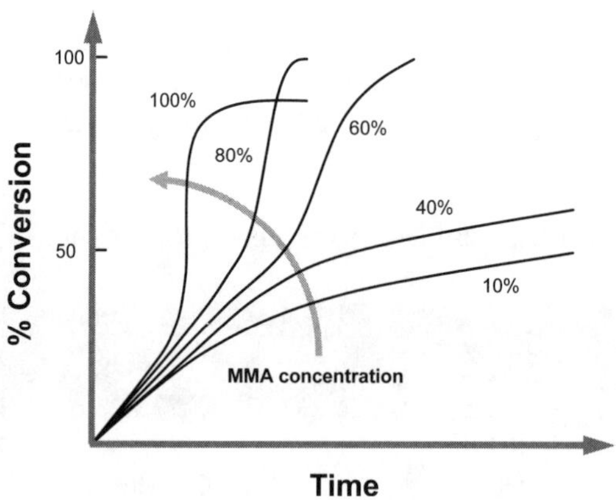

Figure 1.84. Effect of autoacceleration in the polymerization of MMA in benzene solution at various concentrations *(Adapted from Ref. 39)*.

The bulk method has also been traditionally used for industrial production of certain step-growth polymers, such as PET, PBT, PEN and aliphatic polyamides (nylons). Polymerization is carried out at higher temperatures, usually above 250°C, followed by cooling of the macromolecule to a temperature below its semicrystalline melting point. The reaction is then continued in the solid state above the glass transition temperature, but below the melting point. Solid-state polycondensations of this nature usually are conducted above 150°C. This approach has distinct advantages over performing polymerization completely in the melt state, such as producing polymers of higher purity (fewer side reactions at these lower temperatures) and in the economics of the reaction (less energy required). It is noteworthy that this solid-state polycondensation is often mixed with *solid-state polymerization*, which is not conducted in the fluid state (solution, suspension, emulsion, gas, or melt). Rather, reaction is performed by photochemical initiation of specific monomers that satisfy topochemical conditions (appropriate lattice spacings and overall packing of the monomers in the unit cell). Fundamental differences between these two approaches are discussed in the section on solid-state polymerization.

Removal of the condensate is the rate-determining factor in solid-state polycondensation, where greater surface area within the polymerizing solid favors faster evolution of the small molecule. The condensate can be removed from the solid by using static or dynamic vacuum or by exposure to a stream of inert gas. Only in a few cases, such as nylon-6,6, polymerization is started in the presence of an inert solvent (in this case, water) to prevent overheating and to control the start-up process. However, the process is completed as a bulk polymerization (the solvent is removed as the reaction proceeds).

A major disadvantage of bulk polymerization is that the quantity of heat generated is very high for some monomers. Almost all polymerizations are exothermic, especially vinyl monomers which liberate 8 to 20 kcal/mol when a π-bond of the monomer is converted to a σ-bond in the polymer. Heat removal can be a significant problem, particularly when polymerization is rapid and/or the reactor is large. Furthermore, high viscosity complicates heat removal. Thus, the heat of reaction must be addressed when isothermal conditions are to be maintained by special reactor design (e.g. continuous-flow stirred tank reactors and continuous plug flow reactors), which is sometimes very expensive. Despite this disadvantage, bulk polymerization is expanding in commercial processes because of its promise for high purity products, volume efficiency (more polymer in less volume because of neat polymerization or no solvent) and it does not involve solvent removal, recovery or purification.

1.6.2.2. Solution Polymerization

Polymerization of a vinyl monomer in a solvent overcomes the problem of heat management in the bulk polymerization process. The solvent acts as diluent and aids in the transfer of the heat. The solvent also allows easier stirring, since the viscosity of the reaction mixture decreases. However, the presence of solvent may present new difficulties. Chain transfer to solvent can become a problem and most importantly, removal of solvent from the polymer matrix is challenging. Vinyl acetate, acrylonitrile and acrylates are polymerized in solution.

Water possesses some advantages over organic solvents. It is a cheap, clean and environmentally friendly solvent with no chain transfer to solvent. However, for a homogenous polymerization process, its use is limited to water-soluble polymers and monomers. Industrially important water soluble polymers are polyacrylamide, poly(N-vinyl pyrrolidone) and polyacrylic acid. Water-soluble polymers are commonly used in many traditional applications in the food industry, agriculture, ceramics, paper and ink technology, explosives, and textiles. In industry, these polymers are recovered from aqueous solution by spray drying. In the laboratory, polymers are precipitated by pouring the water solution into non-solvents, such as acetone and methanol. Water-soluble azo initiators, peroxydisulfate and redox systems of peroxy compounds, and reducing agents are the main water-soluble initiators (see Appindix-IV).

The slurry-phase process, where monomers, such as isobutene, and catalysts are suspended in a solvent and conducted under high pressure, is mainly used for the production of HDPE. The polyethylene product is not soluble and forms a slurry of suspended solid particles. In contrast, linear low density polyethylene (LLDPE) is also produced under high pressure, but by a solution polymerization process. Ethylene and other co-monomers polymerize under high-pressure in a homogenous fluid phase to form polyethylene in an inert hydrocarbon solvent, such as n-hexane and cyclohexane. The fluid phase in the reactor should be at a pressure higher than the bubble point of the system. The reactor must be operated at a temperature lower than the lower solution temperature (cloud point) of the system and higher than the temperature at which the polyethylene crystallizes. The mixture leaving the polymerization reactor consists of polyethylene, n-hexane and ethylene, and is throttled through a valve reducing the pressure, producing a vapor to recover ethylene and n-hexane for reuse.

Solution polymerization is the only method for most step-growth polymers, due to high melting points of the monomers or being unreactive with co-monomers at lower temperatures. A number of high-performance polymers, such as polyimides, are prepared by this method. The process is advantageous when the solution can be used without separating the polymer, such as in the manufacture of protective coatings. Solution polymerizations are widely used in the textile industry by passing the polymer solution directly into a dope of spinning fibers. However, when the product is marketed in the solid form, the polymer must be separated from the solvent (and sometimes solid catalyst). The solvent, which may be recycled, must be recovered to meet federal regulations.

1.6.2.3. Suspension Polymerization

This method is used mainly to conduct free-radical polymerization of selected vinyl monomers, such as vinyl chloride, styrene and MMA. It is necessary that the initiator (normally an organic peroxide) be soluble in the monomer phase, which is dispersed by comminuting into a dispersion medium (usually water, though methanol is used for styrene and acrylonitrile) to form droplets. Thus, each droplet containing all reactants (i.e., monomer and initiator) acting as a "mini" bulk reactor, with the advantage of heat dissipation to the dispersion medium during polymerization. In addition, a small amount of a stabilizer [e.g., low molecular weight poly(vinyl alcohol), poly(vinyl-pyrrolidone) and hydroxylmethyl cellulose], which hinders coalescence and permits break-up of droplets during agitation, is necessary to obtain a stable dispersion system (Figure 1.85). Polymerization occurs in the monomer droplets that are progressively transformed into sticky, viscous monomer-polymer particles and finally into rigid, spherical polymer particles of size 50-500 μm. The polymer solids content in the fully converted suspension is typically 30-50% w/w. The size distribution of the initial droplets is controlled by the type and speed of agitator, the volume fraction of the monomer phase, and the type and concentration of stabilizer. Control of size distribution is critical because it is directly related to the size of the polymer beads that are formed after polymerization. Polymer beads are applicable to a number of technologies, such as chromatographic separation media (crosslinked ion exchange resin and as supports for enzyme immobilization). The polymer beads may be made porous by the inclusion of an inert diluent (or porogen) to the monomer phase, which may be extracted after polymerization. Although the suspension method represents 80% of PVC world-wide production, molding grade PS and PMMA are also produced to a considerable extent.

A disadvantage of this method is that the polymer must be separated from the dispersant, diluent (if added) and stabilizer, necessitating additional processing steps and equipment. Separation may be accomplished by centrifugation or filtration, and the polymer is subsequently dried, which is usually costly in equipment and energy consumption.

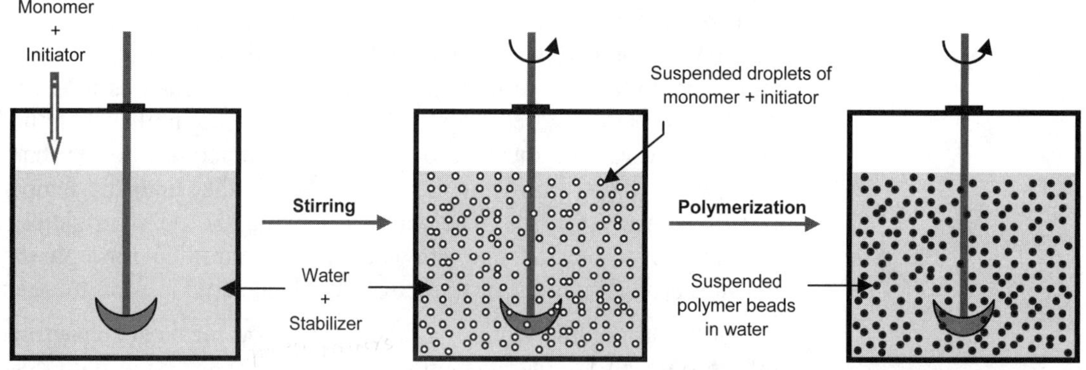

Figure 1.85. Schematics of the situations before and after suspension polymerization.

1.6.2.4. Emulsion Polymerization

Similar to the suspension method, by the nature of chemistry involved, emulsion polymerization employs water as a heat dissipating medium and is limited to only free-radical polymerization. This method is especially suitable for the manufacture of synthetic lattices (water-dispersed polymer), which can be applied directly, such as in paints, paper coatings, barrier coatings, carpet backing, bonding nonovens, and a number of adhesives. The key ingredients for this method are a water-insoluble monomer, a water-soluble initiator and an emulsifier (alternatively called surfactant, usually an amphiphilic long chain fatty acid salt with a hydrophilic "head" and a hydrophobic 'tail', such as sodium dodecyl sulfate and dodecyl trimethyl ammonium bromide). In aqueous solution, under agitation, the surfactant molecules form aggregates, called *micelles*, where the hydrocarbon tails are directed inward and the ionic ends face outward toward the aqueous environment. These micelles have the ability to absorb (swell) monomer molecules due to the formation of a nonpolar "pocket" resulting from the self-assembly of the hydrocarbon ends of the surfactant molecules. The aggregation of surfactant molecules occurs under conditions called the "critical micelle concentration", CMC. Typically, the micelles containing no monomers are very small (~10 nm) and contains only 50 to 100 molecules. The proportion of the ingredients and stirring are adjusted in a way that the surface area of small monomer swollen micelles is much higher (estimated >1000 times) than that of larger monomer droplets (1-10 μm). The droplets act as a monomer reservoir and supply monomers to small monomer swollen micelles, to micelles that have no monomers and to help form new monomer swollen micelles with isolated surfactants (Initial Stage of Figure 1.86).

Since the initiator is water-soluble and insoluble in monomer phase, the polymerization is believed to start with the dissociation of initiator molecules (typically, redox-type, see Appendix-IV) in the aqueous phase. The radicals thus generated react with monomers present in the water phase to form interfacially active free-radical oligomers, which are absorbed into the micelles or continue to grow and adsorb surfactant molecules (Early Stage of Figure 1.86). In either case, this results in the formation of new polymer particles. This process continues until no micelles remain.

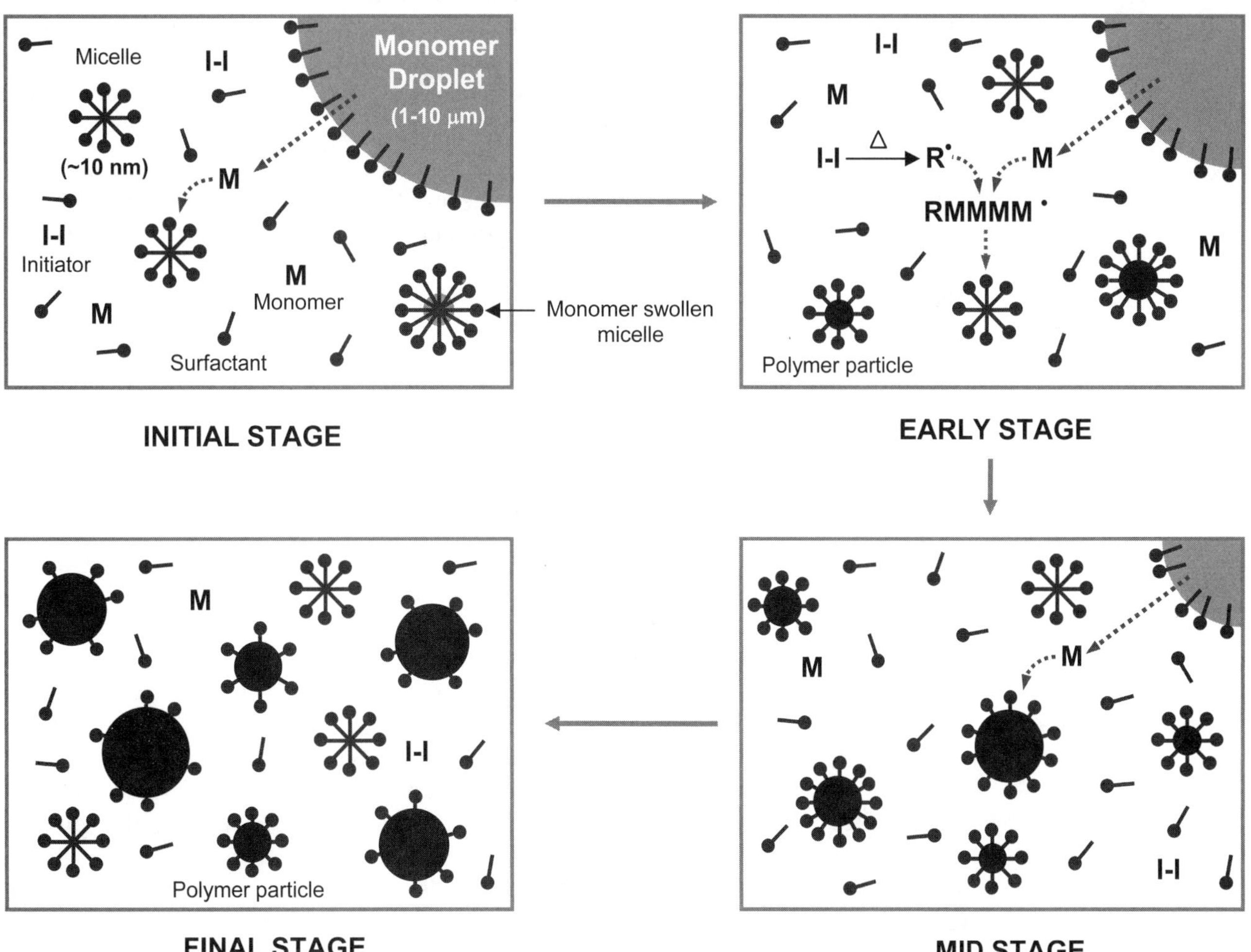

Figure 1.86. Schematics of the possible scenarios of an emulsion polymerization process.

Simultaneously, the polymer particles start to absorb additional monomers, which migrate from the monomer droplets through the water phase. Polymerization then proceeds mainly in the monomer-swollen polymer particles without the formation of new particles (Mid Stage of Figure 1.86). Thus, the growing chain is protected from termination until a second radical diffuses into the micelle. This is why the molecular weight can be so high in emulsion polymerization without slowing the rate of conversion. The monomers consumed by polymer chain growth are replaced by new monomers which continue to migrate from the monomer droplets. Depletion of monomer droplets is prevented by the continuous addition of new monomers. Fresh initiator is also continuously added to the reactor via a separate initiator feed stream.

When the polymer chains become large enough in the micelles undergoing polymerization, the surfactant molecules are slowly ejected from the micelles due to lesser compatibility and form new small monomer swollen micelles by absorbing monomers from the reservoirs. When all the monomers have been added to the reactor, polymerization continues with the conversion of residual monomer in the polymer particles. Gradually, the rate of polymerization decreases until no residual monomer is left (Final Stage of Figure 1.86). The final product, a "dispersion" of polymer particles in water, may be called a polymer colloid or latex, not an "emulsion", because it is no longer an oil-phase solubilized in a continuous phase, but rather finely dispersed discrete solid polymer particles. The major advantages of emulsion polymerization over solution polymerization include the viscosity of the latex (i.e., bulk viscosity) is independent of molecular weight (for solution polymerization, viscosity increases with the progress of polymerization) and extremely high molecular weights (>1,000,000) can be achieved without any viscosity penalty being incurred.

If the polymer product is to be recovered in the solid form, the suspension is usually preferred to the emulsion method because the suspended particles are larger and generally easier to separate and dry. For latex, an additional step, coagulation, is required prior to filtration and drying. Despite these economic considerations, elastomers, such as butadiene rubbers and acrylic elastomers are produced commercially by the emulsion method.

Inverse Emulsion Polymerization

Emulsions are classified according to the nature of the dispersed and continuous phases (*direct:* oil-in-water, *inverse:* water-in-oil, and *double:* water-in-oil-in-water) and their size/stability (*nanoemulsions*, *miniemulsions* and *microemulsions*). The inverse emulsion (IE) process was initially developed as an alternative to acrylamide polymerization in solution, but soon found its way to the field of hydrophilic crosslinked nanoparticle formation (Figure 1.87). IE allows high monomer concentrations while maintaining low bulk viscosities and good heat-transfer throughout the reaction. Heat dissipation in acrylamide polymerizations is quite important, due to the high heat of polymerization of the acrylamide monomer (19.8 Kcal/mol). Emulsification of the aqueous phase in the oil (commonly consisting of hydrocarbons) is achieved by amphiphiles with low *"hydrophilic-lipophilic balance"* (HLB) values; the lower the HLB, the more hydrophobic the emulsifier. Stabilization occurs exclusively through steric effects since the dielectric constant of oils is very low. Unlike direct emulsions (conditions of aforementioned emulsion polymerization), IEs are generally thermodynamically unstable and tend to phase separate with time. Thermodynamic stability is achievable at the expense of high emulsifier concentrations; stable inverse microemulsions usually contain 10-30 wt.% emulsifier, less than 15% v/v aqueous phase and necessitate the presence of co-emulsifiers.

The mechanism of IE polymerization depends strongly on the type of initiator (oil soluble or water soluble) as well as the oil-solubility of monomer(s). For hydrophilic initiators and monomers (homogeneous reaction mixture), the loci of initiation and propagation are the dispersed aqueous droplets, rather than the continuous phase or micellar structures (Figure 1.87). The resulting particle size distribution is, therefore, mainly determined by the nanodroplet size distribution of the IE, provided that reaction kinetics are faster than emulsion break-up.

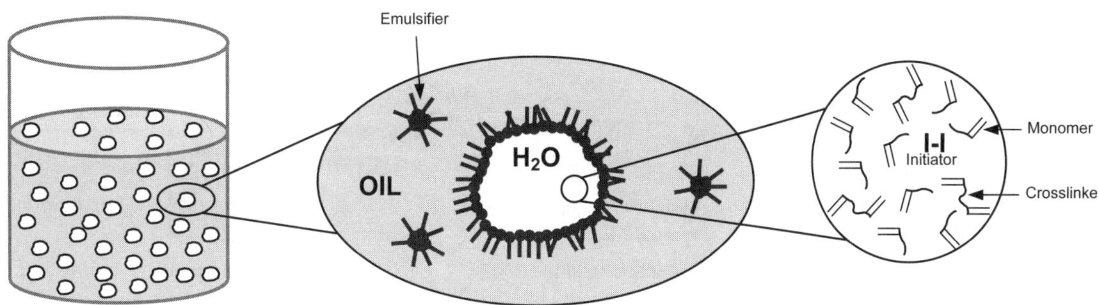

Figure 1.87. A schematic representation of an inverse emulsion polymerization leading to polymer microgels (note the difference from direct micelle shown in Figure 1.86). The loci of polymerization are the emulsifier-stabilized aqueous droplets.

The emulsifiers play an important role in designing nanoparticles through the IE process. Figure 1.88 depicts some of the most used surfactants for inverse microemulsion processes. Among anionic surfactants, the twin-tailed sodium bis(2-ethylhexyl)sulfosuccinate (Aerosol-OT, better known as AOT), is most popular because of the formation of well defined inverse micelles in hydrocarbon solvents. Sodium dodecyl sulfate, the anionic surfactant used extensively in emulsion polymerization, is not suitable in the inverse emulsion process because of its very high HLB number, 42. Fatty acid esters of sorbitan (e.g., sorbitan monostearate, Span-60®, HLB = 4.7, Atlas Chemical) and their polyoxyethylene substituted derivatives (e.g., polyoxyethylenesorbitan monolaurate, Tween-20®, HLB = 14.7) are among the most commonly used nonionics. The sorbitan esters are insoluble in water, but soluble in most organic solvents (low HLB surfactants). The polyoxyethylene substituted products are usually soluble in water and have relatively high HLB values (>14). One of the main advantages of the sorbitan esters and their ethoxylated derivatives is their approval for use as food additives. They are also widely used in cosmetics and some pharmaceutical preparations.

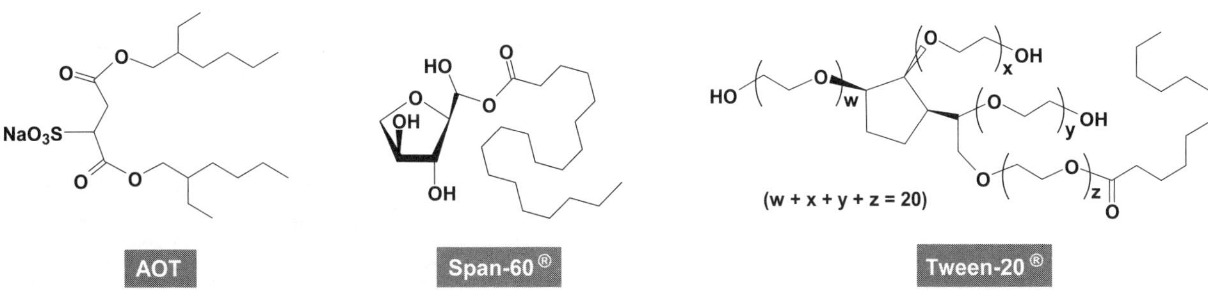

Figure 1.88. Structures of common surfactants in inverse microemulsion processes.

The formulation and application of polymeric nanoparticles enjoy great popularity in both academia and industry. The IE polymerization processes are now becoming very attractive to prepare a variety of polymeric materials, such as polymer-nanoparticle composites and microgels (Figure 1.89).[40] Composites of nanoparticles, such as semiconductors (SiO_2, CdS, ZnS, ZnO, TiO_2) and metals (Pt, Pd, Au, Ag, Cu, Fe), in a polymer matrix are under intense investigation because of their superior electrical, optical, and magnetic properties.

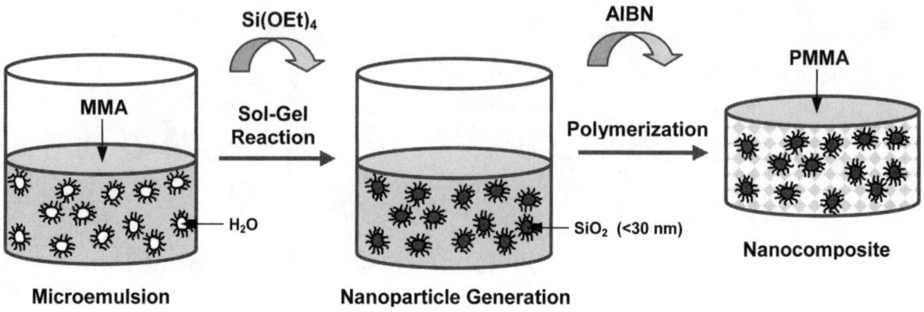

Figure 1.89. Preparation of SiO_2/PMMA nanocomposites by IE polymerization *(Adapted from Ref. 40)*.

1.6.2.5. Interfacial Polymerization

As the name implies, interfacial polymerization occurs at or near the interfacial boundary of two immiscible solutions and allows the synthesis of selected step-growth polymers (such as polyamides, polyureas, polyurethanes, polyesters and polycarbonates), at low temperature with limited side reactions.[41] Interfacial polymerization can directly generate finished products, such as films, fibers and membranes. In a typical polymerization process, the two multifunctional monomers are separately dissolved in two immiscible solvents. Water and an organic solvent (e.g., CH_2Cl_2) or two immiscible organic solvents, e.g., acetonitrile and cyclohexane are commonly used. Due to asymmetric solubility of the monomers in two phases, a very fast reaction often takes place on the organic side, near the interface, and the polymer precipitates quickly, forming a thin dense film (Figure 1.90). The film typically grows to a limiting thickness because the polymer film itself creates a barrier that hinders diffusion and contact between the reactive monomers. Although a variety of polymers can be prepared by interfacial polymerization, commercial exploitation has been limited primarily to polycarbonates and to some extent, a few aromatic polyamides and polyesters. Interfacial synthesis of polyesters involving aliphatic α,ω-diols does not form higher molecular weight products because of its lower reactivity compared to bisphenols, thus promoting the hydrolysis of diacid chloride as the dominant reaction.

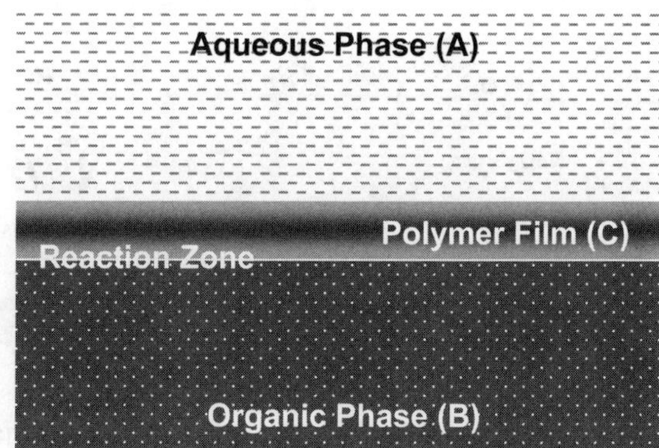

Figure 1.90. Schematic depiction of interfacial polymerization. Reactant **A** (dissolved in the aqueous phase) and reactant **B** (dissolved in the organic phase) diffuse toward one another and react to form polymer film **C**.

The interfacial polymerization technique is now a very popular approach in the field of microencapsulation. Microcapsules possess a unique three-dimensional structure, in which a solution containing a desired solute or an active substance is surrounded by a spherical polymeric film wall. Owing to this unique structure and a capability for arbitrary release of core material to the outer phase, capsules utilizing the interfacial polymerization principle have been widely used in pharmaceutical, agricultural, catalyst and composite products. Microcapsules are commonly prepared in oil-in-water emulsion, where polymerization of monomers proceeds around oil microdroplets containing the core material. For instance, urea-formaldehyde (UF) polymer microcapsules containing a dicyclopentadiene (DCPD, which possesses long shelf-life) monomer core are prepared by acid catalyzed *in situ* polymerization of urea and formaldehyde monomers in an oil-in-water emulsion (Figure 1.91a).[42] These microcapsules (sizes vary from 10-1,000 μm) are used as a healing agent for epoxy composites. When a crack develops under stress in an epoxy composite structure, the microcapsules at the point of the crack are ruptured and release the healing agent (DCPD), which immediately initiates ring-opening metathesis polymerization (ROMP) in the presence of Grubbs catalyst embedded in the epoxy matrix, thus bonding the crack faces (Figure 1.91b).[43] This autonomic healing markedly prolongs the life of structural materials because of adequate strength and excellent bonding of crosslinked polydicyclopentadiene (PDCPD) with the host material.

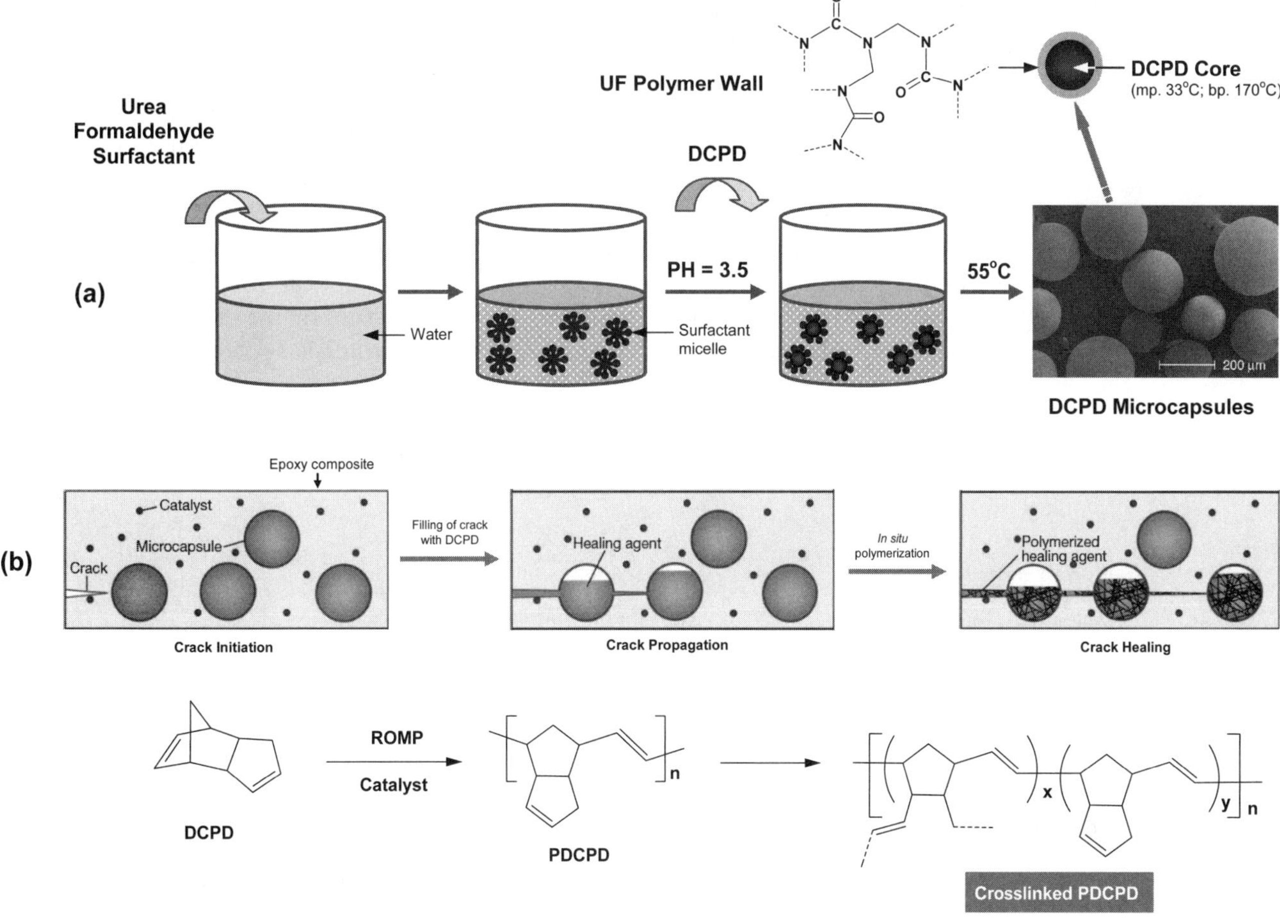

Figure 1.91. (a) Microencapsulation of DCPD utilizing acid-catalyzed *in situ* polymerization of urea with formaldehyde to form a capsule wall. *SEM picture of UF microcapsules is reproduced with permission of Informa Healthcare (Ref. 42).* (b) The autonomic healing concept *(With permission of Nature Publishing Group, Ref. 43).*

1.6.2.6. Solid-State Polymerization

Solid-state polymerization (SSP) traditionally has been divided into two classes: crystal-to-crystal polymerization and equilibrium condensation polymerization. The principles governing these two types are quite different, the former representing topological chemistry, while the latter occurs in the amorphous state of semicrystalline polymers (e.g., bulk polymerization of ethylene glycol and dimethyl terephthalate leading to PET). Topological SSP, better known as *topochemical polymerization*, relies on a suitable arrangement of the reactants in the monomer crystal to permit the necessary contact between reacting groups with only slight vibrations allowed within a crystalline state. The polymerization of diacetylenes and diolefins are sterling examples of topological chemistry. On the other hand, significant molecular motion occurs in polycondensation SSP, mostly in the amorphous phase. This motion facilitates the release of a small condensate molecule (methanol and ethylene, for example, in the case of PET and aforementioned ADMET chemistry, respectively), which can be removed at the surface of the solid to drive the increase in molecular weight.

The diacetylene (DA) monomers comply with topochemical requirements in their monomer crystals and in a highly ordered monolayer monomer assembly prepared by the Langmuir-Blodgett (LB) method. The polydiacetylenes thus obtained are macroscopic single crystals (same size as the monomer crystal) or as a film of a monolayer thickness by the substrate assisted (LB) method. The general guideline for thin-film photopolymerization is adapted from solid-state chemistry. The neighboring diacetylenes are polymerized *via* a 1,4-addition mechanism for which, as illustrated in Figure 1.92, the topochemical requirements include stacking interval (*d*), the tilt angle (θ) between axes of the DA moiety and stacking direction, and the distance between the C_1 and C_4 carbons of adjacent acetylenes are 4.7-5.2 Å, 40°-60°, and not longer than 4 Å, respectively.[44] For example, upon depositing LB films of 10,12-pentacosadiynoic acid onto substrate, the nominal film pressure is regulated at ~20-25 mN/m to achieve the spatial constraints for polymerization. Because of their large π-conjugation, polydiacetylenes (PDAs) exhibit superior nonlinear optical properties and ultrafast (<picosecond) response times compared to traditional inorganic crystals, and are now considered for many applications, such as all optical switches, logic gates and sensors.

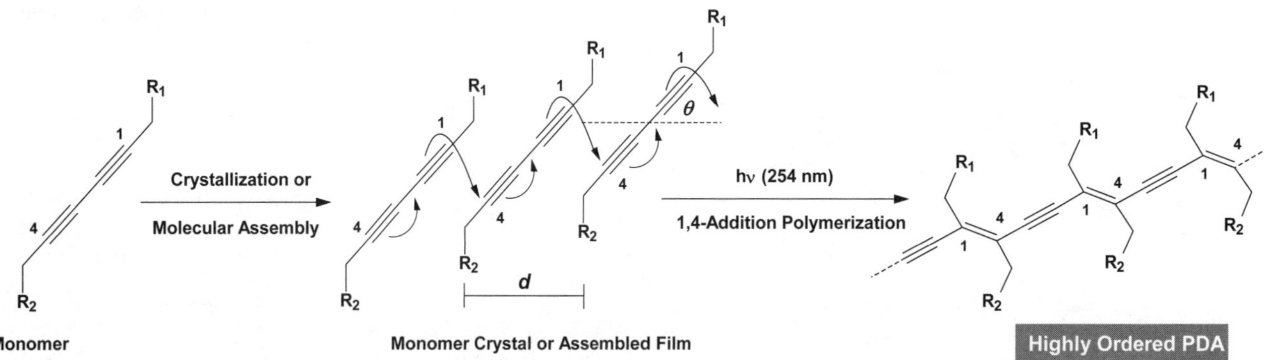

Figure 1.92. Schematic representation of topochemical polymerization of highly ordered diacetylene molecules.

In contrast, topochemical polymerization of suitable diolefinic systems, such as *trans,trans*-1,4-bis(2-phenylethenyl)-2,3,5,6-tetrafluorobenzene, undergo [2+2] photocycloaddition of double bonds of nearest neighbor molecules, resulting in cyclobutane linkages (Figure 1.93). With few exceptions, the prerequisites for this type of photochemical reaction in the solid state are arrangement of molecules in a parallel orientation with a distance (center to center) between molecules of 3.5-4.2 Å.[45] Unlike PDAs, polymers derived from diolefins do not possess extended π-conjugation systems, but they exhibit high thermal stability.

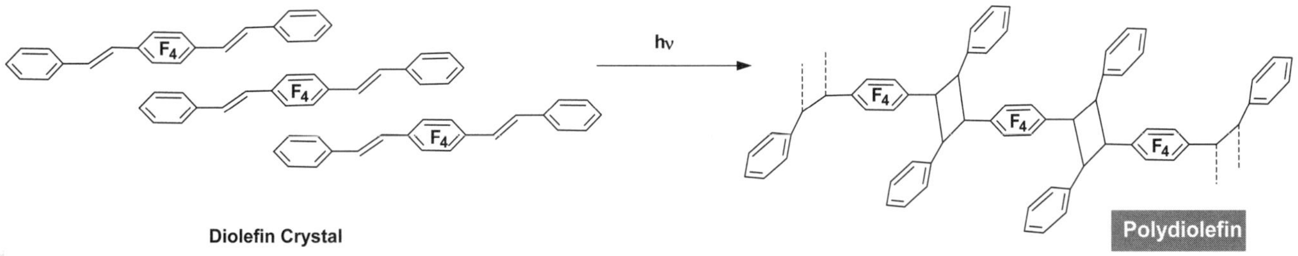

Figure 1.93. Example of a diolefin photopolymerization.

1.6.2.7. Electrochemical Polymerization

Electrochemical polymerization (EP) is an elegant, attractive, and easy strategy, for the preparation of π-conjugated polymers,[46] including the immobilization of metal complexes,[47,48] such as metalloporphyrins, on the electrode surface. The principle is based on the electrochemical oxidation of a suitably designed monomer to form a polymeric film. These films should be electronic conductors to ensure electron-transfer within the matrix and hence, the continuous growth of the polymers. Pyrrole, thiophene, and aniline-based monomers have been the most used compounds for EP. In electrochemical polymerization, a potential is applied across a solution containing thiophene and an electrolyte, producing a conductive polythiophene film on the anode. The quality of an electrochemically prepared polythiophene film is affected by a number of factors. These include the electrode material, current density, temperature, solvent, electrolyte, presence of water, and monomer concentration. Two other important factors are the structure of the monomer and the applied potential. The potential required to oxidize the monomer depends on the electron density in the thiophene ring π-system. Electron-donating groups lower oxidation potential, while electron-withdrawing groups cause an increase. Thus, 3-methylthiophene polymerizes in acetonitrile and tetrabutylammonium tetrafluoroborate at about 1.5 V vs. SCE (saturated calomel electrode), while unsubstituted thiophene polymerizes at about 1.7 V vs. SCE.

The mechanism of EP of pyrrole and thiophene monomers is believed to proceed via the formation of a radical cation with several resonating forms (**A**-**C**). The dimer is formed exclusively by deprotonation of dihydromer dication **D**, produced via α-coupling between two molecules of the resonance form **C**, because of greater unpaired electron density in the α-position (Figure 1.94).[49] The propagation continues via the same sequence: oxidation, coupling, and deprotonation, leading to the formation of oligomers and polymers on the electrode surface. It is worth noting that the polymerization occurs through a step-growth mechanism since a tetramer may form by coupling between oxidized forms of two dimers or one trimer and one monomer (see conducting polymers in Chapter-5 for the EP of aniline). Moreover, the oligomer chain, as well as the delocalization of the unpaired electron, increases progressively and α-coupling will no longer be the only coupling route. The longer the chain length, the higher the number of β-couplings even if the β-positions are sterically inaccessible. These β-couplings are responsible for the poor crystallinity of electrochemically polymerized polypyrrole (PPy) or polythiophene (PTh) films.

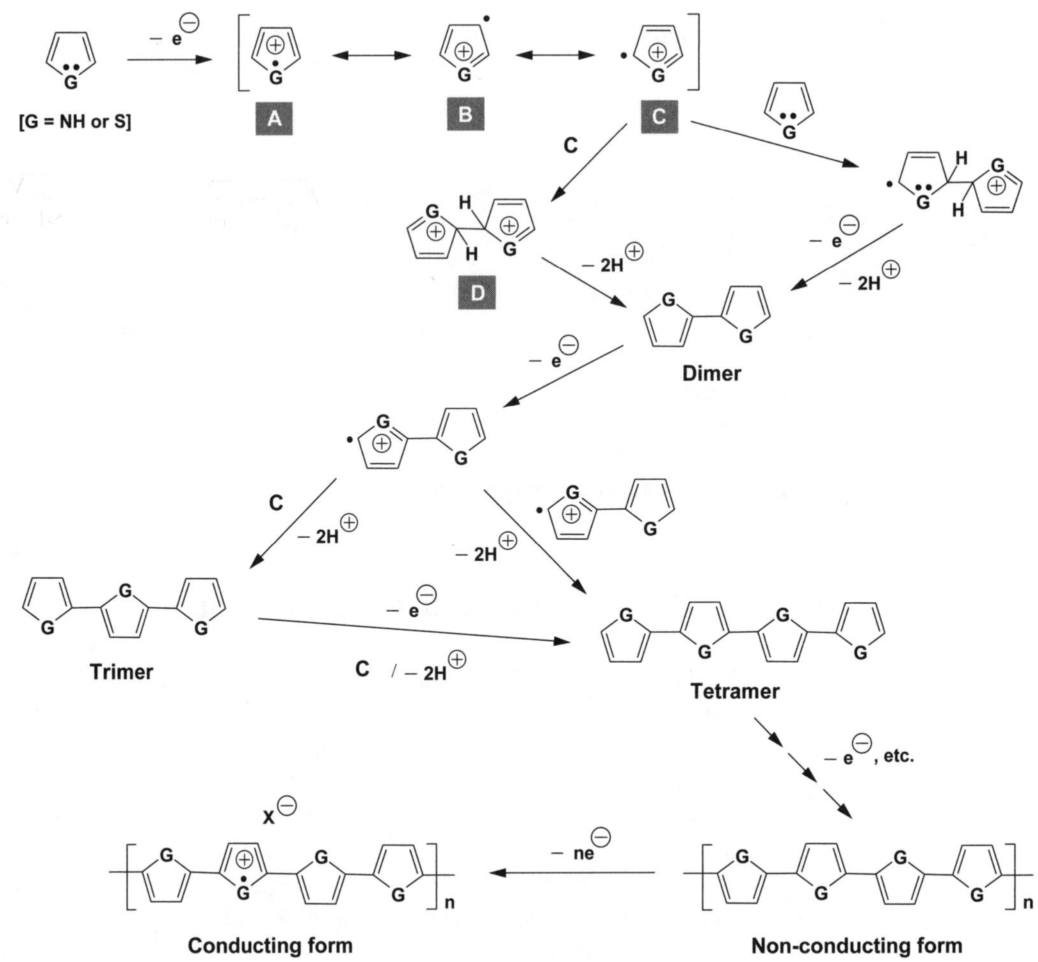

Figure 1.94. Mechanism of electrochemical synthesis of polypyrrole and polythiophene.

Finally, the EP does not produce the neutral non-conducting polymer but rather, its oxidized conducting form (doped). In general, doping is performed at much higher levels (20-40%) in conducting polymers than in inorganic semiconductors (<1%). In fact, the final polymer chain carries a positive charge every 3 to 4 monomer units, which is counter-balanced by an electrolyte anion X, such as ClO_4^- and BF_4^-. Thus, the electrochemically polymerized films consist of about 65 wt.% polymer and 35 wt.% anion. It also appears that the morphology and the physical properties of the polymer films depend largely upon the EP conditions. Therefore, one can induce a supplementary design parameter during the polymerization step by adjusting the solution composition or the electrode potential.[48] Growth of the polymeric films or more precisely, control of the amount of deposited materials (or the polymer film thickness) can be easily achieved by monitoring the total charge passed during the electro-oxidative polymerization process.

The EP of aromatic hydrocarbons, such as benzene, naphthalene, anthracene, pyrene and fluoranthene, leading to polymer films, is very difficult because of their higher oxidation potentials. However, recent studies clearly indicate that boron trifluoride diethyl etherate ($BF_3{\bullet}Et_2O$), BFEE, which exists partially as an ion-pair $[(C_2H_5)_3O^+]BF_4^-$ in diethyl ether, has emerged as an excellent electrolyte system (conduction medium) for EP of aromatic compounds. BFEE presumably interacts with the aromatic monomer, causing a decrease in aromaticity, which leads to a marked reduction in oxidation potential.[50-54] For example, the oxidation potential onset of fluoranthene in BFEE was measured as only 1.07 V vs SCE, which was much lower than that in commonly used electrolytes (1.68 V vs SCE), such as 0.1 mol/L tetrabutylammonium tetrafluoroborate in acetonitrile.[55] The mechanism of the formation of an ion-pair in BFEE is unclear, but it is believed that group exchange and/or a metathesis reaction is responsible for the formation of triethyloxonium tetrafluoroborate (OTFB), as follows:[56]

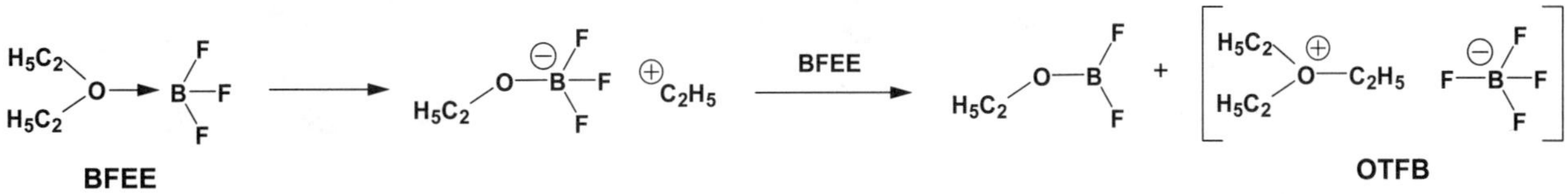

BFEE ⟶ BFEE ⟶ OTFB

It should be noted that the conductivity of BFEE is 2.97×10^{-4} S/cm at 25°C, while that of diethyl ether and liquid BF_3 are 3×10^{-13} S/cm at 25°C and 5×10^{-10} S/cm at -120°C, respectively. Thus, for the first time, high-quality polyfluoranthene (PFAN) films, with good electrochemical properties, conductivity (10^{-2} S/cm), thermal stability, and optical properties, were electrochemically synthesized in pure BFEE by direct anodic oxidation of fluoranthene. Since the first PLED (polymer light-emitting diode) was made in 1990, PFAN has been extensively investigated, owing to its structural similarity with polyfluorene[57,58], an excellent blue light emitting material (see Chapter-5). The results of quantum chemical calculations of fluoranthene monomer and ^{1}H-NMR spectroscopy of dedoped PFAN films indicated that the polymerization occurred mainly at the C_3, C_4, C_{13}, and C_{14} positions via the formation of intermediates **A** through **D** (Figure 1.95).[53] SEM studies indicate that the polymer films are composed of irregular nano-sheets (~200 nm) and resemble a growth of aggregates shaped as blossoms, which suggests the polymer might have acted as its own template during the polymerization.

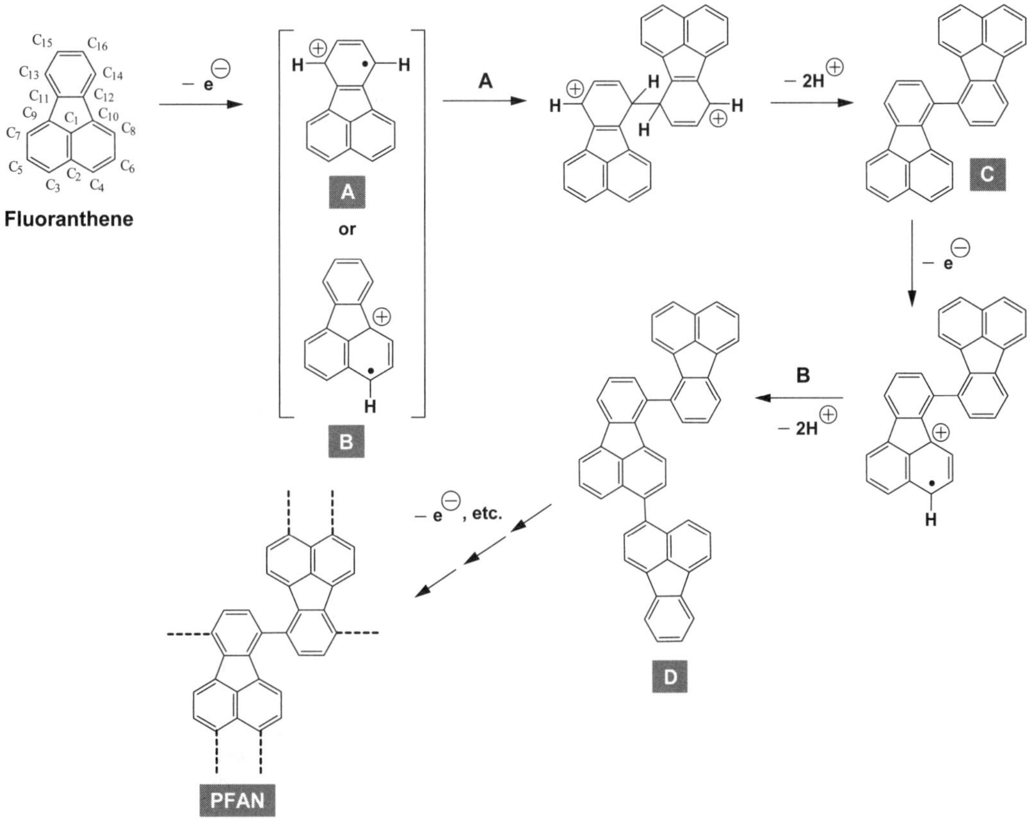

Fluoranthene — A or B — C — D — PFAN

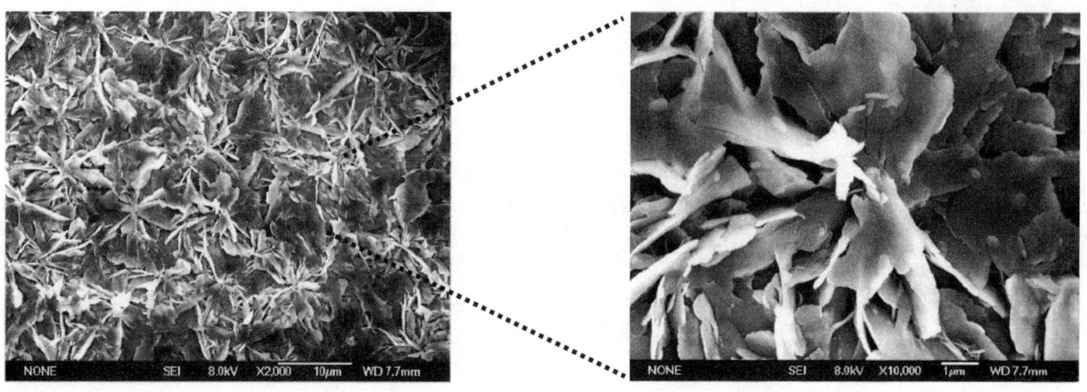

Figure 1.95. Mechanism of electrochemical synthesis of PFAN. *SEM images of a PFAN film are reproduced with permission of the American Chemical Society.*

Finally, among the aforementioned polymerization techniques bulk, solution, suspension and emulsion are industrially important. Their advantages and disadvantages are summarized in Table 1.8.

Table 1.8. Comparison of Major Industrial Methods of Polymer Synthesis

Polymerization Technique	Advantages	Disadvantages
Bulk	Simple process, no solvents, high purity polymers, volume efficiency (more polymer in a small reactor) and inexpensive	Difficulty in managing heat of polymerization. High polydispersity index. Removal of trace amount of unreacted monomers can be a problem, if the polymer is used for food containment.
Solution	Good heat management. Polymer ends up in solution, directly useful for certain applications, such as wire coating and dielectric passivation films for computer chips.	Dry polymers require removal of organic solvent (i.e., associated with environmentally unfriendly/expensive steps: recovery and purification of solvent). Low volume efficiency (high solvent: monomer ratio). Difficult to obtain higher molecular weight due to high viscosity of the polymer.
Suspension	Excellent heat control and water is the preferred solvent. Produces beads that have technological uses (xerographic toner, catalyst carriers, ion exchange resins, substrates for combinatorial synthesis, etc.)	Removal of dispersant and drying are expensive.
Emulsion	Excellent heat control and water is the preferred solvent. Produces very high MW polymer with narrow molecular weight distribution. The product after polymerization is a latex, which has high technological value (paint, coatings and carpet backing). High molecular weight products can be obtained without any viscosity penalty being incurred.	Isolation of solid polymer involves several expensive steps (coagulation, filtration, removal of surfactants, drying and compacting of powders).

General Study Questions:

1. Using five sentences, how would you respond, if you are asked by your friend who is not a chemist, to define polymers.
2. Polymers occur naturally in various forms. Name four of them, including their sources.
3. Write the structural repeat units for the following polymers: ABS, PMP, PPO, SAN, PC, HIPS, SBR, and nylon-4,6.
4. Describe the differences between thermoplastic, thermosetting, and elastomeric polymers with respect to microstructure and general properties. Give three example of each class of polymer.
5. Why does polystyrene behave like a plastic rather than an elastomer at ambient temperatures? Discuss the structural features of a polymer which would make it a useful elastomer.
6. Briefly explain the difference between number average molecular weight (M_n) and weight average molecular weight (M_w) of polymers. Given that a polystyrene sample has a M_w of 110,000 and M_n of 90,000, calculate the polydispersity index (PDI) and comment on the implication of the value you obtain.
7. How would you prepare (a) a very high molecular weight PET and (b) a low molecular weight PET terminated with hydroxyl groups?
8. Discuss the types of phase transition(s) in amorphous, semi-crystalline, crystalline and crosslinked polymers by drawing their specific volume vs. temperature curves. How would you distinguish one from the other experimentally?
9. Define T_g of a polymer. Differential scanning calorimetry (DSC) is the most popular method for obtaining T_g of a polymer. Would the T_g value of a polymer vary if the experiment is conducted at a different rate of heating, e.g., 5, 10 and 15°C/min? Consider HDPE, nylon-6,6, nylon-6,10 and nylon-6,12. Rank them in order of increasing T_g. Justify your answer by citing the primary contributing factor.
10. How would the mechanical and physical properties of thermoplastics change with (a) chain length (degree of polymerization), (b) chain stiffness, (c) side group size, and (d) degree of crystallinity.
11. Write the pentad structures of isotactic, syndiotactic, and atactic polypropylene. Rank them in increasing order of T_g and impact strength. Briefly explain your answer. Name two physical methods you might use to distinguish each from the others.
12. What are the primary differences between T_g and T_m? What will be the effect on T_g if an amorphous sample is cooled faster from its liquid or rubber-like state?
13. The T_g values of polystyrene (PS) and polybutadiene (PB) are 100°C and -105°C, respectively. How many T_gs would you expect in styrene-butadiene random copolymer and styrene-butadiene block copolymer? Explain.
14. Both poly(methyl methacrylate) and polymethyacrylic acid are highly amorphous, but the former exhibits a T_g of 105°C and the latter at 228°C. Offer a reasonable explanation.
15. Certain specific properties or broad-range of properties are not always achievable with a single homopolymer. Copolymerization of two or more monomers is preferred over mixing (physical blending) of two or more homopolymers to create

a broad range of properties in a single polymeric material. Comment on this statement with two examples, including advantages and disadvantages of copolymerization and physical blending.

16. Rank the following polymers in increasing order of T_g. Justify your answer.

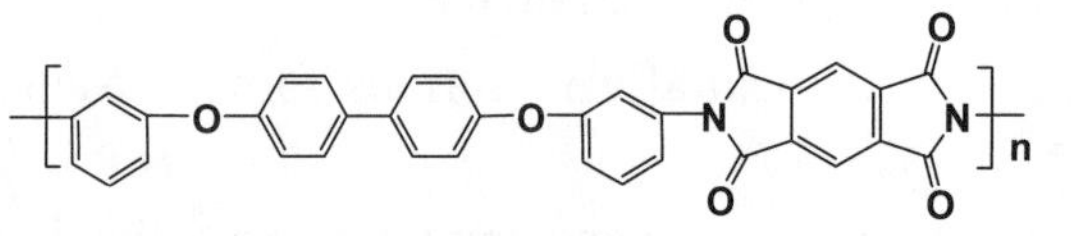

(I)

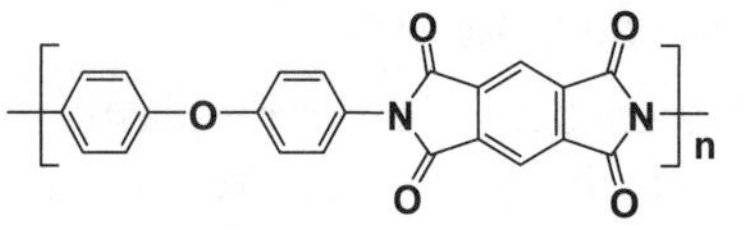

(II)

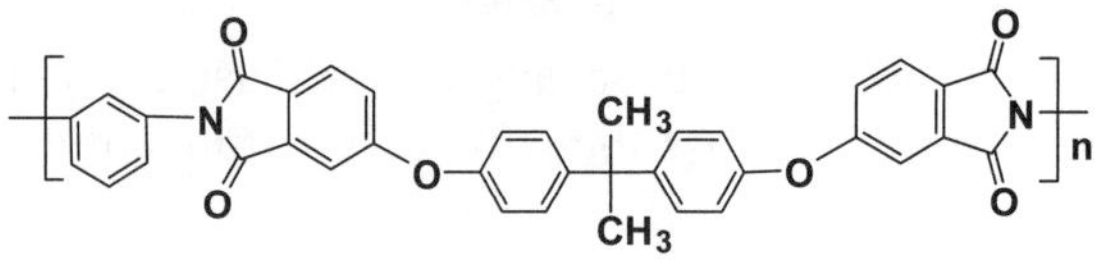

(III)

17. In order to develop a polymer material with a set of specified physical and mechanical properties, it is important to understand the concept of glass transition temperature, T_g, which is the property of the amorphous state of the polymer. How does T_g vary with (a) chain flexing groups, (b) chain stiffening groups, (c) chain symmetry, (d) pendent groups, (e) intermolecular forces and (f) copolymerization and polymer blending. Explain with appropriate examples.
18. Discuss the salient features of various polymerization methods. Compare their advantages and disadvantages.
19. How would a bulk polymerized polystyrene differ from an emulsion polymerized polystyrene in terms of molecular weight and polydispersity?
20. Assign a polymer from PC, PMMA, nylon-6,6 and POM to each of the following set of characteristics: (a) High melting point, high strength, good frictional properties and resistance to fatigue, (b) Highly amorphous, rigid and transparent, but poor impact strength, (c) Strong and tough, but prone to water absorption, and (d) Highly amorphous, rigid, transparent, and high impact strength.
21. Clearly differentiate between chain growth and step growth polymerization. Give three examples of each.
22. Aliphatic polyamides can be successfully prepared using the "nylon rope trick", by interfacial polymerization of a diacid chloride and a diamine. However, the "polyester rope trick" does not seem to work when using the same diacid chloride and an aliphatic diol with the same number of methylene groups as the diamine. Explain.
23. What is different about the polymer formed by anionic polymerization compared to other polymerizations and what type of polymerization does this make possible?
24. Define first-order and second-order phase transitions in polymers. Which experimental method would you use to detect these transitions.
25. Which of the following two polymers will exhibit the higher T_m and why?

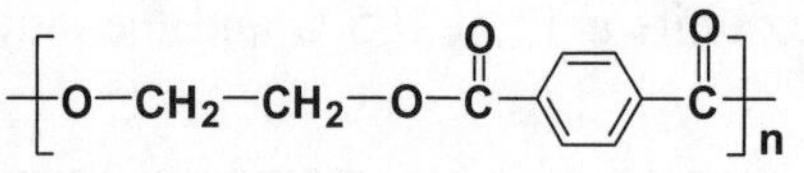

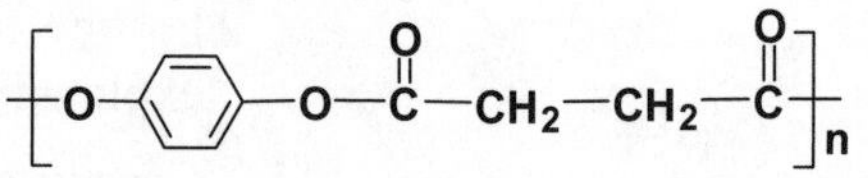

$$\left[O-CH_2-CH_2-O-\overset{O}{\overset{\|}{C}}-C_6H_4-\overset{O}{\overset{\|}{C}} \right]_n \qquad \left[O-C_6H_4-O-\overset{O}{\overset{\|}{C}}-CH_2-CH_2-\overset{O}{\overset{\|}{C}} \right]_n$$

26. Which polymerization process (cationic, anionic or free-radical) would you recommend to polymerize the following monomers: (a) methyl vinyl ether, (b)

acrylic acid, (c) acrylamide, (d) ethylene oxide, and (e) vinyl chloride. Explain the basis of your choice for one process over the others.

27. Listed below are one set each of polyesters and polyamides, including their T_g and T_m values. Write their chemical structures. Which one from each category do you think would be the best fiber for clothing application. Justify your rationale.

Polyesters:

Poly(ethylene succinate) [T_g = -5°C; T_m = 110°C]

Poly(ethylene terephthalate) [T_g = 80°C; T_m = 250°C]

Poly(1,4-butylene adipate) [T_g = -65°C; T_m = 55°C]

Poly(1,4-butylene terephthalate) [T_g = 65°C; T_m = 225°C]

Polyamides:

Polycaprolactam (nylon 6) [T_g = 50°C; T_m = 225°C]

Poly(undecanoamide) (nylon 11) [T_g = -65°C; T_m = 180°C]

Poly(hexamethyl adipamide) (nylon 6,6) [T_g = 60°C; T_m = 255°C]

Poly(hexamethylene sebacamide) (nylon 6,10) [T_g = 40°C; T_m = 240°C]

28. Why is PET a preferred choice over LDPE for beverage containers?

29. Why does a free-radical polymerization process with chain-transfer as a dominant mechanism for termination produce a number of polymer molecules much greater than the number of moles of free-radical initiators used? What would be the effect on molecular weight of the product if you gradually increase the initiator concentrations?

30. Which of the polymers (indicated in parentheses in each category) is best suited for each of the following applications. First, establish the product requirements in each case and then eliminate one by one to arrive at the conclusion. Discuss any compensation (e.g., cost) that you may have considered. (a) Car head lamp cover [PMMA, PC, PMP, COP, PMMI], (b) Heavy duty garbage container [HDPE, PVC, PP, UHMWPE, ABS], (c) Clear water jugs [PS, HDPE, SAN, PET, PMMA], (d) Heavy duty machine gears [HDPE, nylon-6,6, ECO, PTFE, PPO], and (e) Gasket of a pump delivering a hot (100°C) oily organic substance [ABS, PPS, PEEK, PTFE, PVC].

Advanced Study Questions:

31. In applications where polymers will be exposed to elevated temperatures, the heat deflection temperature is often used as a benchmark of high temperature performance. Write a precise definition of the heat deflection temperature (HDT)? What properties of the polymer is HDT most closely related to?

32. What is intrinsic viscosity, $[\eta]$, of a dilute polymer solution? How does it relate to viscosity average molecular weight (M_v)? Under what condition does M_v equal M_w? Draw a typical molecular weight distribution curve showing the locations of M_v, M_n and M_w.

33. Draw a stress-strain curve which would be representative of a hard, tough polymer, such as cellulose acetate. Indicate in the diagram the points, lines, or areas which give (a) the elastic modulus, (b) the yield point, (c) the elongation to break, and (d) the toughness of the polymer.

34. Define the terms tensile modulus, tensile strength, flexural modulus, flexural strength, and creep. Which one of these mechanical properties is most important in designing (a) a car tire, (b) a high-performance composite, and (c) a gasket.
35. What are the fundamental differences between (a) SEM and TEM, (b) WAXD and SAXS, and (c) OM and AFM? What is their range of capabilities?
36. How is the degree of crystallinity of a polymer sample measured by DSC and WAXD? Why is the value obtained by DSC usually higher than that from XRD?
37. Define limiting oxygen index (LOI). Arrange the following polymers in the order of increasing LOI: PVC, PTFE, LDPE and PBO.
38. Rayon (also known as regenerated cellulose) is probably the most misunderstood of all fibers. It is not a natural fiber, yet it is not a synthetic. Rayon is perhaps best characterized as a semi-synthetic fiber, prepared by reaction of cellulose with an alkaline solution of CS_2, followed by acidification of the processed fibers. Write chemical equations for the processing and regeneration steps.
39. What is meant by the 'free volume', V_f, of a polymer? How can you determine the V_f of a polymer sample?
40. Emulsion polymerization is a powerful method for manufacturing polymer emulsions for surface coatings. How can you control (a) particle size and distribution, and (b) average molecular weight?
41. TPX is a semi-crystalline polymer, yet exhibits 90% optical transparency. Explain.
42. Generally, random copolymers exhibit only one T_g, which is in between the T_gs of individual homopolymers. Styrene-Acrylonitrile copolymer (SAN), a random copolymer, typically containing approximately 76% styrene and 24% acrylonitrile, shows a T_g (105°C), higher than that of polystyrene (100°C) and polyacrylonitrile (90°C). Explain.
43. The T_g of a polymer, such as PMMA, can be obtained by measuring the dielectric constant as a function of temperature. Draw and explain the basis of a typical dielectric constant vs. temperature curve. Would the T_g value differ from the one measured at lower frequency compared to that at higher frequency?
44. The T_g of an amorphous or semi-crystalline polymer can be determined by measuring the elastic modulus of the polymer as a function of temperature. Draw a curve showing the relationship between the two functions.
45. The percent crystallinity of a semicrystalline polymer is determined by the density method using the following equation:

$$\textbf{\% Crystallinity} = \left[\frac{\rho_{\text{exptl}} - \rho_{\text{amorph}}}{\rho_{\text{100\% cryst}} - \rho_{\text{amorph}}} \right] \times 100$$

How are the various density (ρ) parameters in this equation obtained experimentally?
46. What is die swell of a polymer? Why is this a significant parameter when designing a pipe with a specific diameter by the extrusion process?

References for Chapter-1:

1. Courtesy of Prof. Joseph E. Armstrong, Illinois State University.
2. Wilks, E. S., *IUPAC Recommendations on Macromolecular (Polymer) Nomenclature*: www.iupac.org/reports/IV/guide-for-authors.pdf.
3. Staudinger, H., *Chem. Ber.,* **57**, 1203 (1924).
4. Mark, H., *Z. Elektrochem.,* **40**, 499 (1934).
5. Houwink, R., *J. Prakt. Chem.,* **157**, 15 (1940).
6. Frisch, H. L.; Mallows, C. L.; Heatley, F.; Bovey, F. A., *Macromolecules,* **1**, 533 (1968).
7. *Properties of Polymers*, van Krevelen, D. W., 3rd Edn., Elsevier, Amsterdam (1990).
8. Dammert, R. M.; Maunu, S. L.; Maurer, F. H. J.; Neelov, I. M.; Niemelä, S.; Sundholm, F.; Wästlund, C., *Macromolecules,* **32**, 1930 (1999).
9. Fox, T. G., *Bull. Am. Phys. Soc.,* **1**, 123 (1956).
10. *Synthetic Fibre Materials*, Brody, H., John Wiley and Sons Inc., New York (1994).
11. *With kind permission of Springer Science and Business Media.* Source: Prevorsek, D. C.; Kwon, Y. D.; Sharma, R. K., *J. Mater. Sci.,* **12**, 2310 (1977).
12. Kamahori, K.; Tada, S.; Ito, K.; Itsuno, S., *Macromolecules*, **32**, 541 (1999).
13. Ziegler, K.; Hozkampf, E.; Breil, H.; Martin, H., *Angew. Chem.,* **67**, 541 (1955).
14. Natta, G., *J. Polym. Sci.*, **16**, 143 (1955).
15. Arlman, E. J.; Cossee, P., *J. Catal.,* **3**, 99 (1964).
16. Arlman, E. J., *J. Catal.,* **5**, 178 (1966).
17. Kaminsky, W.; Kulper, K.; Brintzinger, H.-H.; Wild, F. R. W. P., *Angew. Chem. Int. Ed.,* **24**, 507 (1985).
18. Harlan, C. F.; Mason, M. R.; Barron, A. R., *Organometallics,* **13**, 2957 (1994).
19. Zurek, E.; Woo, T. K.; Firman, T. K.; Ziegler, T., *Inorg. Chem.,* **40**, 361 (2001).
20. Piers, W. E.; Chivers, T., *Chem. Soc. Rev.,* **26**, 345 (1997).
21. Brookhart, M.; Green, M. L. H., *J. Organomet. Chem.,* **250**, 395 (1983).
22. Woo, T. K.; Margl, P. M.; Ziegler, T.; Blöchl, P. E., *Organometallics,* **16**, 3454 (1997).
23. Herisson, P.J.-L.; Chauvin, Y., *Die Makromol. Chemie.,* **141**, 161 (1970).
24. Runge, M. B.; Dutta, S.; Bowden, N. B., *Macromolecules,* **39**, 498 (2006).
25. Schrock, R. R.; Hoveyda, A. H., *Angew. Chem. Int. Ed.,* **42**, 4592 (2003).
26. Webster, O. W.; Hertler, W. R.; Sogah, D. Y.; Farnham, W. B.; RajanBabu, T. V., *J. Am. Chem. Soc.,* **105**, 5706 (1983).
27. Dicker, I. B.; Cohen, G. M.; Farnham, W. B.; Hertler, W. R.; Laganis, E. D.; Sogah, D. Y., *Macromolecules,* **23**, 4034 (1990).
28. Sogah, D. Y.; Hertler, W. R.; Webster, O. W.; Cohen, G. M., *Macromolecules,* **20**, 1473 (1987).
29. Webster, O. W., *J. Polym. Sci. Polym. Chem.,* **38**, 2855 (2000).
30. Osada, Y.; Ross-Murphy, S. B., *Sci. Am.,* **268**, 82 (1993).
31. Simmons, M. R.; Yamasaki, E. N.; Patrickios, C. S., *Macromolecules,* **33**, 3176 (2000).
32. Patrickios, C. S.; Lowe, A. B.; Armes, S. P.; Billingham, N. C., *J. Polym. Sci. Polym. Chem.,* **36**, 617 (1998).

33. Cooper, G. D.; Blanchard, H. S.; Endres, G. F.; Finkbeiner, H., *J. Am. Chem. Soc.,* **87**, 3996 (1965).
34. Hong, S. H.; Sanders, D. P.; Lee, C. W.; Grubbs, R. H., *J. Am. Chem. Soc.,* **127**, 17161 (2005).
35. Wagener, K. B.; Boncella, J. M.; Nel, J. G., *Macromolecules,* **24**, 2649 (1991).
36. Jacobine, A. T. in *Radiation Curing in Polymer Science and Technology: Photopolymerization Mechanisms*, Fouassier, J. P.; Rabek, J. F., Eds., pp. 219-268, Elsevier Applied Science, London (1993).
37. Wilderbeek, H; , van der Meer, M; Bastiaansen, C; Broer, D. J., *J. Phys. Chem. B,* **106**, 12874 (2002).
38. Trommsdorff, V. E.; Köhle, H.; Lagally, P., *Makromol. Chem.,* **1**, 169 (1947).
39. *With kind permission of Wiley-VCH Verlag GmbH & Co KGaA.* Source: Schulz, V. G. V.; Harborth, G., *Makromol. Chem.,* **1**, 106 (1947).
40. *With kind permission of the American Chemical Society.* Source: Palkovits, R.; Althues, H.; Rumplecker, A.; Tesche, B.; Dreier, A.; Holle, U.; Fink, G.; Cheng, C. H.; Shantz, D. F.; Kaskel, S., *Langmuir*, **21**, 6048 (2005).
41. *Condensation Polymers by Interfacial and Solution Methods*, Morgan, P. W., Interscience, New York (1965).
42. Brown, E. N.; Kessler, M. R.; Sottos, N. R.; White, S. R., *J. Microencapsulation,* **20**, 719 (2003).
43. White, S. R.; Sottos, N. R.; Geubelle, P. H.; Moore, J. S.; Kessler, M. R.; Sriram, S. R.; Brown, E. N.; Viswanathan, S., *Nature*, **409**, 794 (2001).
44. Enkelmann, V. in *Advances in Polymer Science: Polydiacetylenes*; Cantow, H.-J., Ed., Vol. 63, pp 91-136, Springer-Verlag, New York (1984).
45. Coates, G. W.; Dunn, A. R.; Henling, L. M.; Ziller, J. W.; Lobkovsky, E. B.; Grubbs, R. H., *J. Am. Chem. Soc.,* **20**, 3641 (1998).
46. Diaz, A. F.; Castillo, J. I.; Logan, J. A.; Lee, W. Y. J., *J. Electroanal. Chem.,* **129**, 115 (1981).
47. Macor, K. A.; Spiro, T. G., *J. Am. Chem. Soc.,* **105**, 5601 (1983).
48. Poriel, C.; Ferrand, Y.; Le Maux, P.; Rault-Berthelot, J.; Simonneaux, G., *Inorg. Chem.,* **43**, 5086 (2004).
49. Sadki, S.; Schottland, P.; Brodie, N.; Sabouraud, G., *Chem. Soc. Rev.*, **29**, 283 (2000).
50. Shi, G.; Li, C.; Liang, Y., *Adv. Mater.,* **11**, 1145 (1999).
51. Li, C.; Shi, G.; Liang, Y., *J. Electroanal. Chem.,* **455**, 1 (1998).
52. Huang, Z.; Qu, L.; Shi, G.; Chen, F.; Hong, X., *J. Electroanal. Chem.,* **556**, 159 (2003).
53. Fan, B.; Qu, L.; Shi, G., *J. Electroanal. Chem.,* **575**, 287 (2005).
54. Lu, G.; Shi, G., *J. Electroanal. Chem.,* **586**, 154 (2006).
55. Xu, J.; Hou, J.; Zhang, S.; Xiao, Q.; Zhang, R.; Pu, S.; Wei, Q., *J. Phys. Chem. B.,* **110**, 2643 (2006).
56. Chen, W.; Xue, G., *Prog. Polym. Sci.,* **30**, 783 (2005).
57. Xia, C.; Advincula, R. C.; Baba, A.; Knoll, W., *Chem. Mater.,* **16**, 2852 (2004).
58. Huang, F.; Wu, H.; Wang, D.; Yang, W.; Cao, Y., *Chem. Mater.,* **16**, 708 (2004).

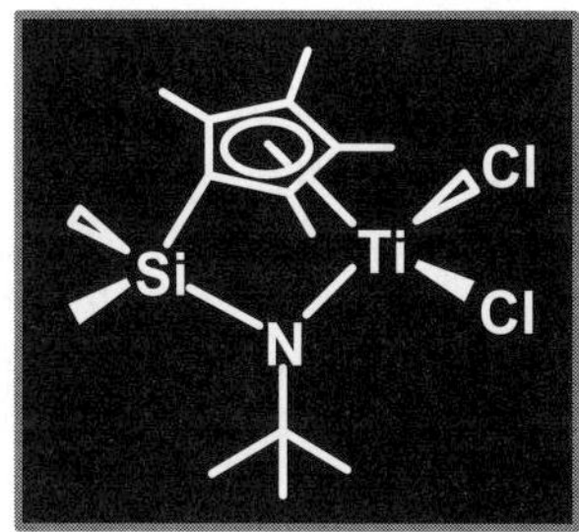

Metallocenes have captured the major theme of this chapter because of their supremacy over Ziegler-Natta catalysts to obtain superior stereoregular polyolefins. For example, the Dow Insite Catalyst above produces high quality long chain branched and linear low density polyethylenes.[1]

CHAPTER-2

GENERAL-PURPOSE POLYMERS

General-purpose polymers, alternatively called *commodity polymers*, are those that directly provide us comfort in our daily lives, normally produced in high volumes (of the order of a billion pounds) and serve a wide range of applications, such as fibers (clothing), plastics (lunch box, grocery bags, food containers), elastomers (shoes, car tires), adhesives (furniture) and coatings (paints). Despite the energy price hike in the past decade, the demand as well as production of these polymers has shown an exponential increase with time. In terms of volume, the general-purpose polymers have the biggest share of the market, several times more than that of the total volumes of engineering and high-performance polymers.

2.1. POLYOLEFINS, ACRYLICS, VINYLS AND STYRENICS

These polymers are grouped into one category because they contain carbon-carbon bonds in the backbone and are primarily made by a chain-growth mechanism via free-radical, co-ordination and/or metathesis polymerizations. Cationic and anionic techniques are also employed to produce a few of these polymers. This section will emphasize their preparation and related research that are promising for future applications.

2.1.1. Polyolefins

Although, by definition, polyolefins comprise a group of polymers that are produced from various olefins (alkenes) or cycloolefins (cycloalkenes), it often signifies the collective name for polyethylenes and polypropylenes, which are the most widely used polymers today. As seen from the classification tree below, there are a variety of useful commercial products, which account for more than half of total worldwide polymer consumption. Polyolefins are extremely versatile and possess a successful combination of properties including flexibility, strength, lightness, stability, impermeability and easy processability. Based on the monomers used, they may be divided into three major categories: polyethylenes, polypropylenes and higher polyolefins. Detailed discussion on their synthesis, including subclassifications, are described below. Since *cycloolefin polymers* (COPs), *cycloolefin copolymers* (COCs) and poly(4-methyl-1-pentene) (PMP) belong to engineering polymers, they are discussed in Chapter-3.

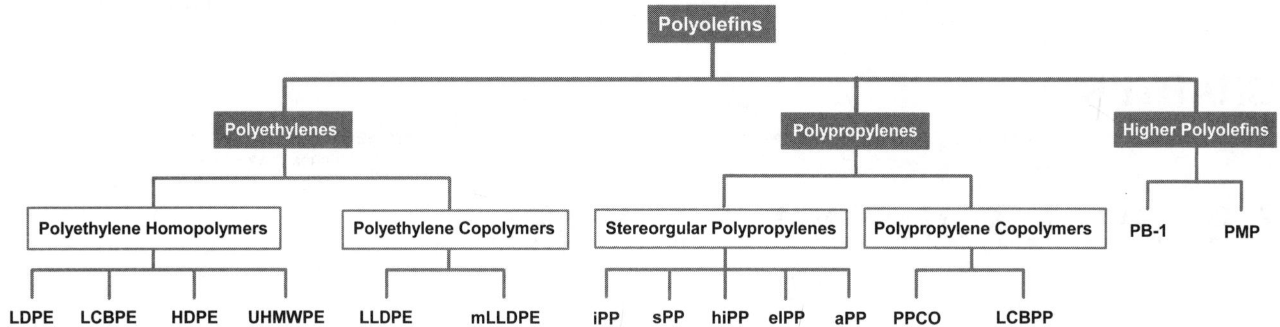

2.1.1.1. Polyethylene Homopolymers

The most important members of this class include LDPE, LCBPE (long chain branched polyethylene), HDPE, UHMWPE (ultra-high molecular weight polyethylene), LLDPE (linear low density polyethylene) and mLLDPE (metallocene derived LLDPE). It is important to stress that all of them are homopolymers except the copolymers LLDPE and mLLDPE.

2.1.1.1a. Low Density Polyethylene (LDPE)

As shown in Figure 2.1, ethylene can be polymerized into various polymer architectures responsible for differences in densities, mechanical, thermal and rheological (processing) properties. LDPE, which possesses extensive "hyperbranched-type" long branching, is produced exclusively under high pressures (75-275 MPa) and high temperatures (125-325°C) in the presence of a free-radical initiator, such as **1** and/or oxygen. As discussed in Chapter-1, free-radical polymerization of ethylene involves both inter- and intra-molecular chain-transfer reactions (Figures 1.44 and 1.45), resulting in short and long branches and leading to lower density and tensile strength, increased malleability and faster biodegradation. Most new LDPE manufacturing plants are now based on tubular reactor design because of their higher production capacity and better heat removal compared to the traditional thick-walled autoclave reactors. Heat management is very important in LDPE production because of the high heat of polymerization of ethylene (0.80 Kcal/g vs. 0.16 Kcal/g for styrene). In a tubular reactor, there is relatively little "back-mixing" since the reaction flow carries the polymer down the tube as it reacts. Once a long-chain branch is started (*via* intermolecular chain-transfer), it is likely to continue to grow rather than interact with another polymer molecule to terminate. The branches formed in this method are longer (as long as the main polymer backbone and 15-25 branches/1000 C atoms) and contain lesser sub-branching. By contrast, the autoclave reactor gives rise to shorter, more "bushy" long chain branching due to the higher level of back-mixing at each stage of the reactor. Thus, the free-radicals have more opportunity to react and terminate with other polymer molecules in the autoclave. The most common household use of LDPE is in garment, grocery and shopping bags.

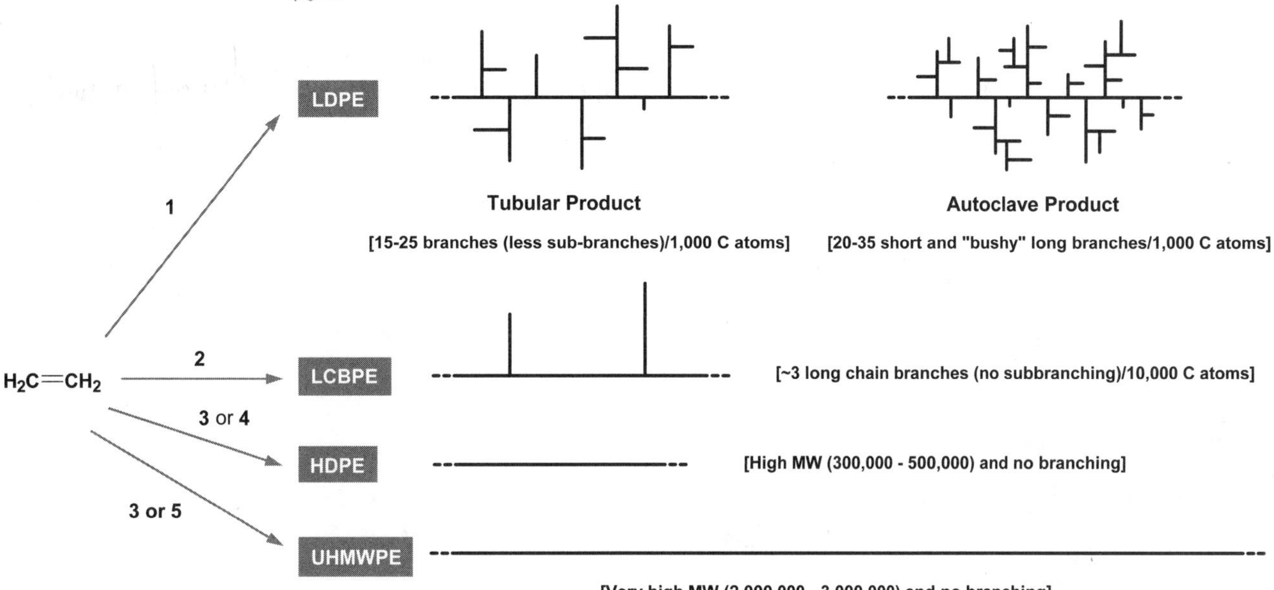

Catalyst	Representative Examples
1	dibutyl peroxide, benzoyl peroxide, diethyl peroxide, oxygen
2	Catalyst: Si, Ti, Cl, Cl, N Co-catalyst: MAO
3	Catalysts: $TiCl_4$, VCl_4; Co-catalysts: $Al(C_2H_5)_3$, $Al(C_2H_5)_2Cl$
4	Catalysts: Ph, Zr, Cl, Cl , Zr, Cl, Cl Co-catalyst: MAO
5	Catalyst: Ti, Cl, Cl Co-catalyst: MAO

Figure 2.1. Synthesis of various grades of polyethylene, including their schematic structures.

2.1.1.1b. Long Chain Branched Polyethylene (LCBPE)

Manufacture of polyethylene with linear long chain branching has been of commercial interest to producers for many years because such a polyethylene structure exhibits an excellent combination of properties, including good processability and high melt strength, which are essential in blow-molding applications. The recent advent of metallocene catalysts, particularly mono-cyclopentadienyl amido complexes, better known as constrained geometry catalyst (CGC)[2,3], has made possible the commercial production, for the first time, of LCBPE (a homopolymer of ethylene). This process is commonly referred to as Dow Insite® technology. The active center of the CGC, such as **2** in Figure 2.1, is based on a Group-IVB transition metal (viz., Ti) covalently bonded to a mono-cyclopentadienyl ring and bridged with a heteroatom unit, forming a constrained cyclic structure. This geometry allows the transition metal center to be open to addition of high α-olefins or macromonomers at high reactivities. CGC polymers are unique in that they have a controlled level of long chain branches (estimated at greater than 250 carbon atoms and branch density ~3 LCBs per 10,000 carbons). Furthermore, the long chains are linear as opposed to hyperbranched and are much longer than those produced by copolymerization of traditional C_3-C_8 comonomers used in LLDPE production (*vide infra*). The branching mechanism involves a critical level of *β*-H elimination of the polymer chain at elevated reaction temperatures (80-90°C) to give a vinyl-terminated macromonomer, which can then reinsert into another growing polymer chain (Figure 2.2). Thus, LCBPE is produced by copolymerization of ethylene with the macromonomers that are formed during the polymerization of ethylene in the presence of CGC. The degree of LCB on polyethylenes can be inferred from rheological data together with a GPC molecular weight distribution and ^{13}C-NMR.[4]

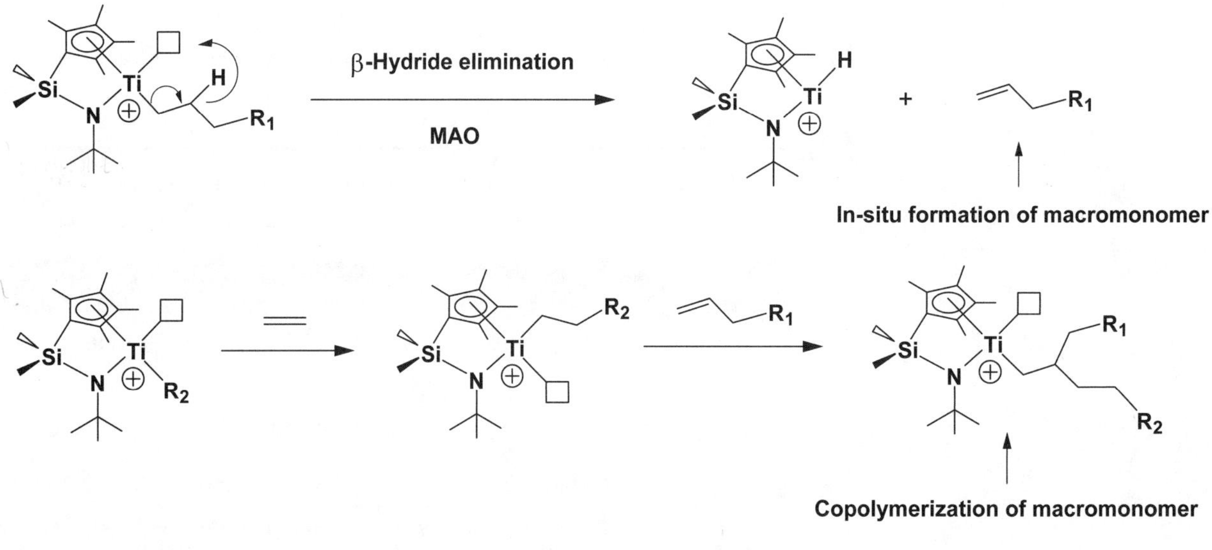

Figure 2.2. Mechanism for the formation of long chain branches in LCBPE.

LCBPE can also be prepared by copolymerizing ethylene with vinyl-terminated macromonomers, a process developed by ExxonMobil (Figure 2.3). The process, although conceptually related to the Dow Insite technology, involves two distinct steps. The first involves the manufacture of nonbranched vinyl macromonomer with a degree of polymerization (DP) in the range of 150-1500 to maintain solubility for the subsequent solution phase polymerization process. In the second step, these macromonomers are copolymerized with ethylene using a CGC-type catalyst to produce a polymer with approximately 1 mol % incorporated macromonomer (i.e., ~5 branches per 1,000 carbon atoms in the main chain). Processability and mechanical properties of these materials are claimed to be identical to those of branched LLDPEs.

Figure 2.3. Synthesis of LCBPE by copolymerization of ethylene and vinyl macromonomer.

2.1.1.1c. High Density Polyethylene (HDPE)

As shown in Figure 2.1, HDPE can be produced via coordination polymerization of ethylene in the presence of Ziegler-Natta or with metallocene catalysts, which allow exclusive formation of a linear polyethylene backbone with very little or no branching, which results in enhanced intermolecular forces and tensile strength. Commercial Ziegler-Natta catalysts, **3**, are a mixture of Group-IVB transition-metal halide as a primary catalyst (e.g., $TiCl_4$ and VCl_4), and an alkylaluminum compound as a co-catalyst (e.g., $AlEt_3$ and $AlEt_2Cl$) dispersed in a magnesium chloride lattice. Depending on the commercial process (solution, slurry or gas-phase), the pressure and temperature vary from 1-7 MPa and 50-80°C, respectively. During polymerization, the transition-metal compound is transformed into the active catalytic species upon reaction with the co-catalyst. Subsequently, the active metal becomes alkylated, and ethylene is inserted into the metal-alkyl bond. The active site is often considered to be a bridging complex between the transition metal and the alkyl aluminum compound, in which one or two ligands are shared between the two metals (see Figure 1.55 in Chapter-1). Since Ziegler-Natta catalysts are microporous solids, gas-phase and slurry processes are commonly used for the production of HDPE. In both cases, in addition to spherical morphology and uniform porosity, the size of catalyst particles (typically, 10-100 μm) is important. Each particle comprises millions of primary crystallites with sizes up to about 15 nm. At the start of polymerization, co-catalyst and monomer diffuse through the catalyst particle and polymerization takes place on the surface of each primary crystallite within the particle. As polymerization proceeds, the initial catalyst support becomes fragmented and dispersed within the growing polymer matrix (Figure 2.4). The morphology of the starting support is replicated in the final polymer so that a spherical support in the size range 10-100 μm will give spherical polymer morphology with a particle size in the general range of 100-3000 μm, depending on the catalyst productivity. The most common household uses are containers for milk and liquid laundry detergent.

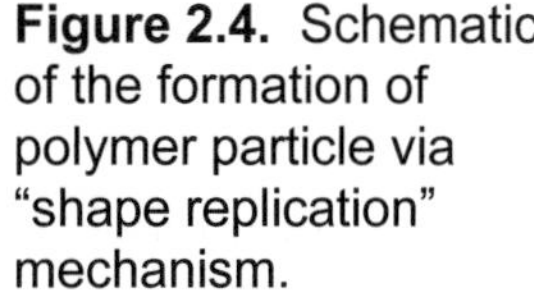

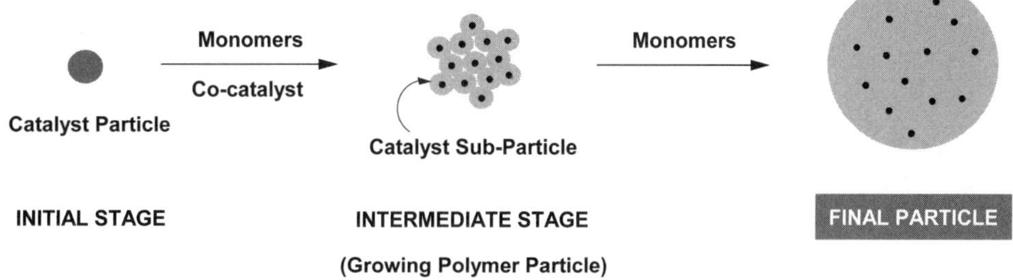

Figure 2.4. Schematic of the formation of polymer particle via "shape replication" mechanism.

Cyclopentadienyl (Cp) complexes of Group-IVB transition-metal halides, such as **4** in Figure 2.1, better known as metallocenes, in conjunction with methylalumoxane (MAO, alternatively called methylaluminoxane) are also used for the production of HDPE and are just entering the market in certain specialty applications. Metallocenes differ from Ziegler-Natta catalysts in that the active site is derived from a single molecular species with defined ligands, which permits formation of products with a narrow molecular weight range (see Chapter-1). It has been projected that advancements in "single-site" chemistry will have a profound impact on the future direction of HDPE markets.

Both bridged (stereorigid) and unbridged metallocenes are used for HDPE. The choice of metal, ligand selection and ligand substitution patterns highly influence the polymerization performance. Unbridged metallocene dichloride complexes exhibit maximum activities when cyclopentadienyl, indenyl, or mixed ligands are used. The catalyst activity [usually expressed as Kg of polymer formed per gram (or mole) of metal (i.e., catalyst) per hour] drops markedly with fluorenyl ligands (Figure 2.5). Moreover, increasing electron donating ability to the ligand substituents appears to increase the activity in the cyclopentadienyl series, whereas steric crowding has a detrimental effect. Overall, the best unbridged catalysts contain zirconium as the metal with either two symmetrical indenyl ligands or mixed ligands (Figure 2.6). Among these superior catalysts, the metallocene with a 2-phenyl substituted indenyl ligand exhibits a dramatic rise in activity and therefore, has been designated in the category of "most active catalysts". No obvious trend in the molecular weights of the obtained polymers was found. When it comes to the choice of metal, catalyst activity generally decreases in the order of Zr>Ti>Hf. It is noteworthy that hafnium complexes produce higher molecular weight polymers than their zirconium analogs. The stronger Hf-carbon σ-bond decreases both bond-making and bond-breaking processes, resulting in lower activity and higher molecular weight. *Note that the data (catalyst activity and molecular weight) cited in this chapter have been collected from different sources, which, in most cases, differ in polymerization conditions. Therefore, the data may not translate proportionally and should be regarded as indicative rather than quantitative.*

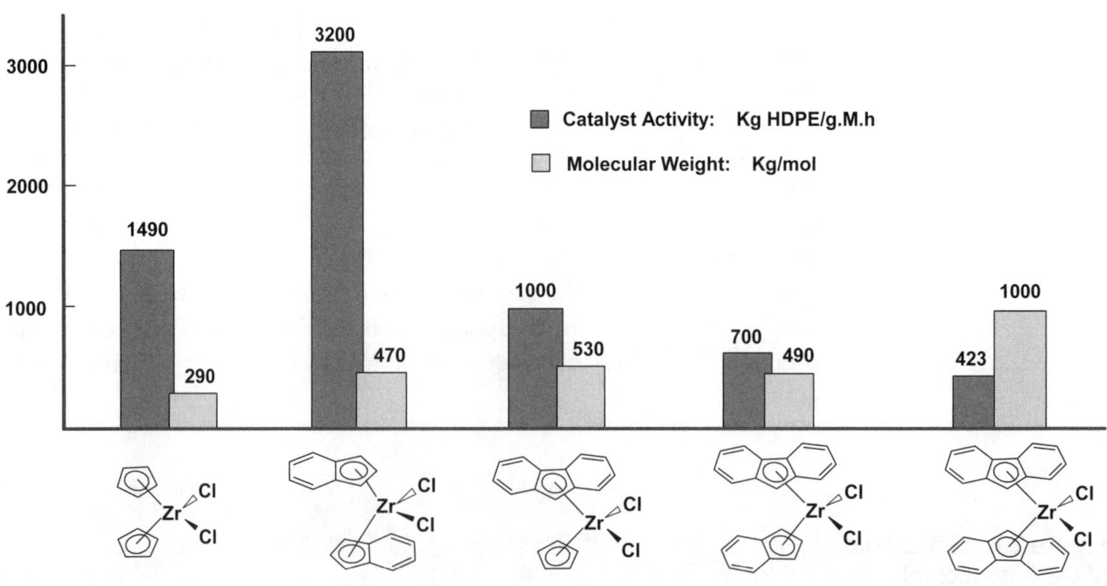

Figure 2.5. Effect of catalyst activity and polymer chain growth as a function of ligand annellation (MAO as the co-catalyst).

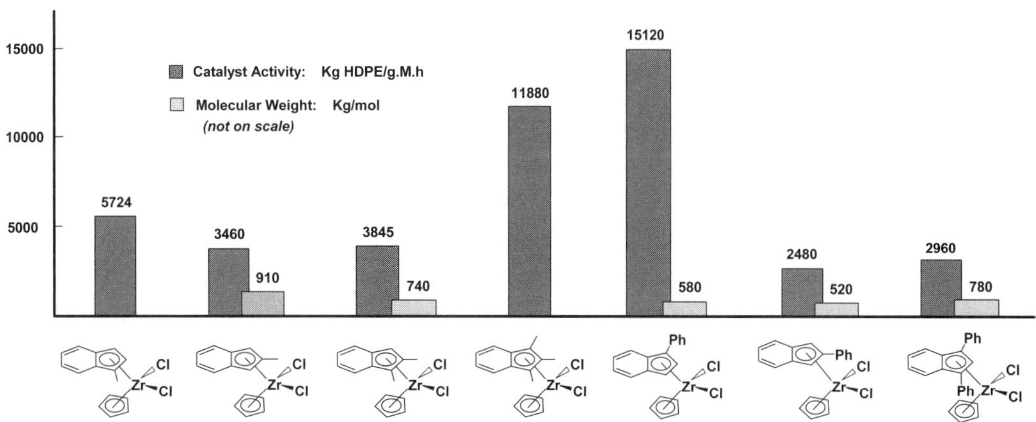

Figure 2.6. Effect of alkyl and aromatic substitutions on aromatic ligands on the catalyst activity and polymer chain growth (MAO as the co-catalyst).

Several zirconium-based bridged metallocene catalysts, designated among the 'top 10 most active catalysts', have also been developed for the production of HDPE. Surprisingly, the most favorable activities were achieved with symmetric fluorenyl ligands, but connected with $-CH_2-CH_2-$ or $-SiMe_2-$ bridging units (Figure 2.7). It is believed that this combination provides desired "bite angle" (angle between the plane of two ligands), electronic effects, and enhanced catalyst-cocatalyst ion-pair separation, necessary for displaying superior catalyst activity. For example, the bigger the bite angle the higher the catalyst activity because of an unforced monomer entrance. In addition, the presence of methyl groups at the 4 and 5 positions of the fluorenyl ligands dramatically increases the catalytic activity compared with the methyl substitutions at other positions. This is attributed to the fact that these positions directly face the active center, thus facilitating catalyst-cocatalyst ion-pair separation. It is noteworthy that if propylene is used as the monomer, the aforementioned catalysts exhibit poor activity, as does the unbridged fluorenyl ligands for ethylene monomer (Figure 2.5). However, one exception was found for an unbridged catalyst, which shows good performance with mixed ligands, viz., *tert*-butylfluorenyl and pentamethyl Cp ligands (Figure 2.7). Too many parameters are involved to determine the overall performance of the catalyst. Tiny changes at the metallocene complex can have a profound effect on the activity of the catalyst and the properties of the polymers.

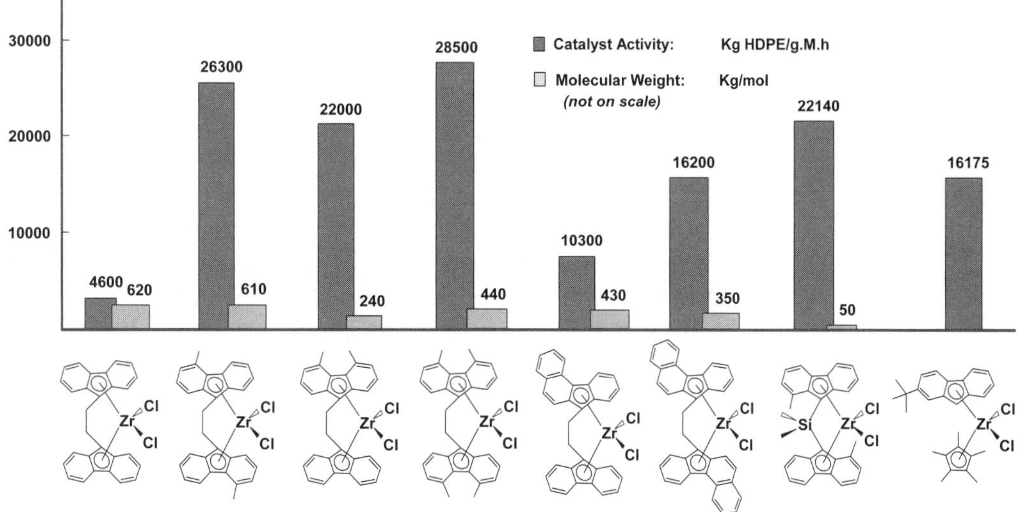

Figure 2.7. Effect of alkyl and aromatic substitutions on aromatic ligands on the catalyst activity and polymer chain growth (MAO as the co-catalyst).

2.1.1.1d. Ultra-High Molecular Weight Polyethylene (UHMWPE)

Although this polymer complies with all the requirements for an engineering polymer, it is discussed here for its similarities in structure with other polyolefins. UHMWPE possesses a structure similar to HDPE, and combines the traditional abrasion and cut resistance of metal alloys with the impact and corrosion resistance of synthetic polymers, making it ideal for fabricating heavy-duty industrial components. Molecular weights of HDPE range from 300,000 to 500,000, compared with 2 to 3 million for UHMWPE, which finds use in high modulus fibers, Spectra® (Honeywell) and Dyneema® (DSM Dyneema, The Netherlands), for bulletproof vests. These fibers are 15 times stronger than steel and three times stronger than that of Kevlar® (DuPont aramide). Due to its low coefficient of friction and high resistance to wear, UHMWPE is used in industrial impact, wear, and sliding applications in both normal and corrosive environments. It is also employed in orthopedic implants, such as artificial hips and knees (Figure 2.8).[5]

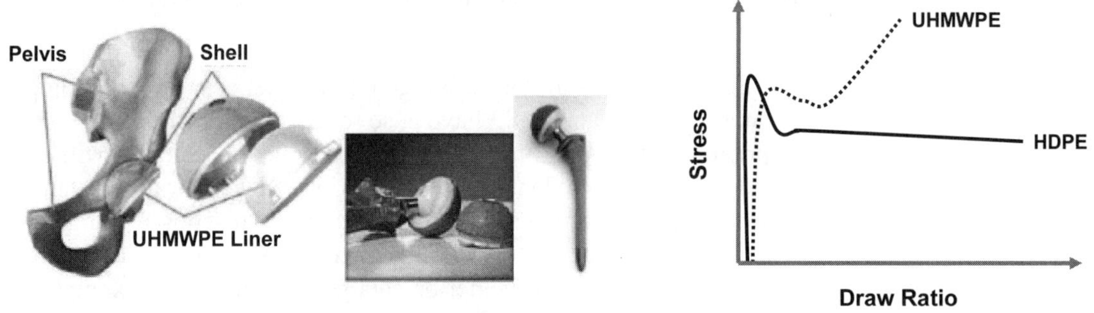

Figure 2.8. *Left:* The use of a UHMWPE component at the interface of metallic components in the artificial hip prosthesis. *Right:* Comparison of mechanical properties of UHMWPE and HDPE.

UHMWPE is primarily produced by the slurry process using a heterogeneous Ziegler-Natta catalyst with hexane as diluent. The catalyst is the same as for HDPE, **3** in Figure 2.1, but the polymerization conditions are different and usually require a longer time prior to termination of polymerization. Since the active sites in such a catalyst system are known to exist relatively close together, the polymer chains grow in close proximity to each other. In addition, a conventional heterogeneous catalyst contains different active sites which exhibit different activities, thereby producing polymers with broad molecular weight distributions. In addition to the chains growing adjacent to each other, the high polymerization temperature (80-100°C) causes crystallization of the polymer chains to be relatively low and the resulting polymer has a very high degree of entanglement. Owing to the nature of this process, essentially every catalyst particle leads to a product polymer particle with (sub) millimeter dimensions (typically, 1 mg polymer particle of a polymer with a 1 million g/mol molecular weight contains 10^{14} entangled chains).

High entanglement density poses restrictions to flow of the chains in the melt, which results in improper fusion of the powder particles. Consequently, UHMWPE is difficult to process via conventional processing routes, such as injection molding and blow molding, because of very high viscosity of the polymer melt. UHMWPE is usually processed via compression molding or ram-extrusion since the former methods would involve a very viscous melt. Regardless of the process applied, all products of UHMWPE suffer from non-homogeneous morphology, which leads to poor long-term mechanical (creep) performance and insufficient lifetime, especially for the artificial implants applications. UHMWPE is a material of choice for artificial orthopedic replacements/implants because of several desirable properties, viz., low coefficient of friction, excellent mechanical properties (superior to HDPE, as shown in Figure 2.8), high wear resistance, good chemical resistance, resistance to environmental stress cracking, dimensional stability over a wide temperature range, high notched impact strength, and high energy absorption at high stress rates. In the past decade, comonomers, such as propylene, are used in the synthesis of UHMWPE to improve long-term properties (mainly to reduce creep under static loading and to increase the yield stress at low strain rates). However, these gains are made at the expense of reductions in the short-term properties, such as the maximum attainable draw ratio, Young's modulus, and the tensile strength of the drawn fibers.

Because of the high processing cost of UHMWPE, demand is less and is limited to specialty applications. At this time, UHMWPE is exclusively produced using Ziegler-Natta catalysts. In the past decade, however, a number of metallocene catalysts have been developed. Some of these exhibit high activity and produce high molecular weights even at room temperature (Figure 2.9). Several parameters need to be addressed in designing a metallocene for UHMWPE. For example, the bite angle of the catalyst should be appropriate so that the β-hydrogen elimination reaction (responsible for lower molecular weight product) is suppressed. In addition, the influence of substituents plays a dominant role in producing a high molecular weight product. In general, high molecular weight polyethylene is obtained by catalysts with bulky substituents in the ligand sphere. One interpretation could be that these substituents partially block the free coordination site that is necessary for the chain transfer step via a *β*-hydrogen elimination reaction. Finally, as mentioned earlier, metallocene complexes with hafnium as the central metal are also known to produce high molecular weight polyethylene, due to a more stable hafnium-carbon bond.

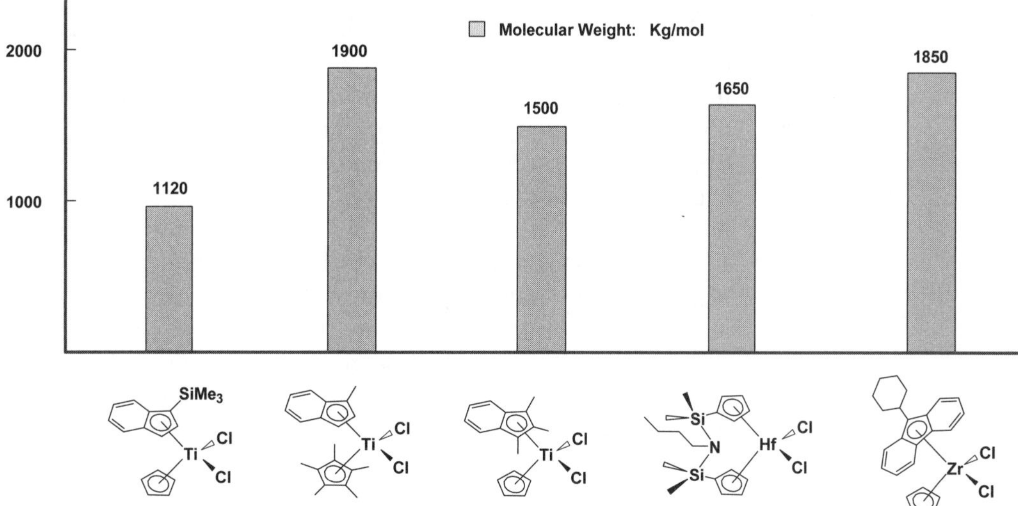

Figure 2.9. Highly promising metallocenes (MAO as the co-catalyst) for the production of UHMWPE.

2.1.1.2. Polyethylene Copolymers

The ethylene-α-olefin copolymers are of great practical importance because of their unique properties, such as high melt strength, exceptional toughness, and convenient processing behavior, leading to superior properties of the final product compared to traditional polymers. Most importantly, copolymerization of α-olefins with ethylene is a common means of tailoring the density and crystallinity of ethylene polymers. Most of the conventional Ziegler-Natta catalysts are, however, less effective in initiating the copolymerization of ethylene with α-olefins, and the copolymers formed are inhomogeneous with regard to comonomer incorporation and molecular weight distribution. The properties and performance of an olefin copolymer are determined by the comonomer content, molecular weight, and molecular-weight distribution and, most importantly, by the comonomer distribution within and between single polymer chains. The development of single site metallocene catalysts for olefin polymerization has opened new opportunities for the synthesis of copolymers with controlled comonomer incorporation, uniform structure, and properties. The unique feature of these metallocene derived ethylene-α-olefin copolymers is that they exhibit both thermoplastic and elastomeric characteristics. These new polyolefin thermoplastic elastomers are described by a new term *plastomers* or POPs, which are especially effective as impact modifiers for conventional polyolefins used in rotational molding (a process for manufacturing large hollow parts) applications. Currently, the most used polyolefin for rotational molding is iPP. However, its applicability in rotational molding is limited, since iPP has a narrow processing window and rotomolded parts suffer from low impact strength. To achieve better properties, it is common practice to blend iPP with impact modifiers, such as ethylene-propylene-diene terpolymers (EPDM) and ethylene propylene rubber (EPR). Such blends of iPP with rubbers are commonly termed thermoplastic olefin blends (TPOs). The availability of POPs suitable for rotational molding has now generated enormous interest, because it would enable rotational molding to enter new high-volume markets, such as production of automotive parts.

2.1.1.2a. Linear Low Density Polyethylenes (LLDPE and mLLDPE)

These are well-controlled ethylene and α-olefin copolymers and exhibit improved properties in comparison with LCBPE, which is produced only from ethylene monomer (Figure 2.2). The major difference in their structures in that the length of branches in LLDPE is short and equal, while LCBPE possesses long branches of uneven length (Figure 2.10). LLDPE can be conveniently prepared by both Ziegler-Natta and metallocene chemistry. Although at the present time Ziegler-Natta catalysts occupy a dominant position, accounting for about 80% of total production, the situation is expected to be reversed by the end of the next decade in favor of metallocenes, due to its evenly distributed branching over the molecular weight distribution, resulting in much improved film performance. mLLDPE distinguishes metallocene-catalyzed polymers from Ziegler-Natta polymers, which are simply denoted as LLDPE. Since the Ziegler-Natta systems contain non-uniform active centers, co-monomer incorporation is highest at the most open catalytic centers, whereas sterically hindered centers will tend to give polyethylene chains with little or no comonomer, thus producing LLDPE with non-uniformly distributed comonomers in the polymer backbone. For example, a LLDPE with a density of 0.918 g/cm^3, produced by gas-phase copolymerization of ethylene and 1-hexene using Ziegler-Natta catalyst, contains approximately 18 butyl groups per 1,000 carbon atoms. By contrast, a LLDPE with the same density can be produced by a metallocene catalyst with a lesser amount of 1-hexene comonomer because of uniform distribution of butyl groups (11-12 groups per 1,000 carbon atoms).

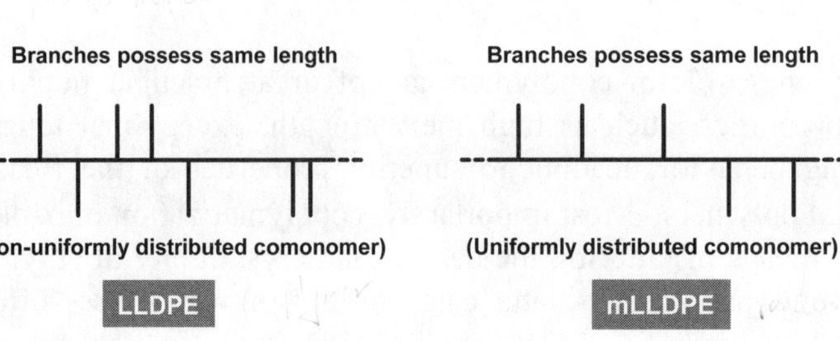

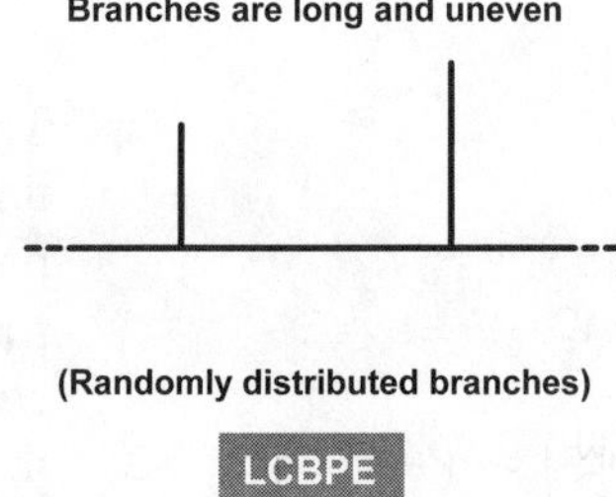

Figure 2.10. Comparison of structures of LLDPE, mLLDPE and LCBPE.

The comonomer for LLDPE can be any α-olefin from C_3 to C_{20}, but the two most common are 1-butene and 1-hexene because they are inexpensive. 4-Methyl-1-pentene and 1-octene are also used, but to a lesser extent. The proportion of comonomer and its distribution along the polymer backbone has a profound effect on the properties of polymers. The higher the proportion of comonomer, the lower the density of the polymer, because of the shortening of the average backbone sequence length for crystallization. Indeed, various grades of polyethylene are prepared by increasing comonomer. For example, 1-2 mol% of comonomer produces *medium density polyethylene* (MDPE, density, 0.940-0.926 g/cm^3; crystallinity, 45-55%), while 2.5-3.5 mol% is used for LLDPE (density, 0.925-0.915 g/cm^3; crystallinity, 30-45%) and >4 mol% for *very low* or *ultra low density polyethylene* (VLDPE/ULDPE, density, <0.915 g/cm^3; crystallinity, <30%). As crystallinity increases, LLDPE becomes more dense and stiffer, and in general, less tough.

Constrained geometry catalysts (CGCs) of *ansa*-monocyclopentadienylamido Group-IV metal complexes are, by far, the best for copolymerization of ethylene with higher α-olefins.[2,3] Most remarkable is the recent development of uniform ethylene/1-octene copolymers which are obtained with the CGCs cited in Figure 2.11. These ethylene/1-octene materials exhibit excellent mechanical properties and melt processability. In addition to their relatively high activity, these catalysts produce high-molecular-weight copolymers with varying levels of comonomer incorporation. The copolymer molecular weight is independent of comonomer incorporation, but dependent on the metallocene structure.

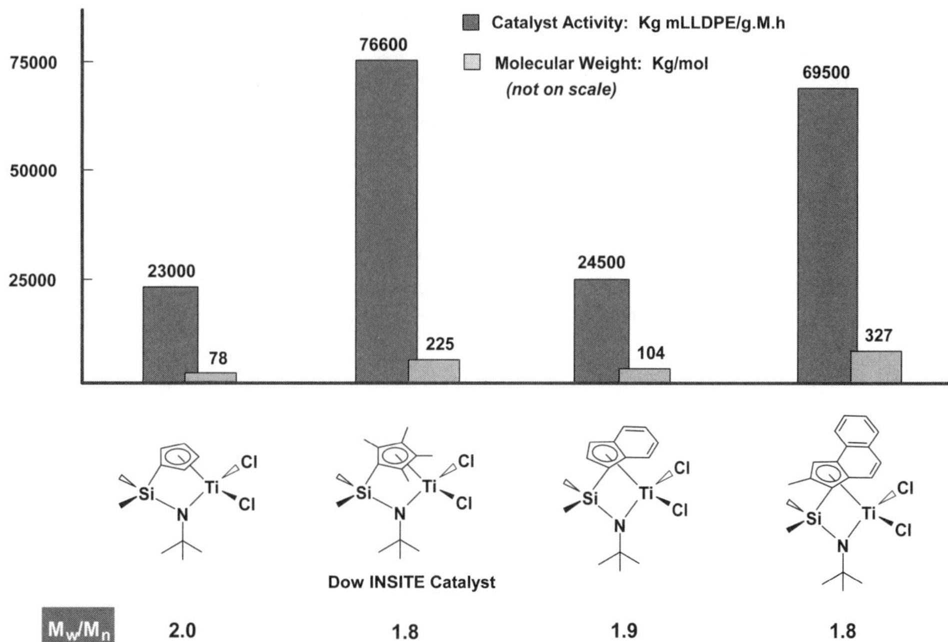

Figure 2.11. Structures of important CGCs for the production of mLLDPE (MAO as the co-catalyst).

Like HDPE, LLDPE is also manufactured by three processes: solution, gas-phase and slurry. In the solution process, ethylene and comonomer are dissolved in a solvent, such as hexane, and fed into a stirred reactor containing active catalyst. The reactor temperature is usually maintained at 200°C with a pressure around 8 MPa. Although this technique offers a quick production rate (the reaction is completed in less than an hour at commercial production rates), the solvent recovery steps are very energy intensive. Another disadvantage of the solution method is that a very high molecular weight product is not achieved because of the very high viscosity of the resulting solution. The gas-phase process, which requires several hours to isolate product, is more versatile because a very high molecular weight product is obtained with a wide range of densities. In this process, ethylene and comonomer are continuously fed into a fluidized bed reactor, which is maintained near 100°C with pressures at 2 MPa. At the present time, the slurry process is used more, because it is usually associated with production of HDPE. In this process, ethylene and comonomer are dissolved in a minimum amount of diluent (hexane) and fed into the reactor containing a catalyst slurry at a set temperature near 100°C and pressure at 4 MPa. After polymerization, the diluent and residual monomers are flashed off for recycling and polymer is conveyed for pelletization.

2.1.1.3. Stereoregular Polypropylenes

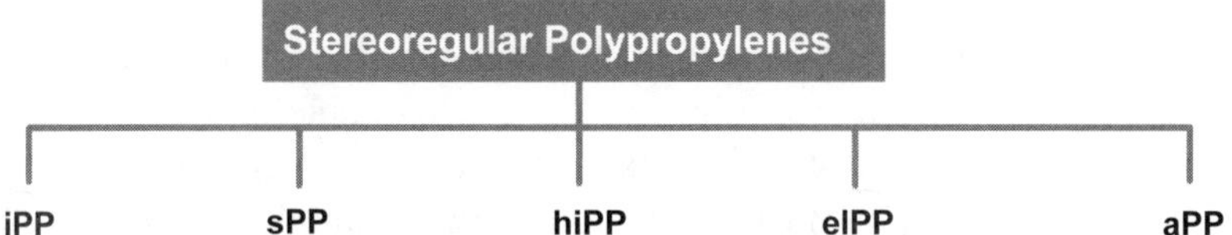

Unlike LDPE, polypropylene (PP) cannot be produced by a free-radical mechanism from propylene monomer because of dominant side reactions which lead to low molecular weight products (see Figure 1.46 in Chapter-1) and/or radical assisted degradation of the PP backbone via a *beta-scission* reaction.[6] In fact, this phenomenon is used by most polypropylene producers to prepare *controlled rheology PP* (CR-PP), which is produced by degrading normal PP (usually refer to iPP) to give a product with a high *melt flow index* (MFI, a measure of the ease of flow of the melt of a thermoplastic polymer), lower molecular weight, narrower molecular weight distribution and hence, easier and more consistent flow. When a peroxide and an iPP mixture are heated (typically, peroxides are added prior to extrusion), the radicals generated *in situ* preferentially attack the tertiary hydrogen atoms of iPP molecules because that carbon-hydrogen bond is more vulnerable than the secondary and primary carbon-hydrogen bonds (Figure 2.12). It is also believed that during this process inversion of configuration (or epimerization) of methyl groups is also a significant side reaction. A high degree of epimerization reduces crystallinity of stereoregular PPs. The peroxide attacks randomly but statistically, the longest molecules are most susceptible to attack. This results in a narrow MW distribution and increased MFI.

As a consequence, the production of stereoregular PPs is exclusively performed by stereoselective polymerization of propylene using transition-metal catalysts, which were developed from the Nobel award-winning work of Karl Ziegler and Giulio Natta in Europe, followed by commercial introduction in the United States in 1957. With Ziegler-Natta catalysis, the control of stereospecificity is limited because the environment around the active center cannot be changed at will. Consequently, these catalysts will only produce stereoregular PPs, depending on the respective enantiofacial selectivity of the different active metal centers on different crystal surfaces. Currently, a major portion of iPP and sPP is produced with Ziegler-Natta catalysts. The most effective are $TiCl_4$-$AlEt_3$ for iPP and VCl_4-$AlEt_3$ for sPP (see Figures 1.55 and 1.56 in Chapter-1).

The growth rate of mPP (polypropylenes made with metallocene catalysts) production has been increasing significantly in recent years and, in fact, revolutionizing the polyolefins industry, because of the flexibility in catalyst design that permits control of properties and access to novel polymeric materials. These advances have spawned a variety of PPs, which are now capturing many non-traditional markets that were not imaginable a few years ago. The driving force comes from their higher impact, stiffness, and crystallinity, a better balance of impact and stiffness, as well as enhanced heat resistance, clarity, gloss, and barrier properties. Polymerization is carried out in either the liquid phase with polymer forming as a slurry of particles, or the gas-phase with polymer forming dry solid particles. Current process development is strongly oriented toward improving catalyst productivity and stereospecificity to make it unnecessary to remove catalyst residues and atactic polymer from the product. ExxonMobil Chemical and Basell North America are the leading producers of mPP.

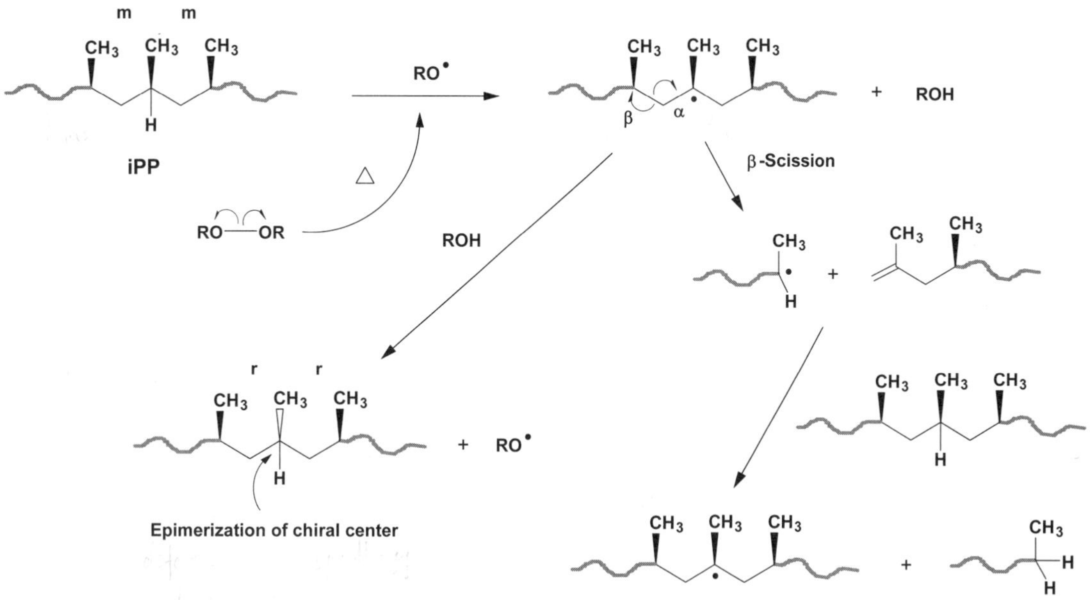

Figure 2.12. Mechanism of radical induced epimerization of chiral centers and β-scission that leads to degradation of iPP backbone.

The major advantage of metallocene polymerization is the degree of control it allows in tailoring of polymer microstructure via ligand geometry. Important elements of chirality in the catalyst-olefin complex include the different non-superimposable orientations of the olefin, the configuration of the tertiary carbon of the last inserted monomer unit, and finally, the chirality of the catalyst itself, either arising from a chiral ligand set or from the metal center being situated in a (pseudo)tetrahedral environment with four different residues. All of these elements will determine the stereospecificity of a polymerization catalyst. In order to efficiently control polymer microstructure, one must control the regioselectivity and the enantiofacial selectivity (stereoselectivity) of the monomer coordination, as well as the stereospecificity of the monomer insertion.

Regioselectivity is governed by which end of the propylene double bond is linked to the metal atom (**M**) of the catalyst and which end to the growing chain. As pointed out earlier (in the α-olefin polymerization mechanism of Ziegler-Natta and metallocene catalysts, see Chapter-1), 1,2-insertion of propylene to the transition metal active center is the energetically preferred regioselectivity. Therefore, consecutive regio-regular insertions will result in a head-to-tail structure (Figure 2.13). Regio-irregularities involving a 2,1-insertion in a series of 1,2-insertions may also occur occasionally, leading to head-to-head and tail-to-tail structures in the polymer chain via an intermediate **A**, which is also responsible for a slowdown of chain propagation due to steric hindrance. Intermediate **A** may also undergo isomerization (known as 1,3-insertion), especially favorable at higher temperature, to a primary ligand, leading to tetramethylene segments in the polymer chain.

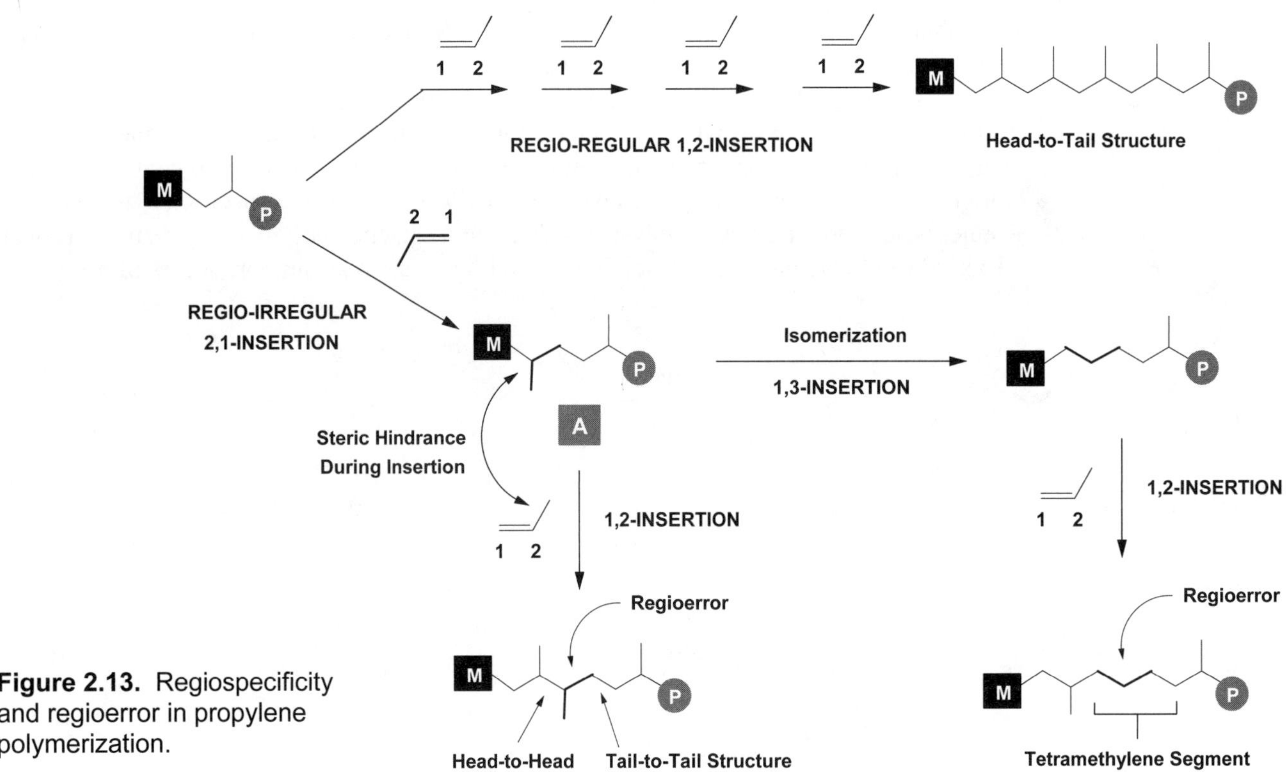

Figure 2.13. Regiospecificity and regioerror in propylene polymerization.

There are two possible sources of stereoregulation in the polymerization of α-olefins.[7-9] As the polymer chain remains connected to the metal of the catalytic center, the stereoconfiguration of the last inserted monomer unit may influence the stereochemistry of the insertion of the next one. If this influence is determining, the mode of stereoregulation is referred to as "chain-end control". If, however, the ligand set of the catalyst is chiral and overrides the influence of the polymer chain end, the mechanism of stereoregulation is referred to as "enantiomorphic-site control". Both modes of stereoregulation are distinguishable by analysis of stereoerror pentads. As shown in Figure 2.14, a stereochemical error is propagated in the former mechanism, while in the latter, a correction occurs, since the ligands direct the stereochemical events.

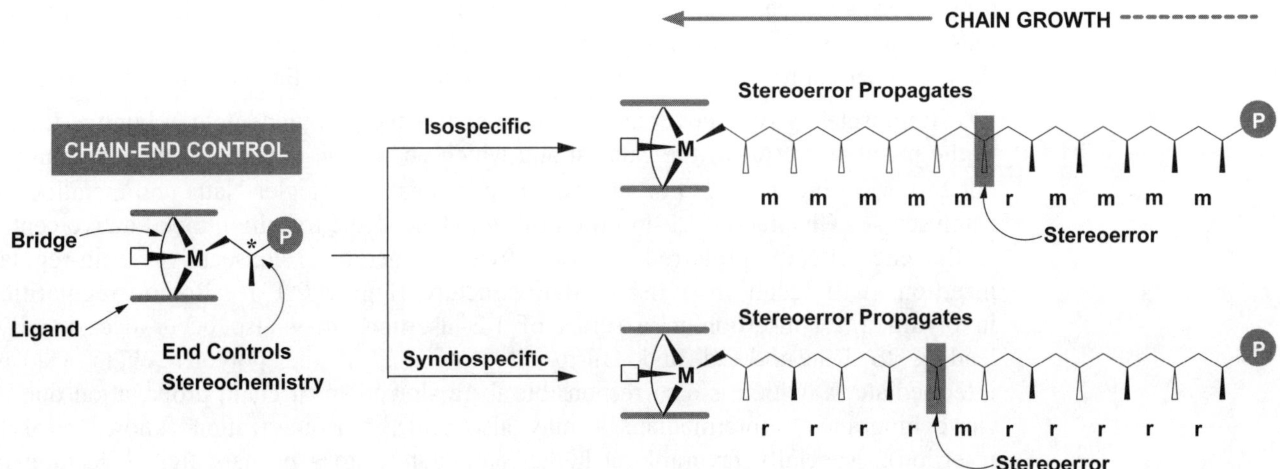

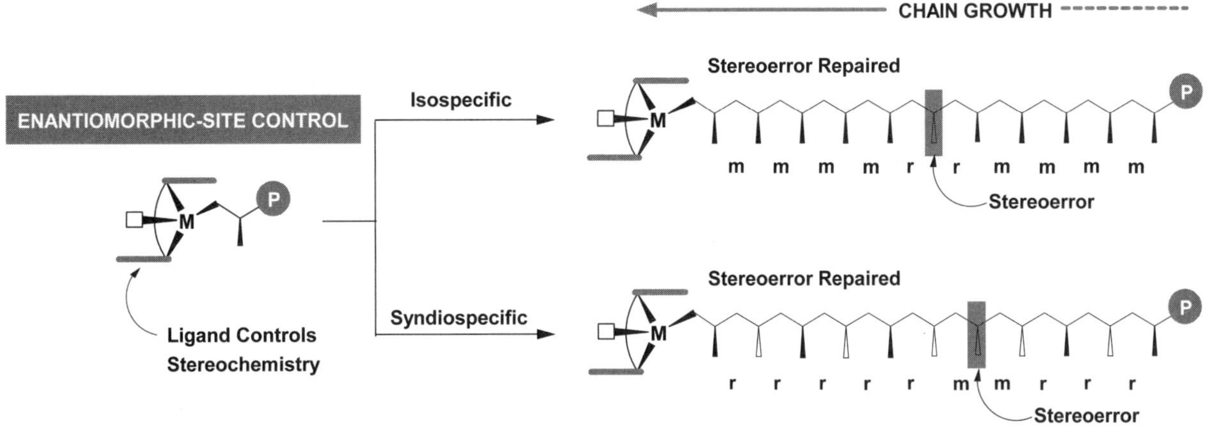

Figure 2.14. Different stereoerror pentads arising from an erroneously inserted monomer unit under chain-end control or enantiomorphic-site control of stereospecificity.

Ewen's symmetry rules

In the past two decades, extensive research has been conducted to achieve high catalyst activity and stereoselectivity. A careful examination of the results of several investigations revealed a predictable relationship between catalyst symmetry and polymer tacticity. This relationship between the metallocenes' structure and the mechanism of the enantioface selectivity is known as *Ewen's symmetry rules* (Table 2.1). Depending on the symmetry of ligand structures, metallocenes are classified into five major symmetry categories, which produce different polymer microstructures.

Table 2.1. Stereocontrol as a Function of Metallocene Symmetry (Ewen's Symmetry Rules)

Ligand Geometry	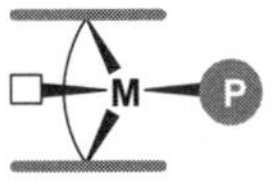	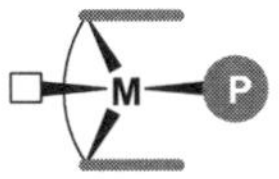	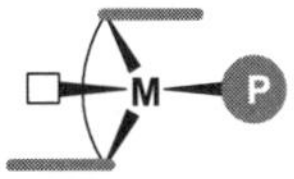	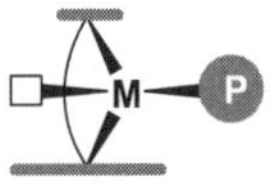	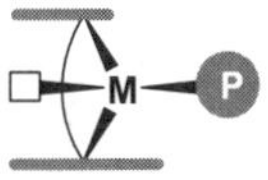
Symmetry	C_{2v} (achiral)	C_s (achiral)	C_2 (chiral)	C_s (prochiral)	C_1 (chiral)
Stereoregulation	Chain-end control	Chain-end control	Enantiomorphic-site control	Enantiomorphic-site control	Variable
Relation of the Two Coordination Sites[a]	Homotopic (N,N)	Diastereotopic (N,N)	Homotopic (E,E)	Enantiotopic (E,E)	Diastereotopic (E,N)
Polymer Microstructure	Atactic	Atactic	Isotactic	Syndiotactic	Variable (isotactic and hemiisotactic)

[a] E = enantioselective site; N = nonselective site

Achiral C_{2v}- or C_s-symmetric Metallocenes: When the metallocene is achiral (C_{2v}- or C_s-symmetric), atactic polyolefins are achieved, although chain-end control may allow for a certain degree of (iso- or syndio-) tacticity at low polymerization temperature. For example, Cp_2ZrCl_2, **6,** yields isotactic PP at low polymerization temperature, while the sterically more encumbered $(C_5Me_5)_2ZrCl_2$, **7**, yields atactic (slightly syndio-enriched) PP and syndiotactic poly(1-butene) (Figure 2.15). Bridged C_{2v}-symmetric metallocenes, such as $Me_2Si(9\text{-}Flu)_2ZrCl_2$, **8**, provide convenient access to high molecular weight atactic polypropylene which performs like an elastomer.

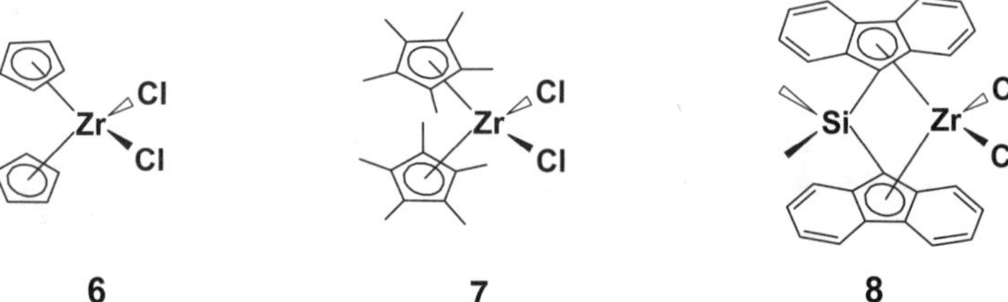

Figure 2.15. Examples of unbridged and bridged C_{2v}-symmetric metallocenes.

Chiral C_2-symmetric metallocenes: In C_2-symmetric metallocenes, such as $C_2H_4(Ind)_2ZrCl_2$, **9**, or $Me_2Si(Ind)_2ZrCl_2$, **10**, the two potential vacant coordination sites are homotopic. Consequently, every newly formed asymmetric center in the growing chain obtains the same configuration, irrespective of the switch in the relative positions of the free coordination site and the polymer chain in two subsequent polymerization steps. Thus, an isotactic polymer results from a C_2-symmetric metallocene. Stereoerrors may arise as an energetic penalty from a 'wrong' enantiofacial orientation of the incoming monomer (Figure 2.16) or more probably, from chain-end epimerization (Figure 2.17). These errors are statistically isolated, giving rise to *rr* error triads. The result is a highly isotactic polymer with *mrrm* stereoerror pentads. It is important to reiterate that, as the two potential free coordination sites of C_2-symmetric metallocenes are homotopic, an active-site epimerization does not cause a stereoerror (*vide infra*). It is also important to stress that, in reality, the chain flip (i.e., 'left to right' or 'right to left') during chain migration (alternatively called *migratory insertion*) involves only a small relative motion between chain end and metallocene.

Prochiral C_s-symmetric metallocenes: The invention of C_s-symmetric (prochiral) metallocenes marked a major turning point in understanding the stereocontrol mechanism of metallocene catalysis and provided access to sPP, a higher melting PP (the theoretical prediction of a fully syndiotactic PP will have T_m of 214°C vs 186°C for fully isotactic PP). In C_s-symmetric catalysts, such as $Me_2C(Cp)(Flu)ZrCl_2$ (**11**) and $Me_2SiMe_2Si(Cp)(Flu)ZrCl_2$ (**12**), the two potential vacant coordination sites are enantiotopic, each leading to an opposite configuration of the newly formed asymmetric center in the growing chain (Figure 2.18). Thus, if polymerization proceeds at alternating coordination sites in subsequent polymerization steps and active site epimerization is excluded, a syndiotactic polymer (recemic stereosequences) is obtained. The stereoerrors observed are *rmmr*-pentads from 'wrong' enantiofacial insertion, and also *rmrr*-pentads due to active-site epimerization, producing an *m* dyad but not affecting the following polymerization step (Figure 2.19). The degree of syndiotacticity is thus determined by the ratio of the rates of propagation and active site epimerization and is, therefore, a function of monomer concentration (pressure) and polymerization temperature. At higher temperature and low monomer concentration (pressure), active site epimerization is expected to be favored, leading to a decrease in syndiotacticity and tendentially atactic polymers. Indeed, at low polymerization temperatures with liquid propylene, **11** can produce syndiotactic polypropylene with very high stereoregularity ([rrrr] > 0.95) and a melting point close to that of highly isotactic polypropylene (T_m>150°C). C_s-symmetric metallocenes are very sensitive to the small variation in the ligand structure or bridging group, which can have a significant effect on the stereoselectivity. For instance, the metallocene with a silylene bridge (Me_2Si) in place of a Me_2C bridge in **11**, performs polymerization of propylene nonstereoselectively without any syndiotactic tendency.

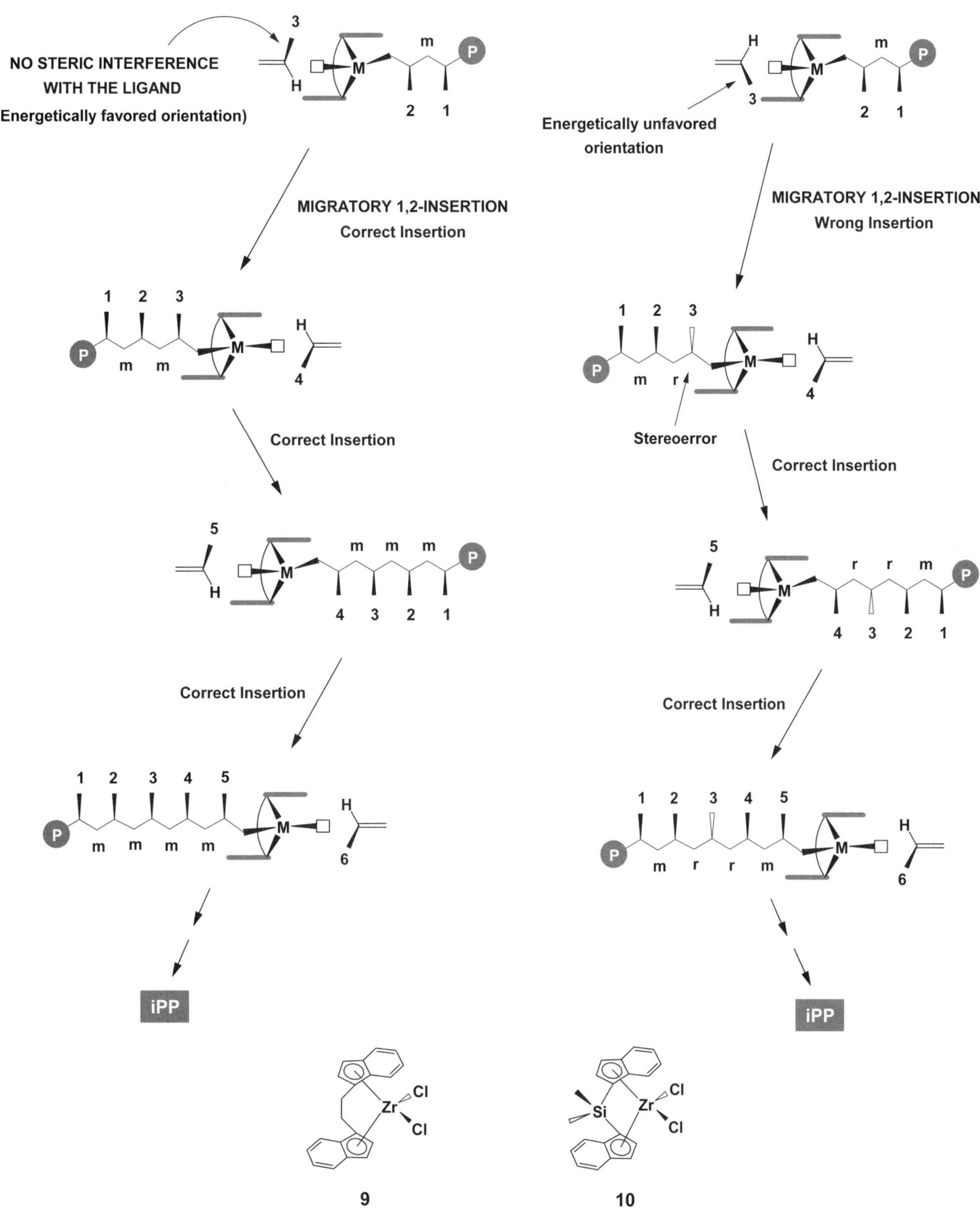

Figure 2.16. Polymerization of propylene with a C_2-symmetric metallocene. *Left:* The steric demand of the ligand forces propylene to approach the active center via an energetically favored enantiofacial orientation leading to isotactic polypropylene (*meso* stereosequences). *Right:* Stereoerror as a result of 'wrong' enantiofacial orientation of propylene. Note that the error is corrected in the next insertion. *Below:* Examples of bridged C_2-symmetric metallocenes.

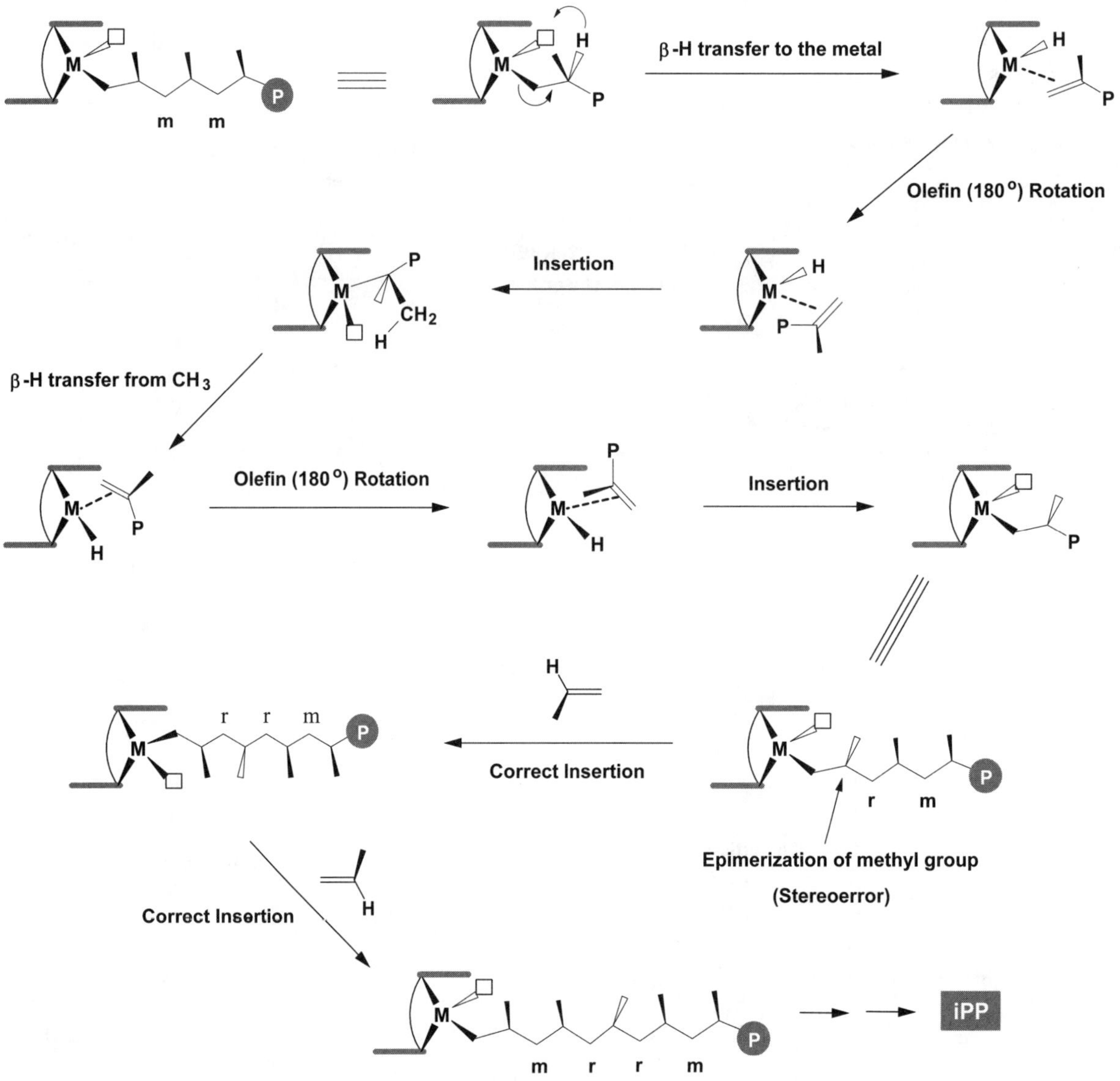

Figure 2.17. Mechanism of stereoerror via chain-end epimerization during the polymerization of propylene with a C_2-symmetric metallocene.

Chiral C_1-symmetric metallocenes: C_1-symmetric metallocenes, which offer two diastereotopic vacant coordination sites to the incoming monomer, can be used to produce polymers with variable microstructures. The stereoselectivity of this class of metallocenes in propylene polymerization is strongly dependent on the structure of the ligand. Chiral C_1-symmetric metallocenes can be derived from C_s-symmetric metallocenes through substitution on the Cp ring or by ring anellation, e.g., **13** and **14**, respectively. In these metallocenes, the site around the t-butyl group or anellated phenyl ring is inaccessible to the sterically demanding polymer chain. Consequently, monomer insertion takes place by a so-called "chain stationary insertion mechanism" (same relative disposition of the monomer and the growing chain). Indeed, experimental results show that **13** produces iPP with relatively high *mmmm* pentad contents, from 77.5% at 60°C in liquid monomer to 87.8% at 50°C (Figure 2.20). By contrast, a methyl substituent on the Cp ring, **15**, polymerizes propylene in a diastereoselective manner to produce isotactic-syndiotactic stereoblock PP. This could only happen if a periodic alternation between a multiple of chain-migratory insertions (leading to the syndiotactic blocks) and a few chain stationary insertion steps (leading to the isotactic blocks) takes place. Apparently, the steric constraint imposed by the methyl group is not large enough to be a driving force for one kind of tacticity.

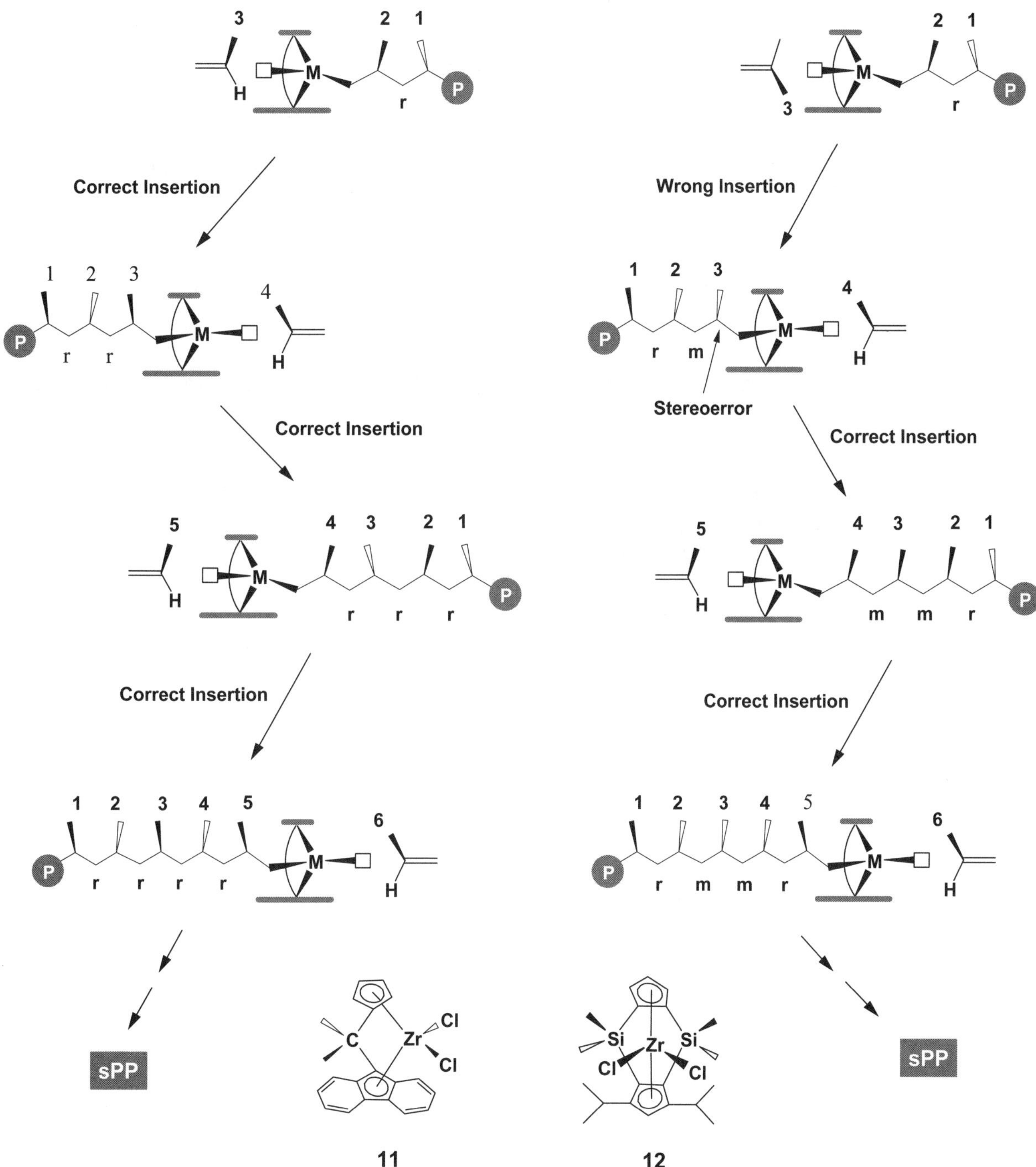

Figure 2.18. Syndiospecific polymerization of propylene with a prochiral C_s-symmetric metallocene. *Left:* Unlike C_2-symmetric metallocenes, the steric demand of the ligand forces racemic stereosequences (energetically favored insertion of propylene leads to sPP). *Right:* Stereoerror as a result of energetically disfavored (wrong) insertion of propylene. Note that the error is corrected in the next insertion. *Below:* Examples of bridged prochiral C_s-symmetric metallocenes.

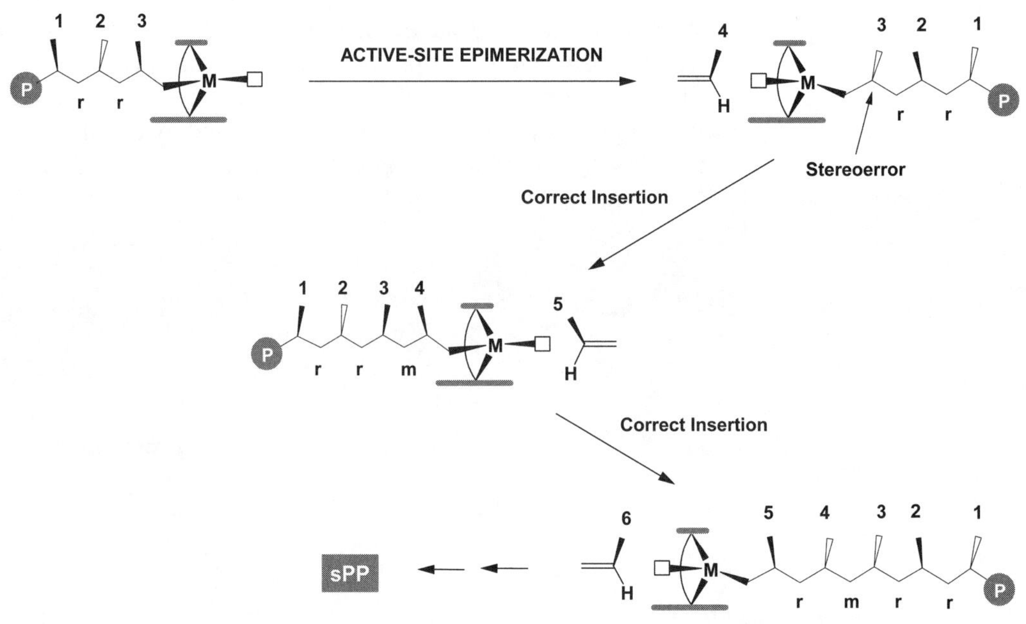

Figure 2.19. Stereoerror in prochiral C_s-symmetric metallocenes due to active-site epimerization.

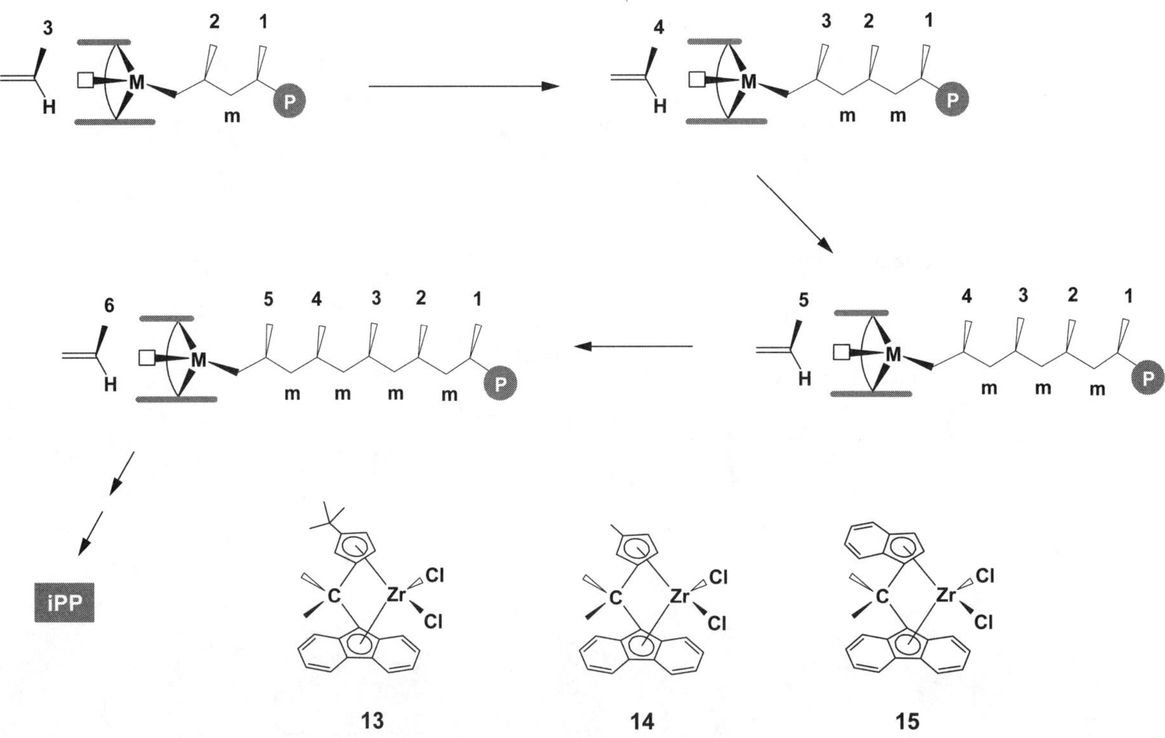

Figure 2.20. Proposed chain stationary insertion mechanism of propylene polymerization with C_1-symmetric metallocenes leading to iPP. *Below:* Examples of bridged C_1-symmetric metallocenes.

In addition to the aforementioned classes of metallocenes, there are two other specific classes of metallocenes which have major significance. Brief descriptions of these classes, oscillating metallocenes and bridged-half metallocenes, are given below:

Metallocenes with Oscillating Structure: In unbridged metallocenes, such as Cp_2MCl_2 or Ind_2MCl_2, the η^5-coordinated aromatic rings rotate freely even at very low temperatures. However, the rotation may become hindered in the presence of a bulky substituent, and the rate of rotation or "oscillation" may be dependent on the temperature. Of special interest are $(2\text{-Ar-Ind})_2MCl_2$ complexes (with M = Zr or Hf, and Ar = phenyl or a substituted aromatic moiety), which give rise to an equilibrium between two rotational isomers: one with quasi-C_2-symmetry and the other with quasi-C_s-symmetry, as illustrated in Figure 2.21.[10] Both rotamers exercise a different stereocontrol during the polymerization of propylene. The enantiomeric *rac*-rotamer (**A**) provides the isotactic block sequences, the achiral *meso*-rotamer (**B**) leads to atactic block sequences. The polymer microstructure can be controlled by varying temperature and pressure. For example, the block length decreases with increasing temperature and the isotactic block lengthens with increasing pressure.

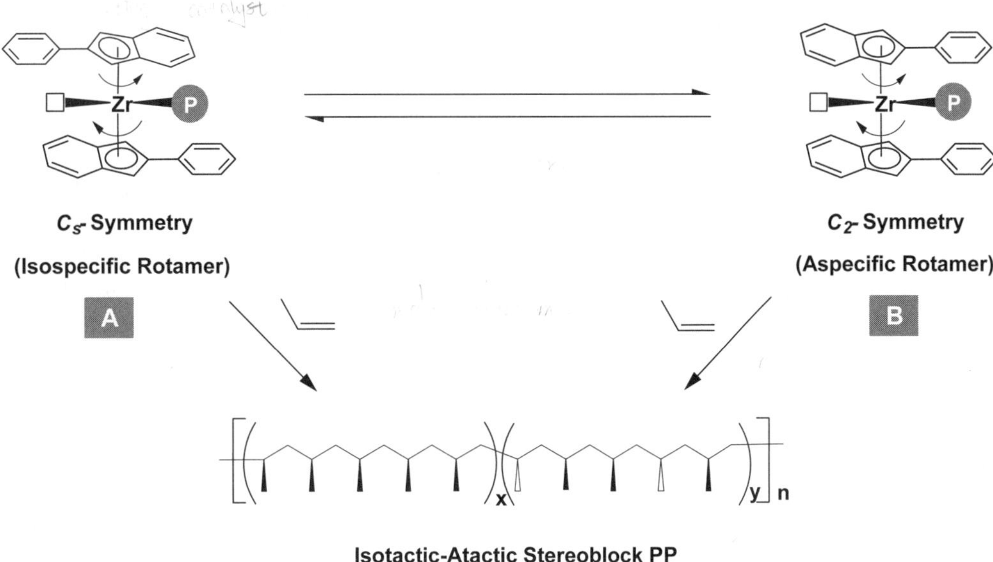

Figure 2.21. The structures of two rotamers of an "oscillating catalyst" for the synthesis of isotactic-atactic stereoblock PP.

Half-metallocenes: Many bridged and unbridged half-metallocenes have interesting catalytic behaviors. For example, $CpTiCl_3$(**16**)/MAO is a highly active catalyst for syndiotactic polymerization of styrene (Figure 2.22). However, such a catalyst cannot perform isospecific polymerization of propylene. As mentioned earlier, another important class of half-metallocenes is constrained geometry catalysts (CGCs, **2** and **17**). In these catalysts, the absence of a second Cp ring and the short bridge result in a very open environment of the transition metal, allowing easier insertion of bulky monomers compared with bis-Cp systems. This special feature endows such catalysts with excellent performance in the copolymerizations of ethylene with higher α-olefins and even with styrene. In the case of propylene polymerization with such catalysts, the resulting atactic polymers have poor regioregularity (with up to 5 mol% of 2,1-insertions). With replacement of Cp by a 9-fluorenyl moiety, the metallocene promotes syndiotactic polymerization of propylene under enantiomorphic-site control. Syndiotactic polypropylene with [*rrrr*] as high as 0.77 was obtained with Me_2Si(9-Flu)(N-t-Bu)$ZrCl_2$, **17**. The stereoselectivity is due to the (pseudo-) C_s-symmetry of the catalytic complex, and the stereocontrol mechanism is analogous to that for the C_s-symmetric *ansa*-metallocenes.

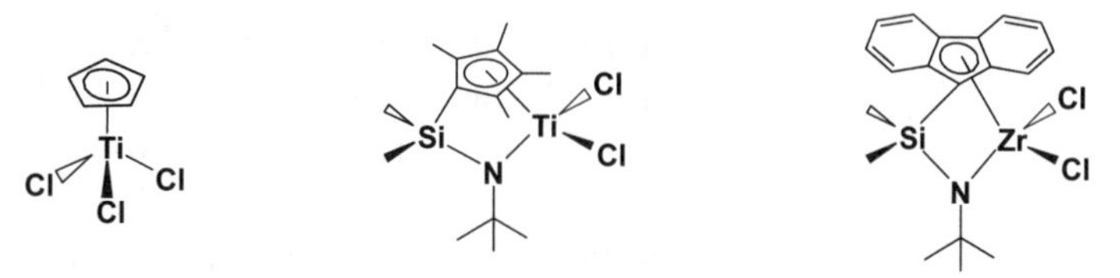

Figure 2.22. Important bridged and unbridged half-metallocenes.

16 2 17

2.1.1.3a. Isotactic Polypropylene (iPP)

As described in the aforementioned section, chiral C_2-symmetric bridged metallocenes are the most successful highly enantioselective polymerization catalysts. Figure 2.23 shows more structures of high performance metallocenes for isospecific propylene polymerization. These metallocenes possess a bridge (1,1' position), connecting two aromatic ligands, that prevents their rotation and locks them in a chiral configuration. In general, variation of the bridging position from 1,1' to other positions lowers catalytic activity and selectivity. The flexibility of the bridge between two ligands is also important. Most metallocenes, especially with indenyl ligands, exhibit stereoselectivity and molecular weight increases in the order $Me_2Si > CH_2CH_2 > Me_2C > CH_2$. Substitution on the indenyl ring has a significant effect on the molecular weight and isotacticity. For instance, an alkyl substituent at position 2,2' increases the molecular weight, presumably due to a combination of steric and electronic influences on the chain-termination process. Enhanced rigidity of the ligand framework combined with a direct steric interaction of the alkyl group with the growing polymer chain decreases the rate of β-elimination. Electron donation from the alkyl substituent may further decrease the local Lewis acidity of the central metal atom, thus reducing its tendency for β-H abstraction. The synergistic effect of 2-alkyl-4-aryl substitution further improves the catalyst rigidity and enhances the stereospecificity. iPP exhibits T_m near 175°C when [*mmmm*] pentad microstructures exceed 99%. The major applications of iPP are in the area of the non-woven industry, such as non-woven fabrics (cigarette and technical filters). Of the world's total non-woven production, iPP is the most common fiber, accounting for about 60% of all fibers. Other applications include carpeting, automotive parts and toys.

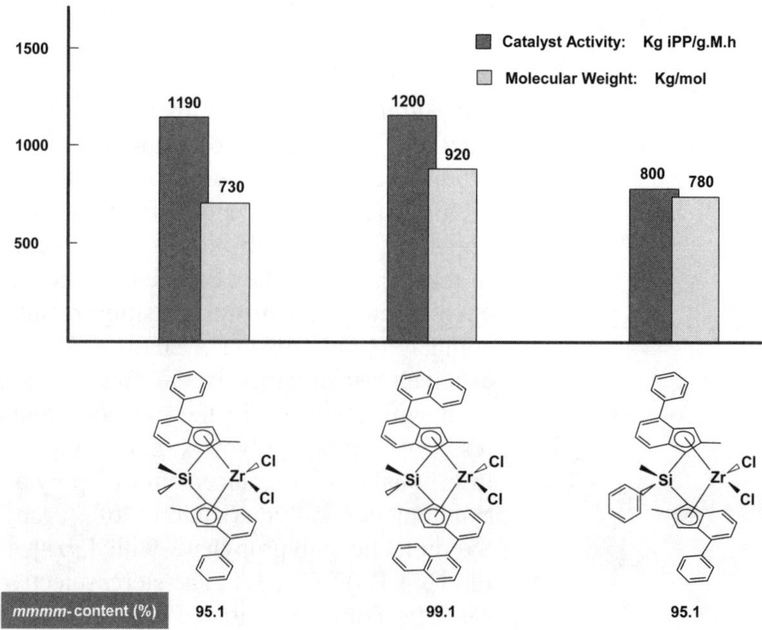

Figure 2.23. Structures of some highly isospecific and active metallocenes for iPP (MAO as the co-catalyst).

2.1.1.3b. Syndiotactic Polypropylene (sPP)

sPP has only recently been made on a large scale. The properties of metallocene derived sPP differ substantially from those of iPP, especially in their considerably higher room temperature impact strength, higher optical clarity, and resistance against UV and gamma radiations. In view of these attributes, the development of high-performance catalysts for sPP is now under intensive research. For the syndiospecific polymerization of propylene, catalysts with C_s-symmetry and a rigid ligand framework are required. Attempts to improve catalyst activity and syndioselectivity have resulted in several second-generation single-site catalysts, including doubly bridged metallocenes, sterically expanded version of **11** and fluorenyl-amido constrained geometry catalysts (CGCs), which provided markedly improved sPP with [*rrrr*] >99% and an unannealed T_m exceeding 155°C (Figure 2.24). It should be noted that while iPP has been prepared with a high pentad (>99.9% *mmmm*) exhibiting T_m near 175°C, fully syndiotactic PP is yet to develop to validate the theoretical prediction of higher T_m (214°C) for sPP.

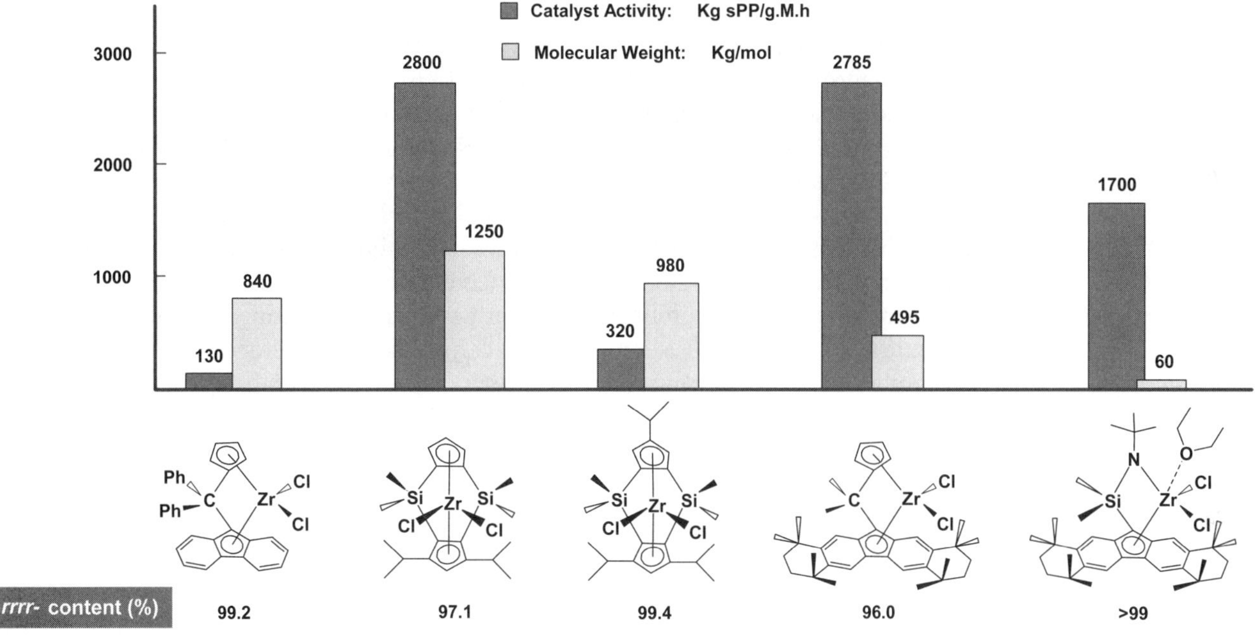

Figure 2.24. Structures and performances of some highly syndiospecific and active metallocenes for sPP (MAO as the co-catalyst).

2.1.1.3c. Hemiisotactic Polypropylene (hiPP)

The polymerization conditions require an isospecific monomer placement in between units of random stereochemistry (see Figure 1.59 in Chapter-1). The proper modification of C_1-symmetric metallocenes provides access to hiPP. The first catalyst that successfully produced hiPP was $Me_2C(3\text{-}MeCp)(Flu)ZrCl_2$ (**14**). The presence of one isospecific site and one aspecific site on the same metal center, together with the requirement of chain migratory insertion with site switching at every or almost every insertion, generates a unique polymer structure (Figure 2.20). The doubly bridged metallocene, **18**, also produces a good quality of hemiisotactic-like PP (Figure 2.25). In general, the synthesis of highly hemiisotactic polymers is very challenging and progress on hiPP is still limited to laboratory research.

Figure 2.25. Structures of two effective metallocenes for hiPP.

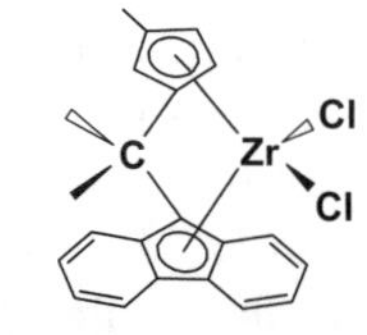

14 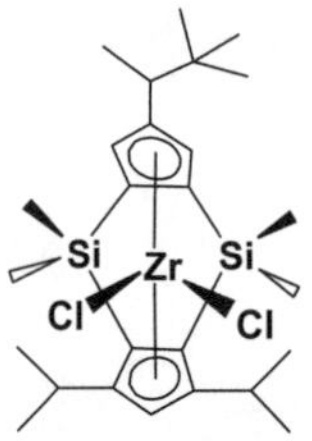 18

2.1.1.3d. Stereoblock Polypropylene (elPP)

This variety of PP, also known as propylene elastomer (elPP), was first prepared with good control using C_1-symmetric *ansa*-metallocenes, such as **19**. Surprisingly, the titanium derivative showed higher activity than its zirconium analog. However, the melting point of the resulting polymer is too low for commercial applications, because the isotactic blocks of the polymer are both short and sterechemically impure, and do not provide adequate size of the crystalline domain (physically linked hard segment) necessary for higher melting and superior elastomeric properties. Subsequently, several other catalysts, **20-22**, have been developed (Figure 2.26). The polymers obtained exhibited various physical properties, from nonelastomeric plastics through flexible plastics to thermoplastic elastomers. The oscillating catalyst, **22**, mentioned earlier in Figure 2.21, is very effective. This catalyst stays in temperature dependent equilibrium between two isomers in which one favors aspecific attack and the other facilitates isospecific orientation. Low temperature and high monomer concentration favors isotacticity. Thus, by controlling the temperature and monomer concentration of polymerization, the properties of elPP can be tuned by creating well-defined blocks of isotactic and attctic PP segments. Finally, these metallocene-derived polyolefin elastomers have become very popular to polymer product designers. As indicated earlier, because of their mix of plastic and elastomeric characteristics, they are now distinguished from other classes of elastomers by the new name "plastomers".

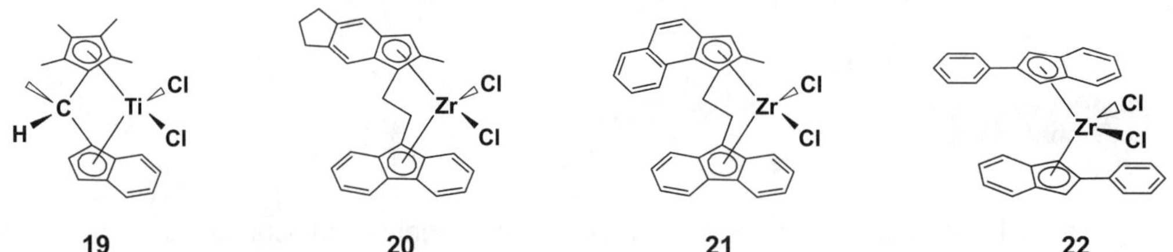

Figure 2.26. Structures of effective metallocenes for elPP.

2.1.1.3e. Atactic Polypropylene (aPP)

Most Ziegler-Natta isospecific catalysts produce low molecular aPP as the by-product during the production of iPP. Because of its highly amorphous nature, aPP lacks the strength characteristics of crystalline isotactic and syndiotactic polymers and finds limited applications, for example, in road paint, in making roofing materials like "roofing felt", and in some sealants, adhesives and compatibilizers. Until recently, there was no formal process for the manufacture of aPP alone due to lower demand. A number of metallocenes are now available to produce high molecular weight aPP. For example, the incorporation of the bulky amido group into the CGC framework (**23** and

24) produces high molecular weight aPPs (>1,000,000 Da) with low polydispersity (<2.0). It is believed that the electronic effect provided by the amido ligation is the likely origin of higher molecular weight (Figure 2.27). Some sandwich metallocenes, such as $[Me_2Si(Flu)_2]ZrCl_2$, **8**, have also been developed, but give molecular weights up to 400,000 at the same reaction temperatures. With the availability of high molecular weight aPP, new applications, such as thermoplastic elastomeric blends with iPP are now under consideration. While blends of aPP and iPP often display interesting flexibility, they generally lack the elastic recovery properties of traditional elastomers.

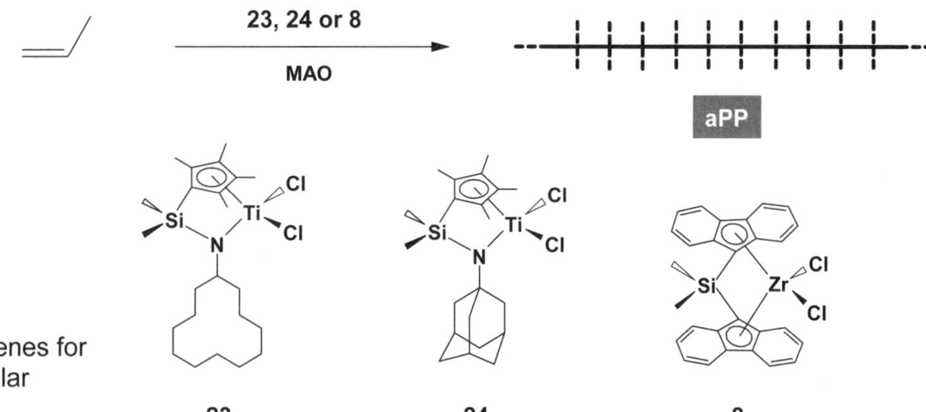

Figure 2.27. Active metallocenes for the production of high molecular weight aPP.

2.1.1.3f. Long Chain Branched Polypropylene (LCBPP)

Commercial iPP has a predominantly linear molecular structure. Despite the huge commercial success with many desirable properties, PP shows a variety of melt-processing shortcomings, such as low melt strength, which limits its applications in some important fabrications, such as thermoforming, blow molding, extrusion coating, and coextrusion of laminates. Most of the early prior art of increasing melt strength of PP was based on post-reactor free-radical processes involving peroxide treatment of linear iPP (see *controlled rheology polypropylene*, CR-PP, *vide supra*). Many studies have focused on optimizing reaction conditions or extruder parameters to promote branch formation while suppressing undesired degradation and cross-linking. However, because of the inherent complexity of free radical reactions, the final product is usually a complex mixture. As a result, PP has been limited in some end-use fabrications. Varying the molecular architecture is one of the most effective methods of tailoring processing characteristics and end-product properties of polymers. For example, long chain branching (LCB) has long been recognized as an ideal solution to improving PP melt strength and processability while maintaining other desirable properties. Unfortunately, the in-situ LCB reaction, which occurs in the case of PE (Figure 2.2), is ineffective with PP because of the limited spatial opening of most isospecific catalyst active sites for incorporating iPP macromonomers, except for the isospecific metallocene catalyst, **25**, which allows a considerable degree of *in situ* generation of LCB during polymerization of propylene (Figure 2.28).[11] This catalyst produces allyl-terminated macromonomers with molecular weights far below the entanglement molecular weight (M_e, the average molecular weight of a chain segment between two adjacent entanglement points) for PP, which has been reported to be 7,000 g/mol.

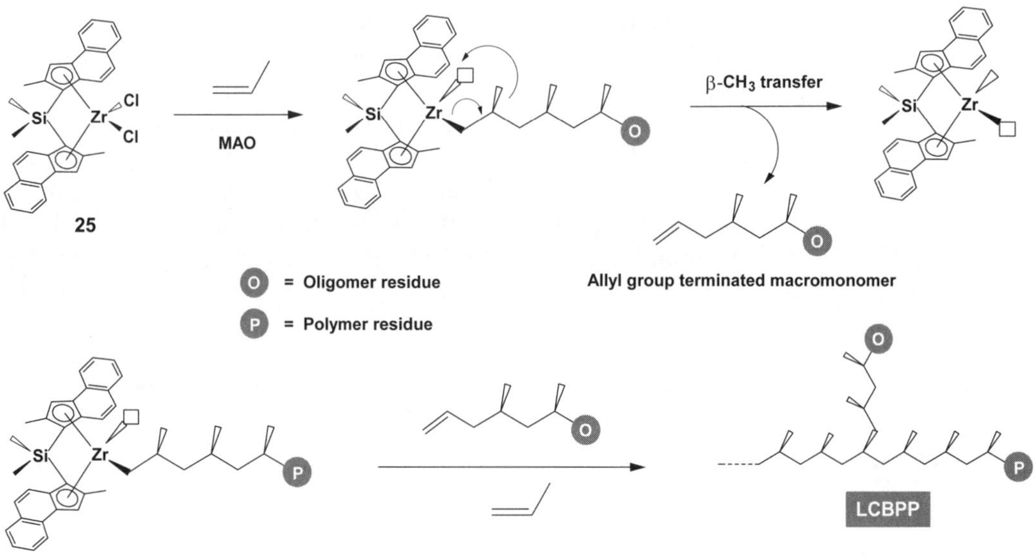

Figure 2.28. Mechanism of formation of LCBPP.

Another method for the preparation of LCBPP is, of course, copolymerization of propylene with polypropylene macromonomer with catalysts used for higher α-olefins. The initial finding of low molar mass products from propylene polymerization with metallocene catalysts was regarded as unfavorable. It is now recognized that metallocene catalysts may be used effectively for directed oligomerization of propylene to give oligomers (macromonomers) with predominantly allyl end groups (Figure 2.29). Thus, metallocene **26** yields a slightly syndiotactic-rich atactic polypropylene with a terminal allyl group (M_w ~ 630 and M_w/M_n ~2.4) and provides opportunity to produce LCBPP.[12]

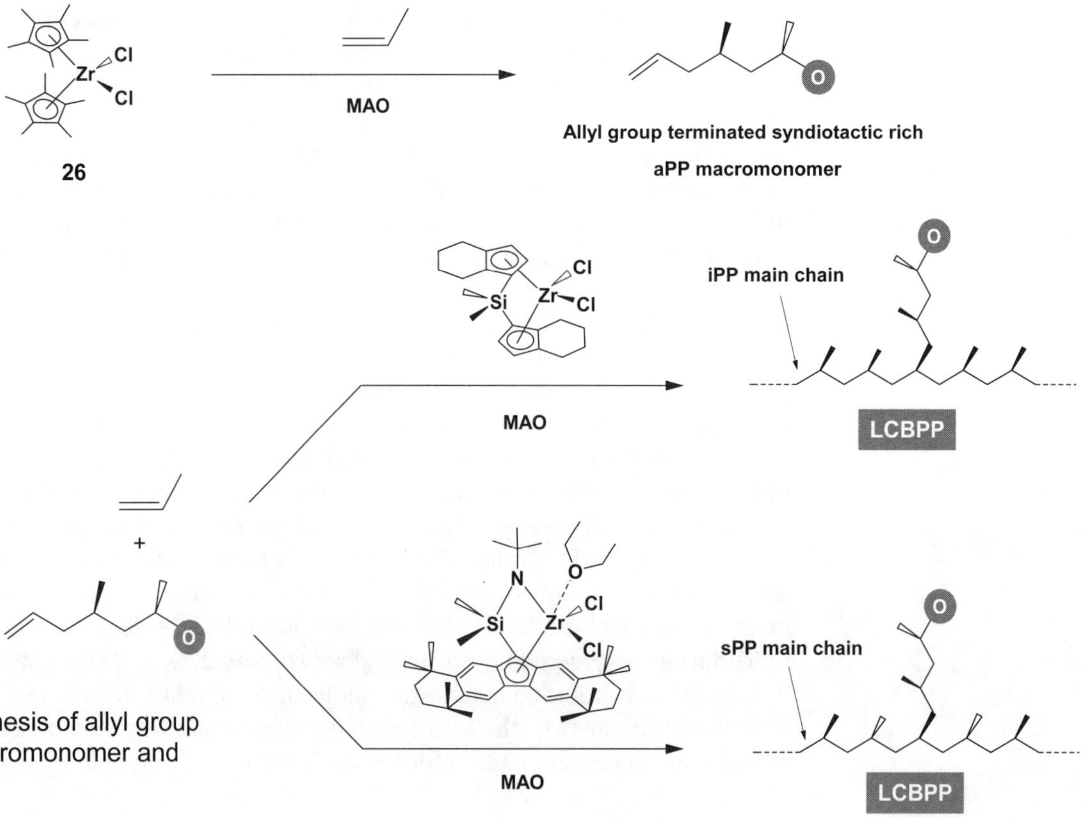

Figure 2.29. Synthesis of allyl group terminated PP macromonomer and related LCBPPs.

The copolymerization of ethylene or propylene with a nonconjugated α,ω-diene, such as 1,9-decadiene, is another important *in situ* in-reactor method for long chain branched polyolefins (Figure 2.30).[13] The diene monomers copolymerize with ethylene or propylene and become pendent vinyl moieties that are further incorporated into growing chains to form H-type long chain branched polymers. A very small amount of diene can introduce a significant level of long chain branches. Compared to the other *in situ* methods, this method suits most catalyst systems and appears to be more efficient and commercially feasible for the production of LCBPP. The degree of LCB in polyethylenes with low levels of branching can be inferred from rheological data, together with a GPC molecular weight distribution and ^{13}C-NMR spectra.[4]

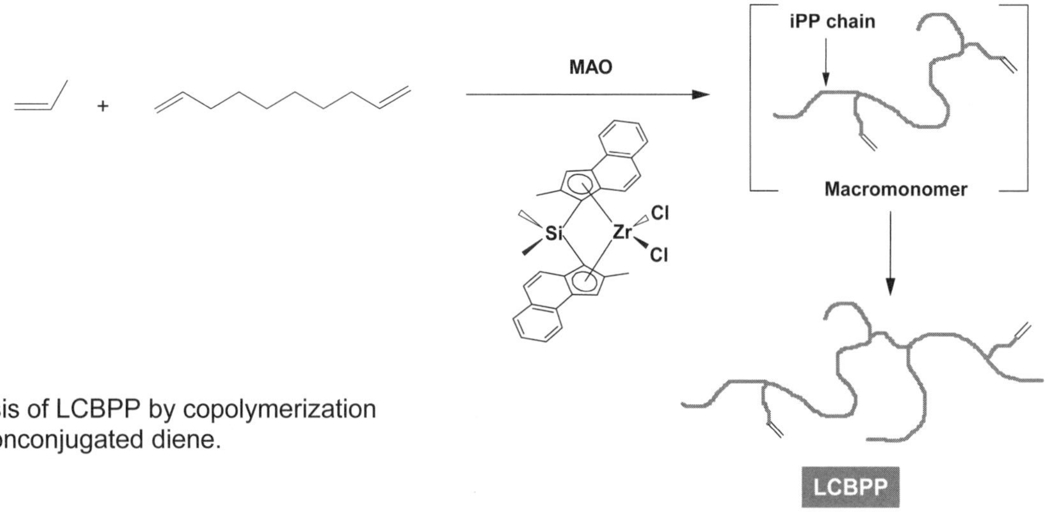

MAO

iPP chain

Macromonomer

LCBPP

Figure 2.30. Synthesis of LCBPP by copolymerization of propylene with a nonconjugated diene.

2.1.1.3g. Propylene Copolymers (PPCO)

The industrially important members of this family include ethylene (E)-propylene (P) copolymers, such as EP elastomer (random and amorphous copolymer, also known as EPM) and EP impact strength modifier (block copolymer). They combine some of the advantages of both homopolymers. For example, iPP is harder and has a higher temperature resistance than HDPE but lower impact resistance and becomes brittle below 0°C. In contrast, the copolymers have 10 times the impact strength of iPP, even in cold temperatures and possesses an exceptionally high strength-to-weight ratio. The primary use of PPCO is in injection molding and thermoforming parts for automotive, appliances and other durable applications. Extensive research has been carried out to relate the physical properties and performance with the chain structure of EP copolymers. The commercial EP copolymers are generally made using homogeneous aspecific vanadium-based and heterogeneous isospecific titanium-based Ziegler-Natta catalysts. The advent of metallocene catalysts has offered a new route to EP copolymers with narrow molecular weight distributions and special stereochemical structures, with both practical and fundamental interest. The structures of recently developed metallocenes, **27** and **28**, for EP copolymers are shown in Figure 2.31. Compound **27** produces rather random ethylene-propylene copolymers with a high affinity to incorporate propene whereas alternating copolymers with percentages of alternating EPE+PEP triads in the range of 61-76% at 50% ethylene incorporation, are obtained with metallocene **28**.[14,15] The structure for the latter is interpreted in terms of a mechanism involving the alternating insertion of olefins at the two heterotopic coordination sites exhibiting different kinetic selectivities for the two comonomers.

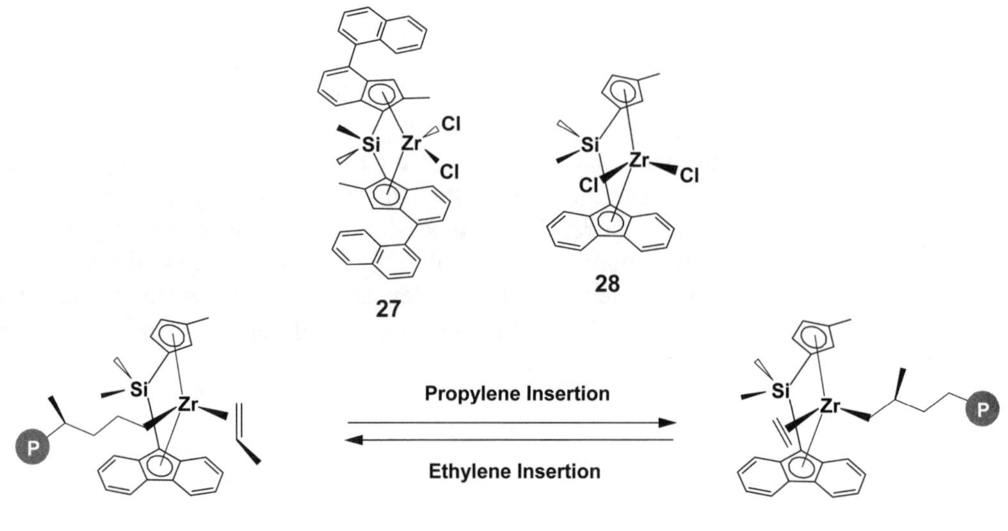

Figure 2.31. Structures of highly active metallocenes (MAO as the co-catalyst) for ethylene-propylene copolymers.

2.1.1.3h. Polyolefin Block Copolymers

In a recent study, a new class of polyolefin block copolymers has been prepared by complete hydrogenation of commercially available SBS triblock and SBSBS pentablock copolymers (Figure 2.32).[16] These polyolefins, such as CEC, which contain blocks of polyethylene (E) and poly(cyclohexylethylene) (C), exhibit superior mechanical properties, higher T_g (~145°C), enhanced UV stability, and a very small *stress-optic coefficient* (which measures how birefringent a medium becomes for a given stress). The saturation of polybutadiene (B) and polystyrene (S) blocks is conducted separately. Homogeneous Wilkinson's catalyst hydrogenates selectively more than 99.5% of the carbon-carbon double bonds of the B block, while the saturation of aromatic rings of the S blocks are performed in the presence of a heterogeneous catalyst, such as Pt on SiO_2.

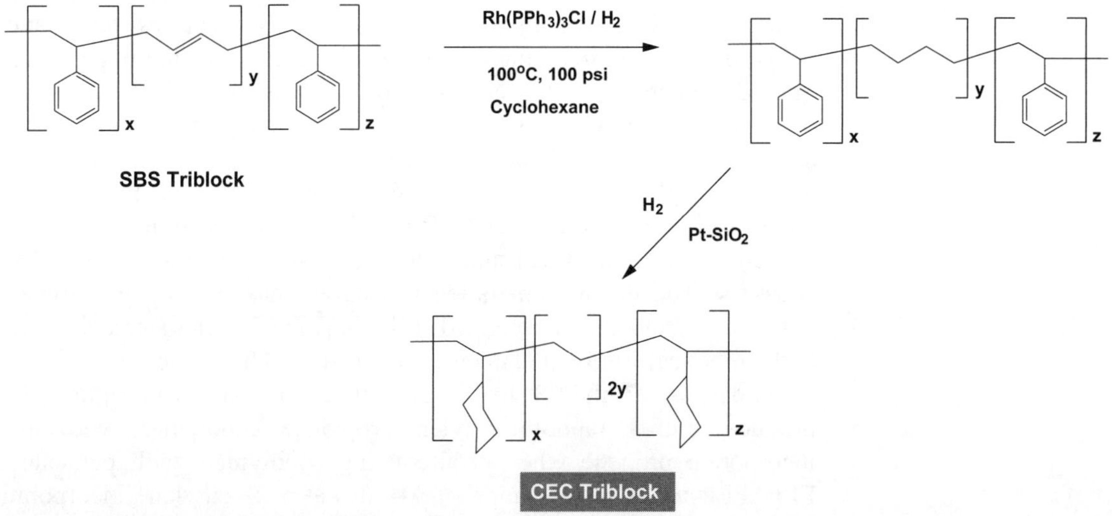

Figure 2.32. Synthesis of polyolefin block copolymers by hydrogenation of SBS triblock copolymer.

2.1.1.4. Higher Polyolefins

The homopolymers of higher α-olefins, such as 1-butene and 4-methyl-1-pentene, possess excellent mechanical strength, rigidity and creep resistance similar to engineering polymers and have been synthesized effectively with Ziegler-Natta and metallocene catalysts. As shown in Figure 2.33, the catalysts **29** and **30** produce isotactic poly-1-butene (PB-1), while the doubly bridged biscyclopentadienyl zirconium dichloride complexes, **31** and **32**, yield highly syndiotactic PB-1. See Chapter-3 for the other important member, poly(4-methyl-1-pentene) (PMP).

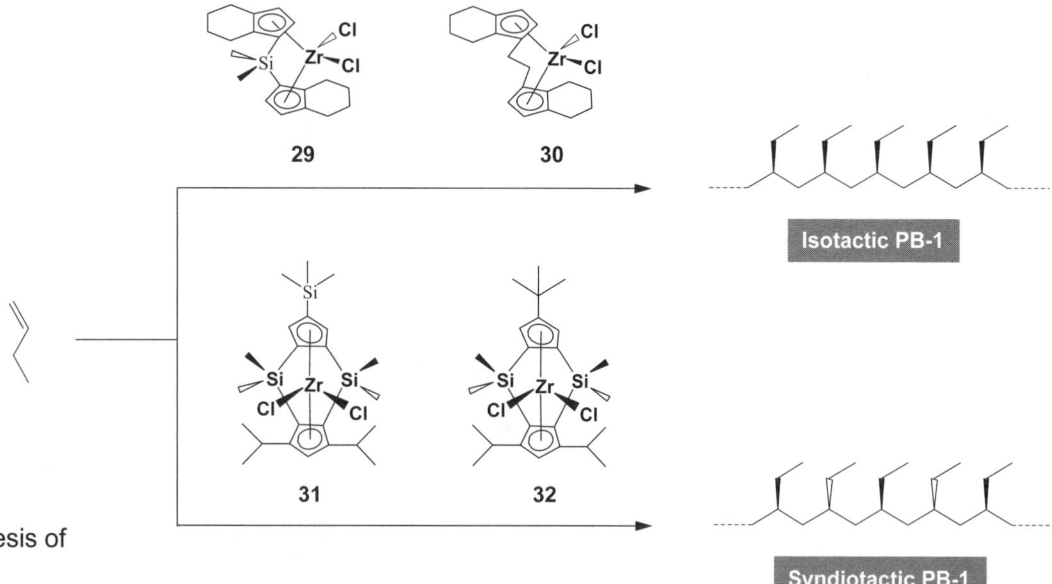

Figure 2.33. Synthesis of poly-1-butene.

Due to PB-1's inherent flexibility in combination with superior mechanical properties compared to other polyolefins (Figure 2.34), as well as excellent creep and burst pressure resistance, pipes produced from this polymer show an ideal balance of performance properties to satisfy the demands of modern heating and plumbing systems. PB-1 forms excellent blends with polypropylene. Incompatibility with polyethylene is used to make peelable PE-based film seals. A major application for PB-1 is seal-peel or easy-open packaging. Typical examples include carton liners (e.g., cereal packaging) and packs for pre-packed delicatessen products like cold meats and cheeses. PB-1 can also be utilized in film modification to increase flexibility and softness without sacrificing clarity. For example, PB-1 is used to modify polypropylene fibers to enhance softness, flexibility and to provide a unique feel.

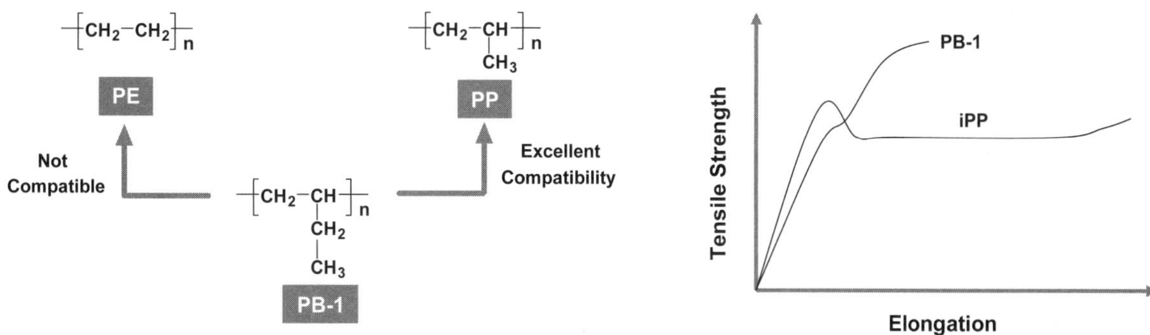

Figure 2.34. Comparison of compatibility and mechanical properties of PB-1 with other polyolefins, such as PE and PP.

2.1.1.5. Polyolefin Fibers

The major proportion of polyolefin fibers is drawn from iPP with the remaining part from LDPE and UHMWPE. Polyolefin fibers differ from other staple fibers in two important aspects: (i) olefin fibers do not absorb moisture and thus possess excellent stain resistance, (ii) the low density of olefin fibers allows a much lighter weight product at a specified size or coverage. For example, 1 kg of iPP fiber can produce fabric, carpet, etc. with much more fiber per unit area than that of other common fibers, such as nylon-6,6, PET and cotton (Table 2.2). However, iPP is much more prone to light-induced degradation compared to LDPE or UHMWPE because of the facile generation of hydroperoxides on the tertiary carbon. It has been established that the light stability is markedly improved in the presence of a *hindered amine light stabilizer* (HALS, e.g., 2,2,6,6-tetramethylpiperidine), which is thought to act as a vehicle to generate a nitroxide radical $>N\text{-}O^{\bullet}$ which then scavenges alkyl radicals or polymer macroradicals to form N-alkoxy derivatives, thus efficiently inhibiting generation of chain propagating alkyl peroxy radicals.[17]

Olefin fibers are manufactured commercially by melt spinning, except for UHMWPE fiber, which is produced by the "gel-spun" technique. In a typical process, a 5-10 wt.% solution of UHMWPE in a hydrocarbon solvent (e.g., decalin, paraffin oil or paraffin wax) is prepared at 150°C to reduce intermolecular entanglements, making it possible to achieve greater fiber orientation. The solution is then cooled to ~135°C to form a gel, porous, crystalline solid with minimal entanglement density. This gel is spun into fibers and then ultradrawn at 120°C to reach the final fiber diameter and strength. The physical and chemical properties of the gel-spun UHMWPE fibers are similar to fibers drawn in the solid-state, except they possess extremely high strength and modulus. It should be noted that the UHMWPE fibers possess strength similar to that of aramid fibers, but provides significant weight savings due to its lower density (0.94 g/cm^3 vs. 1.38 g/cm^3). This low density feature, coupled with high strength and modulus values, has made UHMWPE fibers the most outstanding among the currently available high-performance fibers (see Table 4.2 in Chapter-4).

Table 2.2. Physical Properties of Important Staple Fibers

Property	iPP	UHMWPE	PAN	Nylon-6,6	PET	Cotton	Wool
Density, g/cm^3	0.90	0.94	1.06	1.14	1.32	1.54	1.30
Tenacity, gpd[a]	4.5	34	3.6	8.5	2.4	3.0	3.2
Tensile strength, MPa	43	2860	57	78	55	50	35
Elongation, %	100	3.5	50	40	25	10	30
Limiting oxygen index, %	18	18	18	20	17	18	25
Resistance to sunlight	Poor without stabilizer	Good	Excellent	Poor without stabilizer	Good	Poor	Poor
Resistance to chemicals	Excellent	Excellent	Excellent	Good	Good	Poor	Poor
Abrasion resistance	Excellent	Excellent	Good	Very good	Very good	Good	Good
Moisture regain, 65% r.h, 21°C	0.0	0.0	2.5	5.0	0.4	8.0	15.0

[a] gpd = gram per denier

2.1.1.6. Functional Polyolefins

Despite the great commercial success of polyolefins, some inherent deficiencies in polyolefins, such as a lack of reactive functional groups in the polymer structure, have limited further applications, particularly those in which adhesion, dyeability, paintability, printability or compatibility with other polar polymers is paramount. Logically, this problem can be overcome by introducing suitable functional groups in the polyolefin, which provide interactive properties with other materials, such as pigments, paints, carbon black, glass fiber, and other polymers. As shown in Figure 2.35, the functional polyolefin can be categorized into two main groups: polyolefin with functional groups pendent to the polymer chain (Type-I) and polyolefin with functional group(s) at the end of the polymer chain (Type-II). The latter can be further divided into mono- and di-functional terminated polyolefins and is discussed under metathesis polymerization (Chapter-1) and controlled ionic polymerization (later this chapter).

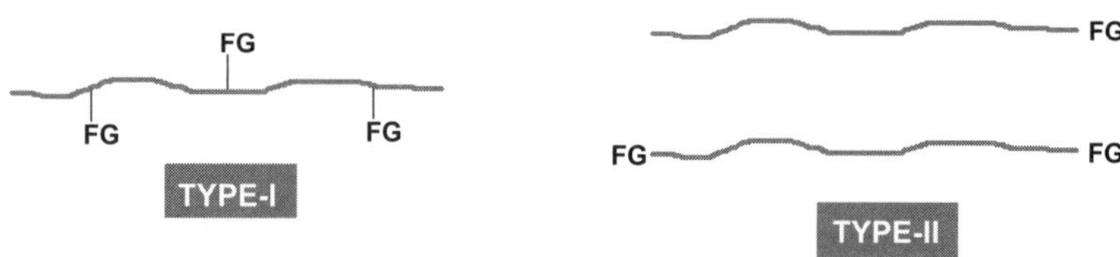

Figure 2.35. Major types of functional polyolefins (FG = functional group).

During the past twenty years, a number of approaches have been developed to produce functional polyolefins.[18] They can be grouped into three categories: (a) chemical modification of the preformed polymer, (b) direct copolymerization of α-olefin with functional monomer, and (c) reactive copolymer approach by incorporating reactive co-monomers that can be selectively and effectively interconverted to functional groups. Currently, most commercial functionalization processes are based on post-polymerization reactions, which usually requires vigorous reaction conditions, due to the inert nature of PE, PP, and EP polymers. The functionalization reaction involves free radical activation of the stable (saturated) polymer chain by breaking some high energy C-H bonds to form free radicals along the polymer chain. Ideally, these polymeric radicals then react with chemical reagents, such as maleic anhydride, which is present in the system. However, many side reactions, such as crosslinking, degradation, and homopolymerization can also occur, and the resulting functional polymer is far from ideal, usually containing low functional group content and by-products.

The direct process could be an ideal one-step reaction if the copolymerization reaction with functional monomers would be as effective and straightforward as the corresponding homopolymerization reaction. The best example in this category is DuPont's polyethylene ionomer (Surlyn®) which is a random copolymer of ethylene and methacrylic acid (EMAA) and is manufactured by high-pressure copolymerization with peroxide initiators, similar to that for the production of LDPE (Figure 2.36).[19] The incorporation of methacrylic acid monomer is intentionally set at low concentration since this monomer is more reactive with itself than with ethylene. This leads to a higher reactivity ratio, around four, for methacrylic acid, and could give a blocky incorporation of methacrylic acid along the polymer chain (see Figure 1.33 in Chapter-1 for the schematic of the domain structure of the ionomer). However, by polymerizing under elevated heat and pressure, the reactivity ratios are driven toward one, thus promoting a random incorporation of the co-monomers. The neutralization of the methacrylic acid units can be accomplished through the addition of an appropriate base in solution, or in the melt mixing of base and copolymer.

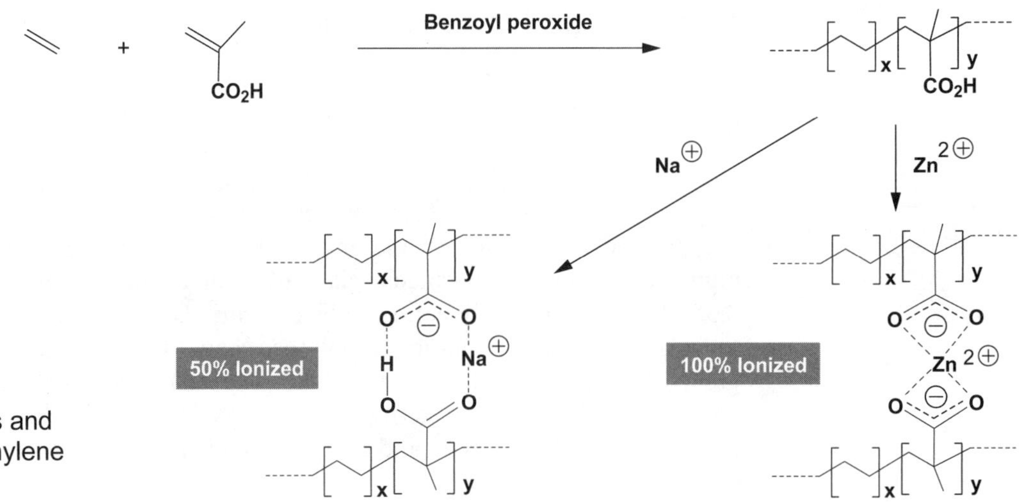

Figure 2.36. Synthesis and ionic bonding in polyethylene ionomers.

Typically, ionomers are defined thermoplastic polymers, which contain small amount of ionic groups (<15 mol%). Ionomers differ from polyelectrolytes in that the latter possesses very high ionic content, usually, in every repeat unit. A variety of grades of Surlyn are made by varying the degree of neutralization and the type of cation, commonly Na^+ (Na-EMAA) or Zn^{2+} (Zn-EMAA). The monovalent alkali acts only through an association of polar ion pairs and not, as the bivalent Zn, through an ionic bonding. This association is considerably less, but allows smooth injection molding and extrusion operations. The polyethylene ionomers are well known for their excellence in flexibility, transparency, toughness, and melt processability. Consequently, they have found extensive applications as coatings and molded parts. Perhaps the best known use for polyethylene ionomers is golf ball covers. In general, the high impact resistance and moldability are required for the covers of golf balls having good play characteristics. The blend of partly neutralized Zn- and Na-EMAA ionomers allows injection or compression molding applied for the blend to make golf ball covers. Due to lower cost, well balanced properties and superior processability, ionomers have now almost outphased the market of *gutta percha* (a natural elastomer containing *trans*-1,4-polyisoprene), long time materials of choice for golf ball covers.

The third functionalization approach is based on protective group chemistry and has achieved a great deal of success. The basic idea is to design a "reactive copolymer intermediate" that can be effectively synthesized and subsequently interconverted to a functional polymer, thus overcoming the chemical difficulties in both post-polymerization and direct processes. The key factors in designing a "reactive" co-monomer include (a) the reactive group must be stable to metallocene catalysts and soluble in hydrocarbon polymerization media, (b) the reactive monomer should have good copolymerization reactivity with α-olefins, and (c) the reactive group must be facile in the subsequent interconversion reaction to a functional (polar) group or form a stable initiator for the polymerization of functional monomers. Several new reactive co-monomers have been successfully incorporated into polyolefins via metallocene catalysis polymerization.[20] The most widely used is 7-octenyl-9-BBN (BBN = 9-borabicyclo[3.3.1]nonane), which, on copolymerization with ethylene, produces functionalized LLDPE (Figure 2.37). The most intriguing feature of the borane functionality is that it can be selectively converted to desirable functional groups (such as OH, NH_2, and halides) under mild reaction conditions. In addition, the borane side groups in polyolefin can then be selectively oxidized at the aliphatic C-B group for graft-form polymerization. The peroxyborane (B-O-O-C) thus formed initiates a controlled radical polymerization in the presence of free radical-polymerizable monomers, such as methacrylates, vinyl acetate, acrylonitrile, etc., at ambient temperature. Successful copolymerization of protected monomer, N,N-bis(trimethylsilyl)-1-amino-10-undecene, has also been carried out in the presence of a CGC catalyst, followed by hydrolysis to afford amino-functionalized LLDPE. The amino functions of the copolymers can readily be used as piers in crosslinking reactions with organic carboxylic acid anhydrides.[21,22]

Figure 2.37. Functionalized polyolefins via 9-BBN protection.

2.1.2. Acrylics

Synthetic polymers derived from acrylic acid or its derivatives, viz., methyl acrylate, methyl methacrylate, acrylonitrile and acrylamide, are called *acrylics*. The most important acrylic polymers are poly(methyl methacrylate) (PMMA), polyacrylonitrile (PAN) and polyacrylamide (PAm). They may be grouped into the following four categories based on their primary uses. A comprehensive discussion on each follows.

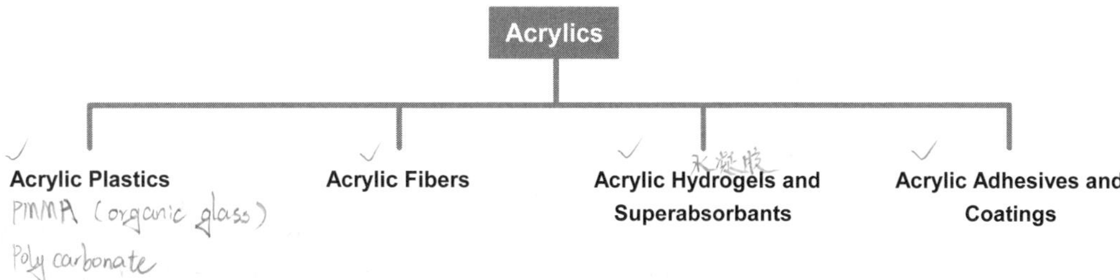

2.1.2.1. *Acrylic Plastics*

Acrylic and methacrylic esters are a versatile group of monomers which lead to a variety of useful commercial polymers. As shown in Table 2.3, the properties of two homopolymers are quite different. For example, the T_g of PMMA is about 100°C higher than that of PAA. The presence of a methyl goup in each repeat unit also provides increased stability, hardness and stiffness. Polymer physical and chemical properties also depend on the alkyl group in the ester part, the molecular weight, and the tacticity of the polymer (see Appendix-II under the effect of pendent groups). Although more costly than many other commonly employed industrial monomers, methacrylics, especially PMMA, have found a wide variety of commercial uses because of their unique balance of physical, optical and mechanical properties. PMMA is essentially transparent in the visible region (400-700 nm) and is capable of serving as a waveguide for visible light with neglible optical loss, which makes it suitable in the area of plastic optical fibers (POF) for digital home appliance interfaces, home networks, car networks and illumination. PMMA is used as a core material (refractive index = 1.49) with fluorinated acrylate (refractive index = 1.43) as clad material. Acrylic ester monomers are primarily used to tailor properties of methacrylic ester copolymers, rather than to prepare acrylic ester homopolymers.

Table 2.3. Comparison of Physical and Mechanical Properties of PMMA and PAA Analogs

Polymer Structure	Abbreviation	T_g (°C)	Density (g/cm^3)	Refractive Index	Tensile Strength (MPa)	Elongation (%)
Poly(methyl methacrylate)	PMMA	105	1.190	1.490	60	4
Poly(methyl acrylate)	PAA	5	1.220	1.479	7	700
Poly(ethyl methacrylate)	PEMA	65	1.119	1.485	33	7
Poly(ethyl acrylate)	PEA	-25	1.120	1.464	<1	1800
Poly(propyl methacrylate)	PPMA	40	1.085	1.484	13	35
Poly(propyl acrylate)	PPA	-45	1.098	1.478	<1	1800
Poly(butyl methacrylate)	PBMA	20	1.055	1.483	7	230
Poly(butyl acrylate)	PBA	-50	1.080	1.474	<1	2000

As depicted in Figure 2.38, the majority of commercial methacrylate ester polymers are produced by bulk (for cast sheets), solution (for coatings and adhesives), emulsion (for paints and paper) and suspension (for molding powders) polymerizations in the presence of free-radical initiators, such as benzoyl peroxide (BPO) and 2,2'-azobisisobutyronitrile (AIBN). The free-radical process generates mainly atactic polymers because of the symmetric nature of the radical species. The tacticity of the polymer backbone has significant influence on the T_g of PMMA. In general, T_g values decrease in the order syndiotactic (110°C) > atactic (105°C) > isotactic (45°C). It is noteworthy that this trend is very different from that of the tacticity observed in PP. This difference is attributed to the presence of an additional polar and larger ester group in each repeat unit, resulting in a helical wormlike polymer chain. According to rotational isomeric state (RIS) calculations, there are conformational differences between iPMMA and sPMMA. The most stable conformation is *trans-trans* (tt) in the two cases, but the racemic tt state of sPMMA is imposed by the backbone, whereas the meso tt state of iPMMA is stabilized by side-group interactions.[23] Moreover, the conformation of the backbone and side chain of amorphous iPMMA seems to be less restricted (higher static chain stiffness) to specific rotational angles than the conformation of the syndiotactic isomer. Interestingly, mixing of isotactic and syndiotactic PMMA produces a stereocomplex in which the sPMMA wraps around the iPMMA to form a double helix; the stoichiometry being 2:1 (s:i) at the monomeric unit level.[24] The melting range of stereocomplexes can extend to temperatures over 200°C (much higher than that of s- or iPMMA), so that structures with very high thermal stability could possibly be built. Compared to iPMMA, the crystalline stereocomplex structures are known to be organized in rather small crystallites, which would cause less light scattering than the more extensive lamellar structures in crystalline iPMMA (important with respect to optical applications).

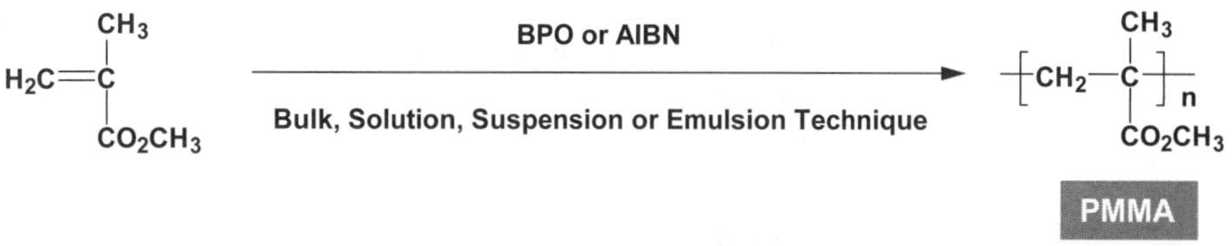

$$H_2C{=}C(CH_3)(CO_2CH_3) \xrightarrow[\text{Bulk, Solution, Suspension or Emulsion Technique}]{\text{BPO or AIBN}} \left[CH_2{-}C(CH_3)(CO_2CH_3)\right]_n$$

PMMA

Figure 2.38. Synthesis of PMMA and the picture of a plastic optical fiber assembly.

While cationic polymerization is not an option due to lack of stabilization of a proton initiated carbocationic species, anionic polymerization is frequently applied to form methacrylic ester polymers. However, the traditional anionic initiator, n-BuLi, is not suitable because of its reactivity toward the ester carbonyl group of MMA, leading to formation of lithium methoxide. The most popular initiator for anionic polymerization of MMA and other polar monomers is 1,1-diphenylhexyllithium, which is prepared *in situ* by adding equimolecular amounts of 1,1-diphenylethylene (DPE) and n-BuLi (Figure 2.39). The anionic polymerization is usually conducted in THF at -78°C and the resulting polymer exhibits narrow molecular weight distributions.

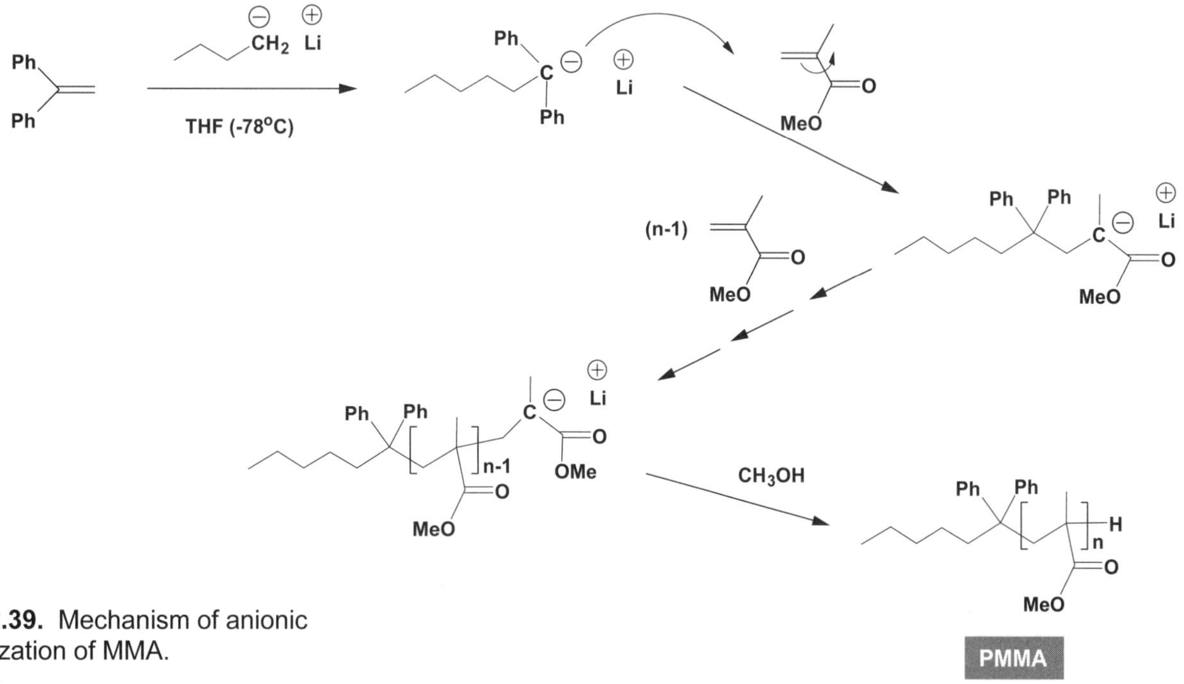

Ph Ph CH_2^{-} Li^{+} THF (-78°C) Ph C⊖ Ph ⊕ Li O MeO

(n-1) O MeO Ph Ph C⊖ ⊕ Li O MeO

Ph Ph n-1 O MeO C⊖ ⊕ Li O OMe CH_3OH Ph Ph n H O MeO

PMMA

Figure 2.39. Mechanism of anionic polymerization of MMA.

In general, most polymerization reactions of MMA by radical, anionic or group transfer polymerization produce atactic or syndio-enriched PMMA with approximately 60 to 70% syndiotacticity (calculated from *rr* triads), due to chain-end control. More recently, the viability of using metallocene complexes as initiators has been investigated for the preparation of stereoregular PMMAs, especially highly syndiotactic PMMA (>99% *rrrr* pentad), which combine properties typical for PMMA with enhanced mechanical and thermal stability. One of the best examples for rational control of PMMA microstructure via metallocene catalyst symmetry is shown in Figure 2.40.[25] While the complex $Me_2CcpIndZrMe(thf)^+BPh_4^-$ (**33**) yields highly iPMMA (94.7% *mm* triad; 91.5% *mmmm* pentad), $Me_2CCp_2ZrMe(thf)^+BPh_4^-$ (**34**) is syndiospecific (89% *rr* triad; 76.9% *rrrr* pentad) at low temperatures. The mechanism involves the formation of a carbon bond via an intramolecular Michael addition, yielding a cyclic intermediate with the polymer chain loosely attached to the catalyst (analogous to group-transfer polymerization). The enchained MMA monomer becomes the ester enolate chain end, situated at the other side of the catalyst wedge as compared to the initial situation. The catalytic cycle is completed by the replacement of the loosely attached polymer chain by a new incoming MMA monomer and another polymerization step analogous to the first one. The catalyst **33** is C_1-symmetric, bearing two substantially different diastereotopic coordination sites at the zirconium center, and apparently, the high isospecificity of **33** is the result of monomer coordination always taking place at the same coordination site. The catalyst **34** is C_{2v}-symmetric, bearing two homotopic coordination sites, which are both aspecific. Consequently, the observed syndiospecificity must be due to chain-end control.

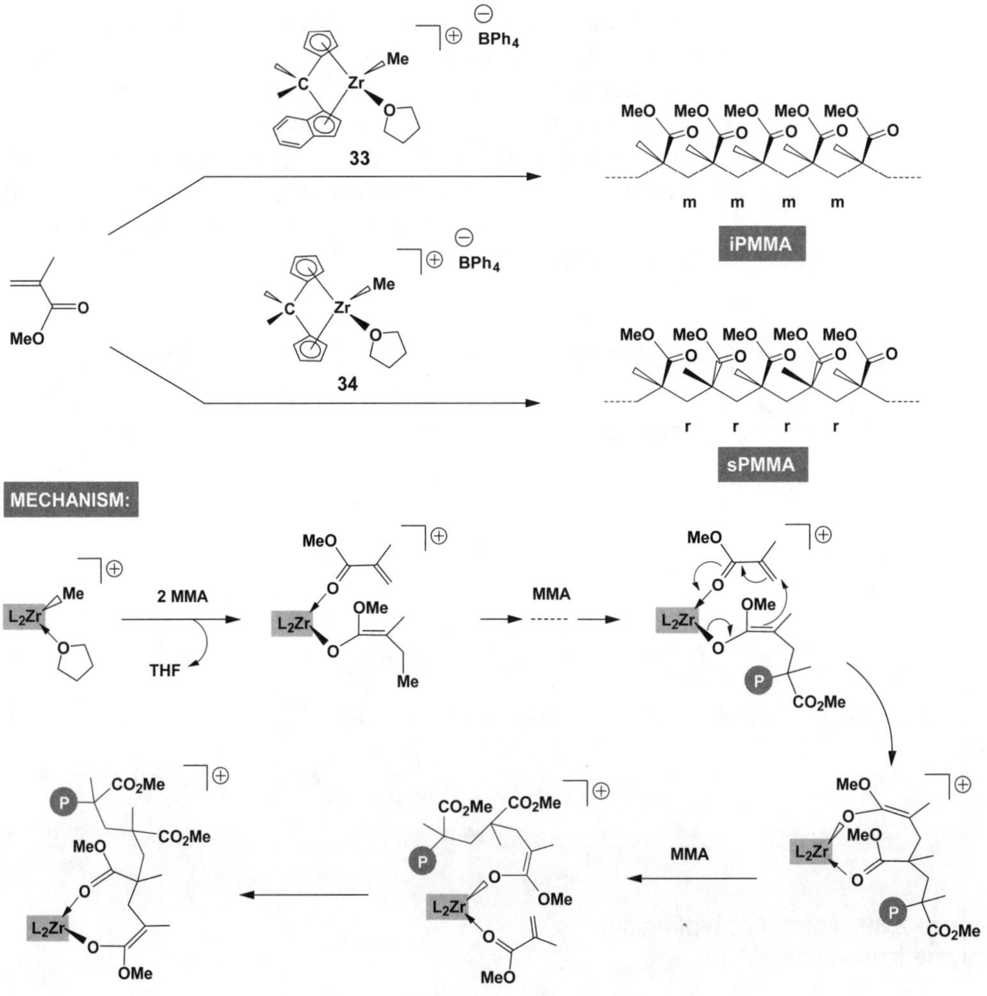

Figure 2.40. Stereospecific polymerization of MMA with single component cationic zirconocene catalysts (i.e., no MAO).

2.1.2.2. Acrylic Fibers

Commercial acrylic fibers, used primarily for the manufacture of apparel, including sweaters and sportswear, as well as home furnishings, viz., carpets, upholstery, and draperies, are produced by copolymerization of acrylonitrile (AN) with at least one other monomer (Figure 2.41). The co-monomers most employed are methyl acrylate (MA) and vinyl acetate (VAc). They increase solubility of the polymers in spinning solvents, modify fiber morphology, and improve the rate of diffusion of dyes into the fiber. For textile end-use acrylics, the most common comonomer is vinyl acetate, followed by methyl acrylate. Other comonomers include halogenated materials (vinyl chloride or vinylidene chloride) to impart flame resistance to fibers, and ionic monomers, such as sodium *p*-vinylbenzene sulfonate (SSS) and sodium methallyl sulfonate (SMAS). Fibers containing 85 wt.% or more of acrylonitrile are usually referred to as *acrylics*, whereas those containing 35-85 wt.% are termed *modacrylics*. More than half of acrylonitrile produced in the world is consumed for the production of acrylic fibers, while the major part of the other half is used for modacrylics, such as ABS and SAN copolymers.

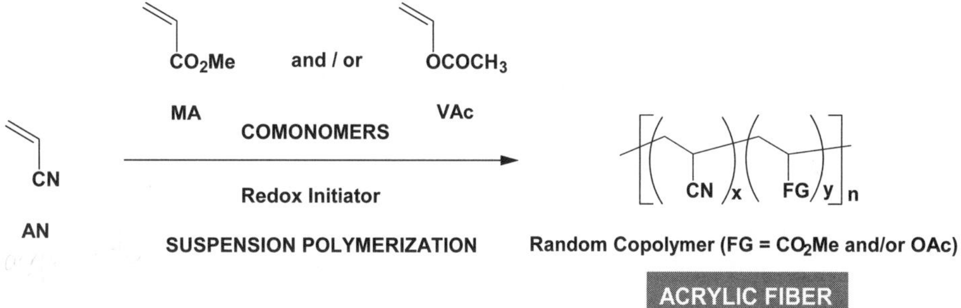

Figure 2.41. Synthesis of acrylic fibers.

The most widely used method of copolymerization of acrylonitrile with its comonomer(s) in the acrylic fibers industry is suspension (aqueous dispersion) in the presence of a redox initiator system, which effectively generates free radicals in an aqueous medium at relatively low temperatures. The most common redox system consists of ammonium or potassium persulfate (oxidizer), sodium bisulfite (reducing agent) and ferric or ferrous ion (catalyst). The best and consistent fiber physical properties are obtained when the molecular weight of the polymer is kept low ($M_w \sim$ 100,000) and the molecular weight distribution is broad (PDI ~ 3), in order to achieve the highest number of terminal functional groups (sulfate and sulfonate) that come from the initiator fragments (Figure 2.42). Because of decomposition or coloration of acrylics before melting, acrylic fibers are produced by solution spinning from a filtered N,N-dimethylformamide (DMF) or N,N-dimethylacetamide (DMAc) solution, followed by removal of the solvent, initially by heat drying and finally in a hot water bath.

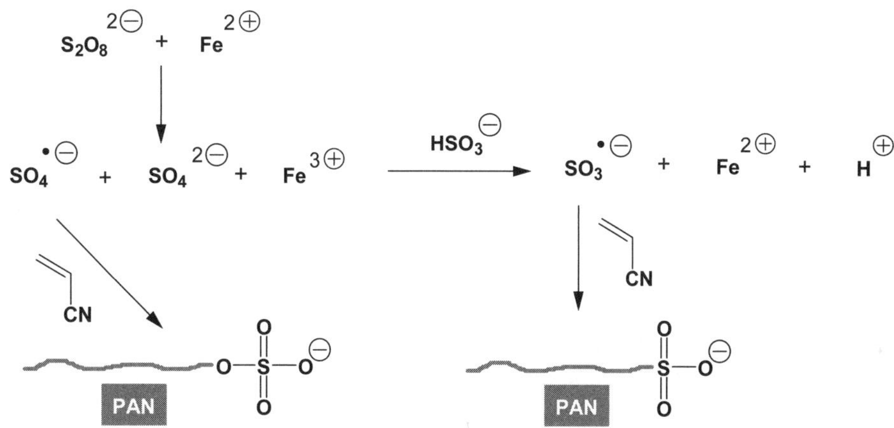

Figure 2.42. Persulfate redox initiation mechanism leading to PAN fibers with terminal hydrophilic functional groups.

The physical properties of acrylic fibers can be characterized as wool-like, with very high elongation and elastic recovery. These elastic properties rank acrylics and wool as compliant fibers, yielding fabric with a characteristically soft handle. Moisture regain, a property that has a great effect on wear comfort, at about 2.5%, is reasonably good, though not as high as that of cotton (8%) or wool (15%). This property can be enhanced by adding hydrophilic comonomers (e.g., SMAS) or by generating a porous internal structure in the fiber. Acrylics have relatively low flame resistance (LOI = 18), comparable to cotton (Table 2.2). Additional flame resistance is necessary for certain end uses, such as children's sleepwear, blankets, carpets, outdoor awnings, and drapery fabrics. This requirement is met by introducing a small proportion of vinyl chloride or vinylidene chloride during copolymerization. The most outstanding property of acrylic fibers is their strong resistance to sunlight. This makes the acrylics particularly useful for outdoor applications, such as awnings, tents, and upholstery for autos and outdoor furniture.

An important application of acrylics is in the production of carbon fibers, which are valued for their unique combination of extremely high modulus and strength and low density (Figure 2.43). Carbon fibers are manufactured by a two-stage thermal treatment of an acrylic fiber made from a very high percentage of acrylonitrile monomer (about 98%) and acrylic acid (2%).[26] The role of the few acid functionalities in the polyacrylonitrile (PAN) backbone is believed to facilitate "ladder polymer" formation

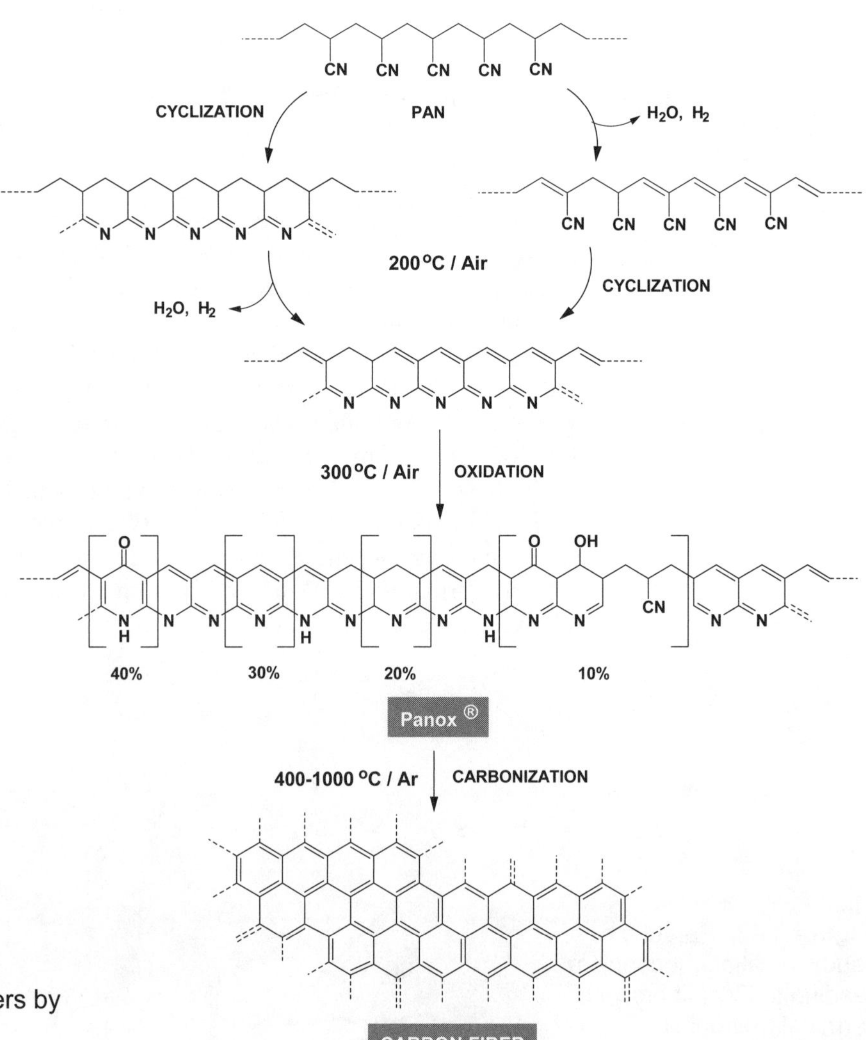

Figure 2.43. Formation of carbon fibers by thermal cyclization of PAN fibers.

during the first stage, called "oxidative stabilization" stage, which is conducted in air at temperatures between 200 and 300°C and under tension to prevent fiber shrinkage. This process involves formation of a ladder structure containing conjugated C=N double bonds along with some carbonyl groups. Prolonged heating in air leads to a color progression, resulting in a black fiber, termed Panox® (SGL Carbo, Germany), which is also useful as a flame-resistant textile. Typical applications of Panox are fire blocking fabrics for seating in aircraft and protective clothing for fire fighters and racing drivers. The stabilized fiber, Panox, is then carbonized (the second stage) in an inert atmosphere at temperatures ranging from 400 to 1000°C to produce carbon fibers. The mechanism of pyrolysis of Panox is very complex and involves many processes, such as chain scission, chain breakdown, by-products evolution or crosslinking, depending on heat treatment history.[26] The principal scission products released during pyrolysis are hydrogen cyanide, ammonia and nitrogen. Depending on the extent of pre-oxidation, various amounts of water, carbon monoxide and carbon dioxide are also formed. In addition, small quantities of hydrogen and methane are released during the carbonization process.

2.1.2.3. Acrylic Hydrogels and Superabsorbants

Hydrogels and superabsorbants are a class of polymer materials that can absorb large amounts of water or aqueous solutions without dissolving. This unique property arises due to the presence of a large numbr of hydrophilic groups, such as hydroxyl, carboxyl and amide, in a three-dimensional (physically or chemically crosslinked) polymer network which provides the strength necessary to retain the shape of the swollen polymer matrix. Thus, the amount of water absorbed can be controlled by adjusting the degree of crosslinking and the number or type of hydrophilic groups. If the amount of absorbed water is between 10-50 wt.%, the materials are classified as *hydrogels*. The dry hydrogel is called a xerogel or dry gel. The superabsorbants normally absorb water in excess of 100 wt.%.

The major applications of hydrogels are in the areas of contact lenses and drug delivery systems. Figure 2.44 shows the structures of widely used monomers and crosslinkers for hydrogel production. High tear strength, good oxygen permeation and high optical clarity are three major design criteria for contact lenses. Hydroxyethyl methacrylate (HEMA), hydroxyethoxyethyl methacrylate (HEEMA) and glyceryl methacrylate (GMA) are widely used as the basic hydrophilic monomers which provide excellent mechanical strength and optical clarity. Some percentage of silicone-based compounds, either as a monomer or crosslinker, is also incorporated to enhance oxygen permeability. Among the crosslinkers, ethylene glycol dimethacrylate (EGDMA) is most common, while N,N'-methylenebisacrylamide (BIS) is extensively used for biodegradable drug delivery systems, because it degrades in the presence of water to produce formaldehyde. Biodegradable hydrogels are useful in the delivery of drugs with poor water solubility or high molecular weight drugs, such as peptide or proteins.

The major applications of superabsorbant polymers (SAPs) are in the area of disposable hygiene products, such as baby diapers and other absorbent personal care products. The monomers and crosslinkers useful for making SAPs are depicted in Figure 2.45. Acrylic acid (AA) accounts for about 80-85% of the raw materials in the manufacture of SAPs. Other important monomers include methacrylic acid (MAA), acrylamide (Am), 2-hydroxyethylmethacrylamide (HEMAm), N-vinyl pyrrolidinone (NVP) and 2-acrylamido-2-methylpropanesulfonic acid (AMPS). BIS and ethylene glycol diacrylate (EGDA) are two of the most prominent crosslinkers.

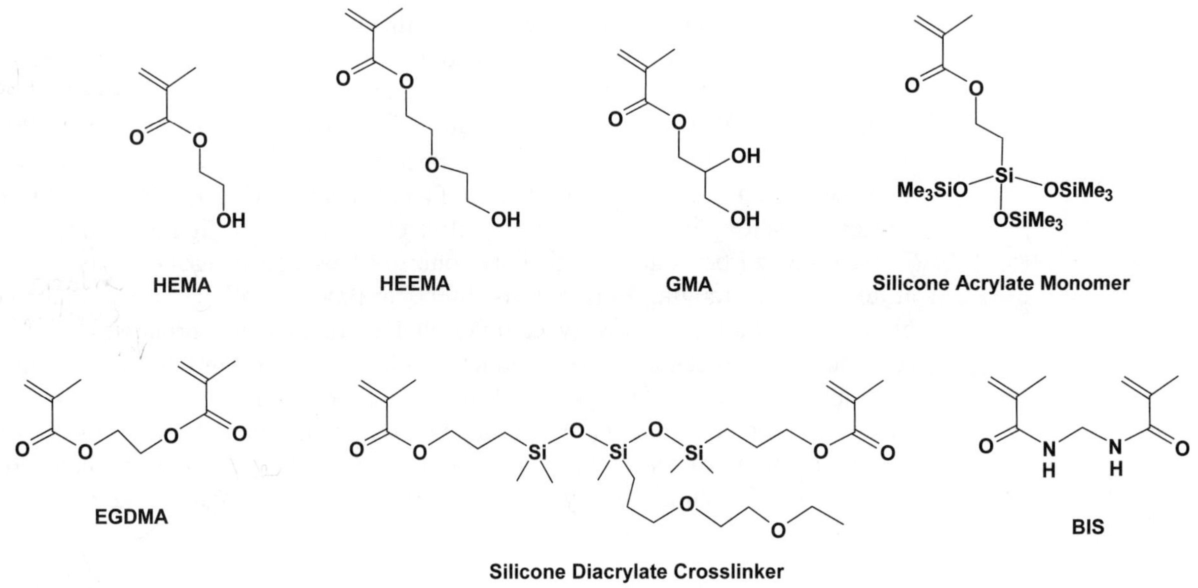

HEMA
HEEMA
GMA
Silicone Acrylate Monomer
EGDMA
Silicone Diacrylate Crosslinker
BIS

Figure 2.44. Structures of common monomers and crosslinkers for hydrogels.

AA
MAA
Am
HEMAm
AMPS
NVP
BIS
EGDA

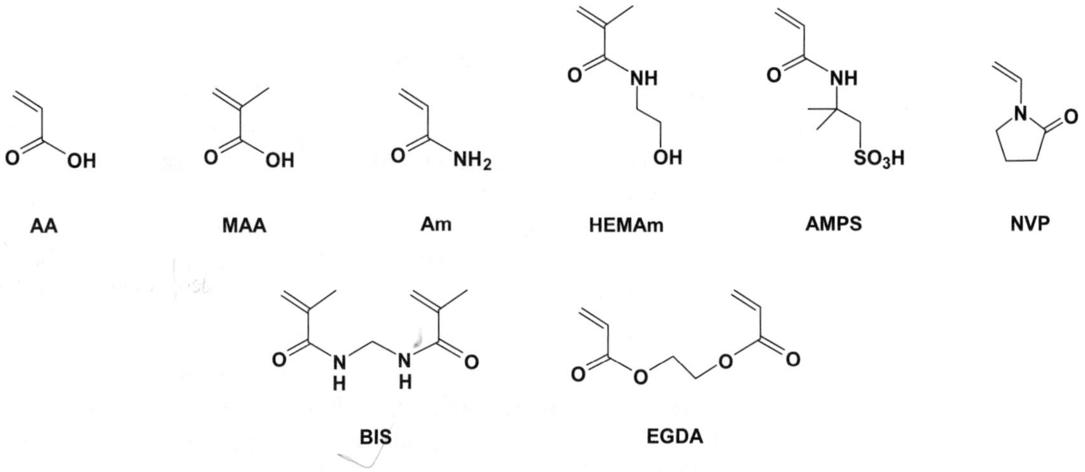

Figure 2.45. Structures of common monomers and crosslinkers for SAPs.

Hydrogels and SAPs are manufactured by free-radical polymerization of appropriate monomer(s) and crosslinker(s) using thermal initiators, such as AIBN and BPO. Suspension polymerization is the preferred route especially when droplets or spheres of the hydrogels or SAPs are desired. After polymerization, the gel particles are dried by hot air, followed by grinding or milling to increase the surface area of the product. A promising new technique for synthesizing uniform polymeric networks in a rapid fashion is *frontal polymerization* (FP).[27] This novel methodology involves the conversion of monomer to polymer in a localized reaction zone that propagates due to the interplay of thermal conduction and temperature-dependent reaction rates. As shown in Figure 2.46, hydrogels prepared by FP, are superior (uniform pore size distribution) to commonly used suspension polymerization. The hydrogels display a morphology in which the microporous structure involves a dispersed microaggregated phase.

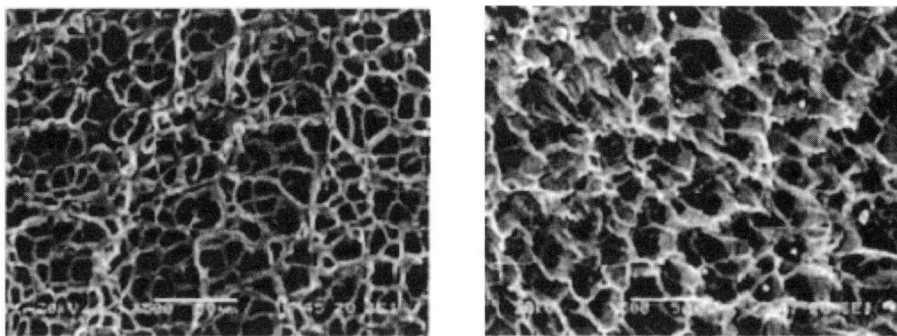

Figure 2.46. Scanning electron micrographs of hydrogels produced by frontal polymerization (Left) and conventional batch polymerization at 60°C (Right). Field of view = (220 x 280) μm^2. *Reproduced with kind permission of the American Chemical Society.*

2.1.2.4. Acrylic Adhesives and Coatings

Adhesives and glues are substances that are capable of bonding two solid materials together at their surfaces. Acrylic adhesives are primarily based on of a mixture containing monomers (viz. acrylic acid and methacrylic acid), crosslinker (e.g., ethylene glycol dimethacrylate) and initiator (e.g., hydroperoxides). Besides metallic products, acrylic adhesives are widely used to bond products like plastics, ceramics and fiberglass. There are many advantages of acrylic adhesives, since they resist severe environmental conditions, bond with minimal surface penetration, bond oily metal alloys with little penetration, offer a faster cure at room temperature, and above all, they are user friendly. Acrylic adhesives are used extensively for packaging in many industries. One of the best known and strongest acrylic adhesives is "Super Glue", or "Krazy Glue". This adhesive is based on cyanoacrylates, which spontaneously polymerize in moist air (Figure 2.47).

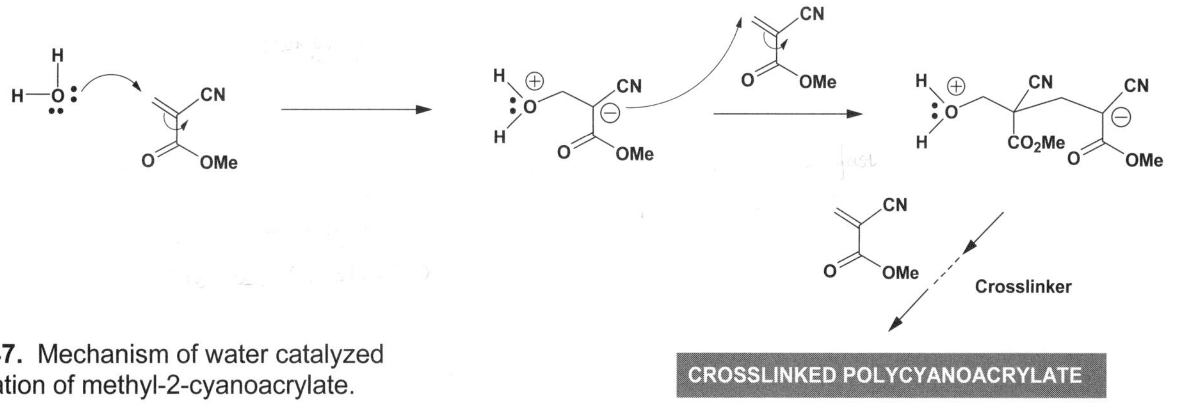

Figure 2.47. Mechanism of water catalyzed polymerization of methyl-2-cyanoacrylate.

Acrylic coatings are based on acrylic and methacrylic ester latex copolymers and are prepared by emulsion polymerization (Figure 2.48). They are attractive in formulating high quality interior and exterior paints or other coating films because of their excellent durability, toughness, optical clarity, and color retention. Copolymers of acrylics, such as vinyl-acrylics and styrene-acrylics are also used for high-performance exterior applications.

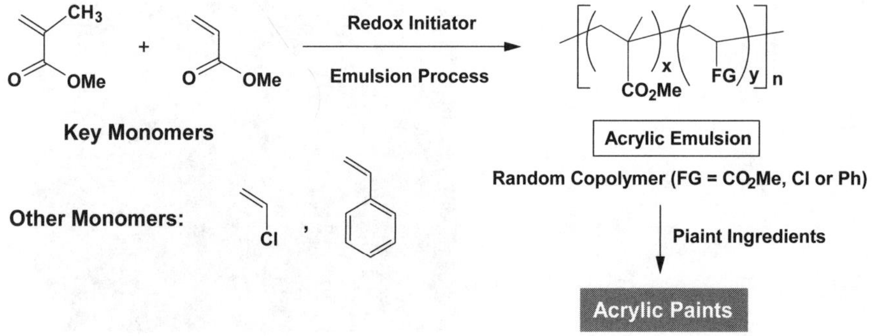

Redox Initiator
Emulsion Process
Key Monomers
Other Monomers:
Acrylic Emulsion
Random Copolymer (FG = CO_2Me, Cl or Ph)
Piaint Ingredients
Acrylic Paints

Figure 2.48. Preparation of acrylic paints.

2.1.3. Vinyls and Vinyl Copolymers

In industry, "vinyl" is used as a shorthand name for polyvinyl chloride (PVC). Most commonly, when a product is referred to as "vinyl", it is comprised primarily of PVC. Occasionally, it also may refer to polyvinylidene chloride (PVDC). In chemistry, however, the term "vinyl" actually has a broader meaning, encompassing a range of different thermoplastic materials, viz. PVC, PVDC, polyvinyl acetate (PVAc), polyvinyl butyral (PVB), and ethylene-vinyl acetate (EVA) copolymers (Figure 2.49). PVC is the second-largest (after polyethylene) and most versatile of all thermoplastics. The construction industry accounts for over 70 percent of its demand. Nearly all (98 percent) of vinyl chloride monomer (VCM) is converted into PVC. It is usually plasticized with low or medium molecular weight materials, such as dioctyl phthalate, trioctyl phosphate, and poly(propylene glycol) esters. The properties can be finely tuned from rigid to soft and flexible by varying the plasticizer content from a few percent to more than 60%. When blended with a high proportion of plasticizer, PVC becomes soft and pliable, providing the useful rubber-like flexible tubing to be found in every well-equipped laboratory. PVC piping is the most widely used plastic piping material because it is environmentally friendly, possesses long service life, is easy to install and handle, and is corrosion resistant, cost effective and widely accepted by codes. Because of environmental concerns relating to the use of PVC, some of the non-chlorinated vinyls are now beginning to be used as direct substitutes for PVC. For example, EVA (industrially familiar by the name "acetate") has been in use for several years as tough films, wire coating, toys and athletic shoes. In the building industry, PVB is now beginning to be employed to replace PVC in carpet backing, as well as in the manufacture of laminated safety glasses for automotive and construction applications. PVAc is extensively used in paints and adhesives, such as white glue.

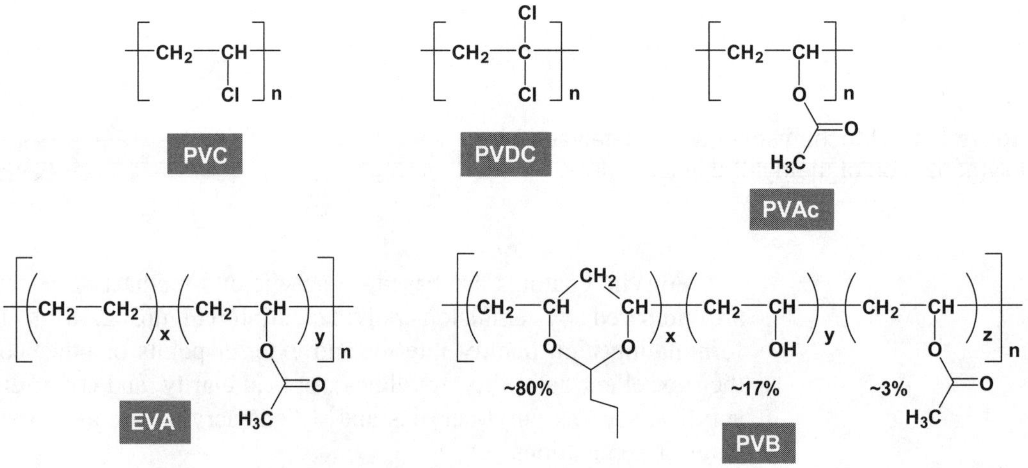

PVC PVDC PVAc
EVA
~80% ~17% ~3%
PVB

Figure 2.49. Structures of most important vinyl homopolymers and copolymers.

Vinyl acetate monomer (VAM) is a key compound for the production of a variety of useful PVC substitutes. Approximately 80 percent of all VAM produced in the world is used to make PVAc and PVA as well as PVB and EVA copolymers. All vinyl homopolymers are manufactured exclusively by the free-radical mechanism, employing suspension and emulsion polymerization methods. Solution polymerization of vinyl acetate is carried out mainly as an intermediate step in the manufacture of PVA and PVB (Figure 2.50). Since vinyl alcohol does not exist because of its rapid tautomerization to acetaldehyde, PVA is manufactured by hydrolysis of PVAc via a base-catalyzed ester interchange with methanol, with elimination of methyl acetate. PVA has excellent film forming and adhesive properties as well as providing good resistance to oil, grease and many solvents. Major applications include use as textile warp sizing, and as a protective colloid for PVAc-based adhesive products. Historically, the value of a warp sizing material has been related to its effectiveness in protecting yarns from breakage due to the forces of weaving, such as stretch, strain and abrasion. PVB is manufactured by reacting PVA with n-butyraldehyde in the presence of an acid catalyst. PVB consists of about 80% of a ring structure formed by intramolecular acetalization.

EVA copolymers resemble elastomeric materials in softness and flexibility, yet can be processed like other thermoplastics. As the amount of vinyl acetate in the copolymer increases, the level of crystallinity found in polythene alone is reduced from about 60% to 10%. This yields products ranging from materials similar to LDPE to flexible rubbers. In fact, EVA has little or no odor and is competitive with rubber and vinyl products in many electrical applications. Common grades usually contain 5-40 wt.% vinyl acetate. Clarity, flexibility, toughness and solvent solubility increase with increasing vinyl acetate content. Of particular note is the retention of flexibility of EVA rubber grades down to -70°C and because they are copolymers, problems due to plasticizer migration are not experienced. EVA copolymers containing 5-40 wt.% vinyl acetate are made by processes similar to those used to make LDPE under high pressure. A medium grade, ~45-50 wt.% vinyl acetate copolymers with rubber-like properties, is prepared by solution polymerization in tert-butyl alcohol. The 75-95 wt.% vinyl acetate emulsion copolymers are produced in emulsion processes under ethylene pressure.

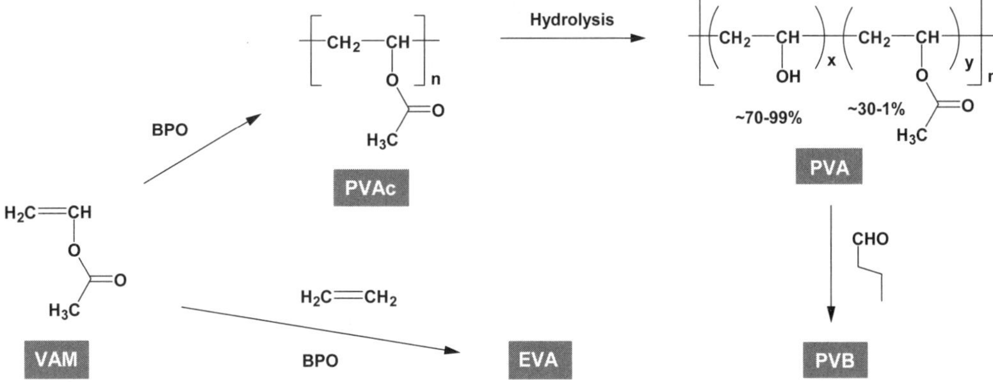

Figure 2.50. Applications of VAM in producing chlorine-free useful polymers.

2.1.4. Styrenics

Styrene homopolymers and copolymers that possess high styrene content are collectively called *styrenics*. The following classification tree depicts most important members of this family. Styrenics find application across a broad range of market segments, such as appliance, automotive, consumer electronics, foam sheets, packaging, toys, and housewares. Brief discussion on each member follows.

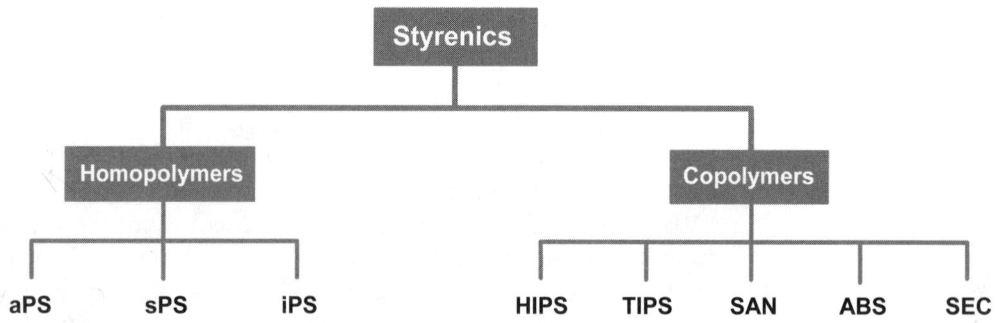

2.1.4.1. Styrenic Homopolymers

The main commercial styrene homopolymer is atactic polystyrene (commonly called polystyrene or PS), which is highly amorphous and exhibits high optical transparency. By contrast, stereoregular styrene homopolymers, syndiotactic polystyrene (sPS) and isotactic polystyrene (iPS), are highly crystalline and display superior thermal and mechanical properties compared with PS.

2.1.4.1a. Atactic Polystyrene (PS)

PS is the most consumed member of the styrenics family. It can be prepared in high molecular weight (M_w = 2-4 x 10^5) with a negligible level of residual monomer, which makes PS very attractive for food packaging applications. Styrene is one of the few monomers that can be polymerized by free-radical, cationic, anionic and coordination mechanisms. Each of the mechanisms has its own advantages and disadvantages. For example, high purity monomer is essential for cationic, anionic and coordination mechanisms. High molecular weight polymers are difficult to make by cationic polymerization because of the instability of polystyrene carbocation, resulting in fast termination (see Figure 1.51 in Chapter-1). The anionic mechanism, especially, produces polymers with narrow polydispersity ($M_w/M_n < 1.1$). All mechanisms yield polymers with a high degree of random orientation of the phenyl group relative to the backbone (i.e., atactic), except for coordination polymerization, which provides access to high melting crystalline tactic PS. Free-radical polymerization, although producing polymers with broad polydispersity ($M_w/M_n > 2$), is the preferred industrial method. The primary reason is that the process does not require high purity monomer, nor is it necessary to remove initiator residues which have a minimal effect on polymer properties. However, anionic and cationic polymerizations are used exclusively in the preparation of styrene-butadiene block copolymers and low molecular weight PS, respectively.

The first commercial manufacture of PS was by spontaneous or thermal polymerization of styrene. When heated in excess of 100°C, styrene acts as its own initiator (Figure 2.51). The pathways of polymerization are believed to involve the formation of a 1,4-diradical (**A**), via the Flory Mechanism[28] and/or a reactive Diels-Alder adduct (**B**), followed by a molecular assisted homolysis between the adduct and another styrene molecule (Mayo Mechanism).[29] Evidence favoring these mechanisms includes isolation/structure determination of the by-products/oligomers and isotope effects. At present, most PS is produced via continuous bulk polymerization with the aid of peroxide initiation. The use of peroxide initiators leads to both process and product advantages, such as increased polymerization rate, narrower polydispersity and most importantly, absence of dimers and trimers, which constitute 1-2% of product by spontaneous polymerization.

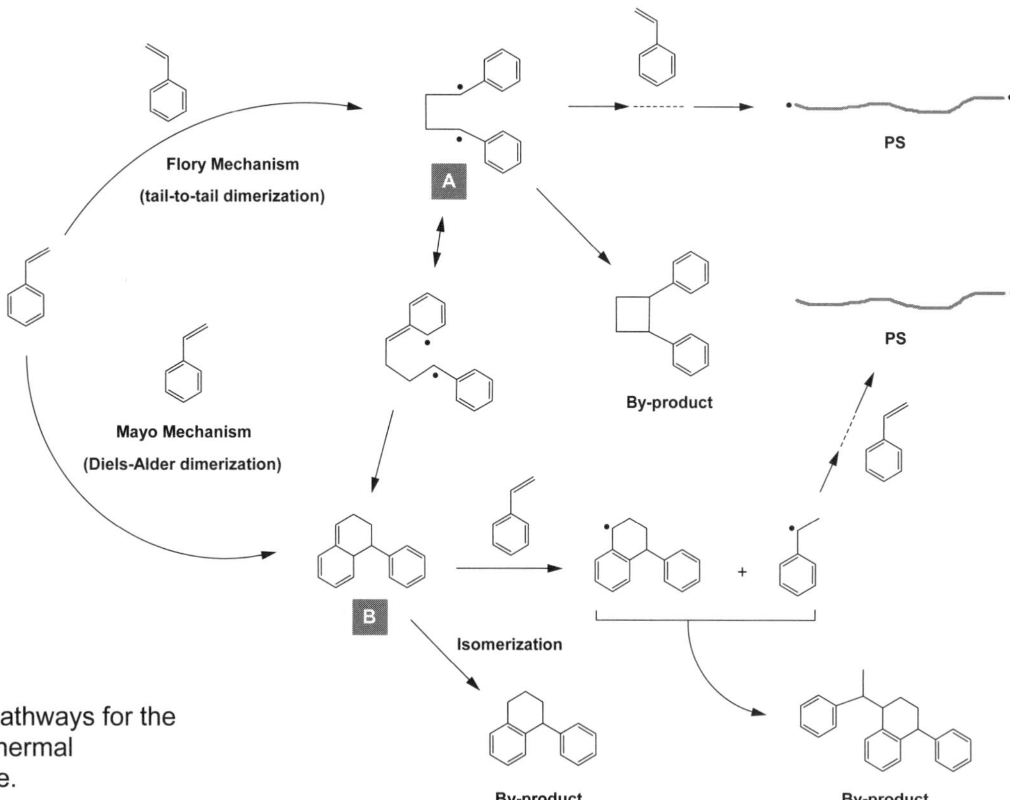

Figure 2.51. Possible pathways for the formation of PS during thermal polymerization of styrene.

It is noteworthy that Styrofoam® (Dow Chemical Company) and related polystyrene-based foam products (e.g., extruded board, extruded sheet and injection-molded structural foams) are produced by mixing volatile liquid blowing agent, such as CO_2 or 1,1,1,2-tetrafluoroethane, with polystyrene under melt and/or high pressure, followed by extrusion and expansion through a die. By contrast, polystyrene loose-fill packaging materials are manufactured by multiple steam expansion of *expanded polystyrene* (EPS) which is produced by impregnating 5-8% of pentane during suspension polymerization. Expansion with steam produces low-density foam in the shape of an S, an 8, or a hollow shell.

2.1.4.1b. Syndiotactic Polystyrene (sPS)

This is a relatively new material having the same T_g as atactic polystyrene in the range of 100°C. However, unlike the atactic form, prepared by free radical or anionic initiators, sPS is a semicrystalline polymer produced by metallocene complexes. The unique features of sPS include rapid crystallization rate, high dimensional stability and high melting point (~275°C, which is the highest melting point of all metallocene homopolymers). These attributes, coupled with its low cost, make it attractive as an alternative to expensive engineering thermoplastics, such as polyamides. Half-sandwich titanocenes or mono-sterically bulky indenyl ligand, along with MAO as cocatalyst, are especially active for the production of sPS with a high pentad (>98% *rrrr*) structure (Figure 2.52).[30] Interestingly, very efficient catalytic behavior in the formation of sPS was also obtained in the presence of metallocene with tetradentate electron-rich trianionic triethoxyamine co-ligand.[31] The mechanism of syndiospecific polymerization of styrene is regarded as a chain-end control process with a partial stabilization of the transition state by the π-bond of the α-phenyl group of the polymer chain in an agostic fashion.

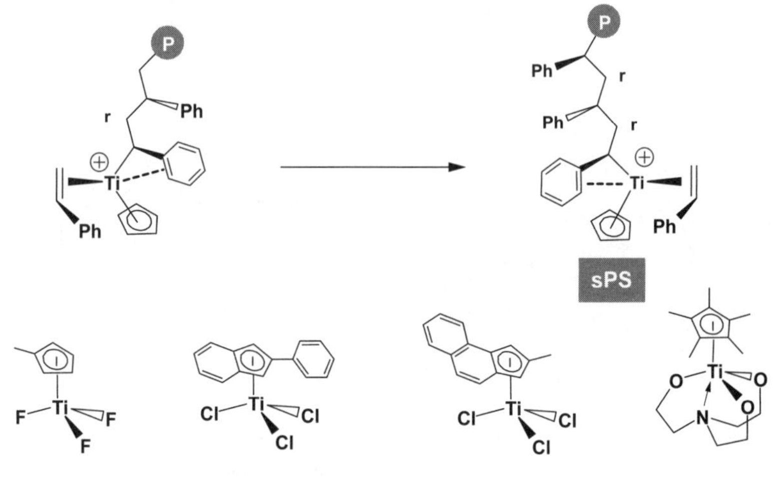

Figure 2.52. Chain-end control driven syndiospecific polymerization of styrene and structures of representative highly effective metallocene catalysts.

2.1.4.1c. Isotactic Polystyrene (iPS)

iPS melts around 230°C and exhibits uncharacteristic melt behavior compared with stereoregular polyolefins and sPS. If a sample of iPS is quenched from its melt, the product is almost amorphous. However, a crystalline sample can be prepared by annealing the sample for a longer time slightly below T_m. This slow rate of crystallization is what has kept iPS from becoming a commercially important polymer. While sPS is produced by half-sandwich titanocenes, iPS, known for almost half a century, is best produced by heterogeneous Ziegler-Natta catalysis (e.g., $TiCl_4$-$AlEt_3$). At this time, there are no metallocenes that can yield high molecular weight iPS with high stereoregularity (>98% *mmmm* pentad). However, a new family of promising non-metallocene Group-IVB metal complexes, e.g., **35**, has been developed for isospecific polymcrization of styrene (Figure 2.53).[32]

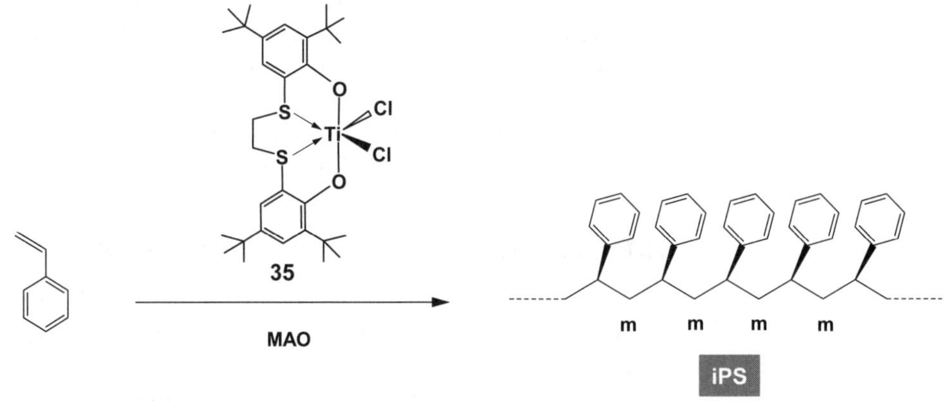

Figure 2.53. Isospecific polymerization of styrene with a non-metallocene titanium complex.

2.1.4.2. Styrenic Copolymers

Styrene can be copolymerized with a variety of monomers, viz., acrylonitrile, butadiene, α-methylstyrene, acrylic acid and maleic anhydride to produce a range of commercially important polymers. Important styrene copolymers include high impact polystyrene (HIPS), poly(styrene-*co*-acrylonitrile) (SAN), and acrylonitrile-butadiene-styrene terpolymer (ABS). Block copolymers of styrene, such as polystyrene-polybutadiene-polystyrene triblock (SBS) and that of random copolymers, such as styrene-butadiene rubber (SBR), are also very useful styrenics and are discussed under elastomers in Section 2.3. Because of good surface quality, high dimensional stability and constant mechanical properties almost up to the softening temperature, most styrenic copolymers, especially HIPS, SAN and ABS meet almost all of the requirements of engineering thermoplastics. By varying the styrene content of these materials, the properties can be adjusted. For example, for SAN, increasing the content of styrene improves stiffness, clarity and processability. The presence of an elastomeric phase in ABS and HIPS improves the impact resistance for engineering applications. Styrenic copolymers can be processed by all the common methods, including injection molding, extrusion and blow molding.

2.1.4.2a. High Impact Polystyrene (HIPS)

PS is too brittle for applications requiring high toughness. There are primarily two approaches to obtain toughened PS. The first involves the incorporation of dispersed rubber particles in a continuous PS matrix, resulting in increased energy absorption during failure, and forms the basis of toughening in HIPS and ABS. The second approach involves the preparation of styrenic block copolymers, created to produce thermoplastic elastomers (*vide infra*). The manufacturing process of HIPS is rather peculiar and is produced by bulk, solution or emulsion polymerization of styrene containing 3-10 wt.% dissolved polybutadiene (PB). Styrene-butadiene rubber (SBR) is also used occasionally as the rubber phase in place of PB. Thus, HIPS is basically a blend of PS and a graft copolymer (PB-*g*-PS) of butadiene and styrene. As shown in Figure 2.54, HIPS displays characteristic phase morphologies, which constitute substructured "salami-like" microphase domains (1-5 μm) of the graft copolymer PB-*g*-PS dispersed in a continuous phase of PS, because PS and PB are incompatible.[33] The domains are not purely elastomeric, but are heavily filled with PS subdomains (see the cartoon). The PB forms only thin lamellar microphases (black portion in the SEM picture), on the outside of the domains and on the inside, between the subdomains. HIPS owes its superior impact strength to these elastomeric microphases.

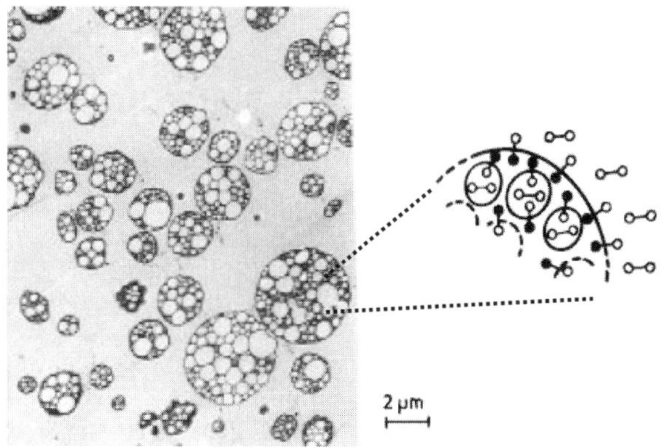

Figure 2.54. *Left:* Salami-like structures in commercial HIPS. *Right:* Schematic of the composition of a microphase where ○-○ is PS (white phase) and ●-○ is graft copolymer PB-*g*-PS (black phase). *Reproduced with kind permission of the American Chemical Society.*

Peroxide initiators, such as *t*-butyl peroxyoxalate, acetyl peroxide, and/or benzoyl peroxide are typically used for the manufacture of HIPS. The free-radicals generated during polymerization attack not only the styrene monomers (leading to PS), but also the PB chains (leading to graft copolymer, PB-*g*-PS). The competition of homopolymerization and graft copolymerization is parameterized by the selectivity of the initiator radicals and is optimized so that the majority of the PB chains contain at least one graft. For example, the t-butoxy and acyloxy free-radicals easily initiate styrene monomer and add to the double bonds of PB rubber, while methyl free-radicals produced from *t*-butyl peroxyoxalate have a strong propensity to abstract allylic H-atoms (Figure 2.55).

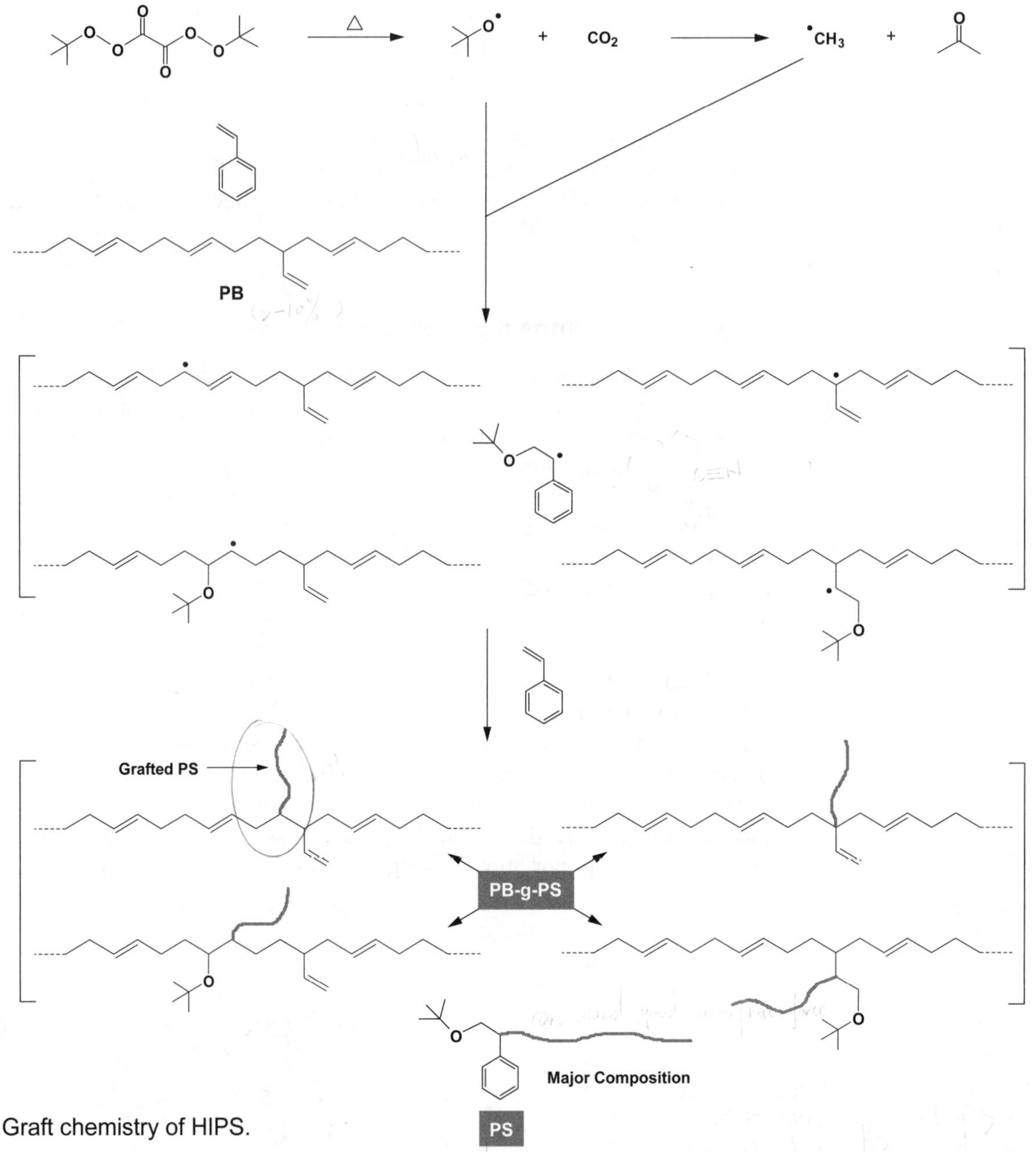

Figure 2.55. Graft chemistry of HIPS.

2.1.4.2b. Transparent Impact Polystyrene (TIPS)

For many applications, optical clarity is a significant advantage. Unlike PS, which is 90% transparent, HIPS polymers are opaque due to scattering of light when passing through two phases (PB-*g*-PS and PS) having different refractive indices. There are two common approaches to introduce transparency into HIPS. The first involves adjustment of the refractive indices of the two phases so that they are nearly the same. Since the refractive indices of PS and PB are 1.59 and 1.51, respectively, the matching can be accomplished by either (a) raising the refractive index of PB through copolymerization with refractive index enhancing comonomers with butadiene, such as styrene, vinylbiphenyl and vinylnaphthalene, or (b) reducing the refractive index of PS through copolymerization with refractive index reducing comonomers with styrene, such as methyl methacrylate. The second approach requires downsizing the sizes of the PS and

PB phases to <20 nm, i.e., much lower than that of the wavelength of visible light. This approach is commercially more receptive and involves physical blending of high styrene content (~75%) specifically tailored styrene-butadiene block copolymer with PS. Thus, the preparation of TIPS (physical blending) is significantly different from that of HIPS (*in situ* grafting). The block copolymers used in the preparation of TIPS are prepared by living anionic polymerization and possess a radial or star block structure with PB at the core and PS at the tip of the arms. The detailed synthesis of star polymers is discussed later in this chapter under tailor-made polymers (Section 2.4.3.3).

2.1.4.2c. Poly(styrene-*co*-acrylonitrile) (SAN)

SAN copolymers are random linear amorphous copolymers, and possess inherent transparency of PS, including superior heat resistance, high load-bearing strength (due to relatively high tensile and flexural strengths), excellent gloss and chemical resistance. These properties, along with reasonable price, provide advantages over other competing transparent thermoplastics, such as PS, acrylics and polycarbonate (PC). SAN copolymers are widely used in housewares, appliances, interior automotive lenses, and medical parts. Commercially, SAN copolymers are manufactured by copolymerization of styrene with 24-30 wt.% acrylonitrile via emulsion, suspension or bulk process using free-radical initiators (Figure 2.56). The kinetics of polymerization is somewhat complex due to the differences in reactivities of styrene and acrylonitrile radicals toward their monomers. The situation is kept under control by batch or continuous addition of styrene (faster reacting monomer) to the reactor.

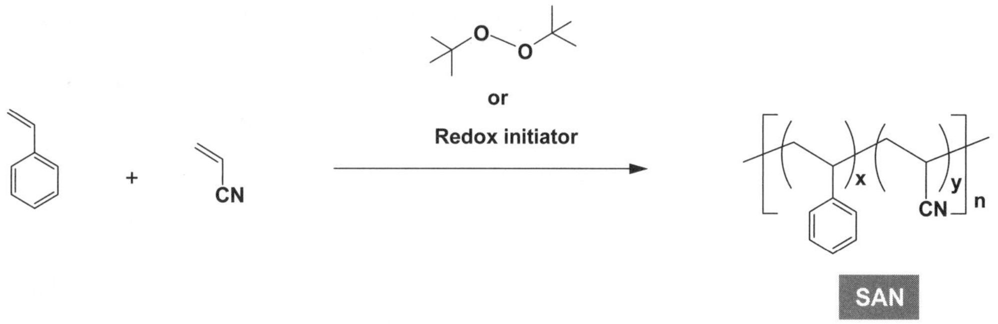

or

Redox initiator

CN

x y CN n

SAN

Figure 2.56. Synthesis of SAN copolymers.

2.1.4.2d. Acrylonitrile-Butadiene-Styrene (ABS)

The creation of ABS is a great example of tailoring of polymer properties through copolymerization and polymerization technology. The three monomers play distinct roles, e.g., butadiene provides the rubbery phase which introduces toughness. Styrene imparts rigidity and processability, while acrylonitrile contributes chemical resistance. For over 50 years, ABS has dominated as the most versatile general-purpose polymer that can be customized by varying the ratio of comonomers to obtain products with a wide range of mechanical and flow properties. Similar to HIPS, ABS is a polymer blend and comprised of a particulate rubber, usually SAN-grafted PB or SBR, dispersed in a thermoplastic matrix of SAN (contrary to PS bulk matrix in HIPS). The presence of SAN polymer chains grafted to the rubber particles makes the rubber compatible with the continuous SAN matrix. It is noteworthy that ABS is blended with polycarbonate (PC) to produce a material which has excellent low temperature toughness and is used for the manufacture of automotive body panels.

Emulsion is the most practiced method for production of ABS, although the bulk method is often used. Butadiene monomer is first converted to polybutadiene latex, which is then pumped into a reactor containing styrene, acrylonitrile, emulsifiers and free-radical initiators. After completion of polymerization, ABS is transferred to a coagulator for isolation of solid product. The grafting mechanism of ABS can be viewed as similar to HIPS, as described in Figure 2.55 (see p. 32 for structure). The only difference is ungrafted SAN (continuous phase) is formed concurrently with SAN-grafted PB (PB-*g*-SAN). The phase morphology of emulsion polymerized ABS is similar to that of HIPS, except that the size of SAN embedded rubber microdomains is relatively smaller (0.2-0.5 μm) compared to that of the bulk method (1-2 μm). Depending on the applications, the comonomer ratios vary from 15-35 wt.% acrylonitrile, 10-30 wt.% butadiene and 40-60 wt.% styrene. Most general-purpose ABS materials contain SAN with 20-30% acrylonitrile content, whereas improved chemical resistance ABS grades employ SAN with acrylonitrile content of about 35%. Standard ABS grades are opaque because of the refractive index mismatch between the two phases. Transparent grades are prepared by increasing the refractive index of the rubber phase through the use of styrene-butadiene rubber, and decreasing the refractive index of the matrix phase through terpolymerization with methyl methacrylate (MMA).

2.1.4.2e. Styrene-Ethylene Copolymers (SECs)

The copolymerization of styrene and ethylene by classical heterogeneous Ziegler-Natta catalysts, free-radical initiators, or metallocene catalysts that are effective for syndiospecific styrene polymerization (Figure 2.52), is not productive because of low yield. Moreover, the composition of the resulting polymers is primarily a mixture of homopolyethylene, homopolystyrene, and varying amounts of styrene-ethylene copolymers with no regio- or stereoregular styrene-styrene sequences. As mentioned earlier, sPS is a very promising new polymer material for a large number of industrial applications. However, a drawback that may limit the scope of applications of sPS is its brittleness. It is postulated that the toughness of sPS may be improved by introducing a small proportion of ethylene comonomer, and therefore, the synthesis of styrene-ethylene copolymers (SECs) having syndiotactic styrene-styrene sequences are of particular interest. Recently, a great deal of success has been achieved with half-metallocene complexes (Figure 2.57). For example, catalyst **36** along with one equivalent of borate cocatalyst, $[Ph_3C][B(C_6F_5)_4]$, is not only good for producing highly active and syndiospecific polystyrene homopolymer, but surprisingly, excellent for styrene-ethylene copolymerization, with great selectivity.[34] The most important features of this copolymerization include high regioselectivity (no tail-to-tail or head-to-head styrene sequences) and formation of no homopolymers. Moreover, the styrene content in the copolymers, which consist of syndiotactic styrene-styrene sequences (blocks) connected by repeated ethylene units, can be easily controlled simply by changing the styrene feed under 1 atm of ethylene, without affecting the microstructure composition of the resulting copolymers.

As shown in Figure 2.58, a quite different promising synthetic route has been developed to obtain SECs with well defined sPS and PE multiblocks. The first step involves the preparation of styrene-butadiene block copolymers (sPS-*b*-PB) using MAO-activated $CpTiCl_3$.[35,36] These copolymers contain highly stereoregular sPS blocks, spanned by polybutadiene (PB) blocks, which consist primarily of *cis*-1,4-butadiene units with a small proportion (~11 mol %) of isolated 1,2-butadiene. These block copolymers were then quantitatively converted to so called “styrene-1-butene-ethylene terpolymers” (sPS-*b*-PE) by selective hydrogenation using *p*-

toluenesulfonhydrazide (THS) in refluxing toluene. These new series of thermoplastic materials possess the crystallinity and melting points of the sPS and PE blocks which can be carefully controlled by regulating the amount of each monomer in the copolymer.

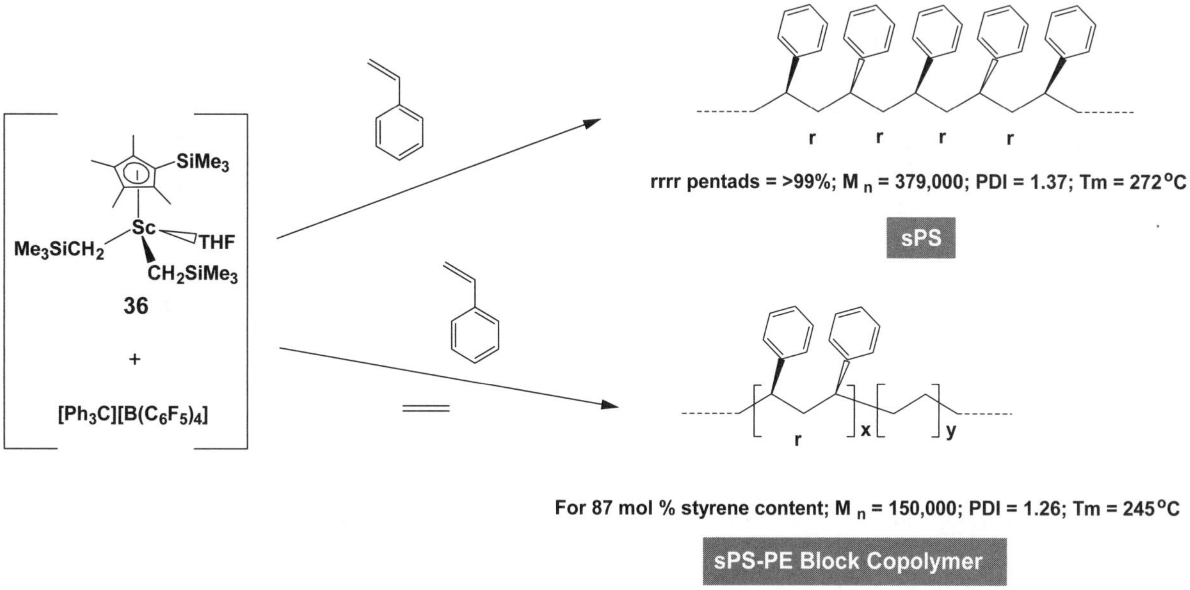

rrrr pentads = >99%; M_n = 379,000; PDI = 1.37; Tm = 272°C

sPS

For 87 mol % styrene content; M_n = 150,000; PDI = 1.26; Tm = 245°C

sPS-PE Block Copolymer

Figure 2.57. Syndiospecific copolymerization of styrene with ethylene.

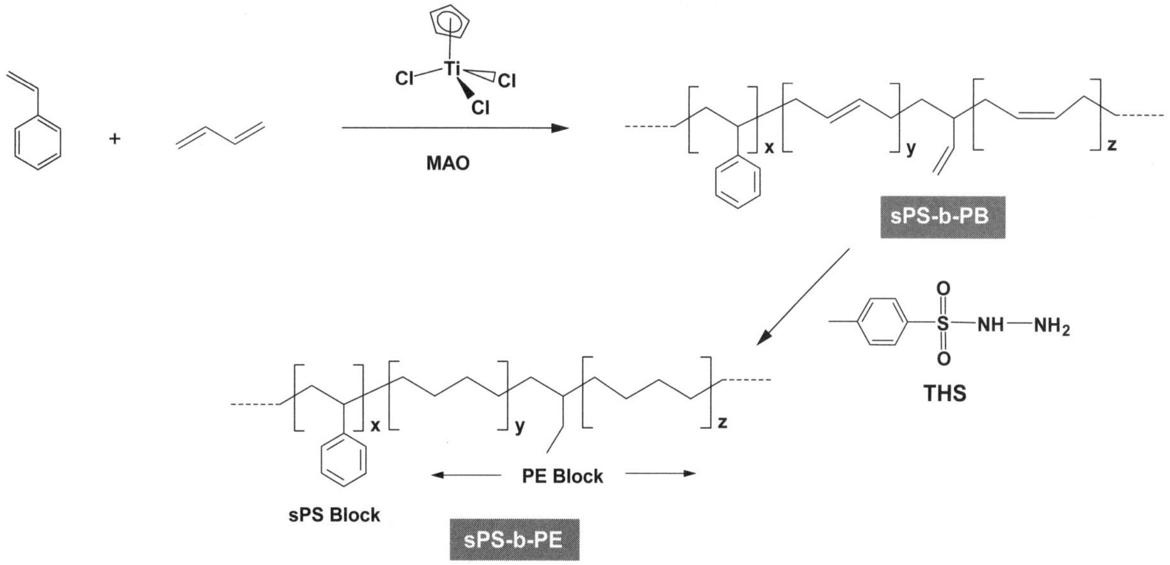

Figure 2.58. Synthesis of sPS-PE multiblock copolymers.

An efficient synthesis of SECs with random (occasional styrene-styrene sequences)/alternating microstructure containing 20-55 mol percent styrene content is also of industrial importance. These copolymers exhibit a single T_g (18°C and 36°C for 23 and 55 mol percent styrene content, respectively) and possess elastomeric properties that are attractive for films, foams, and compatibilizers for PS and α-olefin blends, and as modifiers for bitumens and asphalts. The structures of a few notable catalysts are shown in Figure 2.59.[37,38] Although no regiospecificity or stereocontrol is obtained, both catalysts **37** and **38**, in the presence of MAO, exhibit high activity and produce high molecular weight polymers with unimodal molecular weight distribution. Constrained geometry catalysts, such as **39**, have also been successfully employed in the synthesis of *pseudo*-random SECs. The open ligand environment readily allows the incorporation of bulky comonomers, but precludes the formation of styrene homopolymers. Equally important is the fact that ethylene homopolymers are not observed. However, these catalysts are only capable of producing styrene-ethylene copolymers that contain up to 50 mol % of stereoirregular styrene units. Surprisingly, catalyst **40**, activated by MAO, produces block copolymers in which the PS blocks are isotactic.[39]

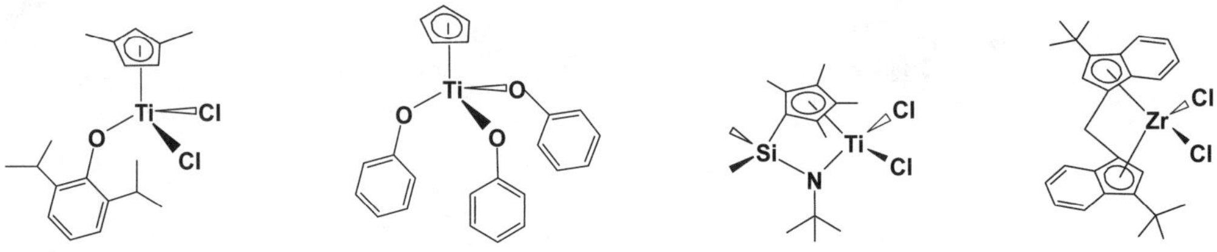

37 38 39 40

Figure 2.59. Structures of catalysts suitable for the synthesis of SECs with random/ alternating microstructures.

2.2. POLYETHERS, POLYESTERS, POLYURETHANES AND POLYSILOXANES

While the previous section was devoted primarily to a variety of chain-growth polymers in which the main chain is composed of carbon-carbon bonds, this section will focus on polymers containing heteroatoms in the main chain. Although not all the polymers discussed in this section are for general-purpose use, they are grouped into one category because most of their primary commercial methods involve step-growth polymerization and synthetic similarity. Cationic and anionic techniques are also employed to produce a few of these polymers.

2.2.1. Polyethers

Among the industrially significant aliphatic polyethers, polyethylene glycol (PEG) and polyethylene oxide (PEO) are most important. PEG and PEO are polymers having an identical structural repeat unit except for chain length. Thus, PEG refers to an oligomer or polymer with low molecular weight, while PEO is used for higher molecular weights. PEG generally is a liquid while PEO is a semicrystalline low-melting solid (T_m ~65°C). Previously well-known aliphatic polyethers, such as polytrimethylene oxide (better known as polyoxetane, POX), and polytetrahydrofuran (PTHF) currently have no significant commercial applications. However, their hydroxyl terminated oligomers are very important as precursor monomers for producing other useful polymers (Figure 2.60). For instance, low molecular weight PTHF (1,000-2,000), commonly called poly(tetramethylene ether) glycol, PTMEG, is primarily used to incorporate the chain segments in elastomeric polyurethane-based Spandex fibers (Lycra®, Dupont), castable polyurethanes and thermoplastic polyesters (*vide infra*). PEG and POX glycol (POXG) are also very useful as monomers for block copolymers. PEG is non-toxic and is used in a variety of products, such as laxatives and skin creams.

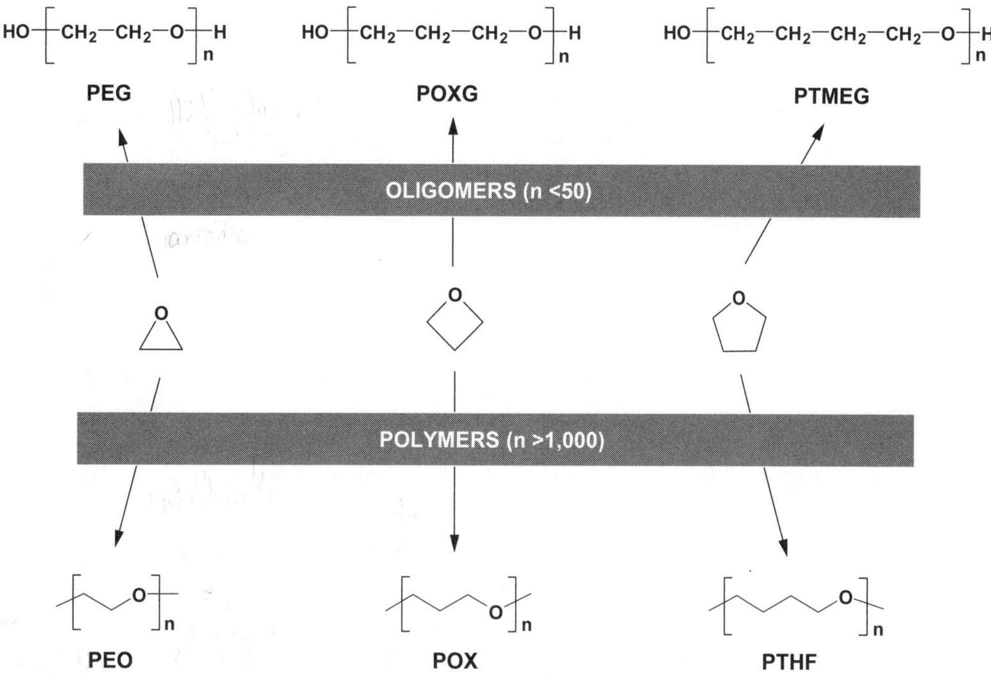

Figure 2.60. Structures of common aliphatic polyethers and their oligomers.

Aliphatic polyethers are conveniently produced by cationic ring-opening polymerization of cyclic ethers, such as ethylene oxide, oxetane and tetrahydrofuran, in the presence a protonic acid catalyst, such as FSO_3H and CF_3SO_3H or Lewis acid, e.g., BF_3 and $AlEt_3$ (Figure 2.61). The propagating species in this polymerization is a tertiary oxonium ion and it is important that the nucleophilicity of the counter anion be low to achieve high ion pair stability. Strong nucleophilic anions, such as Cl^-, are not suitable, because the ion pair is unstable with respect to cyclic ether and the alkyl halide. Under appropriate conditions (e.g., early quenching), the polymerization can be held to low molecular weight hydroxyl terminated oligomers. Anionic ring-opening polymerization of cyclic ethers, especially ethylene oxide, using alkali metal hydroxide or alkoxide, is seldom used to produce (PEG) and monohydroxy oligomers.

Cationic Polymerization Mechanism:

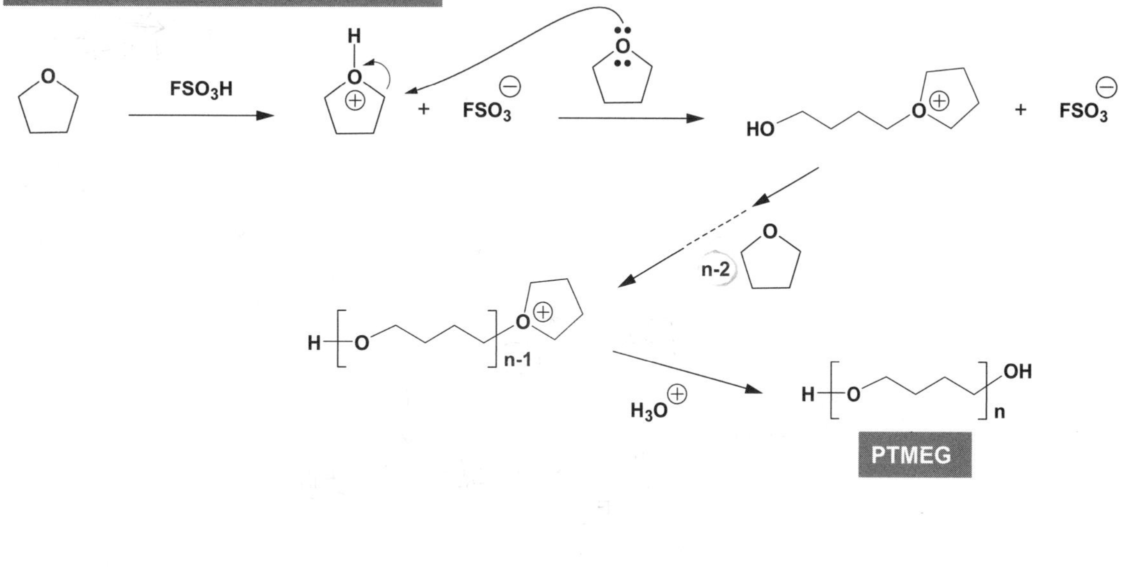

FSO_3H + FSO_3^- HO + FSO_3^-

n-2

H-[O]n-1 H_3O^+ H-[O]n-OH

PTMEG

Anionic Polymerization Mechanism:

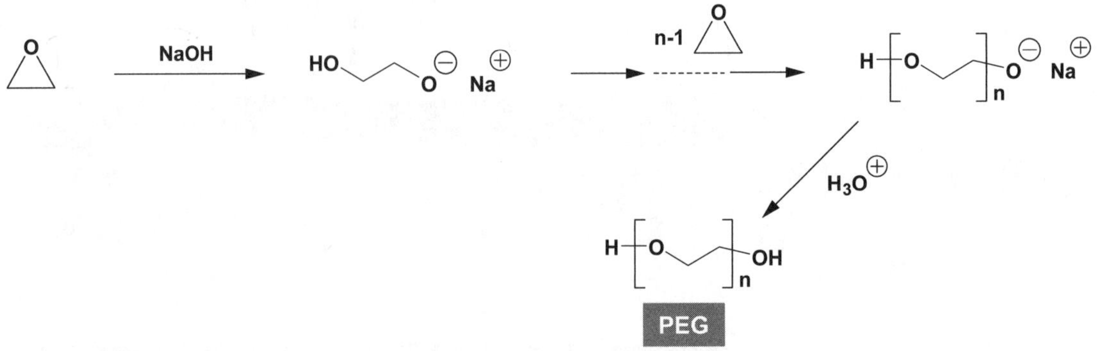

Figure 2.61. The mechanisms of cationic and anionic polymerization of cyclic ethers.

The manufacture of PEO with very high molecular weight (100,000 to several millions) is normally carried out in the presence of alkaline earth metal oxides, alkyl aluminum or alkoxy aluminum compounds over an extended period of time. The mechanism of polymerization is believed to involve a coordinate anionic reaction where ethylene oxide coordinates with the metal atom of the catalyst, followed by nucleophilic attack of the alkoxide at the propagating chain end (Figure 2.62). High molecular weight PEO is especially suitable as the separator and electrolyte in lithium polymer batteries, which carry greater energy for their weight than other lithium-ion battery technologies (see Chapter-5). Among the solvent-free polymer electrolyte systems, PEO is the most studied because of its several attractive features. The main advantages of PEO as a host are its chemical, mechanical and electrochemical stabilities, since it contains only strong unstrained C-O, C-C, and C-H bonds. PEO is very flexible (T_g = -60°C) because of the presence of swivel ether linkages and the repeat unit, -CH_2CH_2O-, provides just the right spacing for maximum dissolution of lithium salts. PEO electrolyte behaves like a rubbery material, due to the presence of sufficient interchain entanglement, and contains both crystalline and amorphous regions (*Note:* the lithium-ion conduction is believed to take place in the latter). PEO electrolytes also exhibit excellent melt processing capability which is very desirable for mass scale production of batteries.

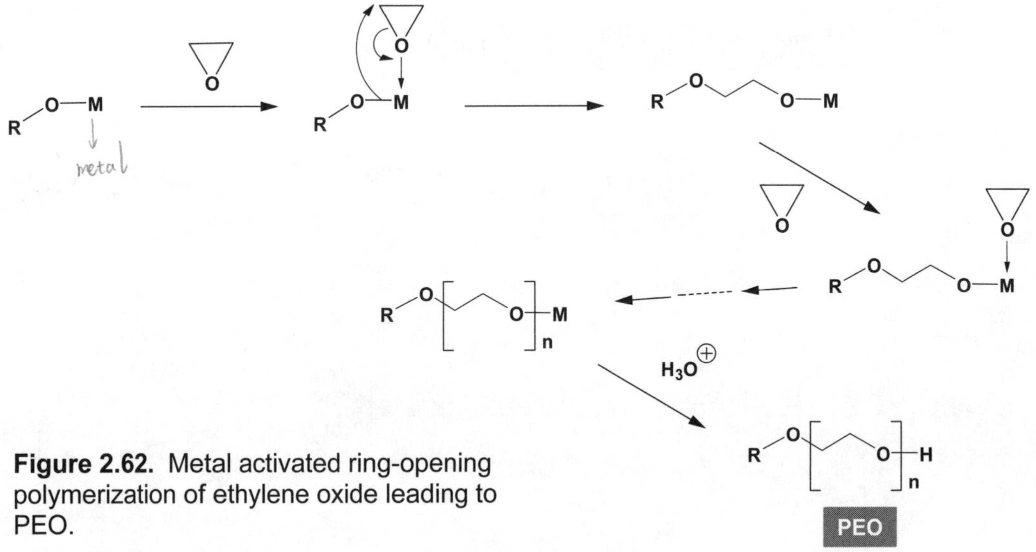

Figure 2.62. Metal activated ring-opening polymerization of ethylene oxide leading to PEO.

2.2.2. Polyesters

Polyesters containing a completely aliphatic backbone are prone to hydrolytic and enzymatic biodegradation. Consequently, they are useful in the area of biomaterials and therapeutic systems. By contrast, polyesters obtained by partial replacement of aliphatic segments with aromatic rings, such as phenylene and naphthylene, exhibit high thermal stability and good mechanical properties, which make them attractive for both general-purpose and specialty engineering applications. In terms of volume, poly(ethylene terephthalate) (PET) is the leader because of its enormous market for fibers, films, and molding plastics. Among the other notable partial aromatic polyesters, poly(butylene terephthalate) (PBT), poly(1,4-cyclohexanedimethylene terephthalate), (PCT), and poly(ethylene-2,6-naphthalene dicarboxylate) (PEN) are important (Figure 2.63). In general, these polyesters have very low moisture permeability and overall resistance to staining by various chemicals and food products. PET and PEN are especially known as superior barrier polymers because of very low permeability of oxygen, nitrogen and carbon dioxide. Besides its optical clarity, PET is an exclusive choice in soda bottles for retaining carbon dioxide over a longer period of time. As mentioned in Chapter-1, PET is a semicrystalline polymer, yet it displays outstanding optical clarity because of a well managed *stretched blow molding* operation during which the sizes of crystallites are kept smaller than that of the visible light wavelength.

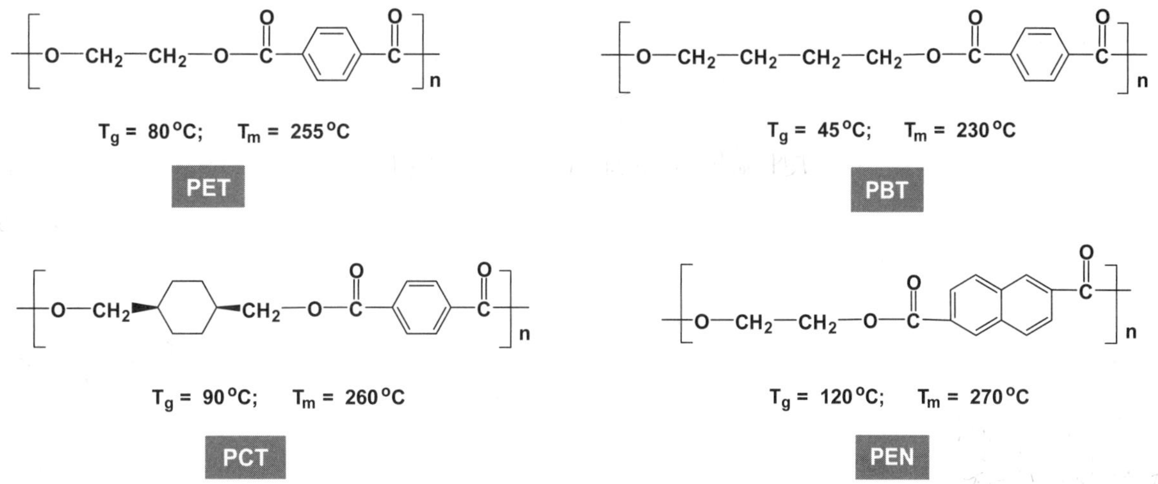

T_g = 80°C; T_m = 255°C

PET

T_g = 45°C; T_m = 230°C

PBT

T_g = 90°C; T_m = 260°C

PCT

T_g = 120°C; T_m = 270°C

PEN

Figure 2.63. Structures and important properties of common partial aromatic polyesters.

Among the spectrum of melt-spinnable fibers, such as polyolefins, acrylics and nylons, partial aromatic polyesters stand at the upper end in terms of T_g and T_m, and thus, provide superior dimensional stability for applications where moderately elevated temperatures are required. In particular, PEN fibers exhibit high tenacity and excellent retention of mechanical properties in a hot/wet environment and consequently find major application in reinforcement of radial passenger and light truck tire carcasses (see Chapter-3 for synthesis). The fibers drawn from PBT, which has a faster crystallization rate than PET, are also important because of their superior dyability (better than PET), resistance to photo-oxidative yellowing (much better than nylons), and excellent resilience and elastic recovery. Fabrics obtained from PET and PBT possess one of the best wrinkle resistance and crease retention properties. More elastic, high resilience and less stiff polyesters include PBT and PCT. They are primarily used in producing high-end carpet yarn.

In the laboratory, these polymers or their derivatives are usually prepared (typically yield low molecular weight) at room temperature by step-growth polycondensation of an aliphatic diol with an aromatic diacid chloride in the presence of an acid acceptor, such as triethylamine. In industry, however, they are manufactured in a two-stage bulk process. In the first stage, the dimethyl ester of the diacid is heated with excess diol in the presence of a catalyst (calcium, zinc or magnesium acetate) to produce primarily the bis(hydroxyalkyl)ester along with a small amount of linear diol-terminated oligomers. In the second stage, excess diol and methanol (transesterified product) are removed under reduced pressure and heating is continued at elevated temperatures until the desired length of the polymer chains (MW ~20,000-40,000) is achieved (Figure 2.64).

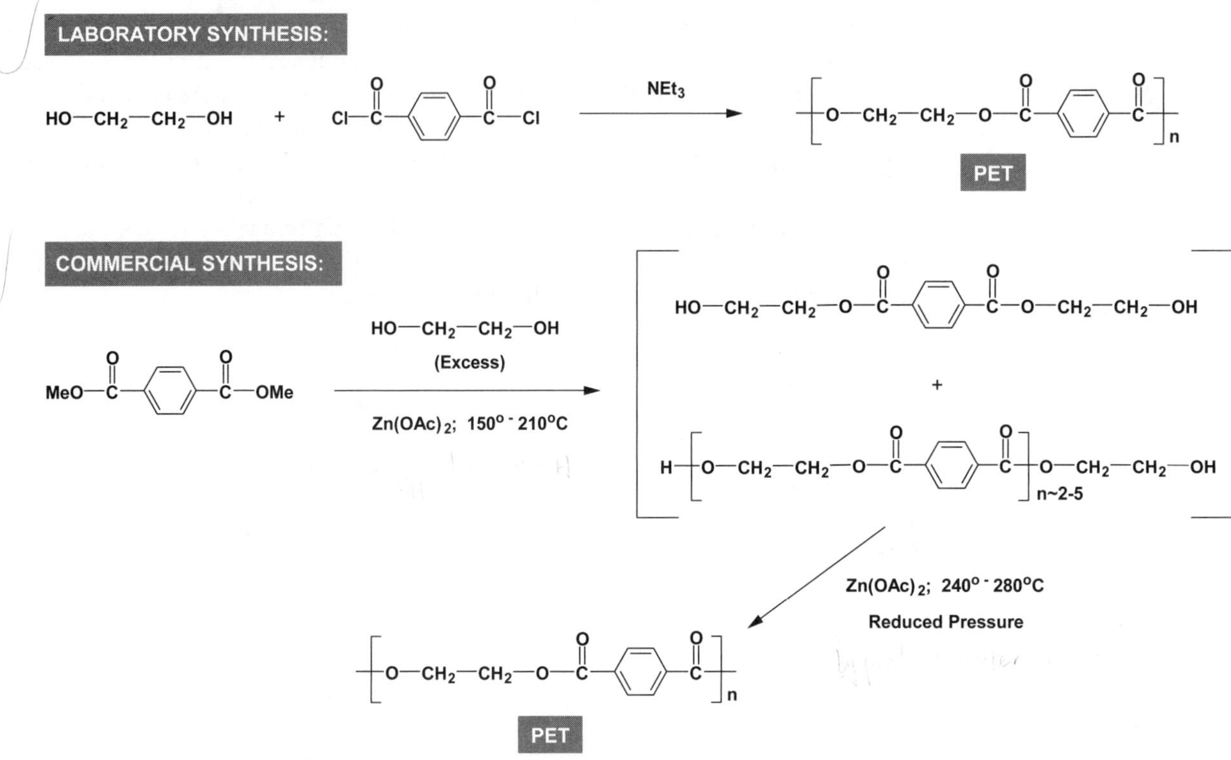

Figure 2.64. Laboratory and commercial syntheses of polyesters (example shown with PET).

Very recently, PBT has been prepared by ring-opening polymerization of a mixture of cyclic PBT oligomers (cPBT), which were obtained *via* pseudo-high dilution condensation of 1,4-butanediol with terephthaloyl chloride in the presence of a tertiary amine, such as 1,4-diazabicyclo[2.2.2]octane (DABCO) (Figure 2.65).[40] Ring-opening polymerization of this oligomer mixture, which melts from 150° to 200°C, thus providing a liquid of low viscosity, affords high molecular weight polymers within minutes. The most effective polymerization initiators, $Ti(OiPr)_4$ and stannoxane, $Bu_2Sn(OCH_2CH_2O)_2SnBu_2$, are thought to operate by Lewis acid activation of the ester group and then transferring a ligand and forming a new ester and an active chain end (initiation step). Propagation continues until all the cyclic oligomers are depleted and the ring-chain equilibration becomes degenerate; the initiator is built into the polymer and is not terminated unless quenched. Because the cyclic oligomers are nearly strain-free, the polymerization is almost thermoneutral and leads to complete equilibration of ester groups (i.e., initiation, propagation, and chain transfer have nearly the same rates). The interesting feature of this polymerization is that complete polymerization of PBT oligomeric cyclics can be achieved at 180-200°C, significantly below the polymer's melting point of 225°C, and with molecular weights as high as 400,000. Polymers formed via such a process are more crystalline than conventionally prepared polyesters. Due to the simplicity in synthesis, the method is more attractive for fiber reinforced composites. This methodology also permits introduction of other cyclic monomers, such as ε-caprolactone (CL), into the polymer backbone. Depending on the CL content, a wide range of cPBT-CL random copolymers with T_g as low as -30°C can be obtained.[41]

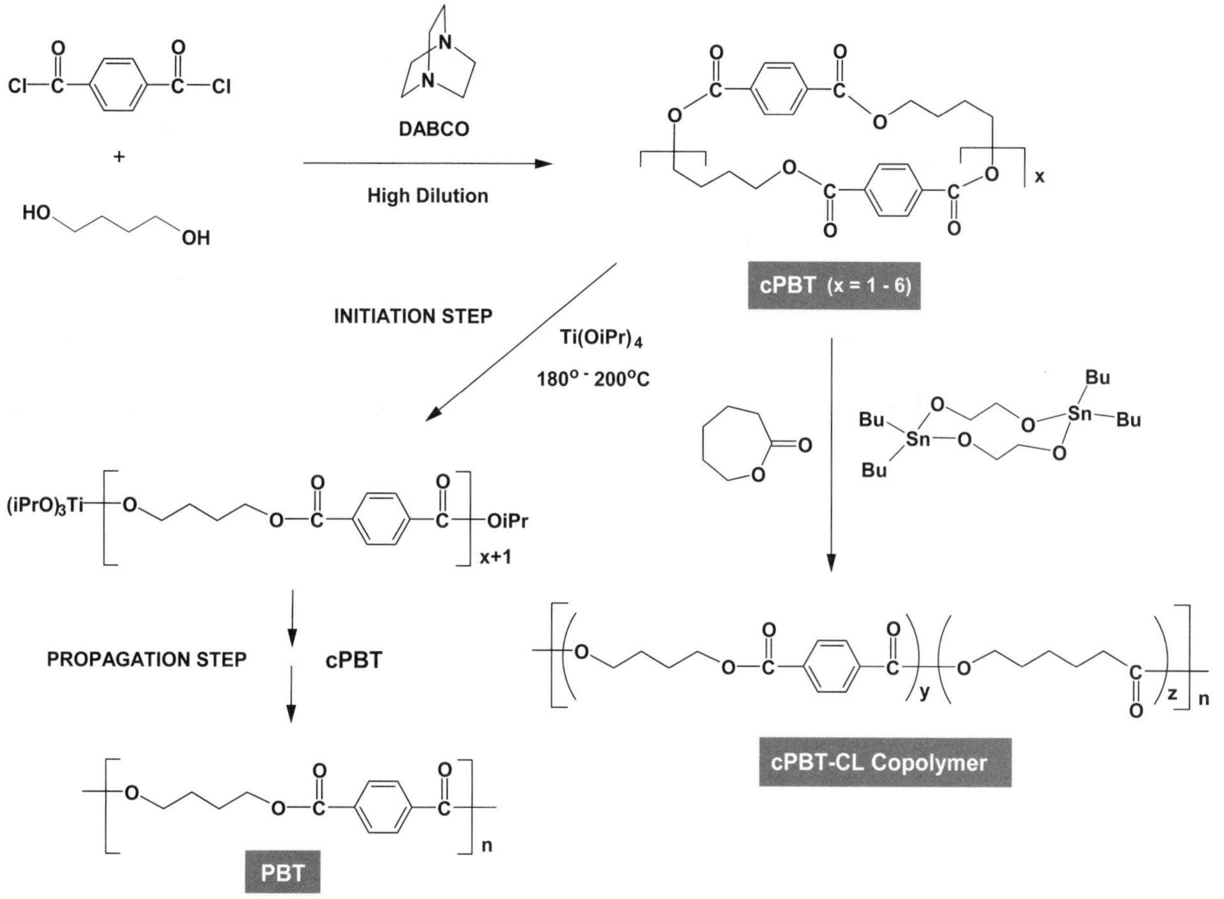

DABCO

High Dilution

cPBT (x = 1 - 6)

INITIATION STEP

$Ti(OiPr)_4$

180° - 200°C

PROPAGATION STEP

cPBT

PBT

cPBT-CL Copolymer

Figure 2.65. Polyesters by ring-opening polymerization of cPBT with and without the presence of CL.

Pure PET fiber is hydrophobic and oleophilic and has poor transport of electrical charge along the fiber. Consequently, during dry seasons, excess static charges, which build up upon contact with other materials, do not quickly leak away, resulting in clinging of fabrics to the skin or discharge of static electricity. This problem is markedly reduced during seasons of higher humidity because the small amount of water absorbed by PET acts as polar, charge-carrying molecules for quicker draining of the static charge. A temporary solution to this problem is the addition of surface lubricants or wetting agents during the manufacture and processing of fibers. However, a permanent solution is copolymerization with low molecular weight poly(ethylene glycol) (PEG). Replacement of a very small proportion of ethylene glycol with PEG improves the moisture absorption characteristics of the modified PET, thus providing both antistatic properties and the ability of water or detergent molecules to lift the oily stains.

2.2.3. Polyurethanes

Polymers containing carbamate, groups, -NHCOO-, are called polyurethanes, although most commercial polyurethanes are associated with a large number of one or several other functional groups (viz., ether, ester, amide and urea) in the polymer backbone. Polyurethanes are used in a wide range of products, such as elastomeric fibers, elastomers, thermoplastics, foams and coatings, and are produced by reaction between a di(or poly)isocyanate and a di(or poly)ol, with the advantage over most other polymerizations in that no byproducts are formed. The versatile properties of polyurethanes are derived from their molecular structure and determined by the choice of building blocks, as well as supramolecular structures caused by atomic interactions between chains. Thus, in linear thermoplastic materials, the ability to crystallize, the flexibility of the chains, and spacing of polar groups are of considerable importance, while in rigid-crosslinked systems, such as polyurethane foams, factors such as density, determine the final properties.

The most common industrial synthetic route for generating isocyanate groups is the phosgenation of amines (Figure 2.66). In small scale preparation, however, thermolysis of bisacylazides (Curtius reaction) is a preferred path instead of using toxic phosgene gas. For most applications, a diisocyanate is chosen, except for high heat resistant rigid foams where a polymeric isocyanate (PMDI) is preferred. The most commonly used diisocyanates include tolylene diisocyanate (TDI), bitolylene diisocyanate (TODI) and 4,4'-methylenebis(phenyl isocyanate) (MDI). Alicyclic diisocyanates, such as isophorone diisocyanate (IPDI) is primarily used in the formulation of rigid coatings, while hydrogenated MDI (HMDI) is excellent for flexible coatings and polyurethane elastomers.

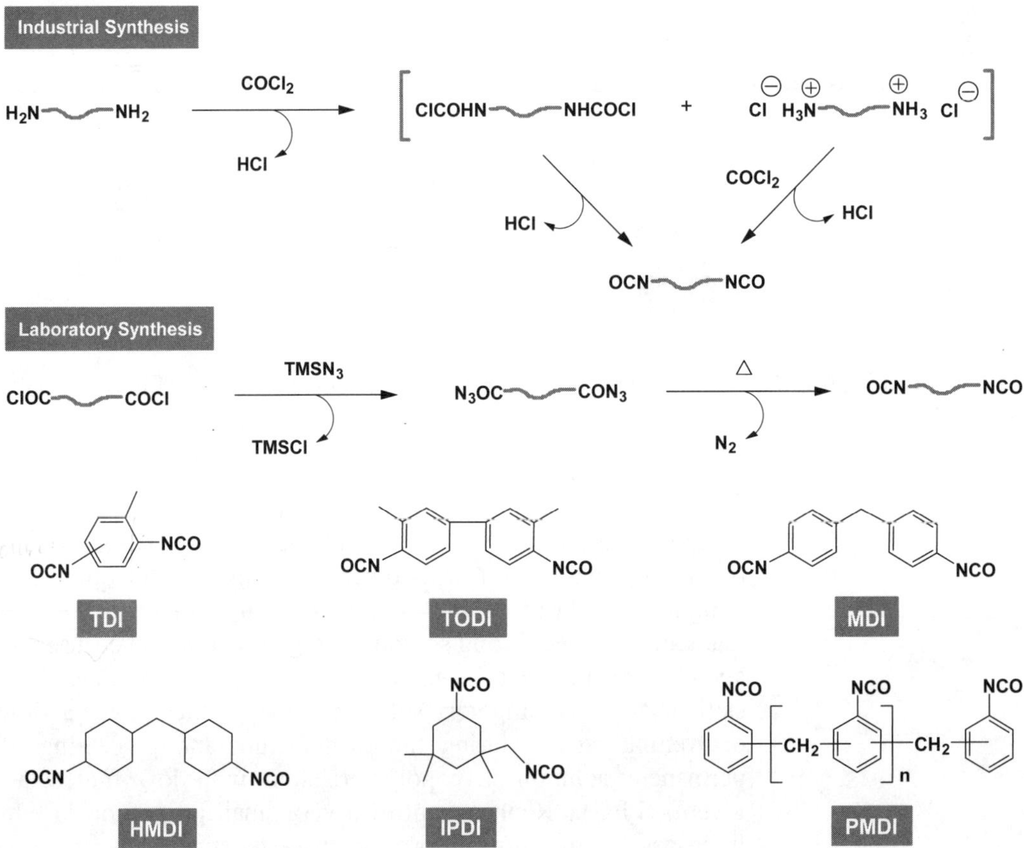

Figure 2.66. Synthetic routes to isocyanates and structures of notable isocyanates.

There are two types of diols used in polyurethane manufacture. One consists of hydroxyl-terminated oligomers, with molecular weight ranging from 500 to 5,000 (Figure 2.67). These diols constitute the flexible segments of the polymer backbone. The economically attractive oligomeric diols are PEG, PTMEG, PETG and glycerol-catalyzed PEG (GPEG). The other type of diols are short-chain molecules, such as 1,3-propanediol, 1,4-butanediol and cyclohexanedimethanol and their major role is to form the hard segments of polyurethane and, of course, the extension of polymer chains (in industry, they are better known as *chain extenders*). The polyurethane segments formed by reaction between diisocyanate and short-chain diol are hard and stiff because of the high concentration of urethane groups.

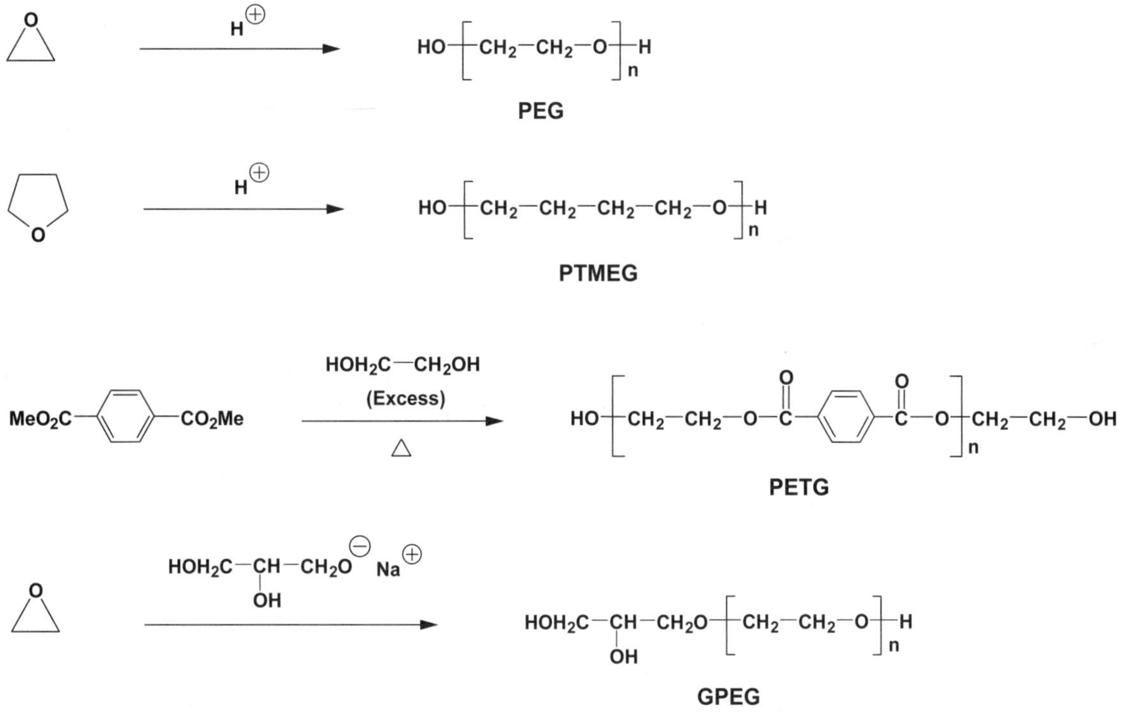

Figure 2.67. Synthetic routes to di(or poly)ols.

Thermoplastic polyurethanes (TPUs) are usually linear ABAB-type alternate copolymers, such as one made by reaction of 1,6-hexanediisocyanate with 1,4-butanediol (Figure 2.68). The unique properties of linear TPUs are attributed to their long chain structure with uniform nylon-like intermolecular hydrogen bonding.

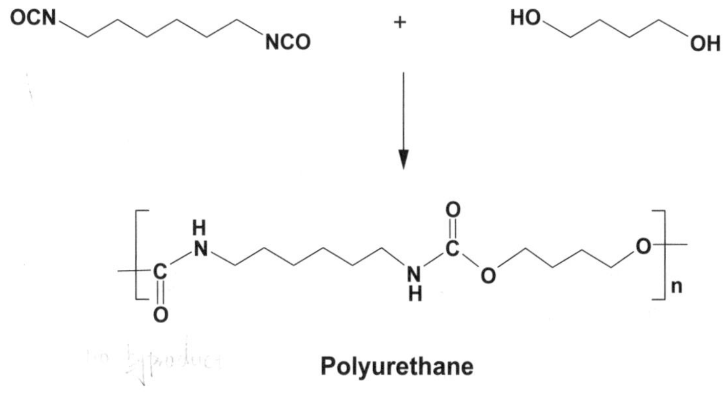

Figure 2.68. Typical synthesis of polyurethane.

At this time, the synthesis of AB-type polyurethane homopolymers is limited to academic exercises and can be performed by cationic ring-opening polymerization of cyclic carbamates, such as tetramethylene urethane (Figure 2.69).[41]

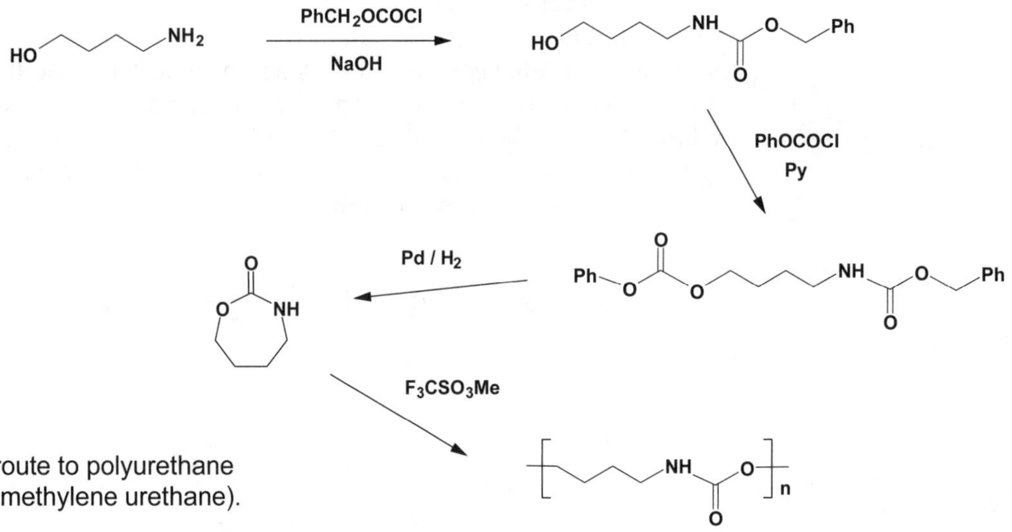

Figure 2.69. Synthetic route to polyurethane homopolymer, poly(tetramethylene urethane).

Thermosetting polyurethanes, which are primarily used for both flexible and rigid foams, cover the largest market segment of polyurethanes. They are produced by reaction of an aromatic di(or poly)isocyanate with a mixture of a low molecular weight polyol and water in the presence of a catalyst mixture. As shown in Figure 2.70, water plays an important role in the chemistry of foam production. The reaction of di(or poly)isocyanate with water generates carbon dioxide gas (which acts as the blowing agent) and a urea derivative (which serves as the chain extender). The heat produced during these reactions is useful by kinetically driving the reactions and for additional expansion of the gas filled bubbles. Because of environmental concerns, the use of co-blowing agents, such as methylene chloride and other halohydrocarbons, are limited to specialty products. For low density flexible polyurethane foams, TDI or MDI is commonly used, while for high heat resistant rigid foams PMDI is preferred. The most common polyols employed in foam production are the oligomers obtained from glycerol or pentaerythritol initiated ring opening polymerization of ethylene oxide or propylene oxide (Figure 2.67). A surfactant, such as PEO-polysiloxane copolymer, is also used in the formulation to facilitate the formation of small bubbles necessary for a fine-cell structure. The role of the catalyst mixture (e.g., dibutyltin dilaurate and DABCO) is to provide the balance between the gelation reaction (urethane formation) and the blowing reaction (urea formation).

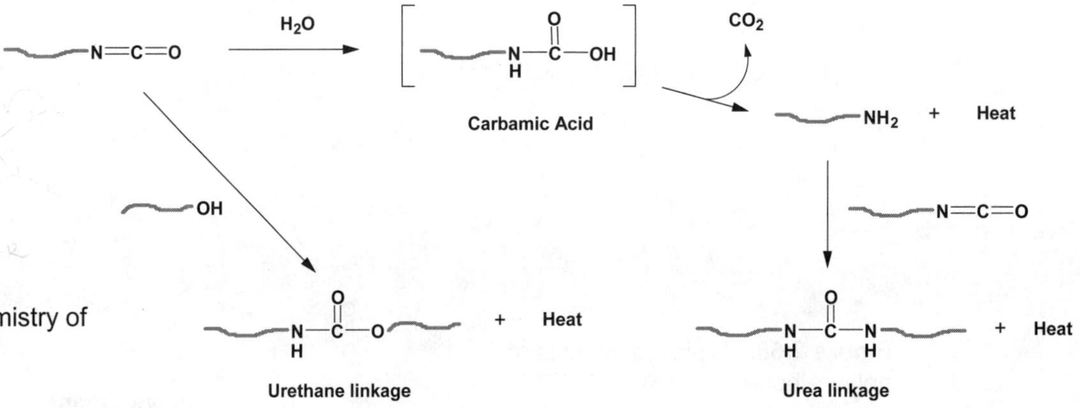

Figure 2.70. Chemistry of polyurethane foam production.

2.2.4. Polysiloxanes

These polymers, better known as *silicones*, possess an unusual array of properties, viz. high thermal and oxidative stability, chemical inertness, low surface tension and insensitivity to temperature changes over the range -50° to 250°C. The most important member of this family is polydimethylsiloxane (PDMS) homopolymer, which is used for medical devices, elastomers, caulking, lubricating oils and heat resistant tiles. PDMS possesses a T_g of -120°C, one of the lowest known values for polymers, because of two types of main-chain flexibility: torsion flexibility and bending flexibility. The former is the ability of the atoms to rotate around a chemical bond, which means that the bond length and angles remain unchanged throughout the process. The latter occurs when there is a large hindrance between non-bonded atoms where there are unfavorable torsion angles. For instance, the Si-O-Si bond is very bendable and can vary between 135 and 180°. In contrast, the O-Si-O bond is rather unbendable and can only vary between 102 and 112°. High molecular weight PDMS, often called *silicone gum*, is prepared by base-catalyzed ring-opening polymerization of the cyclic tetramer of polydimethylsiloxane, octamethylcyclotetrasiloxane. This tetramer is one of the major products of controlled methanolysis of dimethyldichlorosilane and can be separated from the linear oligomer (useful for block copolymers) by vacuum distillation (Figure 2.71). Hydrolysis of dimethyldichlorosilane also produces this tetramer, but in lower yields. When a low molecular weight product (silicone oil) is desired, an acid-catalyzed process is preferred and a chain-stopper (normally hexamethyldisiloxane) is added to block the polymer chain ends with a TMS group.

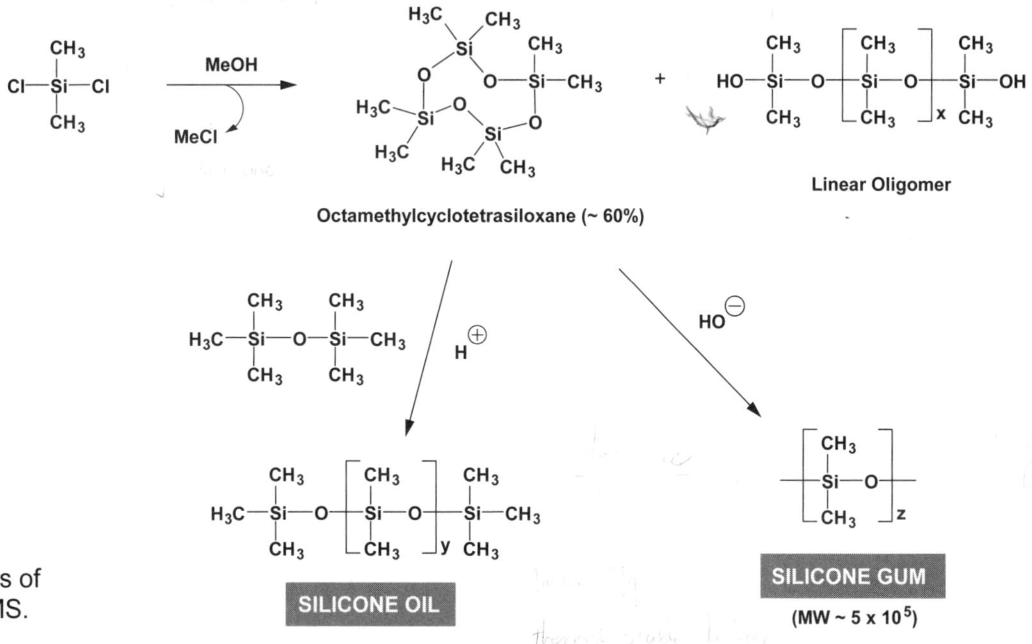

MeOH
MeCl
Octamethylcyclotetrasiloxane (~ 60%)
Linear Oligomer
$H^{\oplus}$
$HO^{\ominus}$
SILICONE OIL
SILICONE GUM
(MW ~ 5 x 10^5)

Figure 2.71. Synthesis of various grades of PDMS.

Silicone elastomers are produced by crosslinking (vulcanization, a commonly used term for crosslinking of rubber with sulfur) silicone gum with a peroxide initiator, such as di-*t*-butyl peroxide and benzoyl peroxide (Figure 2.72). Unlike natural rubber, silicone rubber does not exhibit stretch-induced crystallization, which leads to relatively poor physical properties. Thus, silicone rubber must be compounded with 10-25 wt.% of a reinforcing filler (typically, fumed silica), along with other useful additives (viz., antioxidant and pigment), to improve the final properties of the rubbery product. The mechanism of curing involves free-radical abstraction of a silicon methyl group, followed by dimerization of the methyl radicals to form an interchain ethylene bridge. Silicone rubber is normally fabricated by compression molding of silicone gum compounds at 100-180°C. Silicone rubber keypads are widely used in the "soft push-button" facilities found throughout our daily life, such as calculators, remote controllers, cellphones and cameras. Silicones are also used in shoe insoles because they are non-toxic, non-slippery stable materials with excellent shock absorbing and walking comfort features.

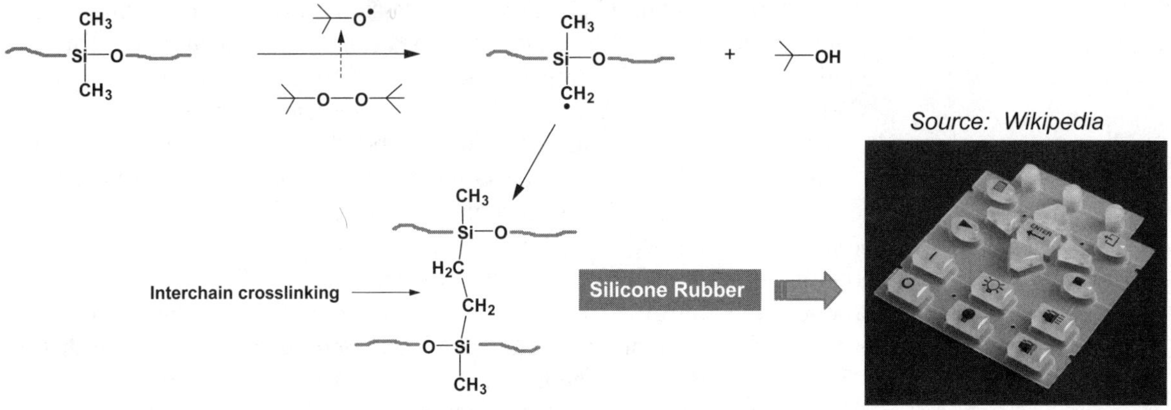

Source: Wikipedia

Interchain crosslinking

Silicone Rubber

Figure 2.72. Mechanism of the formation of interchain crosslinking in silicone rubber.

PDMS is also the principal component of most siloxane random and block copolymers. When dimethyldichlorosilane is hydrolyzed in the presence of other readily hydrolyzable silanes, an array of commercially useful mixed cyclic oligomers and reactive polymers is produced (Figure 2.73). For instance, copolymers **A** (PDMS containing an SiH functionality) and **B** (pendent vinyl group containing PDMS) are used in the formulation of *liquid silicone rubber* (LSR). Unlike the aforementioned heat-cured rubber, which is processed by compression molding, LSR can be processed by liquid injection molding, thus benefiting rapid cycle times and the ability to fill complex mold shapes because of the low viscosity of the compounded dough. The crosslinking is achieved through the hydrosilylation reaction between the silicone hydride group and the vinyl group to form an alkylenic linkage in the presence of a platinum catalyst.

It is interesting to note that the polymers used for LSR can also be used for the production of flexible foamed silicone rubbers, which exhibit superior flame retardancy compared to that of urethane-type foam. Two components prepared separately are mixed at room temperature: one part contains polymer **A**, water, alcohol, platinum catalyst and emulsifying agent, and the other consists of polymer **B** and fillers. Two simultaneous chemical reactions occur when the components are mixed. One is the platinum-catalyzed reaction of hydroxyl groups from water and/or alcohol with SiH of polymer **B** to produce hydrogen gas, which is the source of blowing agent that forms the foam (Figure 2.74). The other reaction is, of course, the aforementioned crosslinking reaction (hydrosilylation), which increases the viscosity which leads to gelation, curing and dimensionally stable foam product. Copolymer **B** is also used in the manufacture of PDMS analogs, such as polymethylalkylsiloxanes, by hydrosilylation of an olefin.

Moisture-curable, one-component, *room-temperature vulcanizable* (RTV) silicones represent one of the largest volume and commercially most successful silicone technologies. Low molecular weight PDMS with silanol end groups are primarily used for this application (see Figure 2.71). The other key ingredients in a typical formulation include excess silane crosslinker (e.g., methyltrimethoxysilane, methyltriacetoxysilane),

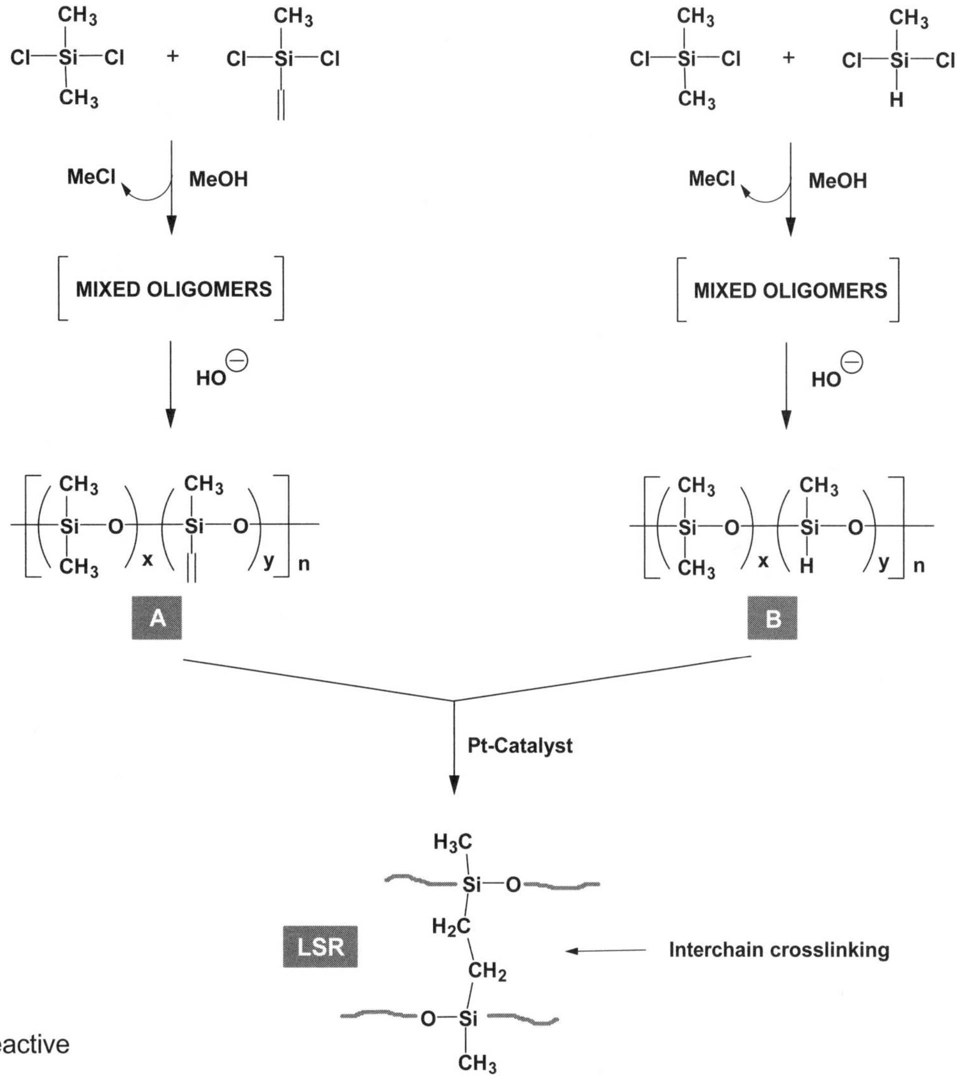

Figure 2.73. Synthesis of reactive polysiloxanes for LSR.

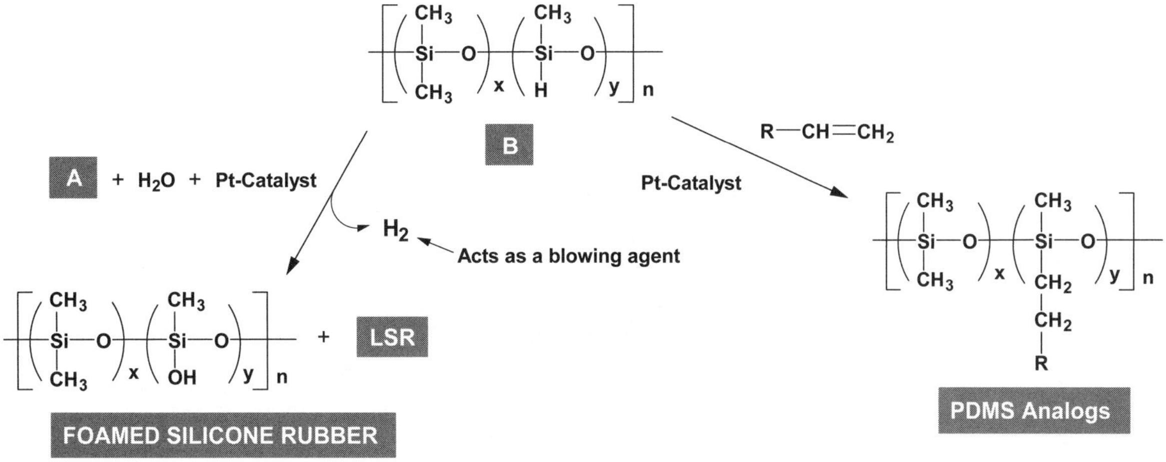

Figure 2.74. The reactions that make copolymer **B** a blowing agent as well as raw material for PDMS analogs.

a cure catalyst (e.g., tin salt) and a reinforcing filler. When exposed to atmospheric moisture, RTV silicones undergo hydrolysis, leading to crosslinked high strength elastomers *via* a polymer intermediate with diol-functionalized end groups (Figure 2.75). The rate of cure of these products is dependent on temperature, humidity and the type of silane crosslinker. For example, RTV silicones, formulated with methyltriacetoxysilane crosslinker, possess long shelf-life and rapid cure-rate compared to that of methyltrimethoxysilane. However, their applications are limited due to odor and the corrosive nature of acetic acid by-product. On the other hand, the formulation involving methyltrimethoxysilane requires a methanol scavenger, such as cyclic alkoxyaminosilanes, to protect the polymer from tin-catalyzed alcoholysis. Major applications of RTV silicones are in the areas of sealants and adhesives.

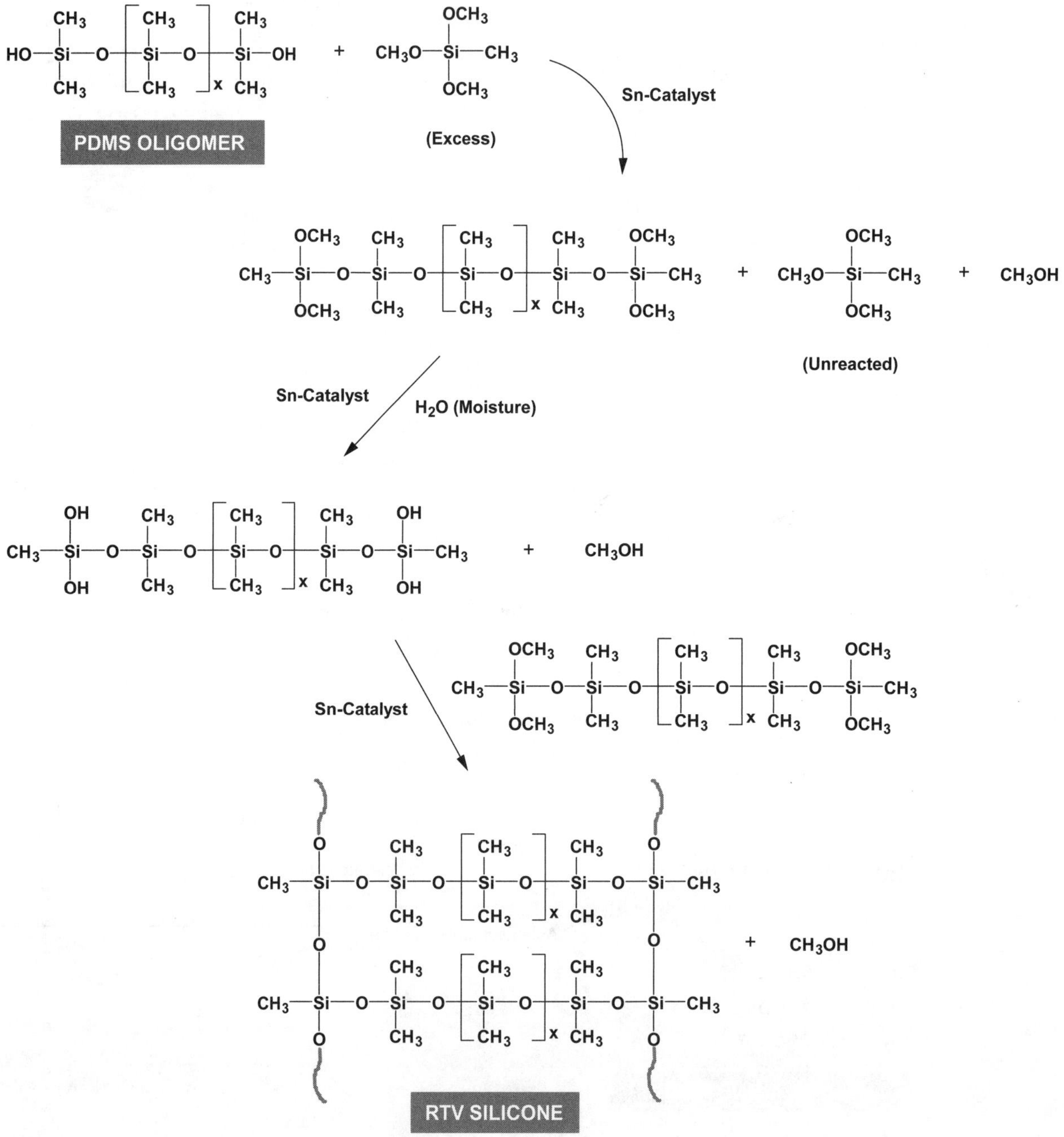

PDMS OLIGOMER + $CH_3O-Si(OCH_3)_2-CH_3$ (Excess) → Sn-Catalyst → methoxy-terminated PDMS + $CH_3O-Si(OCH_3)_2-CH_3$ (Unreacted) + CH_3OH

Sn-Catalyst, H_2O (Moisture) → hydroxy-terminated intermediate + CH_3OH

Sn-Catalyst → RTV SILICONE + CH_3OH

Figure 2.75. Basic chemistry of methyltrimethoxysilane-based RTV silicones.

2.3. ELASTOMERS AND THERMOPLASTIC ELASTOMERS

Although *elastomer* is the modern word to describe polymers that possess rubber-like properties (i.e., exhibit almost perfect reversible elongation and compression up to certain loads), the term *rubber* (originally coined because it can rub out pencil marks) is still associated with several polymers, such as natural rubber and synthetic butyl rubber. As mentioned earlier, the T_g of elastomers must be considerably lower than room temperature (at least -30°C) in order to manifest high local segmental mobility and bond rotations. Elastomers should also have a sufficient number of chemical or physical crosslinks for dimensional stability and restraining chain slippage. Elastomers with chemical crosslinks are, therefore, thermosetting materials, i.e., once the crosslinking operation is performed, they cannot be melted or reprocessed into another shape by heating, unlike thermoplastics. Elastomers are highly amorphous materials with weak interchain interactions. Consequently, they exhibit a fiber-like structure (highly aligned chains along the stretching direction) at high elongation, but retract to their thermodynamically stable configurations upon removal of applied stress, due to lack of interchain forces to stabilize the ordered structure (see Figure 1.31 in Chapter-1). By contrast, elastomers with physical crosslinks exhibit elastomeric behavior due to their two-phase morphology, hard microphases in a soft continuous phase. These materials can be processed like conventional thermoplastics by the application of heat and/or pressure, thus appropriately called *thermoplastic elastomers*.

2.3.1. Natural Elastomers

Elastomers from natural sources have been in use for a very long time (since 1600 BC), primarily for dipped rubber products and weatherproof clothing. However, their widespread use in tires, footwear, latex gloves, foams, coating, etc. did not occur until Charles Goodyear's invention of vulcanization in the early 19th century. Subsequent development of worldwide rubber plantations led to rapid growth of natural rubber products and improvement in latex processing. Today, a variety of trees can produce a good amount of latex (primarily obtained by cutting latex ducts which are in a layer immediately outside the cambium), the raw material for natural elastomers (Figure 2.76). A tapped natural latex typically contains about 35 wt.% of rubber, about 5 wt.% of fatty acids, proteins, carbohydrates, natural antioxidants, etc., and the remainder is water. Depending on the trees, the major polymeric substance present in a latex is either one or a mixture of polymers of the geometrical isomers of isoprene. It is remarkable that the latex obtained from *Hevea brasiliensis* and *Guayule* trees is derived from only *cis*-isoprene, while *Gutta percha* and *Balata* trees produce only *trans* isomer. The molecular weight of the polymers in these lattices is very high (~1,500,000). One notable exception is the *Chicle* tree, which produce latex consisting of relatively low molecular weight *cis*- and *trans*-1,4-polyisoprenes, and confined to limited applications, such as chewing gum.

A major portion of the latex produced worldwide is used for solid rubber technology because of its superior *green strength* (especially tensile and tear strength of uncured rubber compound) and weather resistance compared with synthetic elastomers. About 70% of natural rubber is consumed for tires and tire retreading, 15% for latex products and the rest for various mechanical goods. Solid rubber is obtained from the latex through a series of steps, viz., coagulation, isolation, drying and milling. Most products obtained from natural rubber require compounding (mixing with several ingredients) to improve tensile strength, abrasion resistance, shelf-life, and most importantly, reduction of cost. The major ingredient in rubber compounding is reinforcing filler (e.g., carbon black), which is used often in excess of 50 phr (parts per 100 g of rubber). Other notable ingredients, but used in much less quantities, include sulfur (vulcanizer, introduces chemical crosslinking), accelerator (e.g., mercaptobenzothiazole disulfide, MBTS, enhances rate of vulcanization and provides good distribution of mono-, di- and polysulfidic crosslinks), mineral oil (processing aid, helps fillers and other solid ingredients to disperse well in the rubber), antioxidants, adhesion promoters, pigments, etc.

***Cis-* 1,4-Polyisoprene** **(Hevea and Guayule)**

T_g = - 75 °C; T_m = Amorphous

***Trans-* 1,4-Polyisoprene** **(Gutta percha and Balata)**

T_g = - 55 °C; T_m = 70 °C

Figure 2.76. Structures of polymers present in different species of natural rubber. The picture on right shows collection of latex from a Hevea tree.[43]

Vulcanization is a chemical process where sulfur or other materials introduce crosslinks in the elastomer, resulting in improved mechanical properties. In the absence of an accelerator, a vulcanization process of double bond containing elastomers yields network structures consisting primarily of polysulfidic linkages, which exhibit poor properties, such as very high elongation and low modulus. A generally accepted accelerator-assisted vulcanization mechanism involves insertion of sulfur into the accelerator to form an active sulfurating intermediate, which reacts with a polymer chain at the allylic position to form a polysulfidic pendent group terminated by an accelerator group (Figure 2.77). A polysulfidic crosslink is formed by reaction between this pendent group and another polymer chain. A mono- and/or disulfidic linkage is believed to form during the curing and network maturing periods, when several competing reactions (viz., desulfuration, crosslinking and degradation) occur. The ratio of mono-, di- and polysulfidic crosslinks depends strongly on the ratio of sulfur to accelerator in the formulation.

For latex technology, the tapped latex is first concentrated to ~60% solid content by a centrifugal technique, which separates the latex into a low density rubber-rich concentrate and a denser rubber-poor serum or skim. The concentrate is then separated and mixed with ammonium or potassium laurate (0.01-0.05 wt.%) to increase the stability of the latex. Depending on the applications, the stabilized latex is then mixed with other ingredients, such as a crosslinking agent, antioxidant and pigments. Although fillers do not reinforce latex polymers as they do in dry rubbers, they are primarily used for most applications to adjust processing rheology and to reduce cost of the final product. Major uses of natural rubber latex include surgical gloves, carpet backing, foams and dipped goods. While flexible polyurethane foam holds by far the greatest share of the foam cushioning market in home furnishings, latex foam rubber also occupies an important niche among premium-priced products.

Finally, it is noteworthy that a small percentage of natural and synthetic elastomers is used for making *hard rubber* (also called *ebonite*) products, such as battery boxes and parts, linings and coverings for chemical plants, machined electrical components, chemical resistant pipes, valves, pumps, etc. The formulation is similar to that of tire tread compounds, except for sulfur, which is used in excess of 25 phr, resulting in extensive crosslinking between polymer chains and causing a rise of T_g well above room temperature.

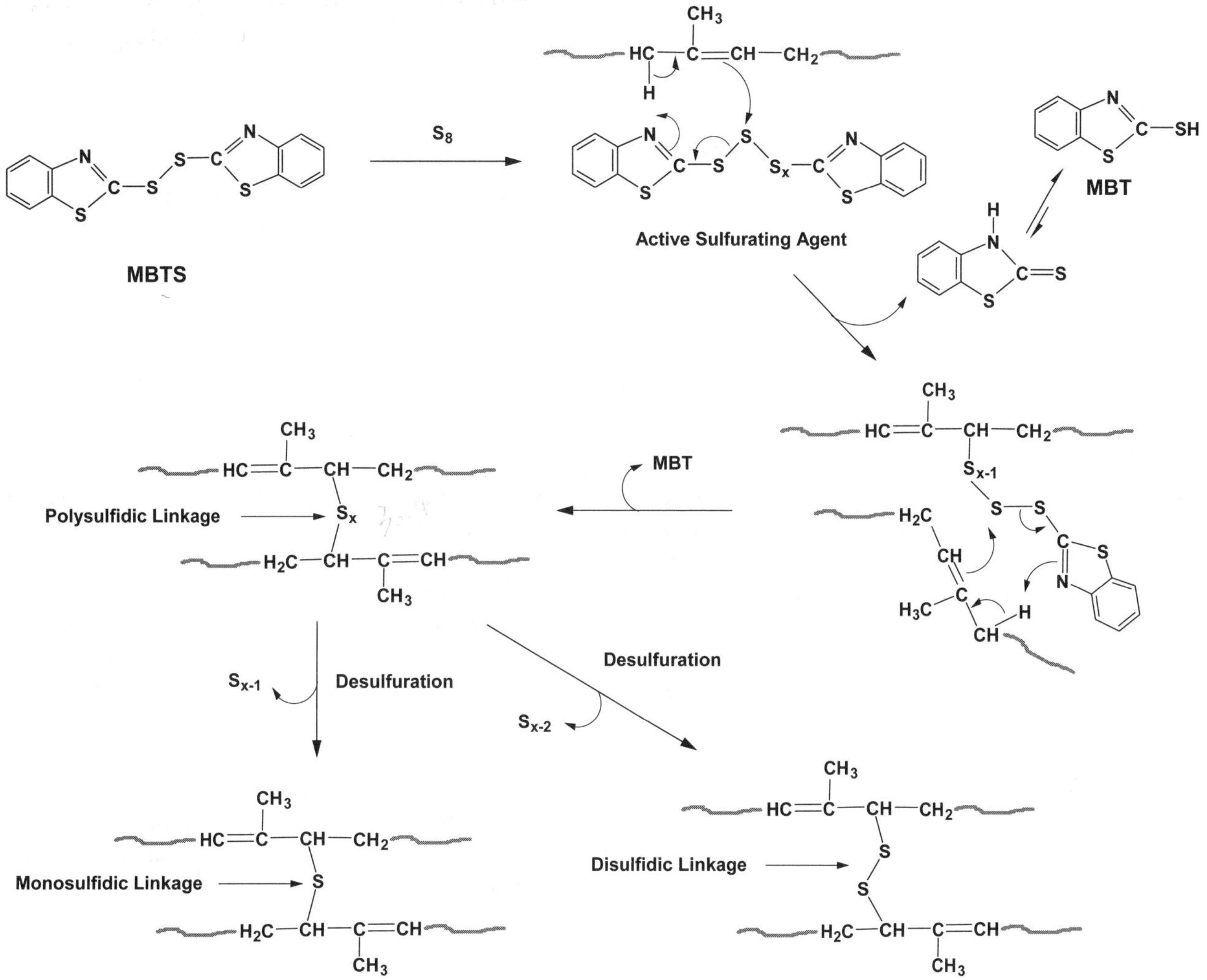

Figure 2.77. Mechanism of accelerator-assisted sulfur vulcanization of elastomers containing double bonds.

2.3.2. Synthetic Elastomers

The origins of synthetic elastomers date back to the first half of the 19th century, when attempts were made to elucidate the composition and structure of natural rubber with the eventual goal of reproducing the material. However, the majority of synthetic elastomers were commercialized in the first half of the 20th century, with the exception of "*synthetic natural rubber*" (virtually 100% *cis*-1,4-polyisoprene) and *cis*-1,4-polybutadiene (with excellent abrasion resistance, especially in tires subjected to severe conditions), which were developed in 1959 and 1961, respectively. Based on use and performance, synthetic elastomers may be grouped into the following five categories. A brief description of these elastomers, with representative examples, is given below.

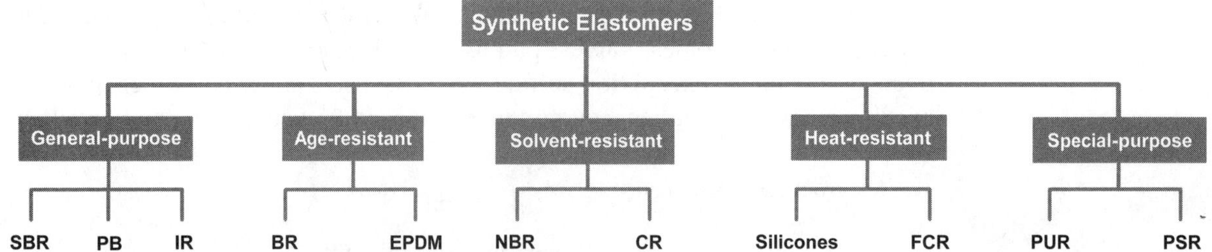

2.3.2.1. *General-Purpose Elastomers*

This class is consumed in very high volume compared with the other classes of elastomers. The notable polymers are styrene-butadiene rubber (SBR), polybutadiene (PB) and polyisoprene (IR). Crosslinking in these elastomers is introduced by sulfur vulcanization.

2.3.2.1a. Styrene-Butadiene Rubber (SBR)

SBR, a random copolymer of styrene and butadiene monomers, is the most important synthetic rubber and represents more than half of all synthetic rubber production. SBR is predominantly used for the production of car and truck tires and tire retread compounds. A good amount of SBR latex also serves as substitutes for natural rubber latex. As shown in Figure 2.78, SBR is commercially prepared by emulsion polymerization of a mixture of two monomers (typically, 75% butadiene and 25% styrene), an emulsifier, an initiator (potassium persulfate) and a chain-transfer agent (n-dodecyl mercaptan). This process leads to more *trans*-1,4 structures in the polymer. The use of a *chain-transfer agent* (also known as a *modifier*) in the amount of about 0.5 weight percent relative to the total weight of the monomers provides the desired molecular weight (M_n ~100,000-200,000). As described in Chapter-1, the thiol (mercaptan) is capable of terminating growing chains and initiating new chains (Figure 1.51). The SBR polymerization system produces a very high molecular-weight polymer in the absence of a chain-transfer agent. A high molecular weight rubber is difficult to process with normal mixing equipment, such as rubber roll mills or Banbury mixers. SBR is highly amorphous and does not crystallize on either heating or cooling. Similar to natural rubber, SBR is compounded with carbon black and vulcanized with sulfur to obtain high strength and abrasion resistance.

$K_2S_2O_8$

Emulsion Process

SBR (T_g = -45°C)

Figure 2.78. Synthesis of SBR.

2.3.2.1b. *Cis*-1,4-Polybutadiene (PB)

PB is a homopolymer of butadiene monomer and its rate of consumption is second to SBR. This very high *cis*-1,4 structure (>90%) and preferred geometry for applications in tires, is prepared by polymerization of butadiene using Ziegler-Natta catalysts. The mechanism involves generation of a coordination complex with one π-bond of the predominant *trans* conformer of butadiene, followed by the formation of a much more energetically stable coordination complex by rotation around the central C-C bond (Figure 2.79). The resulting complex is more stable because both π-bonds of the monomer coordinate to the metal atom (**M**), leading to a five-membered ring transition state, which not only facilitates the formation of a higher percentage of *cis* structure in the polymer, but also 1,4-addition, rather than 1,2-vinyl polymerization.

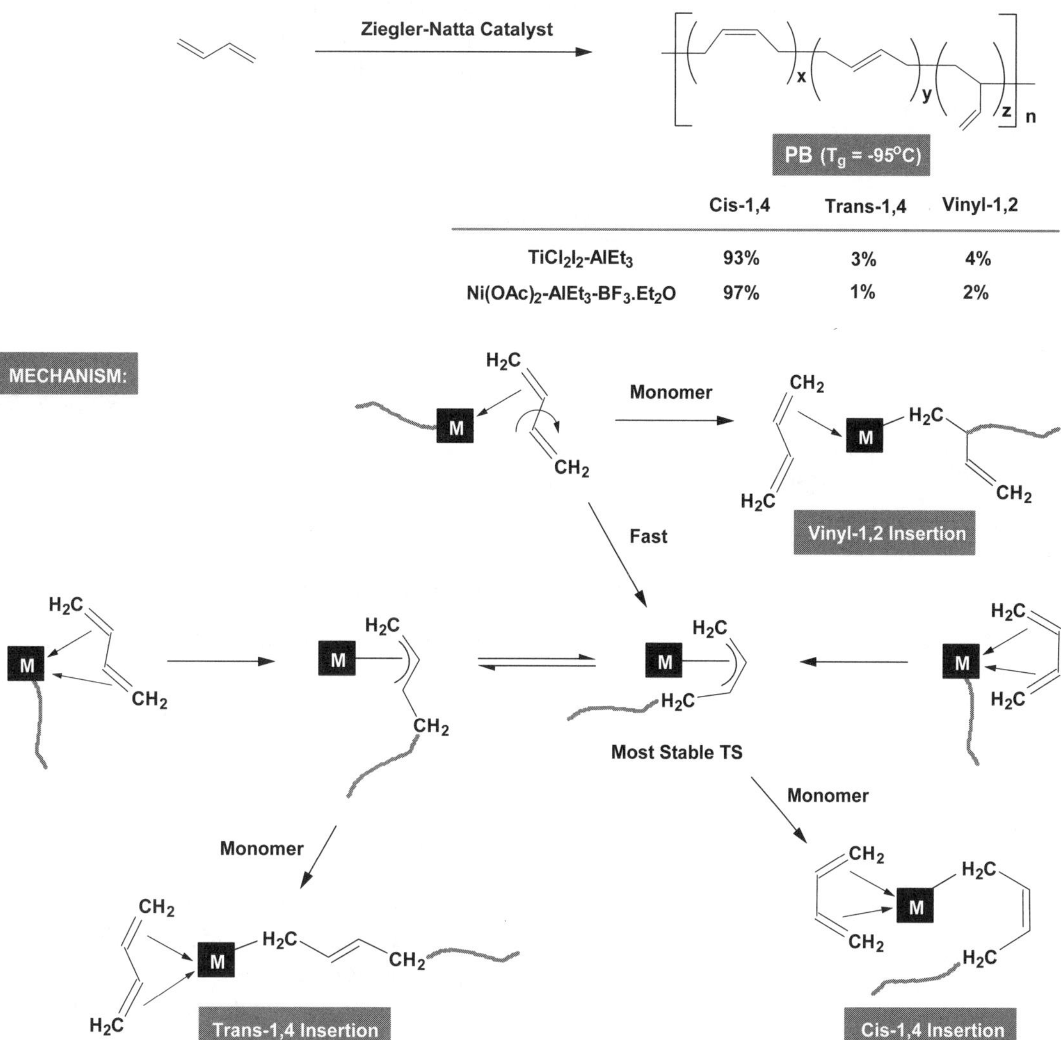

	Cis-1,4	Trans-1,4	Vinyl-1,2
$TiCl_2I_2$-$AlEt_3$	93%	3%	4%
$Ni(OAc)_2$-$AlEt_3$-$BF_3.Et_2O$	97%	1%	2%

Figure 2.79. Synthesis and mechanism of the polymerization of butadiene by Ziegler-Natta catalysts.

Similar to SBR, the desired number-average molecular weight of commercial PB ranges from 100,000 to 200,000. Since PB possesses much lower T_g (-95°C) compared to SBR (-45°C) and natural rubber (-75°C), it is an excellent choice for low temperature tire traction. In addition, PB possesses high resilience (better than natural rubber), which in turn results in a lower heat build-up. Resilience is a measure of recoverable elastic energy in a deformed material. It is the amount of energy released when a load is removed from a specimen and is equal to deformation energy minus electric hysteresis. PB is mainly used for tires, but in combination (blend) with natural rubber and/or SBR, to take advantage of its superior low temperature characteristics and hysteretic properties. PB is also used in the production of block copolymers for thermoplastic elastomers (*vide infra*).

2.3.2.1c. *Cis*-1,4-Polyisoprene (IR)

Similar to polybutadiene, IR with >98% *cis*-1,4 structure is produced by polymerization of isoprene (2-methyl-buta-1,3-diene) monomer in the presence of a Ziegler-Natta catalyst (Figure 2.80). An organolithium initiator, such as BuLi, can also be used to prepare a high molecular weight polymer, but with a relatively lower *cis*-1,4 chain structure. IR is a synthetic substitute for natural Hevea rubber, and can have four possible chain unit geometric isomers: *cis*- and *trans*-1,4-polyisoprene, vinyl-1,2 and vinyl-3,4. The properties and processing of IR is similar to natural rubber, except for the strength, which is slightly lower due to a lower *cis*-1,4 content.

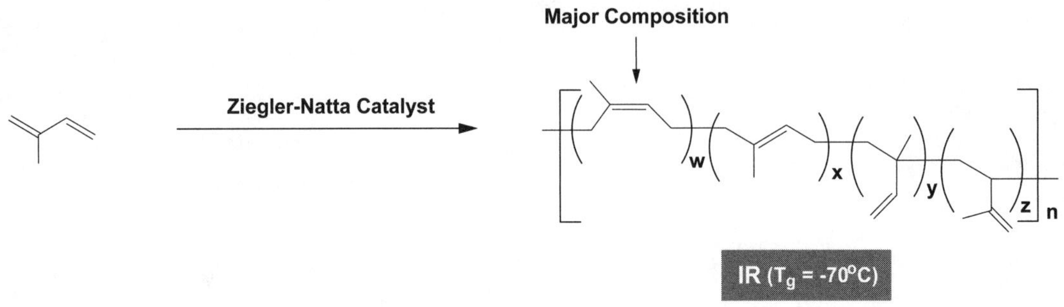

Major Composition

Ziegler-Natta Catalyst

w x y z n

IR (T_g = -70°C)

Figure 2.80. Synthesis of IR by Ziegler-Natta catalysts.

2.3.2.2. Age-Resistant Elastomers

The elastomers that have low unsaturation are called *age-resistant elastomers* because they are less prone to oxidative degradation (i.e., they exhibit good resistance to heat, light and ozone). Examples of this class of elastomers are butyl rubber (BR) and ethylene-propylene (diene) rubber (EPDM).

2.3.2.2a. Butyl Rubber (BR)

This is a random copolymer of isobutylene and isoprene, but the latter is used only in small proportion (<5 mol%), just enough to provide crosslinking sites for vulcanization. BR is produced by cationic polymerization of the monomers using $AlCl_3$ as the initiator and water as the coinitiator at temperatures near -100°C (Figure 2.81). BR is processed and vulcanized similar to SBR to obtain useful properties. BR possesses a T_g of -70°C and exhibits low resilience at room temperature, with high hysteresis loss, which makes it a useful damping rubber. BR possesses remarkable impermeability of air, which led to its widespread use for inner tubes for tires, and for the barrier (inner liner) in tubeless tires.

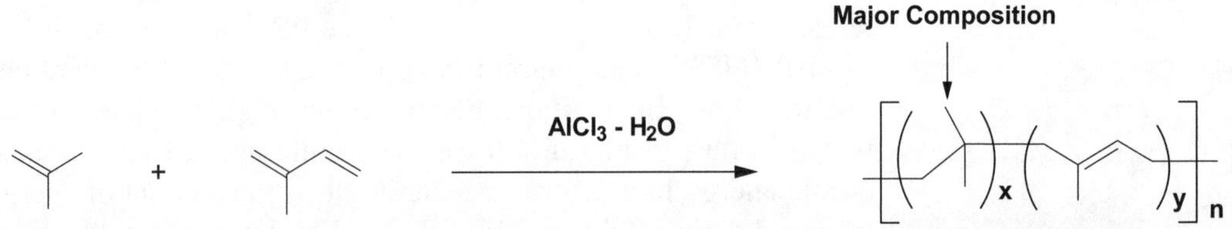

Major Composition

+

$AlCl_3$ - H_2O

x y n

BR (T_g = -70°C)

Figure 2.81. Synthesis of BR by cationic polymerization.

2.3.2.2b. Ethylene-Propylene (Diene) Rubber (EPDM)

This is one of the most versatile, fastest growing and interesting synthetic rubbers. It possesses excellent resistance to heat, oxidation, ozone and weather aging, which provide continued value in demanding automotive, construction, sheet rubber for roofing and mechanical goods applications. EPDM may be regarded as a terpolymer and is produced by copolymerization of monomers in the presence of Ziegler-Natta catalysts, such as VCl_4-$AlEt_2Cl$, or by recently developed metallocenes depicted in Figure 2.31. EPDM is highly amorphous because of its irregular chain structure containing ethylene (~60 mol%), propylene (near 40 mol%) and 1-3 mol% 5-ethylidene-2-norbornene (ENB) units (Figure 2.82). Another notable diene is dicyclopentadiene (DCPD), which is often used in place of ENB as the source of double bonds necessary for sulfur vulcanization.

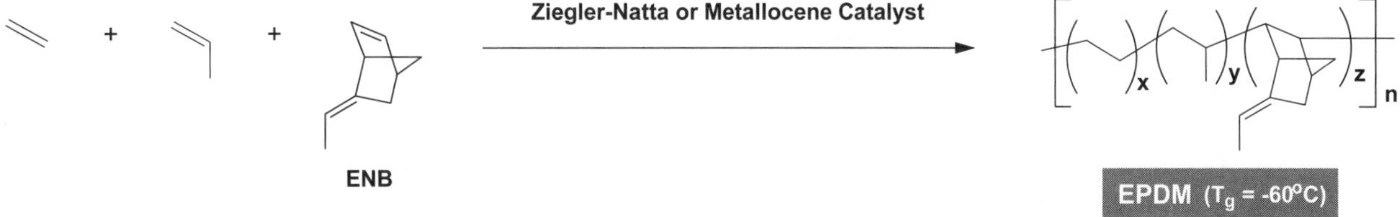

Figure 2.82. Synthesis of EPDM.

2.3.2.3. Solvent-Resistant Elastomers

Elastomers containing polar groups, such as nitrile and chloro, exhibit excellent solvent resistance characteristics. Good examples are nitrile and chloroprene rubbers.

2.3.2.3a. Nitrile Rubber (NBR)

This rubber exhibits excellent resistance to hydrocarbon solvents or oil. It is a random copolymer of 1,3-butadiene and acrylonitrile (Figure 2.83). NBR is manufactured by emulsion polymerization, similar to that used for SBR, resulting in more *trans*-1,4 structure of the butadiene monomer. It is the nitrile group that confers oil resistance to the polymer. Thus, depending on the applications, several grades of NBR are produced in which the acrylonitrile content varies from 10-40 mol%. NBR possesses a slightly higher T_g (varies from -20 to -40°C depending on the acrylonitrile content) compared with other rubbers because of stronger intermolecular dipolar interactions. The desirability of a higher acrylonitrile content for solvent resistance applications, such as gasoline hose, must be balanced against low temperature weather stiffening. The processing is similar to the other rubbers, i.e., requires carbon black and sulfur vulcanization for strength.

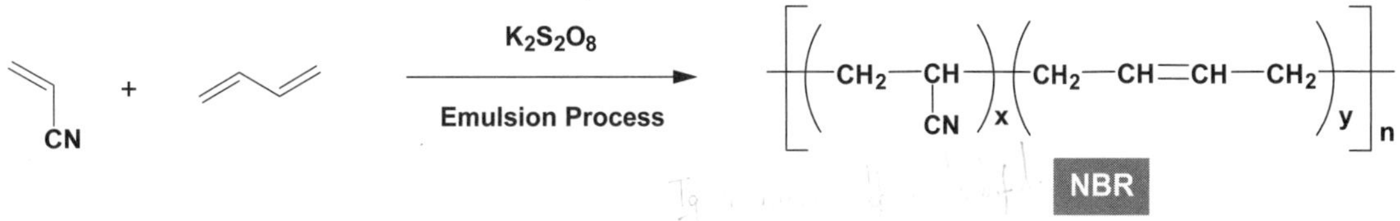

$$\text{CN} + \xrightarrow[\text{Emulsion Process}]{K_2S_2O_8} \left[\left(CH_2-\underset{CN}{CH} \right)_x \left(CH_2-CH=CH-CH_2 \right)_y \right]_n$$

NBR

Figure 2.83. Synthesis of NBR.

2.3.2.3b. Chloroprene Rubber (CR)

This is a homopolymer, better known by the DuPont trade name Neoprene®. Because of its high reactivity, chloroprene (2-chloro-buta-1,3-diene), is difficult to copolymerize with other monomers and thus, does not offer an opportunity for tailoring to produce improved products. Since CR is prepared by emulsion polymerization, the *trans*-1,4 structure predominates over smaller proportions of other isomeric structures, *cis*-1,4, vinyl-1,2, and vinyl-3,4 (Figure 2.84). Even though it is not as solvent-resistant as NBR, it has several advantageous properties, such as resistance to oxidation, ozone attack, and flames (due to the chlorine atoms). Neoprene is the only elastomer, other than natural rubber, that is used in the form of latex for dipping, coating and impregnating applications, because of its high gum tensile strength (i.e., in absence of carbon black), which originates from its *trans* geometry and strong intermolecular dipolar interactions. In addition, CR is extensively used for industrial belts and hoses, seals for buildings and highway joints, etc. Like other rubbers, neoprene can also be processed with carbon black for higher tensile strength. However, vulcanization is typically performed in the presence of a small amount of magnesium oxide or zinc oxide, which reacts with the very labile and reactive chlorine atoms (resulting from 1,2-polymerization of chloroprene). A small proportion of sulfur may be added to the compound to control the rate of vulcanization.

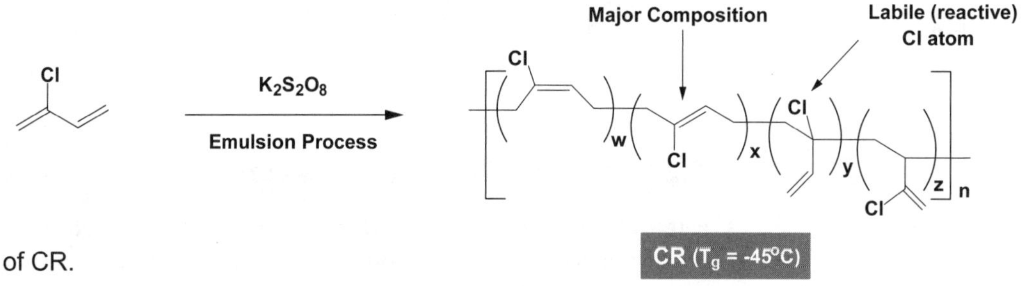

Figure 2.84. Synthesis of CR.

2.3.2.4. Heat-Resistant Elastomers

The only two elastomers that can be used at or above temperatures of 150°C for a prolonged period of time are silicones and fluoropolymers. As discussed in the previous section, the main chain of silicone elastomers does not contain carbon atoms, but instead, a repeating sequence of Si-O bonds. The thermostability of silicones arises from thermal stability of Si-O-Si bond, which is also much more flexible (i.e., can rotate more freely) compared to C-O-C or C-C-C bonds. Consequently, silicone elastomers possess one of the lowest T_g (-120°C) polymers ever made (see Section 2.2.4).

2.3.2.4a. Fluorocarbon Elastomers (FCR)

Due to the presence of a high percentage of fluorine atoms, FCR are the most resistant to heat, chemicals and solvents, but at the same time, they are the most expensive. These elastomers are generally designed for high temperature use (200°C for an indefinite period), with mechanical properties a secondary consideration. However, they have poor low temperature properties, reaching a brittle point at -30°C, compared to nitrile rubber at -40°C. Fluoropolymers derived from perfluoromonomers do not exhibit rubbery properties. Some hydrogen atoms in the main chain are necessary to attain rubbery properties. The monomer that provides the best results is vinylidene fluoride. That is why most fluoropolymers are copolymers of vinylidene fluoride, such as the one shown in Figure 2.85. Emulsion polymerization is used exclusively to produce these polymers, with a molecular weight ranging from 100,000 to 200,000. These polymers must be vulcanized and processed with fillers, such as carbon black and silica to obtain desired properties. Diamine cure systems, such as hexamethylene diamine (HMDA) or a carbon dioxide blocked diamine, such as hexamethylene diamine carbamate (HMDAC), still enjoy some popularity as they enhance rubber-to-metal bonding and the hexamethylene crosslink is mechanically mobile, thereby offering interesting dynamic properties. The very basic character of amine initiates dehydrofluorination at a vinylidene fluoride site, followed by an amine addition (crosslink). The eliminated hydrogen fluoride reacts with magnesium oxide (a compounding ingredient) to form magnesium fluoride and water (which is driven off by an extended high temperature postcure). Peroxides are also added to introduce a parallel crosslinking reaction through methylene groups. Major applications of fluorocarbon elastomers include hoses for the automotive and chemical industries, and seals and gaskets in the marine, oilfield, and chemical process industries.

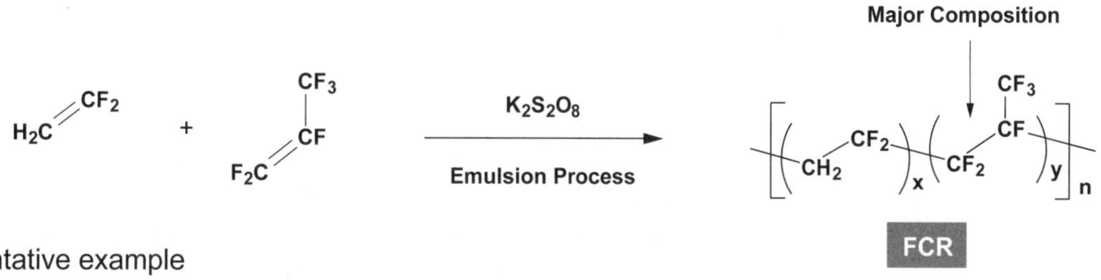

$$H_2C{=}CF_2 + F_2C{=}CF(CF_3) \xrightarrow[\text{Emulsion Process}]{K_2S_2O_8} \left[\left(CH_2-CF_2 \right)_x \left(CF_2-CF(CF_3) \right)_y \right]_n$$

Major Composition

FCR

Figure 2.85. A representative example of fluorocarbon elastomers.

2.3.2.5. Special-Purpose Elastomers

There are a variety of other elastomers, which are consumed in much less quantity than the elastomers discussed above, but offer unique processing features which make them difficult to replace by other polymers. Notable examples are polyurethane (PUR) and polysulfide (PSR) elastomers, which can be employed to develop "castable" elastomers by using liquid low molecular weight prepolymers that can be linked together (chain-extended) and crosslinked into a durable rubber product with negligible shrinkage (Figure 2.86). The section which follows will discuss only PSR, as the chemistry of PUR was elaborated previously (Section 2.2.3).

Figure 2.86. Liquid PUR is used by artists and industry for a variety of design and casting applications, such as sculpture and art casting.[44]

2.3.2.5a. Polysulfide Elastomers (PSR)

Aliphatic polysulfides, better known by its trademark Thiokol® (a product of Thiokol Corporation), are considered the most solvent-resistant rubber (better than nitrile and chloroprene), but it possesses relatively weaker mechanical properties. PSR displays low permeability to gases, water, and organic liquids, low temperature flexibility, and superior resistance to sunlight, ozone, aging, and weathering. This is why its main applications are in the areas of sealants and gaskets for automobiles, and specialty molded items. Polysulfide liquid oligomers with molecular weight 1,000 to 2,500 are made commercially by reaction between bis-chloroethylformal and excess sodium polysulfide (Figure 2.87). The monomer is prepared by acid-catalyzed reaction between 2-chloroethanol and formaldehyde.

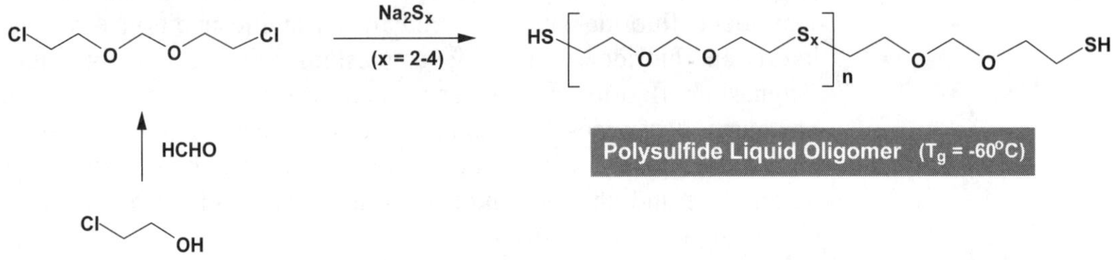

Na_2S_x (x = 2-4)

HCHO

Polysulfide Liquid Oligomer (T_g = -60°C)

Figure 2.87. Synthesis of polysulfide liquid oligomer.

Depending on the applications, a variety of dihalides, such as 1,2-dichloethane and 1,3-dichloropropane, are also used either as a comonomer or a stand alone monomer. During the polymerization reaction, a large amount of high molecular weight polysulfide (>8,000) is formed, which can easily be separated and decomposed into liquid thiol-terminated polysulfide oligomer by reaction with sodium hydrosulfide (NaSH) and sodium sulfite (Na_2SO_3) (Figure 2.88). In fact, polyfunctional polysulfide oligomers, useful for faster crosslinking, are prepared by degradation of crosslinked polysulfide, obtained by reaction of bis-chloroethylformal and 1,2,3-trichloropropane with excess sodium polysulfide.

$$\sim S_x \sim \xrightarrow[Na_2SO_3]{NaSH} \sim SH + \sim S_{x-1}Na + Na_2S_2O_3$$

Figure 2.88. Basic chemical reaction for degradation of high molecular weight linear or crosslinked polysulfide to liquid polysulfide oligomers.

The T_g of polysulfide oligomers depends on the organic dihalide used during polymerization, but is restricted between -30° to -80°C. In general, polysulfides containing the formal group (O-CH_2-O) exhibit a lower T_g compared to those containing only methylene groups of the same chain length. An elastomeric product is made by compounding the low molecular weight liquid oligomer with carbon black and a curing agent. Depending on the curing agent, some formulations can undergo cold vulcanization (useful for preparing solid rocket propellants) while others require heating to produce crosslinked solid product. Metal oxide (e.g., MnO), di- or polyisocyanates (e.g., 1,3-toluene diisocyanate) and low molecular weight epoxy compounds are the most used curing systems for PSR. The crosslinking and/or chain extension reaction between terminal and pendent thiol groups and metal oxide produce disulfide linkages (oxidative coupling reaction), while the latter curatives undergo usual addition reactions.

2.3.3. Thermoplastic Elastomers

Thermoplastic elastomers (TPEs) represent an important class of materials that are rapidly displacing natural and synthetic rubbers, rigid plastics and metals currently found in a variety of products. TPEs are also attractive for "over-molding" onto rigid components for ergonomic or "soft-touch" features. TPEs are block copolymers and generally fall into either an A-B-A triblock motif or segmented $(A\text{-}B)_n$ multiblock pattern (n is typically greater than 25). In principle, A can be any polymer normally regarded as a hard thermoplastic (i.e., hard at room temperature, but fluid upon heating, e.g., polystyrene), and B can be any polymer normally regarded as elastomeric (i.e., softer material that is rubber-like at room temperature, e.g., polybutadiene). It is also necessary that the two blocks, A and B, be thermodynamically incompatible so that the hard blocks can aggregate as intimately dispersed phases (small domains of size ca 20-30 nm) in the bulk of the rubbery matrix (see Figure 1.32 in Chapter-1). Since the role of hard segments is to tie the elastomer chains together in a three-dimensional network through physical crosslinks, the molecular weight of this segment should be much lower compared to the rubbery segment. Thus, in some ways, a TPE matrix is similar to the network formed by vulcanization of conventional rubbers using sulfur crosslinks. The main difference is that in TPEs, the hard domains lose their strength when the material is heated and regains its original integrity when the material is cooled down. Because of phase-separated systems, ABA type TPEs exhibit two T_gs, one for each phase (normally slightly lower than that of their homopolymers). Thus, TPEs have two service temperatures; the soft segment dictates the lower service temperature while the hard segment controls the upper limit. It is noteworthy that block copolymers with structure A-B or B-A-B do not exhibit the characterics of TPEs because of the absence of a continuous physical network, which requires the immobilization of both ends of the elastomer segment in the hard domains. There are five types of commercially important TPEs: styrenic triblock copolymers, thermoplastic olefins, thermoplastic polyurethanes, thermoplastic polyesters and thermoplastic polyamides.

2.3.3.1. Thermoplastic Styrenic Elastomers

The most common TPEs of this class are SBS (styrene-butadiene-styrene) and SIS (styrene-isoprene-styrene) triblock copolymers. Tensile strength of these materials is lower and elongation is higher than SBR or natural rubber, while weather resistance is about the same. The molecular weight of a PS segment varies from 10,000 to 15,000 vs. 50,000 to 75,000 for PB. SBS and SIS triblock copolymers, better known commercially as Kraton® (Kraton Polymers, UK), are produced by sequential anionic polymerization using alkyl lithium, such as *sec*-butyllithium (*s*-BuLi), as the initiator (Figure 2.89). The multi-step polymerization is normally conducted in one pot and in an inert, hydrocarbon solvent under a nitrogen blanket. For example, in the first step, a requisite amount of styrene is polymerized to obtain an oligomeric reactive polystyrene (**S**) block, which is stable (does not undergo termination because of the same charge) and serves as an initiator for the generation of the elastomer block. Thus, a polybutadiene (**B**) block will grow (typically, 93% 1,4-addition with *cis* content less than 40%) on addition of an appropriate amount of butadiene to form a reactive **SB** block. Depending on the required length of polybutadiene block, the SB diblock is either reacted with another appropriate proportion of styrene or with a coupling agent, such as dichlorodimethylsilane or α,α'-dichloro-*p*-xylene, to produce SBS triblock copolymers. The latter approach provides the soft segment with the coupling agent residue at the center of the B block. This method produces a narrow molecular weight distribution product and provides good control of the lengths of the blocks by using stoichiometric amounts of respective monomers. The choice of hard segment usually determines the upper service temperature and/or mechanical properties. For instance, elastomer derived from poly(α-methylstyrene) hard blocks has a higher upper service temperature and tensile strength than that of the elastomer with polystyrene hard blocks.

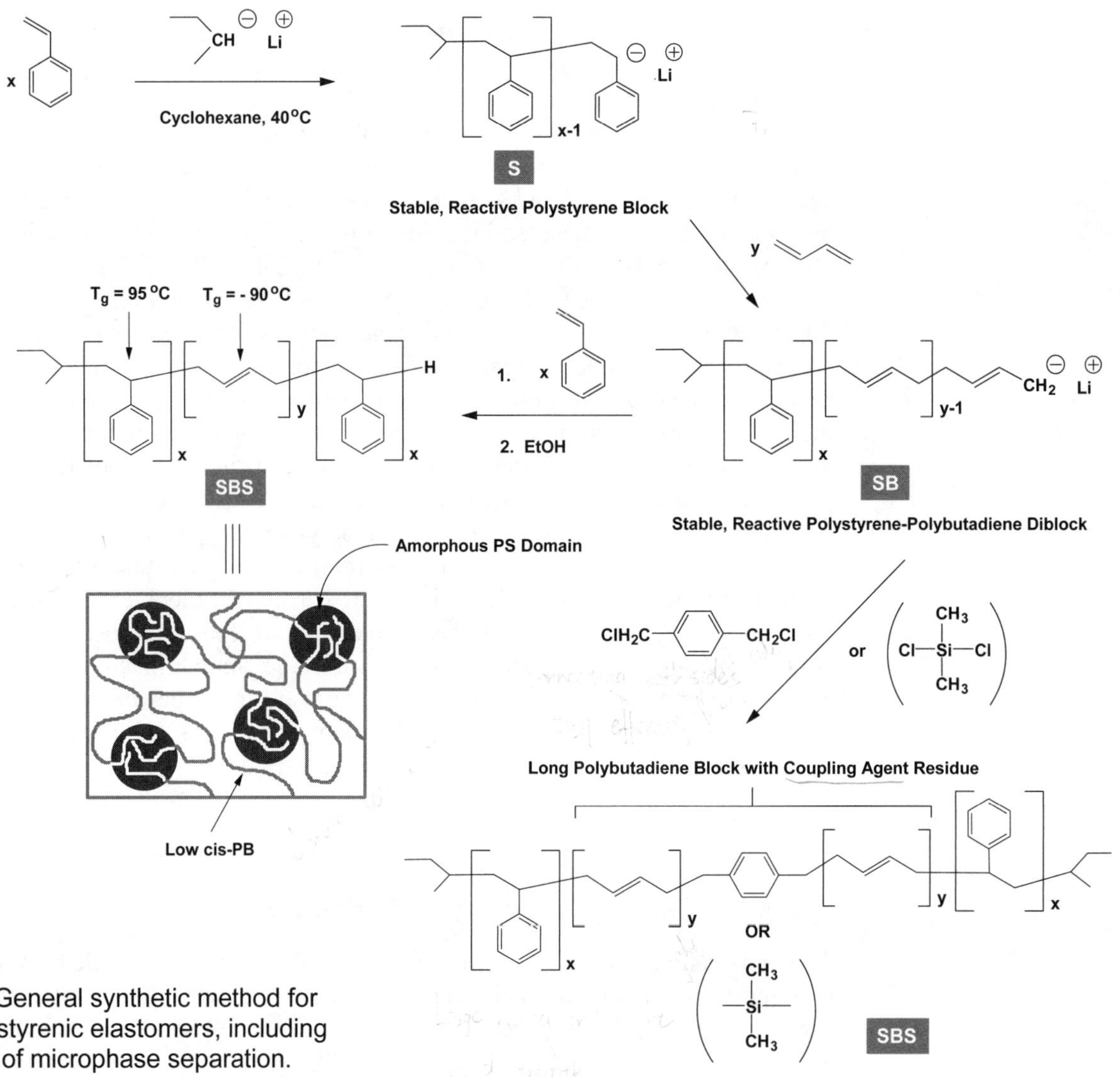

Cyclohexane, 40°C

Stable, Reactive Polystyrene Block

T_g = 95 °C T_g = - 90 °C

1. x

2. EtOH

SBS

SB

Stable, Reactive Polystyrene-Polybutadiene Diblock

Amorphous PS Domain

Low cis-PB

Long Polybutadiene Block with Coupling Agent Residue

Figure 2.89. General synthetic method for thermoplastic styrenic elastomers, including the schematic of microphase separation.

SBS triblock can also be prepared using a bifunctional initiator, such as 1,3-bis(1-phenylethenyl)benzene (PEB), in which the polymer chains grow in an outward direction from the center of the molecule (Figure 2.90). By contrast to the aforementioned method, the **B** block is prepared first, followed by two terminal **S** blocks. This route also provides a well-defined SBS triblock copolymer, ignoring the minor amount of the initiator fragment at the center of the **B** block.

Despite many advantages on the precise control of the copolymer composition and functionality, the alkyllithium reagent in the anionic polymerization is still far less effective in controlling the stereoregularity of either PS or PB blocks. In fact, the lack of stereoregular PS and PB in the anionic SBS material causes some deficiencies of its chemical and mechanical properties. For instance, the tensile strength of the anionic SBS (those prepared by anionic polymerization) is markedly decreased at elevated temperatures and is lost completely at the T_g of the PS block (ca. 100°C) because of the softening of the glassy PS domains, which serve as physical crosslinking sites in these materials. To solve this problem, superior styrene-butadiene-styrene (SBS) triblock copolymers consisting of elastic *cis*-polybutadiene (*cis*-PB) chemically bonded with crystallizable syndiotactic polystyrene (sPS) have been synthesized very recently through a metallocene-catalyzed stereospecific sequential triblock copolymerization of **S** with **B** (Figure 2.91).[45] The ^{13}C NMR analysis of the copolymer product proved that the PS blocks are highly syndiotactic (*rrrr* pentad > 95%), and the PB block contained primarily the *cis*-1,4 structure (>70%).

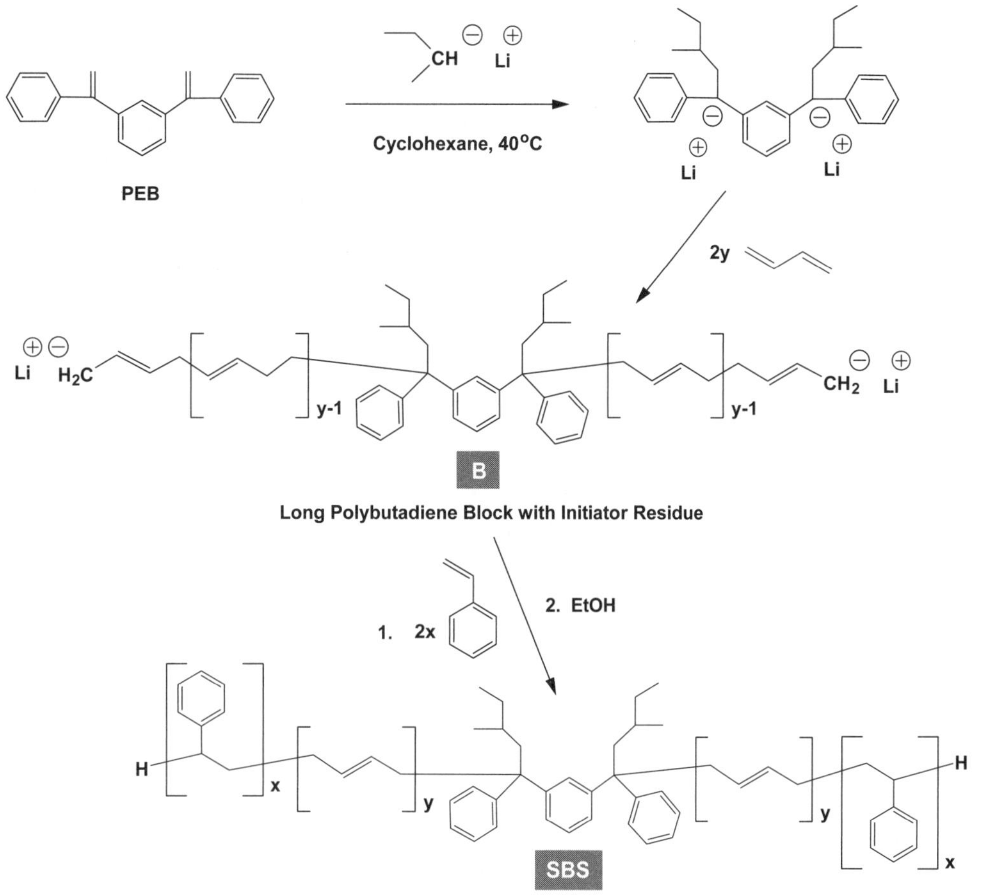

Figure 2.90. Synthesis of SBS triblock copolymer using a bifunctional initiator.

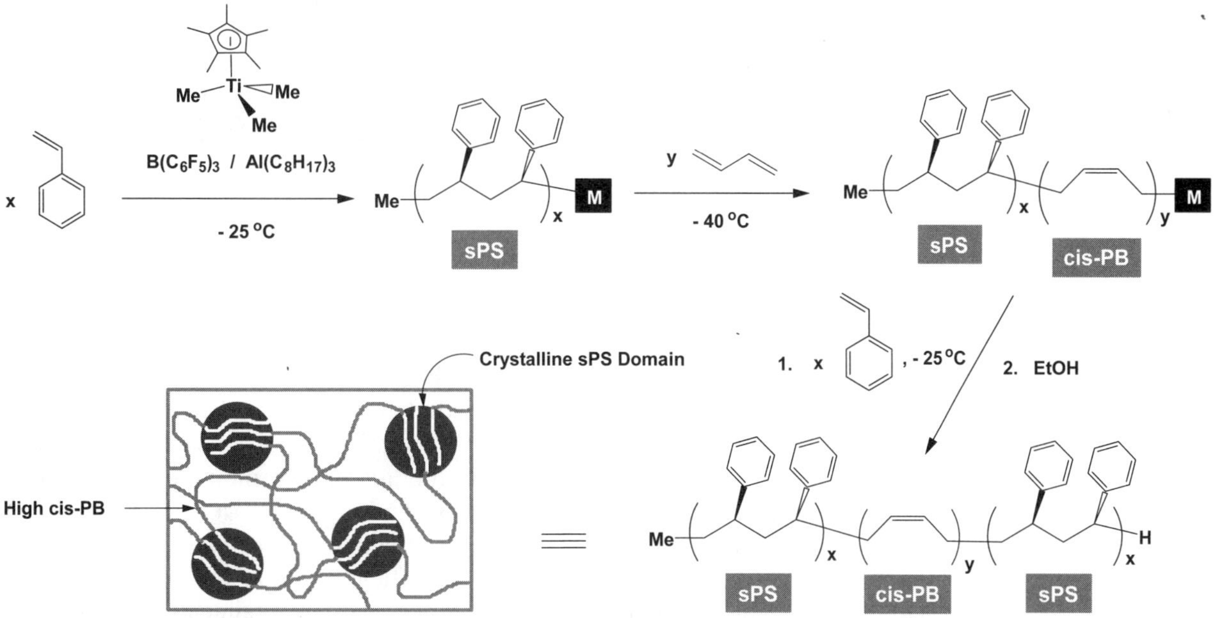

Figure 2.91. Metallocene-catalyzed synthesis of SBS triblock copolymer containing crystalline PS domains and flexible *cis*-PB continuous phase.

Interestingly, in a recent study, a new class of TPEs, PI-*g*-$(PS)_2$, comprised of polyisoprene (PI) backbones with two PS branches grafted at each of several tetrafunctional branch points per molecule has been developed (Figure 2.92).[46] These architecturally controlled multigraft copolymers have been shown to form well-ordered microphase-separated morphologies, which depend on both composition (PS volume fraction) and molecular architecture (number of branch points). For example, the TPE derived from 22 vol.% PS and seven branch points, exhibits high strain at break, which is double that of Kraton®. The synthetic strategy involves the preparation of two reactive monomers, PS-$SiCl_2$-PS and Li-PI-Li, followed by controlled step-growth polymerization of the two monomers. As each step is well established, this methodology offers the control of backbone molecular weight, arm molecular weight, and number and placement of branch points along the backbone.

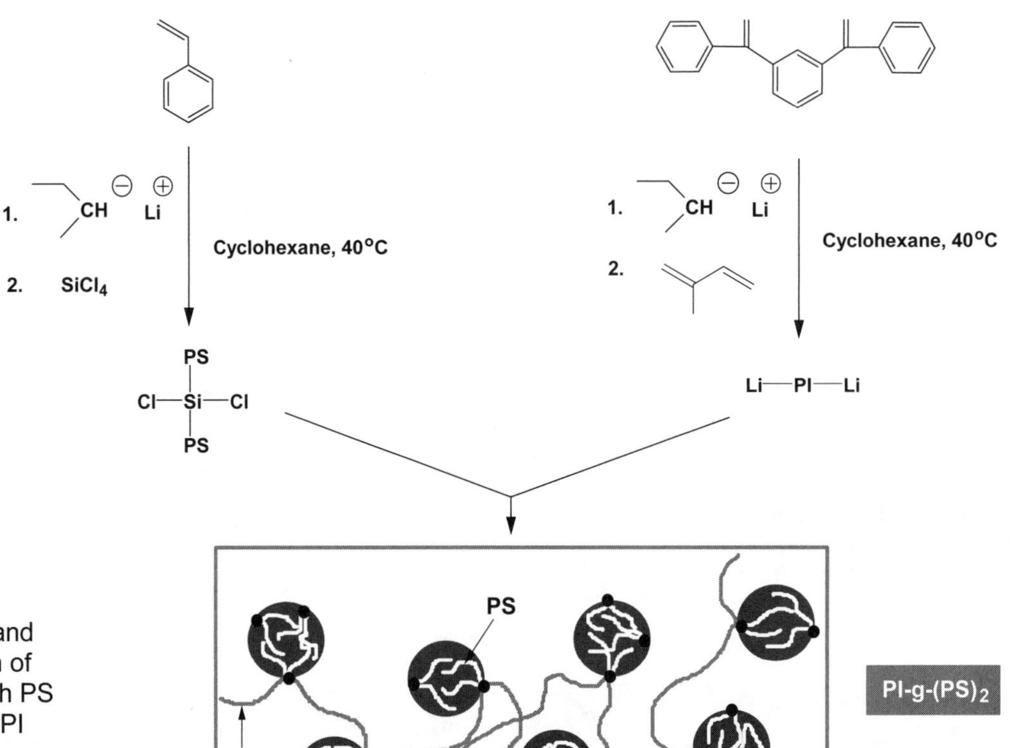

Figure 2.92. Synthesis and schematic representation of multigraft copolymers with PS domains in a continuous PI matrix. *Note:* only one PI molecule with seven branched points is shown for clarity.

2.3.3.2. Thermoplastic Polyolefinic Elastomers

Traditionally, thermoplastic polyolefinic elastomers (TPOs) are produced by blending an amorphous (soft) polyolefin, such as ethylene-propylene-diene (EPDM) copolymers and ethylene-propylene copolymers, with a crystalline (hard) polyolefin, such as iPP and HDPE. These TPOs are used widely in the automotive industry as car bumpers and fascia, because of their light weight, recyclability, low cost, and easy molding into complex geometries, making them a cost-effective alternative to traditional metallic bumper materials. The recent advent of efficient single-site metallocene catalysts, which are capable of copolymerizing with almost any combination of α-olefins, now offer TPOs with superior properties because they provide greater control of polyolefin size dimensions and microstructure. For example, the oscillating catalyst, outlined in

Figure 2.93 (see Figure 2.26 for other catalysts), produces an elastomeric polypropylene (elPP) with well-defined $(A\text{-}B)_n$ type alternating blocks of isotactic and atactic PP segments by controlling the temperature, pressure and monomer concentration of polymerization (*vide supra*).

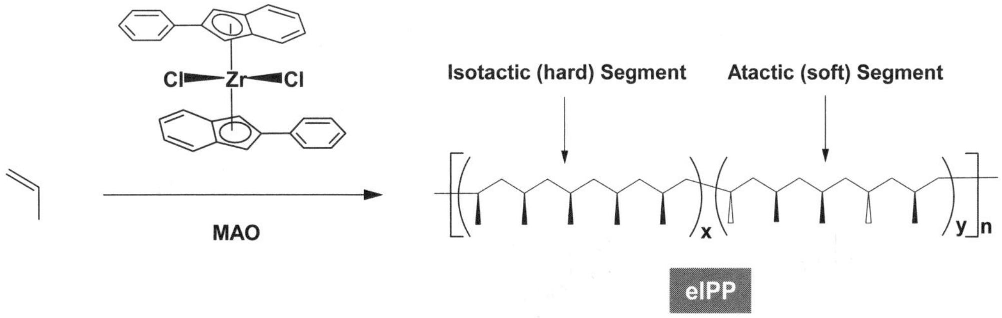

Figure 2.93. $(A\text{-}B)_n$ type TPOs by oscillating catalyst technology.

Another example is Dow's INSITE® constrained geometry catalyst (CGC), which is used to produce TPOs with desired crystallinity, morphology, and tensile stress-strain behavior (Figure 2.94).[47] Under the right conditions, this catalyst can polymerize mixtures of ethylene and α-olefin monomers (usually 1-octene) into $(A\text{-}B)_n$ type block copolymers, rather than into random copolymers. The hard blocks are made of crystalline linear, long polyethylene (HDPE) segments, while the soft rubber-like highly amorphous blocks are constituted of ethylene and α-olefin copolymer segments, usually arranged atactically.

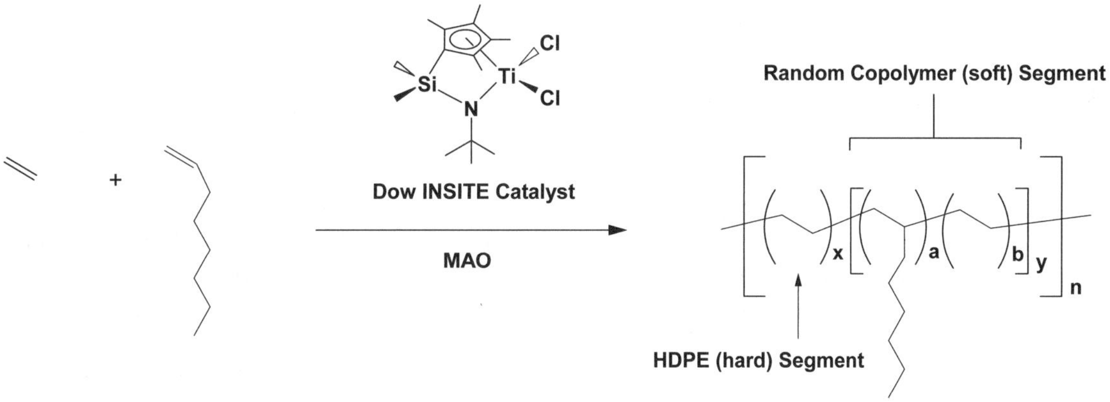

Figure 2.94. $(A\text{-}B)_n$ type TPOs by INSITE catalyst technology.

TPOs with comb branch-block copolymers have also been developed using metallocene catalysts to introduce specific properties, such as good elastic recovery and good high-temperature tensile strength.[48] Conceptually, the synthesis can be divided into two steps: the generation of vinyl-terminated, crystallizable macromonomers, and the incorporation of these macromonomers into an amorphous copolymer backbone. In practice, the two steps may be conducted sequentially or simultaneously. The polymer properties depend on the catalyst pair and the process conditions selected, which determine the populations of reactive macromonomer and the probability of incorporating them into the backbone. One such efficient catalyst pair is depicted in Figure 2.95. In the presence of a mixed ethylene/butene feed the Cp_2ZrCl_2 catalyst, by virtue of its low comonomer incorporating capability, will produce primarily crystalline polyethylene macromonomers. The titanium CGC catalyst, on the other hand, has a higher affinity for comonomers and will consume comonomers and macromonomers during polymerization, which produces a flexible backbone, serving as the continuous phase.

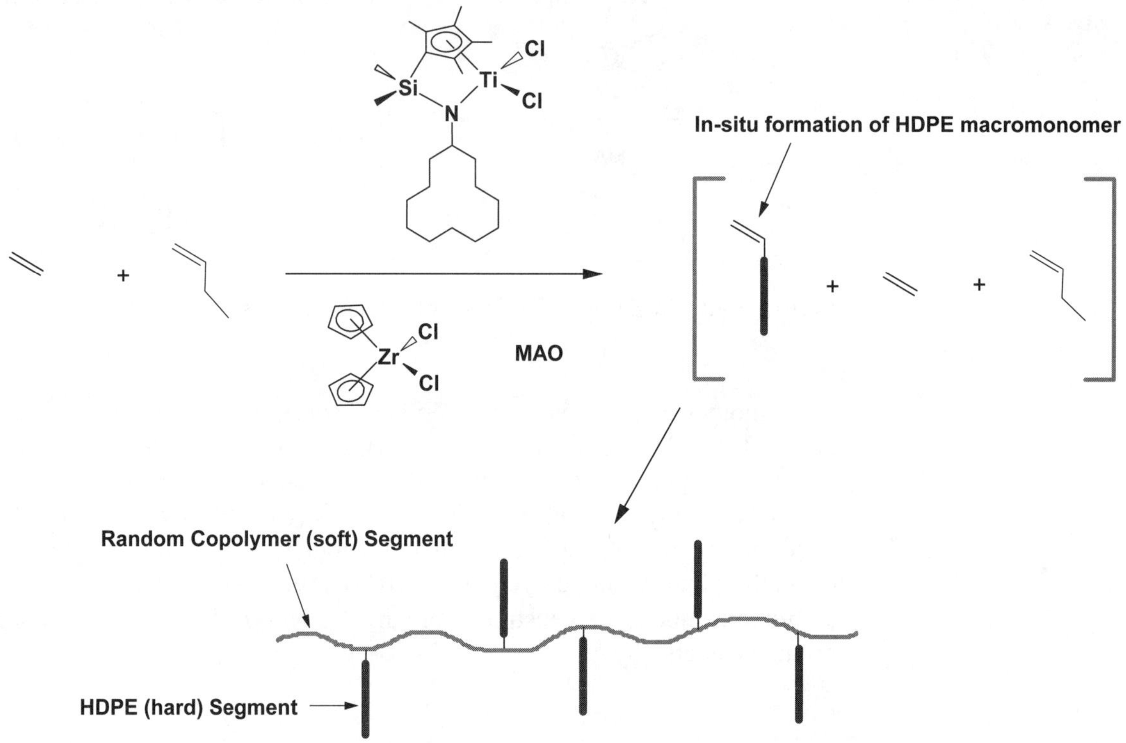

Figure 2.95. Metallocene-catalyzed synthesis of TPOs with comb branch-blocks.

Very recently, a successful preparation of $(A\text{-}B)_n$ type TPOs containing semicrystalline polyethylene (A) and rubbery poly(ethylene-*alt*-propylene) (B) blocks has been accomplished by catalytic hydrogenation of poly(1,4-butadiene-*b*-1,4-isoprene-*b*-1,4-butadiene)$_n$ (BIB) triblock copolymers (prepared by anionic polymerization similar to SBS).[49] In a typical procedure, BIB or related multiblock copolymers are dissolved in cyclohexane and reacted with hydrogen (500 psi) over a porous heterogeneous Pt-Re/SiO_2 catalyst at 140°C (Figure 2.96). Greater than 99% saturation efficiency can be achieved by this method.

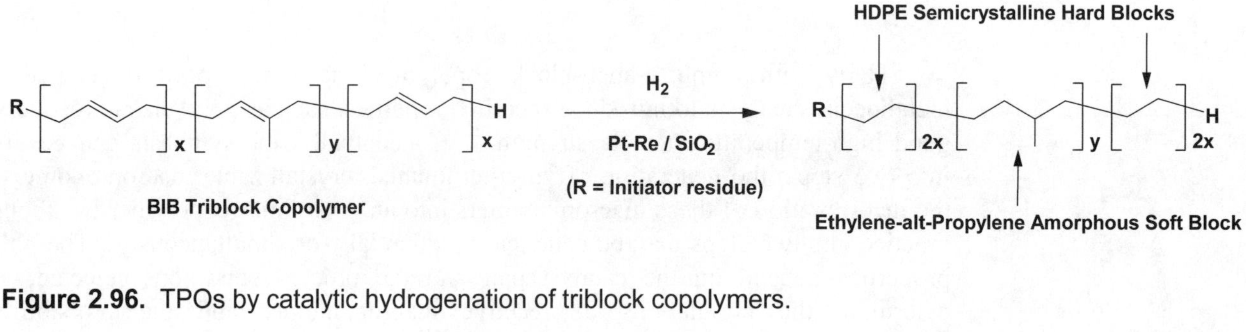

Figure 2.96. TPOs by catalytic hydrogenation of triblock copolymers.

2.3.3.3. Thermoplastic Polyurethane Elastomers

Among segmented copolymers, *thermoplastic elastomeric polyurethanes* (TPUs) are the most widely used. TPUs are linear $(AB)_n$-type multiblock copolymers, comprising soft- and hard-segment blocks. As depicted in Figure 2.97, the representation of the structure of TPU elastomer is very complex, hence a generalized scheme is adopted. The soft-segment blocks are formed by the reaction between a relatively high molecular weight polyester or polyether with terminal hydroxyl groups and a diisocyanate (e.g., PTMEG and MDI), while the hard-segment blocks are produced from a short-chain diol and diisocyanate (e.g., 1,4-butanediol and MDI). TPUs are often prepared via a one-pot procedure, in which the long-chain diol reacts with excess diisocyanate to form an isocyanate-functionalized prepolymer, which subsequently reacts with the chain extender (e.g., a short-chain diol or a diamine), resulting in the formation of the high molecular weight polyurethane. The polyether types are slightly more expensive, but exhibit better hydrolytic stability and low-temperature flexibility than the polyesters. Poly(oxytetramethylene) glycol (PTMEG) in the molecular weight range of 2,000 to 4,000 is often used as the soft segment because of its low T_g, good rubbery elasticity, and high strength. Under ambient conditions, the hard segments are incompatible with the soft segments. Consequently, they aggregate into crystalline microdomains with intense intermolecular hydrogen bonding in the continuous matrix of soft domains. Similar to SBS triblock copolymer, the elastomeric behavior of these materials arises from this aggregation, which provides necessary physical crosslinks between chains. TPU elastomers can also be processed like thermoplastics because of the disruption of the crystalline domains upon heating over the crystalline melting temperature and separation into microphases upon cooling. In general, TPUs possess outstanding abrasion resistance compared with other TPEs, good low-temperature flexibility, and excellent oil resistance to 80°C. Load-bearing capability ranks with the best of the elastomers.

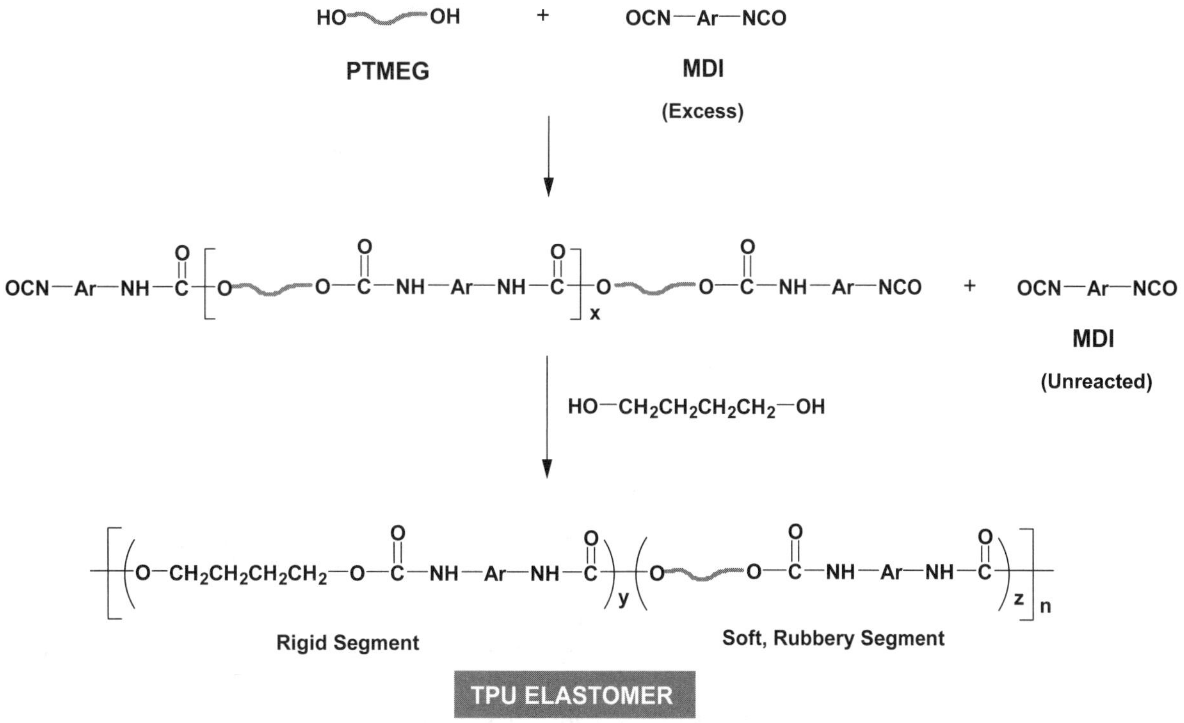

HO〰OH + OCN—Ar—NCO

PTMEG MDI (Excess)

$$OCN{-}Ar{-}NH{-}\overset{O}{\overset{\|}{C}}{-}\left[O\sim O{-}\overset{O}{\overset{\|}{C}}{-}NH{-}Ar{-}NH{-}\overset{O}{\overset{\|}{C}}\right]_x{-}O\sim O{-}\overset{O}{\overset{\|}{C}}{-}NH{-}Ar{-}NCO \; + \; OCN{-}Ar{-}NCO$$

MDI (Unreacted)

$HO{-}CH_2CH_2CH_2CH_2{-}OH$

$$\left[\left(O{-}CH_2CH_2CH_2CH_2{-}O{-}\overset{O}{\overset{\|}{C}}{-}NH{-}Ar{-}NH{-}\overset{O}{\overset{\|}{C}}\right)_y\left(O\sim O{-}\overset{O}{\overset{\|}{C}}{-}NH{-}Ar{-}NH{-}\overset{O}{\overset{\|}{C}}\right)_z\right]_n$$

Rigid Segment Soft, Rubbery Segment

TPU ELASTOMER

Figure 2.97. General synthetic scheme for TPU elastomers.

One of the major shares of the polyurethane market is TPU elastomeric fibers, such as spandex (Lycra®, DuPont). The molecular design is similar to that of TPU elastomers, except for a short-chain diamine, such as hydrazine and 1,2-diaminoethane, which is used as the chain extender in place of a short-chain diol. Thus, the major part of the hard segments is made of polyurea rather than polyurethane. The preferred long soft segment macroglycol is PETMG which makes up about 80% of the total polymer weight. The other 20% is composed of rigid segment materials, viz., MDI and chain extender diamine. Often, a small amount of chain terminating monofunctional secondary amine, e.g., diisopropyl amine, is added to the formulation to control the molecular weight in the range of 50,000 to 100,000. Figure 2.98 shows the simplified reaction scheme for the synthesis of spandex elastomeric fibers. Unlike natural rubber latex-based fibers, spandex polymers do not require a crosslinking step, but the majority of hydrogen bonding required is obtained during stretch drawing of fibers from its melt state. Spandex fibers are superior to latex fibers because they are stronger, lighter, and can be stretched to almost 500% of their length. The "form-fitting" properties of spandex makes it attractive for use in under-garments, swimsuits, bicycle pants and exercise wear.

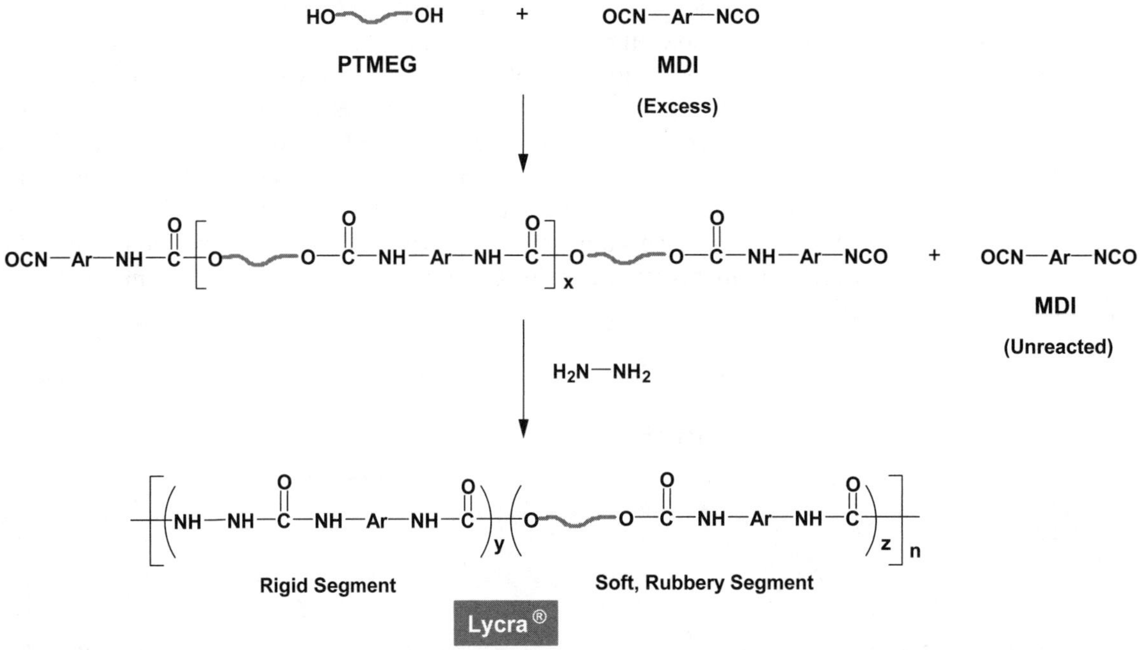

HO~~OH + OCN—Ar—NCO

PTMEG MDI (Excess)

OCN—Ar—NH—C(=O)—[O~~O—C(=O)—NH—Ar—NH—C(=O)]$_x$—O~~O—C(=O)—NH—Ar—NCO + OCN—Ar—NCO

MDI (Unreacted)

$H_2N—NH_2$

—[(NH—NH—C(=O)—NH—Ar—NH—C(=O))$_y$(O~~O—C(=O)—NH—Ar—NH—C(=O))$_z$]$_n$—

Rigid Segment Soft, Rubbery Segment

Lycra®

Figure 2.98. Synthesis of typical spandex elastomeric fibers.

2.3.3.4. Thermoplastic Polyester Elastomers

These TPEs are synthesized in a way similar to the preparation of thermoplastic polyurethane elastomers. The same high molecular weight dihydroxy terminated aliphatic polyether, such as PTMEG, is used as the soft block, which is polymerized to multi-blocks with the oligomeric aromatic hard polyester segment, usually poly(butylenes terephthalate) (PBT), which is formed in-situ by reaction between 1,4-butanediol (chain extender) and dimethyl terephthalate (Figure 2.99). Unlike ABA-type triblock copolymers, these $(AB)_n$-type multiblock copolymers, such as Hytrel® (DuPont), are usually composed of ~55 wt.% of hard blocks and ~45 wt.% of soft blocks. These TPEs provide service over a broad temperature range by maintaining good flexibility and impact strength at temperatures as low as -40°C and significant strength and integrity at temperatures up to about 110°C. Also, they are easier and more forgiving in processing. These materials can be processed by injection molding, extrusion, rotational molding, flow molding, thermoforming, and melt casting.

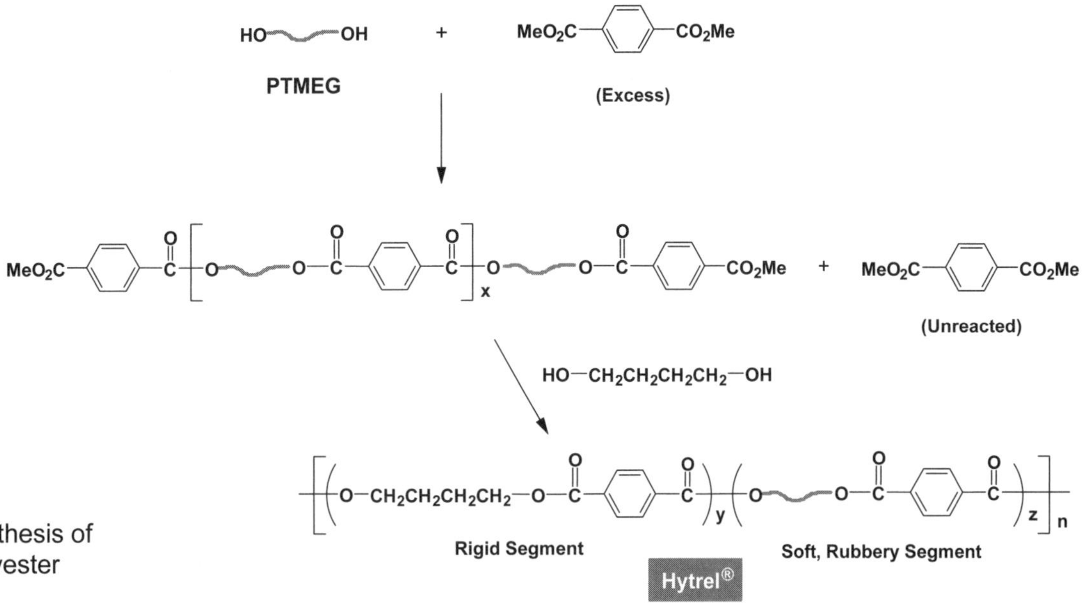

Figure 2.99. Synthesis of thermoplastic polyester elastomers.

In a recent study, the elasticity of these TPEs has been significantly improved by replacement of PTMEG soft segments with poly(ethylene oxide)-*block*-poly(ethylene-*stat*-butylene)-*block*-poly(ethylene oxide) (PEO-*b*-PEB-*b*-PEO) triblock copolymer soft segments containing a nonpolar middle block based on *hydrogenated polybutadiene* (PEB).[50] The incorporation of this strongly incompatible PEB block resulted in increased phase separation between the PBT hard blocks and the soft segment phase, leading to a dispersed PBT phase and hence, to increased elasticity. As depicted in Figure 2.100, the synthesis of dihydroxy terminated PEO-PEB-PEO triblock copolymers was performed by anionic ring-opening polymerization of ethylene oxide in THF using a commercially available HO-PEB-OH (Figure 2.101).

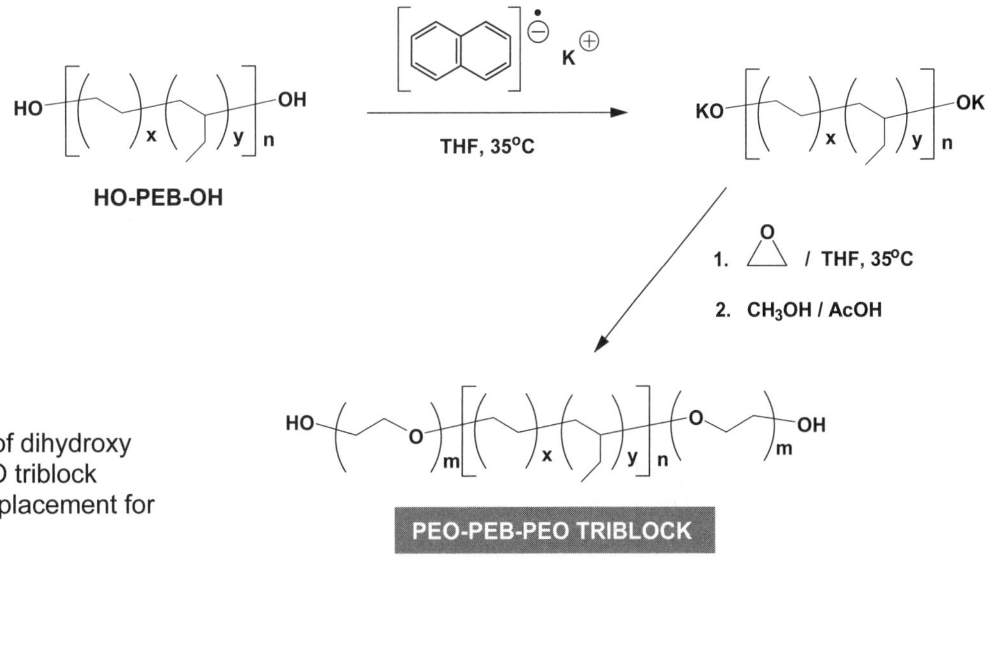

Figure 2.100. Synthesis of dihydroxy terminated PEO-PEB-PEO triblock copolymers as superior replacement for PTMEG.

2.4.3.5. Thermoplastic Polyamide Elastomers

The $(AB)_n$-type multiblock polyamide TPEs, such as Pebax® by Arkema Group, are prepared in a manner similar to thermoplastic polyester elastomers (Figure 2.101). The soft block is normally selected from PTMEG or HO-PEB-OH, while in-situ generated nylon-6,6 is the primary choice for the hard blocks.[51] The amide linkages are formed by reaction between carboxylic and isocyanate groups with elimination of carbon dioxide. The polyamide TPEs are low-density, thermostable (>250°C), high-elongation materials with good solvent and abrasion resistance. They are used especially in automotive, sports, medical, and electric-electronic equipment.

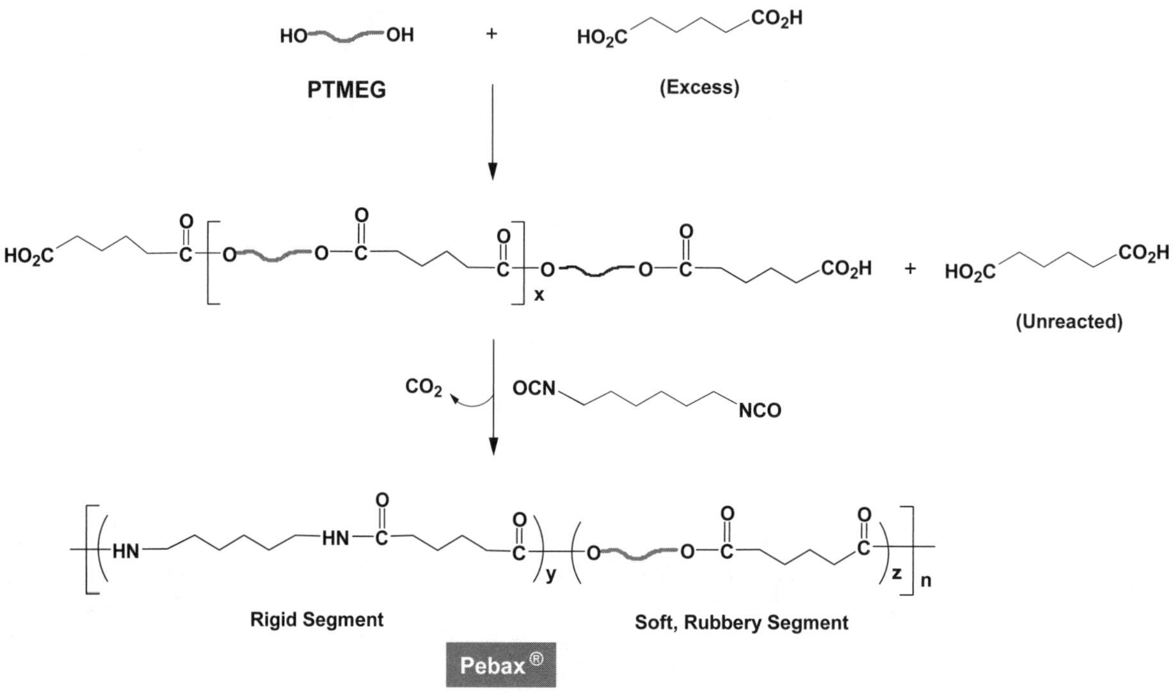

HO~~OH + HO_2C~~CO_2H

PTMEG (Excess)

HO_2C~~C(=O)–[O~~O–C(=O)~~C(=O)]$_x$–O~~O–C(=O)~~CO_2H + HO_2C~~CO_2H (Unreacted)

CO_2 ← OCN~~NCO

[(HN~~HN–C(=O)~~C(=O))$_y$(O~~O–C(=O)~~C(=O))$_z$]$_n$

Rigid Segment Soft, Rubbery Segment

Pebax®

Figure 2.101. Synthesis of thermoplastic polyamide elastomers.

2.4. RECENT ADVANCES IN POLYMER SYNTHESIS

Improvements in synthetic polymer chemistry during the past two decades have been greatly expanded by the development of highly efficient catalyst/initiator systems, which led to polymers with controlled architecture and superior properties. Traditionally, control of molecular architecture has been achieved by living procedures, such as anionic polymerization, which are synthetically challenging and not amenable to significant changes in the macromolecular structure or the presence of functional groups. For example, simple random copolymers of styrene and methyl methacrylate cannot be prepared by living anionic polymerization. Conversely, these random copolymers are trivially prepared using traditional free-radical chemistry; however, the level of control is severely compromised as the polymerization results in ill-defined, polydispersed materials. Moreover, anionic polymerization requires more rigorously controlled reaction conditions and higher purity reactants because the active species can be terminated by impurities, such as oxygen, carbon dioxide, and moisture. The kinetics of anionic polymerization is also very sensitive to the solvent used.

Recent development of “living”/controlled free-radical polymerization (CRP) techniques, which combine the versatility of traditional free-radical polymerization and the control over molecular weight, chemical composition and chain architecture (as in anionic polymerization), seems to be an attractive solution for the facile preparation of a wide variety of polymers, copolymers, and functionalized polymers with predetermined structures and properties. Perhaps the most important advances have been realized in the area of efficient single-site metallocene catalysts, which are capable of copolymerizing almost any combination of α-olefins. Last, but not least, the development of new monomers leading to vastly improved polymer properties and environmentally benign polymerization processes (“green” chemistry) has made a remarkable contribution to the success of polymer science. In this section, a comprehensive outline encompassing the recent proliferation of polymerization procedures, including synthetic strategies to various initiator systems, is presented.

2.4.1. Controlled Free-Radical Polymerization

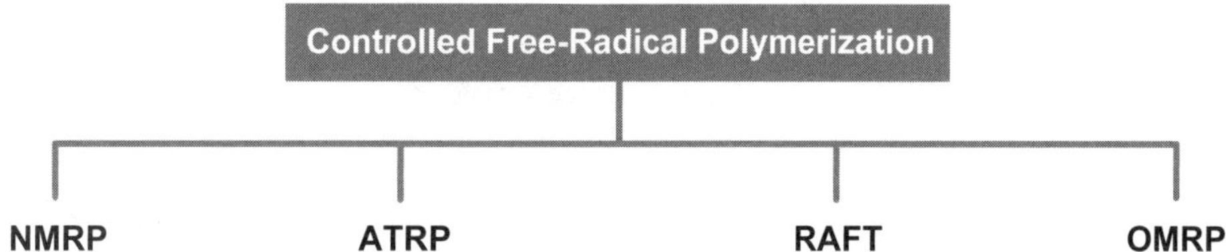

The concept of CRP is based on two principles: reversible termination or reversible transfer. Examples of processes that rely on reversible termination are *nitroxide-mediated controlled free-radical polymerization* (NMRP) and *atom transfer free-radical polymerization* (ATRP). In these processes, species are added which prevent bimolecular termination by reversible coupling. In NMRP, this species is a nitroxide, whereas in ATRP the species is a halide atom, originating from a transition-metal complex to which it can be transferred reversibly. By contrast, *reversible addition-fragmentation chain transfer* (RAFT) is based on reversible transfer. In this process, there is a fast exchange between growing radicals and dormant species via transfer reactions, during which the RAFT-moiety (dithioester) and radical activity are exchanged via an intermediate radical. Very recently, *organometal-mediated free-radical polymerization* (OMRP) has been established as another very efficient process for conducting a CRP. In many respects, all CRPs are similar in their overall scope, although there are a number of subtle differences which affect the applicability and suitability of each system for specific applications. For example, NMRP processes are potentially simpler, since they do not require an added metal complex and this absence leads to a greater functional group tolerance and easier purification (no metal ion contamination). However, the major limitation of NMRP procedures is their incompatibility with most vinyl monomer families. Typically, these are limited to styrene-based systems, and the level of control afforded to homopolymerization of acrylate/methacrylates and even random copolymers with high acrylates/methacrylate levels has been poor. In contrast, ATRP techniques have been successfully applied to a wide range of monomer families, including styrenics, acrylates, methacrylates, and acrylonitrile. Nevertheless, unlike conventional free-radical polymerizations, which exhibit fast propagation rates, all CRPs display significantly longer polymerization times, typically requiring several hours.

2.4.1.1. Nitroxide-Mediated Controlled Free-Radical Polymerization (NMRP)

The general mechanism of NMRP involves reversible activation/dissociation of dormant polymer chains (P_n-R) (Figure 2.102). This additional step in the free-radical polymerization provides the living character and controls the molecular weight distribution. When a dormant species or alkoxyamine dissociates homolytically, a carbon centered radical and a stable nitroxide radical are formed. This is a reversible process and the rate of reversible reaction is close to diffusion control, but at high enough temperatures where dissociation is competitive, the polymeric radicals (P_n•) can add to monomer, which allows step-wise growth of the polymer chains. The nitroxide is a perfect candidate for this process since it only reacts with carbon-centered radicals, is stable and does not dimerize, and in general, couples nonspecifically with all types of carbon-centered radicals (at close to diffusion controlled rates).

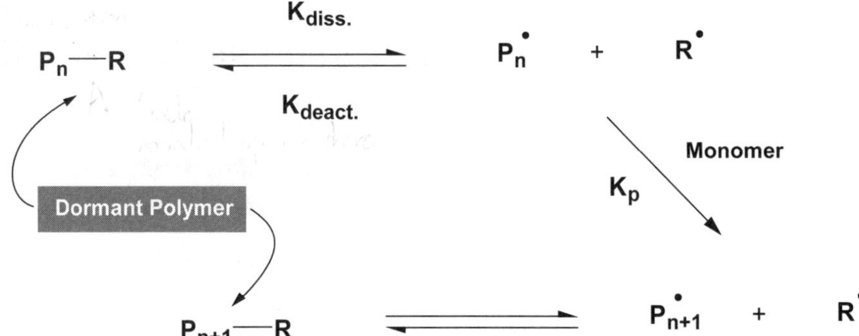

Figure 2.102. Mechanism of NMRP (**R•** = mediating radical, such as TEMPO).

In an ideal NMRP, polymerization is started using an N-alkoxyamine, also called a *unimolecular initiator*, such that reactions other than reversible activation of dormant species and addition of monomer to carbon-centered radicals cannot take place. The unimolecular initiators offer the advantages of fast reaction rates and allow the facile construction of block copolymers and graft copolymers and other complex macromolecular structures. The alkoxyamines consist of a small radical species, capable of reacting with monomer, trapped by a nitroxide, such as 2,2,6,6-tetramethyl-1-piperidinyloxy (TEMPO). Alkoxyamines are conveniently prepared either by trapping nitroxide radical with *in situ* generated benzyl radical or by O-alkylation of an N-hydroxy derivative with an alkyl halide in the presence sodium hydride (Figure 2.103).[52] Upon decomposition of the alkoxyamine in the presence of monomer, polymeric dormant species will form and grow in chain length over time. Since the nitroxide and the carbon-centered radical diffuse away from each other, termination by combination or disproportionation of two carbon centered radicals cannot be excluded. This will lead to the formation of "dead" polymer chains and an excess of free nitroxide. The build-up of free nitroxide is referred to as the *persistent radical effect* (PRE)[53] and slows the rate of polymerization, since it will favor trapping (radical-radical coupling) over propagation.

A more versatile method for the preparation of alkoxyamines by halogen radical abstraction from alkyl halides with a silyl radical has been reported recently (Figure 2.104).[54] This methodology provides access to certain alkoxyamines which are inaccessible by other methods and applicable to the synthesis of primary, secondary, and tertiary *N*-alkoxyamines from a variety of nitroxides. The method permits preparation of *N*-alkoxyamines with hydroxyl and carboxyl functionalities. Incorporation of functionality on the *N*-alkoxyamine provides functional handles to allow for pre- or post-polymerization modification, applications including attachment of polymers to surfaces, or end-capping with affinity labels or biomolecules.

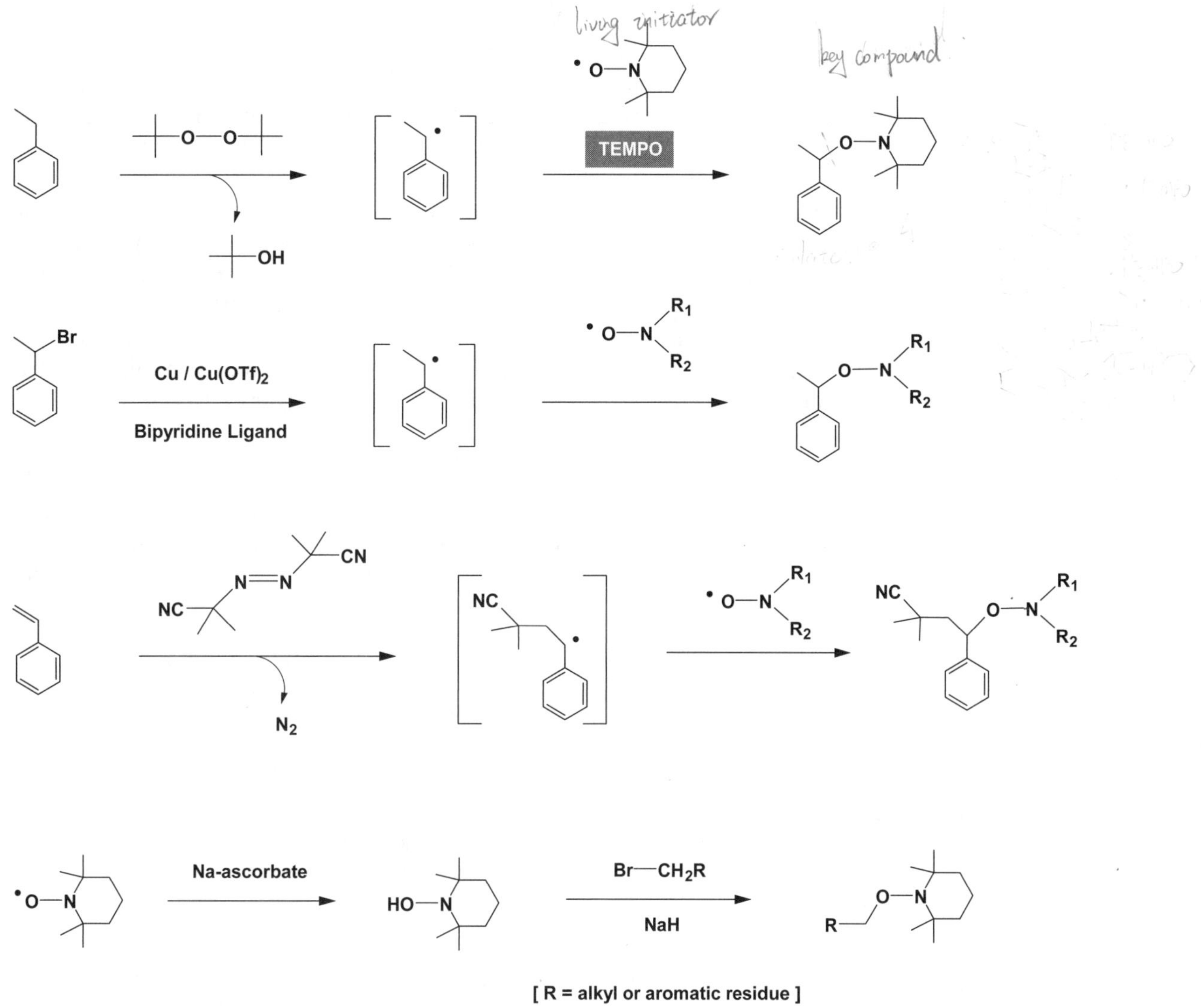
TEMPO
OH
Br
Cu / Cu(OTf)$_2$
Bipyridine Ligand
CN
NC
N_2
Na-ascorbate
Br—CH$_2$R
NaH
[R = alkyl or aromatic residue]

Figure 2.103. General methods for the synthesis of unimolecular initiators.

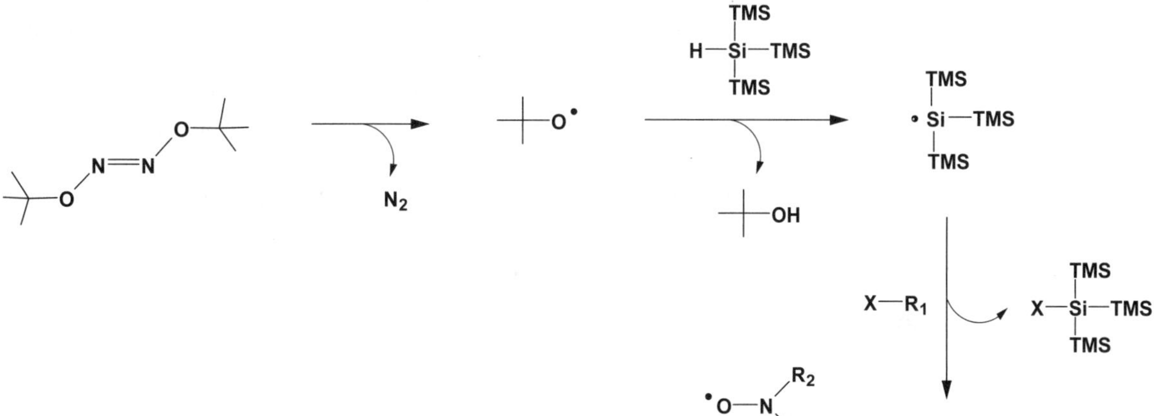
TMS
H—Si—TMS
N_2
OH
X—R$_1$
X—Si—TMS

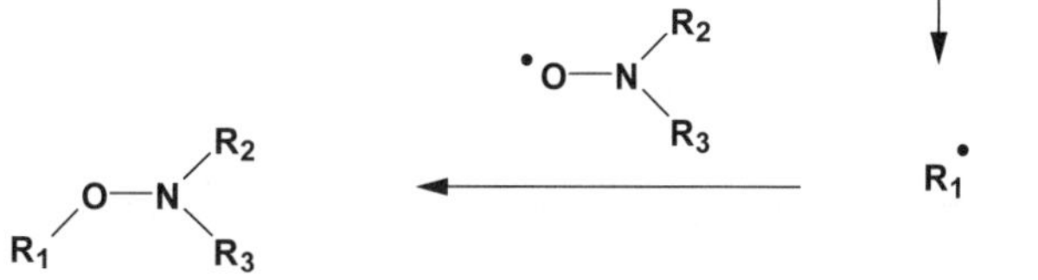

Figure 2.104. Synthesis of unimolecular initiators by halogen radical abstraction from alkyl halides.

To greatly extend the scope of NMRP, especially for controlled polymerization of nonstyrenic monomers, the synthesis of a variety of cyclic and acyclic alkoxyamines that exhibit higher rates of dissociation than the one based on TEMPO, has been conducted. The results indicate that the nitroxide structure plays a crucial role in the success or failure of NMRP, and the key to extending the scope of this reaction is in designing more effective nitroxides. It has been demonstrated that the substituents present on the positions α, α' to the nitroxide function have a significant effect (both steric and electronic) on the homolysis rate constant (k_{diss}) of the corresponding alkoxyamines. Thus, an acyclic alkoxyamine derived from N-*tert*-butyl-N-[1-diethylphosphono-(2,2-dimethylpropyl)] nitroxide (DEPN) is efficient at controlling the radical polymerizations of styrene and alkyl acrylates to afford polystyrene and poly(*n*-butyl acrylate) with polydispersities lower than 1.1, but also allows faster propagation than most other nitroxides investigated thus far (Figure 2.105).[55]

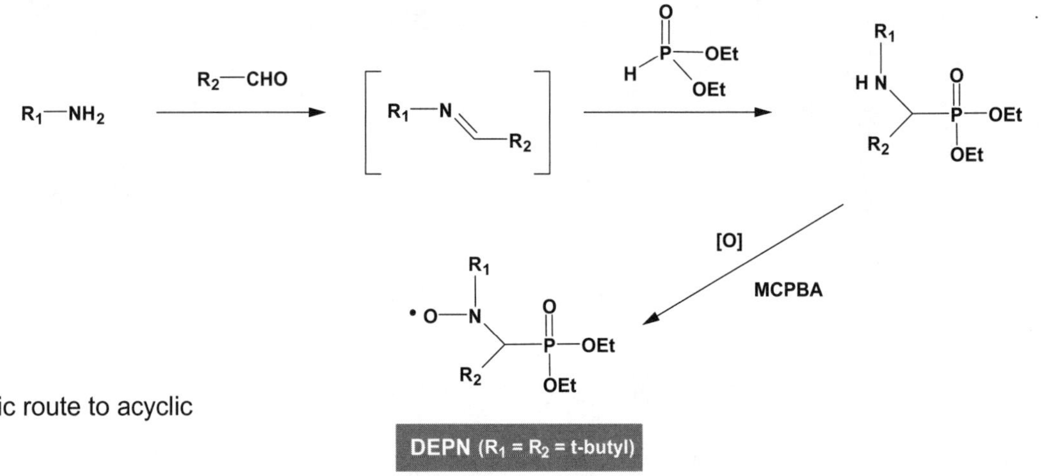

R1—NH2 → (R2—CHO) → [R1—N=CH—R2] → (H—P(=O)(OEt)2) → R1—NH—CH(R2)—P(=O)(OEt)2 → ([O] MCPBA) → •O—N(R1)—CH(R2)—P(=O)(OEt)2

DEPN (R_1 = R_2 = t-butyl)

Figure 2.105. Synthetic route to acyclic nitroxides for NMRP.

A quite different and well used synthetic strategy, involving reductive condensation of tertiary nitro compounds and aldehydes (Figure 2.106), has been described for the synthesis of acyclic α-hydrogen bearing nitroxides, which are prepared by reaction of the resulting nitrones with aryl Grignard reagents, followed by copper(II) catalyzed oxidation at ambient atmosphere.[56-58] In comparison with traditional TEMPO-based systems, the performance of these nitroxides is significantly improved and permits the controlled polymerization of a wide variety of monomer families, viz. acrylates, acrylamides, and acrylonitrile-based monomers. The versatile nature of these initiators can also be used to control the formation of random and block copolymers from a wide selection of monomer units containing reactive functional groups, such as amino, carboxylic acid, and glycidyl. Thorough investigation of a variety of cyclic nitroxides, which exhibit properties similar to that of acyclic nitroxides, has been pursued, but there is less interest because of synthetic complexity and overall yield of the products.

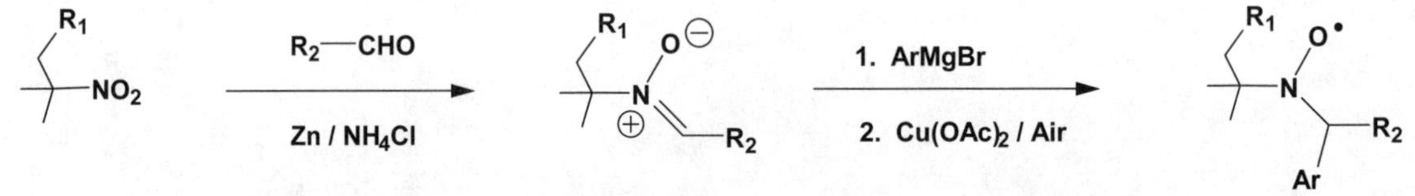

R1, NO2 → (R2—CHO; Zn / NH_4Cl) → nitrone → (1. ArMgBr; 2. $Cu(OAc)_2$ / Air) → nitroxide (R1, O•, N, R2, Ar)

Figure 2.106. Synthetic route to acyclic nitroxides for NMRP.

2.4.1.2. Atom Transfer Free-Radical Polymerization (ATRP)

ATRP employs a different chemistry to establish a dynamic equilibrium between a low concentration of growing radicals and a large amount of dormant chains (Figure 2.107).[59-61] ATRP proceeds via a reversible redox process between an alkyl halide as an initiator and a transition metal (pseudo)halide catalyst based on Cu, Fe, Ni, and Ru (CuBr is most popular). A solubilizing ligating agent is also required to increase the solubility of the metal halide during the reaction. The most common ligating agents are either 2,2'-bipyridine (bipy) or a modified version, such as 4,4'-dinonyl-2,2'-bipyridine (or a triarylphosphine ligand for Ru-based catalyst). The transition metal catalyst abstracts the halogen atom from the initiator (alkyl halide) to generate a radical which initiates and then propagates the polymerization. Monomers that have been successfully polymerized by means of ATRP include styrenes, (meth)acrylates, (meth)acrylamides, and acrylonitrile.

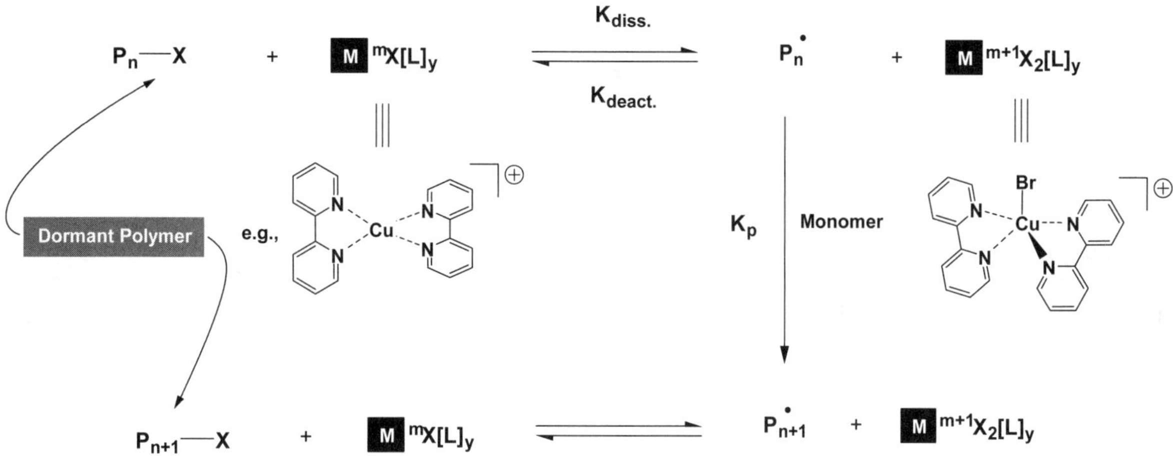

Figure 2.107. Mechanism of ATRP.

For an efficient ATRP, the halide group, X, of the initiator must rapidly and selectively migrate between the growing chain and the transition metal complex. Thus far, bromine and chlorine are the halogens that afford the best molecular weight control. In general, any alkyl halide with activating substituents on the α-carbon, such as aryl, carbonyl, and allyl groups, can potentially be used as ATRP initiators. Figure 2.108 shows examples of commonly used initiators, such as ethyl-2-bromoisobutyrate (EBIB) and 1-phenyl-ethylbromide (PEB), including preparation of initiators from readily available starting materials.[62-64]

Recently, there has been increasing interest in surface-initiated polymerization in both aqueous and non-aqueous media for which ATRP is becoming a valuable tool, leading to novel polymer-grafted materials.[65-67] The reactions depicted in Figure 2.108 are usually used to incorporate initiator sites for grafting. Another example, shown in Figure 2.109, involves reaction between a colloidal silica surface and 3-(dimethylethoxysilyl)propyl-2-bromoisobutyrate to form surface-grafted ATRP initiator. With proper formulation, ATRP of aprotic hydrophilic monomers, such as methoxy-capped oligo(ethyleneglycol) methacrylate (OEGMA), can be conducted in aqueous media to produce polymer-grafted silica particles.[68]

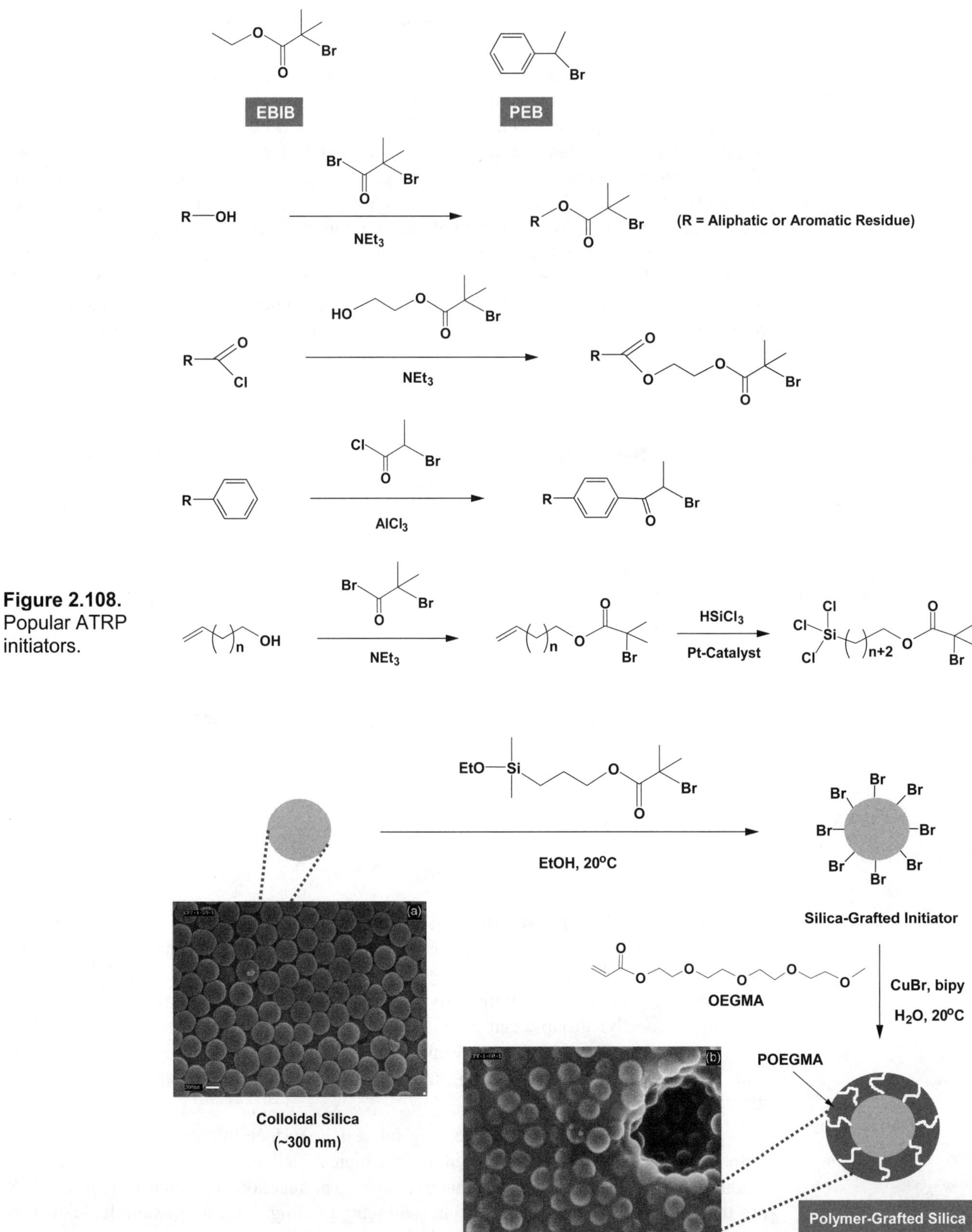

Figure 2.108. Popular ATRP initiators.

Figure 2.109. Synthesis of polymer-grafted silica particles via aqueous ATRP. Scanning electron micrographs of colloidal silica particles (*Left:* before modification; *Right:* after modification with poly(OEGMA), POEGMA. *Reproduced with kind permission of the American Chemical Society.*

Using ATRP, polymers with controlled molar masses and small polydispersities (M_w/M_n = 1.05-1.5) can be obtained. ATRP is capable of polymerizing a wide variety of monomers and is tolerant of many functional groups (except an acid functionality which destroys the metal catalyst by displacing the halogen atom on the metal-ligand complex) present in the monomers and initiators and allows the preparation of end-functionalized polymers, star, comb, or grafted polymers, nanoparticle hybrids, and polymer monolayers (*vide infra*). One notable drawback of ATRP, arising when standard homogeneous catalysts are used, is contamination of the polymer by the ligand/metal complex (e.g., CuBr-bipy). The colored catalyst complex is typically removed by passing through a column of alumina, followed by precipitation of the polymer. Post-polymerization processing to remove catalyst increases the cost of production. Thus, methods that generate a clean polymer solution after reaction and allow for catalyst recycling are desirable.

2.4.1.3. Reversible Addition-Fragmentation Chain Transfer Radical Polymerization (RAFT)

In contrast to the aforementioned CRP processes, RAFT requires a small proportion of a conventional free-radical initiator, such as BPO and AIBN. First, there is a normal reaction to initiate the polymerization (Figure 2.110). In the chain-transfer part, the polymer radical, $\mathbf{P_n}$•, reacts with the S=C moiety of the RAFT agent (thiocarbonylthio compound, **A**, where Z is an activating group that modifies the reactivity of the thiocarbonyl group toward radical addition, and R is a good homolytic leaving group that can initiate polymerization) to form an intermediate radical species **B** that can fragment back to the original polymeric radical species or to a dormant polymeric species **C** and a small radical, R•. This new radical (R•) can subsequently react with monomers to form another growing polymer chain, $\mathbf{P_m}$• (re-initiation). The dormant polymeric RAFT agent **C** acts similar to a RAFT agent, so the new growing polymeric radicals ($\mathbf{P_m}$•) can also add to the S=C moiety of the polymeric RAFT agent **C**, thereby forming an intermediate radical **D**. Hence, the process involves a sequence of reversible addition-fragmentation steps, which result in an equilibrium between active and dormant species (chain equilibrium). This process continues until all monomers are consumed. The effectiveness of **A** in providing living character is attributed to their very high transfer constants which ensure a rapid rate of exchange between dormant and living chains. In fact, the transfer constants are too high to be measured using conventional techniques (e.g., the Mayo method[69]).

The RAFT process offers a significant advantage over other CRPs in its ability to polymerize a variety of monomers, including functional monomers containing acid (e.g., acrylic acid), acid salt (e.g., styrenesulfonic acid sodium salt), hydroxy (e.g., hydroxyethyl methacrylate) or tertiary amino (e.g., dimethylaminoethyl methacrylate) groups. Further, the process is successful with these monomers under a range of reaction conditions, producing polymers with narrow molecular weight distributions around 1.2 and as low as 1.04 while still allowing high molecular weights (M_n~90,000). There are now a variety of methods available for replacing the RAFT end group, which can be an issue from the standpoint of practical applications. Most effective ones include aminolysis (reaction with primary or secondary amine), radical-induced reduction, and thermal elimination (Figure 2.111).[70] It is noteworthy that chain transfer to monomer, polymer, or solvent does not occur in the RAFT process. In addition, the RAFT polymerization can be carried out in a variety of solvents, including benzene, DMF, and ethyl acetate. All these advantages make the RAFT polymerization technique very attractive for the synthesis of block copolymers not amenable to anionic or other controlled free-radical polymerizations (*vide infra*).

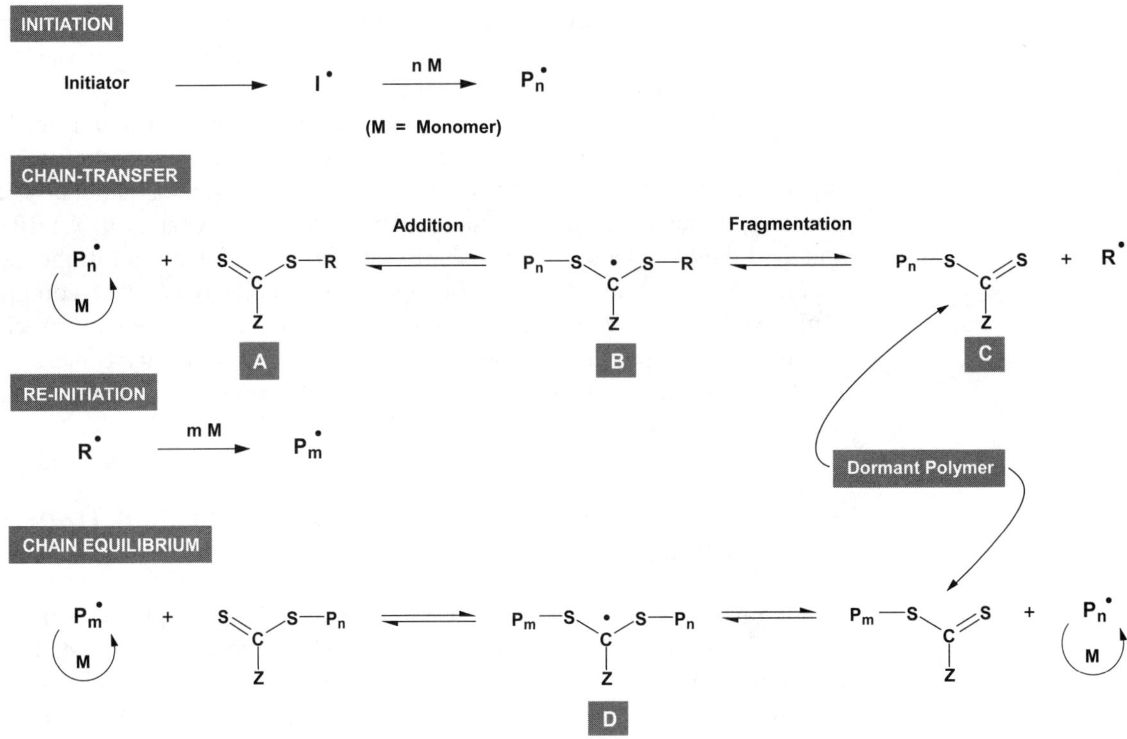

Figure 2.110. Mechanism of RAFT.

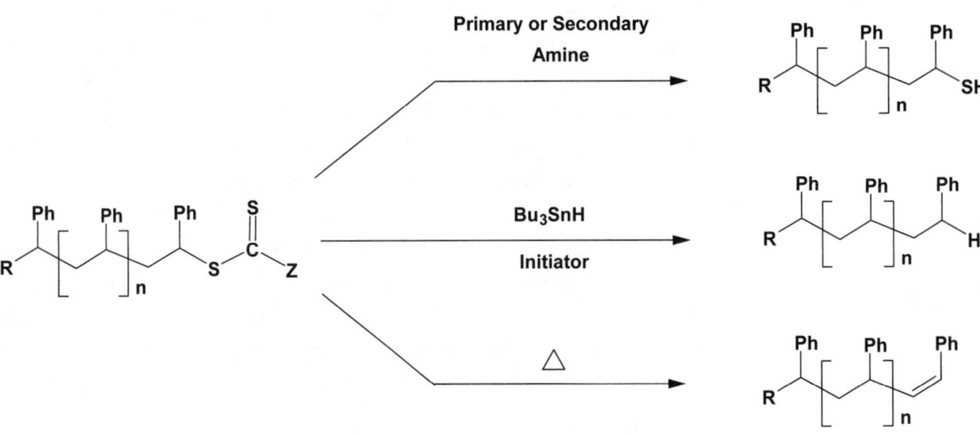

Figure 2.111. Common methods for elimination of RAFT end group.

The requirements for a thiocarbonylthio compound to be effective as a RAFT agent are (i) both rates of addition and fragmentation must be fast relative to the rate of propagation and (ii) the expelled radical (R•) must be capable of reinitiating polymerization. The first requirement ensures the rapid consumption of the initial RAFT agent and fast equilibration of the dormant and active species while the second ensures the continuity of the chain process. Thus, to a large extent, the Z group determines the rate of addition, and the R group determines the rate of fragmentation. Among the most effective RAFT agents, dithioesters have been extensively examined (Figure 2.112).[71-73] Recent studies indicate that phenyl is one of the best Z groups, followed by SCH_3 and CH_3, while cumyl (or 2-phenylprop-2-yl) and 2-cyanoprop-2-yl groups are among the best R groups.

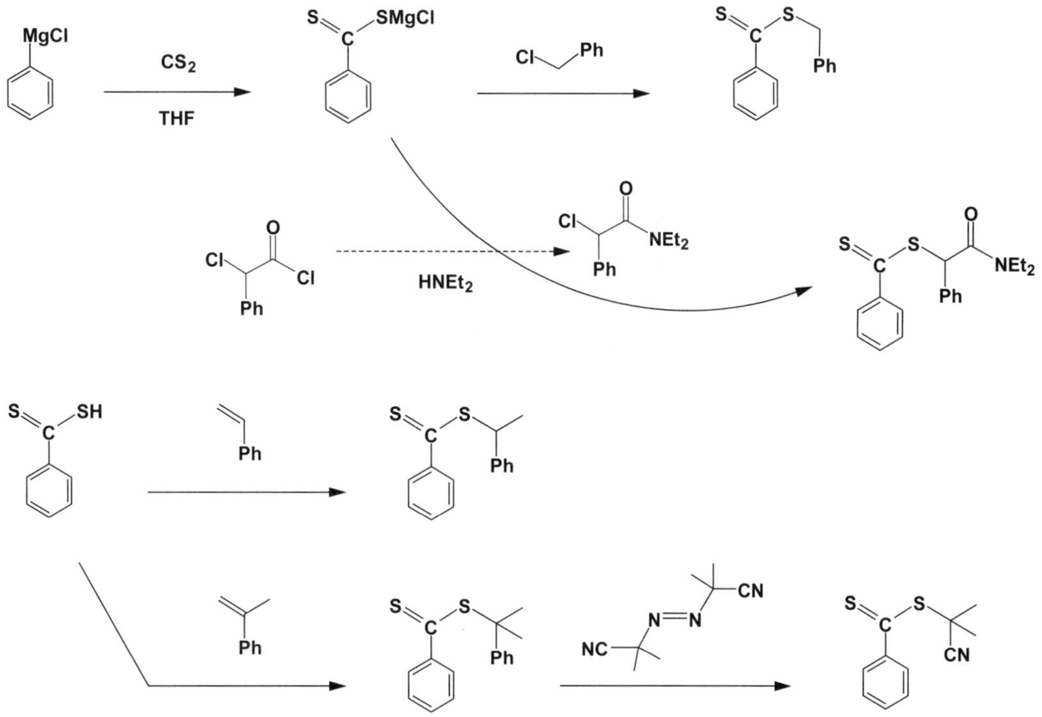

Figure 2.112. Common synthetic routes to dithioester RAFT agents.[74,75]

Recent developments also indicate that trithiocarbonates are potential candidates as RAFT agents. Alkyl thiocarbonates are normally prepared by reacting CS_2 and 33% aqueous NaOH with alkyl halides in the presence of a phase transfer catalyst, such as n-Bu_4NHSO_4.[76] The interesting feature of trithiocarbonates is that they can be prepared with either one or two good homolytic leaving groups. For example, the RAFT agent **X** should give rise to polymers of structure **P$_x$**, whereas **Y**, which can grow in two directions, should yield a polymer of structure **P$_Y$** (Figure 2.113).[77-79] An important consequence is that trithiocarbonates are very suitable for ABA triblock copolymers.

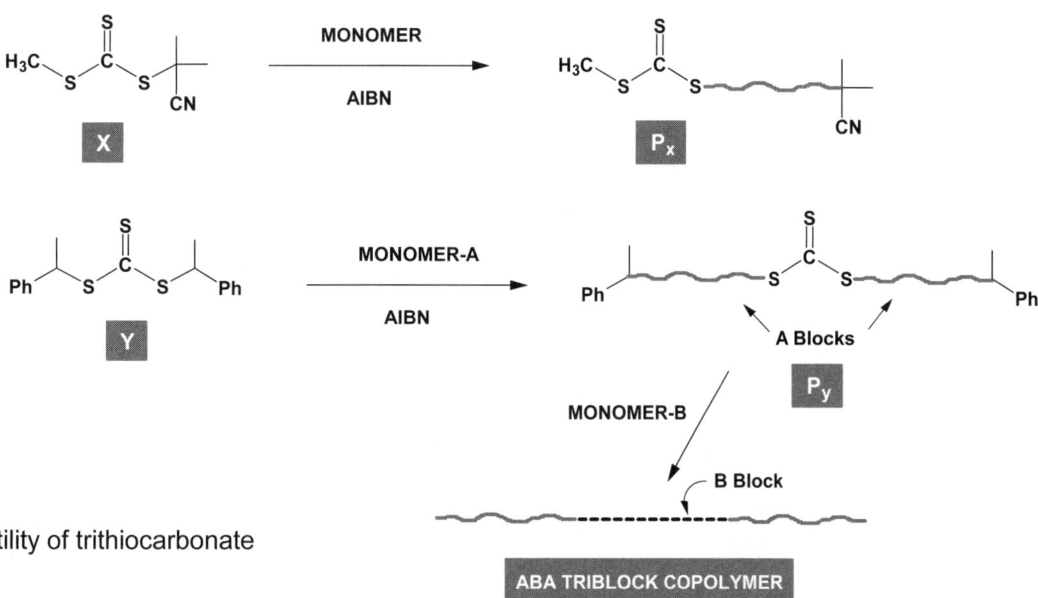

Figure 2.113. Versatility of trithiocarbonate RAFT agents.

2.4.1.4. *Organometal-Mediated Radical Polymerization (OMRP)*

OMRP, a very recently developed CRP technique, exhibits unique features in terms of versatility, molecular weight controllability, functional group compatibility, and ease of polymer-end transformations. This method was first conducted with divalent organotellurium compounds, due to their reversible carbon-tellurium bond cleavage properties upon thermolysis, and now extended to trivalent organostibine compounds.[80] Like the RAFT process, the addition of a small amount of ordinary free radical initiator, such as AIBN, is necessary to lower the temperature of polymerization and significantly enhance the rate of polymerization without forming dead polymer chains. The mechanism of OMRP, as depicted in Figure 2.114, is believed to be initiated by thermal dissociation (TD) of the organotellurium compounds, leading to carbon-centered radicals, which predominantly undergo the degenerative chain transfer (DT)-mediated polymerization (fast direct exchange between growing radicals and dormant species via transfer reactions, without formation of an intermediate radical as observed in the RAFT process). Organostibine compounds show higher reactivity toward the group transfer reaction than organotelluriums and serve as excellent mediators for the highly controlled living radical polymerization of conjugated and unconjugated vinyl monomers (e.g., 1-vinyl-2-pyrrolidinone and vinyl acetate).[81]

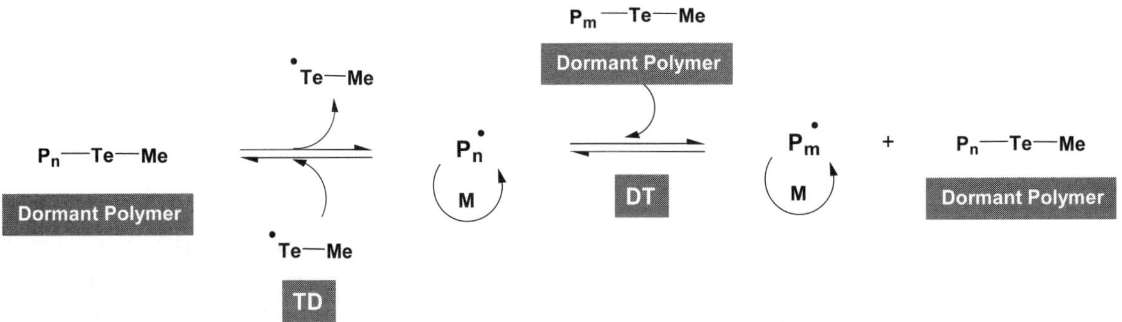

Figure 2.114. Proposed mechanism of OMRP.

2.4.2. Controlled Ionic Polymerization

A number of commercially important polymers, such as styrene-butadiene copolymers, polybutadiene and polyisobutylene, are produced by ionic polymerization. Because of repulsion between active propagating species of same charges, the ionic polymerization is living and a method of choice for tailor-made macromolecules of well-defined structure, as well as polymers of technical interest, such as block, graft, star, ω-functional polymers, macromonomers and macroinitiators. The well-defined polymers obtained by the ionic mechanism possess diversified applications in many areas, e.g., general-purpose polymers, compatibilizers for polymer blends, impact modifiers, textile, optical fibers, etc.

2.4.2.1. *Anionic Polymerization*

Traditionally, monofunctional initiators, such as alkyllithium compounds, have been used for polymerization of styrenes and dienes in hydrocarbon solution (see Section 1.6.1.1c in Chapter-1). The reactivity of these initiators depends on their degree of association. Thus, *n*-butyllithium (*n*-BuLi) is employed commercially to initiate anionic homopolymerization and copolymerization of butadiene, isoprene, and styrene, leading to linear and branched structures. Because of its high degree of association (hexameric), *n*-BuLi-initiated polymerizations are conducted at elevated temperatures (>50°C) to enhance the rate of initiation relative to propagation, essential for obtaining polymers with narrow molecular weight distributions. *sec*-Butyllithium (*s*-BuLi), a tetramer, is used commercially to manufacture styrene-diene block copolymers, because it can initiate styrene polymerization rapidly as compared to propagation and provides opportunity to prepare polystyrene blocks with desired molecular weight and molecular weight distributions. In general, these alkyllithium initiators are not suitable for certain polar monomers, such as alkyl methacrylates, because of extensive side reactions with the functional group of the monomer. The sterically-hindered compounds, such as diphenylhexyllithium (DPHL), are a more versatile class of carbanion-based initiators for controlled polymerization of vinyl, alkyl methacrylate and non-conjugated monomers (e.g., N-vinylpyridine). DPHL is synthesized *in situ* by adding *s*-BuLi to 1,1-diphenylethylene (DPE) immediately before polymerization (Figure 2.115). If DPE is treated with lithium metal, a bifunctional initiator useful for the synthesis of block copolymers is produced (*vide infra*).[82] The standard method of synthesizing a diblock copolymer is by sequential addition of two monomers (A and B). Monomer A is initiated by an alkyllithium or DPHL. Upon consumption of monomer A, monomer B is added to the living polymer A. After consumption of monomer B, an alcohol may be added to terminate polymerization. A variety of block copolymers (di, tri, tetra, etc.) are synthesized in this way with the proper sequencing of addition of different monomers, if each propagating carbanion is capable of initiating the polymerization of the next monomer. The sequencing depends on the electron-withdrawing nature of the substituents of each monomer, which determines the stability of the propagating carbanion. For example, polystyryl carbanions will initiate the polymerization of methyl methacrylate, but the reverse cannot occur. Therefore, when synthesizing a polystyrene-poly(*t*-butyl methacrylate) di-block copolymer, PS-*b*-PBMA, the styrene must be polymerized first (Figure 2.115). However, order of addition is not a problem with monomers, such as styrene, isoprene, and butadiene, due to their similar reactivities.

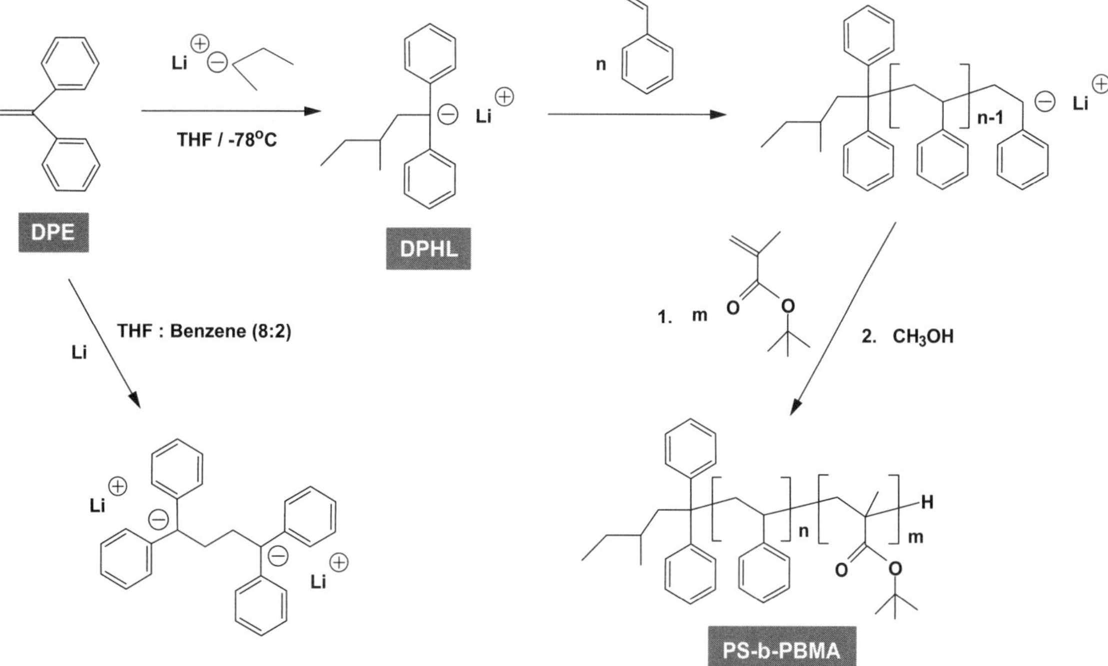

Figure 2.115. Synthesis of block copolymers by using DPHL initiator.

The solvent employed in anionic polymerization has a significant impact on the tacticity of methacrylic and acrylic polymers (Table 2.4).[83-85] For example, a nonpolar solvent, such as toluene, which creates slowly-reacting tight-ion pairs consisting of the living enolate and the cationic counterion, produces a highly isotactic polymer. By contrast, more polar solvents, such as THF, generate more reactive ion pairs, and form a mixture of syndiotactic and atactic triads. The solvent effect is more pronounced in acrylate monomers containing bulkier alkyl groups (e.g., *tert*-butylmethacrylate).

Table 2.4. The effect of solvent on the tacticity of poly(*tert*-butylmethacrylate)

Reaction Conditions	Tacticity (%)			T_g (°C)
	Isotactic	Syndiotactic	Atactic	
DPHL, Toluene, -78°C	~100	0	0	84
DPHL, THF, -78°C	2	52	46	118
AIBN, Bulk, -78°C	0	61	39	123

Bifunctional initiators, which contain two sites to react with monomer, are also used extensively to produce homo- and, especially, symmetrical ABA, BABAB or CABAC-type multiblock copolymers, including telechelic polymers (*vide infra*). The most common of these initiators is 1,3-phenylene-bis(3-methyl-l-phenylpentylidene)dilithium (PEBL), prepared *in situ* by adding two equivalents of *s*-BuLi to l,3-bis(1-phenylethenyl)benzene (BPEB) immediately before polymerization (Figure 2.116).[86] The major advantage of this class of initiators is that polymerization can be conducted in both hydrocarbon (e.g., *n*-hexane, cyclohexane and toluene) and polar aprotic solvents (e.g., THF). For diene polymerization with high (>90%) 1,4-polydiene microstructure, it is essential that the polymerization be conducted in hydrocarbon solvent. Thus, this initiator system is especially suitable for introducing diene monomers in the block copolymers.

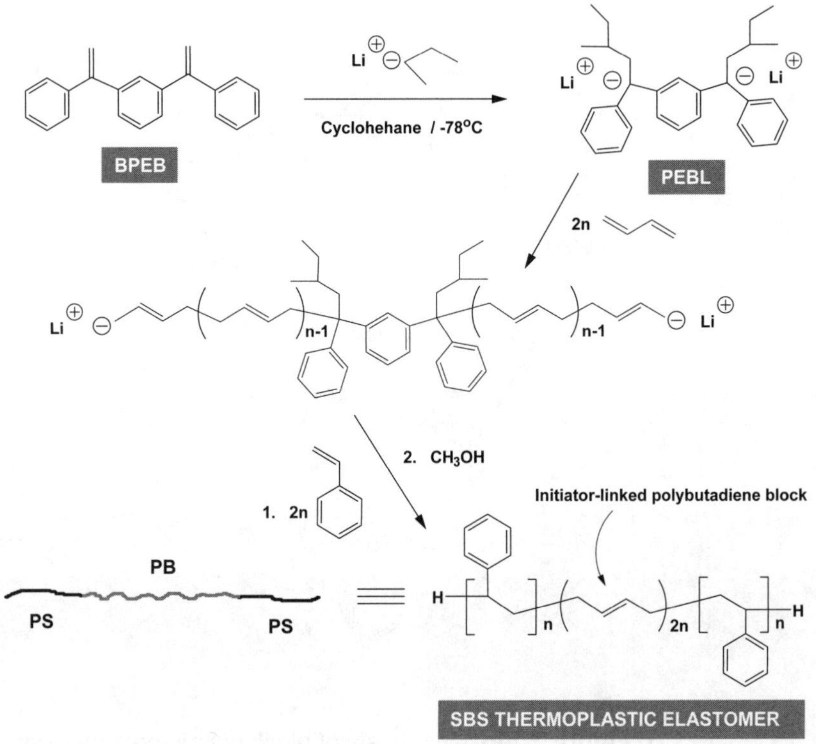

Figure 2.116. Synthesis of ABA block copolymer by using PEBL initiator.

Aromatic radical anions are another interesting class of initiators which can be used as both bifunctional and monofunctional initiators by designing a proper polymerization protocol. They are prepared by reacting an equimolecular amount of alkali metal (lithium, sodium or potassium) and naphthalene in THF. The resulting aromatic radical anion (e.g., sodium naphthalide, often called sodium naphthalenide) transfers an electron to styrene monomer to form monomer radical anions, which rapidly undergo tail-to-tail dimerization to produce a stable dianionic initiator capable of growing polymer chains in outward directions (Figure 2.117). The only major disadvantage of this system is that radical anions can only be formed in polar aprotic solvents, such as THF and glymes, thereby limiting the utility for diene polymerization. In fact, the major use of this type of initiator is in the preparation of *telechelic polymers*, especially low molecular weight polystyrenes with terminal reactive functional groups, by terminating the growing polymer chains with suitable reagents (other methods for telechelic polymers are discussed later in this chapter). For example, a dihydroxy-terminated polymer is obtained by addition of ethylene oxide. Since the resulting alcoholate ion can initiate ring-opening polymerization of ethylene oxide (although the rate of polymerization is low), polyether formation is avoided by quenching the reaction shortly after the addition of ethylene oxide.

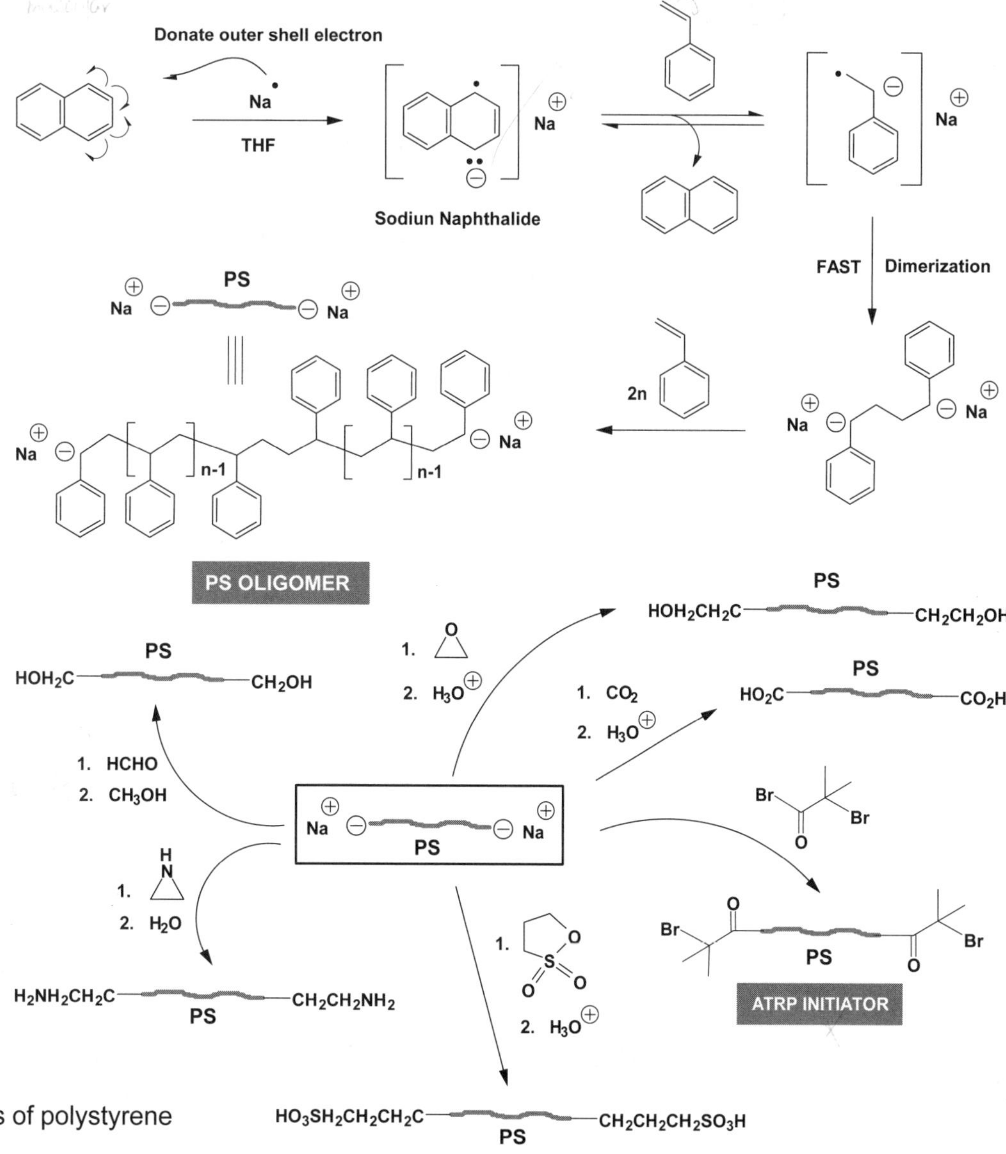

Figure 2.117. Synthesis of polystyrene telechelics.

Sodium naphthalide can also be used with strained ethers (especially ethylene oxide). The mechanism of initiation is quite different and involves nucleophilic addition of the radical anion to the monomer to form a polymer chain with two simultaneous growing ends (Figure 2.118). In this case, sodium naphthalide acts as a bifunctional initiator.

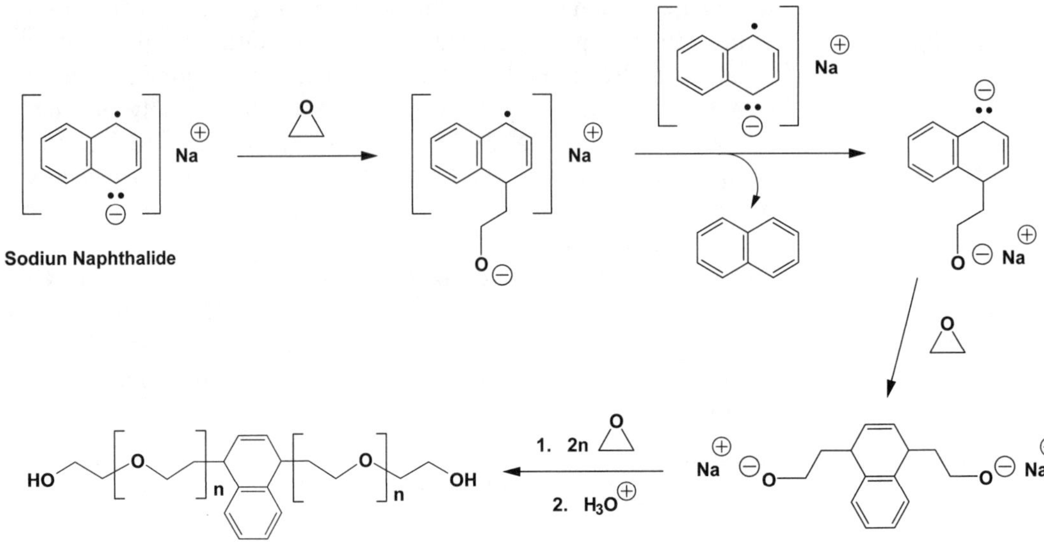

Sodiun Naphthalide

1. 2n

2. $H_3O^{\oplus}$

Figure 2.118. Synthesis of telechelic PEO.

The aromatic radical anions are also used to transform terminal hydroxyl end group(s) to introduce polymer block(s). As shown in Figure 2.119, the synthesis of ABA-type amphiphilic block copolymers, such as PEO-PEB-PEO triblock, is normally performed by anionic ring-opening polymerization of ethylene oxide in THF using HO-PEB-OH, a commercially available poly(ethylene-*stat*-butylene) hydroxy telechelic obtained by hydrogenation of polybutadiene telechelic. The terminal hydroxy groups of HO-PEB-OH are first deprotonated by titration with a 0.5 M solution of potassium naphthalide at 35°C to yield the corresponding bifunctional macroinitiator KO-PEB-OK.[87-89] After addition of ethylene oxide at 0°C, polymerization was carried out at 55°C for 3-4 days. It should be noted that unlike the aforementioned polymerization, the action of potassium naphthalide is monofunctional.

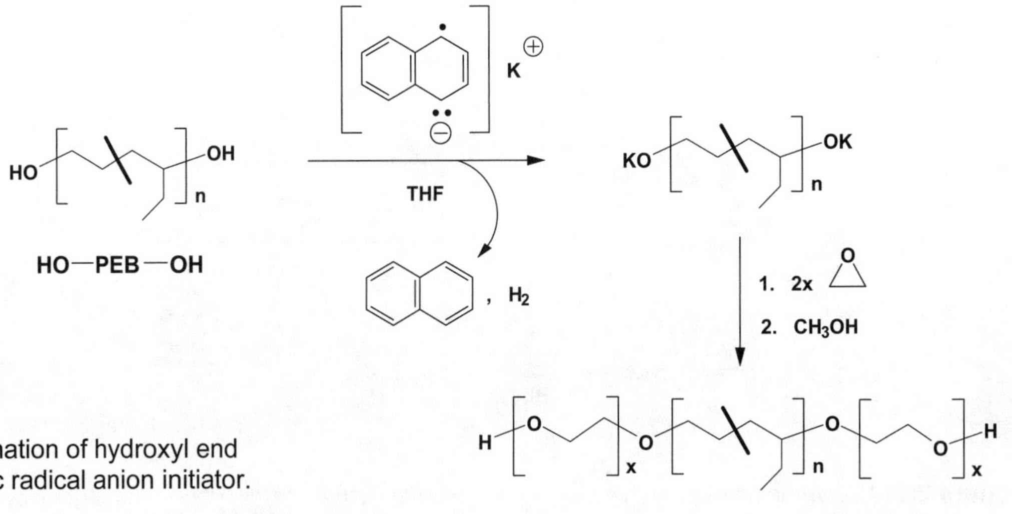

HO—PEB—OH

THF

, H_2

1. 2x

2. CH_3OH

Figure 2.119. Transformation of hydroxyl end groups using an aromatic radical anion initiator.

2.4.2.2. Cationic Polymerization

Polymerization of vinyl monomers by a cationic mechanism has been limited to a narrow range of monomers, viz., isobutylene, styrene and isobutyl vinyl ether, because most other monomers do not have the ability to stabilize a cation at the end of a chain (see section 1.6.1.1b in Chapter-1). Isobutylene is of primary interest because polyisobutylene (PIB) or butyl rubber, which exhibits a combination of attractive properties, such as low T_g, good thermal, oxidative and hydrolytic stability, coupled with high barrier properties, is commercially manufactured only by cationic polymerization of isobutylene. Recent development of initiators and polymerization conditions permits for the first time *quasiliving carbocationic polymerization* (QCP) of isobutylene as well as its copolymerization with other monomers. This leads to a new class of block copolymers with predictable molecular weights, narrow molecular weight distributions, and well defined block junctions.[90] As depicted in Figure 2.120, the initiator and co-initiator are the key elements in QCP, since a necessary condition for obtaining narrow MWD (PDI<1.2) is that the rate of initiation is much higher than the rate of propagation. Unlike conventional cationic polymerization, QCP is performed by added initiator and not by moisture. Mono-, di- and trifunctional cumyl type initiators are frequently used because of flexibility to synthesize linear AB and ABA or star-shaped block copolymers. The catalyst or co-initiator is a Lewis acid, such as $TiCl_4$, BCl_3, $AlCl_3$ and $SnCl_4$. The right selection of Lewis acid depends on different factors, such as the monomer, the M_n of the desired polymer, and the solvent(s), since the crucial point is the acidity of these acids which affects the ionization equilibrium between dormant (inactive) and active species and thereby, the kinetic events. $TiCl_4$ is normally considered to give the best results for M_n >10,000.

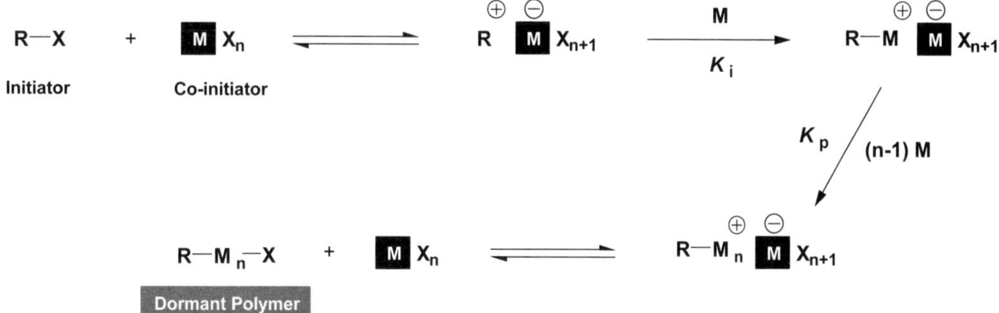

Figure 2.120. Basic reaction steps in QCP.

The choice of solvent or a mixture of solvents is restricted to a few possibilities, because of the solubility of the polymer and the influence of the solvent polarity on the ionization equilibrium of the initiator and the growing chain end. Dichloromethane and a mixture of CH_2Cl_2:n-hexane (40:60 v/v %) are often used. The main problem with CH_2Cl_2 is a relatively high concentration of moisture (about 10^{-3}M). This problem is more or less eliminated by use of a proton trap (e.g., pyridine derivatives, especially 2,6-di-tert-butyl pyridine, DTBP). Another problem is that PIBs with a M_n >2,500-3,000 begin to precipitate in pure CH_2Cl_2, resulting in uncontrolled reaction conditions. n-Hexane, on the other hand, dissolves PIB and is used when high molecular weight material is prepared. However, the presence of n-hexane shifts the equilibrium between inactive and active species toward the inactive one and that is why a strong Lewis acid like $TiCl_4$ is needed when such a solvent mixture is used. Moreover, QCP often requires addition of an electron donor, such as N,N-dimethylacetamide (DMA), which forms a complex with Lewis acid, to reduce the net positive charge of the propagating chain end and thereby, reduce the rate of propagation and rate of transfer/termination.

With proper experimental conditions, QCP can be employed to prepare PIB-based telechelic and block copolymers that otherwise cannot be synthesized (Figure 2.121).[91-93] For example, the end groups of PS-terminated block copolymers prepared by QCP are efficient initiating species for ATRP, thus providing incorporation of methacrylate monomers, which are not amenable to cationic polymerization. The PIB-based telechelic polymers are of recent scientific and commercial importance because of their diverse uses, such as polyurethanes, network polymers and biomaterials (*vide infra*). Significant advances have also been made involving cationic polymerization of novel cyclic monomers, leading to biodegradable polymers.

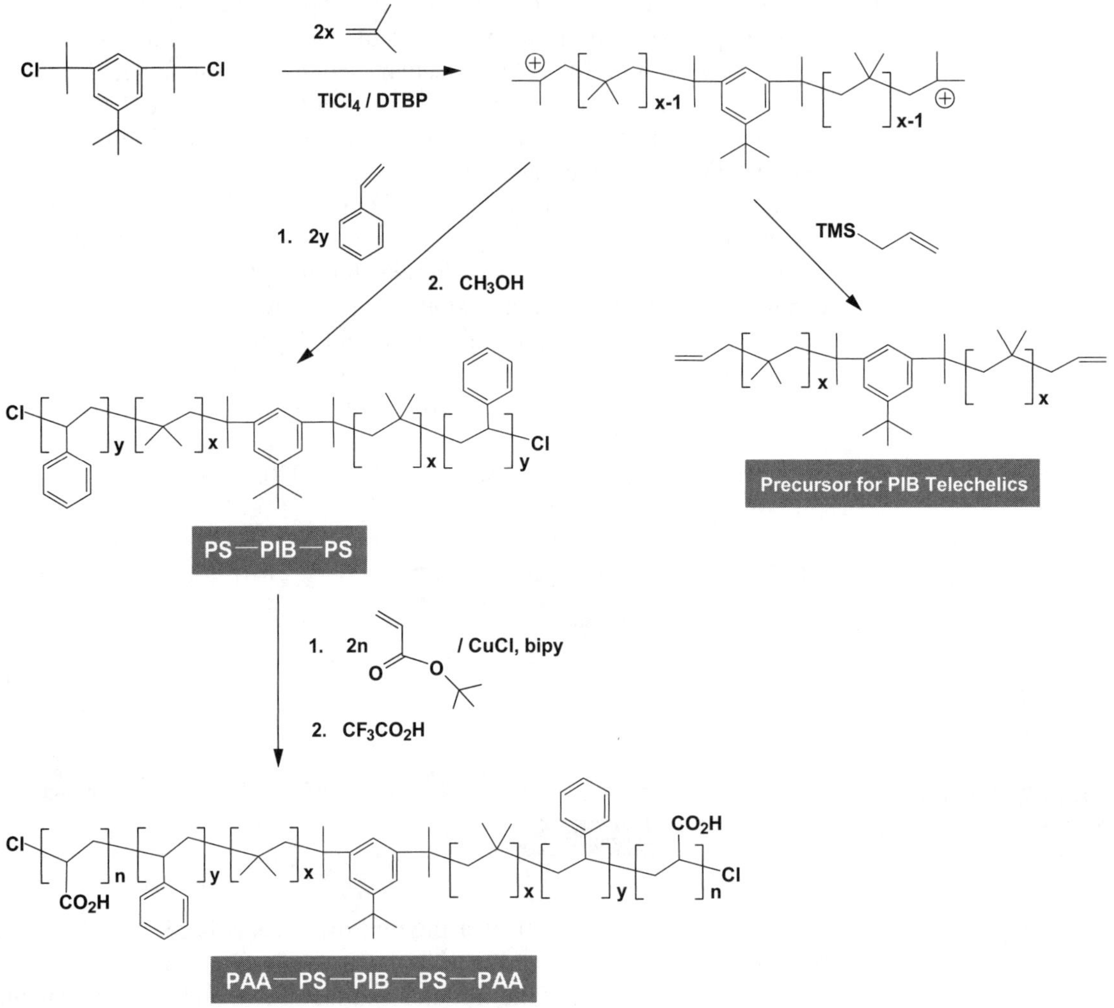

2x

$TiCl_4$ / DTBP

1. 2y

2. CH_3OH

TMS

Precursor for PIB Telechelics

PS—PIB—PS

1. 2n / CuCl, bipy

2. CF_3CO_2H

PAA—PS—PIB—PS—PAA

Figure 2.121. Synthesis of a tailor-made block copolymer by QCP.

The use of functional group-protected initiators, such as **A**, has also been studied for QCP. Figure 2.122 depicts a route for the synthesis of a PIB macromonomer with two aryl hydroxyl groups.[94] This macromonomer has been developed to prepare segmented poly(ether urethaneurea) (PEUU) multi-block copolymers containing PIB branches to impart barrier properties (lower permeability to water vapor and gases) to traditional PEUUs, which are used in a variety of biomedical applications, most prominently as blood sacs in ventricular assist devices and total artificial hearts.

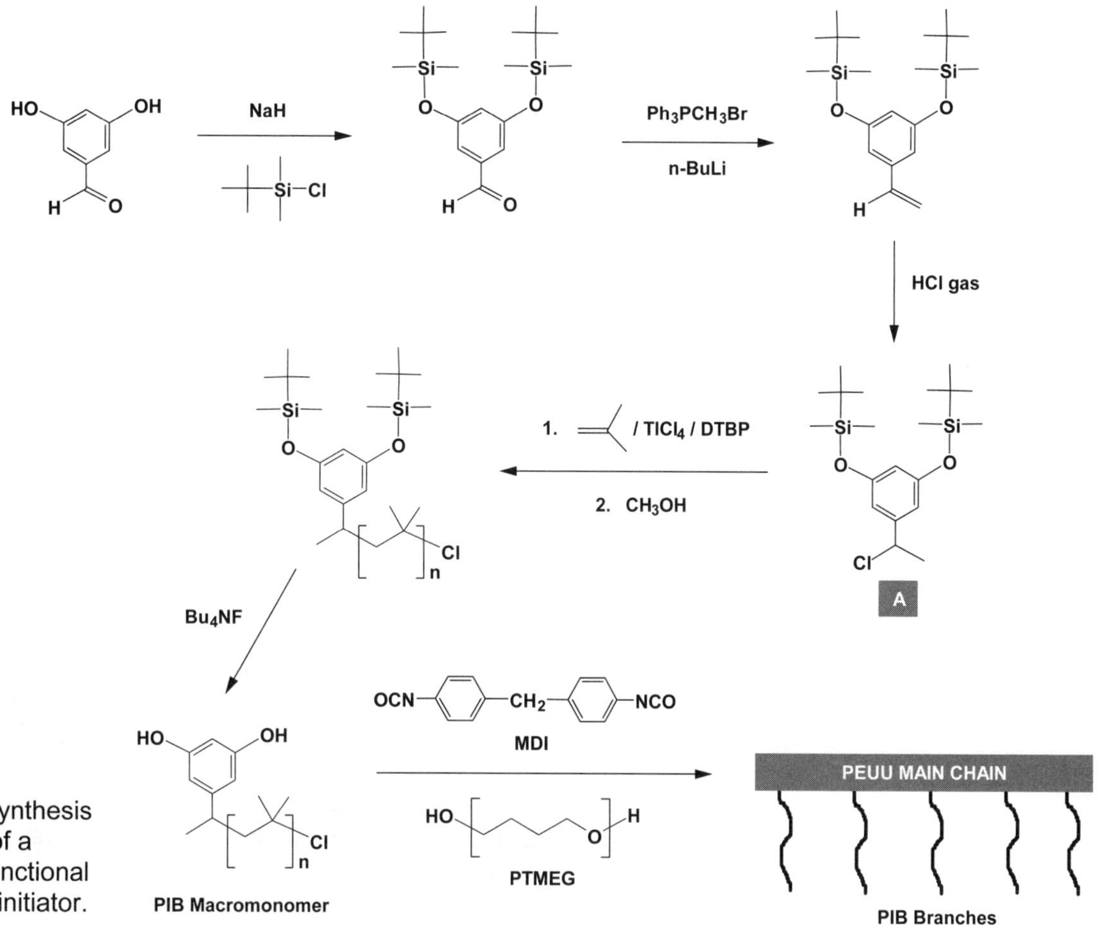

Figure 2.122. Synthesis and application of a representative functional group-protected initiator.

Monomers containing an acidic proton, such as *p*-hydroxystyrene, are difficult to polymerize by conventional ionic mechanisms because of side reactions. Even free-radical polymerization, which is tolerant toward ionic functional groups, is not suitable for *p*-hydroxystyrene. As a result, a protected version, such as *p-tert*-butoxystyrene, *p*-acetoxystyrene and *p*-(*tert*-butyldimethylsilyloxy)styrene, must be used for successful ionic or free-radical polymerization, followed by deprotection to obtain the desired product. Polymers containing phenolic hydroxyl groups are attractive for applications in photoresists, epoxy-curing agents, adhesives, etc. In a recent study, a new class of initiator-activator systems has been developed for direct controlled cationic polymerization of *p*-hydroxystyrene.[95] The interesting feature of these systems is that polymerization can be conducted in the presence of a fairly large amount of water and acetonitrile, a highly polar and strongly coordinating solvent usually not employed in conventional cationic polymerization. This unique feature is believed to originate from the characteristics of $BF_3•OEt_2$, a Lewis acid used in conjunction with the initiator. As illustrated in Figure 2.123, the boron compound apparently generates a carbocationic species by dissociation of the aliphatic C-OH bond in the initiator, such as 4-methoxy-α-methylbenzyl alcohol. The factors contributing to this selective dissociation include the high oxophilicity of BF_3 and the highly polar medium consisting of CH_3CN and water. In addition, $BF_3•OEt_2$ does not undergo decomposition or deactivation even in the presence of water and the phenolic group. Thus, this novel initiating system for unprotected phenol, viz., *p*-hydroxystyrene, offers access to styrenic amphiphilic polymers.

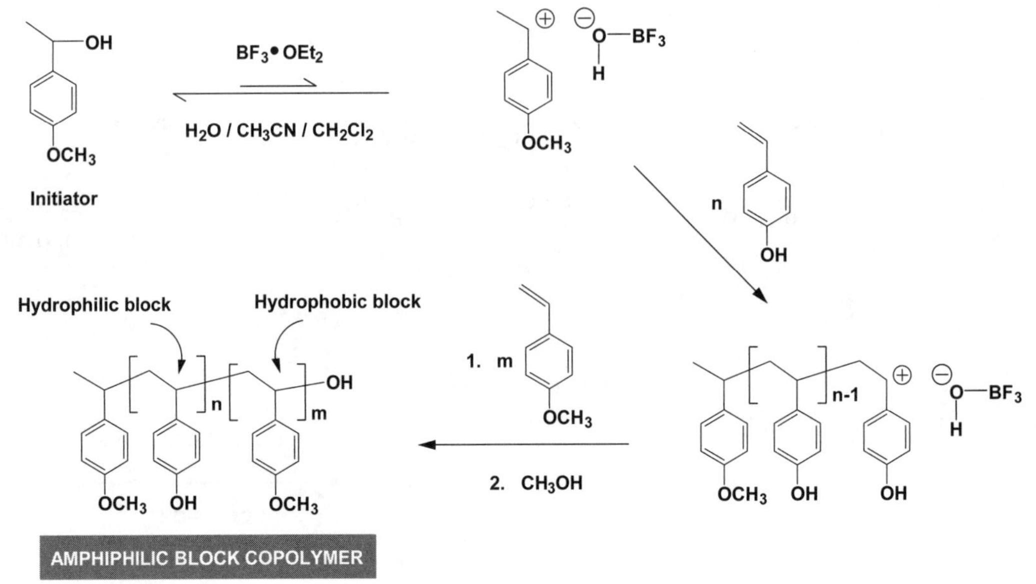

Initiator

$BF_3 \bullet OEt_2$

H_2O / CH_3CN / CH_2Cl_2

Hydrophilic block

Hydrophobic block

1. m

2. CH_3OH

AMPHIPHILIC BLOCK COPOLYMER

Figure 2.123. Synthesis of styrenic amphiphilic block copolymers by controlled cationic polymerization.

Alkyl vinyl ethers, such as butyl vinyl ether, are another class of monomers that have been studied extensively by controlled cationic polymerization.[96-99] A wide variety of initiating systems have been employed, mostly combinations of a protonic acid (e.g., HCl, HI, CF_3CO_2H, etc.) and a Lewis acid (e.g., $ZnCl_2$, $SnCl_4$, $EtAlCl_2$, etc.) or iodine. The protonic acid, which serves as an initiator, readily reacts with the vinyl monomer to form a stable dormant species containing a carbon-halogen or related adduct (Figure 2.124). The Lewis acid, acting as a catalyst or activator, generates a carbocationic growing species to trigger controlled propagation. This methodology is very popular for the preparation of alkyl vinyl ether-based block copolymers.[100,101]

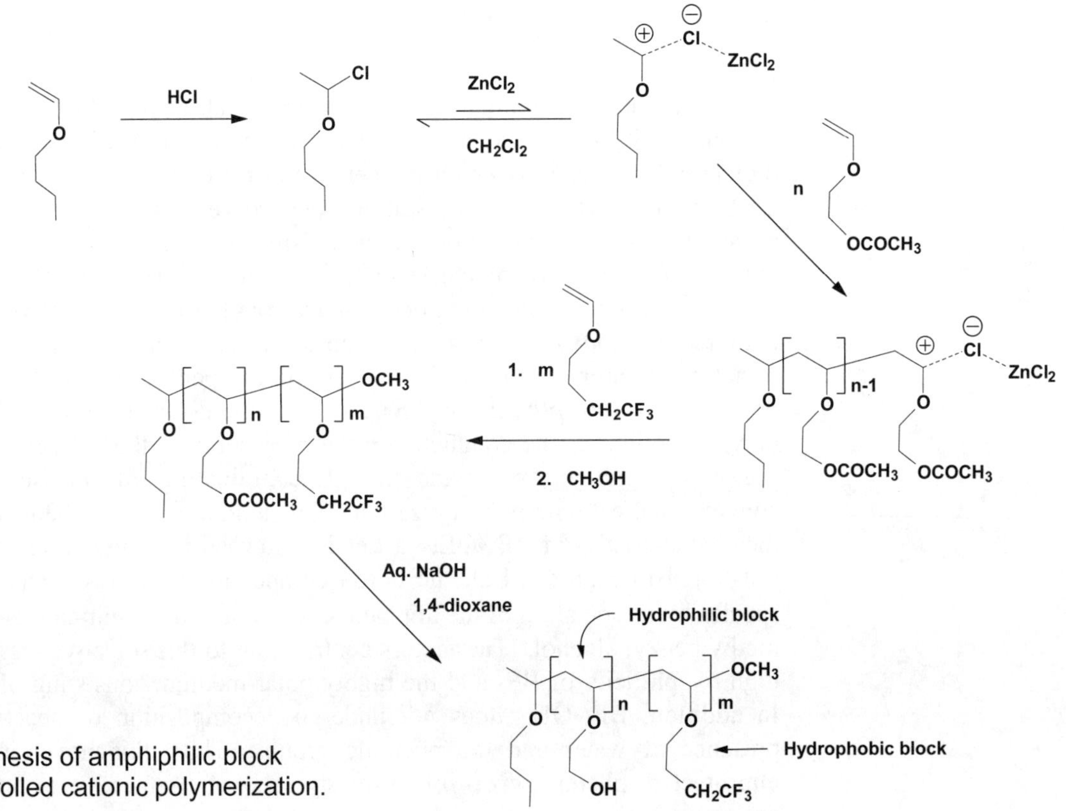

HCl

$ZnCl_2$

CH_2Cl_2

1. m

2. CH_3OH

Aq. NaOH

1,4-dioxane

Hydrophilic block

Hydrophobic block

Figure 2.124. Synthesis of amphiphilic block copolymers by controlled cationic polymerization.

2.4.3. Tailor-made Polymers

As mentioned earlier, conventional free-radical polymerization is not well suited for the synthesis of advanced polymer architectures. Even the synthesis of di- or triblock copolymers is hardly possible by this technique. The primary reason is the occurrence of continuous initiation and termination of chains, which result in the early generation of dead polymer chains that no longer participate in the polymerization process. Acquiring control over macromolecular architecture constructed with one or more types of monomers has become an increasingly important challenge in polymer chemistry, because, depending on the nature of the monomers, the number and lengths of the block segments, as well as the chain architecture (linear, branched, graft, star, etc.), a wide range of polymers with interesting properties can be achieved. The interest in novel polymer architecture stems from their unusual mechanical, thermal, dilute solution and melt properties. The recent advent of the aforementioned controlled polymerization techniques, coupled with judicious choice of synthetic strategy, now offers ready access to complex macromolecules with a high level of homogeneity with regard to molecular weight characteristics and architectural structure. Consequently, synthesis of polymers with tailored mechanical, optical, electrical, ionic, barrier and other physical properties is no longer a distant goal. In general, these molecular architectures can be grouped into three primary categories: graft, block and star polymers. Dendritic polymers have also been the subject of intense research and are discussed in Chapter-5.

2.4.3.1. Graft Copolymers

There are four major approaches for the synthesis of graft polymers, "grafting onto", "grafting from", "grafting through" and "modular".[102] Each approach provides access to polymers with different backbone and branch compositions. Branches are usually distributed randomly along the backbone, although the preparation of well defined structures is possible with proper selection of synthetic strategy. As shown in Figure 2.125, the "grafting onto" approach requires a polymer (which serves as the backbone chain) with randomly distributed functional groups, and oligomeric reactive species capable of coupling with the functional groups to form branches. By contrast, the "grafting from" approach involves preparation of a backbone polymer containing randomly substituted active sites capable of initiating polymerization (branch formation) when a second monomer is added. The "grafting through" or "macromonomer" approach involves simple copolymerization of a macromonomer (an oligomeric or polymeric substance bearing a polymerizable end group) with another monomer. It is noteworthy that the direct polymerization of a macromonomer results in a polymacromonomer which exhibits low conformational entropy and high compactness because of the presence of a branch point in each repeat unit. Often, the properties of the backbone polymer are not identifiable because of extremely low backbone polymer content compared to branches. Consequently, macromonomers are copolymerized with another monomer to obtain desired properties of the backbone polymer. The "modular" approach allows better control over branch point placement in a graft copolymer. In this strategy, the backbone polymer is generated in discrete segments (or "modules"), which are subsequently linked together, along with the side chains, using suitable coupling chemistry. In all the approaches, the homogeneity of the branches depends on the method used for the preparation of branches.

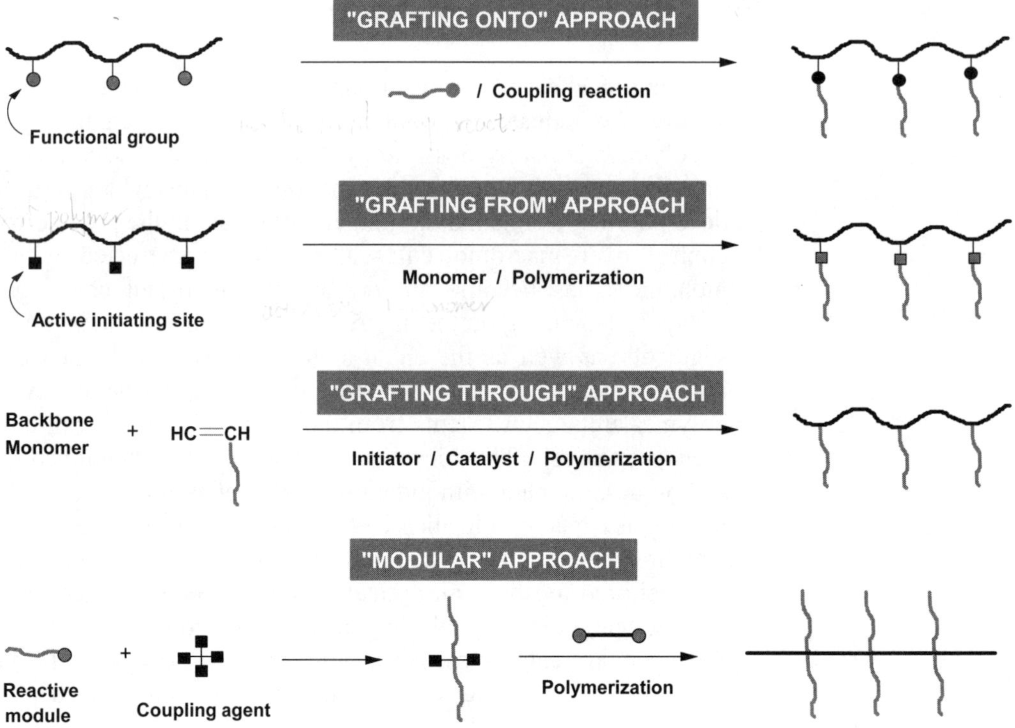

Figure 2.125. Schematics of the common synthetic approaches for graft copolymers.

2.4.3.1a. The "Grafting onto" Approach

The backbone polymers, **A**-**C**, bearing functional groups, are usually prepared by chemical modification of a polymer or copolymerization of appropriate monomers. The choice of polystyrene (PS) and polybutadiene (PB) as backbone polymer is common in this approach because of ease of functionalization, such as chloromethylation of PS and hydrosilylation of PB (Figure 2.126). The coupling reaction is normally conducted by using an excess amount of anionic oligomeric intermediates, **41**-**45**, prepared by living anionic polymerization. This approach permits incorporation of block copolymers in the branches by using living block anionic intermediates.

Functionalized Backbone Polymers:

PS → (CH_3OCH_2Cl / $SnCl_4$) → **A** (CH_2Cl)

PB (High 1,4) → ($HSiMe_2Cl$ / Pt-Catalyst) → **B** (—Si(Cl)—)

PB → ($HSiMeCl_2$ / Pt-Catalyst) → **C** (Cl—Si—Cl)

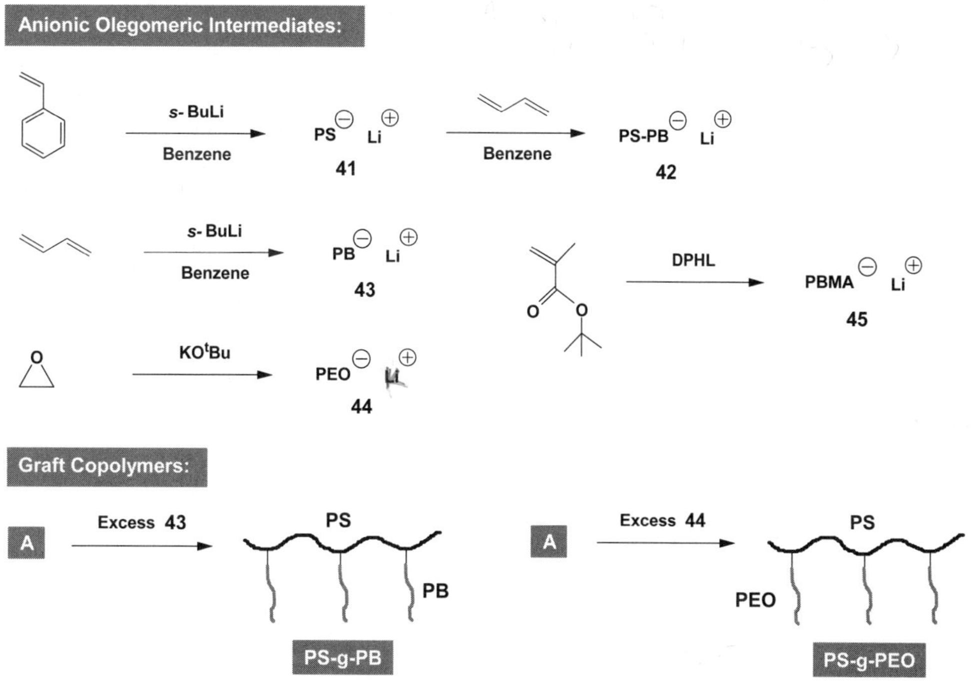

Anionic Olegomeric Intermediates:

s-BuLi, Benzene → PS⊖ Li⊕ 41 → Benzene → PS-PB⊖ Li⊕ 42

s-BuLi, Benzene → PB⊖ Li⊕ 43

DPHL → PBMA⊖ Li⊕ 45

KO^{t}Bu → PEO⊖ Li⊕ 44

Graft Copolymers:

A → Excess 43 → PS, PB: PS-g-PB

A → Excess 44 → PS, PEO: PS-g-PEO

Figure 2.126. Synthesis of graft copolymers by "grafting onto" approach (illustrated with only two examples from several possibilities).

It is often necessary to employ two or more mechanistic approaches for the synthesis of graft polymers with complex molecular architecture. As shown in Figure 2.127, NMRP can be combined with living anionic polymerization to prepare novel graft polymers, such as (PS-*g*-PI)-*b*-PS and (PS-*g*-PS)-*b*-(PS-*g*-PI).[103] It is important to emphasize that NMRP not only provides polymers with functional groups directly on the polymer backbone chain, but is also compatible with anionic oligomeric intermediates (i.e., the resulting polymer retains its living character that permits further molecular tailoring).

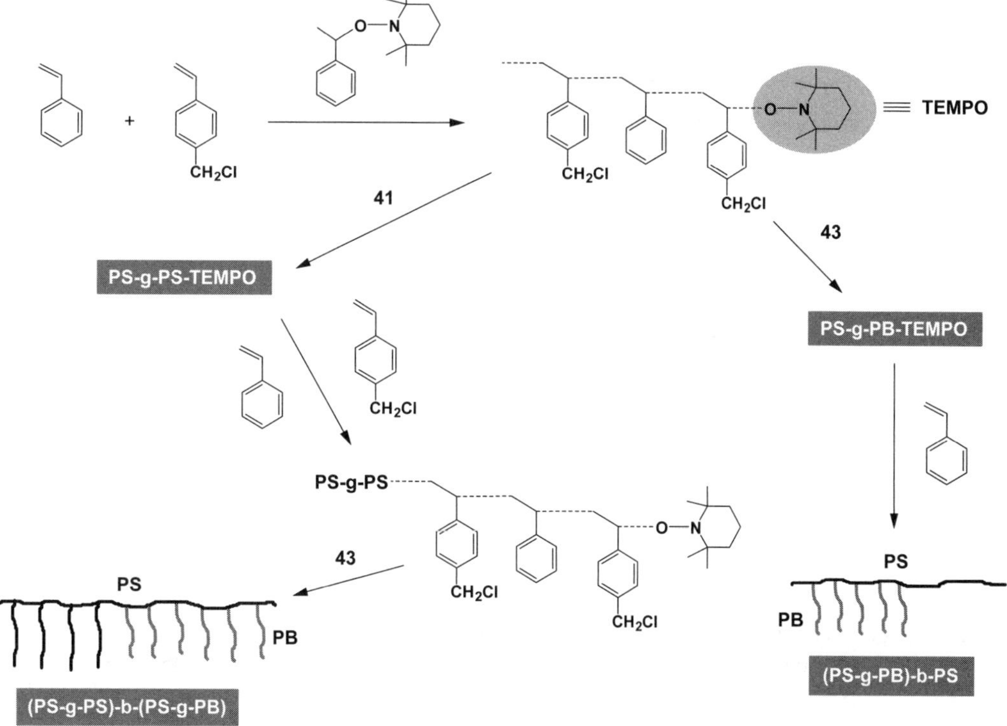

Figure 2.127. Synthesis of graft copolymers with complex molecular architecture. (Shown with butadiene and styrene. Other monomers like isoprene and methacrylates could also be used as branches.)

2.4.3.1b. The "Grafting from" Approach

The backbone polymers having active sites capable of initiating polymerization with the second monomer(s) are also prepared by chemical modification of a polymer or homo or copolymerization of appropriate monomers. A good example to demonstrate this approach is the preparation of PMMA, PS or PS-*b*-PMMA grafted poly(ethylene-*co*-styrene).[104] The initiating sites are introduced to the polymer backbone by standard benzylic bromination (Figure 2.128). Subsequent use of the ATRP method (CuBr and pentamethyldiethylenetriamine, PMDETA) permits homo or copolymeric graft chains to the backbone polymer. This approach is quite attractive because of the relatively wide scope of monomers that can be employed, the stability of the initiator, the simple polymerization procedure, and good control of graft structure.

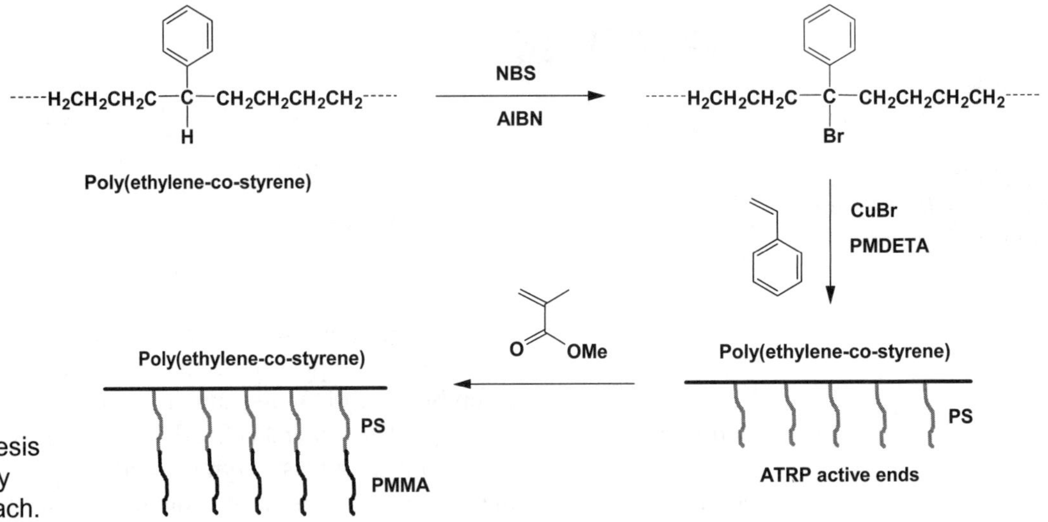

Figure 2.128. Synthesis of graft copolymers by "grafting from" approach.

Figure 2.129 illustrates the preparation of another type of precise graft copolymer architecture by employing the ATRP technique.[105] The backbone polymer is obtained by acyclic diene methathesis (ADMET) chemistry, which, by and large, provides backbone structure that is not achievable by other polymerization methods, as in this case, an ATRP initiating substituted polyethylene containing a small number of unsaturated double bonds. It is important to point out that, unlike other methods, this strategy provides introduction of well-defined branch substitutions to the backbone polymer.

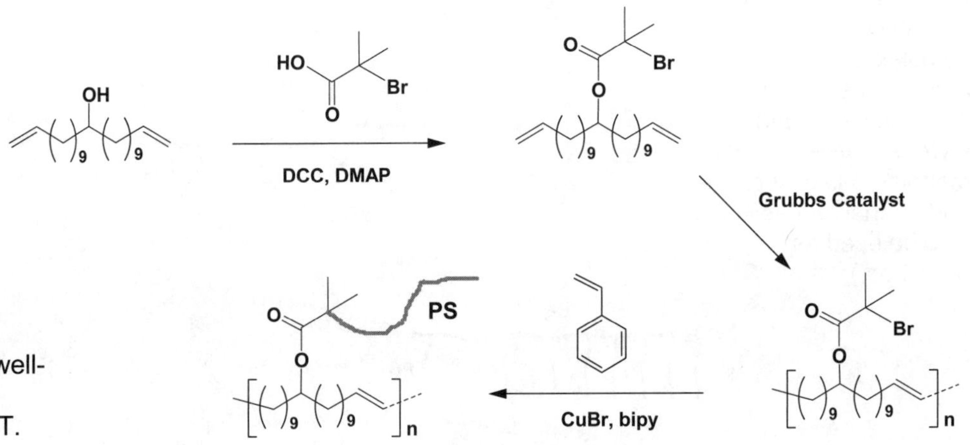

Figure 2.129. Synthesis of well-defined graft copolymers by combining ATRP and ADMET.

Living anionic polymerization can also be used to develop novel amphiphilic block-graft copolymers via the "grafting from" approach. As shown in Figure 2.130, the backbone block copolymer (ABA-type) was obtained employing living anionic polymerization by sequential addition of monomers, styrene (**S**) and 4-*t*-butoxystyrene. The protected *t*-butyl groups in the B block, poly(*t*-butoxystyrene), can be quantitatively removed by treatment with HBr, thus allowing grafting of PEO chains through hydroxystyrene(**HS**) units via anionic ring-opening polymerization of ethylene oxide (**EO**).

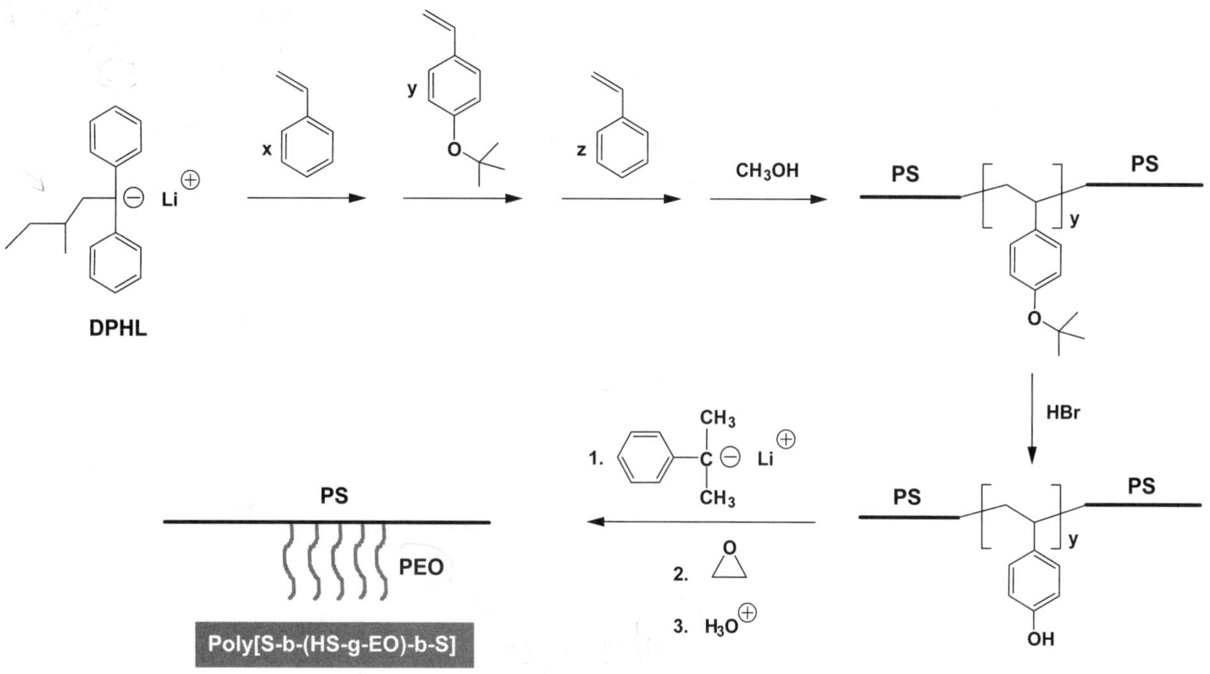

Figure 2.130. Synthesis of block-graft copolymers by anionic polymerization.

2.4.3.1c. The "Grafting through" Approach

In this approach, the backbone polymer is usually prepared by copolymerization of macromonomer with another monomer. Thus, how random the placement of branches on the backbone will be depends on the reactivity ratios of the macromonomer and the comonomer. In general, the graft copolymers obtained by this approach possess increased compositional and molecular weight heterogeneity due to marked changes in the ratio of the concentration of the two monomers in the mixture during the course of the copolymerization. Depending upon the degree of polymerization, comonomer ratio and the size of the side chains, the polymers obtained by this approach adopt two types of conformation and shape: starlike (for those having a small number of branches) or bottle-brush type (as the number of branches increases, as in polymacromonomer). As shown in Figure 2.131, synthetic methods to yield a variety of styrene and methacrylate macromonomers, including a norbornene (NB)-containing macromonomer for ROMP, are now available for the preparation of graft copolymers.[106-111]

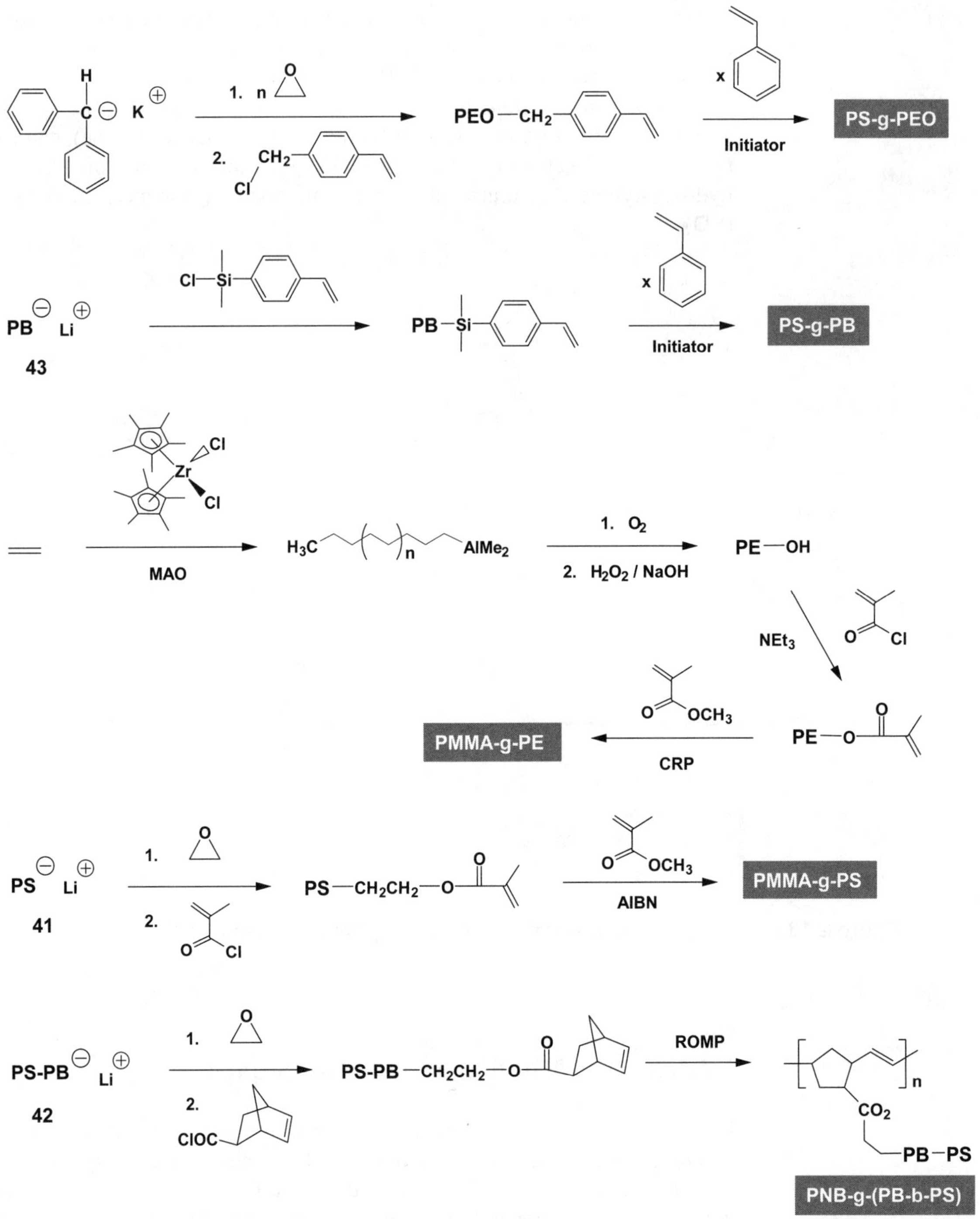

Figure 2.131. Common synthetic strategies to prepare macromonomers and related graft copolymers.

2.4.3.1d. The "Modular" Approach

This approach is especially suitable for poly(isoprene-*g*-styrene)s or poly(styrene-*g*-isoprene)s having multiple regularly spaced branch points. The strategy involves the synthesis of polystyrene and polyisoprene segments ("modules") having reactive anions at one or both chain ends. These modules, along with proper selection of chlorosilane, afford well-defined polymer materials having trifunctional (comb-type), tetrafunctional (centipede-type), and hexafunctional (barbwire-type) branch points (Figure 2.132).[112,113] Since the backbone polymer is produced by the step-growth mechanism, the polymers obtained are polydispersed. However, this approach provides access to polymers with more complex architectures, including well-defined placement of branches. It is important to stress that the modular derived centipede copolymer with 22 vol % PS and seven branch points exhibits properties like thermoplastic elastomers (TPEs) and displays a surprisingly high strain at break of about 2100%, double that of commercial TPEs, such as SBS (Kraton®). These superior properties, believed to be due to the combination of two branches at each branch point, combined with the large number of branch points per molecule, allows the elastic PI backbone to couple into a large number of reinforcing PS domains.

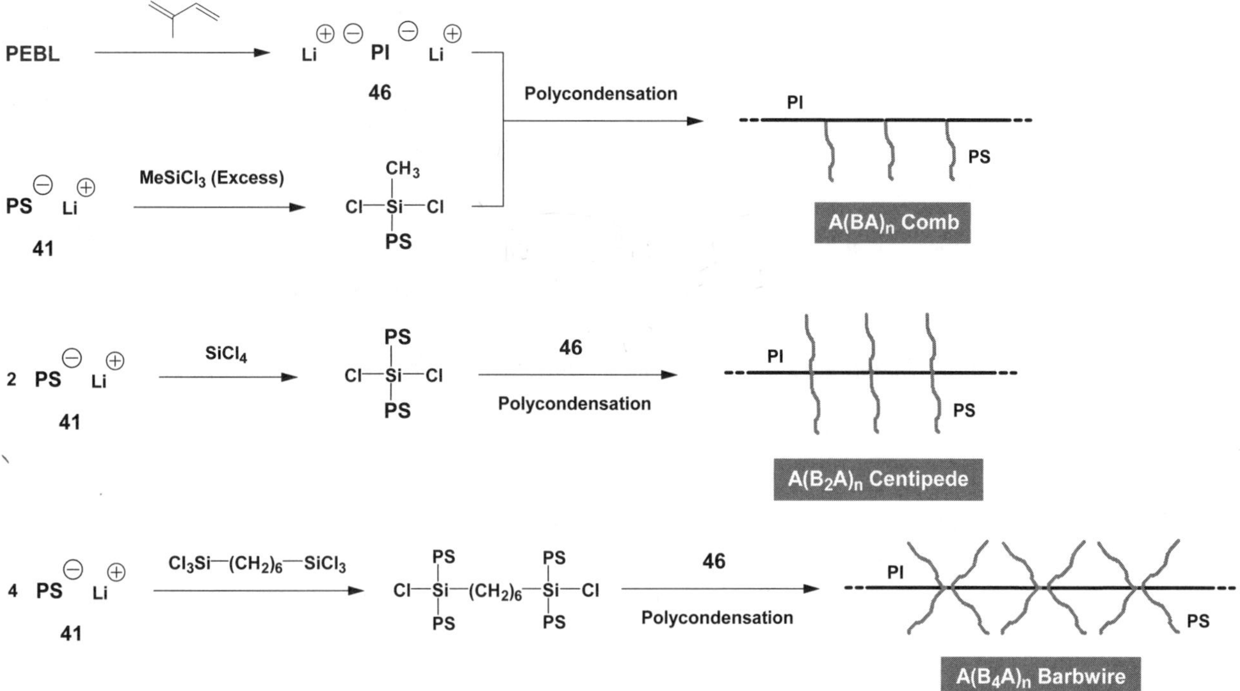

Figure 2.132. Synthesis of multi-graft polymer architectures.

2.4.3.2. Block Copolymers

There are two major approaches for the synthesis of block polymers, "telechelic" and "sequential".[114] Each provides access to polymers with different backbone compositions. As shown in Figure 2.133, the "telechelic" approach requires α,ω-functionalized polymer blocks and is especially suitable for $(AB)_n$-type copolymers. By contrast, the "sequential" approach requires α or α,ω-active polymer block, which can be extended to di- or multi-block polymers, viz., AB, ABC, ABA, etc. by sequential addition of monomers. However, recent advances in synthetic chemistry now permit combining both approaches to produce novel, exquisitely structured block copolymers endowed with tailored mechanical, optical, electrical, ionic, barrier and other physical properties. For example, ABA-type block copolymers have been prepared by sequential polymerization of a difunctional macroinitiator obtained by functionalization of a telechelic polymer (*vide infra*).

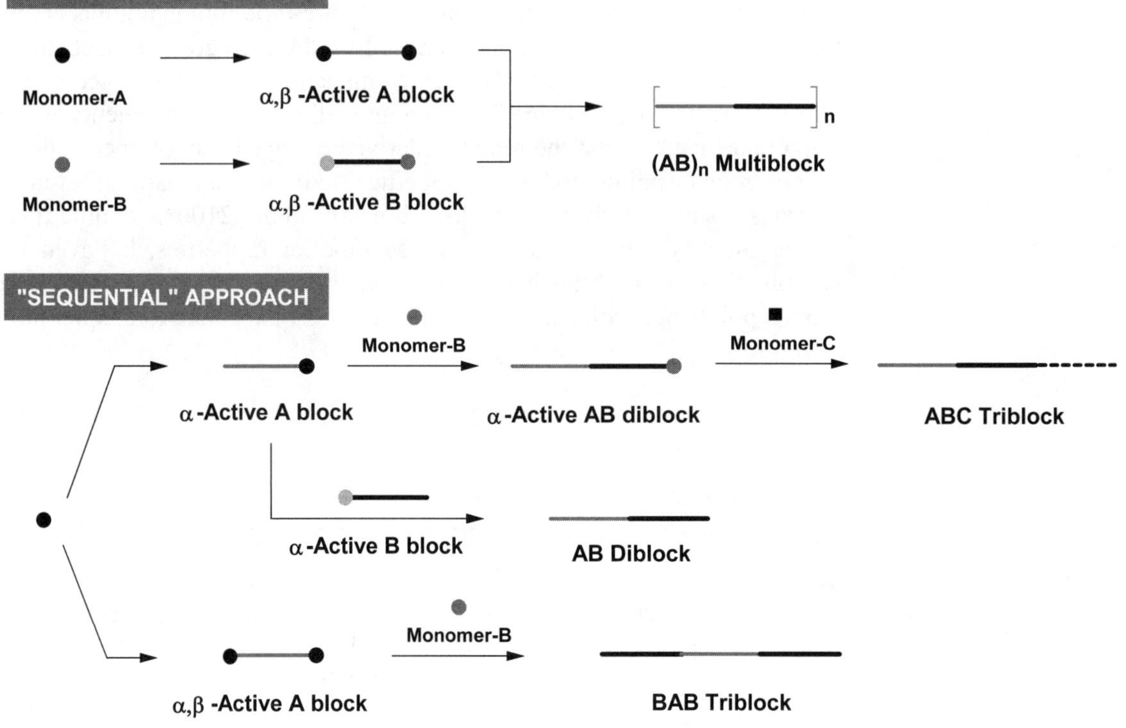

Figure 2.133. Schematics of the common synthetic methods for block copolymers.

2.4.3.2a. The "Telechelic" Approach

The backbone polymers in this case are usually prepared by step-growth polymerization of two mutually reactive telechelic polymers (low molecular weight with α,ω-bifunctional reactive groups), which can be obtained by several methods (Figure 2.134). As mentioned previously (Figure 2.117), living anionic polymerization offers an excellent route to a variety of telechelic PSs. If a living PS sample, generated by using a bifunctional anionic initiator, is terminated with oxirane, a dihydroxy-terminated PS (**T_1**) is obtained. Step-growth polymerization represents the simplest way to synthesize telechelic polyesters (**T_2**), polyamides (**T_3**) and polyurethanes (**T_4**), by terminating with appropriate excess monomer. Cationic polymerization can also be used to prepare telechelic polyethers (e.g., **T_5**, see also Figure 2.61).

$Li^{\oplus}\ {}^{\ominus}PS^{\ominus}\ Li^{\oplus}$ → 1. (oxirane) 2. $H_3O^{\oplus}$ → HO–PS–OH (**T_1**)

ClOC–C_6H_4–COCl (Excess) + HO–CH_2CH_2–OH → TEA → ClOC—PET—COCl (**T_2**)

H_2N—$(CH_2)_6$—NH_2 (Excess) + ClOC—$(CH_2)_4$—COCl → TEA → H_2N—PA66—NH_2 (**T_3**)

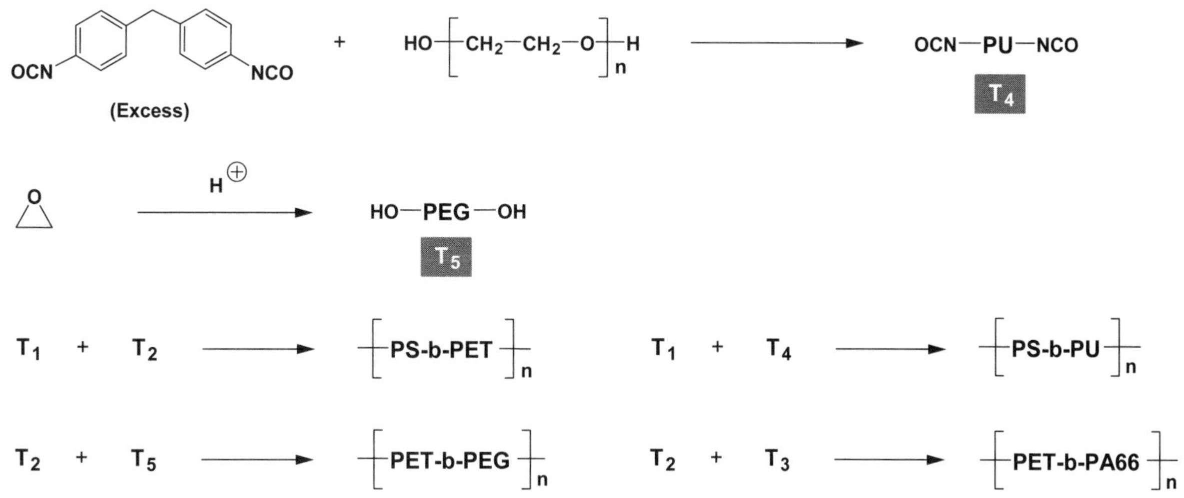

Figure 2.134. Synthesis of widely used telechelic polymers and related $(AB)_n$ multiblock copolymers.

When it comes to polybutadiene (PB) telechelics, the ROMP technique is preferred over living anionic polymerization because of 100% 1,4-microstructure and simplicity in preparation.[115] Thus, the ROMP of 1,5-cyclooctadiene (COD) in the presence of a chain transfer agent (CTA) containing protected functional groups (PFGs) produces telechelic PBs end-capped with a reactive functional group, such as amino, hydroxyl and carboxy (Figure 2.135). These telechelics are attractive as building blocks for tailor-made block copolymers, including reaction injection molding leading to network polymeric materials. Several similar polynorbornene (PNB) based telechelics have also been prepared by using norbornene in place of COD.[116] These polymers are expected to complement or substitute for other telechelic polyalkenamers currently used in industry.

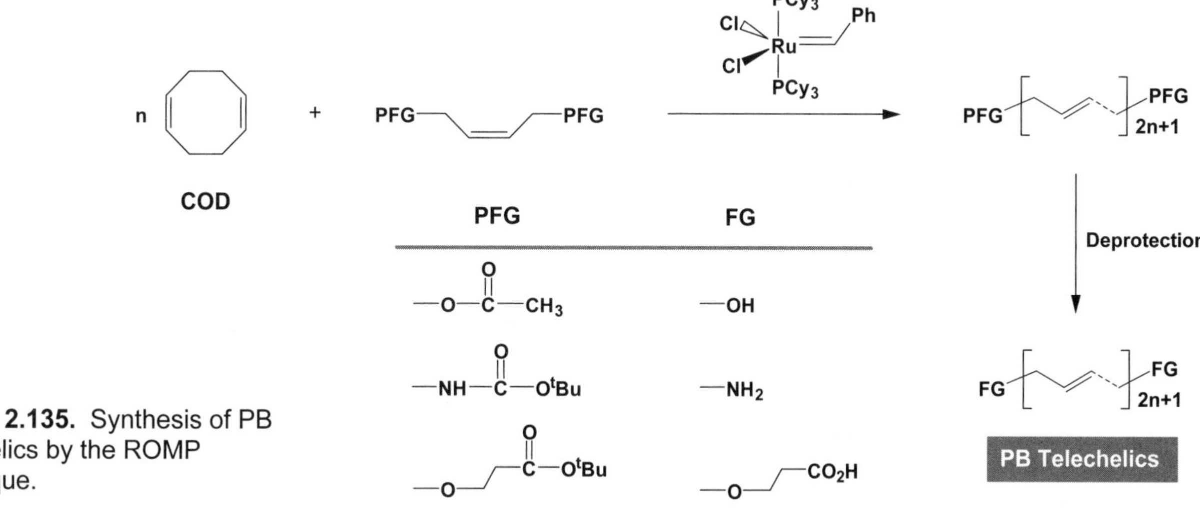

Figure 2.135. Synthesis of PB telechelics by the ROMP technique.

The aforementioned synthetic strategy, ROMP in the presence of CTA, has been successfully coupled with other CRP techniques, especially RAFT and ATRP, to build polymer blocks in outward directions to give ABA-type block copolymers.[117,118] Thus, if a suitable ATRP or RAFT group-substituted CTA is used with COD, one can devise an alternate route to SBS and MBM triblock copolymers (M = methyl methacrylate). The interesting feature of this cross-polymerization strategy is that, like the living anionic technique, polymerization can be conducted in "one-pot" by sequential addition of monomers (Figure 2.136). It is important to emphasize that the living anionic route can produce SBS with high 1,4-linked butadiene content, but cannot yield MBM triblock copolymer because of side reactions with the functional group.

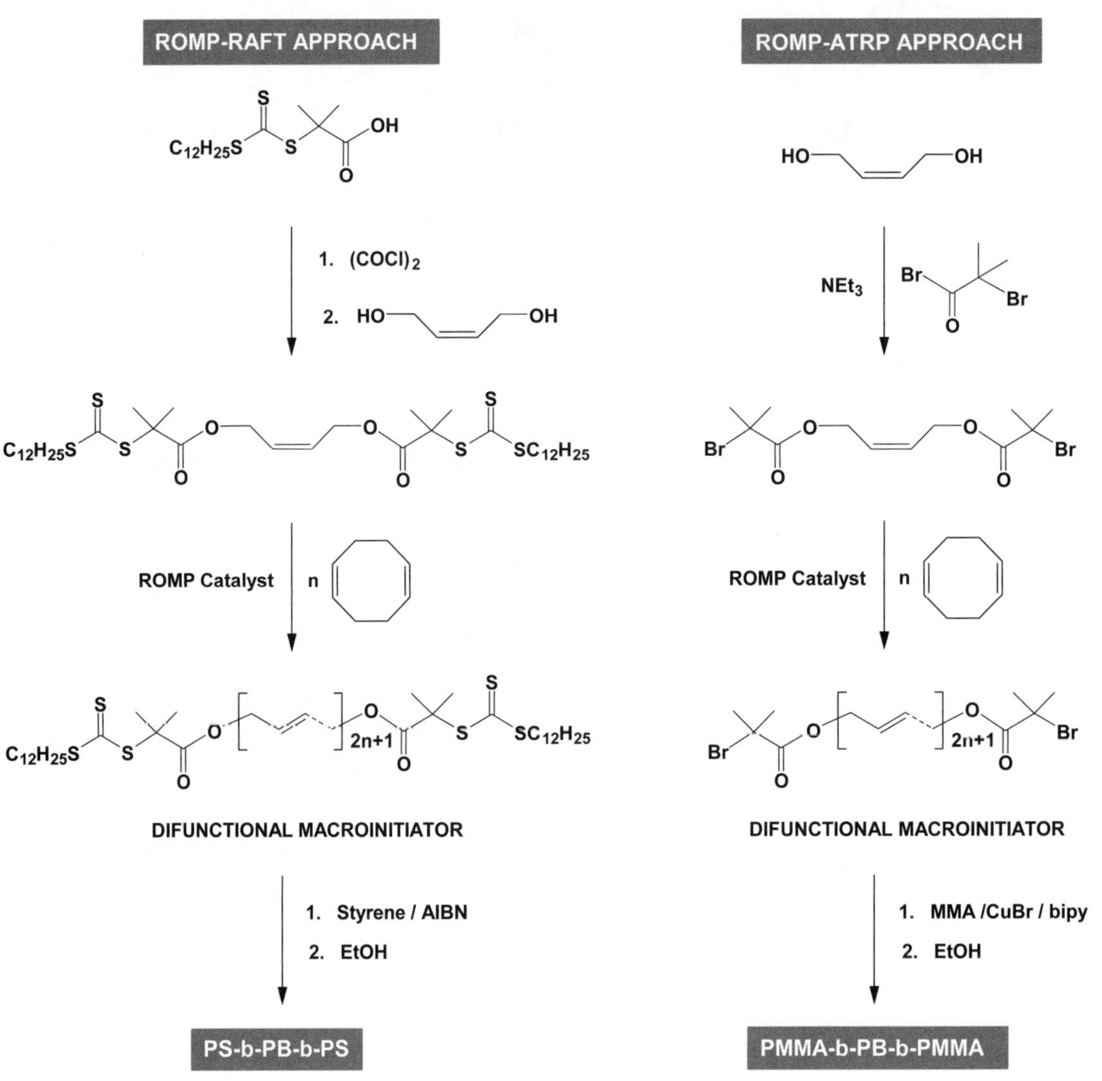

Figure 2.136. Synthesis of block copolymers by the tandem ROMP-CRP approach.

Recently, several novel block copolymer systems have been obtained by using step-growth polymerized telechelic polymers.[119,120] A notable system contains a rigid polysulfone (PSU) center block flanked by two flexible poly(n-butyl acrylate) (PBA) soft blocks (Figure 1.137). The methodology involves preparation of a difunctional macroinitiator by coupling a telechelic PSU with an appropriate CRP-initiating species, which can be used to initiate the polymerization of monomers, viz., styrene or butyl acrylate, to yield block copolymers with novel physical properties. For example, the triblock copolymer (PBA-*b*-PS-*b*-PBA) with a central polysulfone segment (25 wt.%) organizes in supramolecular aggregates with a periodicity from 10 to 12 nm.

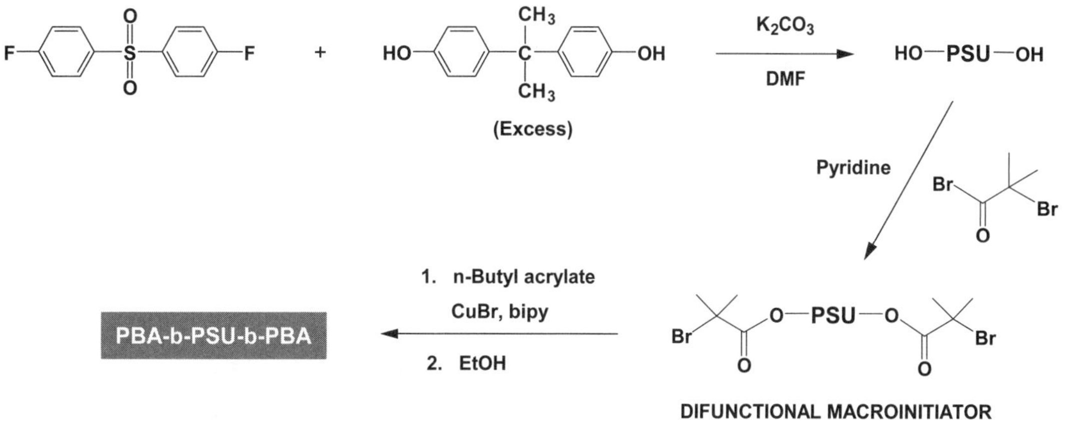

Figure 2.137. Synthesis of a block copolymer by cross-polymerization strategy.

2.4.3.2b. The "Sequential" Approach

The backbone polymers of this approach are usually prepared by controlled free-radical and/or ionic polymerization mechanisms. ABC-type block copolymers are conveniently achieved in "one-pot" by sequential addition of monomers to a monofunctional anionic or CRP active species. Often, other polymerization techniques, such as cationic ring-opening, are included in the strategy to obtain polymers with specific properties. An excellent example is the preparation of polylactide-poly(*N*,*N*-dimethylacrylamide)-polystyrene (PLA-PDMA-PS) triblock copolymer in developing hydrophilic pores containing nanoporous polystyrene materials, which are attractive for biological applications, such as antibody or enzyme immobilization and selective transport and separation of biomolecules (Figure 2.138).[121] Each block plays a distinct role: PLA is the etchable component, PDMA is the hydrolytically stable hydrophilic and water-soluble component, and PS is the matrix material. The interesting feature of this triblock copolymer is the formation of highly ordered cylindrically shaped PLA microphases when subjected to heat-induced shear alignment. Thus, hydrolytic removal of these PLA segments provides microporous PS substrates with hydrophilic PDMA in the inner surface of the pores. The SEM picture inserted in the figure below demonstrates the existence of a nanoporous structure arranged on a hexagonal lattice, with an average pore diameter of 19±2 nm and an average principal spacing of 29±2 nm. Several examples relate to ABA-type block copolymers by adding monomers to a bifunctional living anionic or CRP active species already cited in the previous sections while introducing these living polymerization mechanisms (e.g., Figures 2.113, 2.116, 2.119 and 2.121).

AB-type diblock copolymers can be obtained either by addition of monomers to a living polymer chain or by coupling of two α-active polymer blocks. With proper selection of polymerization mechanisms, a variety of diblock copolymers with novel molecular architecture has been synthesized. In this way, well-defined polynorbornene PNB-*b*-PS was prepared via termination of living ROMP with an anionically polymerized macromolecular aldehyde (Figure 2.139).[122] Because of the presence of norbornene units in the polymer backbone, the upper service temperature of the block copolymer is expected to be much higher than that of PS while some attributes of PS, such as processability and transparency, are also expected to be important features of the material.

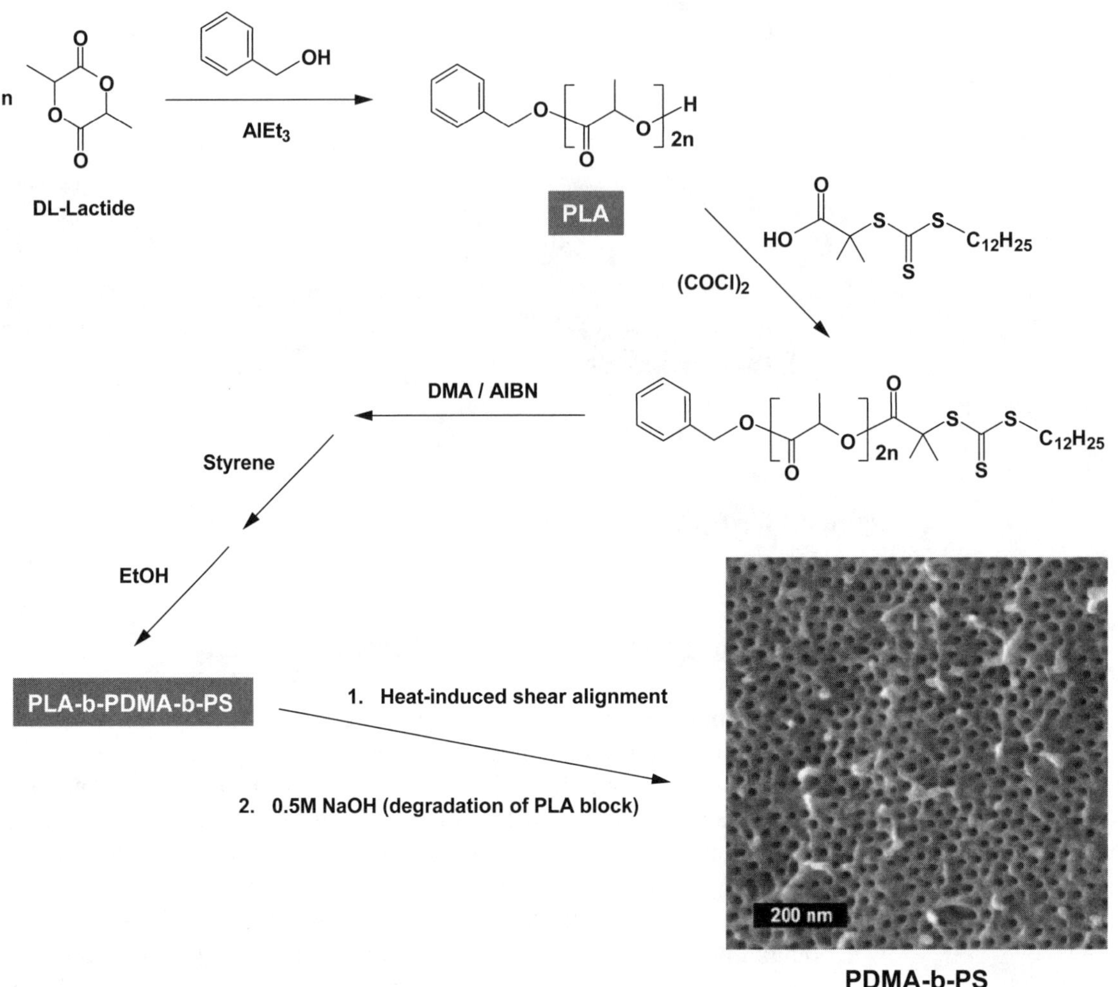

Figure 2.138. Synthesis of a nanoporous material by selective cleavage of one block. *SEM picture is reproduced with kind permission of the American Chemical Society.*

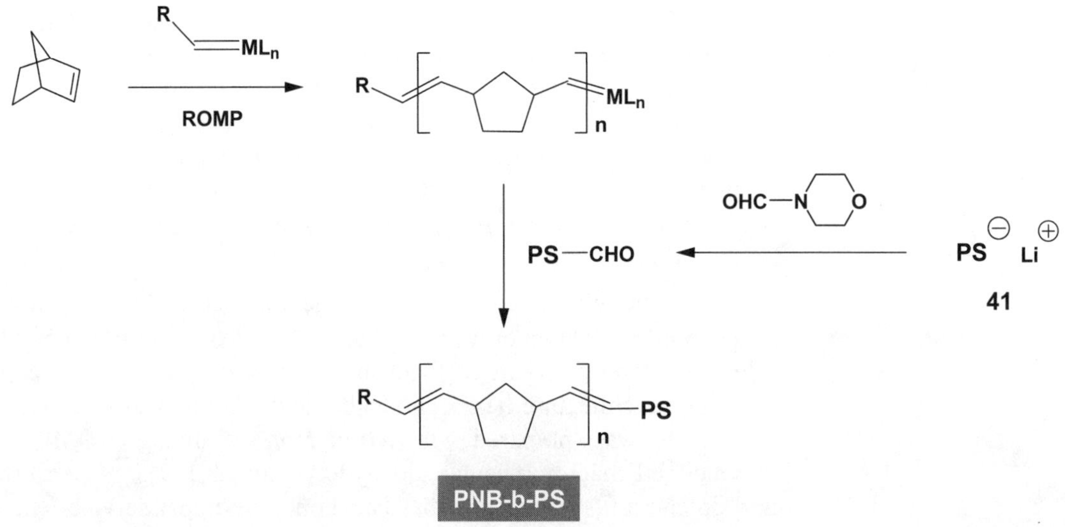

R
ML_n
ROMP
R
ML_n
n
OHC—N O
PS—CHO
PS $^{\ominus}$ Li $^{\oplus}$
41
R
PS
n
PNB-b-PS

Figure 2.139. Synthesis of a well-defined diblock copolymer.

2.4.3.3. *Star-shaped Polymers*

Polymers with star-shaped architectures are usually prepared by two approaches: "core-first" and "arm-first". In the "core-first" approach, the arms are grown from an initiating species containing multiple active sites (Figure 2.140). Thus, the number of arms depends on the number of active sites on the initiator. The length of the arms is controlled by the ratio of grams of monomer to moles of active sites. This approach is applicable to both living ionic and CRP techniques. In the "arm first" approach, the grown arms react with a coupling agent containing multiple linking sites to conform the star-shape. Living anionic polymerization methods are ideal for the synthesis of this class of polymers. Both methods, however, allow the introduction of arms with polymer blocks. Since precise control of molecular weight and polydispersity is a distinguishing feature of anionic polymerizations, the latter approach offers relatively better control in terms of arm length and microstructure.

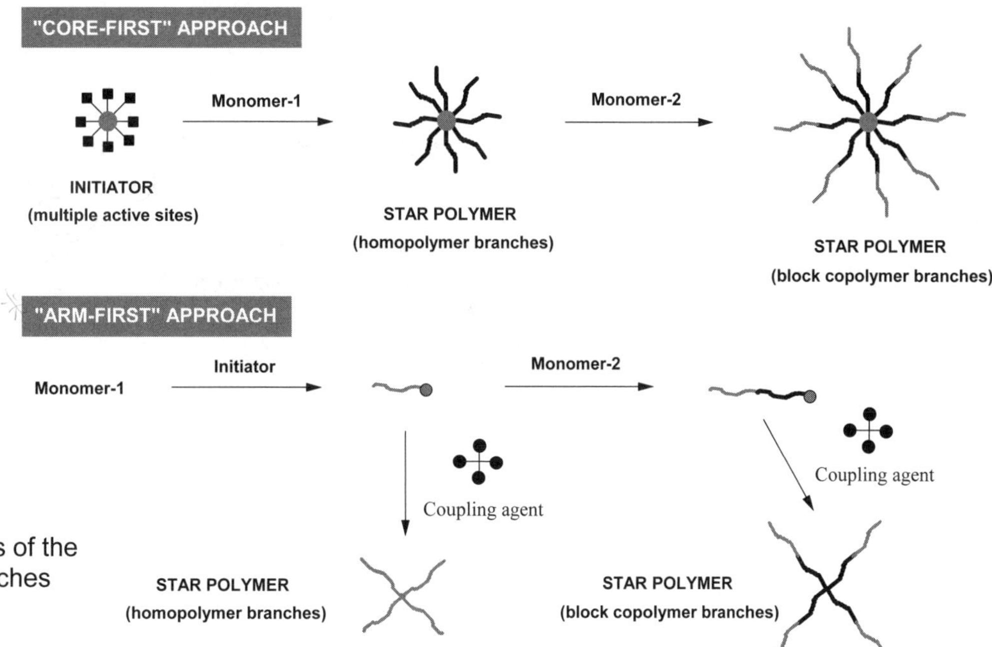

Figure 2.140. Schematics of the common synthetic approaches for star-shaped polymers.

2.4.3.3a. The "Core-first" Approach

In this case, a bis-unsaturated monomer, usually divinylbenzene (DVB), is polymerized first under dilute conditions using s-BuLi or lithium naphthalide to form small, stable microgel particles coated with metal organic functions, which subsequently serve as initiating sites for the living anionic polymerization of suitable monomers.[123,124] The branches that emanate from the core are fitted with anionic sites at their outer ends, thus providing opportunities for block copolymerization and/or for functionalization of the branches at their outer ends (Figure 2.141). It is important to reiterate that if acrylate monomers, such as *tert*-butyl acrylate (TBA) and 2-acetoxyethyl acrylate (AcOEA), are used as a part of the strategy, LiCl must be added to avoid side reactions, such as nucleophilic attack on the carbonyl group.[125,126] Often, the intermediate addition of 1,1-diphenylethylene (DPE) serves the same purpose, but not as a substitute for LiCl. The interest in acrylate monomers lies in the fact that the functional groups present in the acrylate polymer blocks can be hydrolyzed to hydrophilic groups, e.g., carboxylic acid for TBA and hydroxyl for AcOEA. Finally, this approach produces star polymers with a large number of arms, which markedly differ in a polymer sample, i.e., one molecule may have 5 and another 50.

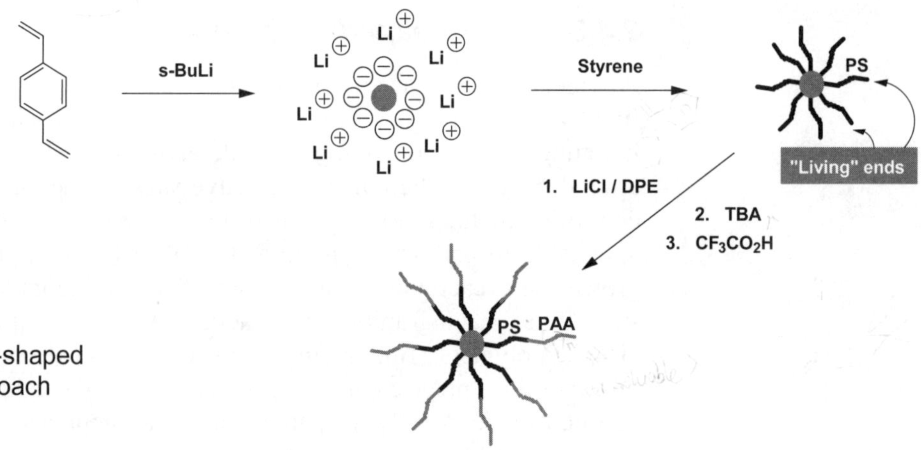

Figure 2.141. Synthesis of star-shaped polymers by the "core-first" approach (PAA = Polyacrylic acid block).

Star polymers with exact, but a lesser number of arms (usually less than 6) are best synthesized by using a multifunctional DVB anionic initiator[127], such as 1,3,5-tris(1-phenylethenyl)-benzene, or a CRP initiator[128], e.g., 1,2,4,5-tetrakis(bromomethyl) benzene (Figure 2.142). Branches with multiple polymer blocks can also be grown from each active site of the initiator by sequential addition of monomers. Since the outer ends of all branches are functionalized, this approach provides opportunity to place peripheral functionalities and combine with other polymerization mechanisms, including incorporation of sub-branches. For example, diphenylmethylpotassium (DPMK)-induced ring-opening anionic polymerization of ethylene oxide can be employed if the terminal ends of an ATRP initiated star polymer is modified with a monofunctional or difunctional amino alcohol.

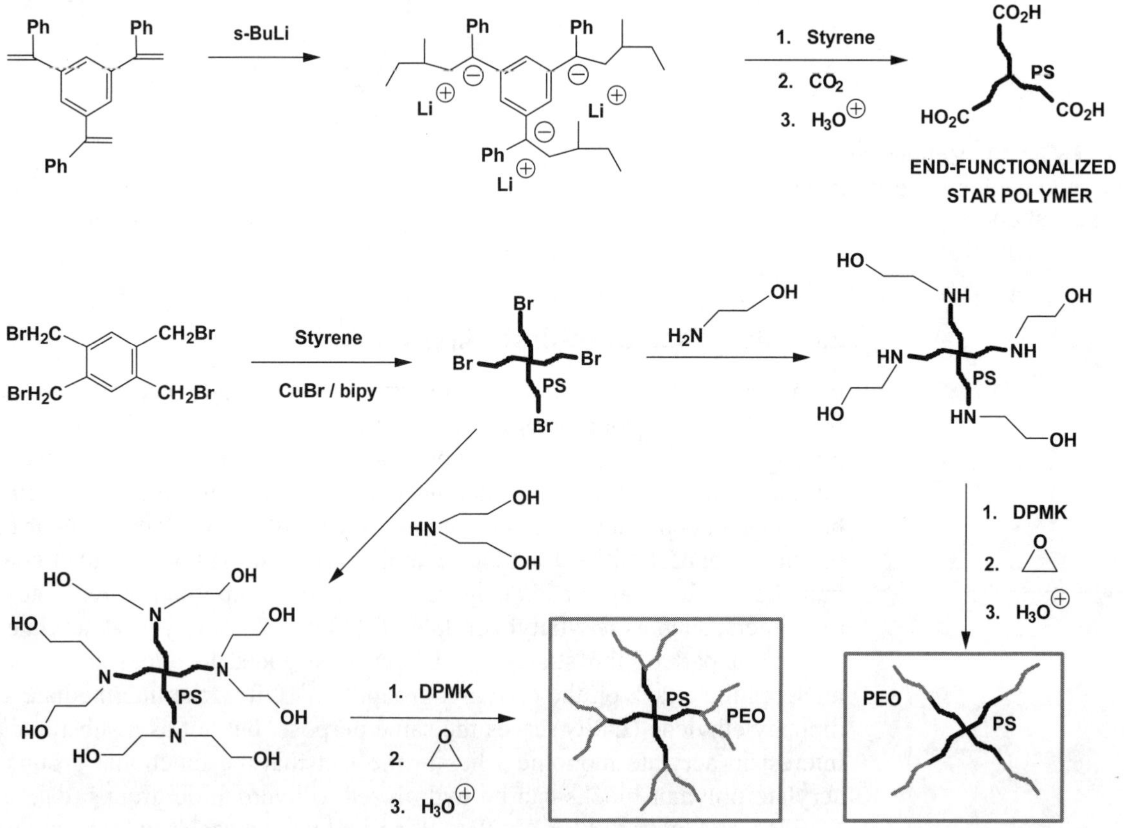

Figure 2.142. Synthetic strategy to well-defined star-shaped polymers.

2.4.3.3b. The "Arm-first" Approach

This route is more popular and provides access to more complex molecular architectures that are not possible with the "core-first" approach because of the flexibility in the preparation of arms in the form of a homopolymer or block copolymer with linear and/or comb structures. Star-branched polymers with well-defined architectures are synthesized mainly by terminating living anionic polymers (arms) with multifunctional chlorosilanes. Commercial star block thermoplastic elastomers, especially the *K-Resin® family* (Chevron-Philips Chemical Co.), are manufactured by this method (Figure 2.143). Another strategy involves reactions of living anionic polymers with a specifically designed bifunctional reactant, 4-(chlorodimethylsilyl)styrene (CDMSS), which contains a silyl chloride group capable of quantitatively terminating a living chain and a polymerizable vinyl group capable of addition and maintenance of a living reaction site. Thus, very slow addition of a certain amount of CDMSS (chlorosilane coupling is much faster than addition with a vinyl group) to a living anionic polymer system leads to a convergent hyperbranched core (**A**) with only one living anionic reactive site, a quite different situation from that of DVB, where many living anionic sites are formed.[129-131] This strategy is now becoming more attractive because of ease of preparation (often in "one-pot") and access to novel molecular architectures, e.g., star-*block*-linear-*block*-star triblock polystyrene polymers with identical stars at each end of a linear block (*"pom-pom" polymers*), polymers with star-shaped branching at the ends of each arm, etc., by sequential addition of appropriate monomer(s) and CDMSS.

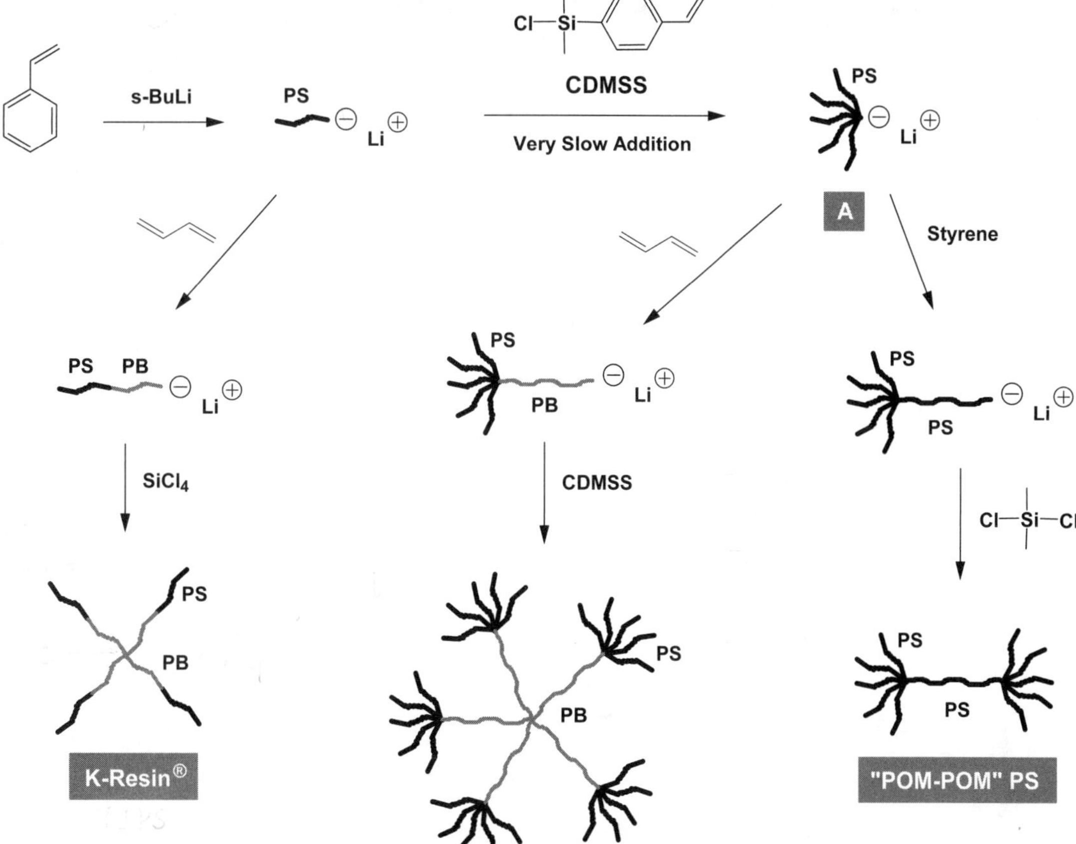

Figure 2.143. Synthesis of complex molecular architectures by the "arm-first" approach.

Complex asymmetric star-branched polymers whose arms differ in molecular weight or chemical composition (mixed arm or *"miktoarm"*) have been extensively investigated because of their unique physical properties and morphologies consisting of branched architectures and heterophase structures. A recently developed "iterative methodology" is considered well suited for synthesizing both regular and asymmetric starbranched polymers,[132] and involves only two sets of reactions for the entire synthetic sequence: a linking reaction between a living anionic polymer with a bi-functional anionic initiator, such as BPEB, followed by an *in-situ* reaction of the resulting dianionic species with a specifically designed coupling agent, 1-[4'-(4'-bromobutyl)phenyl]-1-phenylethylene (**X**), for introducing DPE moieties into the polymers (Figure 2.144). Thus, well-defined miktoarm star polymers can be prepared by proper selection of living anionic polymers (arms). If a tri-functional anionic initiator is used, such as 1,1-bis[3'-(1"-phenylethenyl)phenyl]ethylene (BPPE), three new arms will be formed after each iteration.

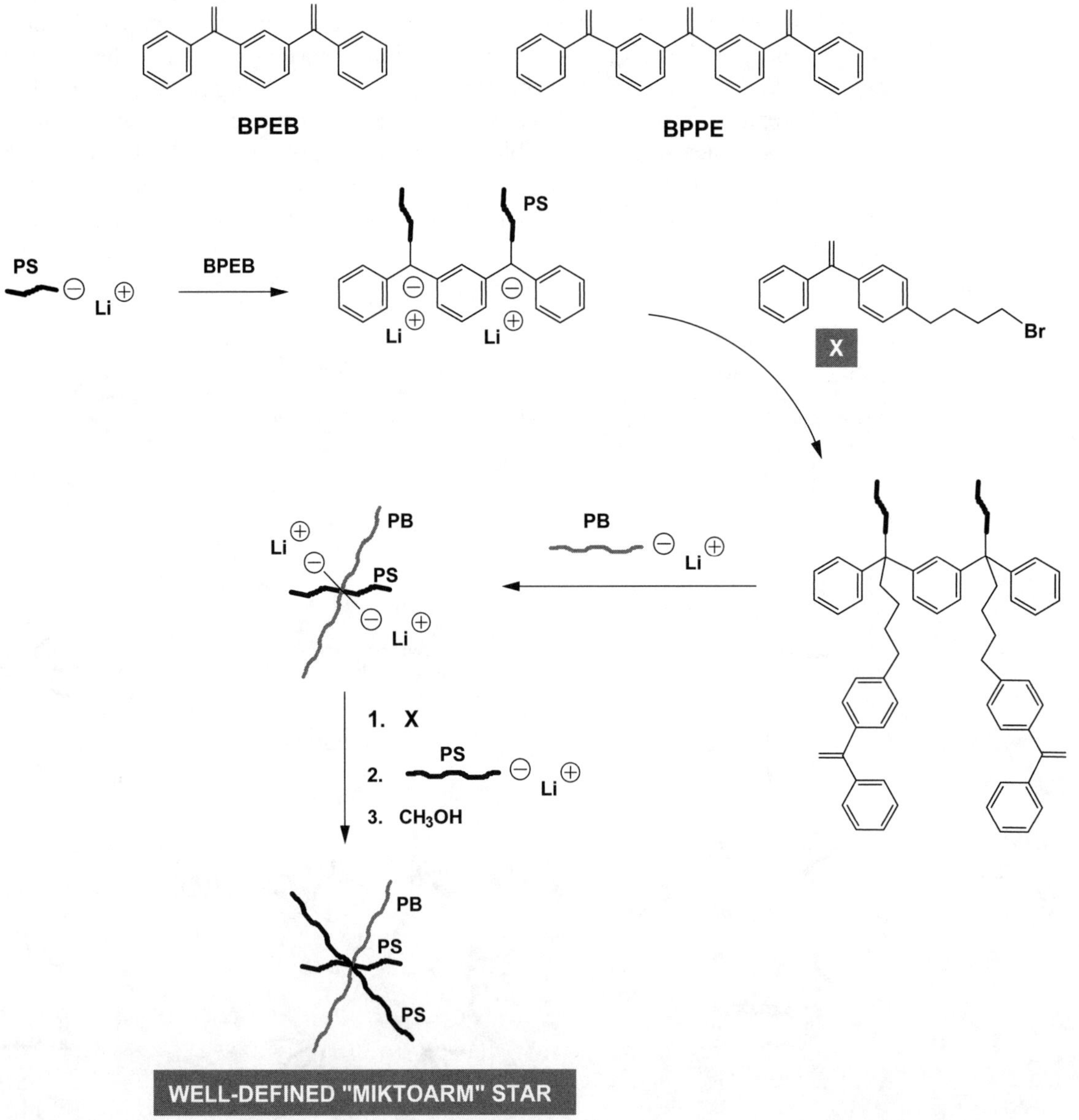

BPEB

BPPE

PS BPEB PS Li Li Li X Br PB Li PB Li PS Li

1. X

2. PS Li

3. CH_3OH

PB PS PS

WELL-DEFINED "MIKTOARM" STAR

Figure 2.144. Synthesis of complex molecular architectures by the "arm-first" approach.

Another popular strategy for synthesis of miktoarm star polymers has also been described by slight modification of the "core-first" approach. As mentioned earlier, when *s*-BuLi reacts with a small amount of DVB, a highly crosslinked polydivinylbenzene core containing several living anionic centers is formed, a basis for the "core-first" approach. If an appropriate living polymer chain (arm) is used in place of *s*-BuLi, a star polymer is formed, consisting of a core with several living anionic centers, which can be used to grow another set of new arms using suitable monomers.[133] A recently reported work has extended this principle to the living cationic polymerization, in order to gain access to vinyl ether derivatives, such as isobutyl vinyl ether (IBVE) and 2-acetoxyethyl vinyl ether (AcOVE), which are not suitable by the anionic method.[134] Figure 2.145 shows a synthetic strategy for a new class of amphiphilic star polymers containing heteroarms with asymmetric lengths by combining "arm-first" and "core-first" approaches. These star polymers exhibit properties that differ from those of the corresponding linear polymers. For example, amphiphilic star polymers with longer hydrophobic segments are superior in host-guest interactions with small organic molecules than the linear amphiphilic counterpart, due to a high accumulation of polar functional groups that stem from the multi-branched structures of star polymers.

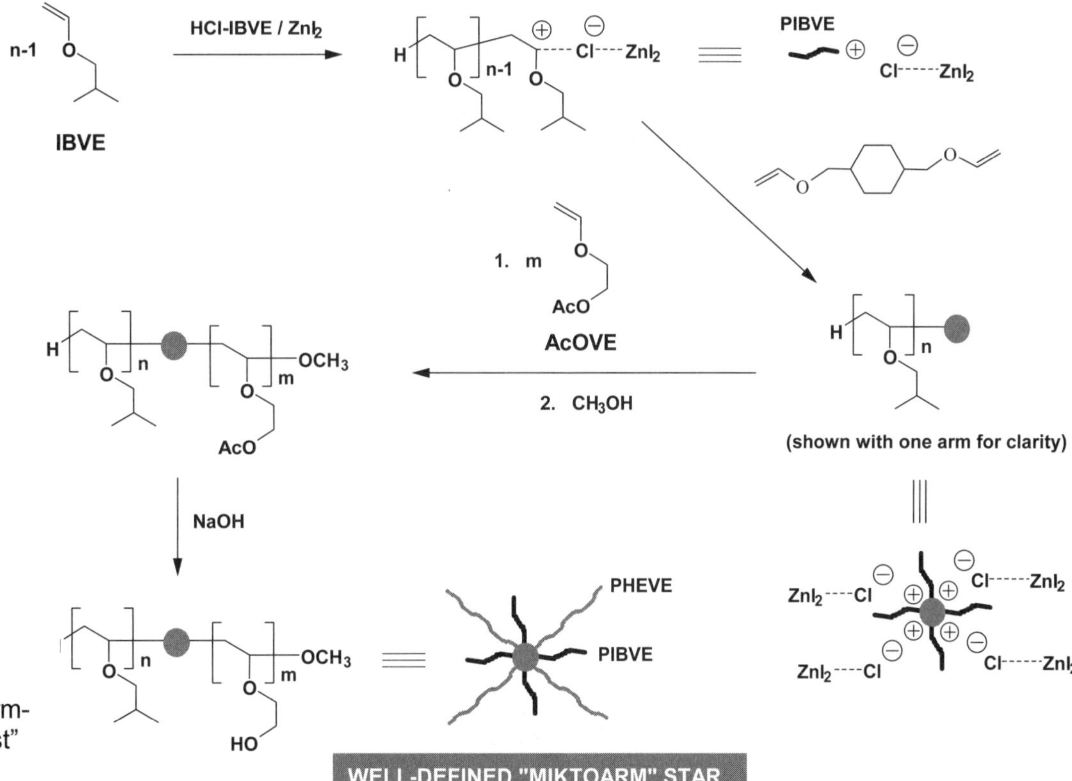

Figure 2.145. Synthesis of asymmetric star polymers by the combination of "arm-first" and "core-first" approaches.

2.4.4. Advanced Catalyst/Initiator Systems

In the past decade, the development of new efficient catalyst/initiator systems has been the subject of intense research leading to unprecedented polymer architectures. The most significant is, perhaps, metallocene catalysts. The aim of this section is to emphasize underlying chemistry involved in the preparation of various classes of metallocenes discussed earlier in this chapter. A rather comprehensive discussion is also presented on important promising non-metallocene catalysts and free-radical initiators.

2.4.4.1. Metallocene Catalysts

As discussed earlier, metallocenes of Group-IV early transition metals, especially Ti, Zr and Hf, are most important because they exhibit superior activity, including longterm stability on storage. Based on their synthetic methodologies, they can be grouped into three categories: unbridged-metallocenes, *ansa*-(or bridged) metallocenes and constraint-geometry catalysts (CGCs).[135,136]

2.4.4.1a. Unbridged-Metallocenes

There are several synthetic avenues to unbridged-metallocene derivatives, including half-metallocenes. The most common routes are outlined in Figure 2.146. The symmetrical metallocenes are prepared by reaction of two equivalents of lithiated ligand with one half equivalent of metal tetrachloride. By contrast, the unsymmetrical metallocenes are prepared exclusively via a half-metallocene intermediate, which is obtained by reaction between the trimethylsilyl (TMS) derivative of the ligand and metal tetrachloride or by treatment of an amide complex of the ligand with a chlorinating reagent, such as trimethylsilyl chloride (TMSCl). In general, the lithiated analog of the ligand that exhibits high electronic stability is preferred in reaction with the half-metallocene of the other ligand.

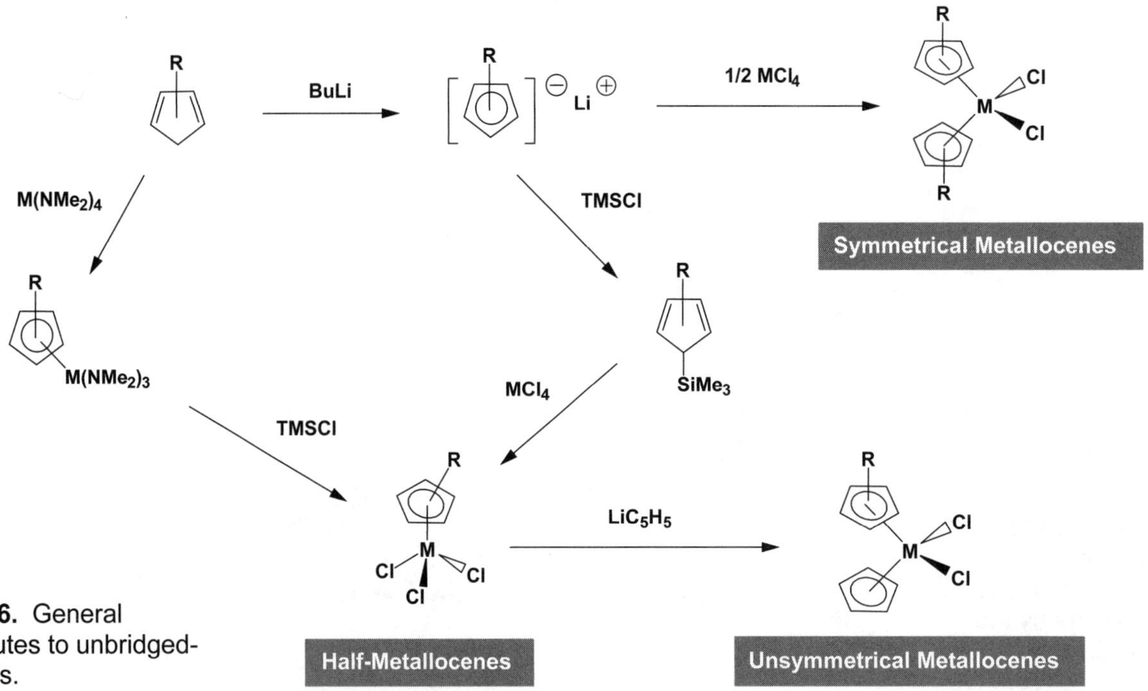

Figure 2.146. General synthetic routes to unbridged-metallocenes.

Besides cyclopentadiene and its derivatives, a variety of benzannulated ligands have been used to synthesize unbridged metallocenes. 2-Arylindenyl ligands are one of the most important because the unbridged 2-arylindenyl metallocenes (also called "oscillating catalyst") can change geometry between at least two conformations during the polymerization reaction of propylene, leading to stereoblock polymers (see Figure 2.26). These ligands are prepared by the action of an arylmagnesium bromide on 2-indanone, followed by dehydration of the resulting tertiary alcohol (Figure 2.147).[137] Several alkylated derivatives of 2-arylindene have also been prepared by subsequent treatment of the ligand with *n*-BuLi and alkyl halide.[138]

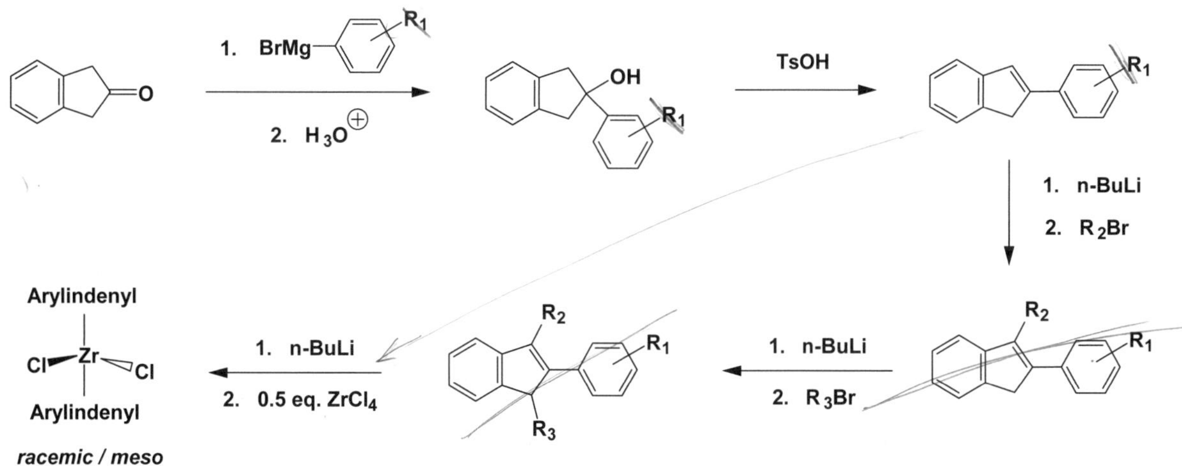

Figure 2.147. Synthetic route to arylindenyl ligands suitable for the preparation of oscillating catalysts.

2.4.2.1b. *Ansa*-Metallocenes

These complexes have received considerable attention owing to recent success in the development of stereospecific polymerization catalysts by strategic placement of substituents on the ligands, which are connected through one (singly-bridged) or two (doubly-bridged) positions. The presence of a bridging group restricts the mobility of the ligands, providing a more rigid system that renders the activation of their C-H bonds more difficult. This feature helps to stabilize lower oxidation states of metallocene complexes. An *ansa*-metallocene can have either C_2-, C_s-, or C_1-symmetry, depending upon the substituents on the two ligands and the structure of the bridging unit. The tacticity of polypropylene varies predictably with the structure of the metallocene catalyst: C_{2v}-symmetric metallocenes generally afford atactic polypropylene; C_2-symmetric metallocenes produce highly isotactic polypropylene; C_1-metallocenes also produce isotactic polypropylene, but generally with less stereospecificity. Whereas the types of isospecific metallocene catalysts are structurally highly variable, syndiotactic polypropylene has been produced using essentially a single type of C_s-symmetric ansa-metallocene catalyst.

The most common symmetrical bidentate ligands containing a single bridge include silyl or methylene connectors (Figure 2.148). The former is formed by reacting dichlorodimethylsilane with an appropriate lithiated cyclopentadienyl species, while the latter is introduced prior to the construction of cyclopentadienyl moieties. However, in both cases, the singly-bridged bidentate ligands can be deprotonated with 2 equivalents of n-BuLi, followed by treatment with metal tetrachloride to obtain the corresponding *ansa*-metallocenes, which usually contain mixtures of racemic (*dl*) and meso diastereomers. The application of other metallation methods is often employed to synthesize either pure racemic or meso product.[139-142]

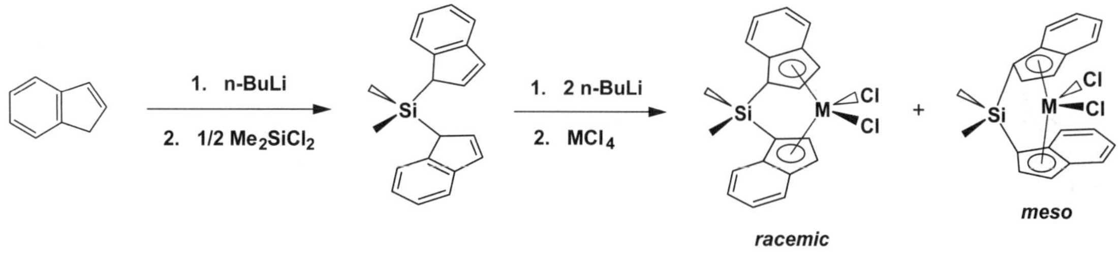

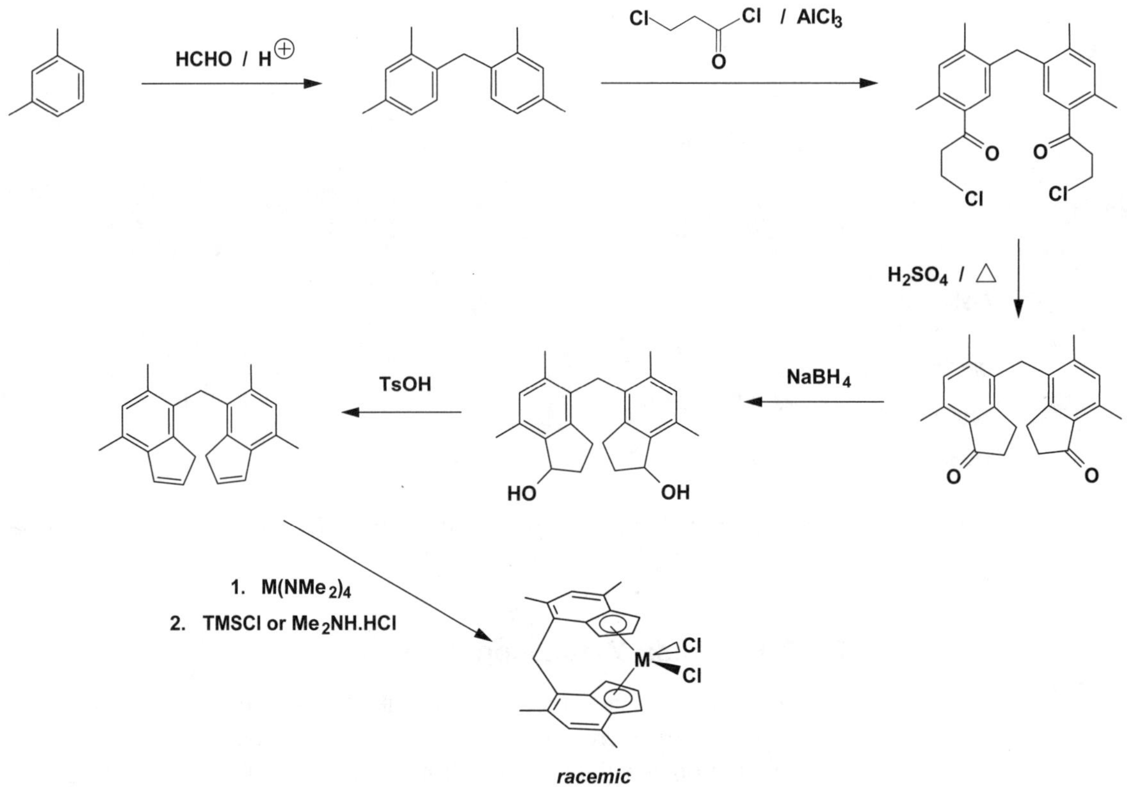

Figure 2.148. Synthesis of singly-bridged metallocene complexes with symmetrical ligands.

Singly-bridged metallocene complexes with unsymmetrical ligands are best prepared by reacting lithiated species of the bulky ligand with the fulvene derivative of the other ligand (Figure 2.149).[143] This approach provides access to C_s-symmetric *ansa*-metallocenes, which are especially suitable for highly stereoregular syndiotactic PP, devoid of stereoerrors ([*r*] > 98%), with melting point exceeding 150°C (*vide supra*).

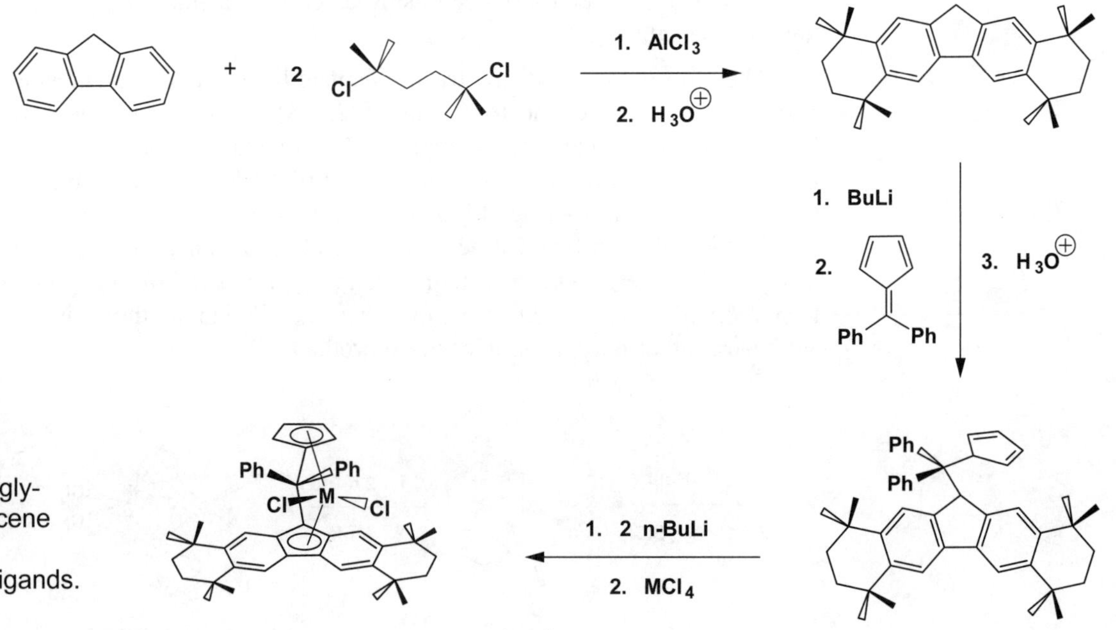

Figure 2.149. Synthesis of singly-bridged metallocene complexes with unsymmetrical ligands.

Unsymmetrical doubly-bridged *ansa*-metallocenes are also suitable for syndiospecific polymerization of propylene, provided they are incorporated with special features, such as C_s-symmetry, cyclopentadienyls of differing size and steric bulk flanking the metallocene wedge with an open region in center. Figure 2.150 depicts the synthesis of one such molecule which contains 1,2-$[SiMe_2]_2$ linking of cyclopentadienyl and 3,5-diisopropylcyclopentadienyl groups.[144-146] The interesting feature of this approach is that the ligand design allows systematic variation of the cyclopentadienyl substituent (R) contained in the mirror plane, permitting C_1-symmetric catalysts, which are suitable for obtaining isotactic PP.

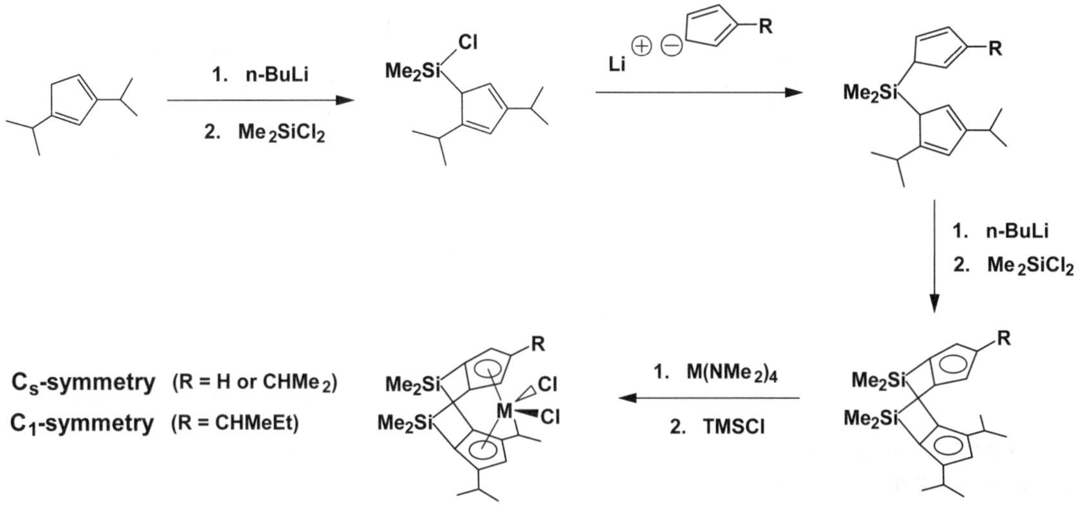

Figure 2.150. Synthesis of doubly-bridged metallocene complexes.

2.4.4.1c. Constraint-Geometry Catalysts

As mentioned earlier, these catalysts have the advantages of a relatively open active site which permits easy incorporation of higher olefins, leading to polyethylene copolymers, resistance toward counterions, such as methylalumoxane (MAO), temperature stability up to 160°C, and providing higher molecular weight polymers when compared to the *ansa*-metallocenes. Among the CGCs, titanium cyclopentadienylsilylamido complexes are highly active. The most common synthetic route to CGCs involves a metathetical reaction of a dilithium derivative of the ligand and $TiCl_4$.[147-149] Figure 2.151 shows the preparation of the dilithium derivative of the ligand.

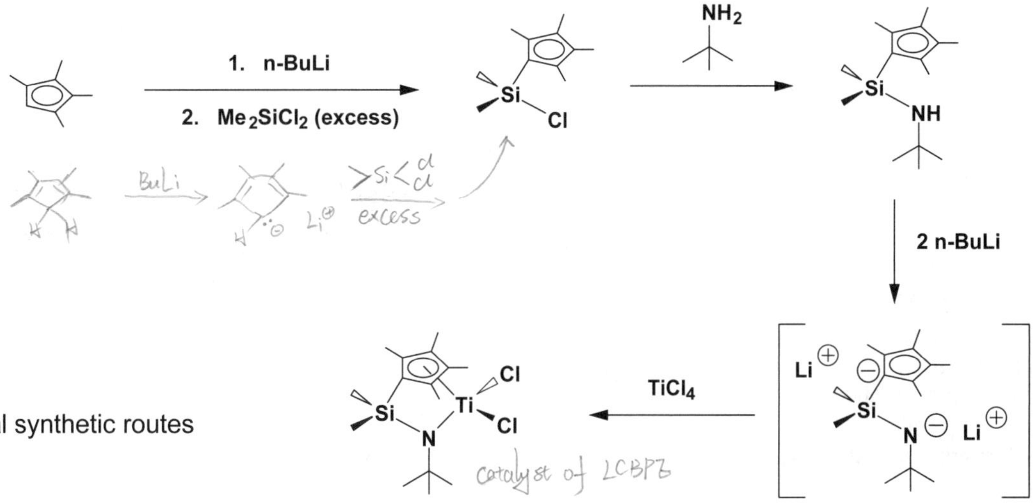

Figure 2.151. General synthetic routes to CGCs.

A slightly different method was reported recently to prepare heteroatom-substituted constrained-geometry complexes in order to enhance catalyst efficiency and polymer molecular weight.[150] The route involves reaction between a lithiated ligand and N(*tert*-butyl)-N-(1-chloro-1,1-dimethylsilyl)amine (Figure 2.152). The 3-amino-substituted complex exhibits the highest catalytic activity and forms the highest molecular weight ethylene-octene copolymers that have ever been reported for this class of catalysts. The higher efficiency of these catalysts is believed to be due to an increase in electron density at the metal center.

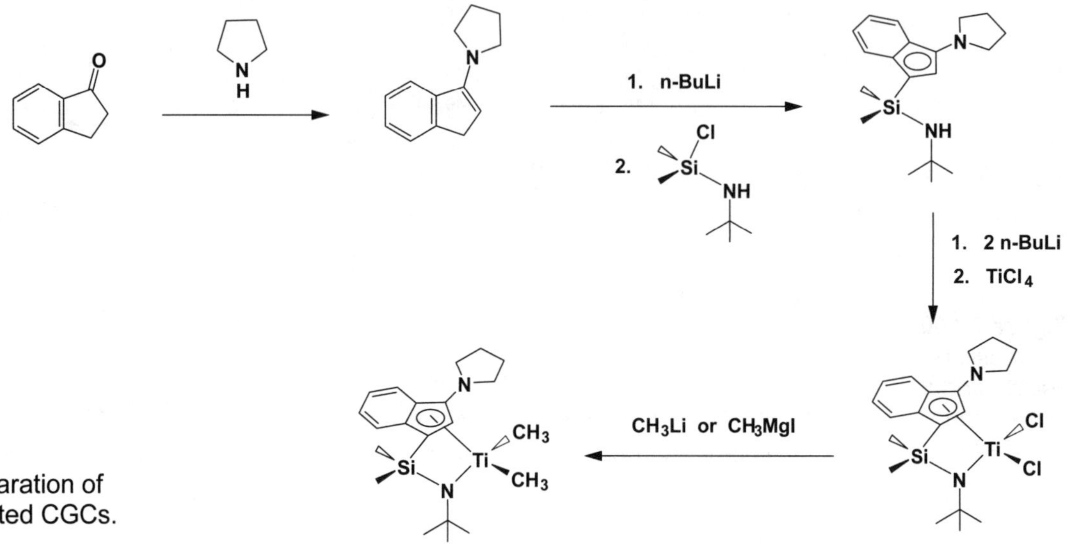

1. n-BuLi

2.

1. 2 n-BuLi

2. $TiCl_4$

CH_3Li or CH_3MgI

Figure 2.152. Preparation of heteroatom-substituted CGCs.

An interesting application of CGC is in the direct preparation of a new type of chiral, C_1-symmetric titanocene imido complex *via* a "one-pot" reaction from a constrained-geometry complex (Figure 2.153).[151] Although the titanocene imido complex itself is active for MMA polymerization, the addition of an activator, such as $Al(C_6F_5)_3$, substantially enhances the polymerization activity to produce syndiotactic PMMA. This result is in sharp contrast to that for $Me_2C(Cp)(Ind)ZrMe^+$, a chiral zirconocene cation having similar ligation but with a terminal methyl group, which produces isotactic PMMA *via* a site-controlled mechanism.

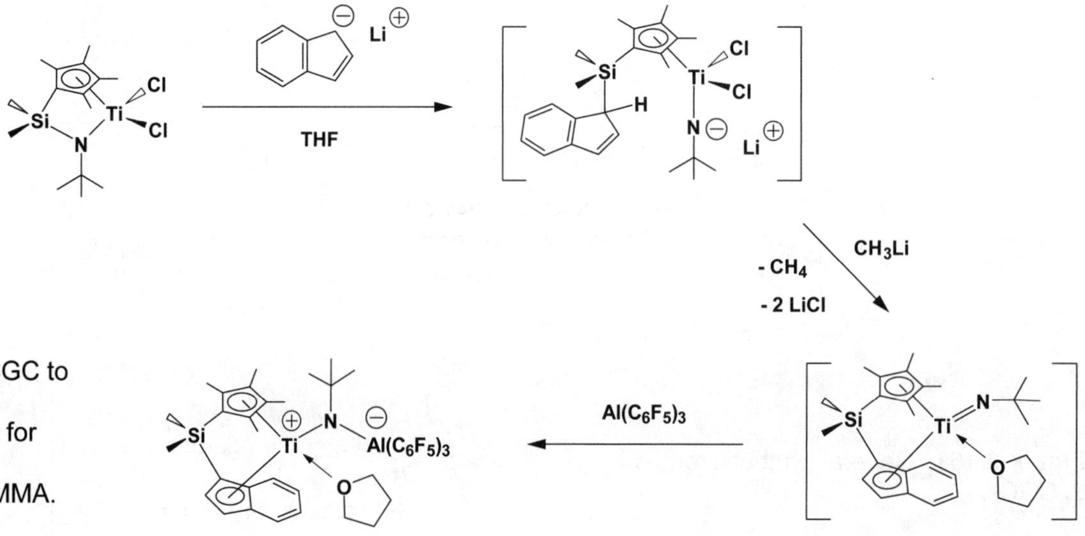

THF

CH_3Li

$- CH_4$

$- 2\ LiCl$

$Al(C_6F_5)_3$

Figure 2.153. Modification of a CGC to a highly active C_1-symmetric catalyst for syndiospecific polymerization of MMA.

2.4.4.1d. Immobilization of Metallocenes

In summary, metallocenes are homogeneous systems that offer higher versatility and flexibility for the synthesis and control of the microstructures of polyolefins. For instance, metallocenes can be tailored to produce polyolefins with specific stereoregularity, a high degree of tacticity and a narrow molecular weight distribution. High-density polyethylene, polypropylene with different stereostructures (atactic, isotactic, syndiotactic, hemiisotactic, etc.), and random copolymers of ethylene with higher α-olefins are examples of most remarkable products. The use of metallocene catalysts for the preparation of novel elastomers may also have significant commercial impact. However, despite their numerous advantages, several issues need to be addressed before metallocene catalysts can be accepted widely in industry. At present, two major problems exist: (1) difficulty in controlling polymer morphology and reactor fouling (a phenomenon where polymer sticks to reactor walls and agitator blades) with soluble homogeneous catalysts and consequent incompatibility with currently used slurry and gas-phase processes and (2) the very large amount of MAO needed to achieve maximum metallocene catalytic activity. As used in Ziegler-Natta catalysis, immobilization of homogeneous metallocene catalysts on a solid support, such as silica, Al_2O_3 and $MgCl_2$, has been regarded as a viable solution to these problems. Heterogenization allows morphology control by "replication phenomena", which leads to uniform polymer particles (product beads instead of a fine powder, making the product easier to handle, Figure 2.154), narrow particle size distribution and high bulk density. The single-site nature of the catalyst, however, provides polymers with narrow molecular weight distributions. Additionally, immobilization of the catalyst can reduce the formation of dormant sites, which, in principle, makes it possible to decrease the required amount of cocatalyst, including the only way to run a metallocene polymerization without solvent in a gas-phase reactor.

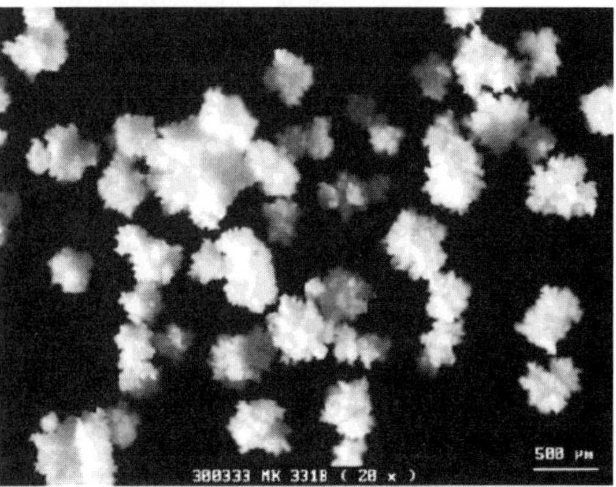

Figure 2.154. Visual microscopy images of polymer particles obtained from an immobilized metallocene system. *Reproduced with kind permission of the American Chemical Society.*[152]

The most common method to immobilize homogeneous metallocene catalysts consists of physisorption of metallocenes on a support that is pretreated with MAO or other cocatalysts. Whereas this method results in heterogeneous catalysts, leaching remains one of the major problems. Improvement of this and alternative immobilization techniques, viz. catalyst tethering, remains a topic of great importance. The most studied support material for tethering is silica, because of its versatility and robustness, and the advantage of a history of varied chemistry being performed on it. There are two primary synthetic strategies to tether the catalyst on silica surfaces.[153] The first involves step-by-step construction of the ligand and subsequently, the catalyst on the silica surface, while the second requires preparation of a metallocene derivative that is a selectively reactive tether that targets a specific function on the silica surface. In theory, the latter process should offer the best hope of forming uniform single active sites, because constructing the complex on the surface usually involves steps that are nonselective or that eliminate potential catalyst poisons or need rigorous purification to remove byproduct from the support. However, both strategies suffer from disadvantages in that the catalyst's steric and electronic environment always differs from the homogeneous cousin it is trying to mimic, and usually less effectively.

The surface of pure silica gel is covered with silanol groups, at a maximum concentration of 8 Brønsted acid OH groups per nm^2.[154] They are mostly found as geminal or isolated pairs and are neither very acidic nor very basic ($pK_a \approx 6$). The hydroxylated surface is hydrophilic and easily adsorbs moisture from the air. This physically adsorbed water can be desorbed by raising the temperature to near 200°C (Figure 2.155). In the course of this heating, partial dehydroxylation of the silica gel takes place, reducing the number of OH groups per nm^2 to approximately 5.5 (approximately 5 wt.% silanol groups attached to 300 m^2/g silica). One-half of these OH groups are geminal pairs; the other half, vicinal. The number of hydroxyl groups decreases continuously as the temperature is raised, until at a temperature of 600-800°C, an almost completely dehydroxylated silica with approximately 1 OH group per nm^2 remains. Nevertheless, both hydroxylated silica and dehydroxylated silica materials are efficient for tethering processes.

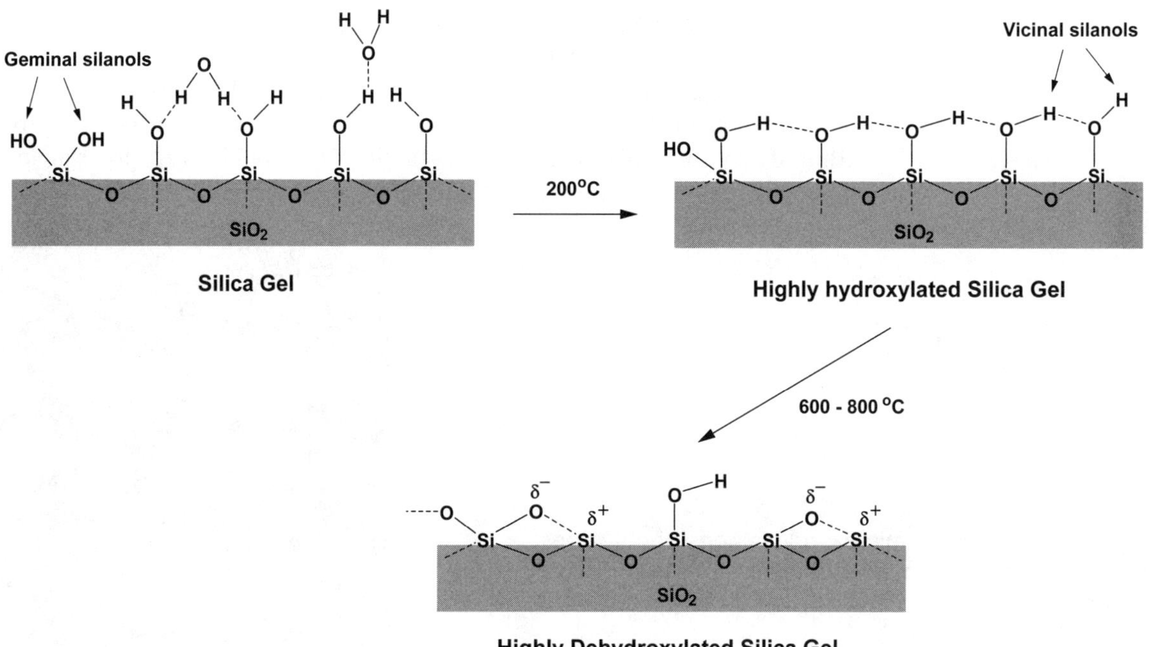

Figure 2.155. Chemistry of a silica gel surface as a function of temperature.

As shown in Figure 2.156, hydroxylated or partially modified silica is normally used for step-by-step solid-phase synthesis of immobilized catalysts. A variety of synthetic procedures can be used to introduce ligands covalently linked to the support. The resulting supported catalysts are quite active in ethylene polymerization in combination with MAO. Analysis of the polymer produced showed slightly broad molecular weight distributions ($M_w/M_n \approx 3$), indicating the existence of several active centers arising from nonselective or competitive reaction on the silica surface.

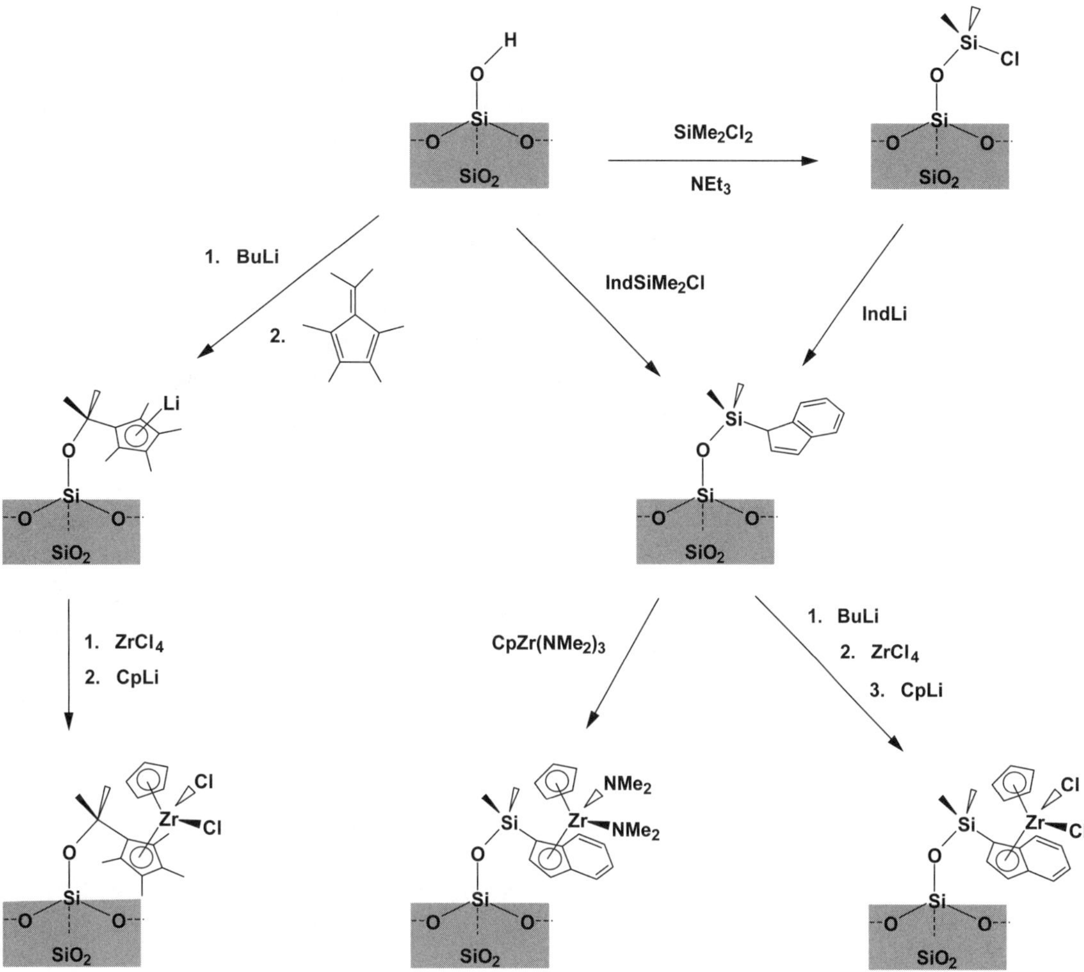

Figure 2.156. Synthesis of supported metallocenes through ligand attachment on silica surface.

Strategies for construction of immobilized bis-indenyl and fluorenyl *ansa*-metallocenes have also been developed (Figure 2.157). Interestingly, the bis-indenyl derivatives, when activated with MAO, produced polyethylene of good bulk density, low polydispersity index (~ 2.1) and no reactor fouling. Such a narrow molecular weight distribution is surprising when one considers the numerous possible side reactions that can occur on the silica surface, especially when excess organolithium complexes are employed. Supported bis- fluorenyl *ansa*-metallocene complexes, however, showed low activities (~60 times less active than that of the homogeneous model compound) in ethylene polymerization.

Immobilization of constrained geometry catalysts (CGCs) via construction on a surface has been very successful, as this strategy produces a more "accurate" CGC mimic (Figure 2.158).[155,156] The standard method involves anchoring of an aminosilane, viz., $(MeO)_3Si(CH_2)_3NH_2$, on the silica surface, followed by treatment with Me_2SiCp^*Cl to obtain a CGC precursor ligand. In general, the activities of the less sterically hindered unsubstituted immobilized cyclopentadienyl complexes are higher than those of the corresponding tetramethyl-substituted complexes, while the latter produces narrower polydispersity. It has also been established that tailoring the silica support structure in supported CGC catalysts can markedly affect the catalyst activity and the resulting polymer properties. For example, a CGC catalyst constructed over a spatially patterned aminosilica material exhibits a 10x increase in ethylene polymerization activity compared to that of a CGC prepared via a standard aminosilane treatment of silica materials. The standard method leads to multiple types of sites due to steric crowding on the support and the heterogeneous nature of the support surface. Figure 2.158 shows steps involved in obtaining a spatially patterned aminosilica material, i.e., isolated aminopropyl groups, utilizing a process called "molecular patterning technique". A patterning agent, in this case a trityl group capped aminosilane, [3-(trimethoxysilanyl)propyl]-(3,3,3-triphenylpropylidene)amine), is used to control the effective spacing of aminosilane groups on a silica surface. The large trityl groups on the patterning agent prevent incorporation of the silane on the surface at sites immediately adjacent to each other. After this functionalization, any additional, unreacted silanols on the surface are covered via treatment with hexamethyldisilazane (HMDS). Thus, uniformly spaced aminopropyl groups on the silica surface can be obtained by selective hydrolysis of the trityl groups from the functionalized surface.

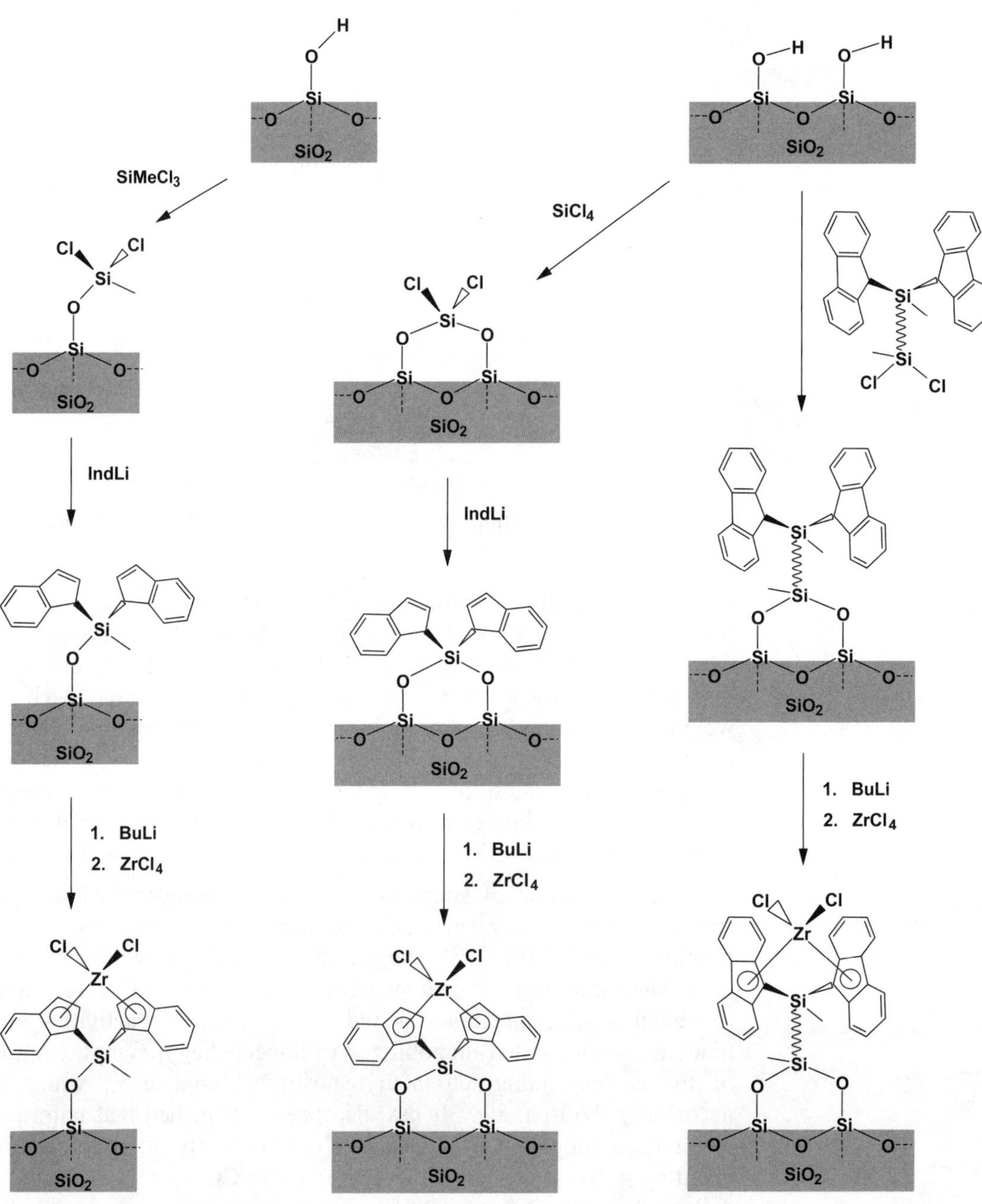

Figure 2.157. Synthesis of supported *ansa*-metallocenes through ligand attachment on silica surface.

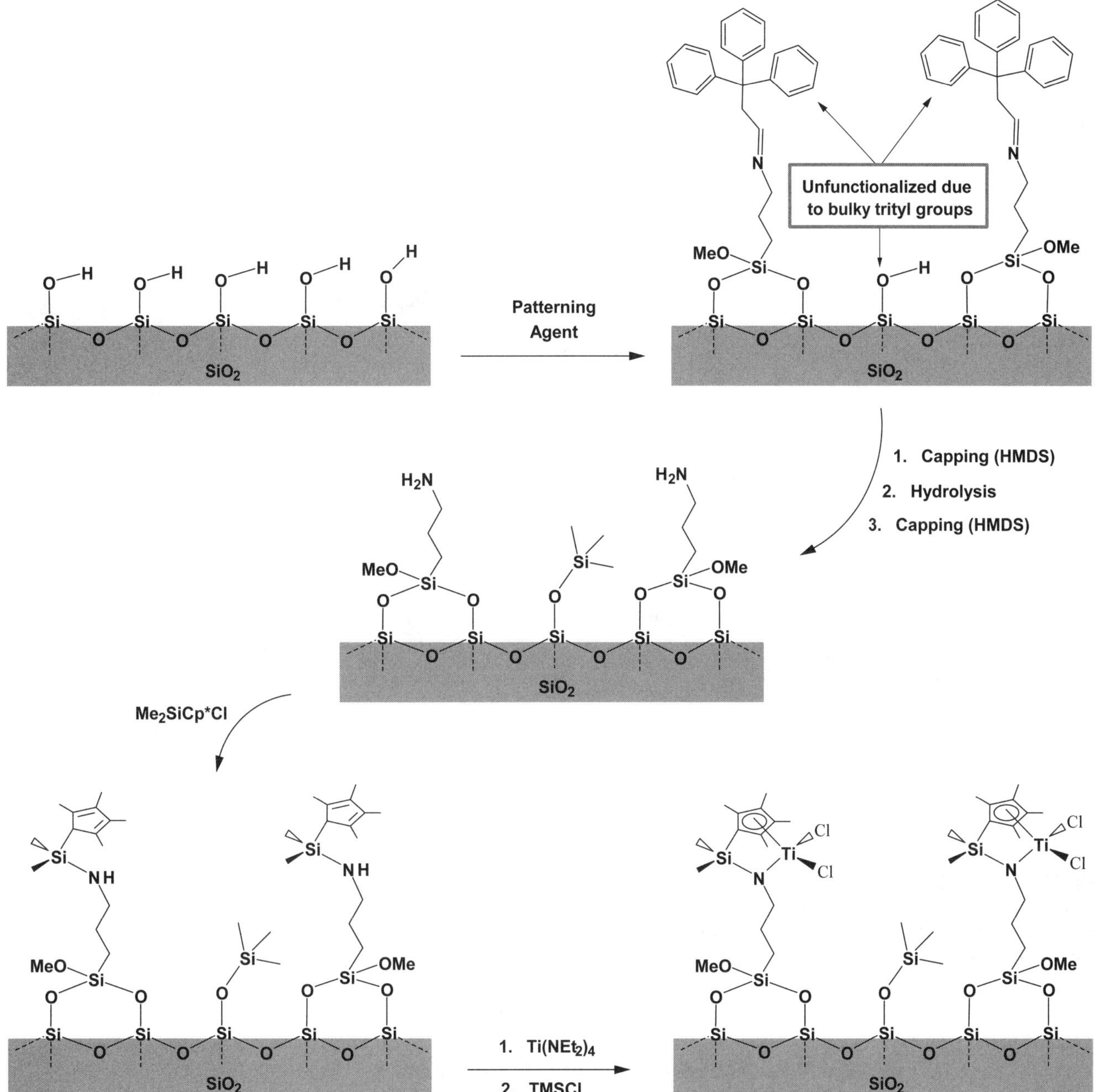

Figure 2.158. Synthesis of well-defined supported CGC via the "molecular patterning technique".

Metallocenes containing reactive functional groups have also been directly attached to dehydroxylated or hydroxylated silica surfaces. Various examples of anchor chemistry have been developed. Most notable ones include reaction between (i) a dehydroxylated silica and a metallocene complex containing a *tert*-butyl ether functionality[157] and (ii) a vinyl-modified hydroxylated silica and a metallocene complex containing a MeSiH bridge[158] or involving reactions utilizing hydrosilylation chemistry (Figure 2.159). Both methods offer opportunities to study the effect of tether length on catalytic performance with longer tethers (C_8) providing increased activity. Interestingly, in the latter route, higher catalyst loading leads to decreased catalytic activity.

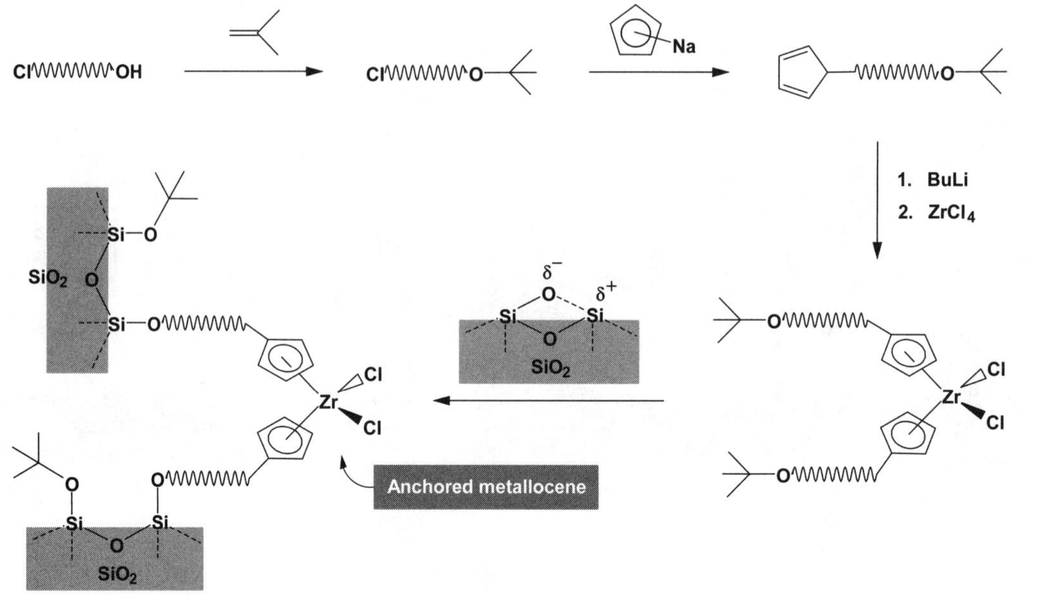

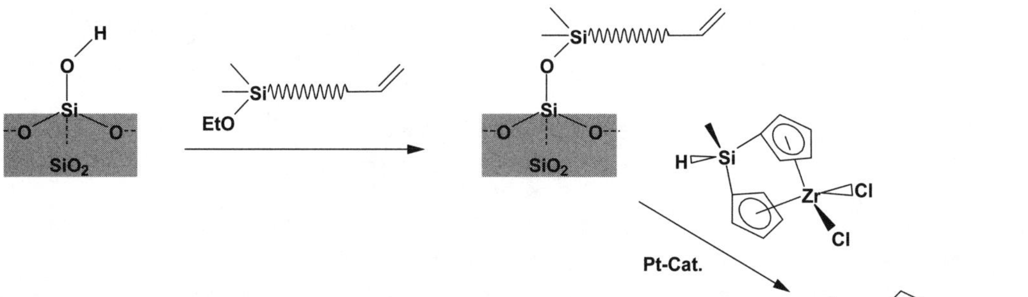

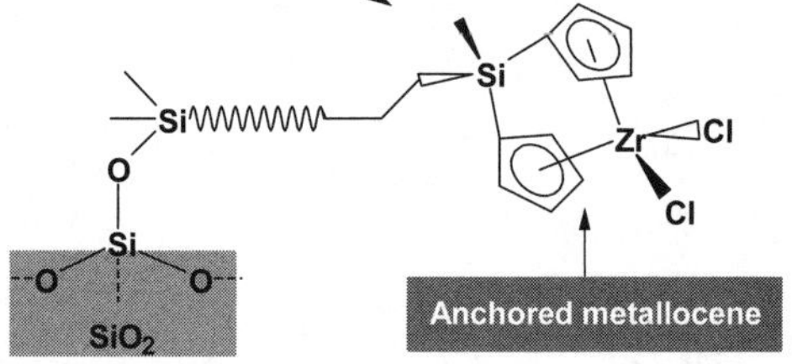

Figure 2.159. Synthesis of anchored metallocenes through a coupling reaction between a metallocene derivative containing a reactive tether and a specific function on the silica surface.

2.4.4.2. Non-metallocene Catalysts

Following the successful design and application of Group-4 metallocenes, there has been a concerted effort to develop "non-metallocene" catalysts for polymerization of α-olefins.[159,160] Among the various catalyst systems, Ni and Pd-α-diimine, Group-4 transition metal bis(phenoxyimine), and bis(phenolate) catalysts have made the most spectacular breakthroughs in this field. The Ni and Pd-α-diimine catalysts possess several key features, such as being highly electrophilic, cationic metal centers, sterically bulky aryl-substituted α-diimine ligands, and noncoordinating counterions. They are capable of not only polymerizing ethylene, α-olefins, and cyclic olefins to high molecular weight polymers. The polyethylenes produced by these systems are distinguished from those made with metallocenes by their structure, having branches along the main polymer backbone and branches on these branches (a "hyperbranched" structure). Branches in these polyolefins form as a result of fast chain isomerization reactions (Figure 2.160). The topology of the polymers is strongly affected by the olefin pressure: under low pressure, highly branched structures are obtained, whereas high pressure gives rise to structures with linear side chains. It is noteworthy that in the polymerization catalyzed by Pd-diimine complexes, the average number of branches is pressure independent, while for the Ni-based system, it is strongly affected by the pressure. Branching in olefin polymerization catalyzed by diimine complexes can be controlled to some extent by the polymerization temperature and the substituents on the catalyst.

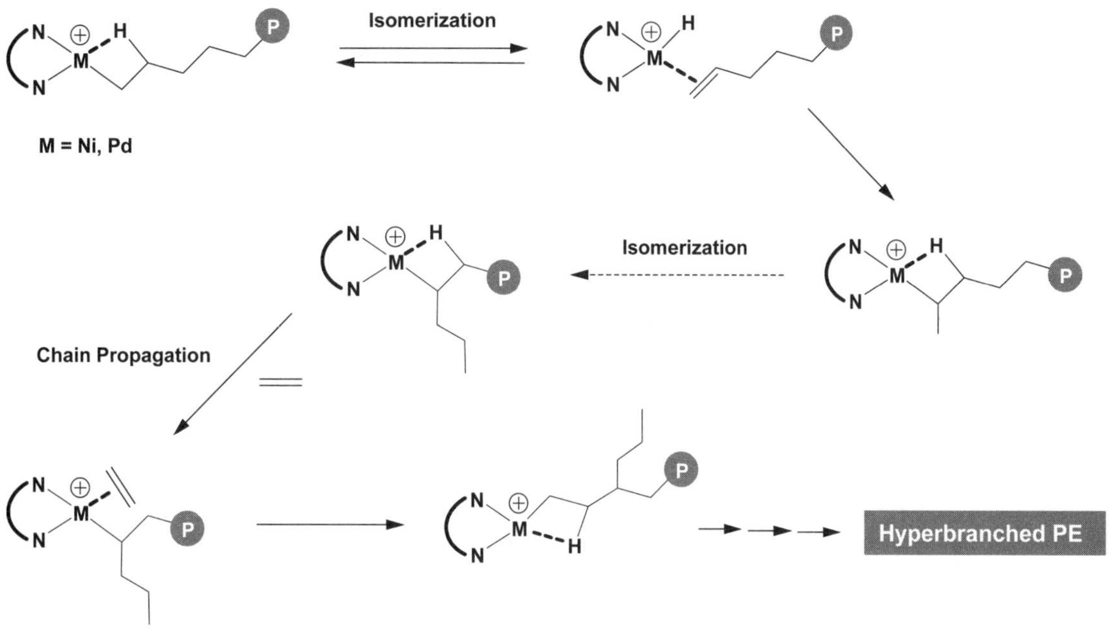

Figure 2.160. Ni and Pd-α-diimine chain propagation/chain isomerization steps in the mechanism of ethylene polymerization.

The Ni-catalysts are usually prepared as its dihalide form by simple ligand exchange of a Ni-complex, such as (1,2-dimethoxyethane, dme)$NiBr_2$, with an α-diimine ligand (Figure 2.161). The Pd-catalysts are rather easier to prepare by using alkyl-containing precursors, such as (1,5-cyclooctadiene, COD)$PdCH_3Cl$. The α-diimine ligands are normally obtained by condensation of an α-diketone with two equivalents of an alkyl- or arylamine, often catalyzed by a Lewis or Bronsted acid. Thus, the backbone and aryl substituents can be readily varied, enabling the preparation of arrays of ligands with independent control over the steric and electronic effects at the metal center. Similar to metallocenes, the cationic form of these catalysts is obtained by using appropriate co-catalysts, such as MAO and sodium tetrakis[3,5-bis(trifluoromethyl)phenyl]borate, $NaBAr_4$.

Group-IV transition metal bis(phenoxyimine) catalysts are also attractive to prepare polyethylene with activities comparable to or exceeding those of metallocene catalysts. Titanium complexes can produce syndiotactic polypropylenes with stereoregularities ranging from moderate to high, depending on the precatalyst structure and the polymerization conditions. Also, titanium complexes bearing fluorinated N-aryl groups polymerize ethylene and propene in a living fashion.[161,162] These catalysts are prepared by reacting an appropriate amount of metal tetrachloride with a ligand, which is conveniently obtained by Schiff base condensation between a fluorinated aniline and a salicylaldehyde (Figure 2.162). The important features of these catalysts include simple synthesis and ease of structure modification by varying the aniline and phenol moieties of the ligand.

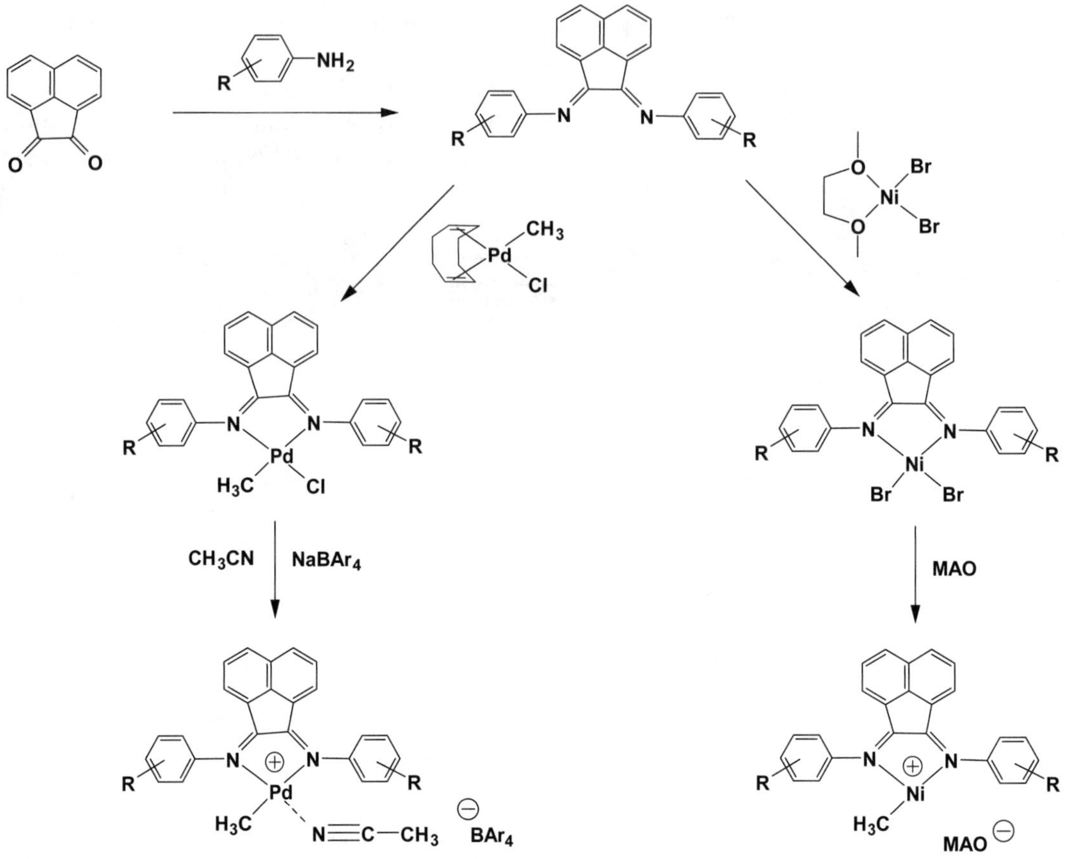

Figure 2.161. Synthesis of Ni and Pd-α-diimine catalysts.

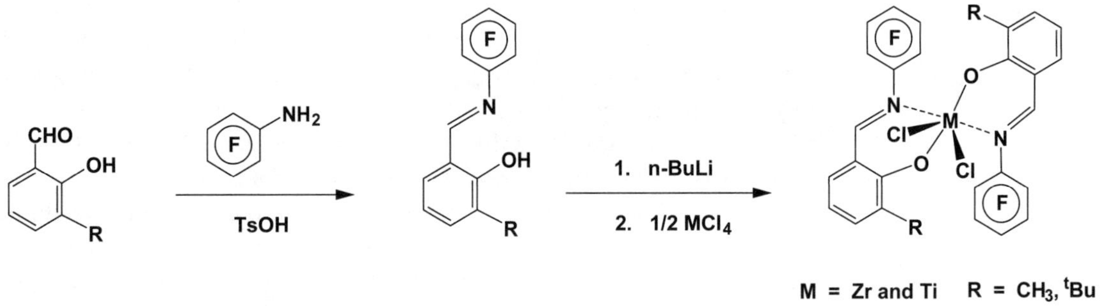

M = Zr and Ti R = CH_3, ^{t}Bu

Figure 2.162. Synthesis of Group-IV transition metal bis(phenoxyimine) catalysts.

A slight variation of bis(phenoxyimine) catalysts, which consist of phenoxyketimine ligands, has been examined recently (Figure 2.163).[163] The special feature of these catalysts is that they are active for living ethylene polymerization, even though the aniline moiety is not fluorinated. The synthetic route to phenoxyketimine ligands is uncommon and rather complex compared to that of bis(phenoxyimine) ligands. However, the pathway allows for incorporation of a variety of substituents, especially electron-withdrawing groups, such as trifluoromethyl, into the ligand framework.

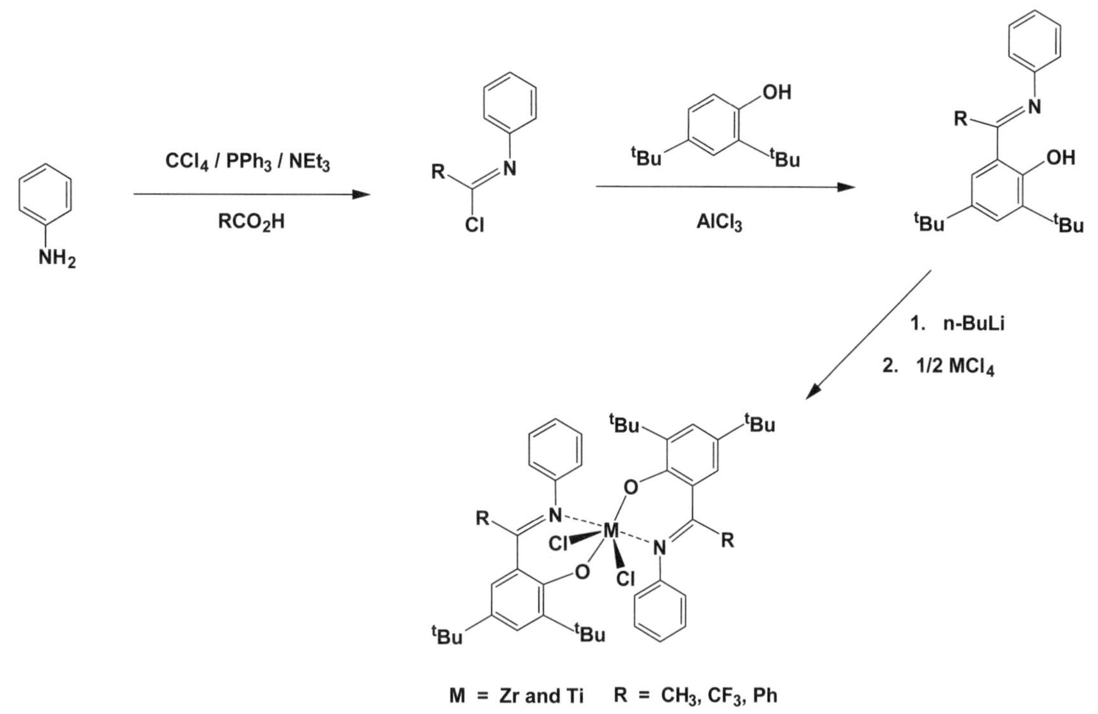

Figure 2.163. Synthesis of Group-4 transition metal bis(phenoxyketimine) catalysts.

Group-IV transition metal bis(phenolate) complexes are also regarded as versatile catalysts for olefin polymerization.[164-166] These complexes usually consist of sulfur or diamine-bridged bis(phenolato) ligands (Figure 2.164). In particular, the sulfur-bridged titanium catalyst is very active for isospecific styrene polymerization and also produces iPS-*b*-iPP-*b*-iPS which is inaccessible using *ansa*-metallocene catalysts. By contrast, the diamine-bridged complexes are effective for higher α-olefin polymerization. The combination of electron-withdrawing groups on the phenolate rings that cause an increase in activity and a small titanium center that is sensitive to ligand steric bulk leads to highly active high-olefin polymerization catalysts which provide varying degrees of stereocontrol. These catalysts also exhibit a high propagation/termination ratio that leads to polymers of unusually high molecular weights.

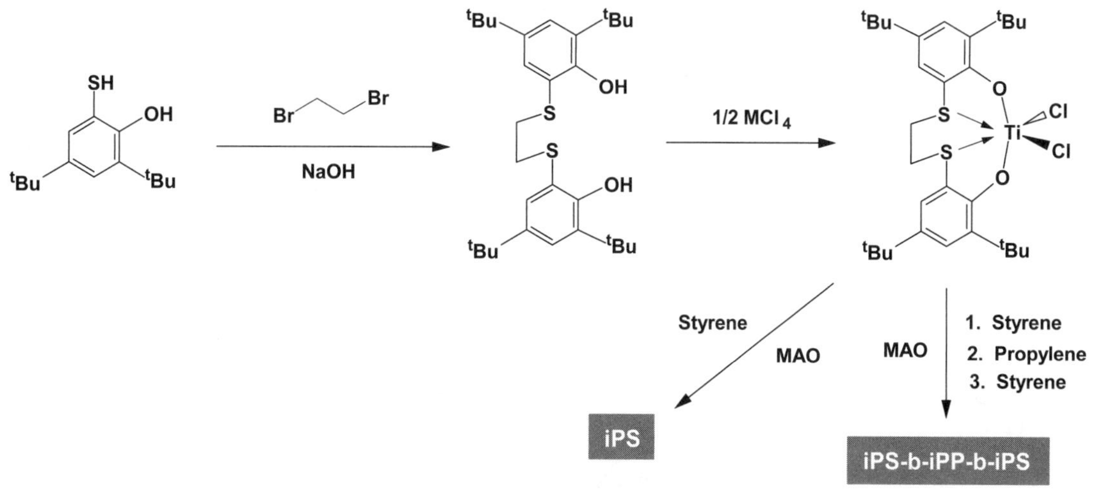

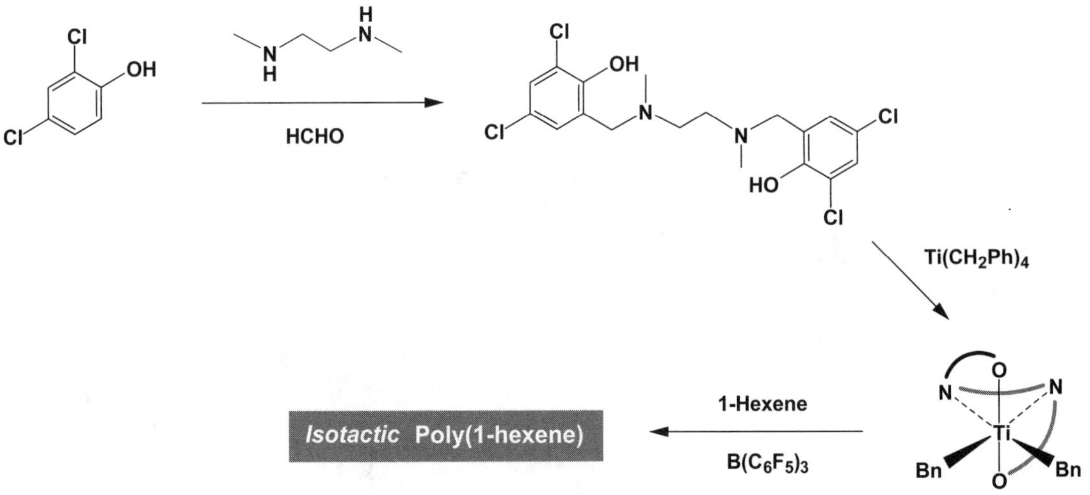

Figure 2.164. Synthesis of Group-IV transition metal bis(phenolate) catalysts.

2.4.4.3. Free-Radical Initiators

In the past two decades, a variety of novel organic peroxide and aliphatic azo initiators have been developed to obtain both process (polymerization rate) and product (narrower polydispersity) advantages. Currently, a major portion of PS is produced via continuous bulk polymerization with the aid of peroxide initiation. Peroxides are generally preferred over azo initiators for initiation of styrene polymerization because they are more efficient (less in-cage decomposition reactions). The use of difunctional peroxide initiators, such as diperoxyketals and peroxyesters, is now under consideration because of their theoretical ability to form fragments which can initiate polymer growth from two different sites within the same fragment, ultimately leading to "*double-ended PS*".[167] If double-ended PS chains are produced, higher molecular weight PS can be obtained at faster rates than by using monofunctional initiators. The synthesis of difunctional peroxide initiators involves a simple procedure starting with readily available starting materials (Figure 2.165). For example, 1,l-bis(*tert*-butylperoxy)cyclohexane is prepared by acid catalyzed condensation of cyclohexanone and *tert*-butyl hydroperoxide, while the peroxyester analog is obtained by condensation of a diacid chloride with *tert*-butyl hydroperoxide.

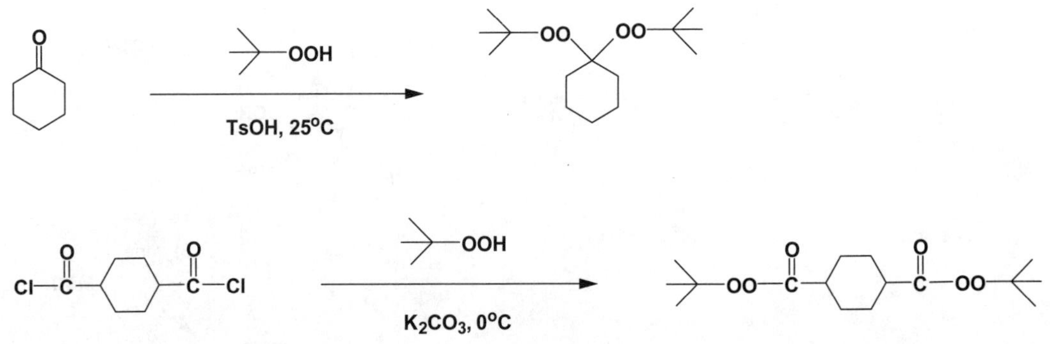

Figure 2.165. Synthesis of difunctional peroxide initiators.

In principle, an alkoxyl radical could be generated from an alkyl hydroperoxide, a dialkyl peroxide, or an alkyl peroxyester. Although peroxyesters and dialkyl peroxides give alkoxyl radicals readily upon decomposition, they are generally not soluble in water. Some alkyl hydroperoxides are soluble in water but clean homolysis of their O-O bonds is not commonly observed, except in some metal catalyzed decomposition. Considering the applications of alkoxyl radicals in a wide range of polymerization processes, especially microemulsion methods, a convenient scheme for the formation of these radicals in aqueous medium is extremely important because microemulsion polymerization, for example, can produce nanosized stable lattices that are not easily obtained from other systems. Figure 2.166 outlines strategies for the incorporation of a water-soluble functionality into an aromatic peroxyester and a hydrophobic tail to traditional azo-type initiator, such as AIBN.[168,169] The latter, amphiphilic AIBN, is applicable to interfacial free-radical polymerization of hydrophobic dibutyl maleate and hydrophilic PEG-divinyl ether monomers to form liquid-core polymer capsules, which have wide-ranging applications in high efficiency encapsulation and controlled delivery of drugs, dyes, enzymes, and many other substrates.

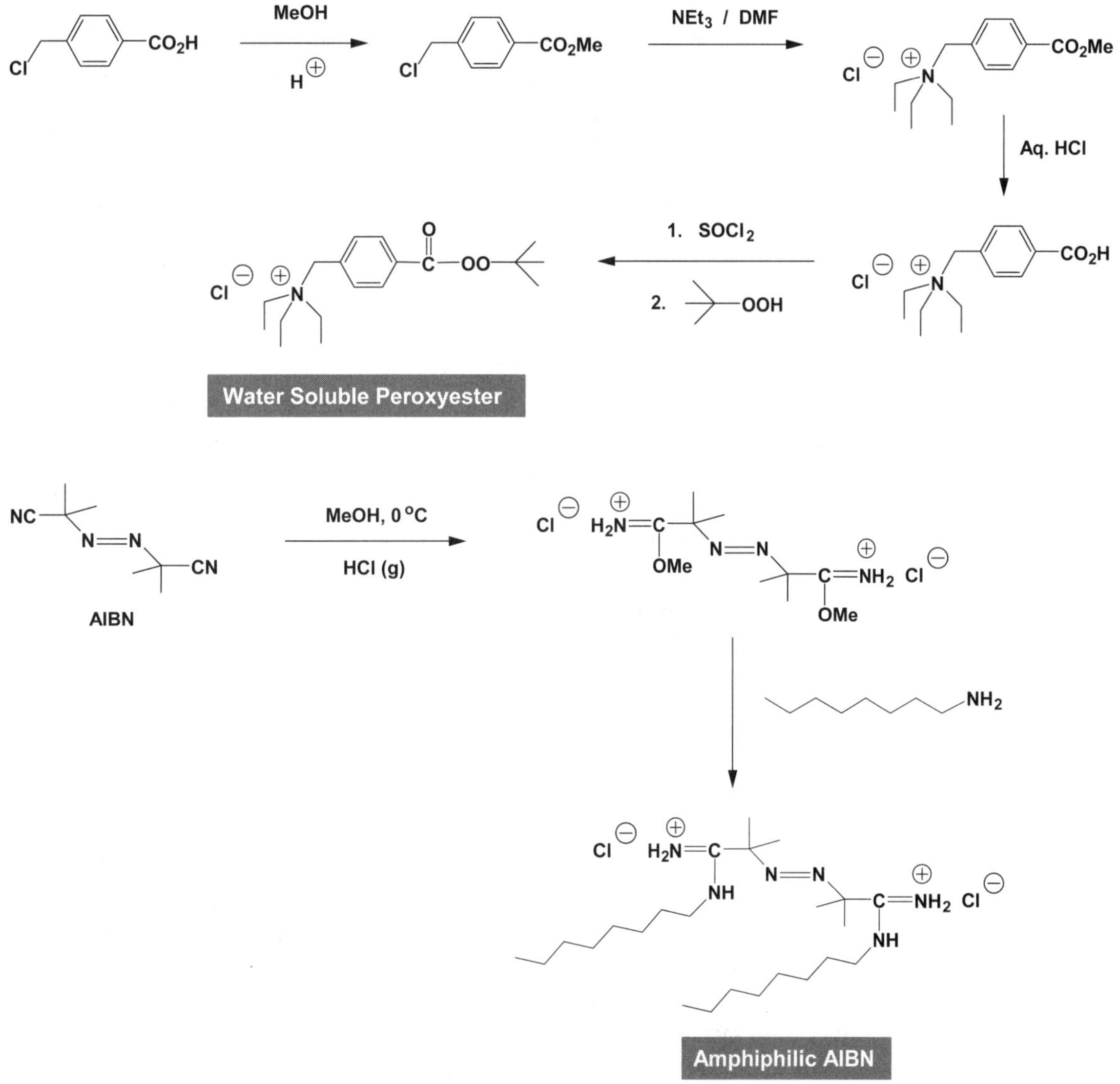

MeOH
$H^{\oplus}$
CO_2H
Cl
CO_2Me
NEt_3 / DMF
Aq. HCl
1. $SOCl_2$
2. OOH
Water Soluble Peroxyester

NC
N=N
CN
AIBN
MeOH, 0 °C
HCl (g)
H_2N=C
OMe
C=NH_2 Cl
NH_2
NH
Amphiphilic AIBN

Figure 2.166. Synthesis of representative water soluble and amphiphilic initiators.

2.4.5. Green Polymer Chemistry

In recent years, there has been a growing concern over the emission of volatile organic solvents, especially ozone-depleting substances (such as chlorofluorocarbons, CFCs), used as a medium for polymer synthesis and polymer processing. Supercritical carbon dioxide (SCD) has been regarded as an alternative (green solvent) to volatile organic solvents, because it is environmentally benign, a natural resource, nontoxic, nonflammable, inexpensive, and possesses an easily accessible critical point (T_c of 31.1°C and a P_c of 7.38 MPa) around which SCD exists as a low viscosity medium with a tunable density. Moreover, SCD can be easily removed from the polymerization reactor simply by depressurizing the reactor (leaving dry polymer products) and is inert toward free-radicals and cations.[170,171] Moreover, a significant research has already been aimed at demonstrating the utility of SCD in polymer processing, such as foaming, blending, coating and additive impregnation. All of these specific processes are based on the ability of SCD to swell and plasticize a polymer.[172]

When SCD is considered as a polymerization medium, its solvent strength toward reactants, reagents and products is of major concern. Carbon dioxide is a low dielectric solvent, which behaves with good approximation like a hydrocarbon solvent concerning solubility of volatile nonpolar molecules of low molar mass. On the other hand, it is a weak Lewis acid with a significant quadrupole moment which provides a major contribution to its solubility parameter, thus allowing it to dissolve some polar molecules, such as methanol. As a result, CO_2 is a good solvent for most vinyl monomers and initiators, but is exceedingly poor for most hydrocarbon polymers. The only classes of polymers which have exhibited good solubility in SCD under relatively mild conditions ($T < 100$°C and $P < 35$ MPa) are amorphous fluoropolymers, silicones, and polycarbonate-polyether copolymers. Owing to this solubility consideration, CO_2 has been used as a free-radical homogeneous polymerization medium only for highly fluorinated amorphous polymers, while heterogeneous (dispersion) techniques have been adopted in the case of other vinyl monomers.

Figure 2.167 shows representative examples of homogeneous polymerization of fluorinated monomers in SCD.[173-178] In general, the yield, molecular weight and polydispersity of the polymers formed in SCD are comparable to those obtained from the conventional solvents, such as CFCs. Some polymerizations in SCD offer unique advantages that are very attractive from a commercial standpoint. First, the traditional route to fluoropolymers involves heterogeneous (emulsion or suspension) polymerization of fluoromonomers in aqueous media. With aqueous initiators, unstable carboxylic acid and acid fluoride end groups are generated, which, owing to their thermal instability, must be removed before processing the polymer melt. A possible way to reduce the level of thermally unstable end groups is the use of aprotic solvent, such as chlorofluorocarbons (CFCs) or perfluorocarbons, perfluoroalkyl sulfide, and perfluorinated cyclic amines, which, however, are too expensive and/or not environmentally friendly. In contrast, the SCD process allows the use of a suitable initiator, such as bis(perfluoro-2-propoxypropionyl) peroxide, $[CF_3CF_2CF_2OCF(CF_3)C(O)O]_2$, which eliminates the formation of deleterious end groups.[177] Second, conventional synthesis of poly(TFE-*co*-VAc) in water emulsions produces a mainly branched structure (see mechanism inserted in Figure 2.167), while a predominantly linear structure is obtained in SCD.[174] Third, the reduction in melt viscosity of poly(bisphenol-A carbonate), due to swelling in SCD during the step-growth melt polymerization of bisphenol-A and diphenyl carbonate, leads to increased reaction rates and increased production quality (color, higher purity lower residual monomer, etc.).[176]

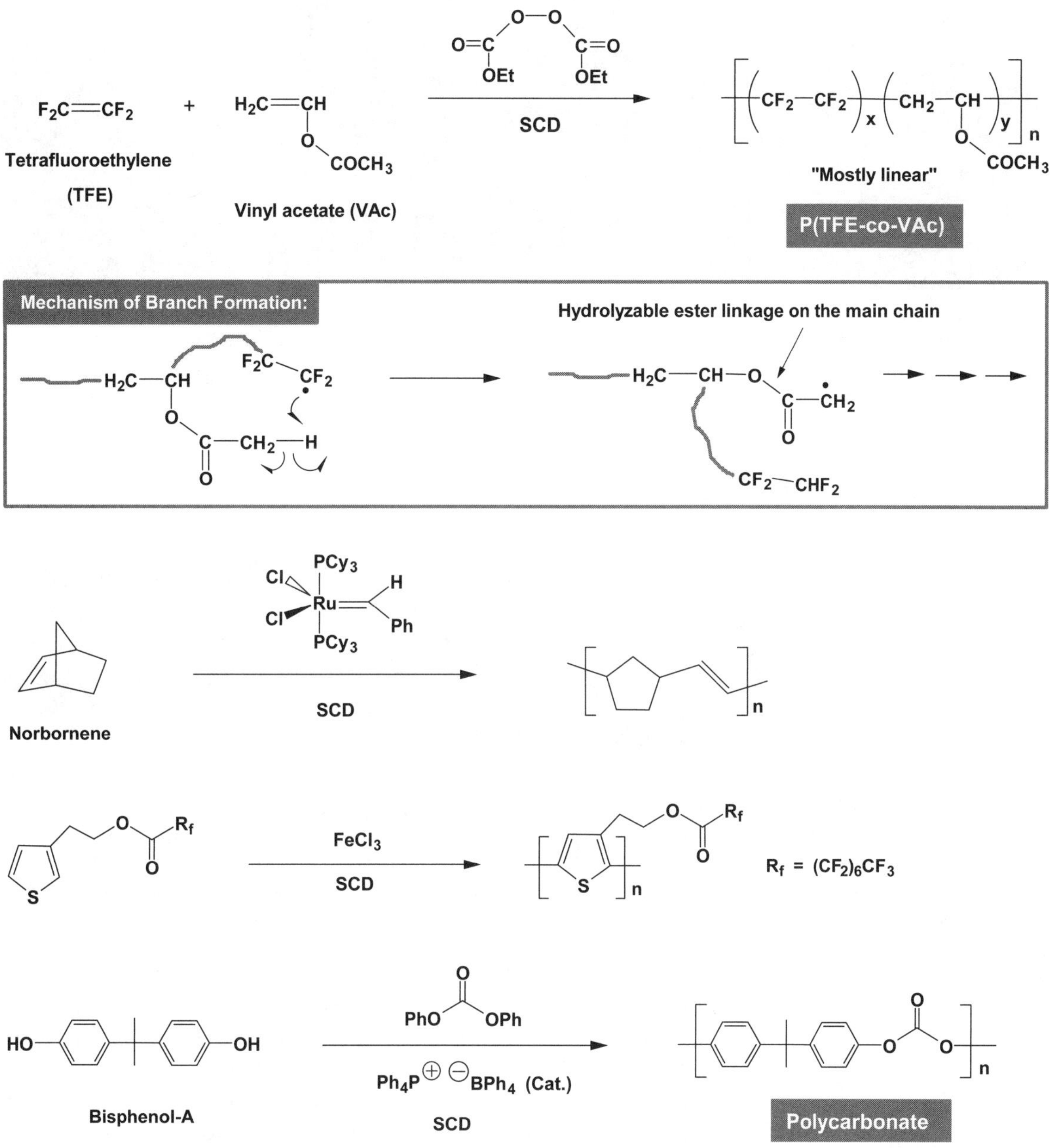

Figure 2.167. Successful synthesis of representative polymers prepared in SCD under homogeneous conditions.

Dispersion polymerization of vinyl monomers, such as styrene, methyl methacrylate and 1-vinyl-2-pyrrolidone, has also been performed in SCD.[179-182] The addition of a specifically designed stabilizer is required for improved yields and molecular weights, including some control of polymer morphology (Figure 2.168). The successful stabilizers for dispersion polymerization in SCD include poly(dimethylsiloxane) (PDMS), poly(fluorooctyl acrylate) (PFOA) and related block copolymers. Such stabilizers, often described as "CO_2-philic", have been shown to act effectively for polymerization of vinyl monomers in which the polymer is insoluble in SCD but the monomer is soluble. The interaction of the stabilizer with the growing polymer particle through van der Waals' forces or dipolar interactions leads to effective stabilization and hence, control of polymer morphology.

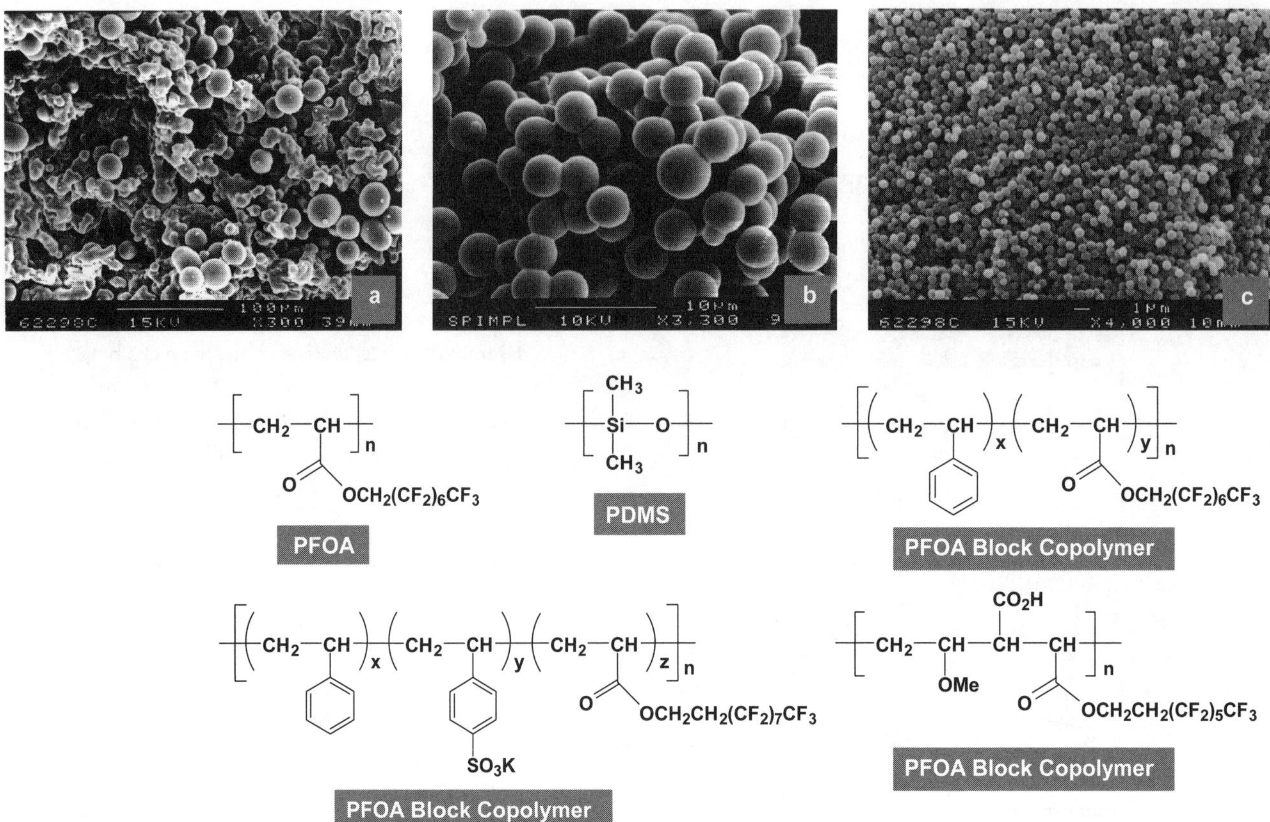

Figure 2.168. Control of polymer morphology by varying the concentration of stabilizer: SEM pictures of poly(1-vinyl-2-pyrrolidone) particles with varied amounts of POFA (a = 0, b = 0.25 and c = 6 w/v %). *Below:* Structures of selected stabilizers useful for polymerization of vinyl monomers in SCD. *Pictures reproduced with kind permission of the American Chemical Society.*

Recently, for the first time, a one-pot synthesis of novel block copolymers has been successfully accomplished in SCD by combining two independent polymerization mechanisms, enzymatic ring-opening polymerization (ROP) of ε-caprolactone (ε-CL) and atom-transfer radical polymerization (ATRP) of methyl methacrylate (MMA).[183] The two catalysts, Novozym-435 (an immobilized enzyme) for ROP and CuBr/bipy for ATRP, used to initiate the polymerization, seem to tolerate each other and smoothly perform their respective polymerization process without interrupting the other (Figure 2.169). A key advantage of the SCD is that the ATRP can occur in the SCD plasticized polycaprolactone (PCL) that is formed, as well as in the ε-CL monomer/SCD solution. The lengths of constituent blocks can be tailored by simply adjusting the levels of catalysts, i.e., lower the level of catalyst, lower the size of the block.

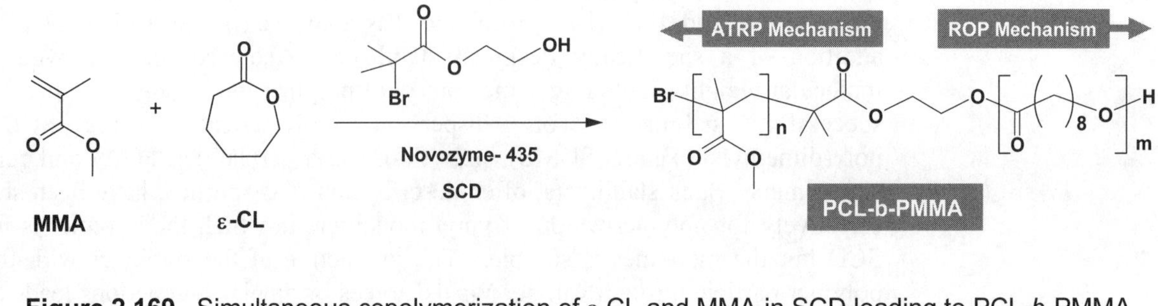

MMA + ε-CL → (Novozyme- 435, SCD) → PCL-b-PMMA

ATRP Mechanism | ROP Mechanism

Figure 2.169. Simultaneous copolymerization of ε-CL and MMA in SCD leading to PCL-*b*-PMMA.

Finally, the application of SCD as a green solvent in photolithography (a process typically used in the semiconductor industry for transferring geometric shapes on a mask to the surface of a silicon wafer) has been successfully employed to develop submicron features on substrates.[184] Figure 2.170 demonstrates that the methodology requires a fluoropolymer, which must be very soluble in SCD and form an SCD insoluble intermediate upon exposure to deep-UV light in the presence of a *photoacid generator* (PAG), such as bis(4-*tert*-butylphenyl)iodinium triflate. A di-block copolymer containing poly(tetrahydropyranyl methacrylate) and poly(fluorinated methacrylate) blocks is found suitable for this approach since tetrahydropyranyl protective groups are easily removed in the presence of an acid catalyst, thus inducing the solubility change. The methodology has the capability to resolve features as small as 0.2 μm, indicating the remarkable potential of this class of polymers as photoresists and the SCD development technique.

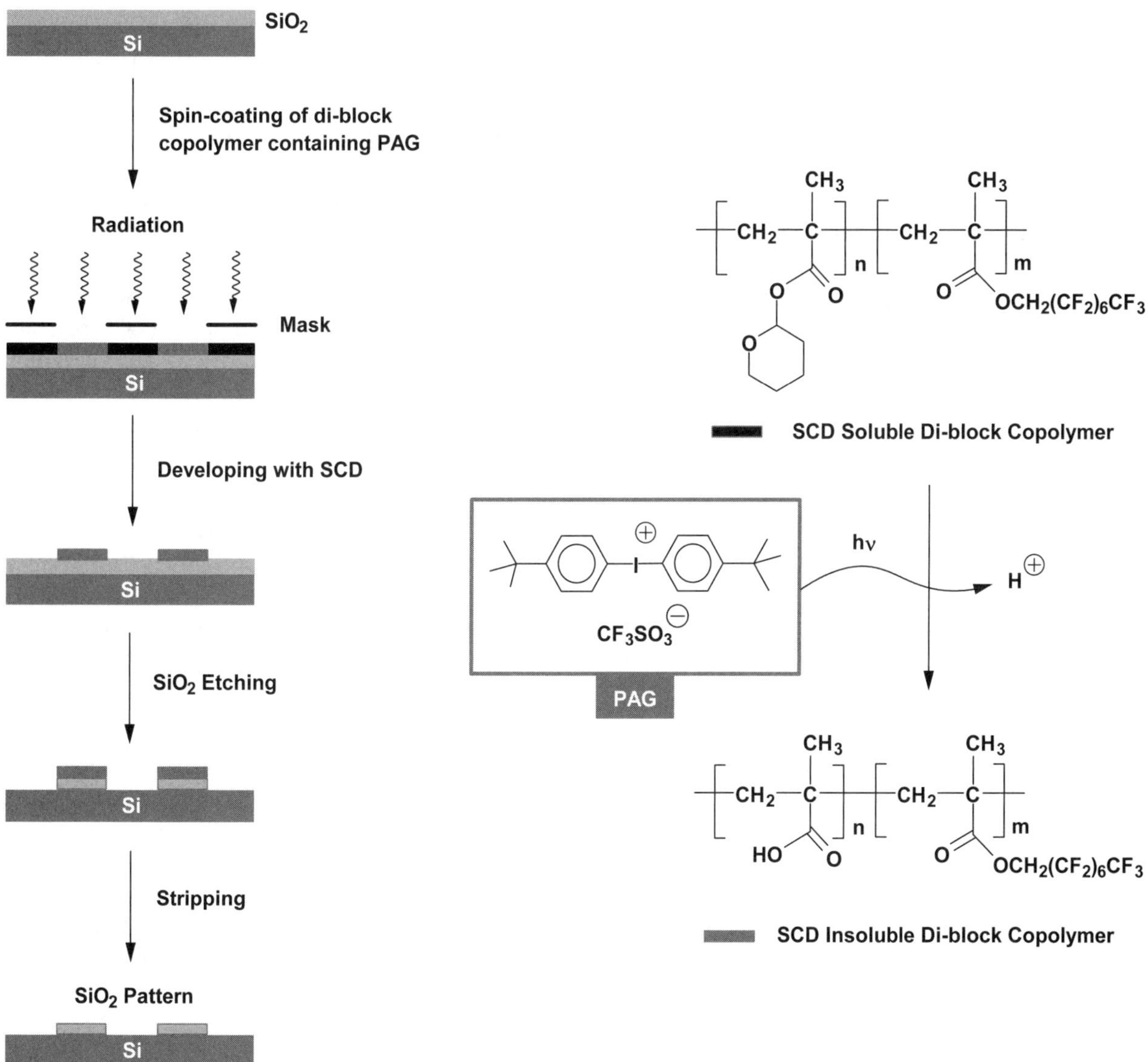

Figure 2.170. Imaging process and associated chemistry involved in a negative-tone SCD developable partially fluorinated diblock copolymer.

2.5. FUTURE OUTLOOK

Among the general-purpose polymers, polyolefins, such as LDPE, LLDPE, HDPE and PP, are the most consumed. LDPE has been serving us for over half a century and continues to dominate as one of the most coveted general-purpose polymers in the future, owing to its well-balanced cost, performance and properties. The major portion (48%) of LDPE is used in the production of films for food- and non-food packaging. LLDPE, because of its controlled branching, provides unique properties and is now one of the fastest growing polyolefins, due to its use in the non-food packaging film market by offering a balance of toughness and stiffness, including excellent optical clarity and gloss. Since non-food packaging requires stronger films that allow downgauging, saving material and reducing cost, LLDPE seems to be the answer. It has been capturing some portion of the market of LDPE and HDPE. However, extrusion coating of paper and paperboard, the second largest application segment (24%) of LDPE, continues to be a growth area for LDPE, largely because it is easier to process than LLDPE. Demand for both PP and HDPE will continue to grow, driven by a number of advantages and improvements in manufacturing. Packaging, fabrics, carpets and rugs, housewares, and motor vehicles will remain the largest markets for PP, with blow-mold containers and injection molded products for HDPE.

Another important factor that would significantly boost the popularity, as well as production of polyolefins, is the advent of "single-site catalyst" (e.g., metallocenes) technologies, which offer polymer producers an unprecedented degree of customization during polymerization, by facilitating the cost-effective production of polymers with enhanced performance qualities, such as higher strength, improved clarity and better processability. In view of these attributes, single-site polymers (those produced using single-site catalysts), such as long chain branched polyethylene (LCBPE), are often called "next-generation" polyolefins. At this time, the majority of these polyolefins are made using metallocene catalysts, and the term "*metallocene polymers*" is also used as a catch-all for all next generation polyolefins. However, it is noteworthy that there are several efficient new catalyst systems that are single-site but not metallocene.

In the *acrylics* arena, polyacrylic acid (PAA) captures the major share because of strong demands for superabsorbent materials (diapers and hygienic products), water treatment products and detergent applications. Opportunities for polyacrylate esters/copolymers include radiation-cured acrylic coatings, ink and pressure sensitive adhesives. In the past decade, there has been strong growth in these areas of acrylics because of the continued acceptance of acrylics as a preferred chemistry.

Polyvinyl chloride (PVC) is the second-largest (after polyethylene), most versatile of all thermoplastics and represents 98% of total *vinyls* consumption. The construction industry accounts for over 70 percent of its total production (pipe, siding, window profile, etc.). Hence, demand correlates closely with economic growth or decline in construction. Other notable, but much less consumed vinyls are poly(vinyl acetate) and poly(vinylidene chloride). Beginning in the past decade, there has been movement toward banning PVC because of serious concerns about human health and environmental pollution during its production, use and afterlife. For example, the production process creates highly toxic waste, such as dioxin and organochlorines. These waste products can find their way into water and the food chain. In order to make PVC pliable, chemical plasticizers, such as di(2-ethylhexyl) phthalate (DEHP) is added. There is evidence that these chemicals may leach from discarded products and find their way into the environment. Moreover, there is strong evidence that in fires (e.g., during incineration), PVC gives off great volumes of toxic fumes, including dioxin emissions. All these concerns indicate, perhaps, that sooner or later replacement of PVC in several critical markets is unavoidable. Thus, it remains a challenge for polymer chemists and manufacturers to develop suitable cost-effective alternatives without sacrificing the advantages of PVC.

Styrenics have found use in almost every plastic application and are available as rigid products, both opaque and transparent, and as films, sheet, foams and elastomers. Styrenics also form an important part of alloys/blends and thermoplastic elastomers. Styrene block copolymers (SBCs) can be rigid or elastomeric. Rigid SBCs have found applications in packaging, medical devices, toys, etc. Elastomeric SBCs are used as impact modifiers, adhesives, sealants and asphalt modifiers. Styrenic alloys/blends have found a wide array of applications, such as automotive, electronic enclosures, appliances, etc. Extruded and expanded foams are important in food and nonfood packaging, while oriented polystyrene film/sheet has been used in both food and nonfood packaging. All these applications demonstrate that styrenics are very much involved in our daily lives and are projected to maintain a modest growth rate into the future.

Synthetic elastomers continue to hold their unique position among synthetic polymers because of the expansion of the automobile industry and no viable substitute. Interestingly, the demand for natural rubber latex in the area of medical gloves (60% of total latex consumption) has been increasing because of the advent of AIDS and other pandemic diseases, and the need to protect healthcare workers from infection.

Finally, it can be concluded that the overall future outlook of general-purpose polymers is very promising. However, recent advances and changes in polymer- and elastomer-related technologies are unprecedented, driving the potential for massive structural changes in the polymer industry. For example, single-site catalyst technologies are now under consideration for mass scale production of styrenics and acrylics. Technological developments will particularly impact the markets for mid-range polymers, including polyolefins, PVC, elastomers, and engineering plastics/styrenics. These advances will strongly promote inter-material competition based on the new polymers and subsequently, drive strategic redirection of the industry, creating a new paradigm known as "Polymers In Transition".

2.5.1. Environmental Issues

Besides concern about PVC, there are several other general-purpose polymers, especially polyolefins, styrenics and synthetic rubbers, which pose serious environmental hazards arising from after-use polymer waste. While these materials do not use or leach toxic chemicals, they are not bio-degradable and fill landfills quickly. The major portion of polymeric waste comes from packaging applications. Other areas of high polymeric waste include: construction, automotive, agricultural and electrical components. In an effort to recycle these polymers more effectively, a variety of strategies have been developed, viz., feedstock recycling (processing of plastics into basic chemicals), mechanical recycling (re-processing of the plastic materials into new products), and valuable energy recovery (from waste plastic through incineration).

The plastics industry has now adopted a coding system to identify the type of plastic so that they can be categorized for recycling purposes (Table 2.5). Despite the wide range of recycled plastics applications, the actual amount of waste which is returned to the material cycle is relatively small. Currently, recycled plastics are rarely used in food packaging (the biggest single market for plastics) because of food safety cencerns. A method of addressing this problem is by enclosing the recycled plastic between layers of virgin plastic to ensure the packaging conforms to hygienic standards.

Another constraint on use of recycled plastics is that, to be economically viable, plastic processors require large quantities of recycled plastics, manufactured to tightly controlled specification at a competitive price in comparison to that of virgin polymer. This is a challenging task, particularly because of the diversity of sources of waste plastics, the wide range of polymers and the high potential for contamination of plastics waste. As a result, there has been serious concern about the continuation of the recycling program.

Table 2.5. Polymer Recycling Codes

Recycling code	Polymer	Major Household Items
1	**PET**	Drink bottles and oven-ready meal trays.
2	**HDPE**	Bottles for milk and detergent liquids.
3	**PVC**	Food trays and shampoo bottles.
4	**LDPE**	Grocery bags and food-wrap films.
5	**PP**	Microwaveable meal trays.
6	**PS**	Foamed meat or fish trays, hamburger boxes and egg cartons, vending cups, plastic cutlery, protective packaging for electronic goods and toys.
7	**OTHER**	Any other plastics that do not fall into any of the above categories, e.g., melamine, which is often used in plastic plates and cups.

Polymer recycling is also employed in the rubber industry, primarily for used tires. Existing methods of tire disposal include: landfill, energy recovery, retreading, and reuse for low value products, such as sports surfaces, noise barriers and roofing materials. Compared to plastics, rubber recycling is much more controlled and simple. Plastics involve a very complicated and expensive recycling procedure.

Additives that impart controlled degradation behavior to conventional thermoplastics are becoming a popular strategy. Such additives are known as *prodegradant concentrates*, and are generally based on catalytic transition metal compounds, such as cobalt stearate or manganese stearate. The additive is typically used at levels of 1-3% and leads to additional costs between 10-35% over that of polyethylene. An alternate approach is the use of bio-degradable plastics for packaging applications. A number of manufacturers have been exploring alternatives derived from non-renewable fossil-fuels. Such alternative "bio-plastics" include polymers made from plants, sugars, and plastics grown inside genetically modified plants or micro-organisms. There are a number of concerns over the use of degradable plastics. First, these plastics will only degrade if disposed of under appropriate conditions. For example, a photodegradable plastic will not degrade if it is buried in a landfill site where there is no light. Second, they may cause an increase in emissions of methane, a greenhouse gas released when materials biodegrade anaerobically. Third, the mixture of degradable and non-degradable plastics may complicate plastics sorting systems. The use of these materials may also lead to an increase in plastics waste and litter, if people believe that discarded plastics will simply disappear.

General Study Questions:

1. Write the structure of a representative catalyst and/or monomer(s) for each of the following equations:

   (a) Ethylene $\xrightarrow{?}$ LDPE

   (b) Propylene $\xrightarrow{?}$ iPP

   (c) Styrene $\xrightarrow{?}$ sPS

   (d) ? $\xrightarrow{?}$ LLDPE

   (e) ? $\xrightarrow{?}$ PMP

2. Polystyrene is rigid with excellent dimensional stability, but possesses very poor impact resistance. How could you improve its impact strength?
3. Explain how LDPE, LLDPE, HDPE and UHMWPE differ in terms of structure and properties. Distinguish them as being homopolymers or copolymers.
4. How are the two commercially important impact grade polystyrenes, high impact (HIPS) and transparent impact (TIPS), prepared? Discuss their advantages and disadvantages.
5. Polyvinyl alcohol is a useful polymer for films and adhesives. What monomer is used for the production of PVA?
6. Why do clothing made of PET display static electricity during winter? What would you suggest to offer a permanent solution. Also, discuss any compromise you have to make.
7. Describe anionic polymerization with styrene monomer as an example.
8. Why is hydrogen introduced during the metallocene-catalyzed manufacture of HDPE?
9. After use polymer waste is a major concern for general-purpose polymers. What major strategies have been implemented to address this issue. Comment on the pros and cons of these strategies.
10. Name and write the structures of at least two polyolefins which are thermoplastics, elastomers and plastomers.
11. Based on density, a variety of polyethylene (such as HDPE, LDPE, MDPE, LLDPE, VLDPE and ULDPE) is sold in the marketplace. How are they prepared?
12. Why does styrene monomer require a strong nucleophile, such as n-butyl lithium, for anionic polymerization, whereas cyanoacrylate monomer undergoes polymerization in the presence of water?
13. What is the basic difference between poly(ethylene glycol) (PEG) and poly(ethylene oxide) (PEO)? Which preparative method(s) would you choose to synthesize them? Write one major application of both polymers.
14. What is the difference between olefinic plastomers and olefinic elastomers?
15. Why do monomers possessing allylic structures, such as $CH_2{=}CHCH_2OCOCH_3$, polymerize (free-radical) only to low molecular weight oligomers?
16. Write the chemical structures of ABS and SBS copolymers. Discuss the role of each monomer in these copolymers.

17. PE is produced commercially by the free-radical process, but PP is produced by coordination polymerization. Why can't propylene polymerize by free-radical polymerization?
18. Write the mechanism for the cationic ring-opening polymerization of (i) ethylene oxide and (ii) caprolactone.
19. Discuss briefly the synthesis and properties of representative age-resistant, solvent-resistant and heat-resistant elastomers.
20. HDPE, PP and poly-1-butene (PB-1) possess similarities in that they are all composed of aliphatic hydrocarbon chains. Why is HDPE miscible with PP, but not with PB-1?
21. In 1839, Charles Goodyear discovered vulcanization by heating natural rubber with sulfur at around 130°C. When vulcanization is performed using 2-3 wt.% of sulfur, the product is more durable than virgin natural rubber and is extensively used in automobile tires. Write the mechanism of vulcanization. What would be the properties of the product if natural rubber was treated with 20-30 wt.% of sulfur at 130°C?
22. Write the mechanisms, using a standard monomer, for three major controlled free-radical polymerization methods: NMP, ATRP and RAFT.
23. How can you synthesize polybutadiene by metathesis polymerization? Write the structures of the monomer and catalyst systems.
24. Write one synthetic strategy for the preparation of each of the following: (i) bulk, (ii) graft and (iii) star copolymers.
25. Why does T_g of stereoregular PPs increase in the order i>s>a, whereas for PMMA it is s>a>i?
26. How is SBS thermoplastic elastomer produced commercially? Would BSB triblock copolymer exhibit thermoplastic behavior as SBS does?
27. Outline a synthetic method for the preparation of each of the following oligomers: (i) Polystyrene with CO_2H group at both chain ends (ii) Polybutadiene with a hydroxyl group at both chain ends (iii) polyethylene terephthalate with a hydroxyl group at both chain ends.

Advanced Study Questions:

28. Name two commercially available graft copolymers. How do their methods of preparation vary for multi-graft polymers, such as centipede-type polymer?
29. Which of the following two catalysts would produce iPP and which sPP? Explain the different behavior of the two catalysts using stereochemical arguments and illustrate the structures of the two types of polypropylene.

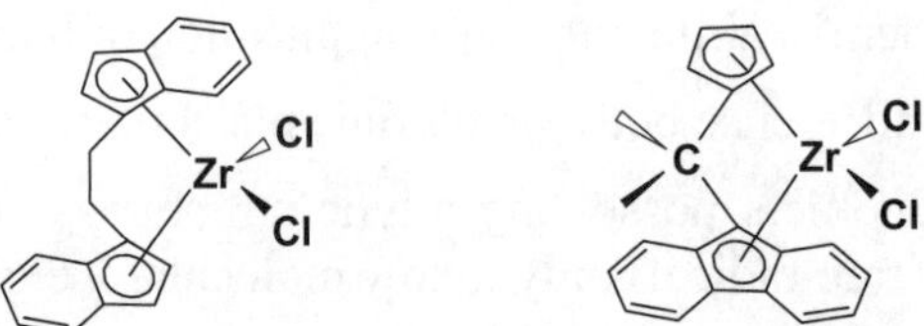

30. Write the symmetry of the following metallocenes. If propylene is the monomer, predict the microstructure (pentad geometry) of the resulting polymers.

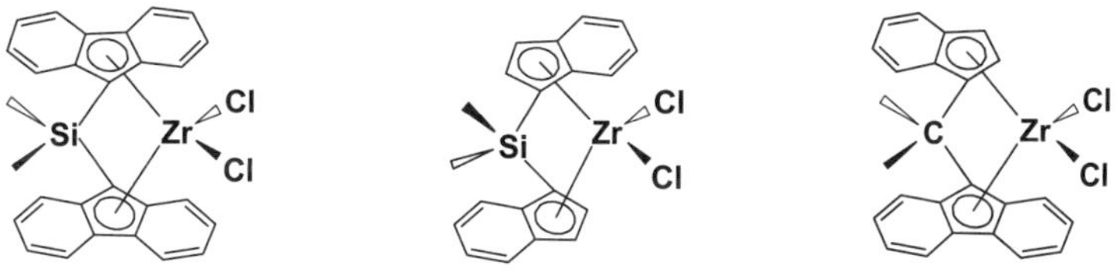

31. The following bifunctional initiators (**I-IV**) are useful for living anionic polymerization of symmetrical multiblock copolymers. Suggest a convenient synthetic route for each.

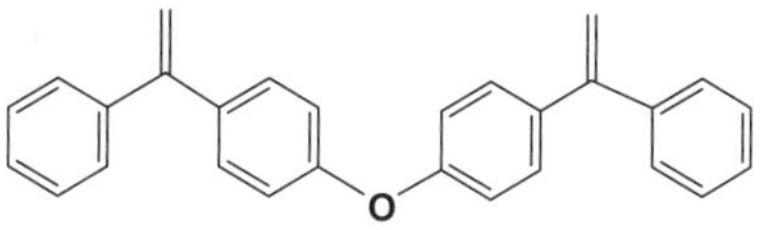

I 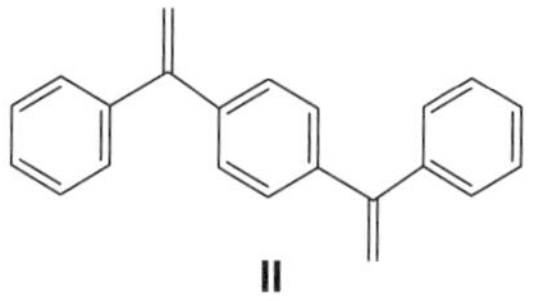 **II**

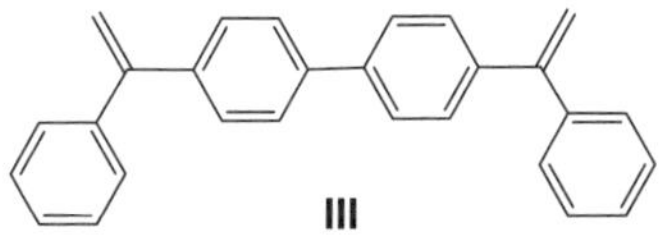

III 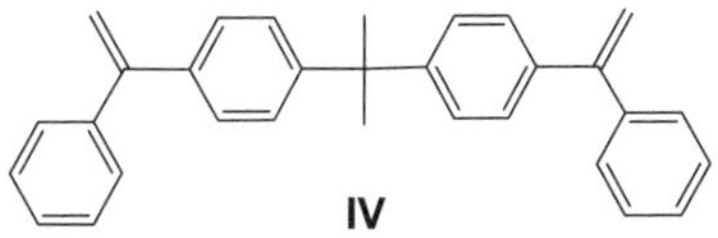 **IV**

32. Fluoroquinolones are a group of synthetic antimicrobial agents that exhibit excellent potencies and a broad spectrum of activity against a variety of Gram-positive and Gram-negative bacteria, as well as mycoplasmas. Norfloxacin (**A**) is a member of the fluoroquinolone antibiotics. In order to reduce toxicity, **A** is often functionalized with a hydrophilic polymer chain, such as polymer-**1**. Starting from **A**, suggest a synthetic strategy to obtain Polymer-**1**.

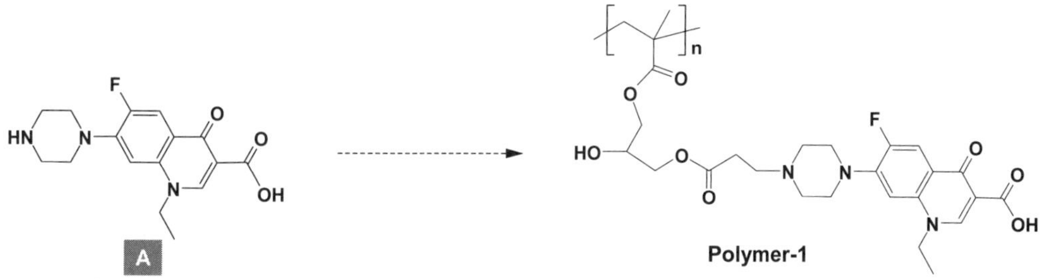

A **Polymer-1**

33. What synthetic strategy would you use to prepare PEO-*b*-PS-*b*-PMMA?

34. The ABC terpolymer, polystyrene-*b*-poly(acrylic acid)-*b*-poly(n-butyl methacrylate), PS-PAA-PnBMA, which consists of a central long polyelectrolyte end-capped by two different hydrophobic short blocks, exhibits interesting properties, such as being self-organized hierarchically from flower-like micelles to dendron-like micellar aggregates and eventually to a three-dimensional physical network. Outline a synthetic route to this amphiphilic triblock copolymer.

35. Propose a synthetic strategy for the preparation of the following star polymer containing arms with different polymer segments.

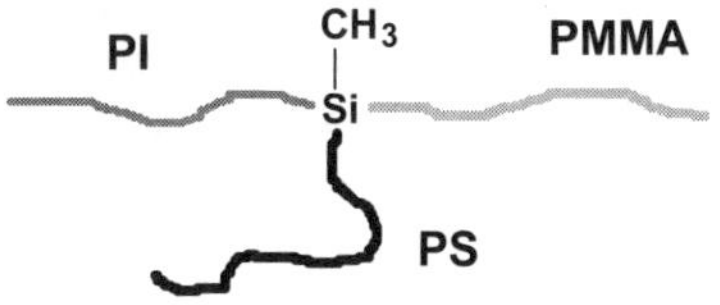

PI CH_3 PMMA Si PS

36. The following initiator is used especially to produce ABC miktoarm star polymers. Devise a synthetic strategy for the preparation of a star polymer containing the following arms: PS, PB and PEO.

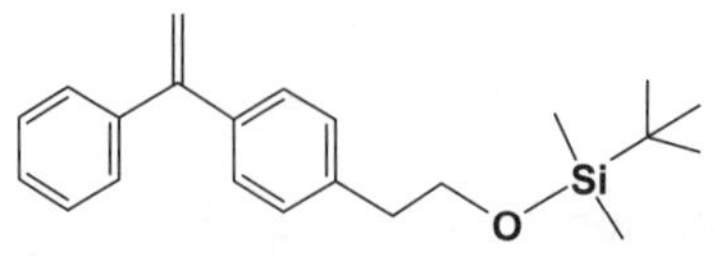

37. Besides chlorosilanes, several coupling agents have been used to prepare fixed-arm star polymers. How many arms would you expect to form if **B** is used as the coupling agent. Write the mechanism of the reaction.

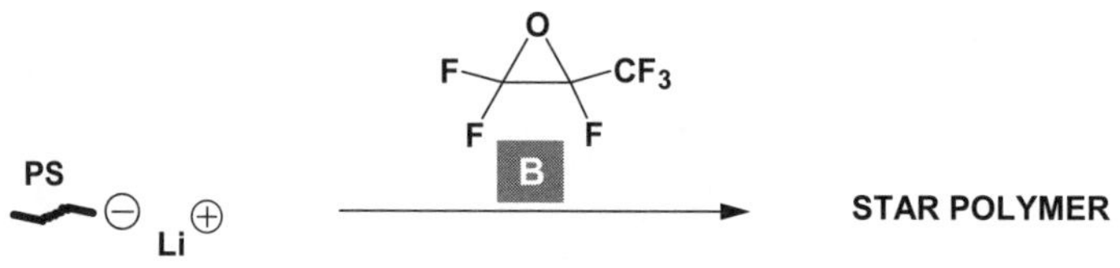

38. Which polymerization technique would you select to synthesize an amphiphilic diblock copolymer containing **C** as hydrophobic block and **D** as hydrophilic block? Write the total synthetic scheme.

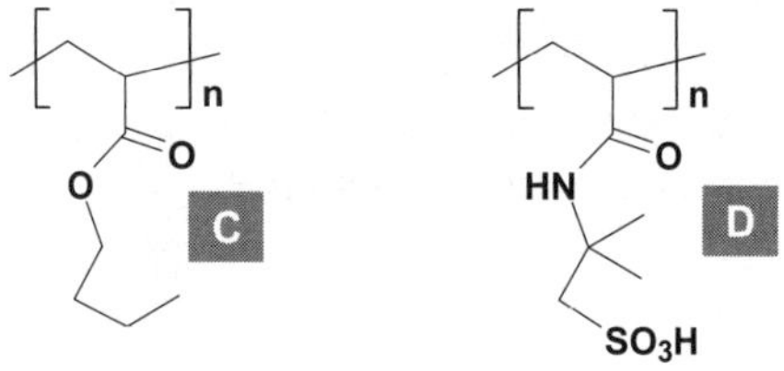

39. Tethering surfaces with polymer brushes provides a versatile method for tailoring surface properties, such as wettability, friction, and protein/cell adhesion. As depicted in the cartoon **E**, ATRP is an efficient method for growing tapered copolymer brushes on a silicon wafer by gradual addition of 2-hydroxyethyl methacrylate (HEMA) to methyl methacrylate (MMA). Which ATRP initiator would you choose to perform the operation? The surface properties of these tapered copolymer brushes can be reversibly altered by selective solvent treatment. In the cartoon **F**, which orientation will be preferred for methanol and methylene chloride? Offer a reasonable discussion in support of your answer.

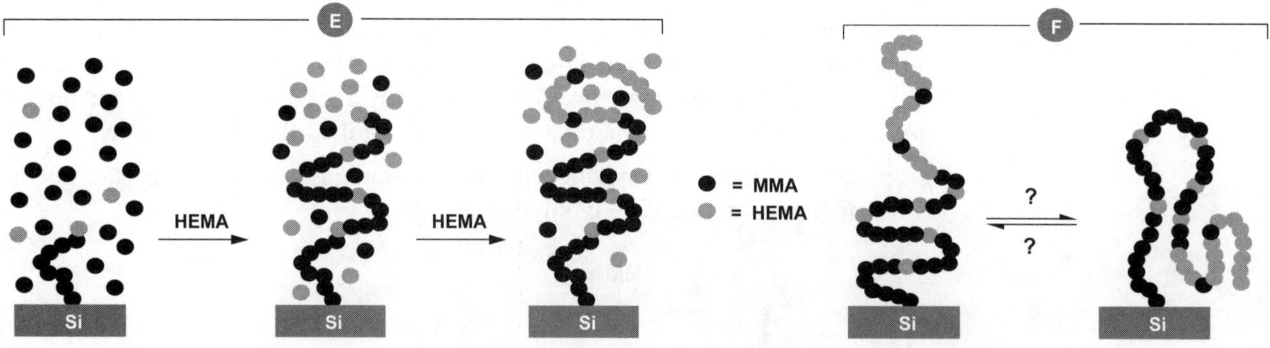

40. Identify the polymer prepared by the following synthetic scheme and discuss the rationale or motivation for the synthesis of such a polymer.

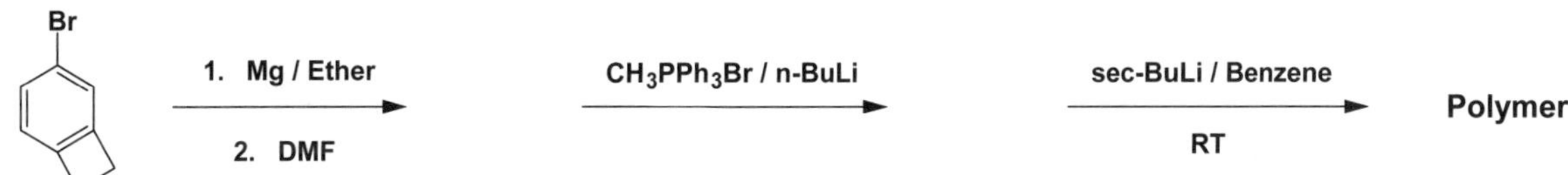

41. The following is a convenient synthetic route to doubly-bridged *ansa*-metallocenes containing ethylene bridges. Identify the reagents needed to accomplish the synthetic scheme. Predict the symmetry of the metallocene complex.

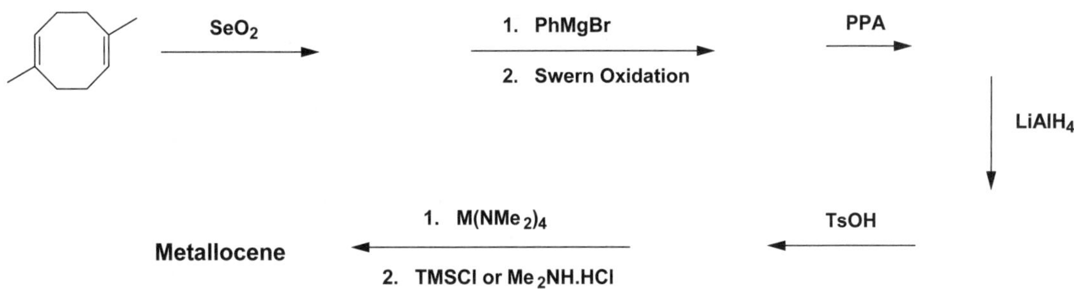

42. Outline synthetic strategies for the following telechelic polymers.

HO — OH, n

H_2N — NH_2, n

43. In the following sequence, the bridge connecting the aromatic rings is thought to be an essential and integral part of the chelating ligand system. The bridge provides the rigidity and maintains the requisite symmetry for stereospecific polymerization reactions. Complete the synthetic scheme for the following metallocene complex.

1. ^tBuOK, n-BuLi
2. I_2

1. Cl–C(=O)–Cl / $AlCl_3$
2. H_2SO_4 / Δ

$NaBH_4$

TsOH

1. $M(NMe_2)_4$
2. TMSCl or $Me_2NH.HCl$

Metallocene

44. Devise a synthetic route to the following star-shaped amphiphilic polymer containing a PEO core and PS corona.

OH_2C, CH_2O, C, OH_2C, CH_2O — PS, PEO

45. Identify the structures of all intermediates and the metallocene complex in the following synthetic scheme:

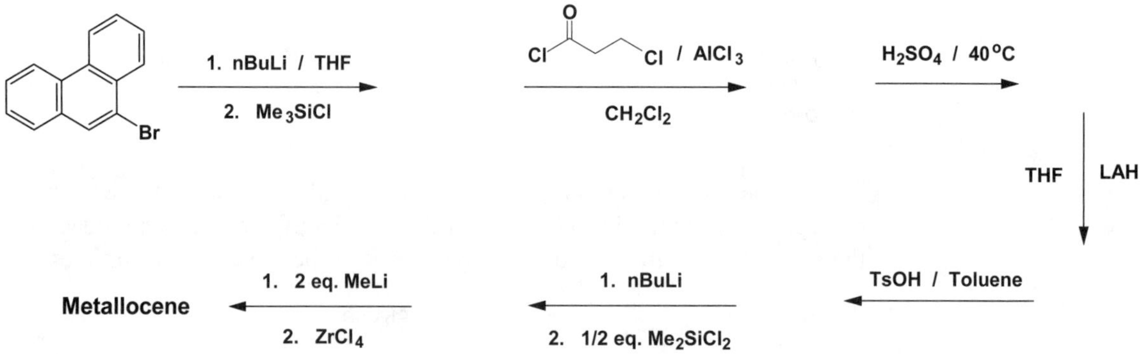

1. nBuLi / THF
2. Me_3SiCl

/ $AlCl_3$
CH_2Cl_2

H_2SO_4 / 40°C

THF LAH

TsOH / Toluene

1. nBuLi
2. 1/2 eq. Me_2SiCl_2

1. 2 eq. MeLi
2. $ZrCl_4$

Metallocene

46. Very recently, a series of interesting iptycene-containing *cis*-1,4-polybutadienes has been synthesized by thermally initiated radical polymerization of butadiene-elaborated anthracene, tetracene and pentacene scaffolds. The following scheme outlines the total synthesis of a representative example of this class of polymers. Because of the presence of the iptycene-based superstructure, these polymers exhibit very high T_g, (>145°C) excellent thermal stability and possess high degrees of free volume that can be used in applications benefiting from low densities, such as high-performance (low-*K*) dielectric coating materials for semiconductor devices. Identify all intermediates and the structure of the polymer.

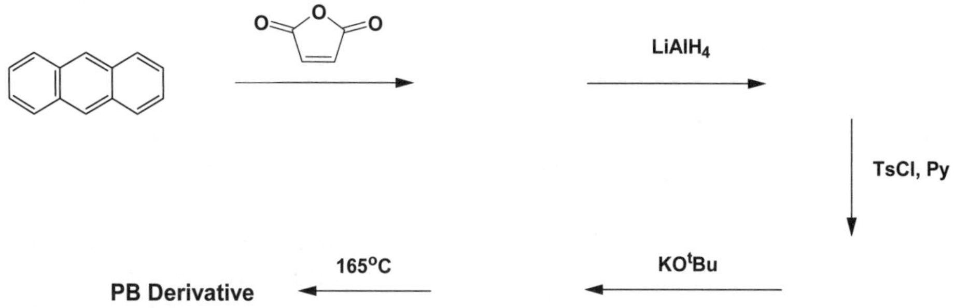

$LiAlH_4$

TsCl, Py

KO^{t}Bu

165°C

PB Derivative

47. The following is the synthetic reaction scheme for a highly stable half-metallocene catalyst for the stereospecific polymerization of styrene. Identify the metallocene along with all the intermediates.

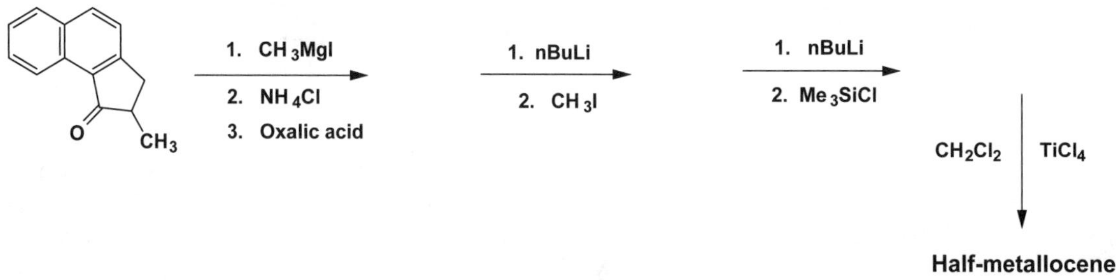

1. CH_3MgI
2. NH_4Cl
3. Oxalic acid

1. nBuLi
2. CH_3I

1. nBuLi
2. Me_3SiCl

CH_2Cl_2 $TiCl_4$

Half-metallocene

References for Chapter-2:

1. *Metallocene-based Polyolefins: preparation, properties and technology,* Scheirs, J.; Kaminsky, W., Eds., Wiley, Chichester, England (2000).
2. Shapiro, P. J.; Bunel, E.; Schaefer, W. P.; Bercaw, J. E., *Organometallics,* **9**, 867 (1990).
3. Xu, G.; Ruckenstein, E., *Macromolecules,* **31**, 4724 (1998).
4. Wood-Adams, P. M.; Dealy, J. M., *Macromolecules,* **33**, 7481 (2000).
5. Kelly, P. A.; O'Connor, J. J., *J. Biomechanics,* **34**, 1599 (2001).
6. Zhou, W.; Zhu, S., *Ind. Eng. Chem. Res*., **36**, 1130 (1997).
7. Ewen, J. A.; Elder, M. J.; Jones, R. L.; Haspeslagh, L.; Curtis, S.; Cheng, H. N. in T. Keii and K. Soga, Eds., *Catalytic Olefin Polymerization-Studies in Surface Science and Catalysis*, Elsevier, New York, 1990, p. 439.
8. Ewen, J. A.; Haspeslagh, L.; Elder, M. J.; Atwood, J. L.; Zhang, H.; Cheng, H. N. in W. Kaminsky and H. Sinn, Eds., *Transition Metals and Organometallics as Catalyst for Olefin Polymerization*, Springer-Verlag, Berlin, 1988, p. 281.
9. Ewen, J. A.; Elder, M. J.; Jones, R. L.; Haspeslagh, L.; Atwood, J. L.; Bott, S. G.; Robinson, K., *Makromol. Chem., Macromol. Symp.,* **48/49**, 253 (1991).
10. Coates, G. W.; Waymouth, R. M., *Science*, **267**, 217 (1995).
11. Weng, W.; Hu, W.; Dekmezian, A. H.; Ruff, C. J., *Macromolecules,* **35**, 3838 (2002).
12. Shiono, T.; Azad, S. M.; Ikeda, T., *Macromolecules,* **32**, 5723 (1999).
13. Ye, Z.; AlObaidi, F.; Zhu, S., *Ind. Eng. Chem. Res.,* **43**, 2860 (2004).
14. Fan, W.; Leclerc, M. K.; Waymouth, R. M., *J. Am. Chem. Soc.,* **123**, 9555 (2001).
15. Piel, C.; Karssenberg, F. G.; Kaminsky, W.; Mathot, V. B. F., *Macromolecules,* **38**, 6789 (2005).
16. Lim, L. S.; Harada, T.; Hillmyer, M. A.; Bates, F. S., *Macromolecules,* **37**, 5847 (2004).
17. Malatesta, V.; Ranghino, G.; Montanari, L.; Fantucci, P., *Macromolecules*, **26**, 4287 (1993).
18. Chung, T. C., *Functionalization of Polyolefins*, Academic Press, San Diego, 2002
19. Lundberg, R. D. In *Ionomers: Synthesis, Structure, Properties and Applications*; Tant, M. R., Mauritz, K. A., Wilkes, G. L., Eds.; Blackie Acad. and Prof. Publ.: London, 1997, p. 477.
20. Boffa, L. S.; Novak, B. M., *Chem. Rev.,* **100**, 1479 (2000).
21. Chung, T. C.; Janvikul, W., *J. Organomet. Chem.*, **581**, 176 (1999).
22. Schneider, M. J.; Schafer, R.; Mulhaupt, R., *Polymer*, **38**, 2455 (1997).
23. Sundararajan, P. R., *Macromolecules*, **19**, 415 (1986).
24. Schomaker, E.; Challa, G., *Macromolecules*, **22**, 3337 (1989).
25. Frauenrath, H.; Keul, H.; Hocker, H., *Macromolecules*, **34**, 14 (2001).
26. Fitzer, E., Frohs, W. and Heine, M., *Carbon*, **24**, 387 (1986).
27. Washington, R. P.; Steinbock, O., *J. Am. Chem. Soc.,* **123**, 7933 (2001).
28. Flory, P. J., *J. Am. Chem. Soc.,* **59**, 241 (1937).
29. Mayo, F. R., *J. Am. Chem. Soc.,* **90**, 1289 (1968).
30. Kaminsky, W.; Lenk, S.; Scholz, V.; Roesky, H. W.; Herzog, A., *Macromolecules*, **30**, 7647 (1997).
31. Kim, Y.; Hong, E.; Lee, M. H.; Kim, J.; Han, Y.; Do, Y., *Organometallics*, **18**, 36 (1999).
32. Capacchione, C.; Proto, A.; Ebeling, H.; Mulhaupt, R.; Moller, K.; Spaniol, T. P.; Okuda, J., *J. Am. Chem. Soc.,* **125**, 4964 (2003).
33. Fischer, M.; Hellmann, G. P., *Macromolecules,* **29**, 2498 (1996).
34. Luo, Y.; Baldamus, J.; Hou, Z., *J. Am. Chem. Soc.,* **126**, 13910 (2004).

35. Grassi, A.; Caprio, M.; Zambelli, A.; Bowen, D. E., *Macromolecules*, **33**, 8130 (2000).
36. Zambelli, A.; Caprio, M.; Grassi, A.; Bowen, D. E., *Macromol. Chem. Phys.,* **201**, 393 (2000).
37. Xu, G.; Lin, S., *Macromolecules,* **30**, 685 (1997).
38. Nomura, K.; Okumura, H.; Komatsu, T.; Naga, N., *Macromolecules*, **35**, 5388 (2002).
39. Caporaso, L.; Izzo, L.; Sisti, I.; Oliva, L., *Macromolecules*, **35**, 4866 (2002).
40. Brunelle, D. J.; Bradt, J. E.; Serth-Guzzo, J.; Takekoshi, T.; Evans, T. L.; Pearce, E. J.; Wilson, P. R., *Macromolecules,* **31**, 4782 (1998).
41. Tripathy, A. R.; MacKnight, W. J.; Kukureka, S. N., *Macromolecules*, **37**, 6793 (2004).
42. Kusan, J.; Keul, H.; Hocker, H., *Macromolecules*, **34**, 389 (2001).
43. Photo taken by the author of this book in a home-grown rubber plantation near Krabi, Thailand.
44. Picture reproduced with kind permission of Smooth-on.com. (http://www.smooth-on.com/Sculpture-and-Art-/c1239/index.html).
45. Ban, H. T.; Kase, T.; Kawabe, M.; Miyazawa, A.; Ishihara, T.; Hagihara, H.; Tsunogae, Y.; Murata, M.; Shiono, T. *Macromolecules*, **39**, 171 (2006).
46. Weidisch, R.; Gido, S. P.; Uhrig, D.; Iatrou, H.; Mays, J.; Hadjichristidis, N., *Macromolecules*, **34**, 6333 (2001).
47. Bensason, S.; Stepanov, E. V.; Chum, S.; Hiltner, A.; Baer, E., *Macromolecules*, **30**, 2436 (1997).
48. Markel, E. J.; Weng, W.; Peacock, A. J.; Dekmezian, A. H., *Macromolecules*, **33**, 8541 (2000).
49. Koo, C. M.; Hillmyer, M. A.; Bates, F. S., *Macromolecules*, **39**, 667 (2006).
50. Schmalz, H.; van Guldener, V.; Gabrielse, W.; Lange, R.; Abetz, V., *Macromolecules*, **35**, 5491 (2002).
51. Zaschke, B.; Kennedy, J. P., *Macromolecules*, **28**, 4426 (1995).
52. Hawker, C. J.; Bosman, A. W.; Harth, E., *Chem. Rev.,* **101**, 3661 (2001).
53. Fischer, H. *Macromolecules*, **30**, 5666 (1997).
54. Braslau, R.; Tsimelzon, A.; Gewandter, J. *Org. Lett.*, **6**, 2233 (2004).
55. Grimaldi, S.; Finet, J.-P.; Le Moigne, F.; Zeghdaoui, A.; Tordo, P.; Benoit, D.; Fontanille, M.; Gnanou, Y., *Macromolecules*, **33**, 1141 (2000).
56. Benoit, D.; Chaplinski, V.; Braslau, R.; Hawker, C. J., *J. Am. Chem. Soc.,* **121**, 3904 (1999).
57. Miura, Y.; Nakamura, N.; Taniguchi, I., *Macromolecules*, **34**, 447 (2001).
58. Moigne, F. L.; Tordo, P., *J. Org. Chem.,* **59**, 3365 (1994).
59. Patten, T. E.; Matyjaszewski, K., *Adv. Mater.,* **10**, 901 (1998).
60. Matyjaszewski, K.; Xia, J., *Chem. Rev.*, **101**, 2921 (2001).
61. Kamigaito, M.; Ando, T.; Sawamoto, M. *Chem. Rev.,* **101**, 3689 (2001).
62. Wang, X.-S.; Armes, S. P., *Macromolecules*, **33**, 6640 (2000).
63. Huang, X.; Lu, G.; Peng, D.; Zhang, S.; Qing, F., *Macromolecules*, **38**, 7299 (2005).
64. Matyjaszewski, K.; Miller, P. J.; Shukla, N.; Immaraporn, B.; Gelman, A.; Luokala, B. B.; Siclovan, T. M.; Kickelbick, G.; Vallant, T.; Hoffmann, H.; Pakula, T., *Macromolecules*, **32**, 8716 (1999).
65. Granville, A. M.; Boyes, S. G.; Akgun, B.; Foster, M. D.; Brittain, W. J., *Macromolecules*, **37**, 2790 (2004).
66. Xu, C.; Wu, T.; Mei, Y.; Drain, C. M.; Batteas, J. D.; Beers, K. L., *Langmuir*, **21**, 11136 (2005).

67. Hong, C.-Y.; You, Y.-Z.; Wu, D.; Liu, Y.; Pan, C.-Y., *Macromolecules*, **38**, 2606 (2005).
68. Perruchot, C.; Khan, M. A.; Kamitsi, A.; Armes, S. P.; von Werne, T.; Patten, T. E., *Langmuir*, **17**, 4479 (2001).
69. Mayo, F. R., *J. Am. Chem. Soc.,* **90**, 1289 (1968).
70. Moad, G.; Chong, Y. K.; Postma, A.; Rizzardo, E.; Thang, S. H., *Polymer,* **46**, 8458 (2005).
71. Chong, Y. K.; Krstina, J.; Le, T. P. T.; Moad, G.; Postma, A.; Rizzardo, E.; Thang, S. H., *Macromolecules*, **36**, 2256 (2003).
72. Takolpuckdee, P.; Mars, C. A.; Perrier, S.; Archibald, S. J., *Macromolecules*, **38**, 1057 (2005).
73. Takolpuckdee, P.; Mars, C. A.; Perrier, S., *Org. Lett.,* **7**, 3449 (2005).
74. Ramadas, S. R.; Srinivasan, P. S.; Ramachandran, J.; Sastry, V. V. S. K., *Synthesis*, 605 (1985).
75. Thang, S. H.; Chong, Y. K.; Mayadunne, R. T. A.; Moad, G.; Rizzardo, E., *Tetrahedron Lett.*, **40**, 2435 (1999).
76. Lee, A. W. M.; Chan, W. H.; Wopng, H. C., *Synth. Commun.,* **18**, 1531 (1988).
77. Mayadunne, R. T. A.; Rizzardo, E.; Chiefari, J.; Krstina, J.; Moad, G.; Postma, A.; Thang, S. H., *Macromolecules*, **33**, 243 (2000).
78. Lai, J. T.; Filla, D.; Shea, R., *Macromolecules*, **35**, 6754 (2002).
79. Lai, J. T., *Tetrahedron Lett.,* **42**, 557 (2001).
80. Goto, A.; Kwak, Y.; Fukuda, T.; Yamago, S.; Iida, K.; Nakajima, M.; Yoshida, J., *J. Am. Chem. Soc.,* **125**, 8720 (2003).
81. Yamago, S.; Ray, B.; Iida, K.; Yoshida, J.-i.; Tada, T.; Yoshizawa, K.; Kwak, Y.; Goto, A.; Fukuda, T., *J. Am. Chem. Soc.,* **126**, 13908 (2004).
82. Sioula, S.; Tselikas, Y.; Hadjichristidis, N., *Macromolecules*, **30**, 1518 (1997).
83. Allen, R. D.; Long, T. E. *Synthesis of Tactic Poly(Alkyl Methacrylate) Homo and Copolymers,* in Advances in Polymer Synthesis, ed. B. M. Culbertson, McGrath, J. E., New York: Plenum Publishing Co., 1985.
84. Liu, W.H.; Nakano, T.; Okamoto, Y., *Polym. J.*, **31**, 479 (1999).
85. Kilian, L. *Synthesis and Characterization of Responsive Poly(Alkyl Methacrylate) Topologies,* Dissertation, VA Polytech. Inst. & State Univ., 2004.
86. Tung, L. H.; Lo, G. Y.-S., *Macromolecules*, **27**, 2219 (1994).
87. Schmalz, H.; Abetz, V.; Lange, R.; Soliman, M., *Macromolecules*, **34**, 795 (2001).
88. Hillmyer, M. A.; Bates, F. S., *Macromolecules*, **29**, 6994 (1996).
89. Allgaier, J.; Poppe, A.; Willner, L.; Richter, D., *Macromolecules*, **30**, 1582 (1997).
90. Storey, R. F.; Curry, C. L.; Hendry, L. K., *Macromolecules*, **34**, 5416 (2001).
91. Storey, R. F.; Scheuer, A. D.; Achord, B. C., *Polymer*, **46**, 2141 (2005).
92. Kennedy, J. P.; Ivan, B. *Designed Polymers by Carbocationic Macromolecular Engineering: Theory and Practice*; Hanser Publishers: Munich, 1992.
93. Ivan, B.; Kennedy, J. P., *J. Polym. Sci, Polym. Chem. A.,* **28**, 89 (1990).
94. Weisberg, D. M.; Gordon, B., III; Rosenberg, G.; Snyder, A. J.; Benesi, A.; Runt, J., *Macromolecules*, **33**, 4380 (2000).
95. Satoh, K.; Kamigaito, M.; Sawamoto, M., *Macromolecules*, **33**, 5830 (2000).
96. Miyamoto, M.; Sawamoto, M.; Higashimura, T., *Macromolecules*, **17**, 2228 (1984).
97. Percec, V., Tomazos, D., *Adv. Mater.,* **4**, 548 (1992).
98. Omenat, A.; Lub, J.; Fischer, H., *Chem. Mater.,* **10**, 518 (1998).
99. Satoh, K.; Kamigaito, M.; Sawamoto, M., *Macromolecules*, **33**, 748 (2000).
100. Kamigaito, M.; Sawamoto, M.; Higashimura, T., *Macromolecules*, **25**, 2587 (1992).
101. Matsumoto, K.; Mazaki, H.; Nishimura, R.; Matsuoka, H.; Yamaoka, H., *Macromolecules*, **33**, 8295 (2000).

102. Hadjichristidis, N.; Pitsikalis, M.; Pispas, S.; Iatrou, H., *Chem. Rev.,* **101**, 3747 (2001).
103. Tsoukatos, T.; Pispas, S.; Hadjichristidis, N., *Macromolecules*, **33**, 9504 (2000).
104. Liu, S.; Sen, A. *Macromolecules*, **34**, 1529 (2001).
105. O'Donnell, P. M.; Wagner, K. B., *J. Polym. Sci. Part-A. Polym. Chem.,* **41**, 2816 (2003).
106. Castle, T. C.; Hutchings, L. R.; Khosravi, E., *Macromolecules*, **37**, 2035 (2004).
107. Pantazis, D.; Chalari, I.; Hadjichristidis, N., *Macromolecules*, **36**, 3783 (2003).
108. Han, C. J.; Lee, M. S.; Byun, D.-J.; Kim, S. Y., *Macromolecules*, **35**, 8923 (2002).
109. Wang, Y.; Huang, J., *Macromolecules*, **31**, 4057 (1998).
110. Tsukahara, Y.; Yai, K.; Kaeriyama, K., *Polymer*, **40**, 729 (1999).
111. Heroguez, V.; Amedro, E.; Grande, D.; Fontanille, M.; Gnanou, Y., *Macromolecules*, **33**, 7241 (2000).
112. Uhrig, D.; Mays, J. W., *Macromolecules*, **35**, 7182 (2002).
113. Iatrou, H.; Mays, J. W.; Hadjichristidis, N., *Macromolecules*, **31**, 6697 (1998).
114. Hamley, I. W., Ed., *Developments in Block Copolymer Science and Technology*, John Wiley & Sons, Chichester, 2004.
115. Morita, T.; Maughon, B. R.; Bielawski, C. W.; Grubbs, R. H., *Macromolecules*, **33**, 6621 (2000).
116. Bielawski, C. W.; Benitez, D.; Morita, T.; Grubbs, R. H., *Macromolecules*, **34**, 8610 (2001).
117. Bielawski, C. W.; Morita, T.; Grubbs, R. H., *Macromolecules*, **33**, 678 (2000).
118. Mahanthappa, M. K.; Bates, F. S.; Hillmyer, M. A., *Macromolecules*, **38**, 7890 (2005).
119. Gaynor, S. G.; Matyjaszewski, K., *Macromolecules*, **30**, 4241 (1997).
120. Tsolakis, P. K.; Koulouri, E. G.; Kallitsis, J. K., *Macromolecules*, **32**, 9054 (1999).
121. Rzayev, J.; Hillmyer, M. A., *Macromolecules*, **38**, 3 (2005).
122. Notestein, J. M.; Lee, L.-B. W.; Register, R. A., *Macromolecules*, **35**, 1985 (2002).
123. Hadjichristidis, N.; Pitsikalis, M.; Pispas, S.; Iatrou, H., *Chem. Rev.,* **101**, 3747 (2001).
124. Tsitsilianis, C.; Lutz, P.; Graff, S.; Lamps, J. P.; Rempp P., *Macromolecules*, **24**, 5897 (1991).
125. Hautekeer, J. P.; Varshney, S. K.; Fayt, R.; Jacobs, C.; Jerome, R.; Teyssie, P., *Macromolecules*, **23**, 3893 (1990).
126. Wang, J. S.; Jerome, R.; Warin, R.; Teyssie, P., *Macromolecules*, **26**, 5984 (1993).
127. Quirk, R. P.; Tsai, Y., *Macromolecules,* **31**, 8016 (1998).
128. Francis, R.; Taton, D.; Logan, J. L.; Masse, P.; Gnanou, Y.; Duran, R. S., *Macromolecules*, **36**, 8253 (2003).
129. Knauss, D. M.; Al-Muallem, H. A.; Huang, T.; Wu, D. T., *Macromolecules*, **33**, 3557 (2000).
130. Knauss, D. M.; Huang, T., *Macromolecules*, **35**, 2055 (2002).
131. Knauss, D. M.; Huang, T., *Macromolecules*, **36**, 6036 (2003).
132. Hirao, A.; Higashihara, T., *Macromolecules*, **35**, 7238 (2002).
133. Hadjichristidis, N.; Pitsikalis, M.; Pispas, S.; Iatrou, H., *Chem. Rev.,* **101**, 3747 (2001).
134. Kanaoka, S.; Nakata, S.; Yamaoka, H., *Macromolecules*, **35**, 4564 (2002).
135. Halterman, R. L. In Metallocenes: *Synthesis-Reactivity-Applications; Togni, A., Halterman*, R. L., Eds.; Wiley-VCH: New York, 1998, p. 455.
136. Qian, Y.; Huang, J.; Bala, M. D.; Lian, B.; Zhang, H.; Zhang, H., *Chem. Rev.,* **103**, 2633 (2003).

137. Greifenstein, L. G.; Lambert, J. B.; Nienhuis, R. J.; Fried, H. E.; Pagani, G. A., *J. Org. Chem.*, **46**, 5125 (1981).
138. Kravchenko, R.; Masood, A.; Waymouth, R. M., *Organometallics*, **16**, 3635 (1997).
139. Schneider, N.; Huttenloch, M. E.; Stehling, U.; Kirsten, R.; Schaper, F.; Brintzinger, H. H., *Organometallics*, **16**, 3413 (1997).
140. Kukral, J.; Lehmus, P.; Feifel, T.; Troll, C.; Rieger, B., *Organometallics*, **19**, 3767 (2000).
141. Resconi, L.; Jones, R. L.; Rheingold, A. L.; Yap, G. P. A., *Organometallics*, **15**, 998 (1996).
142. Halterman, R. L.; Combs, D.; Khan, M. A., *Organometallics*, **17**, 3900 (1998).
143. Miller, S. A.; Bercaw, J. E., *Organometallics*, **23**, 1777 (2004).
144. Herzog, T. A.; Zubris, D. L.; Bercaw, J. E., *J. Am. Chem. Soc.,* **118**, 11988 (1996).
145. Veghini, D.; Henling, L. M.; Burkhardt, T. J.; Bercaw, J. E., *J. Am. Chem. Soc.,* **121**, 564 (1999).
146. Baar, C. R.; Levy, C. J.; Min, E. Y.-J.; Henling, L. M.; Day, M. W.; Bercaw, J. E., *J. Am. Chem. Soc.,* **126**, 8216 (2004).
147. Okuda, J., *Chem. Ber.,* **123**, 1649 (1990).
148. Xu, G.; Ruckenstein, E., *Macromolecules*, **31**, 4724 (1998).
149. Grandini, C.; Camurati, I.; Guidotti, S.; Mascellani, N.; Resconi, L.; Nifant'ev, I. E.; Kashulin, I. A.; Ivchenko, P. V.; Mercandelli, P.; Sironi, A., *Organometallics*, **23**, 344 (2004).
150. Klosin, J.; Kruper, W. J., Jr.; Nickias, P. N.; Roof, G. R.; De Waele, P.; Abboud, K. A., *Organometallics*, **20**, 2663 (2001).
151. Jin, J.; Chen, E. Y.-X., *Organometallics*, **21**, 13 (2002).
152. Koch, M.; Stork, M.; Klapper, M.; Mullen, K.; Gregorius, H., *Macromolecules*, **33**, 7713 (2000).
153. Severn, J. R.; Chadwick, J. C.; Duchateau, R.; Friederichs, N., *Chem. Rev.,* **105**, 4073 (2005).
154. Chien, J. C. W., *Top. Catal.*, **7**, 23 (1999).
155. McKittrick, M. W.; Jones, C. W., *J. Am. Chem. Soc.,* **126**, 3052 (2004).
156. McKittrick, M. W.; Jones, C. W., *Chem. Mater.,* **17**, 4758 (2005).
157. Lee, B. Y.; Oh, J. S., *Macromolecules*, **33**, 3194 (2000).
158. Tian, J.; Soo-Ko, Y.; Metcalfe, R.; Feng, Y.; Collins, S., *Macromolecules*, **34**, 3120 (2001).
159. Ittel, S. D.; Johnson, L. K.; Brookhart, M., *Chem. Rev.,* **100**, 1169 (2000).
160. Gibson, V. C.; Spitzmesser, S. K., *Chem. Rev.,* **103**, 283 (2003).
161. Mitani, M.; Mohri, J.; Yoshida, Y.; Saito, J.; Ishii, S.; Tsuru, K.; Matsui, S.; Furuyama, R.; Nakano, T.; Tanaka, H.; Kojoh, S.-i.; Matsugi, T.; Kashiwa, N.; Fujita, T., *J. Am. Chem. Soc.,* **124**, 3327 (2002).
162. Lamberti, M.; Gliubizzi, R.; Mazzeo, M.; Tedesco, C.; Pellecchia, C., *Macromolecules*, **37**, 276 (2004).
163. Reinartz, S.; Mason, A. F.; Lobkovsky, E. B.; Coates, G. W., *Organometallics*, **22**, 2542 (2003).
164. Segal, S.; Goldberg, I.; Kol, M., *Organometallics*, **24**, 200 (2005).
165. Capacchione, C.; Proto, A.; Ebeling, H.; Mulhaupt, R.; Moller, K.; Spaniol, T. P.; Okuda, J., *J. Am. Chem. Soc.,* **125**, 4964 (2003).
166. Capacchione, C.; De Carlo, F.; Zannoni, C.; Okuda, J.; Proto, A., *Macromolecules*, **37**, 8918 (2004).
167. Drumright, R. E.; Kastl, P. E.; Priddy, D. B., *Macromolecules*, **26**, 2246 (1993).
168. Wang, L.; Liu, X.; Li, Y., *Macromolecules*, **31**, 3446 (1998).
169. Scott, C.; Wu, D.; Ho, C.; Co, C. C., *J. Am. Chem. Soc.,* **127**, 4160 (2005).

170. Kendall, J. L.; Canelas, D. A.; Young, J. L.; DeSimone, J. M., *Chem. Rev.,* **99**, 543 (1999).
171. Cooper, A. I., *J. Mater. Chem.,* **10**, 207 (2000).
172. Tomasko, D. L.; Li, H.; Liu, D.; Han, X.; Wingert, M. J.; Lee, L. J.; Koelling, K. W., *Ind. Eng. Chem. Res.,* **42**, 6431 (2003).
173. Baradie, B.; Shoichet, M. S., *Macromolecules*, **35**, 3569 (2002).
174. Lousenberg, R. D.; Shoichet, M. S., *Macromolecules*, **33**, 1682 (2000).
175. Ganapathy, H. S.; Hwang, H. S.; Lim, K. T., *Ind. Eng. Chem. Res.,* **45**, 3406 (2006).
176. Gross, S. M.; Givens, R. D.; Jikei, M.; Royer, J. R.; Khan, S.; DeSimone, J. M.; Odell, P. G.; Hamer, G. K., *Macromolecules*, **31**, 9090 (1998).
177. Romack, T. J.; DeSimone, J. M.; Treat, T. A., *Macromolecules*, **28**, 8429 (1995).
178. Furstner, A.; Ackermann, L.; Beck, K.; Hori, H.; Koch, D.; Langemann, K.; Liebl, M.; Six, C.; Leitner, W., *J. Am. Chem. Soc.,* **123**, 9000 (2001).
179. Carson, T.; Lizotte, J.; Desimone, J. M., *Macromolecules*, **33**, 1917 (2000).
180. Giles, M. R.; O'Connor, S. J.; Hay, J. N.; Winder, R. J.; Howdle, S. M., *Macromolecules*, **33**, 1996 (2000).
181. Ye, W.; DeSimone, J. M., *Macromolecules*, **38**, 2180 (2005).
182. Huang, Z.; Shi, C.; Xu, J.; Kilic, S.; Enick, R. M.; Beckman, E. J., *Macromolecules*, **33**, 5437 (2000).
183. Duxbury, C. J.; Wang, W.; de Geus, M.; Heise, A.; Howdle, S. M., *J. Am. Chem. Soc.,* **127**, 2384 (2005).
184. Sundararajan, N.; Yang, S.; Ogino, K.; Valiyaveettil, S.; Wang, J.-G.; Zhou, X.; Ober, C. K.; Obendorf, S. K.; Allen, R. D., *Chem. Mater.,* **12**, 41 (2000).

Strong, clear architectural glazing with polycarbonate, which is one of the most versatile engineering thermoplastics because of its extraordinary durability (250 times stronger than float glass and many times stronger than acrylic) coupled with outstanding optical transparency and UV resistance.[1]

CHAPTER-3

ENGINEERING POLYMERS

Engineering polymers are classified by temperature resistance between 100°C and 150°C for a long period of time. They possess good strength and durability and exhibit superior thermal stability compared to those of general-purpose polymers. Other important features include moldability and a good balance between mechanical properties during a long time period over a wide range of dynamic and static conditions. Interestingly, most of the engineering polymers developed between 1950 and 1980 are still in use. Since then, the number of new families of engineering polymers has slowed markedly, primarily because of the growing costs for the introduction of a new material as well as competition with tailored grades of existing polymers. The latter include, those crossing over from commodity to engineering plastics (e.g., iPP and sPS) and new blends and fiber (glass, carbon, etc.) reinforced composite materials. Among the new entries, aliphatic polyketones (alternating copolymers of carbon monoxide with ethylene and/or propylene) have experienced significant growth because of cheap feedstocks and exceptional thermal, mechanical and processing properties. The recent development of Pd-based single-site catalysts, which provide access to syndiotactic styrene-carbon monoxide copolymer and norbornene-carbon monoxide copolymer, has further enhanced the scope of polyketones. A notable new entry is poly(ethylene naphthalate) (PEN), which has emerged in as an engineering polymer in great demand for fiber, film and molded material applications.

3.1. POLYCARBONATES

Bisphenol-A (BPA)-polycarbonate, PC, is the most important member of this family. PC was first developed by General Electric which commercialized the product with the trademark Lexan® in 1957 to compete with die-cast metals. Transparency, scratch resistance, excellent toughness, thermal stability, high T_g (150°C) and, most importantly, excellent impact resistance at room temperature (well below its T_g!), make PC one of the most widely used engineering thermoplastics (Figure 3.1). It is believed that both the high impact strength and excellent amorphous character of PC are due to the presence of the V-shaped 2,2-diphenylpropane moiety which provides adequate free-volume, including low conformational barriers to rotation.[2] In addition, two flexible ether linkages on both sides of the 2,2-diphenylpropane moiety further facilitates phenyl ring-flipping and cis-trans isomerization about the carbonate group, resulting in dissipation of stress during impact (Figure 3.1).[3,4] Thus, PC is ideal for parts requiring load-bearing capability or energy management. Compact discs, eyeglass lenses, shatterproof glass, electrical components, safety helmets and headlamp lenses are typical applications of PC.

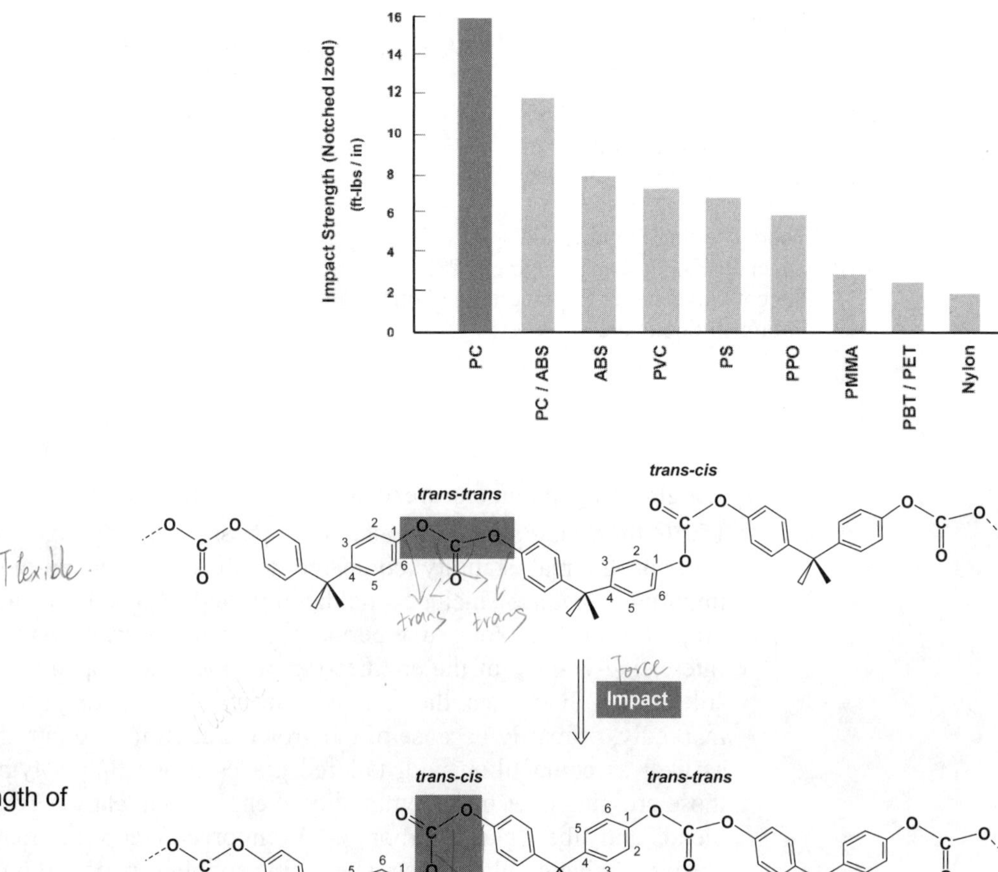

Figure 3.1. Impact strength of common thermoplastics. Below: Conformational changes of PC on impact.

PC is manufactured commercially by two different processes: (i) Schotten-Baumann reaction of phosgene and BPA in an amine-catalyzed interfacial polycondensation reaction, and (ii) base-catalyzed *trans*-esterification of diphenyl carbonate with BPA. Although, a major proportion of PC is now obtained by the interfacial route, the trend is shifting towards the use of more environmentally benign procedures, such as *trans*-esterification in supercritical CO_2 (see green chemistry at the end of Chapter-2, Section 2.4.5) and oxidative carbonylation of BPA (see Section 3.11.5 later in this Chapter). The interfacial route involves slow addition (bubbling) of phosgene gas through a well-stirred mixture of water and methylene chloride containing BPA and a tertiary amine catalyst (~ 0.1 mol %) with concurrent addition of sodium hydroxide to maintain a pH between 10 and 12. A small amount (1-5 mol %) of a chain stopper, such as phenol and 4-*t*-butylphenol, is added to the mixture to control the molecular weight of PC. The mechanism of polymerization is believed to proceed via BPA chloroformate, **A**, which undergoes base-catalyzed reaction with BPA to form carbonate linkages (Figure 3.2). Methylene chloride is the most favored solvent because of high solubility of PC (~350 g/L at 25°C), and low flammability and toxicity. Thus, at the end of the polymerization, the PC, obtained in the methylene chloride layer, is separated from all impurities by thorough washing with water followed by evaporation of the solvent.

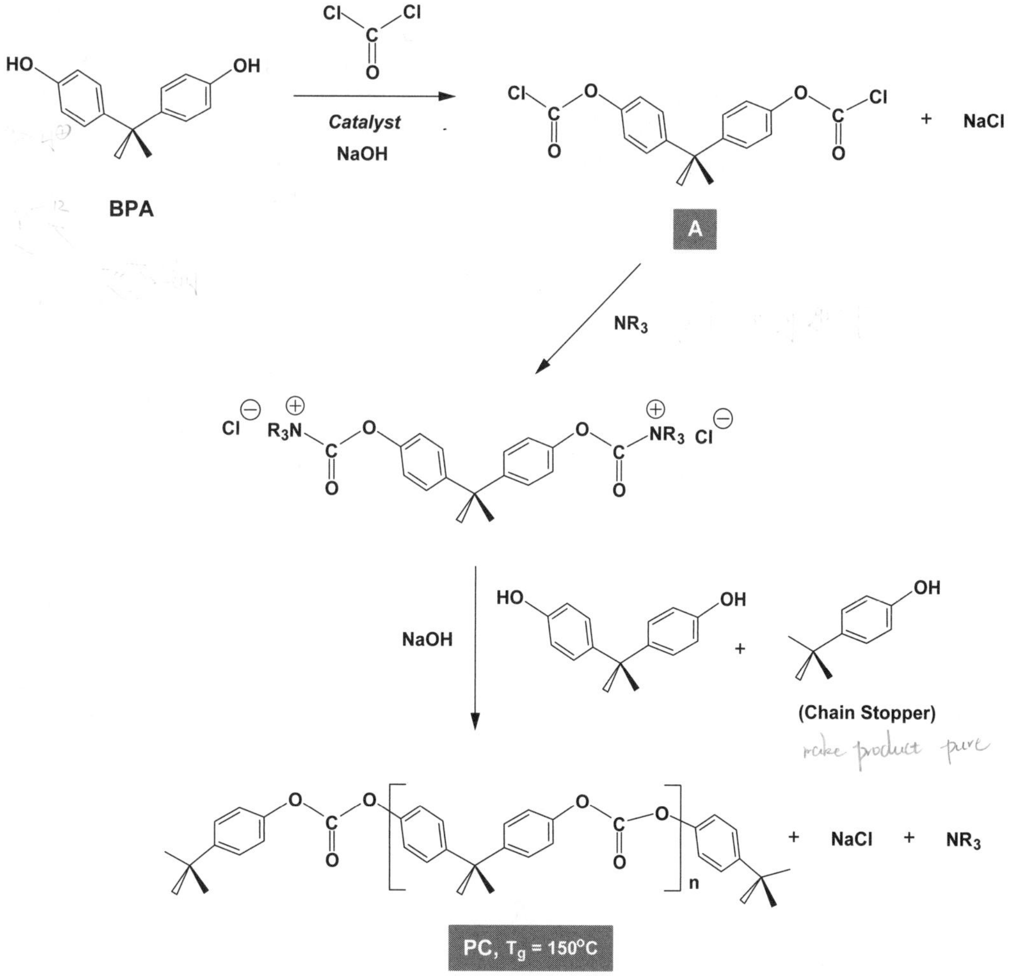

Figure 3.2. Synthesis of PC by interfacial polymerization.

By contrast, the traditional *trans*-esterification route is conducted in melt phase (180-270°C) in the absence of chlorinated solvent or phosgene, thus producing neat PC directly (Figure 3.3). A small amount (~0.01 mol%) of base catalyst, e.g., tetraalkylammonium or tetraalkylphosphonium hydroxide, is required to facilitate the *trans*-esterification of diphenyl carbonate (DPC) with BPA. The by-product, phenol, is removed from the reactor under high vacuum to drive the equilibrium toward PC. In this process, the addition of a chain stopper is unnecessary as the by-product can serve that purpose.

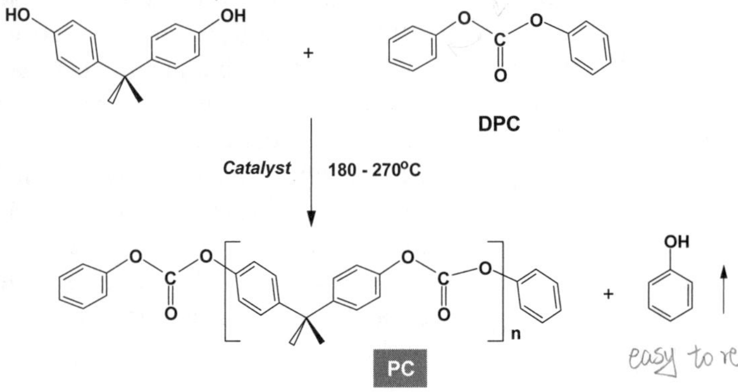

Figure 3.3. The *trans*-esterification route to PC.

Besides PC, a variety of aromatic polycarbonates has been developed for tailoring customized processing and thermal and mechanical properties of PC (Figure 3.4). For example, the replacement of BPA with 1,1'-spiro(3,3'-dimethyl-6-hydroxyindan) (SBI) or tetramethylbisphenol (TMB) leads not only to a polycarbonate with much higher T_g, but an increase in molecular weight between entanglements, M_e, which is only around 2,000 (i.e., about eight repeating units) for PC.[5] The M_e is an important factor for both the processability and mechanical properties of a polymer. If the weight-average molecular weight, M_w, is close to the critical molecular weight for entanglement coupling, M_c ($\approx 2M_e$), the polymer loses its strength. On the other hand, viscosity increases by the 3.4th power of M_w from M_c onward. Therefore, for good processability, it is desirable to keep M_w as low as possible (especially for high T_g polymers) without affecting mechanical properties. As described in Figure 3.4, most of these polymers have been prepared by the newly introduced bischloroformate method, a slight twist of the commercial phosgenation process. The bischloroformate derivatives are prepared by reaction of a bisphenol derivative with phosgene in the presence of a base, N,N-dimethylaniline (DMA), and a catalyst, N,N-dimethyl-4-aminopyridine (DMAP).[6-8]

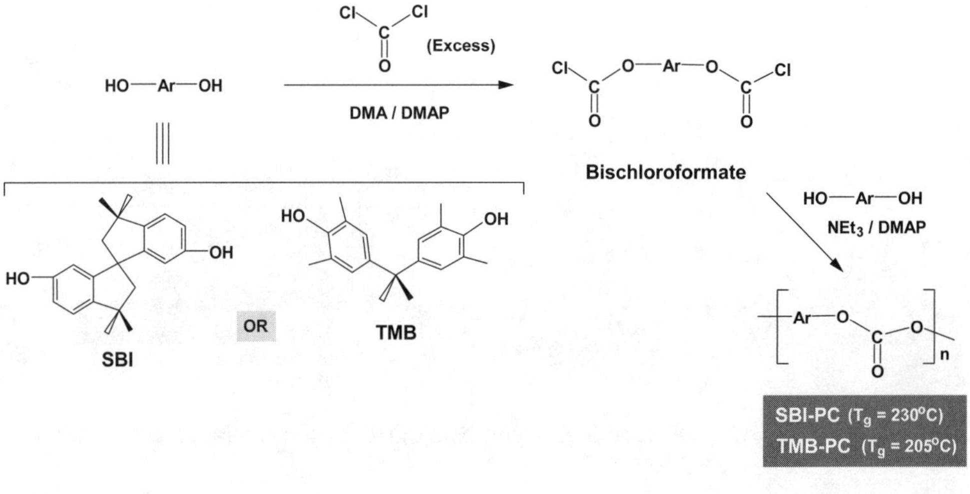

Figure 3.4. Synthesis of important PC analogs.

Although the above developments are still concentrated in laboratory research, a variety of polyester carbonate copolymers, prepared by a "one-pot" reaction, is now under commercial consideration to improve the processing characteristics of PC (Figure 3.5). The polymers containing 1,4-cyclohexylene dicarboxylate moieties in the backbone exhibit superior thermal and processing properties because of smooth cooperative conformational (chair-to-boat-to-chair) transitions of neighboring cyclohexyl rings.[6-8]

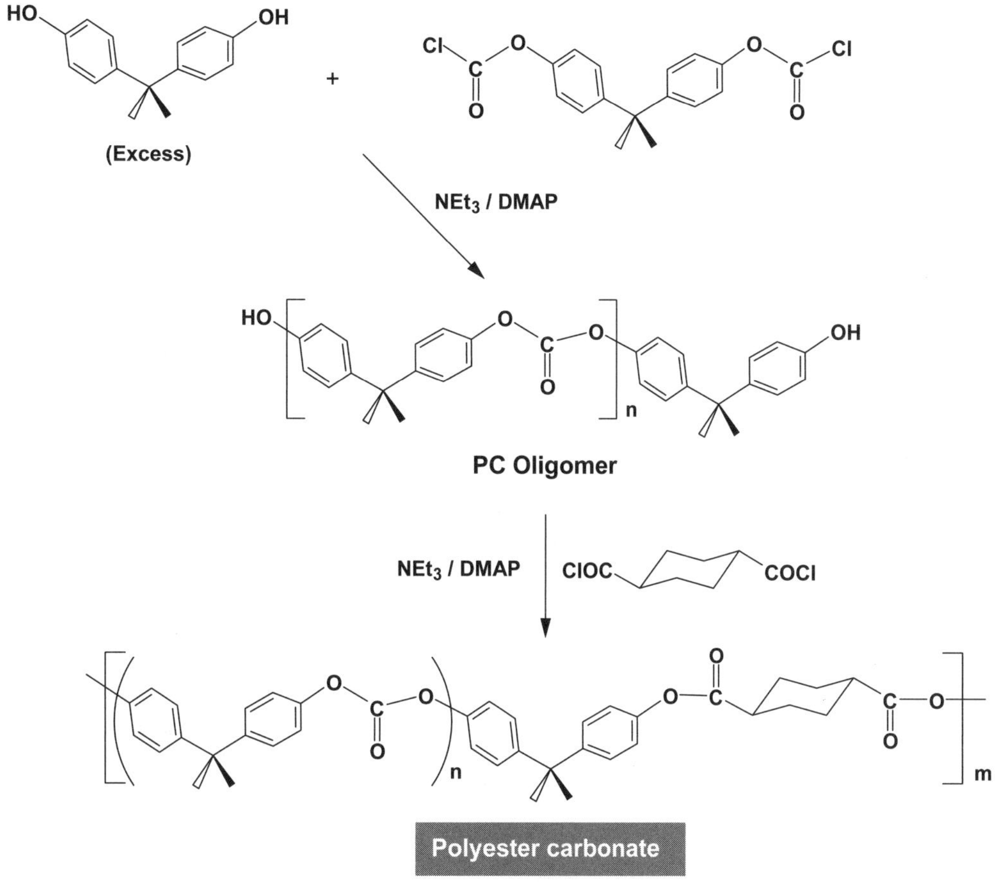

HO OH (Excess) + Cl C O O O C Cl O

NEt_3 / DMAP

HO O C O O n OH

PC Oligomer

NEt_3 / DMAP ClOC COCl

O C O O n O C O C O O O m

Polyester carbonate

Figure 3.5. "One-Pot" synthesis of polyester carbonate.

Despite the remarkable balance of outstanding mechanical properties, good heat tolerance, and excellent optical quality, PC suffers from relatively poor solvent resistance and low surface hardness. Modification of PC by crosslinking while maintaining its thermoplastic nature is a successful approach for addressing these deficiencies because any degree of crosslink density provides improved ignition resistance in these materials, due to the absence of melt dripping. The use of 4-hydroxybenzocyclobutene (BCB)[9,10] in conjunction with 4-*t*-butylphenol as a chain stopper in the synthesis of PC, has been regarded as a viable solution to this issue (Figure 3.6).[11,12] Indeed, when heated above 200°C, the PC containing low terminal BCB content is transformed to a long-chain branched product, which exhibits high melt strength attractive for blow molding, thermoforming and injection molded products. In contrast, the BCB-terminated PC containing high BCB content leads to a crosslinked product with high solvent resistance characteristics.

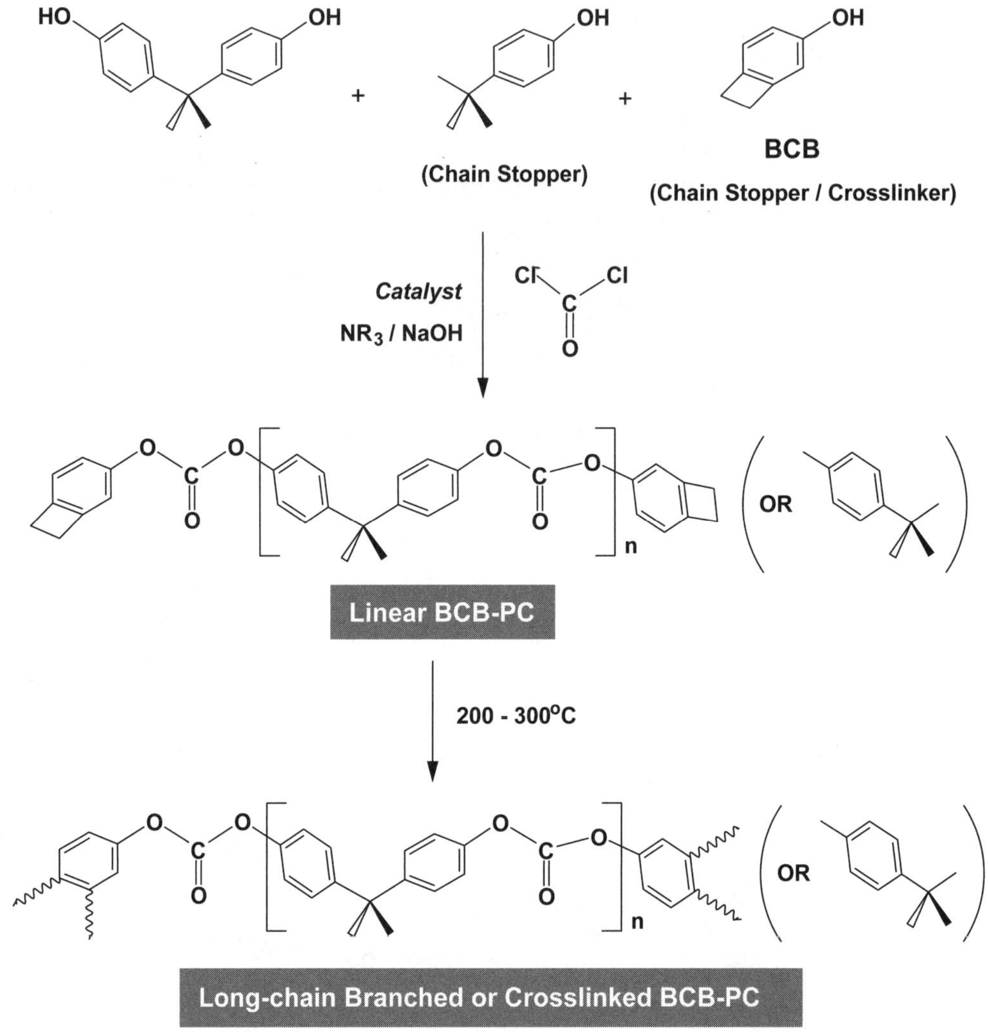

HO OH + OH + OH
(Chain Stopper) BCB (Chain Stopper / Crosslinker)
Catalyst NR_3 / NaOH
Linear BCB-PC
200 - 300°C
Long-chain Branched or Crosslinked BCB-PC

Figure 3.6. Synthesis of long-chain branched/crosslinked PC.

3.2. NYLONS

Nylons generally refer to aliphatic polyamides (PA) which contain a majority of amide linkages attached to aliphatic or alicyclic segments, while aramids are those aromatic polyamides in which the amide linkages are flanked by two aromatic rings. In the traditional system, the name includes the word "nylon" followed by either one or two numbers. If the nylon is made from an A-B monomer there will be only one number (e.g., nylon-6 or PA6). If there are two numbers, the nylon was prepared from two A-A and B-B monomers (e.g., nylon-6,6 or PA66). For nylons derived from A-B monomers, the integer tells the number of carbon atoms in the monomer. For nylons made from A-A and B-B monomers, the first figure represents the number of carbon atoms in the diamine monomer and the second corresponds to the number of carbon atoms in the diacid or diacid chloride monomer. When an aromatic diacid is used instead of an aliphatic diacid, the nomenclature is modified to reflect the isomeric form of the aromatic diacid, with the term polyphthalamide (PPA) used to distinguish these polymers from those of solely aliphatic raw materials (see Section 3.7, Semi-aromatic Polyamides). Thus, nylon-6,T (or PA6T) is produced by the condensation of hexamethylene diamine with terephthalic acid.

Nylon-6,6 and nylon-6 are the most popular members of the family (>90% of total nylon consumption), as Kevlar® and Nomex® are for aramids (see Chapter-4). It is noteworthy that nylon-6,6 and nylon-6 are isomers that share the same empirical formula ($C_6H_{11}NO$), density (1.14 g/cm^3), refractive index (1.530) and many other properties, such as thermal behavior between the T_g and T_m windows that are important in fiber melt-spinning and drawing and in fiber-to-fabric processing. However, their softening and melting temperatures differ (nylon-6 softens at 170°C and melts at 220°C, whereas for nylon-6,6, they are 235°C and 260°C, respectively) because of variations in the alignment of molecular chains and crystallization behavior. In general, T_m increases as the number of methylene groups between amide linkages decreases, due to severe restrictions of segmental motions by hydrogen bonding. For even-even nylons, such as nylon-6,6, and nylon-6,12, the monomers have a center of symmetry and the amide groups are easily placed at top of one another, readily forming hydrogen bonds which facilitate the rate of crystallization. By contrast, in even nylons, such as nylon-6, that have no center of symmetry, the amide groups are in the correct positions only if the polymer chains are aligned in an antiparallel direction, resulting in a slower rate of crystallization. Other types of nylon, such as even-odd and odd nylons, also differ in their rates of crystallization.

In general, nylons are strong, tough and resistant to abrasion, fatigue and impact. Their major use are in the production of general-purpose synthetic fibers (viz. carpeting, clothing, and tire cord) and engineering plastic components (e.g., bearings and gears, due to good abrasion resistance and self-lubricating properties), whereas aramids are used particularly as high-performance composites due to their excellent thermal, mechanical, and chemical properties. Figure 3.7 shows that nylons, primarily nylon-6, are most commonly used as face fibers in the carpet industry. In recent years, there has been increasing interest in polyamides that exhibit T_m and mechanical properties intermediate to those of nylons and aramids in order to satisfy stringent requirements for high temperature automotive and electronic parts. Nylon-4,6 (T_m = 295°C) and several semi-aromatic nylons (*vide infra*) seem to be very satisfactory for this purpose.

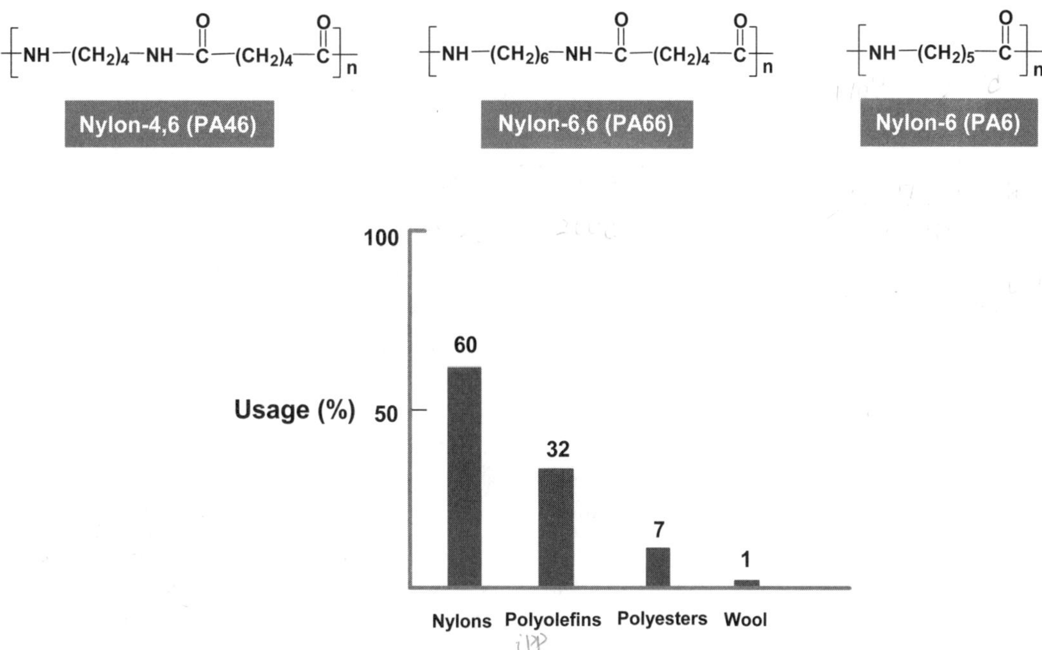

Figure 3.7. Structures of important nylons and relative use of common face fibers for carpeting applications.

Although polyamides have been prepared by several routes, only melt (bulk) polymerization, ring-opening polymerization, and low-temperature solution polymerization are employed in commercial manufacture. The first two methods are normally used for nylons while the last is convenient for aramids. Melt polymerization is especially suitable for high molecular weight **AABB** type (where **A** represents the amine group and **B**, the carboxyl group) nylon copolymers, such as nylon-6,6, which was first prepared by Wallace H. Carothers in 1936. Currently, most nylons are made by direct amidation between a diamine (**AA**) and a diacid (**BB**) at higher temperatures, with removal of water under reduced pressure (Figure 3.8). The first step of the process normally involves the preparation of pure salt, e.g., hexamethylene diammonium adipate for nylon-6,6. For apparel fiber applications, the M_n of nylon-6,6 is adjusted in the range of 12,000-15,000, with >20,000 for high strength yarn for tires and engineering thermoplastic uses. Table 2.2 in Chapter-2 compares some of the important properties of nylon-6,6 fiber with respect to commonly used staple fibers. It should be noted that the melt method is not suitable for high molecular weight aramids, due to the low reactivity of aromatic amines compared with aliphatic amines, because of the resonance effect of phenyl groups.

$$H_2N-R_1-NH_2 \quad + \quad HO_2C-R_2-CO_2H \longrightarrow \overset{\oplus}{H_3N}-R_1-\overset{\oplus}{NH_3}\ \ \overset{\ominus}{O_2C}-R_2-\overset{\ominus}{CO_2}$$

$$\xrightarrow[-H_2O]{210 - 270^{o}C} \left[NH-R_1-NH-\overset{O}{\overset{\|}{C}}-R_2-\overset{O}{\overset{\|}{C}} \right]_n$$

	R_1	R_2	T_m (^{o}C)
Nylon-6,6	$-(CH_2)_6-$	$-(CH_2)_4-$	265
Nylon-4,6	$-(CH_2)_4-$	$-(CH_2)_4-$	295
Nylon-6,12	$-(CH_2)_6-$	$-(CH_2)_{10}-$	215
Nylon-MXD,6	$-H_2C(m\text{-}C_6H_4)CH_2-$	$(CH_2)_4$	265

Figure 3.8. Synthesis of nylon copolymers by melt polymerization of a diacid and a diamine.

Nylon-6 is prepared by *ring-opening polymerization* of ε-caprolactam, rather than bulk synthesis of ε-aminocaproic acid. However, higher homologs of AB polyamides, such as nylon-11, are obtained by the bulk method at higher temperatures from the corresponding amino acid analogs. Pure, dry ε-caprolactam does not polymerize when heated at higher temperatures, but polymerizes slowly (12-24 h) in the presence of water and a catalytic amount of ε-aminocaproic acid (Figure 3.9). When ε-caprolactam containing water is heated initially to 265°C, little ring opening occurs. However, with time, the concentrations of both amino and carboxyl groups gradually increase as a result of monomer hydrolysis. The presence of ε-aminocaproic acid is believed to initiate ring opening of ε-caprolactam at an early stage, followed by a progressive increase in the rate. A carboxyl-catalyzed addition of an amine end to the cyclic monomer may cause the polymer chain to grow. At higher temperatures, condensation between the terminal amino and acid groups also contributes to the growth of polymer chains. For apparel fiber applications, the M_n of nylon-6 is adjusted to the range of 18,000-20,000.

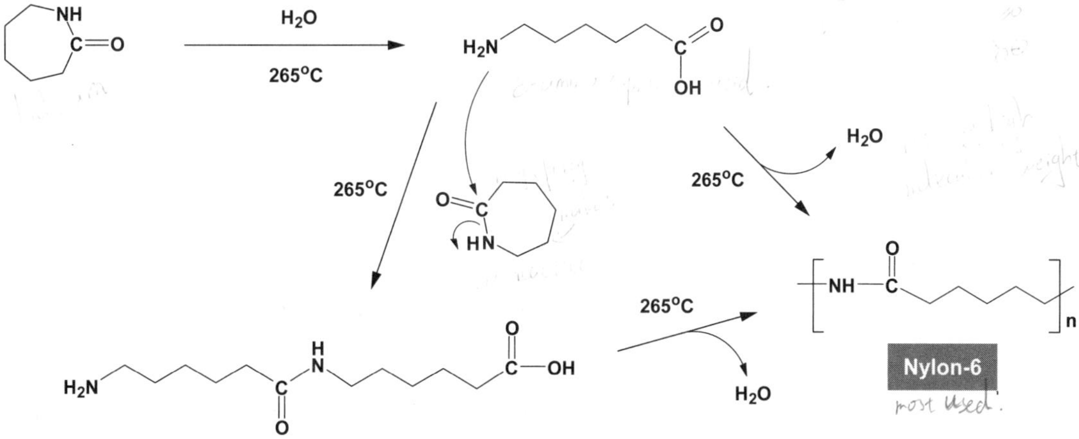

Figure 3.9. Hydrolytic ring-opening polymerization of ε-caprolactam.

Non-hydrolytic ring-opening polymerization of ε-caprolactam, leading to nylon-6, can also be performed at higher temperature (~265°C) in the presence of a small amount of strong base, such as a metal hydride or an alkoxide, which abstracts the amide hydrogen from the monomer (Figure 3.10). This polymerization is much faster (2-4 h) than the hydrolytic method, but requires complicated reactor design for managing the heat of polymerization. It is important to note that this polymerization is still inaptly called an "anionic polymerization" although there is no anionic center at the propagating chain end. According to a recently proposed classification, the reaction belongs to the category "polymerization via electrophilic propagating species", reacting with anionic monomer.

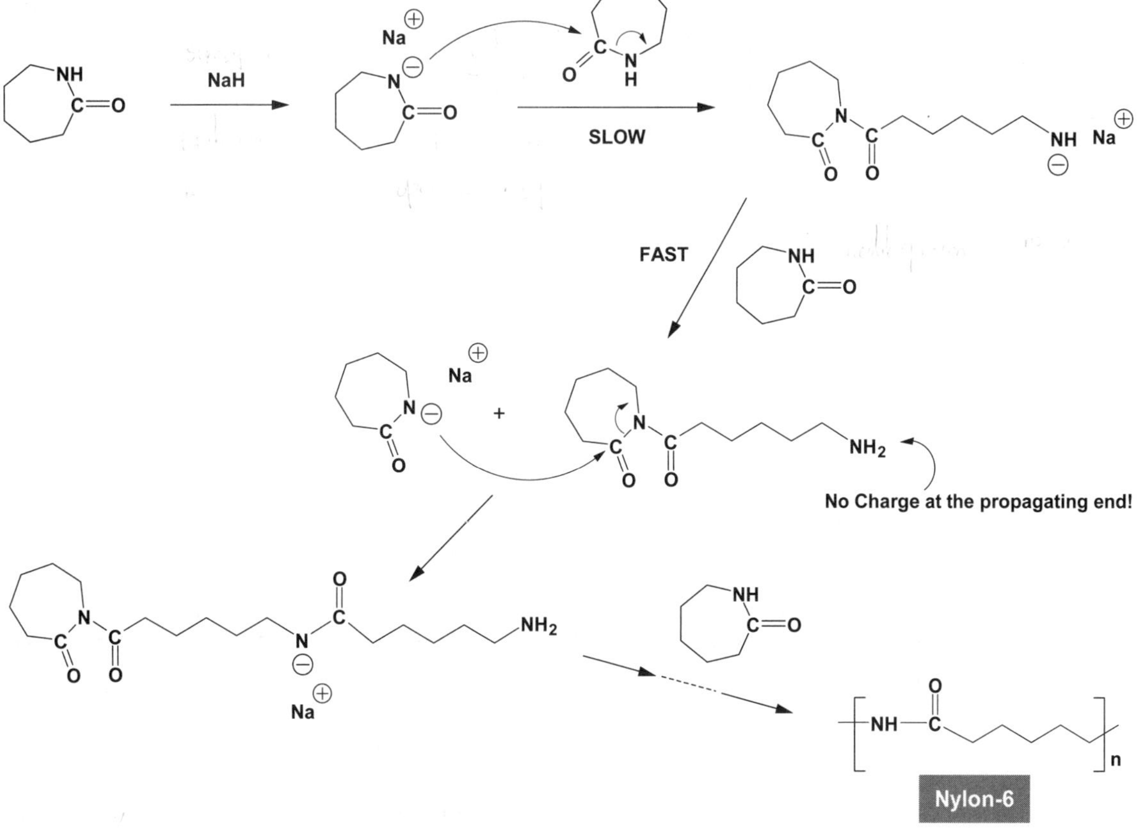

Figure 3.10. Non-hydrolytic ring-opening polymerization of ε-caprolactam.

A very promising manufacturing method for obtaining nylon-6 nanoparticles has been developed recently by utilizing the aforementioned non-hydrolytic ring-opening polymerization of ε-caprolactam in heterophase using the inverse miniemulsion process.[13] The advantage of this process is that the droplets themselves are the locus of reaction and become particles. Unlike the suspension process, which can only lead to micron-sized particles, miniemulsion allows the production of stable particles in the nanometer size range (50-500 nm). Besides the formation of higher molecular weights, more effective heat dissipation during the synthesis and simplicity in reactor design, the nanometer-sized polymer products obtained by this method offer excellent melt processability because of a lower heat deflection temperature compared to that of bulk polymer products. As shown in Figure 3.11, an inverse miniemulsion system is prepared by ultrasonication of a mixture of a concentrated dimethyl sulfoxide (DMSO) solution of ε-caprolactam, a catalytic amount of NaH, and a paraffin oil (Isopar M) phase containing a block copolymeric surfactant, poly(ethylene-*co*-butylene)-*b*-polyethylene oxide. The miniemulsion, which is very stable at higher temperatures for several hours, is subsequently transferred to an oil bath at 150°C to allow polymerization to occur.

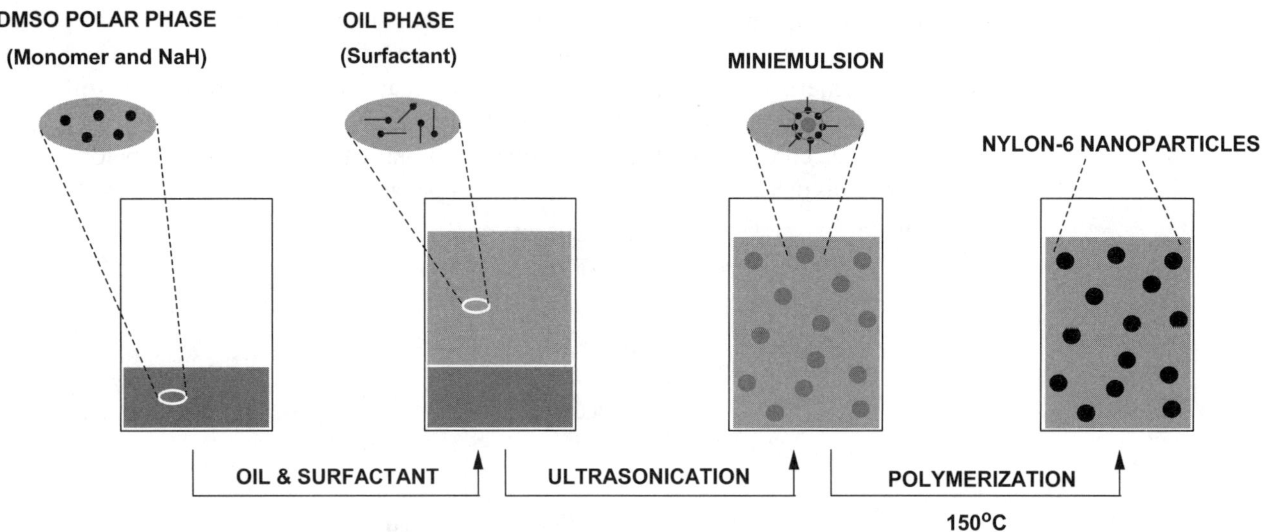

Figure 3.11. Synthesis of nylon-6 nanoparticles by a miniemulsion process.

In general, nylons are opaque, but Trogamid CX® and Trogamid T® polyamides, both manufactured by Degussa, Germany, are very transparent because of the presence of highly flexible cycloaliphatic diamine or substituted diamine residues in the main chain (Figure 3.12). Trogamid T is a highly amorphous polymer, while Trogamid CX is semicrystalline, in which the crystallites are so small (a property known as microcrystallinity) that they do not scatter visible light. Therefore, these polyamides are clear as glass. They possess higher resistance to chemicals and stress cracking than other amorphous transparent plastics, in addition to the mechanical advantages of amorphous compounds. The unique combination of properties of these transparent polyamides permits their use over a broad, diverse application spectrum, such as water management, filter technology, laboratory and medical technology, the manufacture of eyeglasses, or bottles for the cosmetics industry. Similar to nylon-6,6, they are prepared by melt polymerization of appropriate monomers (see Semi-aromatic Polyamides, *vide infra*).

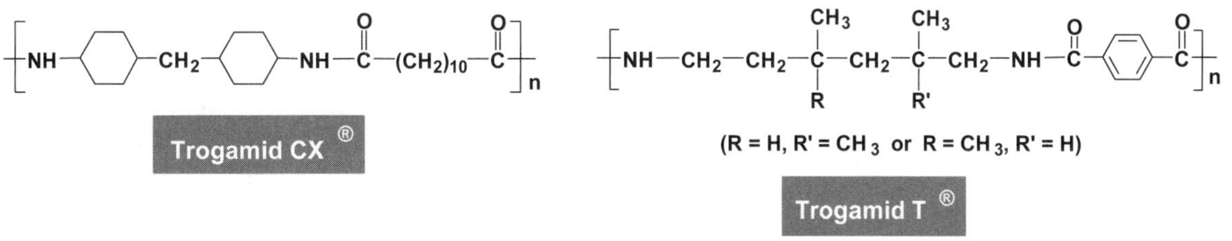

Trogamid CX®

(R = H, R' = CH_3 or R = CH_3, R' = H)

Trogamid T®

Figure 3.12. Structures of transparent polyamides.

3.3. CYCLOOLEFIN POLYMERS (COPs) AND CYCLOOLEFIN COPOLYMERS (COCs)

Homopolymers of cycloalkenes are commonly called COPs, while copolymers of cycloalkenes with ethylene or 1-alkenes are COCs. There are several kinds of commercial COPs and COCs based on different types of cyclic monomers and polymerization methods. Homopolymerization of cyclomonomers, such as cyclobutene, cyclopentene, norbornene, and dimethanooctahydronaphthalene (DMON), can be performed, without ring-opening reactions, using metallocene catalysts (e.g., **1** and **2**) to produce a variety of COPs (Figure 3.13). In general, these polycycloalkenes show extremely high melting points (e.g., polycyclopentene, about 400°C, but for other cycloolefin polymers it is near or above 500°C), rendering it difficult for these polymers to be subjected to conventional melt processing operations, such as extrusion. Therefore, these COPs are of less commercial interest.

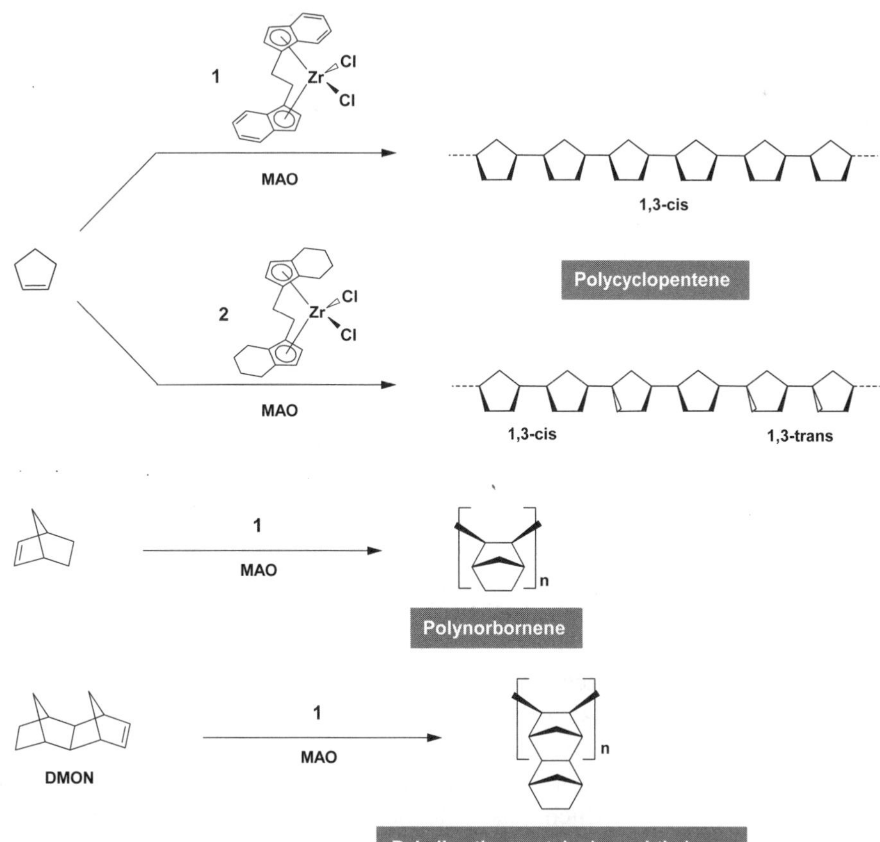

Figure 2.13. Metallocene derived COPs.

It is important to point out that only polymerization of cyclopentene produces polycyclopentene with 1,3-enchainment of the monomer. As shown in Figure 3.14, the mechanism involves a 1,2-insertion of cyclopentene followed by β-H elimination, olefin rotation and reinsertion. Apparently, the intermediate derived from 1,2-insertion of cyclopentene monomer is too sterically crowded to permit insertion of another monomer and instead, isomerizes prior to subsequent monomer insertion. If catalyst **1** is used for polymerization, the product is exclusively 1,3-*cis* configured polycyclopentene, while the chiral metallocene catalyst **2** produces both 1,3-*cis* and 1,3-*trans* configured polycyclopentene. The mechanism involving *trans* geometry is the result of intramolecular isomerization of the olefin hydride intermediate to the opposite olefin diastereoface via a σ-CH complex.[14]

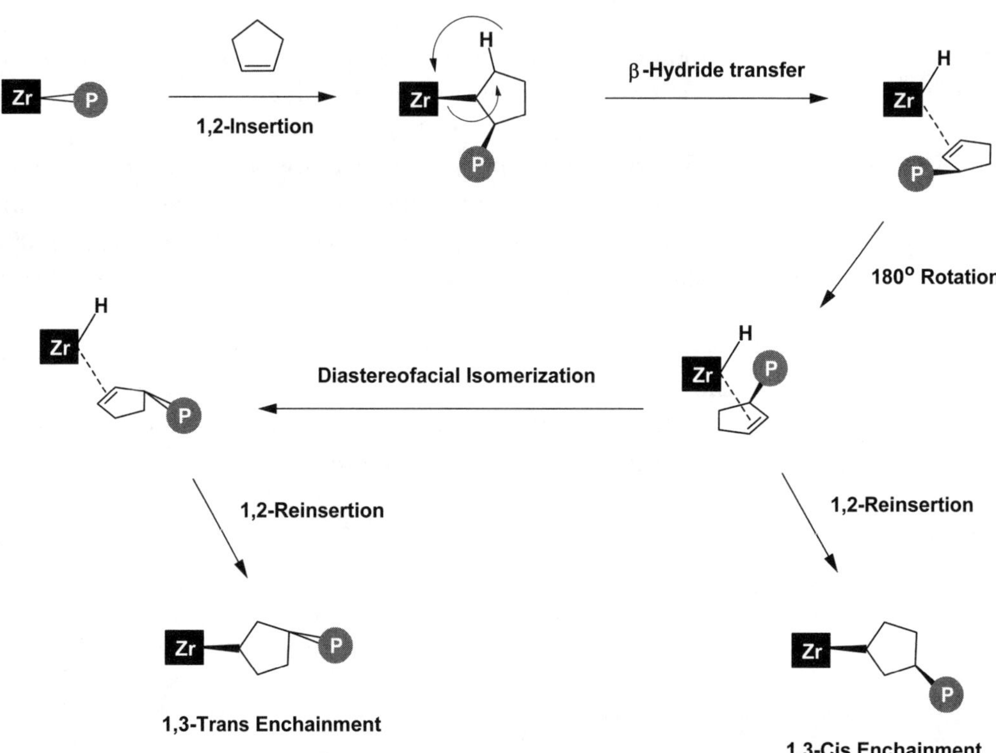

Figure 3.14. The mechanism of 1,3-enchainment during the metallocene-catalyzed polymerization of cyclopentene.

Ring-opening metathesis polymerization (ROMP) of various cyclic monomers, such as norbornene, and its derivatives, followed by hydrogenation, has also been employed to produce COPs of high commercial interest (Figure 3.15). In fact, the first commercial cycloolefin polymer product, prepared by ROMP, was introduced in 1991 by Zeon Chemical, Japan, under the tradename Zeonex®. Unlike metallocene derived COPs, ROMP derived COPs are melt processable because of the presence of a flexible ethylene unit between two alicyclic rings. Zeonex is an amorphous COP possessing excellent precision molding behavior, low birefringence and high transparency, which makes it very suitable for camera lenses and prisms, optical disks and optical films. Other beneficial characteristics include excellent chemical resistance, low moisture absorption and thermal resistance (features a T_g of 140°C and heat stability over 200°C), which makes Zeonex attractive for medical devices (vials, syringes, etc.) and electronic parts applications.

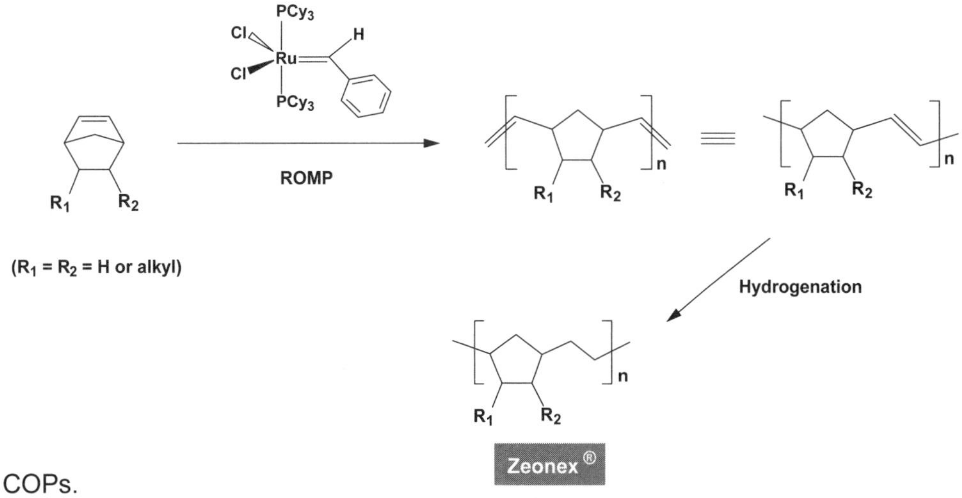

Figure 3.15. ROMP derived COPs.

In order to improve the processing characteristics of metallocene derived COPs, a variety of COCs have been developed by copolymerization of cycloalkenes with ethylene or propylene. The COC that has attracted most attention is ethylene-norbornene (E-N) copolymer, produced by continuous solution polymerization of ethylene and norbornene in a hydrocarbon solvent in the presence of a metallocene catalyst (Figure 3.16). The monomer ratio in solution controls the ratio of monomer units in the final polymer.

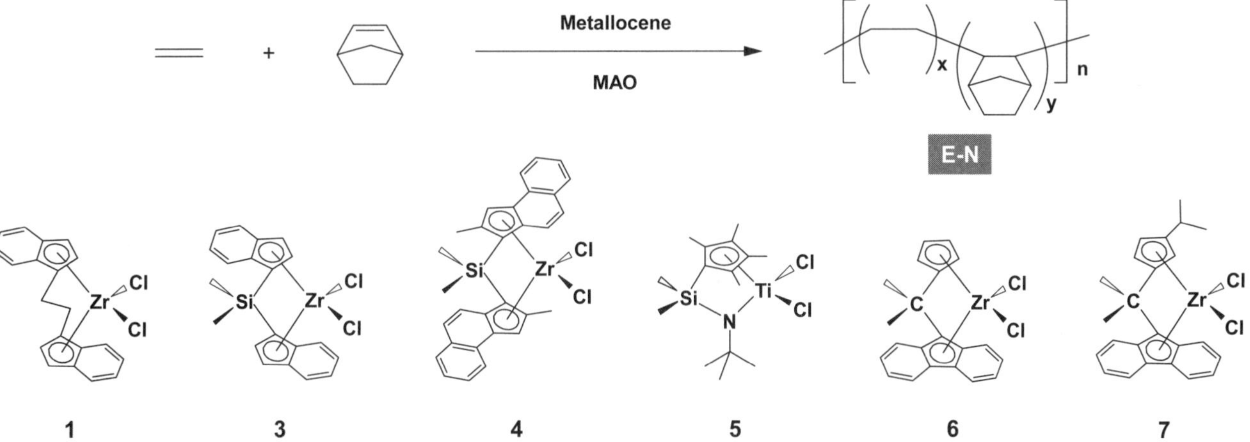

Figure 3.16. Structures of efficient metallocene catalysts for E-N copolymers.

The properties of E-N copolymers depend on several parameters, such as the co-monomer composition, the distribution of co-monomers within the chain, and the chain stereoregularity. Metallocene structure is the key for producing a controlled copolymer microstructure needed to produce a quite distinctive, totally amorphous COC. Recently, a variety of catalytic systems composed of C_2-symmetric (**1**, **3**, **4**), CGC (**5**), C_s-symmetric (**6**), and C_1-symmetric (**7**) metallocenes have been used to prepare high percentages of NENEN pentads.[15] Isotactic, alternating E-N copolymers with percentages of NENEN pentads up to 21% and norbornene incorporation up to 40% were obtained with the C_1-symmetric metallocene **7**. It is concluded that in E-N copolymerizations with this catalyst, both N and E are inserted at the same open site

(Figure 3.17).[16] Norbornene undergoes a Cossee's chain migratory insertion and after every insertion the copolymer "chain back skips" to its original position. The synthesis of alternating E-N copolymers, possible only at very high N/E feed ratios, derives from the impossibility of having two consecutive norbornene insertions. The isotacticity is a consequence of norbornene insertion always occurring at the same site with the same face. The E-N copolymers derived from CGC catalyst **5** show the highest catalytic activity, exhibiting remarkably high melting points (~250°C), and containing both *meso* and *racemic* alternating E-N sequences as well as isolated norbornene units.[17,18]

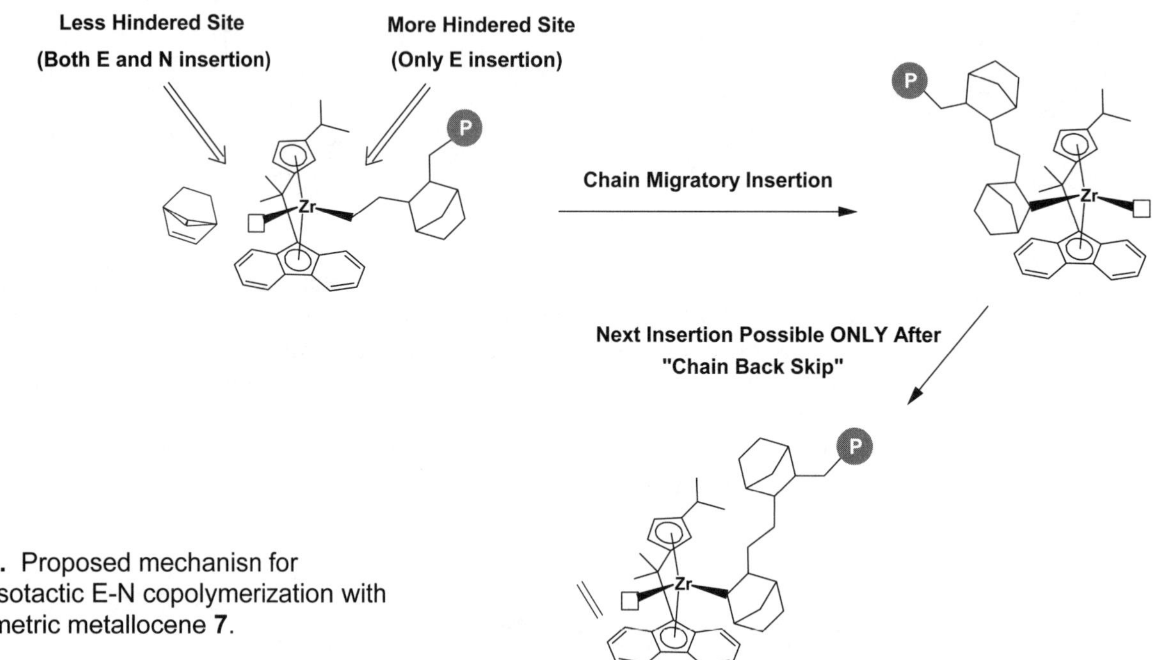

Figure 3.17. Proposed mechanisn for alternating isotactic E-N copolymerization with the C_1-symmetric metallocene **7**.

The T_g of commercially available COCs (e.g., Topas® by Ticona, Germany and Apel® by Mitsui Chemical, Japan) ranges from 70°C to 180°C and is controlled by adjusting norbornene content. COCs also exhibit excellent transparency, near zero birefringence, low density, low water uptake, and good chemical resistance. The presence of alicyclic rings in the main chain also confers superior mechanical properties, especially high tensile strength and modulus. It is noteworthy that these physical properties match closely with those of PS, PC and PMMA, but COCs have the advantage of good compatibility with polyethylene and high temperature resistance, if needed. In fact, COCs are now in competition with PC, PS and PMMA in applications requiring transparent, high-performance plastics with relatively high heat distortion temperatures (see Table 1.14 in Chapter-1 for other optical properties). Moreover, COCs are blendable and coextrudable without needing a tie layer for most polyolefins. One of the most common uses for COCs in packaging is in a blend with LDPE or LLDPE, where the addition of 10% COC can triple the tensile modulus of the base polyethylene while maintaining or improving optics. Higher levels of high T_g COC are employed to produce further high temperature property enhancement, e.g., high T_g COC/PE blends are being used to produce steam sterilizable blisters for medical applications. Best of all, COCs can be processed using conventional cast or blown film equipment. With their versatility and ease of use, COCs are becoming more and more familiar to film/packaging professionals.

3.5. POLYACETALS

Polyacetals are produced by bond opening and polymerization of the carbonyl group of an aldehyde. Polyoxymethylene (POM), commercially known as Delrin® (DuPont), is the simplest member of this family. POM is a crystalline thermoplastic polymer first introduced to industry in 1956 as a replacement for die-cast metals. POM is extremely rigid without being brittle. It has a high crystalline melting point (180°C), is very strong and possesses good frictional properties and resistance to fatigue. Moisture has little to no effect on POM, and because of this, the dimensional stability of close tolerance fabricated items is excellent. It is commonly used as a direct replacement for metals due to its stiffness, dimensional stability and corrosion resistance. POM is naturally opaque and can be reinforced with glass fibers for increased stiffness. Typical applications are water-pump parts, pipe fittings, zippers, car instrument housings, bearings, and gears. The polymer is commercially prepared by cationic polymerization of formaldehyde or trioxane in the presence of BF_3 dibutyl etherate as initiator with a trace of water as co-initiator (Figure 3.18). Since the hydroxyl end group of POM is unstable (readily initiates depropagation to formaldehyde, sometimes called unzipping), the product obtained after polymerization is acetylated with acetic anhydride containing sodium acetate (0.1 wt.% based on anhydride).

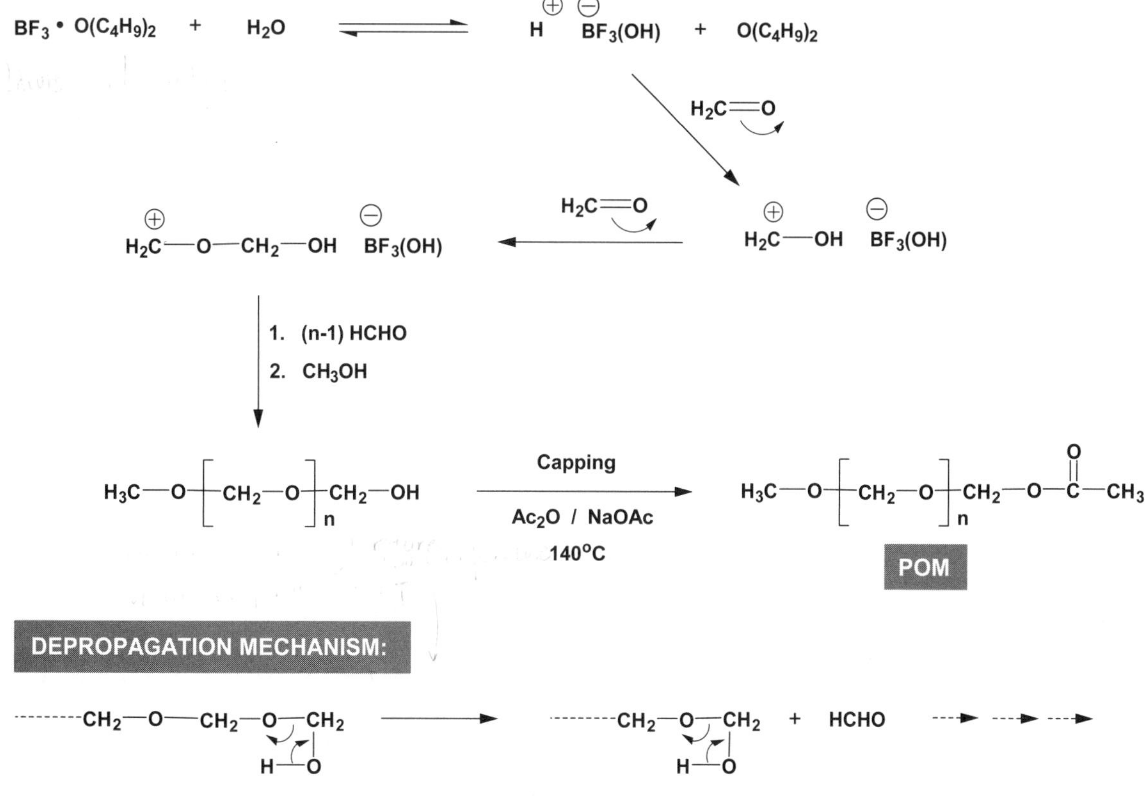

Figure 3.18. Commercial synthesis of POM and depolymerization mechanism of deprotected POM.

Recently, the synthesis of POM has been improved by using an organometallic initiator, such as dibutyltin dimethoxide, which provides POM with high molecular weights, a narrow-molecular-weight distribution ($M_w/M_n \approx 2$), and minimal polymer deposit on the reactor wall.[19] The proposed mechanism involves fast insertion of formaldehyde into the Sn-O linkage (Figure 3.19). Since the initiator possesses two methoxy groups, chain propagation may take place through both Sn-O linkages. A very small amount of chain-transfer agent (methanol) is continuously fed to the polymerization reactor to control the molecular weight of the polymer as well as to reactivate the initiator species. The study showed that the molecular-weight distribution of the polymer is an important factor for producing a tough material. The polymer with a narrow-molecular-weight distribution produced a material with a high impact strength while the polymer with a broad molecular weight distribution ($M_w/M_n > 3$) had a low impact strength.

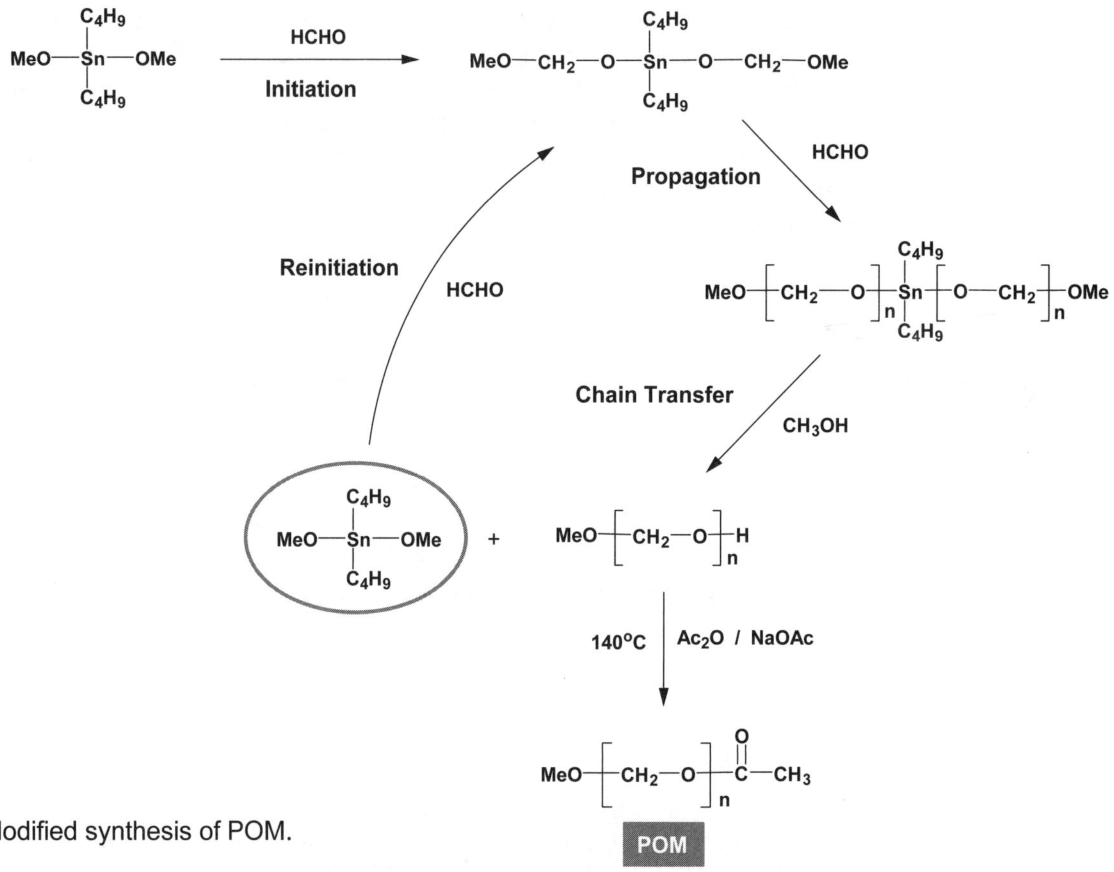

Figure 3.19. Modified synthesis of POM.

The polyacetal prepared by copolymerization of trioxane and ethylene oxide has also attracted much attention because of high stability of the polymer under acidic and/or ambient conditions.[20] The copolymerization conditions are slightly different from the homopolymerization of formaldehyde discussed in Figure 3.18. To obtain a polymer with a high degree of stability, the water content in the monomer should be minimized because water leads to polymer chains terminated with unstable hydroxyl groups. Indeed, the polymerization is conducted in the presence of boron trifluoride dibutyl ether as the initiator, without water as co-initiator (Figure 3.20). Second, methylal is used as a chain-transfer agent to control the molecular weight of the copolymer, including end-capping with the methoxy groups. Thus, this process eliminates the acetylation end-capping step. Several other acetal copolymers, such as those obtained by cationic polymerization of methyl glyoxylate, an aldehyde containing an ester group in addition to the aldehyde function and a cyclic acetal, viz., 1,3-dioxolane and 1,3-dioxepane, are also under recent investigation for specialty applications.[21-23]

$$\text{trioxane} + \text{ethylene oxide} \xrightarrow{BF_3 \cdot O(C_4H_9)_2} \overset{\ominus}{F_3BO}-CH_2-\left[\left(O-CH_2\right)_{x-2}\left(O-CH_2-CH_2\right)_{y-1}\right]_n-O-CH_2-\overset{\oplus}{CH_2}$$

$$\xrightarrow[-BF_3]{H_3C-O-CH_2-O-CH_3} H_3C-\left[\left(O-CH_2\right)_{x}\left(O-CH_2-CH_2\right)_{y}\right]_n-O-CH_3$$

Acetal Copolymer

Figure 3.20. Synthesis of an acetal copolymer.

3.5. ALIPHATIC POLYKETONES (PKs)

PKs, ethylene-carbon monoxide copolymer (ECO) and ethylene-propylene-carbon monoxide copolymer (EPCO), are a relatively new and unique family of aliphatic polymers derived from equal proportions of ethylene and carbon monoxide, often with an additional few percent of higher olefin (usually, propylene) for property and processability adjustment.[24] For instance, random incorporation of 6 mol% propylene in the polymer backbone results in a reduction in T_m from 260 to 220°C. This family of semi-crystalline polymers (Carilon® aliphatic polyketone, Shell Chemicals) exhibits many of the properties of other engineering polymers, such as polyamides and polyacetals, with processing similar to polyolefins. Mechanical properties are characterized by preservation of high levels of stiffness, toughness, and strength over a broad temperature range. They also exhibit excellent thermal stability, chemical resistance and tribological performance (in particular, PKs have a low coefficient of friction and a low wear factor against steel), which make them especially suitable for gears and machine components (see photo on the left). PKs are compatible or miscible with a broad range of other polymers, including polyolefins and PVC, and they are readily filled and reinforced. Since there are high concentrations of carbonyl groups in the polymer backbone, PKs are sensitive to UV radiation, leading to slow degradation of the polymer backbone.

PKs are prepared at low temperatures and pressures by slurry polymerization of carbon monoxide and olefin monomers in the presence of a Pd-based catalyst (Figure 3.21).[25] The copolymerization proceeds exclusively via alternate insertion of CO and olefin monomers. As shown in the reaction mechanism, the chain propagation involves the insertion of carbon monoxide into the Pd-alkyl bond and of ethylene into the Pd-acyl bond. The reasons for the perfect alternation of the comonomers were found in the thermodynamically disfavored double carbon monoxide insertion (i.e., pure CO polymerization) and in the low coordination ability of ethylene with respect to carbon monoxide, combined with a more rapid insertion of the latter (much lower activation barrier) in the alkyl intermediates. It is also suggested that the pure alternation arises from the formation of a stable five-membered cationic palladium metallocycle (**A**) by an electrostatic interaction of the oxygen of the carbonyl moiety and the cationic palladium center "back-biting" effect, which may be opened only by a CO molecule. Several studies indicate that the rate of migratory insertion of carbonyl alkyl complexes is ca. 2000 times faster than their ethylene analogs and the possibility of consecutive ethylene insertions will occur roughly 1/106 times, thus explaining why the perfectly alternating structure of the PKs is obtained in this system.[26,27] When two olefins are used, they are randomly incorporated in the perfectly alternating CO/olefin terpolymers to a degree which is equally proportional to their concentration and relative rate of incorporation.

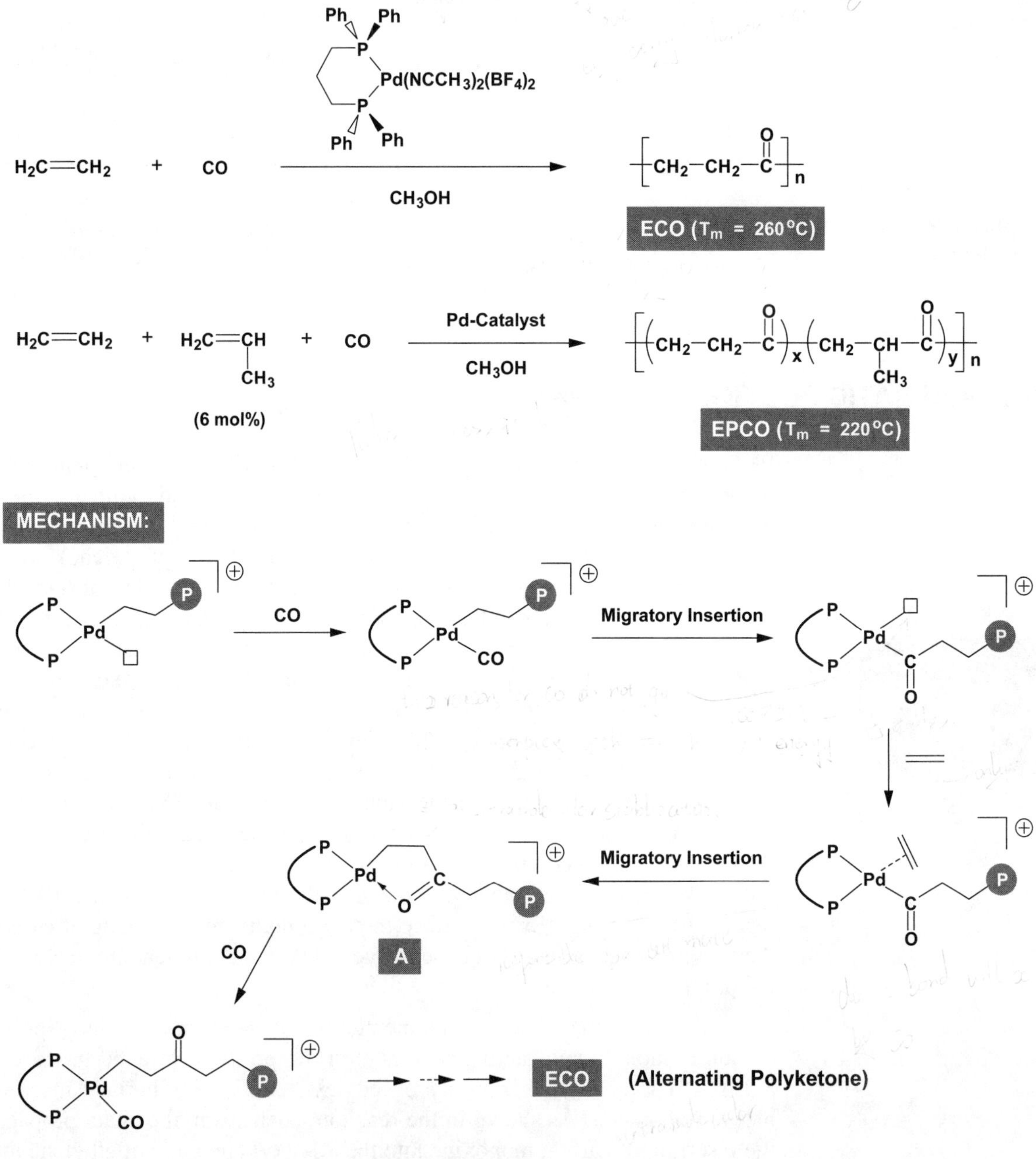

Figure 3.21. Formation of alternate CO-ethylene copolymer by successive migratory insertion reactions.

The synthesis of random copolymers of CO and ethylene (i.e., non-alternating polyketone) has also been the subject of a recent study on tailoring the properties of PKs. Neutral palladium(II) complexes containing a phosphine sulfonate chelate are especially suitable for extra incorporation of ethylene up to 30%, relative to the alternating polyketone structure.[28] These catalysts produce copolymers with very high molecular weights ($M_w = 370{,}000$), low polydispersity ($M_w/M_n \approx 2$), and T_m in the range of 220-230°C. Figure 3.22 shows a typical synthetic route to a representative catalyst. It should be noted that a requirement is the presence of an alkoxy group in the *ortho*-position of the unsulfonated phenyl rings of the ligand for incorporation of a higher proportion of ethylene in the polymer backbone.

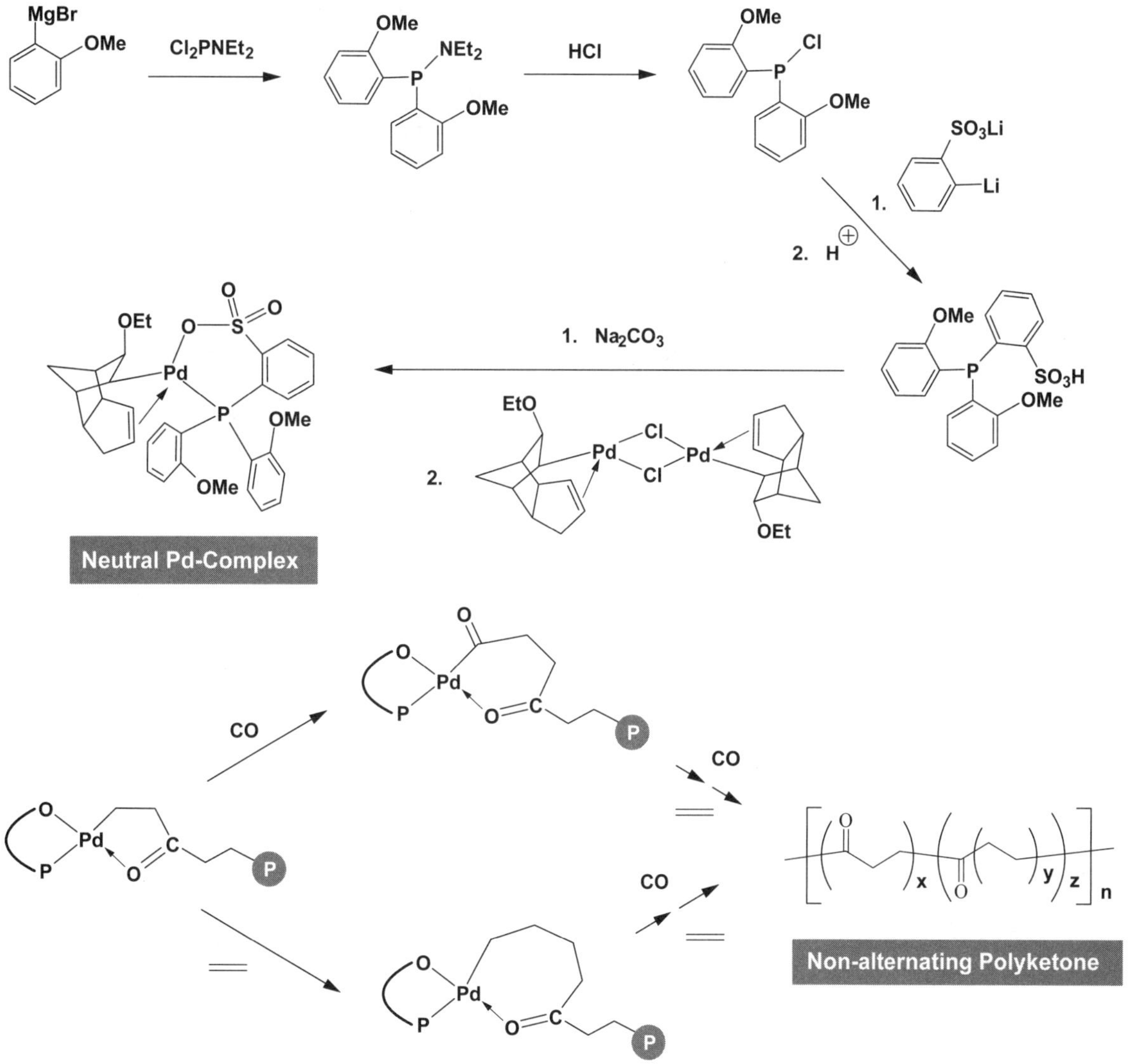

Figure 3.22. An effective catalyst system for CO-ethylene copolymer containing oligoethylene segments.

It is noteworthy that electron-deficient olefins, such as methyl acrylate, vinyl acetate and vinyl chloride, are unsuitable for the alternating copolymerization with carbon monoxide because of stronger chelation of the carbonyl oxygen to the metal center of the five-membered cationic palladium metallacycle. This chelation is thought to obstruct the subsequent CO insertion, which requires replacement of the intramolecular ketone-coordination by intermolecular CO-coordination. Moreover, the electronegative substituent (carbonyl group of methyl acrylate) on the α-carbon retards the subsequent CO insertion to the metal-carbon bond by lowering the nucleophilicity of the migrating α-carbon atom. However, recent increased interest in the development of new catalysts, such as BINAPHOS-Pd(II) and DDPPI-Pd(II), for polymerization has led for the first time to alternating copolymerization of CO and fluoroalkenes with a general formula CH_2=CH-CH_2-C_nF_{2n+1} (Figure 3.23).[29-31] These catalysts are also effective for an isotactic alternating copolymerization of propylene (or higher α-olefins) and carbon monoxide.[30]

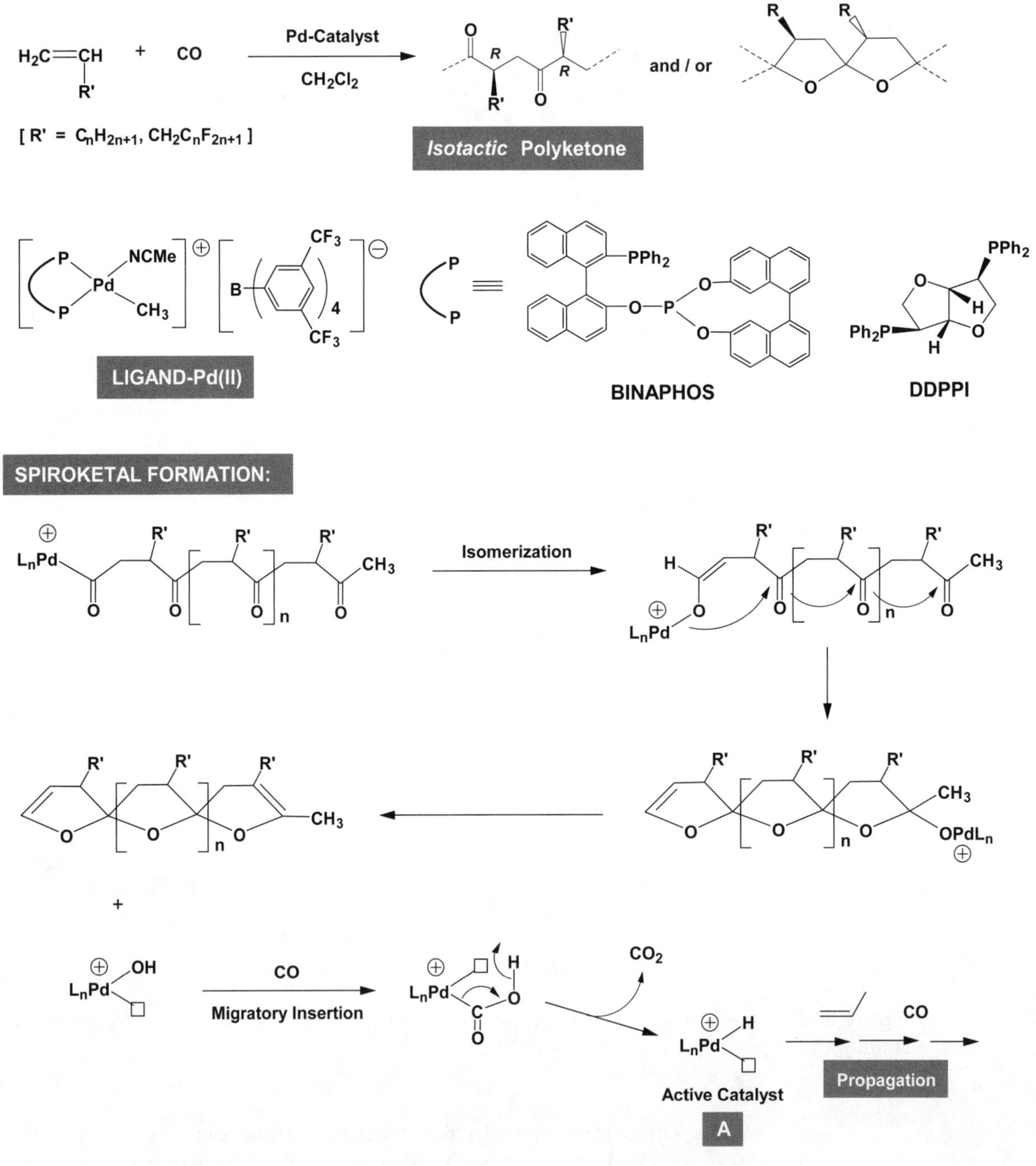

Figure 3.23. New catalyst systems for alternating copolymerization of CO and α-olefins.

Unlike regioregular α-olefin homopolymers, these copolymers have a directionality along the polymer backbone due to the incorporation of CO (i.e., the pendent alkyl groups in an isotactic polyketone will have alternate arrangements). With few exceptions, the alternating regio- and stereoregular copolymerization of propylene or higher α-olefins with carbon monoxide usually produces more stable spiroketal repeat units (Thorpe-Ingold effect) instead of the expected ketone repeat units. For example, the copolymer obtained from CH_2=CH-CH_2-C_8F_{17} exists as a mixture of polyspiroketal and polyketone, while that from CH_2=CH-CH_2-C_4F_9 is a pure polyspiroketal. However, in most cases, the pure poly(1,4-ketone)s can be obtained by dissolving the copolymers containing spiroketal and 1,4-ketone units in 1,1,1,3,3,3-hexafluoro-2-propanol and reprecipitating with methanol. The formation of spiroketal linkages is believed to occur after several chain propagation cycles and the first step is the isomerization of the acylpalladium complex to a palladium enolate by a hydride migration (Figure 3.23).[29] Nucleophilic attack of the enolate oxygen atom to the neighboring carbonyl group leads to the tandem acetalization to form the spiroketal skeleton. Elimination of hydroxide gives the first series of polymer, which was detected with lower intensities in MALDI-TOF mass spectra. The generated palladium hydroxide may be reduced to form a hydridopalladium complex, possibly via hydroxide migration to the coordinated carbonyl to form a hydroxycarbonylpalladium (**A**) followed by a β-hydride elimination to produce carbon dioxide. The generated palladium hydroxide is reactivated, possibly via hydroxide migration to the coordinated carbonyl, to again form a hydroxycarbonylpalladium followed by a β-hydride elimination to produce carbon dioxide.

3.6. POLY(PHENYLENE OXIDE)S

Poly(2,6-dimethyl-1,4-phenylene oxide), generally referred to as PPO, possesses high strength, excellent heat resistance (T_g = 210°C and T_m = 265°C) and good dimensional stability, similar to the members of high-performance rigid engineering thermoplastics, e.g., polyethersulfone (see Chapter-4). However, deficiencies, viz. natural brittleness, poor processability (high melt viscosity) and solvent resistance, prohibit its broader application in high-performance applications. Consequently, most commercial products, (e.g., Noryl®, General Electric), are a blend or "alloy" with polystyrene or high impact polystyrene (HIPS), which acts as a cost-effective extender. PPO is completely miscible with polystyrene in all proportions as each blend exhibits a single T_g and no crystalline melting point (Figure 3.24).[32] The alloy can be injection molded and has mechanical properties similar to those for nylon. It is used for automotive parts, domestic appliances, and parts requiring good dimensional stability. PPO is prepared commercially by oxidative polymerization (also called *oxidative coupling*) of 2,6-dimethylphenol (2,6-xylenol) with copper-amine complexes (e.g., CuCl-pyridine) under oxygen in toluene, nitrobenzene or methylene chloride (Figure 3.24). Green synthesis of PPO has also been successfully conducted in supercritical carbon dioxide using a CuBr-pyridine catalyst and a small amount (< 3 wt./vol %) of PS-*b*-POFA as stabilizer.[33] Polymerization proceeds at around room temperature and is an ideal economical reaction that does not require any leaving groups for producing the polymer. Substituent groups at the 2,6-positions of the phenolic OH moiety are necessary to prevent formation of unwanted branched and/or crosslinked polymers. The mechanism of polymerization is believed to proceed via the formation of an aryloxy radical by oxidation of 2,6-dimethylphenol with the oxidized form of the copper-amine complex.[34] The chain propagation begins with tandem coupling between two aryloxy radicals to form a quinone ether which enolizes to form a dimer (see Figure 1.79 in Chapter-1 for detailed reaction mechanism). A very small proportion (< 3%) of colored 3,3',5,5'-tetramethyl-4,4'-diphenoquinone (TMDQ), formed as a result of *p-p* coupling of two aryloxy radicals, is separated during work-up. It is important to reiterate that although the mechanism involves radical intermediates, the chain propagation follows step-growth kinetics.

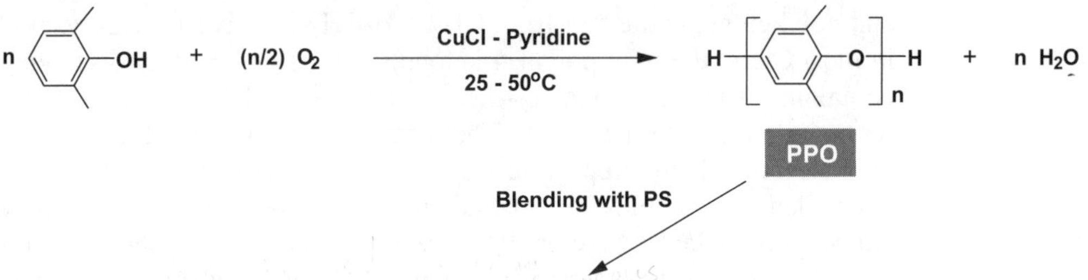

n ArOH + (n/2) O_2 —(CuCl - Pyridine, 25 - 50°C)→ H–[Ar–O]$_n$–H + n H_2O

PPO

Blending with PS

PPO:PS (w/w)	100:0	84:16	58:42	22:78	0:100
T_g (°C)	210	190	140	120	105
Density (g cm^{-3})	1.025	1.007	0.982	0.974	0.973

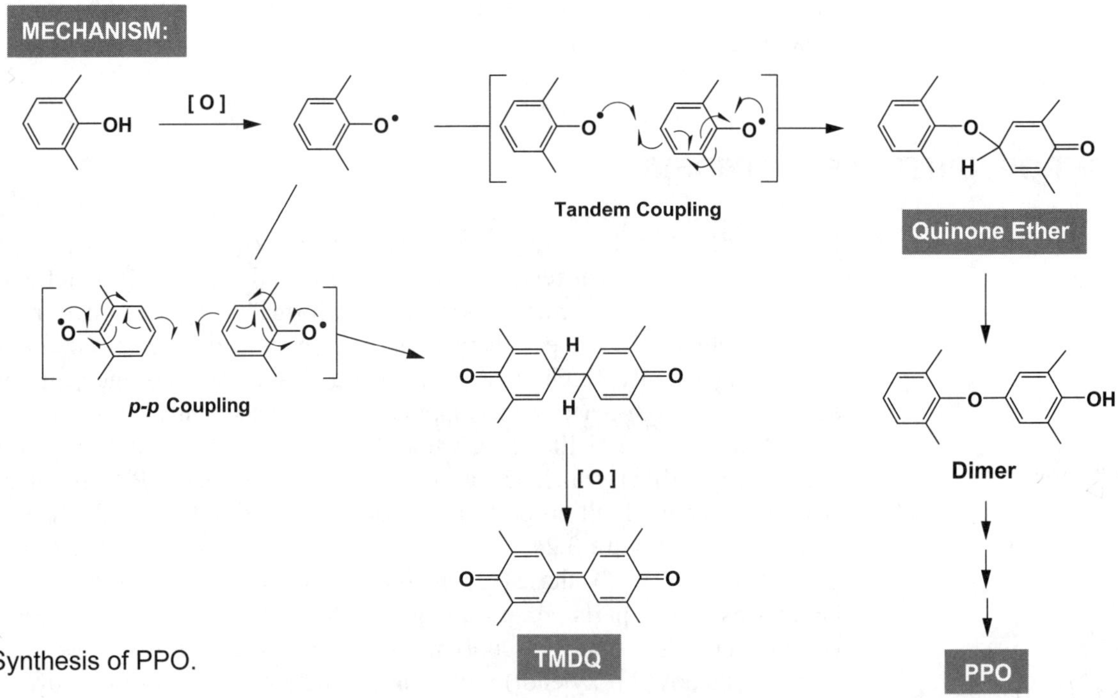

MECHANISM:

[O]

Tandem Coupling

Quinone Ether

p-p Coupling

H

H

[O]

Dimer

TMDQ

PPO

Figure 3.24. Synthesis of PPO.

Among the 2,6-substituted poly(phenylene oxide) analogs, poly(2,6-difluoro-1,4-phenylene oxide) (F_2PPO) has received considerable interest because of the development of new catalyst systems which permit polymerization of 2,6-difluorophenol to produce high molecular weight products. An effective catalyst system consists of copper(II) dichloride with peralkylated amine ligands, such as 1,4,7-triisopropyl-1,4,7-triazacyclononane (TACN) as the catalyst and a less coordinating base (e.g., 2,6-diphenylpyridine, to avoid ligand-exchange reaction) in chlorobenzene (Figure 3.25).[35,36] It is noteworthy that the conventional Cu-pyridine catalyst does not produce

F_2PPO. Improvement in polymer properties include high solubility in organic solvent (89 wt.% in THF) and superior thermal stability (~ 50°C better than PPO), owing to the higher strength of the C-F bonds than the aliphatic C-H bonds in CH_3 groups.

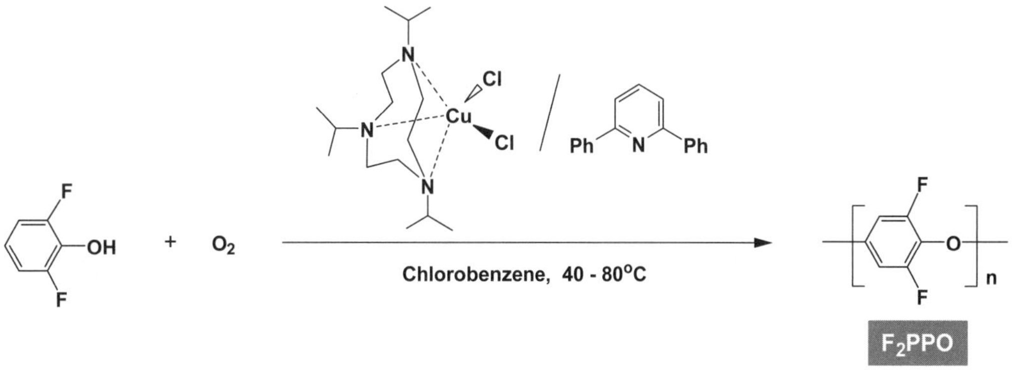

Figure 3.25. Novel catalyst systems for the polymerization of 2,6-difluorophenol.

3.7. SEMI-AROMATIC POLYAMIDES

Semi-aromatic (i.e., aliphatic-aromatic) polyamides have been developed to extend the boundaries of nylons and to satisfy more stringent high temperature automotive and electronic applications. The most important member of this family, nylon-6,T (or PA6T), is obtained by thermal copolymerization of hexamethylene diamine and terephthalic acid (TPA) (Figure 3.26). It is often called high-temperature nylon, because of its high T_g (180°C) and T_m (370°C) compared to nylon-6,6 (T_g = 60°C and T_m = 265°C). By contrast, its isomeric form, PA6I, possesses high transparency and good adhesion properties, but exhibits much lower T_m (195°C), thereby not suitable for applications requiring long term thermal exposure near 150°C. In general, copolyamides that melt above 300°C are difficult to process because of their high melt viscosities and greater susceptibility toward thermal oxidative degradation. For this reason, the commercial grades of PA6T, better known as polyphthalamide (PPA), are manufactured by addition of isophthalic acid (IPA) and adipic acid comonomers during copolymerization to lower the T_m from 370°C to ~300°C. Thus, PPA, manufactured under trade names Zytel®-HTN (DuPont) and Amodel® (Solvay Advanced Polymers), can be obtained in several grades by varying the composition of the monomers. The TPA portion is believed to be about 65% while the proportion of adipic acid and IPA are adjusted to obtain desired properties, viz., fast crystallization rate similar to PA66 and lowering of T_m. Polyamides that have a slow crystallization rate are inconvenient for fabrication via melt processing (especially, melt spinning) because they remain tacky for a long time. TPA and adipic acid, known as *isomorphic monomers* because they produce amide segments in the polymer chains similar in size, which permit exchange or replacement of each other in the crystal lattice, constitute a major portion of the diacid fraction. The percent crystallinity and the rate of crystallization do not differ much from that of PA66. Moreover, PPA possesses excellent mechanical properties (e.g., strength, stiffness, fatigue, creep resistance) and property retention over a broad temperature range.

Other notable semi-aromatic polyamides include nylon-MXD,6 and nylon-6,3,T. The former is a crystalline polymer produced through polycondensation of *meta*-xylylene diamine (MXDA) with adipic acid, while the latter, commercially known as Trogamid-T® (Degussa, Germany), is a highly amorphous, transparent material prepared from TPA and isomeric mixtures (2,2,4 and 2,4,4) of trimethylhexamethylenediamine (Figure 3.27). Unlike PPA, neither of these polymers are useful in stringent high temperature applications. Interestingly, nylon-MXD,6 is primarily used in the area of specialty films because it exhibits excellent gas barrier performance (much superior to nylon-6 or PET) in a humid atmosphere, while nylon-6,3,T finds major applications in transparent casing for high-voltage switch, filter cups, and flow meters.

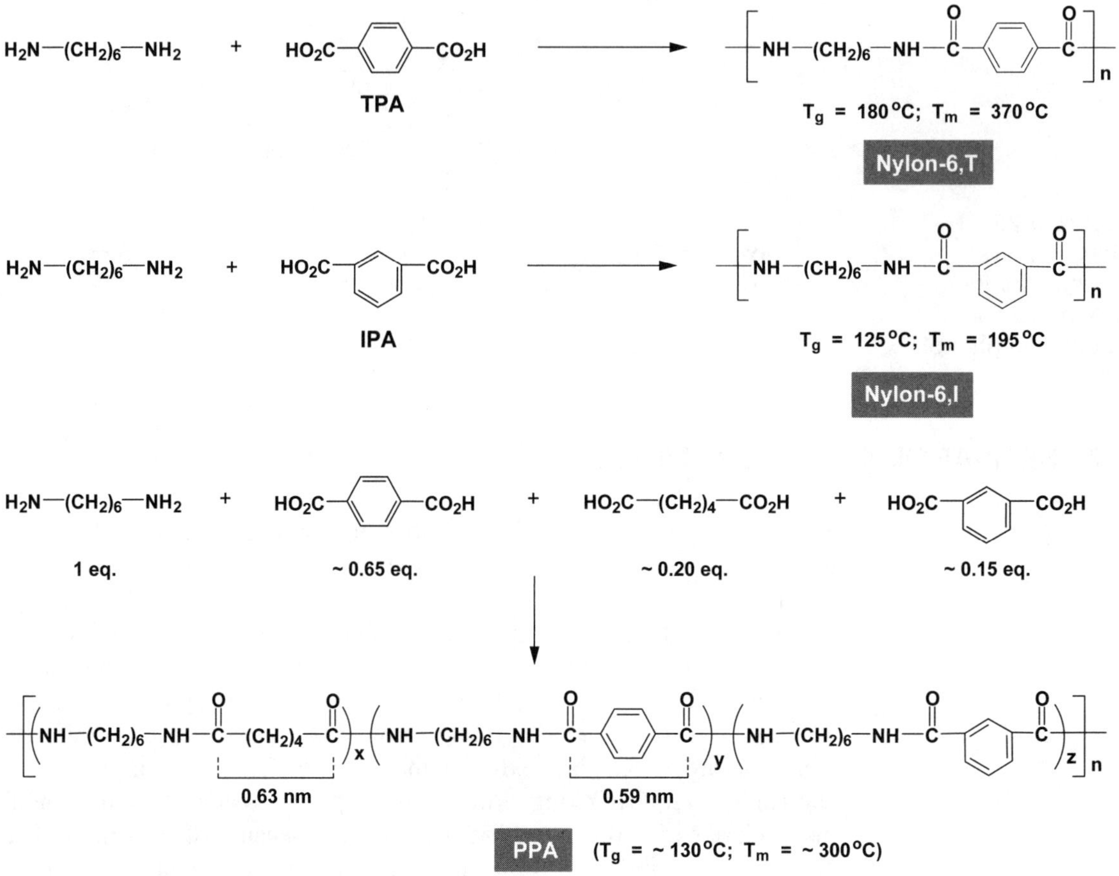

TPA

T_g = 180 °C; T_m = 370 °C

Nylon-6,T

IPA

T_g = 125 °C; T_m = 195 °C

Nylon-6,I

1 eq. ~ 0.65 eq. ~ 0.20 eq. ~ 0.15 eq.

0.63 nm 0.59 nm

PPA (T_g = ~ 130 °C; T_m = ~ 300 °C)

Figure 3.26. Structures and compositions of semi-aromatic polyamides.

MXDA

T_g = 95 °C; T_m = 235 °C

Nylon-MXD,6

Nylon-6,3,T (T_g = 150 °C)

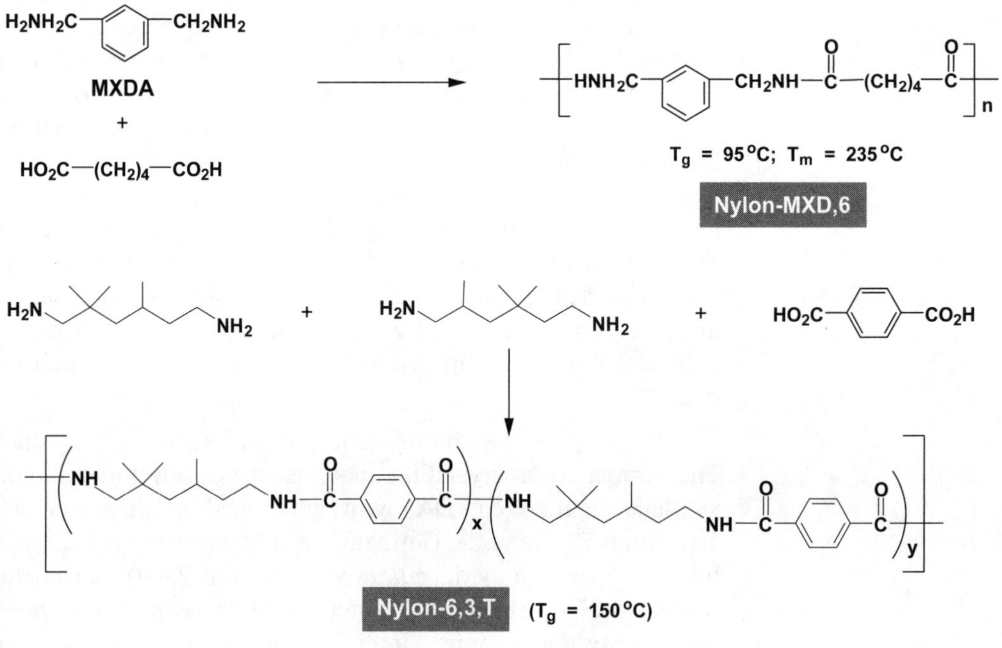

Figure 3.27. Structures and compositions of specialty semiaromatic polyamides.

3.8. POLYARYLATES

Aromatic polyesters prepared from aromatic diols and dicarboxylic acids are commonly called polyarylates (PARs). The most successful products, known commercially as Ardel® (BP plc), are prepared by polycondensation of bisphenol-A with a mixture of the diphenyl esters of terephthalic and isophthalic acids (Figure 3.28). PARs are amorphous (because of the presence of bent 2,2-diphenylpropane moieties in the main chain), 87% visibly transparent and characterized by their relatively high T_g (~200°C), resistance to UV, and inherent flame retardancy. When Ardel is exposed to UV light, it undergoes molecular rearrangement resulting in formation of protective layers that essentially serve as a UV stabilizer. This UV stability, combined with superior retention of optical, mechanical and thermal properties (substantially superior to polycarbonates), make polyarylate an ideal choice for any application where weathering effects could pose a problem. Important applications include semiconductor components, transportation (interior panels for buses and aircrafts), glazing parts (solar collectors and appliances) and other optical uses.

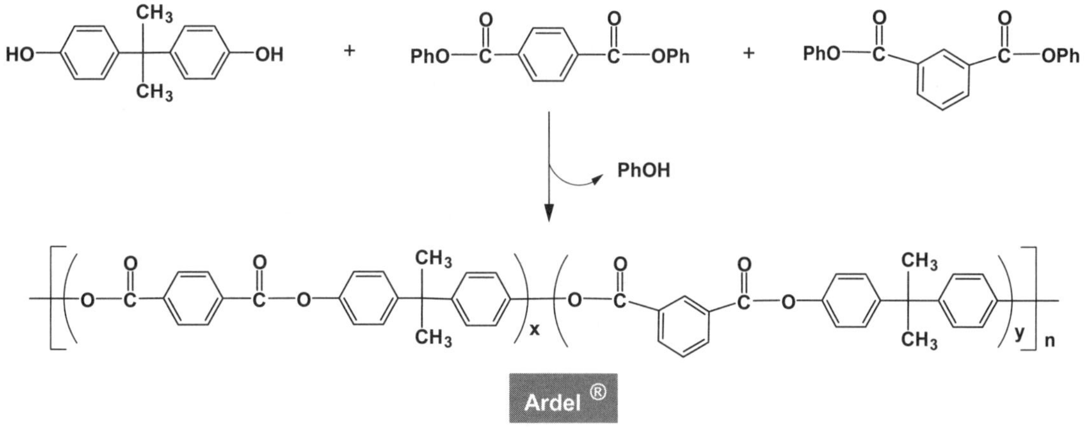

HO–C₆H₄–C(CH₃)₂–C₆H₄–OH + PhO–C(=O)–C₆H₄–C(=O)–OPh + PhO–C(=O)–C₆H₄–C(=O)–OPh

↓ – PhOH

Ardel®

Figure 3.28. Synthesis of PARs.

3.9. THERMOSETTING POLYMERS

Thermosetting polymers (also called thermosets or network-forming polymers) are primarily used to construct polymer composite materials. A polymer composite is defined as a combination of at least two chemically distinct phases, the polymer matrix and the reinforcement (e.g., glass and carbon fibers), which at the microscopic scale are separated by a distinguishable interface. In the composite, the thermosetting polymer holds the reinforcement in place, transfers the external loads to the reinforcement, and protects the reinforcement from the environment. If individual fibers are fractured, the matrix will redistribute the load to the surrounding fibers, thus preventing the complete failure of the material. Consequently, the composite products exhibit a broad range of mechanical, chemical, thermal and physical properties. As shown in the chart on the next page, there are four major classes of thermosetting polymers. A majority of polymer composite products are based on unsaturated polyesters and epoxies, due to their low cost, high mechanical strength and low density when manufactured with glass or carbon fibers. Other important thermosetting polymers used for composites are phenol-formaldehydes (phenolics), urea-folmaldehydes and melamine-formaldehydes. In contrast to crosslinked elastomers or rubbers, the crosslink density in thermosets is much higher. Consequently, the T_g of thermosets is well above room temperature, often not detectable by traditional methods, such as differential scanning calorimetry (DSC), due to lack of segmental motion caused by a high degree of crosslinking. A brief description of each class follows.

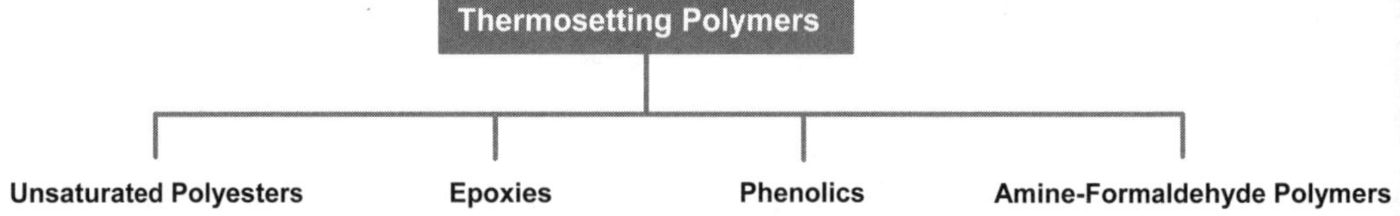

3.9.1. Unsaturated Polyesters

Unsaturated polyesters (UPEs) are one of the most important matrix polymers for commodity *fiber-glass-reinforced plastic* (FRP) composite materials, alternatively called *glass-fiber-reinforced plastic* (GRP) in Europe and elsewhere. They are obtained in a two step process; first, unsaturated and saturated acids or anhydrides reactwith diols in a polycondensation reaction (Figure 3.29). Second, the resulting linear low molecular weight polyester is dissolved in styrene (25 and 35 wt.%) along with other ingredients, such as initiator, inhibitor and promoter into a highly viscous syrup-like material; in which form the UPE is sent to the end-user. Besides the free-radical initiator (e.g., benzoyl peroxide) for curing (or crosslinking), a small proportion of inhibitor is required to avoid self-curing during storage, and a promoter is necessary for polymerization to occur at lower temperatures. Styrene acts as both a crosslinking agent and as a viscosity reducer so that the polymer can be processed with reinforcement materials prior to curing, leading to a rigid thermoset. Styrene is replaced with *t*-butyl styrene in specialty FRP to achieve much less shrinkage during curing. Three reactions may occur during the curing process: (1) between the vinyl groups of UPE and styrene, (2) between the vinyl groups of styrene molecules; and (3) the reaction among the vinyl groups of UPEs. Due to the slow rate of reaction (3), it is believed that curing is dominated by reactions (1) and (2). Commercial production of UPEs is performed by melt polycondensation of unsaturated and saturated acids or anhydrides with glycols (Figure 3.29). No solvents are used and the water formed is continuously removed, in order to force the esterification reaction towards completion. The condensation temperature is typically between 170 and 230°C. At the end of the condensation, vacuum is often applied to remove the remaining water from the viscous melt.

Typically, the UPE has a molecular mass between 2,000 and 10,000 with four to six C=C bonds per molecule. The molecular mass is regulated by the diol/dicarboxylic acid ratio. Usually, the diol is used in excess, as suitable diols are liquids, while the dicarboxylic acids and anhydrides are solids. A high molecular mass will give greater hardness, tensile and flexural strength of the final cured material. If the molecular mass is too low, the mechanical properties of the cured product will be poor. If too high, molecular mass increases the viscosity of the uncured UPE syrup, which will cause problems in processing with reinforcing materials.

The adjustment of the molar ratio of unsaturated dicarboxylic acid and saturated dicarboxylic acid (maleic anhydride and phthalic anhydride) is an important criterion to tailor the properties of the composite. This ratio controls the reactivity of the UPE and also, the crosslinking density of the final network. If the saturated dicarboxylic acid is in molar excess, the reactive unsaturated bonds will be distributed in the polyester chain sparsely, and reactivity of the UPE will be lower. If the unsaturated dicarboxylic acid is used in a molar excess, the reactive double bonds will be distributed much more densely, and reactivity will be higher, because of a larger number of reactive sites in each polyester chain. This will also give a much denser network in the cured polymer, which will result in a brittle material with poor mechanical properties. For this reason, commercial UPEs are usually formulated using an excess of saturated acid.

UPEs are very versatile since processing into a composite product can be performed using several techniques, such as hand lay-up and spray lay-up lamination, casting and compression molding. Since UPE composites exhibit excellent electrical properties, superior dimensional stability and good thermal resistance (service temperature 170°C; intermittent use 260°C), they find applications in the areas of marine, automotive, electric and electronic, building, construction, sport and leisure, and furniture. A special use is in gel coats, which are used as colored and protecting surface coatings in composites.

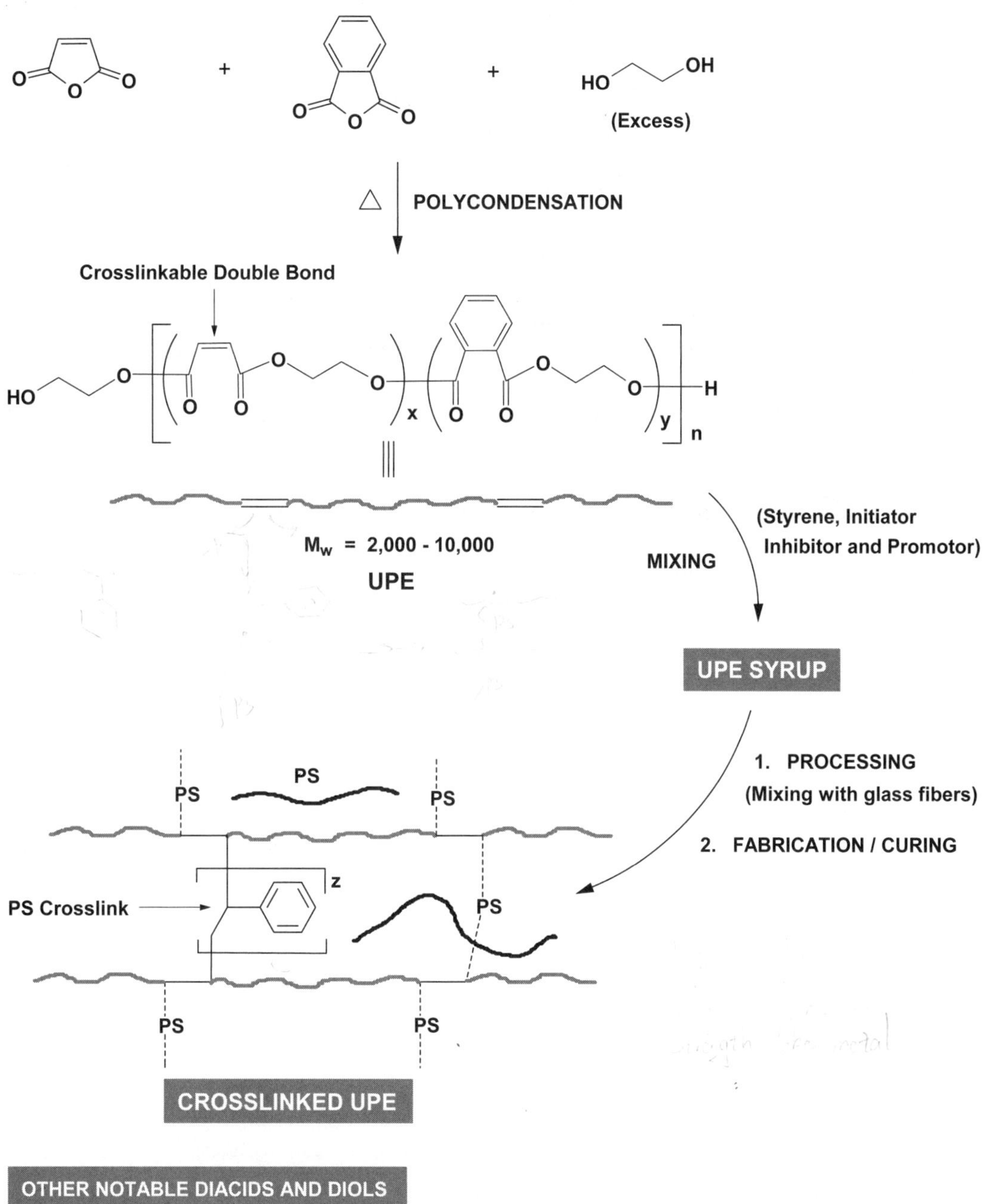

Figure 3.29. Synthesis and processing steps for the manufacture of a typical UPE composite.

3.9.2. Epoxies

Epoxies, in the uncured form, contain two or more epoxide groups, which react with a curing agent (often called *hardener*) to form a thermoset. Epoxies bond with nearly all materials, e.g., wood, metal, glass, and most importantly, they exhibit little or no shrinkage on cure. The most used epoxy compound, diglycidyl ether of bisphenol-A (DGEBA) (n ≅ 0.2 in Figure 3.30), is prepared by reaction between bisphenol-A and epichlorohydrin in the presence of a catalytic amount of sodium hydroxide. Depending on the reaction conditions (monomer feed ratio and base concentration), the degree of polymerization can be controlled from 1 to 35. The lower oligomers are liquid while the higher oligomers (n > 2) are low melting solid epoxy compounds (SECs). DGEBA is especially suitable for composite applications because of ease of mixing with reinforcement materials. By contrast, SECs are widely used in the coating industry due to the formation of a longer backbone between crosslinks through terminal epoxy groups, providing desired flexibility and toughness. Multifunctional primary and secondary aliphatic (e.g., diethylenetriamine, DTA) and cycloaliphatic amines (e.g., isophorone diamine, IDA) account for ~50% of all the curing agents. As shown in Figure 3.27, a primary amine can react with two epoxide groups, while a secondary amine reacts with one epoxide group. The reaction between the pendent secondary hydroxyl group (resulting from the epoxy-amine reaction or present in the epoxy segment) and an epoxide is also believed to be a small part of the crosslinking process. Since aromatic amines (e.g., 4,4'-diaminodiphenyl sulfone, DADPS) are less basic (lower electron density on nitrogen atom due to π-conjugation) than to aliphatic and cycloaliphatic amines, they are less reactive toward epoxies, but provide longer pot-lives and require elevated temperatures for curing. Aromatic amine cured epoxy composites exhibit better chemical, mechanical and thermal properties than composites cured with aliphatic and cycloaliphatic amines. Consequently, they are widely used in aerospace, PCB laminates and electronic encapsulations.

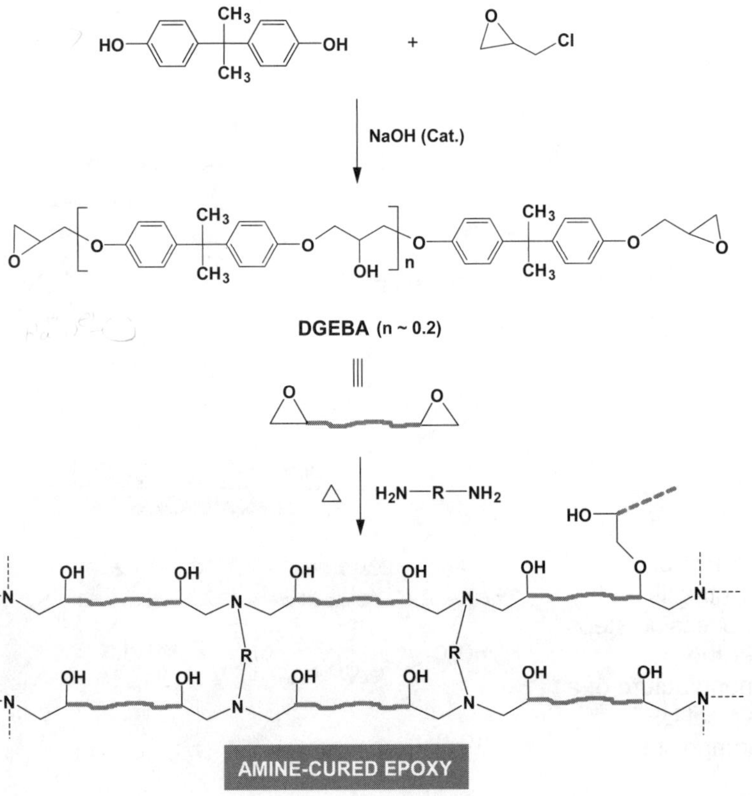

NaOH (Cat.)

DGEBA (n ~ 0.2)

$H_2N—R—NH_2$

AMINE-CURED EPOXY

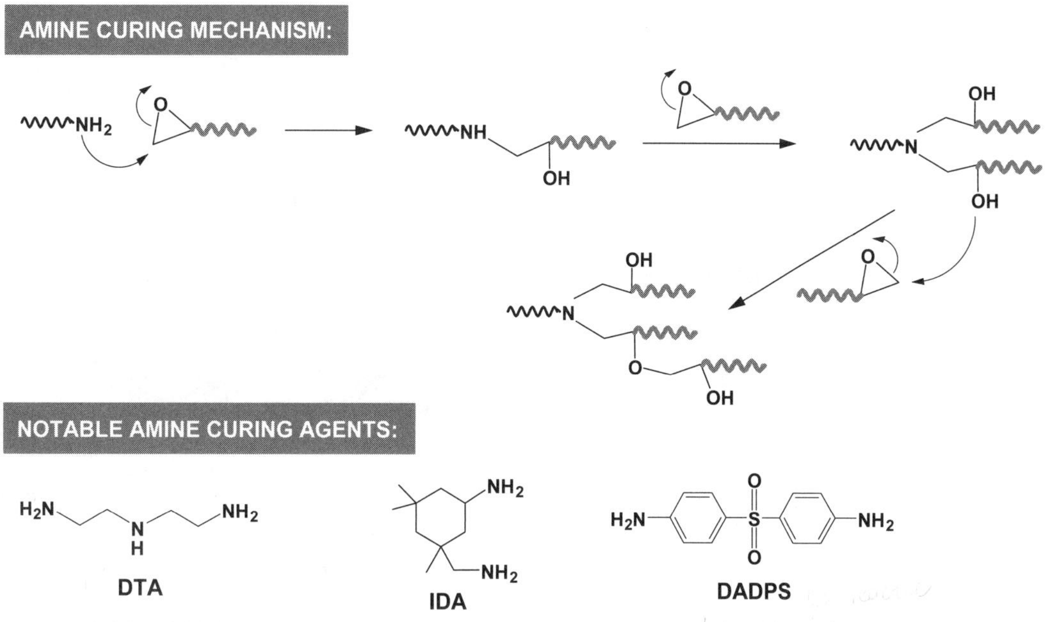

Figure 3.30. Synthesis and amine curing of an epoxy compound.

Oligomeric polyesters terminated with carboxylic acid groups is the second most important class of epoxy curing agent. In fact, they are now becoming the primary choice over the toxic aromatic amine curing agent in environmentally friendly powder-coating technologies, and rapidly advancing as a leading epoxy curing agent. Oligomeric polyesters are prepared by polycondensation of terephthalic acid and neopentyl glycol. Trimellitic anhydride is often added to introduce multifunctionality for obtaining higher crosslink density in the thermoset. The combination of another acid, anhydride and glycol can also be used to tailor the viscosity of the premix and mechanical properties of the thermoset. The mechanism of curing involves reaction between a carboxylic acid and an epoxide group, followed by esterification of the newly formed hydroxyl group with another acid group (Figure 3.31). Major applications of polyester cured epoxies are in the area of powder coating of metal and wood surfaces, which include automotive, furniture, appliances, machinery and equipment.

Aromatic mono- and dianhydrides, including cycloaliphatic analogs, belong to another very important class of epoxy curing system and are especially used in the fabrication of composites requiring high thermal, mechanical and electrical properties, such as PCB laminates, mineral filled composites, and electrical casting and encapsulations. The addition of a small proportion (0.5 – 2.5 wt.%) of epoxy material, tertiary amine (e.g., benzyldimethylamine), or other Lewis base to the formulation is essential to facilitate curing at a faster rate and at lower temperature (~150°C). The mechanism of curing involves the formation of a betaine (internal salt) by reaction between a base and an anhydride. Propagation occurs by attack of the betaine carboxylate ion with an epoxide, followed by attack of the resulting alkoxide to another anhydride moiety (Figure 3.32). The most common anhydride is methyltetrahydrophthalic anhydride (MTHPA), followed by phthalic anhydride (PA). Tetrachlorophthalic anhydride (TCPA) is used for composites requiring flame-retardant properties. The dianhydrides, such as benzophenonetetracarboxylic dianhydride (BTDA), are employed when a product with high crosslinking density and a high heat distortion temperature (HDT) in excess of 275°C is desired.

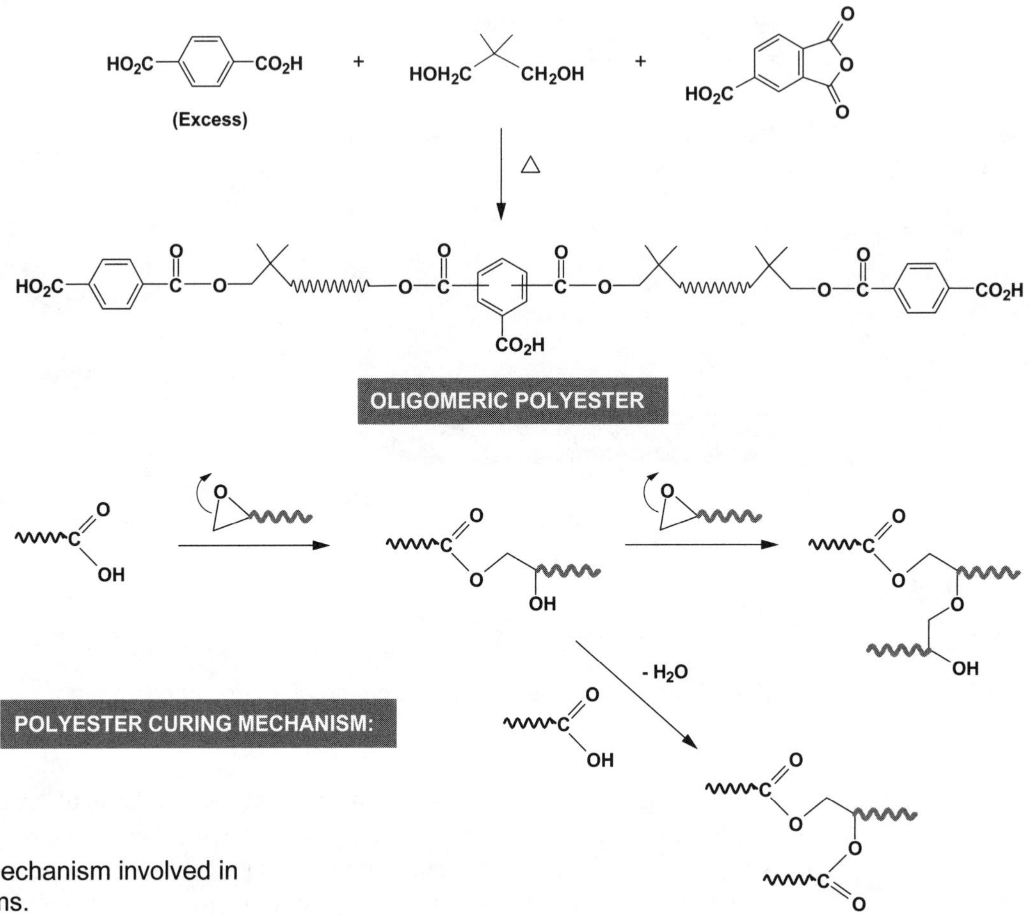

Figure 3.31. Curing mechanism involved in epoxy-polyester systems.

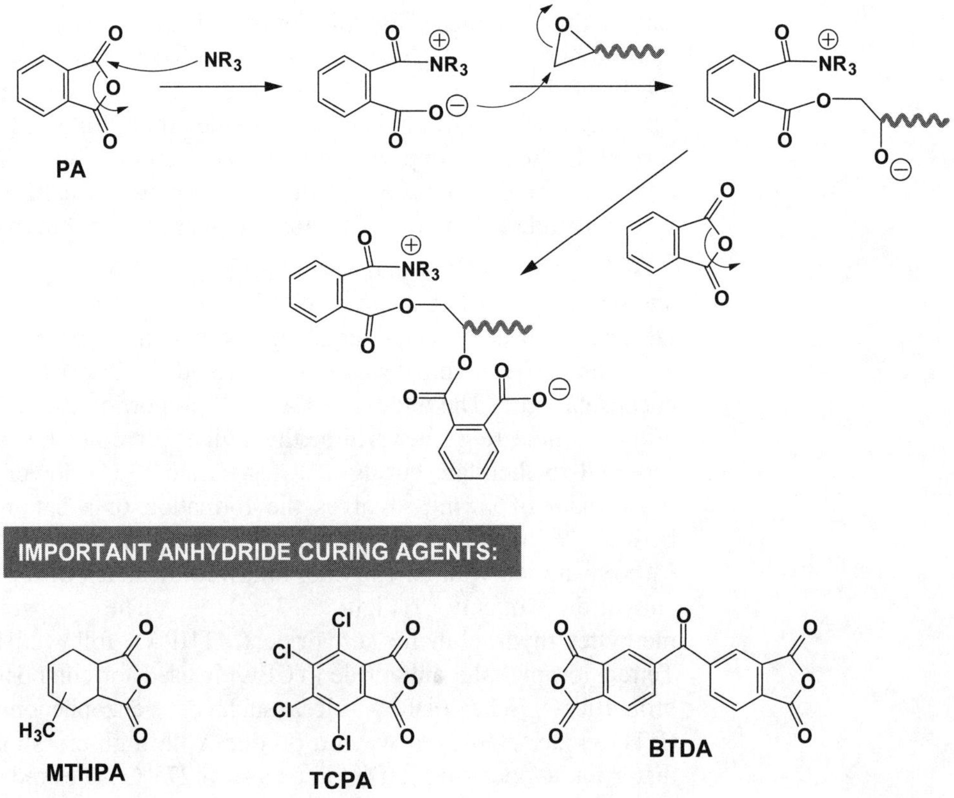

Figure 3.32. Curing mechanism involved in epoxy-anhydride systems.

Besides DGEBA and SECs, a variety of epoxy compounds are commercially available to meet the demands for specialty composites (Figure 3.33). For example, the cured thermosets obtained from epoxy-phenol novolac (EPN) and epoxy-cresol novolac (ECN) compounds exhibit thermal and chemical resistance superior to DGEBA because of higher crosslinking density resulting from multi-epoxide groups (*vide infra*). These improved properties are useful for aerospace composites and liners for pumps and other chemical process equipment. Another notable compound containing multi-functional epoxy groups is the tetraglycidyl ether of tetrakis(4-hydroxyphenyl)ethane, TGEPE. This product is used primarily in the formulation of high temperature resistant adhesives and electrical laminates for high density printed circuit boards (PCBs). Very recently, two epoxy compounds, the diglycidyl ether of tetramethyl biphenol (DGETB) and diglycidyl ether of 1,5-dihydroxy naphthalene (DGEDN), have been developed in response to the increased performance requirements set by the semiconductor industry. These materials are crystalline solids, but their low melt viscosity allows very high reinforcement material loading (~ 90 wt.%), leading to highly amorphous composite materials which exhibit low coefficient of thermal expansion (CTE) and outstanding thermal, moisture and crack resistance. These attributes are ideal for advanced semiconductor processes, such as surface mount technology (SMT), a method for constructing electronic circuits in which the components are mounted directly onto the surface of PCBs.[37]

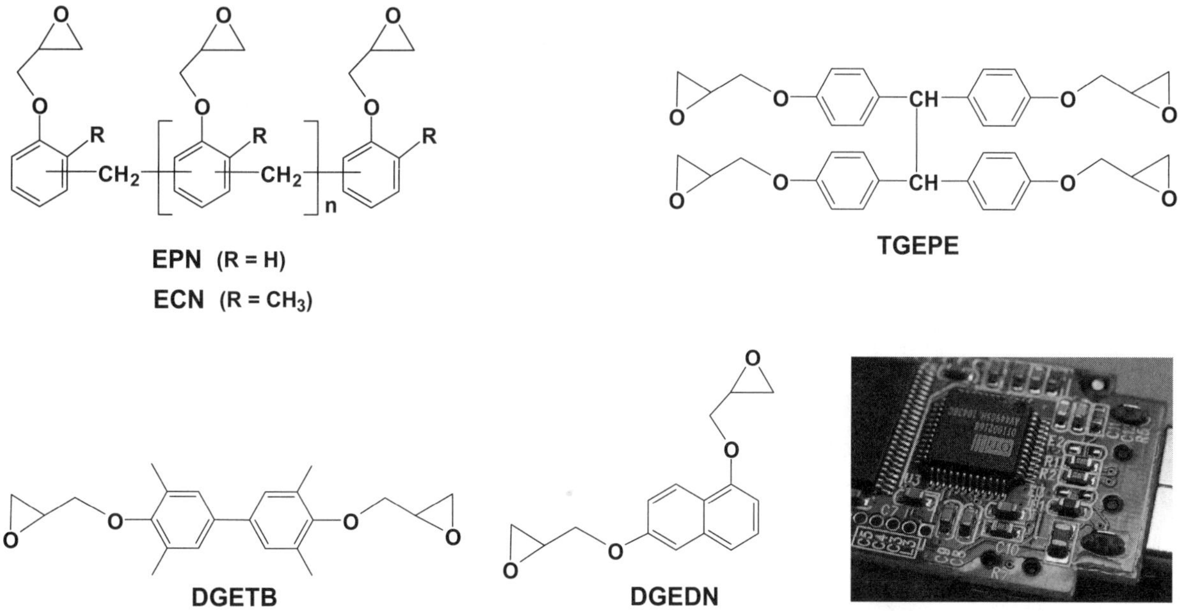

EPN (R = H)
ECN (R = CH_3)

TGEPE

DGETB

DGEDN

Figure 3.33. Structures of specialty epoxy compounds. Photo: PCB fabricated by SMT.[37]

3.9.3. Phenolics

Phenolics are credited with being the first commercialized (Bakelite) wholly synthetic polymer. In the pre-cured stage, they are low molecular weight polycondensation products of phenols and aldehydes, in particular, phenol (P) and formaldehyde (F). Since phenol possesses two *ortho* and one *para* reactive sites and formaldehyde is difunctional, different molecular architectures can be achieved by varying the molar ratio of reactants as well as the amount and type of catalyst, resulting in three classes of phenolics: novolacs, *high-ortho* novolacs, and resols.

Novolacs are produced from an excess of phenol (F/P ≈ 0.5 – 0.8) in the presence of an acid (e.g., sulfuric acid or *p*-toluenesulfonic acid) with a pH <3. They are slightly branched polymers (tri-substituted phenol at the branch points) with molecular weights of 500 – 5,000 and glass-transition temperatures of 45 – 70°C. The novolac reaction is believed to proceed through methylene-linked bisphenol intermediates, as depicted in Figure 3.34. In aqueous solution, formaldehyde exists in the form of methylene glycol (**MG**). In the presence of an acid, MG is converted into a hydrated cation which adds to

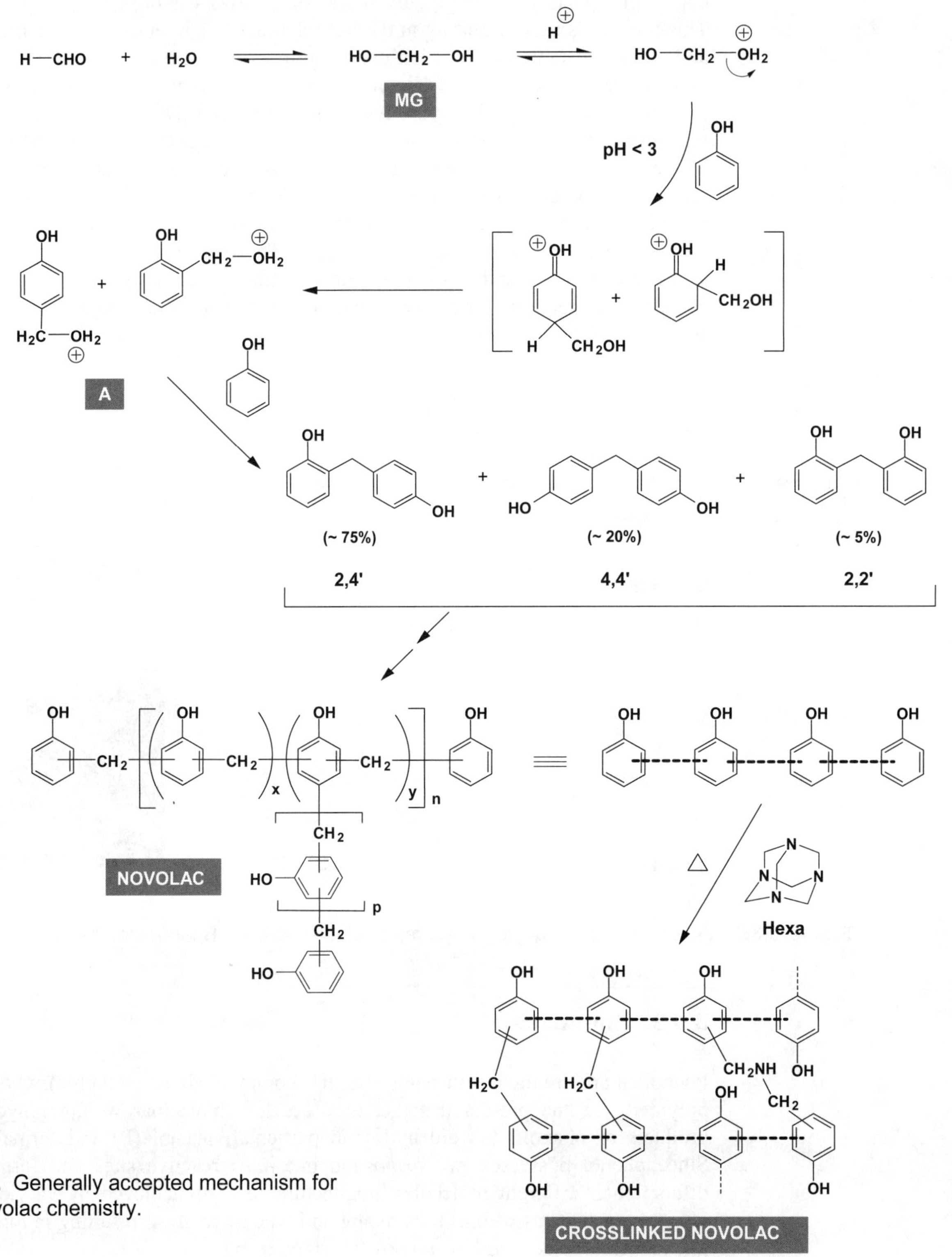

Figure 3.34. Generally accepted mechanism for complex novolac chemistry.

the ortho or para position of phenol to form a hydrated benzylic ion (**A**). This, in turn, reacts with the ortho or para position of a free phenol to form methylene-linked bisphenol intermediates. Novolacs contain ~75% of ortho-para (2,4') linkages, ~20% of para-para (4,4') linkages, and ~5% of ortho-ortho (2,2'). Since there are no self-reacting groups present in novolacs, crosslinking is accomplished by reaction with 5 – 15 wt.% hexamethylenetetramine (hexa), a latent formaldehyde source ("masked formaldehyde"), which is manufactured by reaction of formaldehyde and ammonia. Thus, similar to the condensation of phenol and formaldehyde, the majority of crosslinks in the cured novolacs are methylene bridges between aromatic rings, along with some dibenzylamine linkages. Novolacs can be formulated with 40-70 wt.% fillers, such as wood flour, nylon, glass fiber and graphite to produce low cost, high compressive strength, low-creep, high gloss, and thermal resistant (e.g., 150°C for wood filled; intermittent use 220°C) composite molding materials. It is important to mention that a variety of substituted phenols, such as cresols, xylenols, 4-*t*-butylphenol, 4-phenylphenol, bisphenols, and resorcinol, can be used in place of phenol or in combination with phenol to produce specialty novolacs. The only aldehyde which performs well, other than formaldehyde, is furfural.

In comparison, as the name indicates, *high-ortho* novolacs have a large number of *ortho-ortho* repeat units and are prepared exclusively from phenol and formaldehyde monomers (F/P ≈ 0.5 – 0.8), but in the presence of a catalyst, usually zinc acetate, in the range of pH 4.5 – 7. The catalyst imparts a significant ortho-directing effect by chelating both phenol and MG and consequently, almost 100% *o*-methylol phenol (OMP) is produced in the first step (Figure 3.35). The subsequent reaction of OMP with phenol has less chelate-directing influence, which is evident from the formation of equal quantities of 2,2' (~45%) and 2,4' (~45%) methylene-linked bisphenol intermediates. High-ortho novolacs possess no branching (negligible tri-substituted phenol) with molecular weights of 500 – 1,800 and glass-transition temperatures of 45 – 50°C. They are also cured with hexa, but require only one-third of the time to that of novolacs, because of the availability of more reactive unsubstituted *para* positions. Besides composite molding materials, high-ortho novolacs are used as effective curing agents for epoxies, including the synthesis of epoxidized novolacs for applications requiring multi-functional epoxide groups and high crosslink density (*vide supra*).

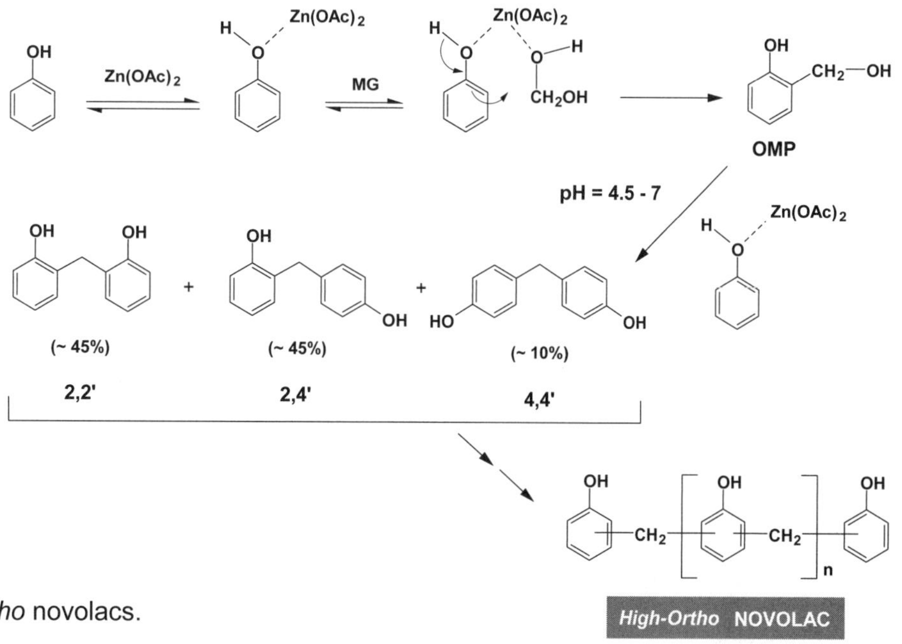

Figure 3.35. Synthesis of *high-ortho* novolacs.

Resoles are produced from excess formaldehyde (F/P ≈ 1.2 – 1.8) in the presence of a base (sodium hydroxide or calcium hydroxide) at a pH ~10. They are highly branched oligomeric tri-substituted phenolic compounds with molecular weights of 280 – 500 and glass-transition temperatures of 30 – 40°C. A generally accepted mechanism for the complex resole reaction is outlined in Figure 3.36. The *ortho* and *para* mono-methylolated phenols are believed to form initially via nucleophilic attack of phenolate ion on formaldehyde. In the second step, further consumption of formaldehyde by mono-methylolated phenols occurs to produce di and/or tri-methylolated phenols. Simultaneous nucleophilic displacement reactions between methylolated phenols with empty *ortho* and *para* positions also occur to form methylene-linked bisphenol intermediates. Involvement of an *ortho* or *para* quinone methide (**QM**) intermediate is also thought to be an alternate route to methylene-linked bisphenol. Unlike novolacs, resoles do not require hexa to make network polymers. The crosslinks are formed by reactions involving a large number of methylol groups, with the elimination of water

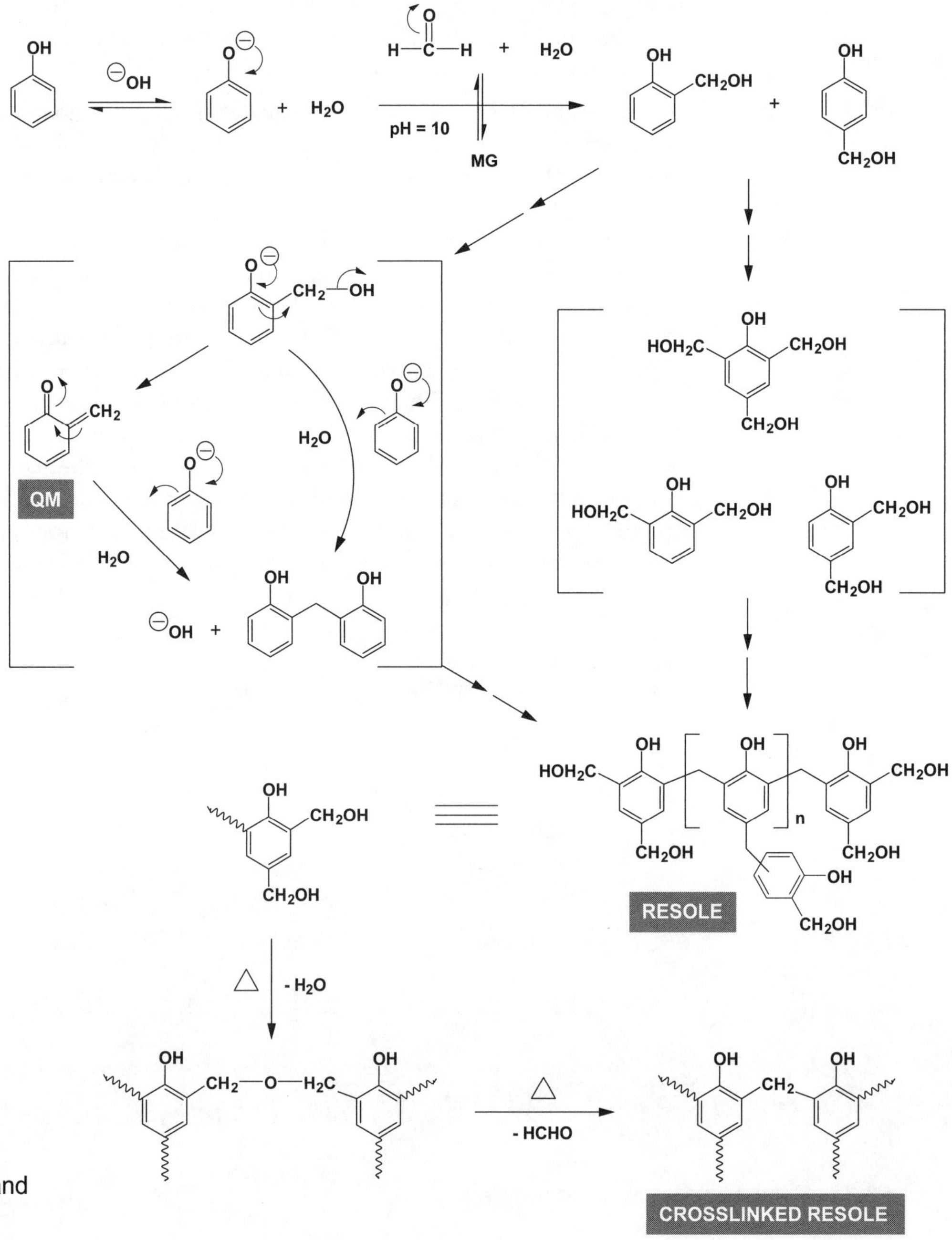

Figure 3.36. Synthesis and curing of resoles.

and formaldehyde as volatile products. Most formulations use a small proportion of amines, such as melamine, as a formaldehyde scavenger. Major applications of resoles include glass-reinforced electrical circuit board laminates, car brake linings (when filled with glass, metal powder, etc.), plywood adhesives, and appliance handles, knobs and bases.

3.9.4. Amine-Formaldehyde Polymers

Urea-formaldehyde (UF) and melamine-formaldehyde (MF) polymers are the two important members of this family. The former accounts for over 80% of total amine-formaldehyde polymer consumption because it is very cheap. Similar to the other thermosetting polymers, the preparation of amine-formaldehyde polymers involves two-steps: (1) addition reaction between formaldehyde and amine, usually at room temperature, to form a viscous syrup containing mixtures of methylolated amine species, and (2) condensation reactions of methylolated amine species by the application of heat and pressure in the presence of an acid catalyst, such as phosphoric acid, leading to a crosslinked polymer containing primarily ether and methylene bridges, along with a small amount of a cyclic ring between amine residues (Figure 3.37). Unfilled UF thermosets are transparent, but susceptible to hydrolysis, hence not suitable for applications involving higher relative humidity or increased moisture resistance. By contrast, MF thermosets exhibit outstanding stability against hydrolysis, extreme hardness, excellent colorability and arc-resistant characteristics, but they are more expensive than UF. Most UF polymers are melamine-fortified (10 - 30 mol%) to obtain balanced properties. Moreover, MF thermosets have much higher crosslink density (only ether and methylene bridges and no cyclic ring between melamine residues) compared to UF thermosets, because of the presence of one additional amino group on melamine as well as higher reactivity of melamine amino groups towards formaldehyde. Molding powders of these polymers are also available for compression and transfer molding products and are made by homogeneous mixing of fillers (e.g., wood flour and silica) with the uncured syrup. Major applications of UF polymers involve adhesives or binders for wooden materials (e.g., plywood and particle board) and expanded thermosets, while MF polymers find extensive use in laminates and chemically resistant coatings, parquet flooring, and rigid electrical and decorative products, including popular colorful, rugged dinnerware.

Urea

(Major)

(Major)

(Minor)

UF THERMOSET

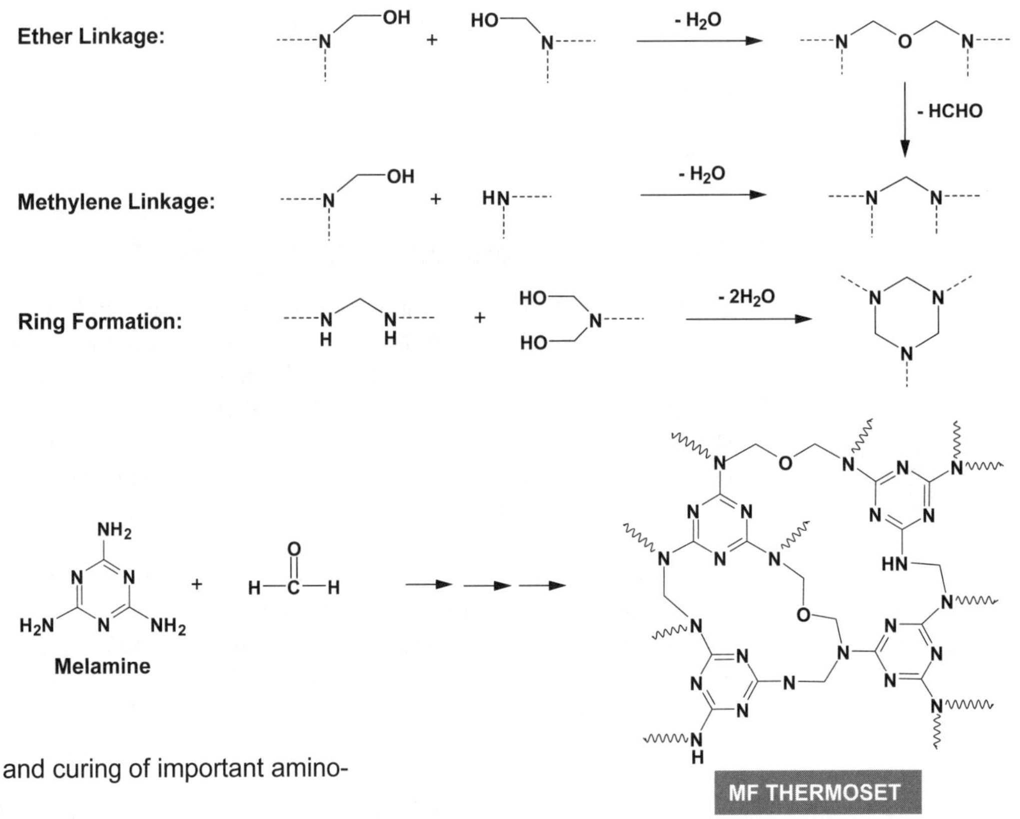

Ether Linkage:

Methylene Linkage:

Ring Formation:

Melamine

MF THERMOSET

Figure 3.37. Synthesis and curing of important amino-formaldehyde polymers.

3.9.5. Specialty Thermosetting Polymers

In addition to the aforementioned materials, a few other classes of thermosetting polymers, viz., dicyanates and bismaleimides, have been developed specifically for selected applications. The synthesis of representative members and their crosslinking chemistry are depicted in Figure 3.38. Dicyanates, often called polycyanurates for the cured structure that they produce, are prepared by reacting cyanogen bromide with a diphenol compound, such as 4,4'-(1,3-phenylenediisopropylidene)bisphenol (PDB).[38] The curing of dicyanates is accomplished by cyclotrimerization of nitrile groups without formation of volatiles in the presence of a metal coordination catalyst, such as copper acetylacetonate, $Cu(Acac)_2$ to form a network structure containing triazine or cyanurate rings. The cured product exhibits high T_g (~250°C), and outstanding mechanical and electrical properties (low dielectric constant and loss factor), coupled with low moisture absorption, which is especially required for composite circuit boards in aircraft and satellites. Similar to dicyanates, bismaleimides do not produce any volatiles during curing. These compounds are prepared by reaction of maleic anhydride with a diamine. Bismaleimides can be tailored with a range of properties by using an appropriate aliphatic or aromatic amine. They can be cured via several chemical pathways, e.g., free-radical, Michael addition and Diels-Alder cycloaddition reactions. However, for high performance composites, aromatic bismaleimides, such as 4,4'-bismaleimidodiphenylmethane (BMI) and a peroxide initiator are used. Bismaleimides have made a significant impact in fast cure (within seconds) die-attach adhesives for semiconductor chips which are readily attached to substrates, thus facilitating a high rate of production. They are also used in high-performance fiber-reinforced composites and thermal resistant coatings.

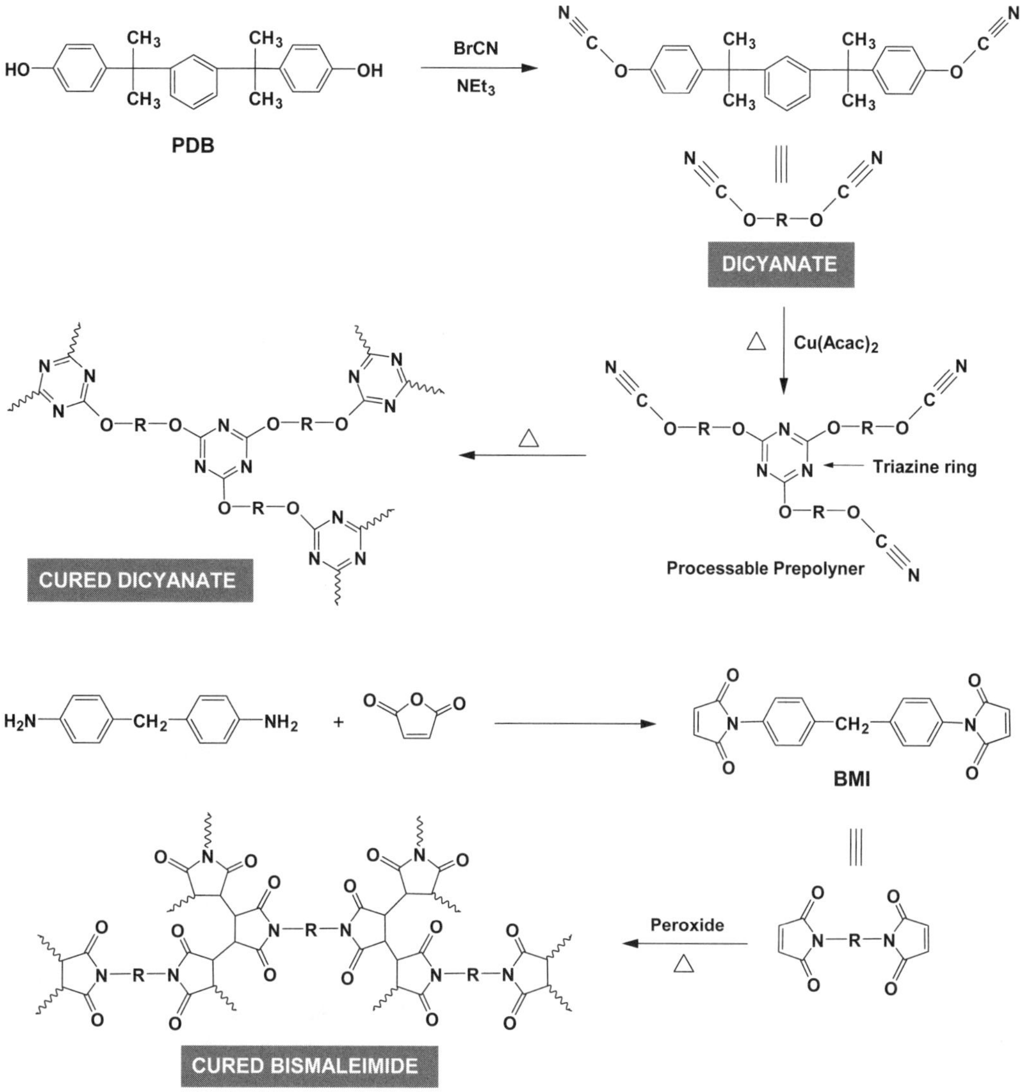

Figure 3.38. Synthesis and curing of dicyanates and bismaleimides.

3.10. SPECIALTY ENGINEERING POLYMERS

In addition to the aforementioned major polymers, there are several other useful polymers, which are produced in lesser amounts, as described below:

3.10.1. Poly(N-methyl methacrylimide) (PMMI)

PMMI, Pleximid® (Röhm, Germany), also known as poly(N-methylglutarimide), a thermoplastic molding compound, is a modified PMMA and obtained by aminolysis of PMMA with methylamine in an extruder (Figure 3.39). The introduction of cyclic imide units in the PMMA backbone offers a series with outstanding properties, such as high modulus of elasticity, low tendency to creep and expand thermally, together with high chemical resistance, particularly toward alcohols. It also exhibits unsurpassed rigidity for an amorphous, non-reinforced thermoplastic, superior resistance to high temperatures and UV light, as well as transparency and excellent weather resistance.

PMMI also meets the stringent requirements regarding heat deflection temperature under load (150 - 170°C for PMMI depending on imidation vs. 109°C for PMMA), optical transparency (90% for PMMI vs. 93% for PMMA) and weather resistance that apply to the auto and lighting industries, such as road and signal lights, ship navigation lights, and car head/tail-lamp lenses.

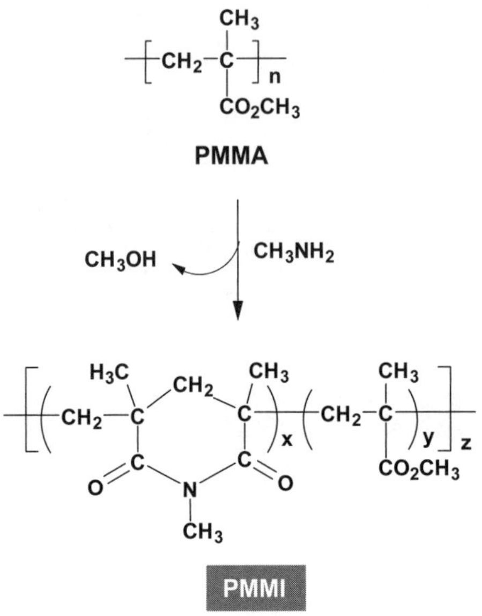

Figure 3.39. Synthesis of PMMI.

3.10.2. Poly(4-methyl-1-pentene) (PMP)

Commercial grades of PMP, (e.g., TPX®, Mitsui Chemical), are stereoregular copolymers (head-to-tail isotactic sequences), which are produced by Ziegler-Natta polymerization of 4-methyl-1-pentene in the presence of 3-5 mol% of 1-hexene or higher linear α-olefin to improve mechanical and processing properties and to prevent haze formation. The commonly used catalyst system is $TiCl_4$-$Al(C_2H_5)_3$ in $MgCl_2$ support, the same catalyst employed for the manufacture of iPP.

Isotactic PMP crystals consist of polymer chains in the helix conformation, accounting for seven monomer units per two helix turns. Despite being a semi-crystalline (~60% crystalline domains) polymer, PMP exhibits very high optical transparency (90-92%) and the lowest density of all thermoplastics (0.84 g/cm^3). It is transparent because, unlike other polyolefins, its crystalline and amorphous phases have the same index of refraction. The primary reason for low density is a very loose space packing of the polymer helix. This means that it compares well with acrylics (transparency = 90-92%) and polystyrene (88-92%) for optical use, but has only 70% of their density. Among all transparent thermoplastics, PMP has the best resistance to distortion at high temperature and superior impact strength (2-3 times better than polystyrene and acrylics). PMP withstands repeated molding, even at 150°C, including an intermittent exposure to temperatures as high as 175°C (soft soldering temperature). It has a melting temperature (T_m) of 245°C and a glass transition (T_g) of 50°C. The dielectric constant of PMP is the lowest among all synthetic polymers reported in the literature (2.12 at 25°C and 10^2-10^4 Hz), including a low dielectric loss angle (dissipation factor at 10 MHz = 1.5 x 10^{-4}), surpassing those of other polyolefins and polyfluoroolefins. Its mechanical properties are comparable to other polyolefins at room temperature, whereas its thermal properties closely resemble those of typical engineering plastics, such as nylon and polycarbonate.

The applications of PMP are founded on its high optical transparency, superior dielectric properties, low bulk density, high thermal stability, and chemical resistance. Moreover, PMP is an inert, nontoxic material and compliant with FDA regulations and the health standards of other countries. Consequently, the major portion of PMP production (>40%) goes for the manufacture of medical equipment, such as hypodermic syringes, blood collection and transfusion equipment. Other important applications include light covers, chemical laboratory ware, high-frequency electrical insulation, and radar components.

Although heterogeneous Ziegler-Natta catalysts are now used for the manufacture of PMP, a number of effective homogeneous systems (e.g., metallocenes) have been developed to obtain products with high stereoregularity and low polydispersity index. For example, the *rac*-$Me_2Si(2\text{-}MeBenz[e]Ind)_2ZrCl_2$ produces isotactic PMP with a polydispersity index of 2.1 and a high stereoregularity, [*mmmm*] = 94.1%. As shown in Figure 3.40, the intermediate steps in the synthesis of the metallocene involve a mixture of products, but the desired product is obtained as a pure microcrystalline insoluble material, allowing effective separation from other isomers in the last step.[39,40] The metallocene is also very active in terms of productivity [5,200 Kg/(mol of metal)(mole of monomer)h] and chain length (M_w = 168,000).

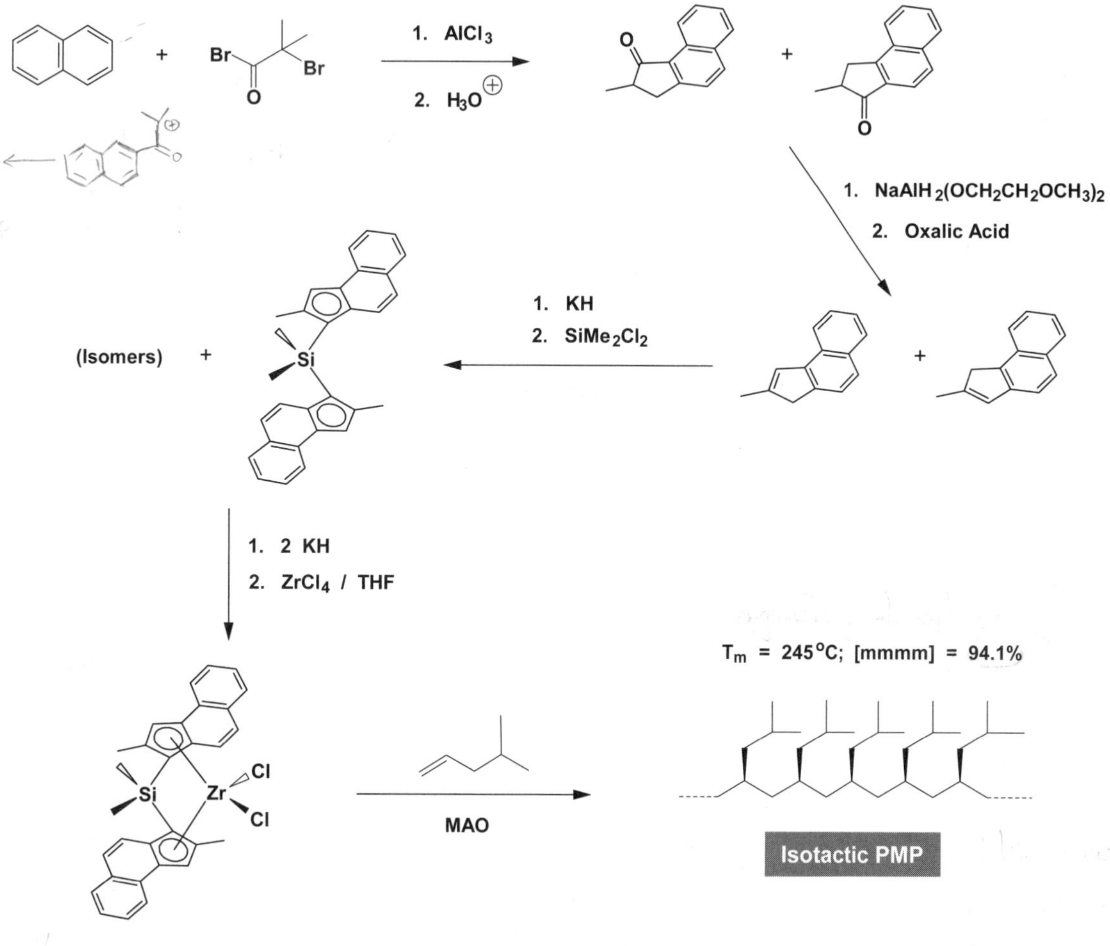

1. $AlCl_3$
2. $H_3O^{\oplus}$

1. $NaAlH_2(OCH_2CH_2OCH_3)_2$
2. Oxalic Acid

1. KH
2. $SiMe_2Cl_2$

(Isomers) + Si

1. 2 KH
2. $ZrCl_4$ / THF

Si Zr Cl Cl

MAO

T_m = 245°C; [mmmm] = 94.1%

Isotactic PMP

Figure 3.40. Synthetic route to a zirconocene complex for obtaining isotactic PMP.

Recently, a new sterically expanded zirconium fluorenyl-amido complex has been prepared to produce syndiotactic PMP (Figure 3.41).[41] The steric environment of the metal center in this complex is unique, which permits a monomer incorporation ability far superior to those obtained from the best titanium-based systems, such as Dow Insite® CGC. The catalyst synthesis is facile and scalable, while the starting materials are accessible and inexpensive, making it an ideal candidate for commercial utilization.

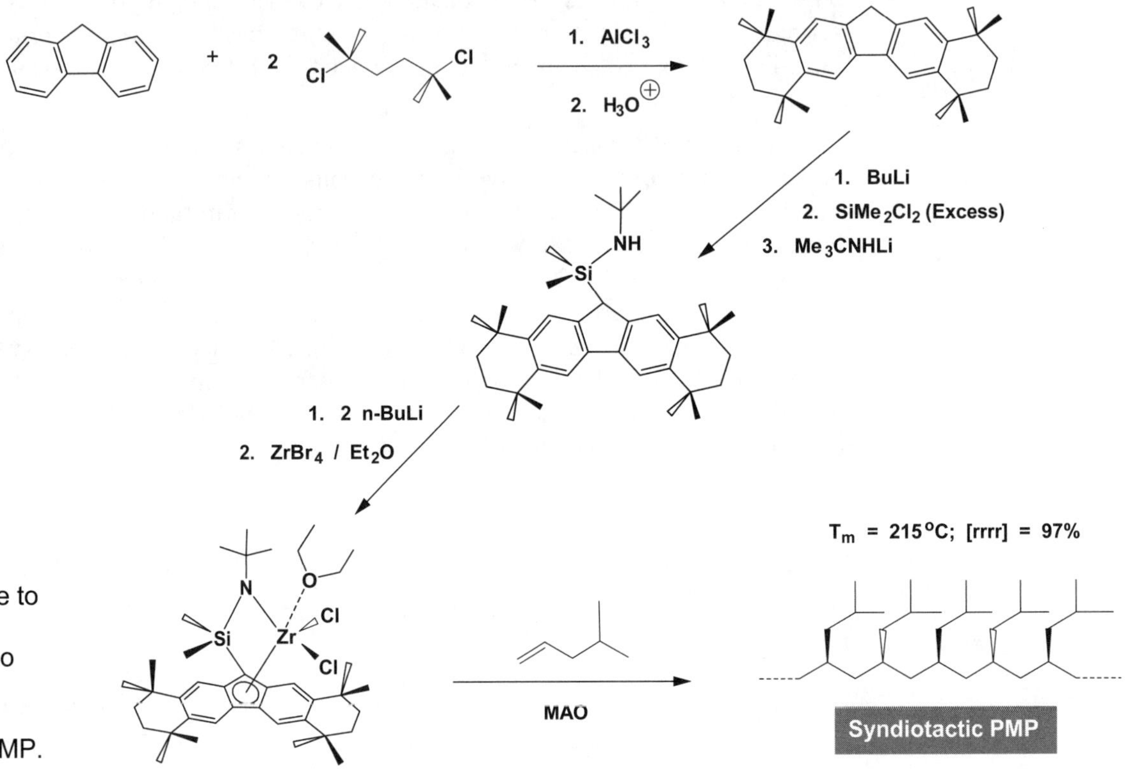

1. $AlCl_3$
2. $H_3O^{\oplus}$

1. BuLi
2. $SiMe_2Cl_2$ (Excess)
3. Me_3CNHLi

1. 2 n-BuLi
2. $ZrBr_4$ / Et_2O

MAO

T_m = 215°C; [rrrr] = 97%

Syndiotactic PMP

Figure 3.41. Synthetic route to a zirconium fluorenyl-amido complex for obtaining syndiotactic PMP.

3.10.3. Poly(ethylene 2,6-naphthalate) (PEN)

This is a semi-crystalline high-end engineering thermoplastic, known for over 50 years. Major production did not occur until the early 1990s when the raw material, dimethyl-2,6-naphthalenedicarboxylate (NDC) became readily available on a larger scale and in high purity at an affordable price (Figure 3.42). The incorporation of a naphthalene ring (double ring structure) in the main chain provides greater rigidity to the polymer backbone than does the benzene ring in PET, which leads to (i) improved thermal properties (low thermal shrinkage, 0.6% vs. 1.3% for PET; continuous use temperature, 150°C vs. 100°C; T_g = 125°C vs. 80°C and T_m = 270°C vs. 250°C), (ii) enhanced mechanical properties, such as tensile modulus and creep resistance, and (iii) superior barrier performance toward oxygen, carbon dioxide and water vapor (at least three times better than PET!). The versatile properties of PEN offer a broad range of applications, such as magnetic tape, medical parts requiring steam sterilization, hot food containers and high performance industrial fibers (superior to both nylon-6,6, and PET), as well as reinforcement cord for tires and automotive belts. Similar to PET, PEN is manufactured by melt-phase polycondensation of NDC and ethylene glycol in the presence of an effective ester-exchange catalyst, such as zinc acetate, but the challenge for the PEN process is greater because of higher T_m and melt viscosity values.

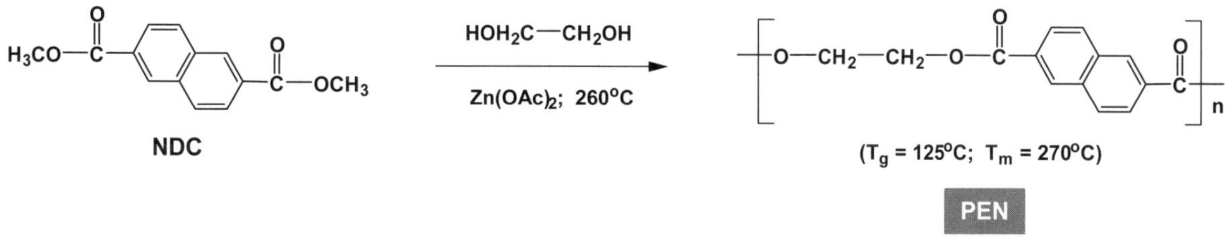

Figure 3.42. Commercial synthesis of PEN.

Similar to poly(butylene terephthalate) (PBT, Figure 2.70), PEN and poly(butylene 2,6-naphthalate) (PBN) have also been synthesized on a laboratory scale via ring-opening polymerization of cyclic oligomers, with the advantage that PEN or PBN can be prepared from low-viscosity precursors under solvent-free conditions (Figure 3.43).[42] Cyclic oligomers primarily consisting of a trimer of PEN and dimer of PBN, are prepared by reaction of 2,6-naphthalenedicarbonyl dichloride with the corresponding diol in the presence of a base, diazabicyclo[2.2.2]octane (DABCO). Ring-opening polymerization of cyclic material is performed in the melt using 1 mol% titanium isopropoxide catalyst. The molecular weights of PEN and PBN obtained by this method are usually lower than those of commercial samples.

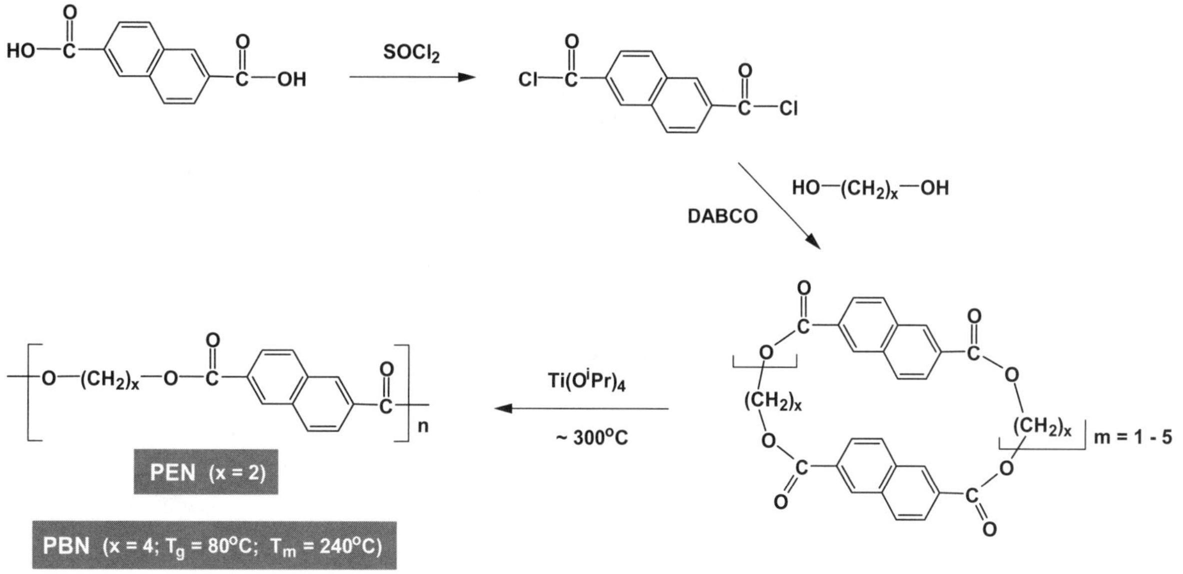

Figure 3.43. Synthesis of PEN by ring-opening polymerization.

3.10.4. Poly(*p*-xylylene)s

The most prominent member of this family is poly(*p*-xylylene) (PPX), known in the industry as "Parylenes", which possess similarities with polystyrene (PS) in that they have the same molecular formula of their repeat units. Amazingly, their properties and methods of polymerization show quite a contrast. While PS is highly amorphous, PPX has an appealing combination of high degree of crystallinity, high thermal stability (T_m ~400°C), good mechanical properties, excellent solvent resistance, low dielectric permittivity, and outstanding barrier properties. Compared with PS, PPX is preferentially prepared by chemical vapor deposition (CVD) or a vapor coating process, better known as the Gorham-method,[43-45] a room temperature process that requires no catalyst, solvent, or initiator. The method involves vapor phase vacuum pyrolysis of [2.2]paracyclophane, PCP, (at temperatures above 550°C and at pressures of less than 1 Torr) to quantitatively cleave into two monomer (1,4-quinodimethane, QDM, or *para*-xylylene) units. These species are adsorbed onto a substrate surface at room temperature and spontaneously polymerize, yielding linear high-molecular-weight (2,000 – 3,000 repeat units) transparent pinhole-free thin films (1 – 100 nm depending on process conditions) (Figure 3.44). Thus, PPX conformal coatings are useful in a range of applications, such as packaging of electronic components (e.g., circuit boards, semiconductors and hybrid circuits, including insulating layers in integrated circuits and thin-film transistors), medical device fabrication (metal part of implant devices), and artifact conservation.

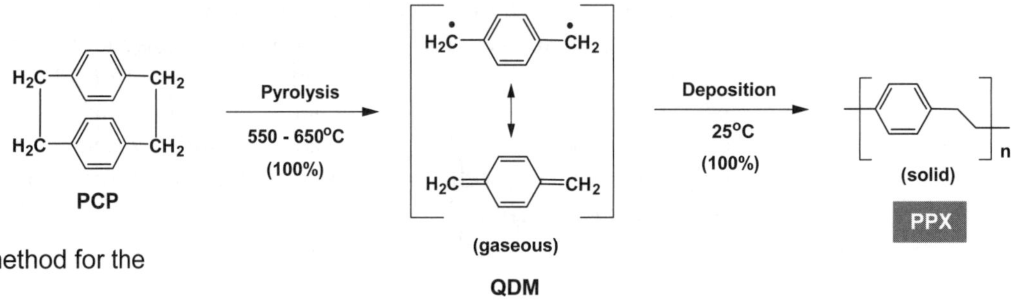

Figure 3.44. Gorham method for the preparation of PPX.

A variety of PPX analogs have been synthesized starting with either functional group substituted PCP derivatives[46] or by surface modification of PPX films[47,48] to obtain distinct chemical and optical properties. Among these, Parylene-HT, poly(α,α,α',α'-tetrafluoro-*p*-xylylene), has received most attention because of recent new scalable methods for the synthesis in high yields of the CVD precursor, 1,1,2,2,9,9,10,10-octafluoro[2.2]paracyclophane, the bridge-fluorinated version of PCP (industrially known as **AF4**) (Figure 3.45). Both reductive dimerization of *p*-bis(chlorodifluoromethyl)benzene in the presence of zinc dust and Mg(0)-promoted defluorinative silylation of commercially available 1,4-bis-(trifluoromethyl)benzene followed by CsF-catalyzed 1,6-elimination, produce AF4 in yields of ~60%.[49-51] Parylene-HT exhibits a low dielectric constant (2.25 vs. 2.65 for PPX), high thermal and oxidative stability (< 1 wt.% loss at 450°C in air), low moisture absorption (< 0.1%), and chemical inertness due to the presence of very stable C-F bonds.

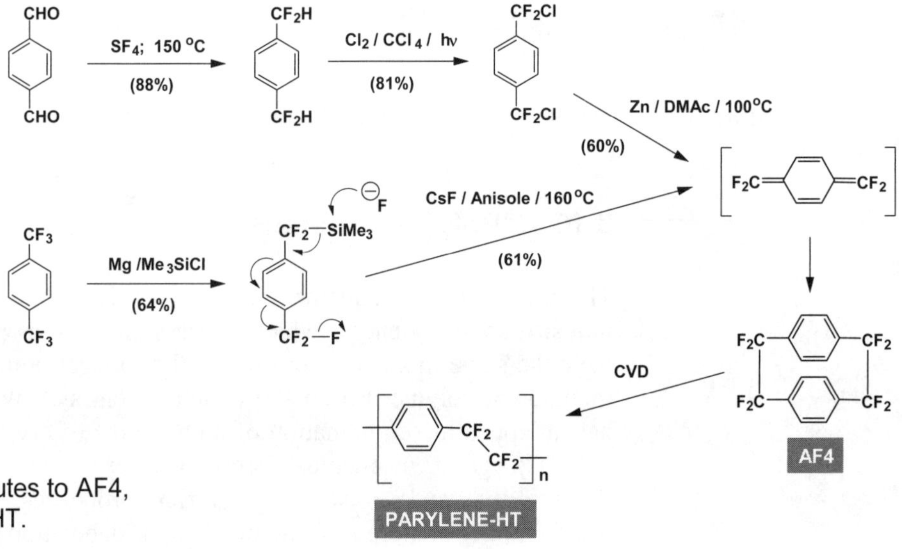

Figure 3.45. Efficient synthetic routes to AF4, precursor compound to Parylene-HT.

PPX derivatives have also been synthesized by solution methods. As an example, the generation of 1,4-quinodimethanes in dioxane by base-induced dehydrohalogenation of 4-halogenomethyltoluenes, better known as the Gilch-method[52,53], is especially suitable for nonvolatile or temperature-sensitive starting materials (Figure 3.46). The reaction mechanism favors a radical 1,6 polymerization via corresponding 1,4-quinodimethanes originating from 4-halogenomethyltoluenes. Organosoluble polymers

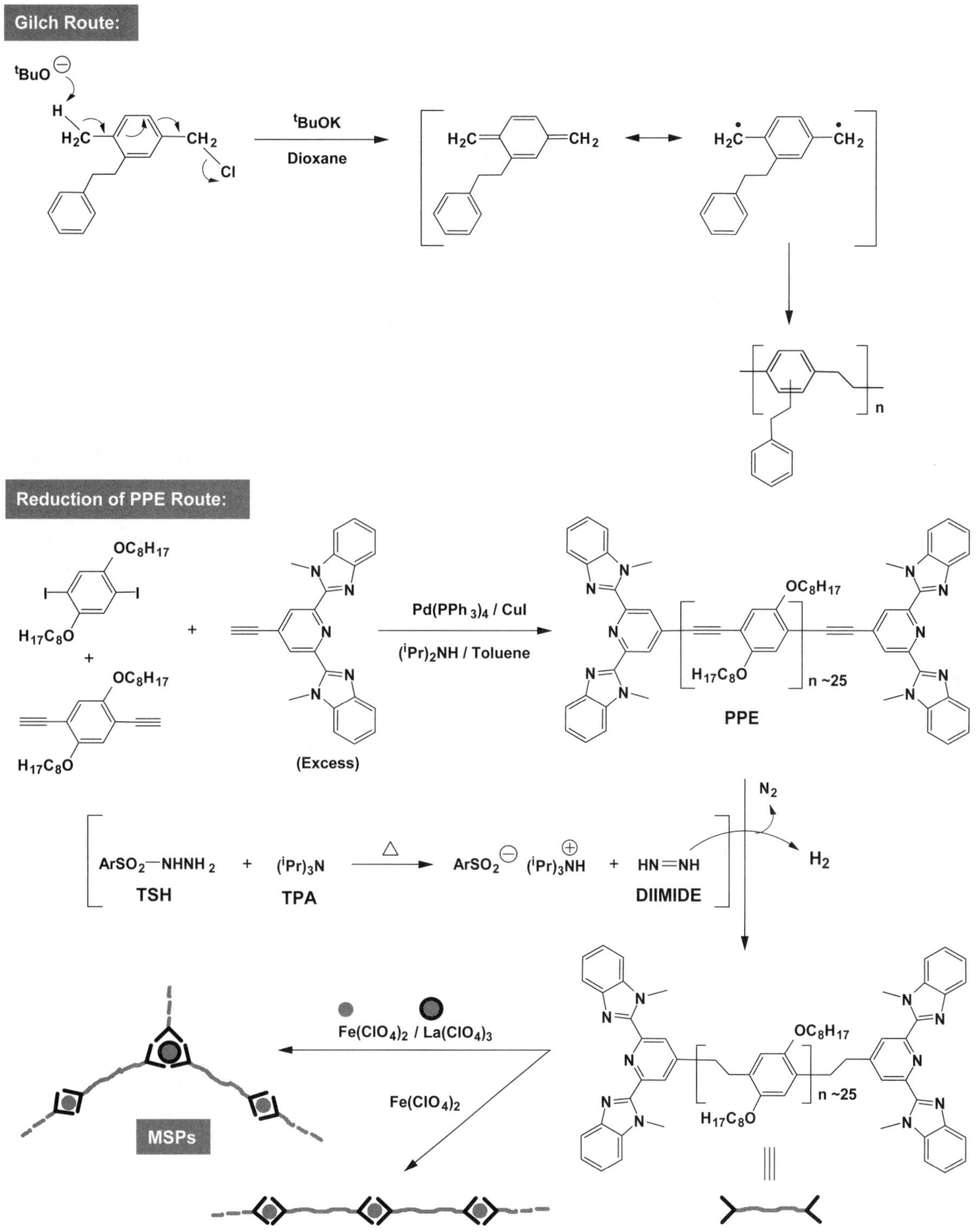

Gilch Route:

$^tBuO^{\ominus}$ H H_2C CH_2 Cl ^tBuOK Dioxane H_2C CH_2 $H_2\dot{C}$ $\dot{C}H_2$ n

Reduction of PPE Route:

OC_8H_{17} I I $H_{17}C_8O$ + + OC_8H_{17} $H_{17}C_8O$ N N N N N (Excess) $Pd(PPh_3)_4$ / CuI $(^iPr)_2NH$ / Toluene OC_8H_{17} $H_{17}C_8O$ n ~25 PPE

$ArSO_2$—$NHNH_2$ + $(^iPr)_3N$ △ $ArSO_2^{\ominus}$ $(^iPr)_3NH^{\oplus}$ + HN=NH TSH TPA DIIMIDE N_2 H_2

$Fe(ClO_4)_2$ / $La(ClO_4)_3$ $Fe(ClO_4)_2$ MSPs OC_8H_{17} $H_{17}C_8O$ n ~25

Figure 3.46. Alternate methods for the synthesis of PPX derivatives.

with high molecular weights can be obtained by this method using a bulky group substituted 4-halogenomethyltoluene. Relatively low molecular weight PPX derivatives can also be prepared by either diimide reduction[54,55] or by high temperature catalytic hydrogenation[56,57] of conjugated poly(*p*-phenylene ethynylene) (PPE) derivatives (see Chapter-5 for the synthesis of monomers). Since diimide reduction involves mild conditions, reaction of PPE with *p*-toluenesulfonhydrazide (TSH) and triisopropylamine (TPA) in hot toluene provides an opportunity to prepare PPX derivatives with temperature-sensitive moieties. As shown in Figure 3.46, this strategy can be used to prepare PPX-based ditopic ligands, which are suitable for novel processable, thermostable *metallo-supramolecular polymers* (MSPs).[58,59]

3.11. RECENT ADVANCES IN ENGINEERING POLYMERS

Synthesis of new monomers, development of novel polymerization techniques, and/or design of superior catalyst systems have been the primary goals of polymer synthesis laboratories in both academic laboratories and industry. In the past decade, several significant advances have resulted on various fronts of polymer chemistry. This section highlights some examples with strong commercial potential.

3.11.1. New Comonomers for PET

Among the new comonomers developed for improvement of specific properties of PET, conformationally rigid 2,2,4,4-tetramethyl-1,3-cyclobutanediol [CBDO, ~50/50 cis/trans][60] and multi-ring fused dimethyl 2,6-anthracenedicarboxylate (MADC)[61-63] are important. CBDO, now commercially available, is conveniently prepared in high yield in two steps (Figure 3.47). First, pyrolysis of isobutyric acid or isobutyric anhydride produces a cyclic diketone, thought to form via dimerization of a dimethylketene intermediate. Second, catalytic hydrogenation of the diketone affords a mixture of cis/trans CBDO. The random copolyesters, CBDO-PETs, obtained by transesterification of dimethyl terephthalate (DMT) with the combination of CBDO and ethylene glycol or higher diol, exhibit attractive combinations of physical properties, including thermal stability, UV stability, clarity, low color, and higher T_g up to 170°C (T_g of PET = 80°C). The incorporation of rigid tetramethylcyclobutylene groups in the polymer backbone not only enhances the T_g, but also markedly improves (~10 folds higher than PET) impact resistance (similar to polycarbonate at ~40 mol% CBDO content).

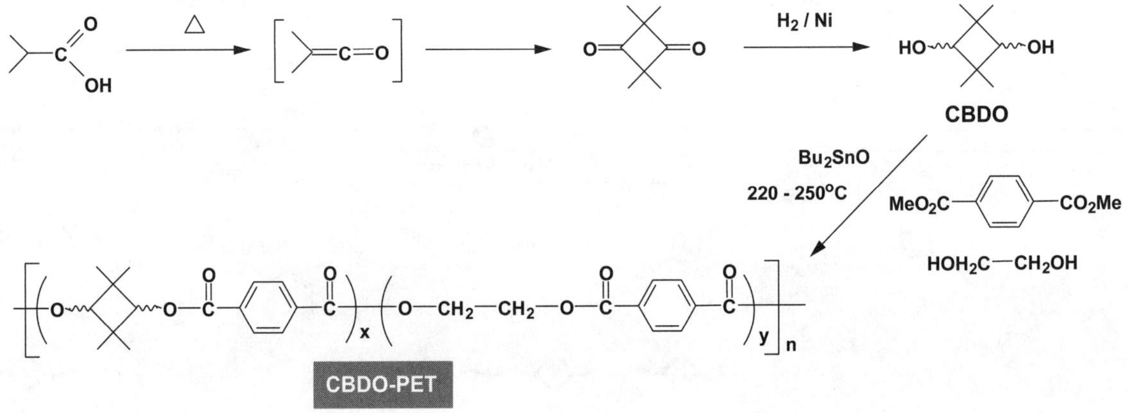

Figure 3.47. Synthesis of high impact, amorphous terephthalate copolyesters.

By contrast, introduction of a small proportion of an anthracenedicarboxylate unit into PET slightly increases the T_g, but decreases the T_m, an observation quite different from PEN where both T_g and T_m increase simultaneously. The increase in T_g is attributed to the rigid anthracene units in the main chain, while the decrease in T_m is due to a disruption of crystallinity by the anthracene units. However, the interesting feature of these random copolyesters, MADC-PETs, is that they can be crosslinked by either photochemical reaction (face-to-face dimerization through the 9- and 10-positions of the anthracene units) or by thermal-assisted Diels-Alder cycloaddition in the presence of bis-maleimide crosslinker.[61] The monomer, MADC, is not commercially available and has been prepared by multiple steps, as shown in Figure 3.48.

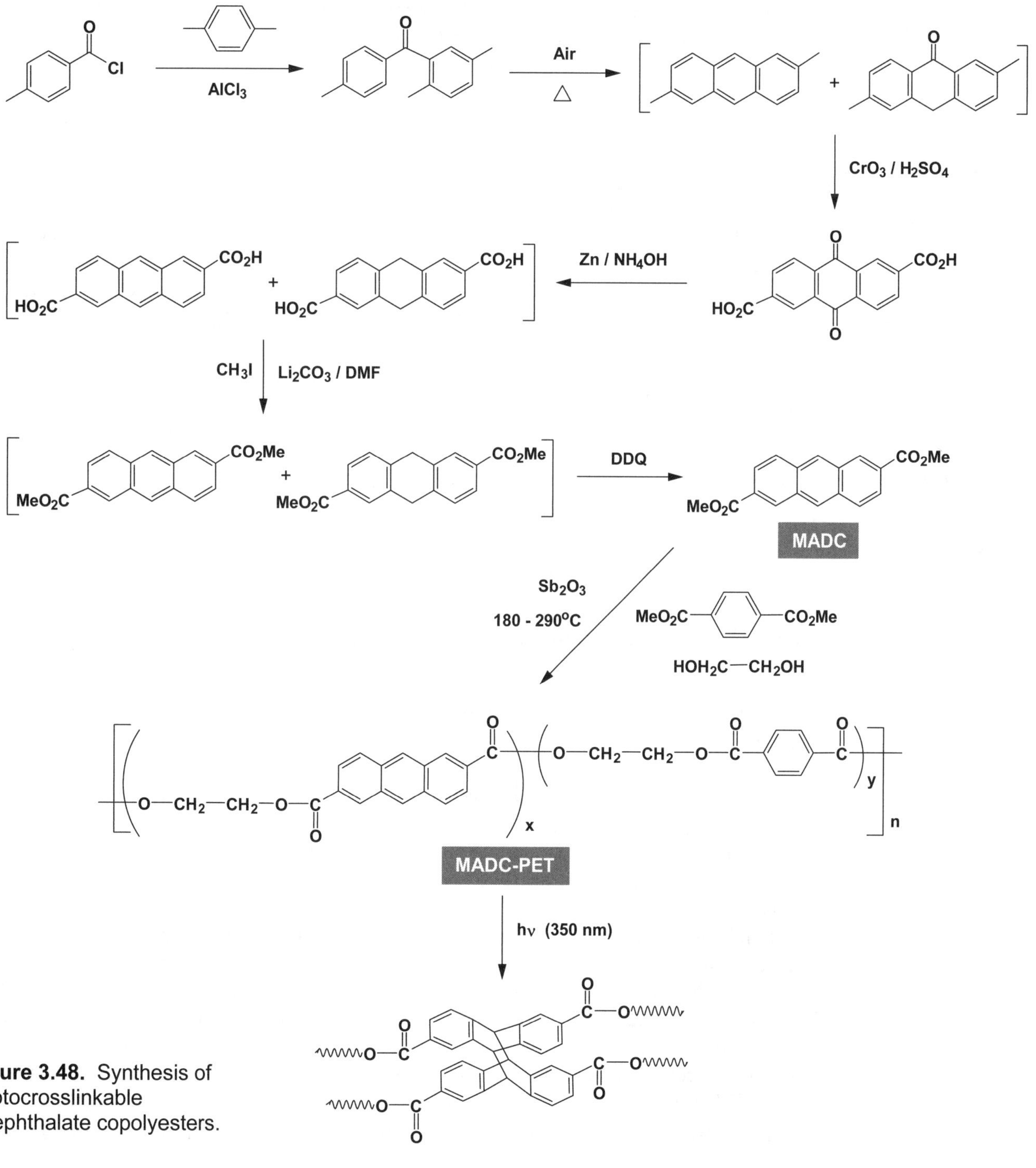

Cl
$AlCl_3$
Air
Δ
+
CrO_3 / H_2SO_4
CO_2H
HO_2C
CO_2H
HO_2C
Zn / NH_4OH
CH_3I
Li_2CO_3 / DMF
CO_2Me
MeO_2C
DDQ
MADC
Sb_2O_3
180 - 290°C
MeO_2C
CO_2Me
$HOH_2C—CH_2OH$
$O—CH_2—CH_2—O—C$
x
y
n
MADC-PET
hν (350 nm)

Figure 3.48. Synthesis of photocrosslinkable terephthalate copolyesters.

3.11.2. Semi-fluorinated Polyethers

Semi-fluorinated polyethers containing octafluorobiphenyl or perfluorocyclobutyl units are gaining increased interest because of their ease of synthesis coupled with low surface energy, thin-film forming, thermal and electrochemical properties. The former class of polymers are readily prepared by nucleophilic displacement of two *para* fluorine atoms of decafluorobiphenyl (DFBP) with an alkanediol or arenediol in the presence of a base (Figure 3.49).[64-70] Sodium hydride is an excellent base for alkanediol, while it produces only low molecular weight polymers for arenediol. The use of propylcarbamoyl-masked arenediol (from reaction of arenediol and propyl isocyanate) markedly improves the yield and molecular weight, even in the presence of a mild base, such as potassium carbonate. As expected, these polymers are highly thermostable (>400°C). The aromatic analogs are amorphous and especially suitable for the preparation of high temperature proton-exchange membranes for fuel cells.

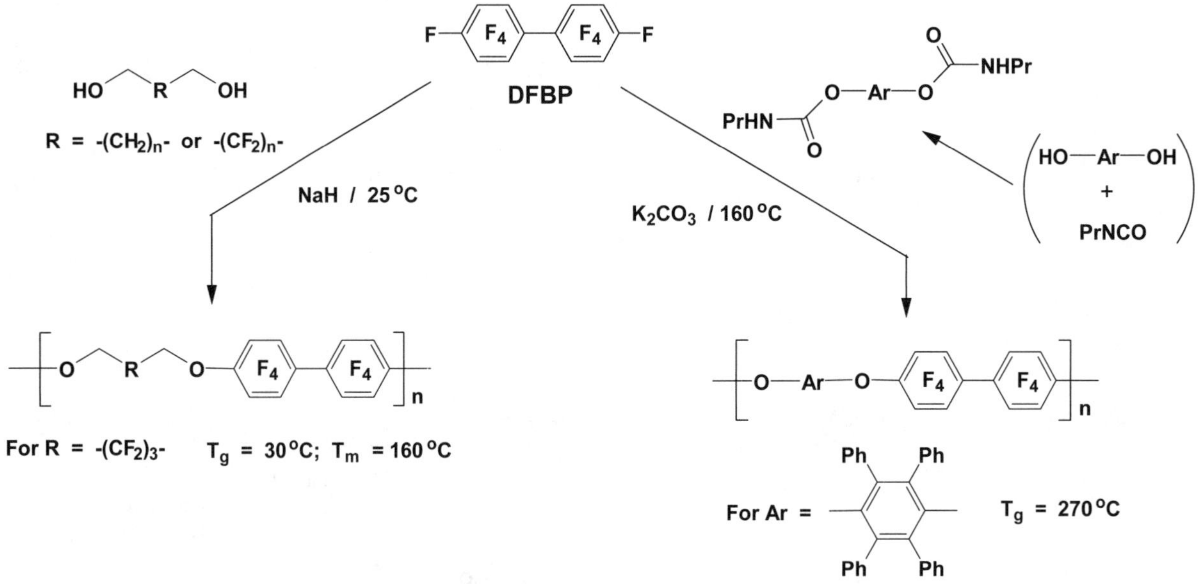

Figure 3.49. Synthesis of semi-fluorinated polyethers containing octafluorobiphenyl units.

The thermal [2π + 2π] cyclopolymerization of aromatic trifluorovinyl ether (TFVE) monomers offers a versatile route to a unique class of linear and network semi-fluorinated polymers containing the perfluorocyclobutyl (PFCB) linkage.[71-73] Polymerization of TFVE monomers proceeds by a thermal radical-mediated step-growth mechanism in which two TFVE groups undergo head-to-head cycloaddition to form the more stable di-radical intermediate, followed by rapid ring closure to give a mixture of *cis*- and *trans*-1,2-disubstituted PFCB units (Figure 3.50). Cyclodimerization is favored thermodynamically for fluoroolefins due to increased double-bond strain, a lower C=C π-bond energy, and the strength of the resulting fluorinated C-C single bond adducts, in contrast to most hydrocarbon analogs. The aromatic TFVE monomers are prepared by fluoroalkylation of phenol, followed by zinc-mediated elimination of the resulting bromo intermediate. The PFCB-containing polyethers, PFCB-PE, generally combine the thermomechanical properties of polyaryl ethers with fluorocarbon segments and exhibit excellent processability, optical transparency, high-temperature performance, low dielectric constants, and transparency at telecommunication wavelengths. Thus, depending on the choice of aromatic residue, the range of applications of PFCB-PE includes components for optical devices, thermostable coatings and composites. This includes the preparation of novel PFCB aromatic ether-based ABA triblock copolymer (A: polystyrene block; B: perfluorocyclobutyl aromatic ether-based fluoropolymer block) via a combination of atom transfer radical polymerization (ATRP) of styrene and thermal step-growth cycloaddition polymerization of TFVE monomer.[74,75]

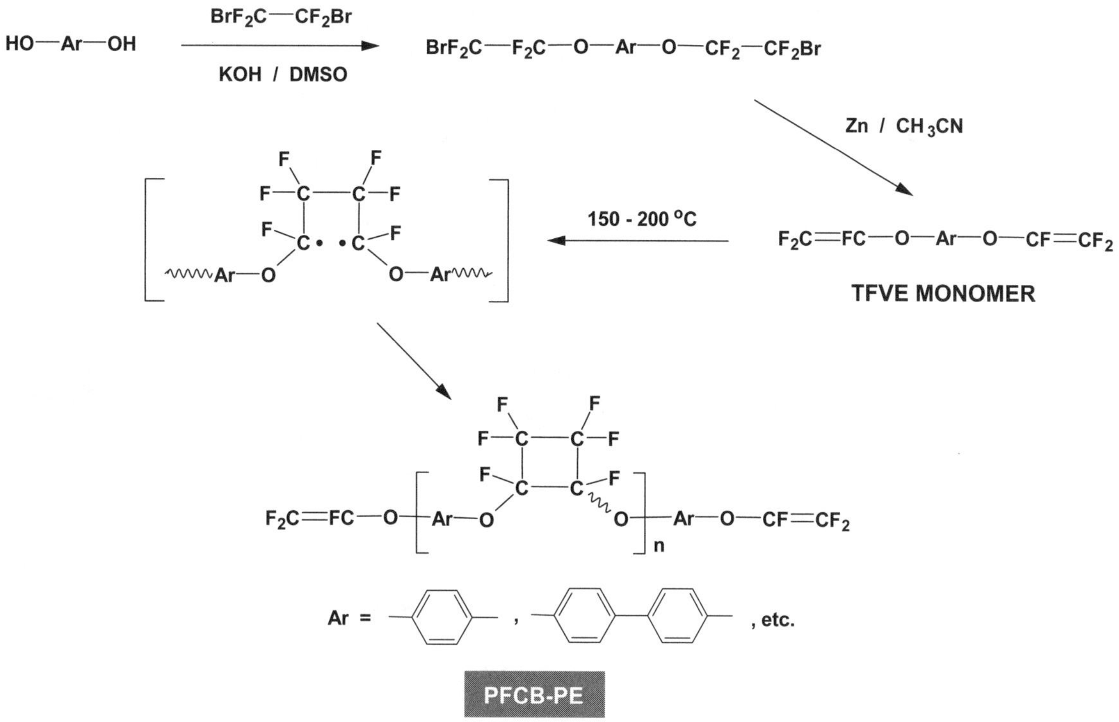

Figure 3.50. Synthesis of semi-fluorinated polyethers containing PFCB units.

3.11.3. Styrene-Carbon monoxide Copolymer

Since the regiochemistry (head/tail orientations) and stereochemistry (tacticity) of styrene insertion have a strong influence on the physical and mechanical properties of alternating styrene-carbon monoxide (SCO) copolymers, several highly active enantioselective catalysts have been developed. Polymer stereoregularity is usually tuned by the choice of ligand. Planar achiral precursors (C_{2V} or C_s symmetry) give highly syndiotactic polyketones, due to chainend control produced by the interaction of the growing chain with the incoming styrene comonomer, while C_2-symmetric chiral catalysts provide enantiomorphic site-controlled propagation to give isotactic microstructures.[76] As shown in Figure 3.51, the cationic bioxazoline Pd(II) complex, BOX-Pd(II), produces a highly isotactic optically active polymer, while an α-diimine Pd(II) complex, DIM-Pd(II), yields copolymer containing more than 92% syndiotactic microstructure. Both polymerization reactions can be conducted at room temperature and at low carbon monoxide pressure (1-4 atm).[77-79] A very recently developed cationic dendritic N,N'-iminopyridine Pd(II) complex, DIP-Pd(II), has also been found very suitable for the syndiospecific copolymerization of CO and 4-*tert*-butylstyrene.[76]

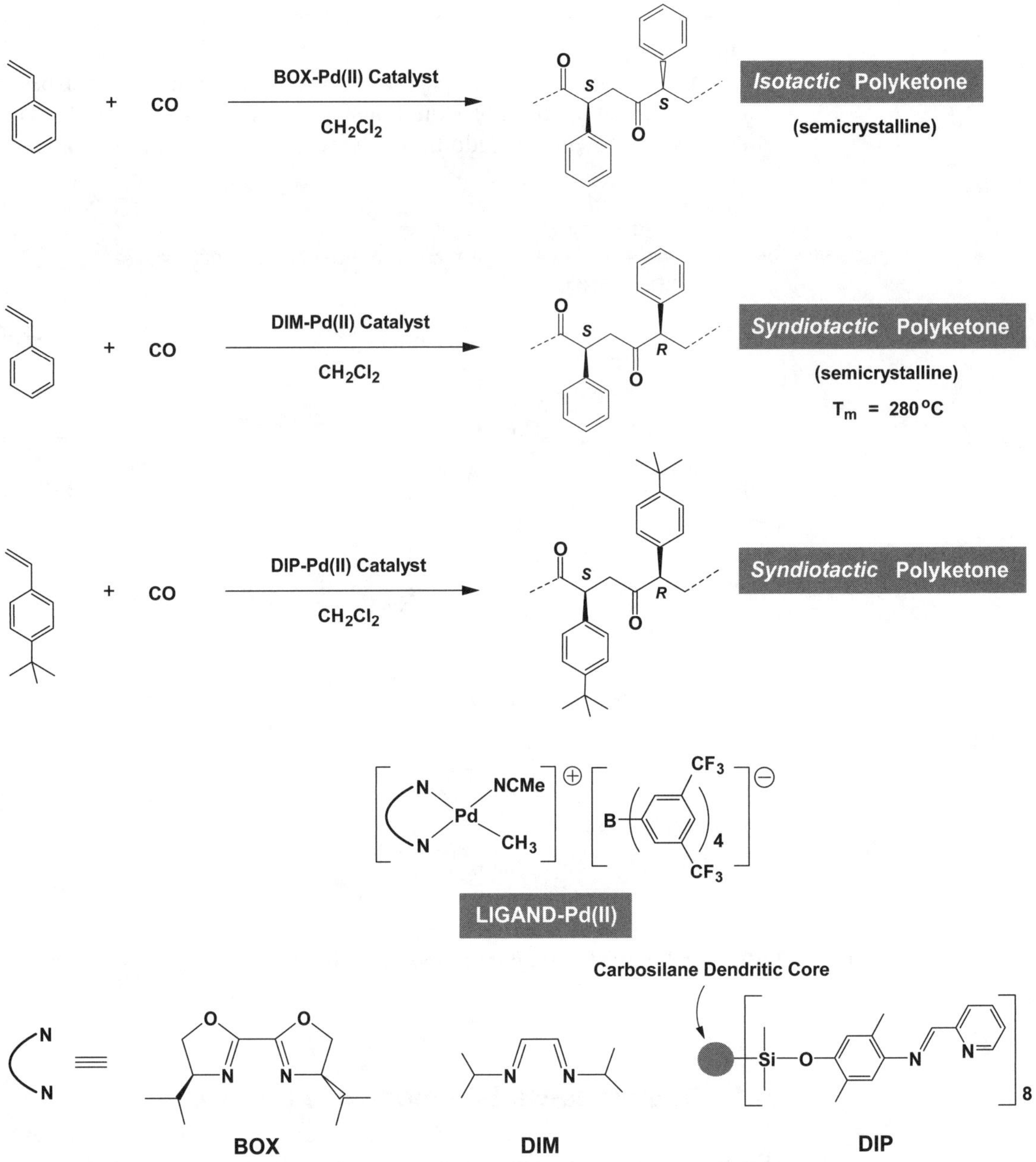

Figure 3.51. Catalyst systems for the synthesis of alternating stereoregular styrene-carbon monoxide copolymers.

3.11.4. Norbornene-Carbon monoxide Copolymer

Several attempts have been made to prepare the alternating norbornene-carbon monoxide (NCO) copolymer because, unlike the norbornene homopolymer (which is amorphous), the NCO copolymer is crystalline with a glass transition temperature of 160°C, which is very high for a polyketone (e.g., T_g of ECO = 15°C). Unfortunately, the cationic palladium(II) complexes used for ECO or EPCO are ineffective, owing to the formation of low molecular weight polymers. It has been observed recently that the activity of such complexes is markedly improved if the classical diphosphane chelate is replaced by arsene and sulfur donors (Figure 3.52). With weaker donor atoms in the chelate, the activity of the complex in norbornene homopolymerization is significantly lower than that of the corresponding phosphane complexes, thus providing potential for copolymerization of norbornene with carbon monoxide. Indeed, under the same reaction conditions used for ECO, NCO copolymer is obtained in good yield and found to have a high molecular weight (M_w = 14,200) relative to the oligomers obtained with phosphane ligands.

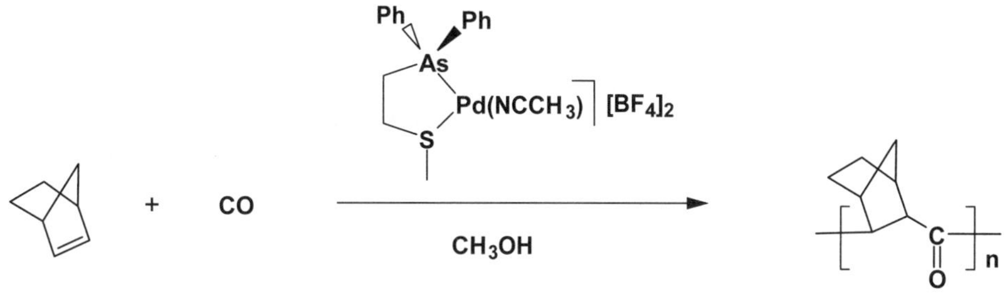

Figure 3.52. Catalyst for the synthesis of alternating norbornene-carbon monoxide copolymer.

Norbornadiene and its derivatives have also been investigated as comonomer for copolymerization with carbon monoxide. The best result was obtained with 7-tert-butoxynorborna-2,5-diene in the presence of a catalytic amount of $Rh_6(CO)_{16}$. The copolymerization does not occur in the absence of water and amine, indicating that copolymerization may be initiated by a [Rh]-H species generated from reaction of rhodium carbonyl with water and amine (Figure 3.53).[80] Under similar conditions, norbornene produces only low molecular weight products. This may imply that the unused double bond of norbornadiene may be involved in stabilizing the terminal [Rh] species of the growing polymer chains. The copolymer is soluble in a variety of organic solvents, such as acetone, chloroform, benzene, and THF, and possesses a molecular weight of 24,500 and a molecular weight distribution of $M_w/M_n \approx 1.38$.

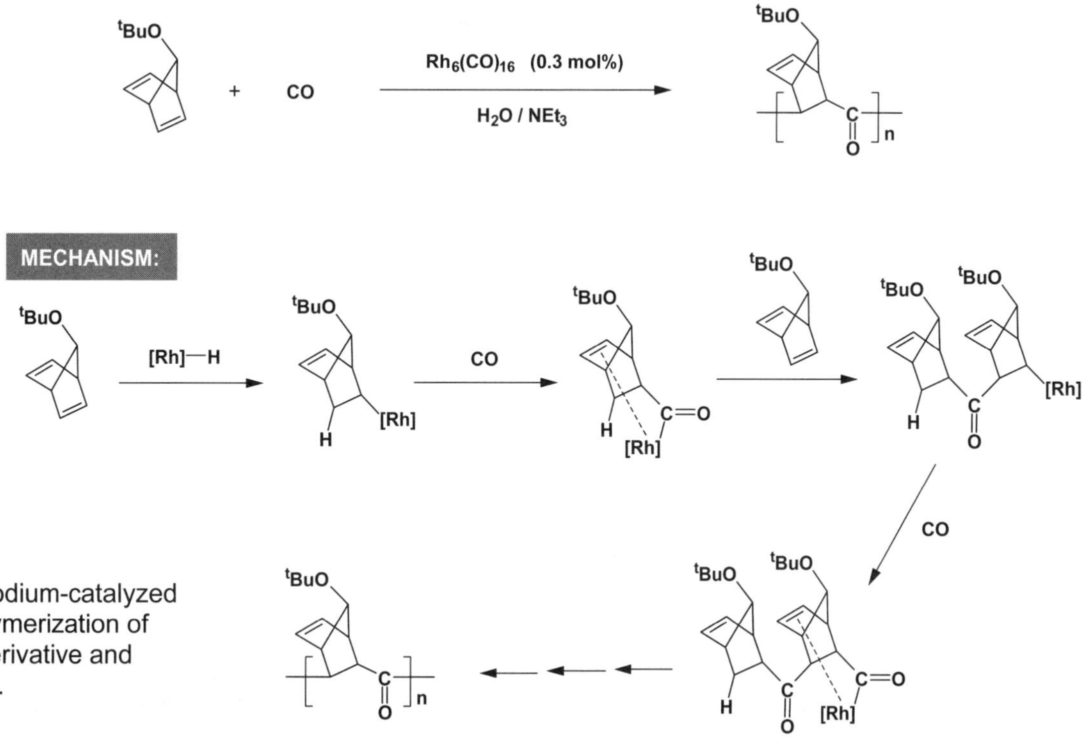

MECHANISM:

Figure 3.53. Rhodium-catalyzed alternating copolymerization of norbornadiene derivative and carbon monoxide.

3.11.5. Direct Synthesis of Polycarbonates

In the past decade, the introduction of aromatic polycarbonates, such as PC, via an environmentally benign route (i.e., without use of phosgene or its derivatives) has been the subject of intense research. As shown in Figure 3.54, the most effective catalyst system consists of the Pd-carbene complex, [1,1'-disubstituted-3,3'-methylenediimidazolin-2,2'-diylidene]palladium(II) dibromide, an inorganic redox co-catalyst (a cerium or manganese complex), an organic redox co-catalyst (hydroquinone), an organic onium salt (tributylphosphonium bromide), and a dehydrating agent (3Å molecular sieves).[81,82] This system produces close to industrially useful molecular weights (M_w = 24,000 and M_n = 9,400) and in reasonably high yields (~80%). At this time, the prospect of commercialization of this strategy is promising.

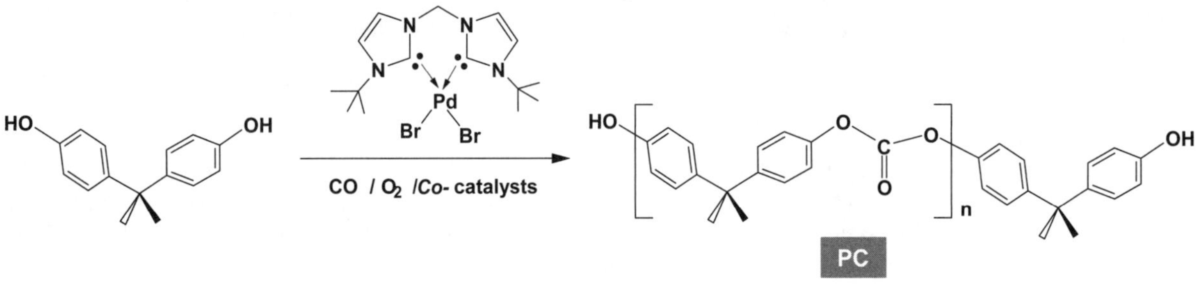

Figure 3.54. Synthesis of PC by oxidative carbonylation of BPA.

Recent advances in catalyst design have also permitted the synthesis of novel aliphatic carbonates by copolymerization of propylene oxide or ethylene oxide and carbon dioxide.[83] These polymers, i.e., poly(propylene carbonate) and poly(ethylene carbonate) are useful for several applications, such as binders for metals and ceramics, lost-foam casting (a machined foam pattern is dip-coated or sprayed with a thin ceramic film) and coatings. Among other epoxide monomers studied by this environmentally benign route, 1,2-cyclohexene oxide (CHO) and its derivatives are important (Figure 3.55).[84-87] The resulting polymers, e.g., poly(cyclohexyl carbonate) (PCHC), exhibit T_g near 115°C (about 35°C lower than that of traditional PC) and thermal stability in excess of 250°C.

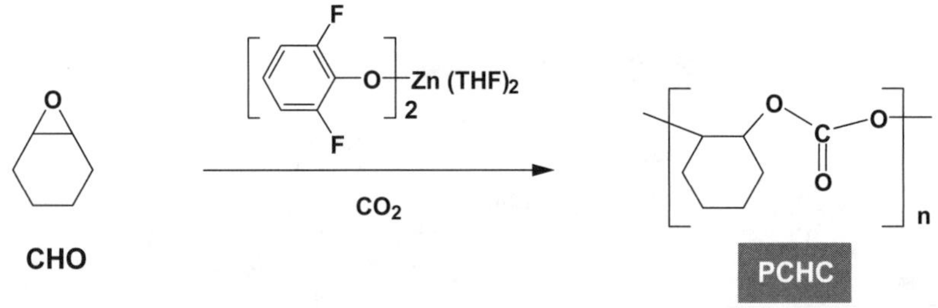

Figure 3.55. Synthesis of PCHC.

3.11.6. New Method to Polyamides

There are three conventional methods for the synthesis of polyamides. First, melt polymerization, which is used in industry for the production of nylons (aliphatic polyamides) with high molecular weights. However, this technique is not suitable for high molecular weight aromatic polyamides because of the low reactivity of aromatic amines compared with aliphatic amines, owing to the resonance effect of the aryl ring.

Second, polymerization of acids and amines in the presence of a stoichiometric amount of condensing agents, such as N,N'-dicyclohexylcarbodiimide (DCC). Third, low-temperature solution polymerization, where activated acyl derivatives, such as acid chlorides, react with amines to form polyamides. This approach is used exclusively for the preparation of aromatic polyamides, even though use of acid halides is environmentally undesirable. In a recent study, 3,4,5-trifluorophenylboronic acid (TBA) was shown to be a highly effective catalyst for the direct polycondensation of acids and amines in high boiling solvents, such as m-terphenyl and N-butyl-2-pyrrolidinone (NBP), leading to aramids, semi-aromatic nylons and nylons (see Chapter-5).[88] As shown in Figure 3.56, this methodology produces industrially useful molecular weights, except for nylons. The mechanism is believed to proceed via an active (acyloxy)boron complex, generated *in situ* by condensation of TBA with a carboxylic acid.

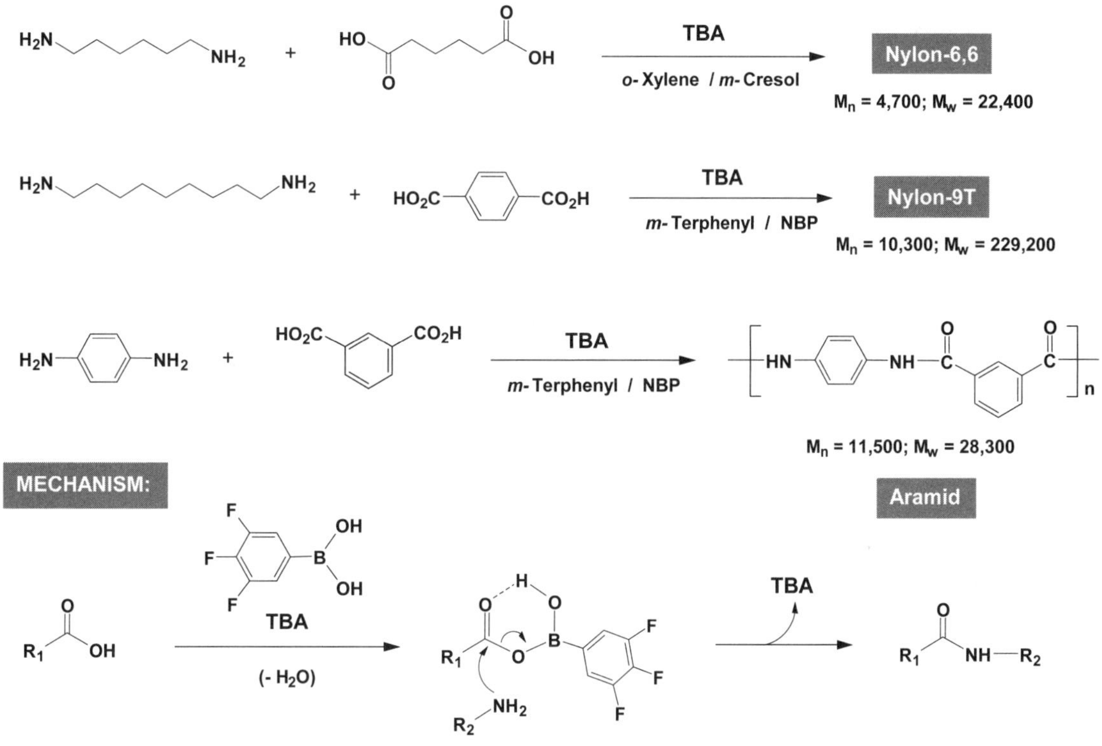

H_2N–(CH₂)₆–NH_2 + HO–C(=O)–(CH₂)₄–C(=O)–OH →(TBA; *o*-Xylene / *m*-Cresol) **Nylon-6,6**
M_n = 4,700; M_w = 22,400

H_2N–(CH₂)₉–NH_2 + HO_2C–C₆H₄–CO_2H →(TBA; *m*-Terphenyl / NBP) **Nylon-9T**
M_n = 10,300; M_w = 229,200

H_2N–C₆H₄–NH_2 + HO_2C–C₆H₄–CO_2H (meta) →(TBA; *m*-Terphenyl / NBP) [–HN–C₆H₄–NH–C(=O)–C₆H₄–C(=O)–]$_n$
M_n = 11,500; M_w = 28,300
Aramid

MECHANISM:

R_1–C(=O)–OH →(TBA; (- H_2O)) (acyloxy)boron complex of 3,4,5-trifluorophenylboronic acid + R_2–NH_2 → (– TBA) R_1–C(=O)–NH–R_2

Figure 3.56. Polyamides by direct polycondensation of an amine and an acid.

3.11.7. Polybenzoxazines

Polybenzoxazines may be considered as a spin-off member of the phenolics family because the monomers, benzoxazines, are also prepared from phenol and formaldehyde, but in conjunction with an aliphatic or aromatic amine (Figure 3.57).[89,90] Unlike phenolics, they have tremendous flexibility in molecular design for monomers and consequently, a versatile performance for polymers.[91] Moreover, the monomers can be polymerized to the corresponding polybenzoxazines in the absence of strong acid or basic catalysts and without producing by-products. In addition to the important advantages of phenolics, such as heat resistance, good electrical properties, and flame retardance, polybenzoxazines exhibit unique characteristics, such as low water absorption, relatively low dielectric constant, superior dimensional stability, and near-zero curing shrinkage, which overcome the shortcomings of most thermosets. A possible explanation for these unusual properties is the presence of extensive inter- and intramolecular hydrogen-bonds and Mannich-base linkages ($-CH_2-NR-CH_2-$, where R is an amine residue).[92,93] The mechanism of polymerization is thought to proceed via thermally induced opening of the $O-CH_2$ bond of the oxazine ring. The driving force is the relief of strain of the oxazine ring, which exists in a distorted semi-chair conformation with the nitrogen and the carbon between oxygen and nitrogen sitting, respectively, above and below the benzene ring plane.[94]

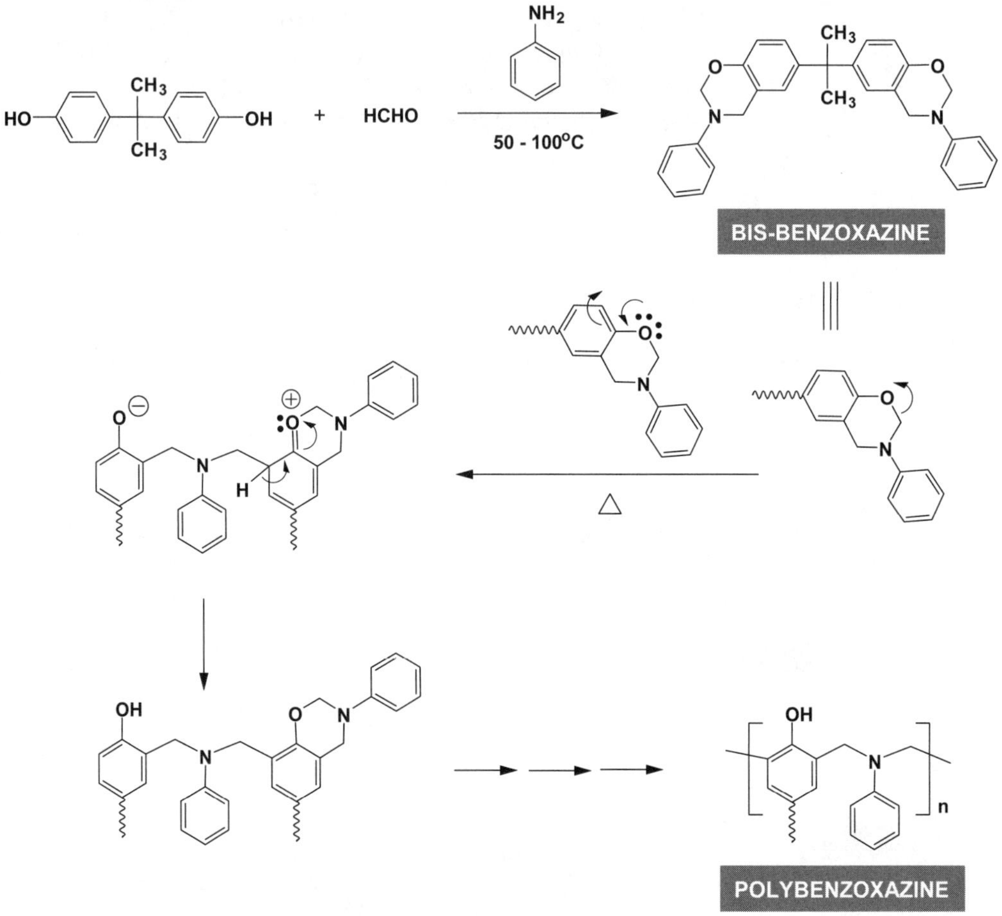

Figure 3.57. Synthesis and thermal crosslinking of a representative bis-benzoxazine.

A recent study demonstrated that bis-benzoxazine monomers containing arylpropargyl ether groups markedly improve thermal properties (e.g., enhancement of T_g by ca. 100 – 140°C and product decomposition temperature by ca. 20 – 40°C) without affecting the mechanical properties (Figure 3.58).[95,96] The enhanced thermal stability is attributed to the formation of additional crosslinks via intramolecular Claisen-type rearrangement, without the evolution of any volatiles. Currently, polybenzoxazines are not substituted for phenolics. However, the very promising developments of the past few years point to increasing use of polybenzoxazines, including new applications that are not achievable with phenolics. For example, the benzoxazine monomer, prepared from bisphenol-A, aniline, and formaldehyde, has been formulated with a polyamine crosslinker to give a composition which can be coated on zinc phosphate-treated steel panels. The panels can be cured to give coatings having excellent mechanical and protective properties. These compositions are also useful for corrosion inhibition of metals and as potting and laminating resins.

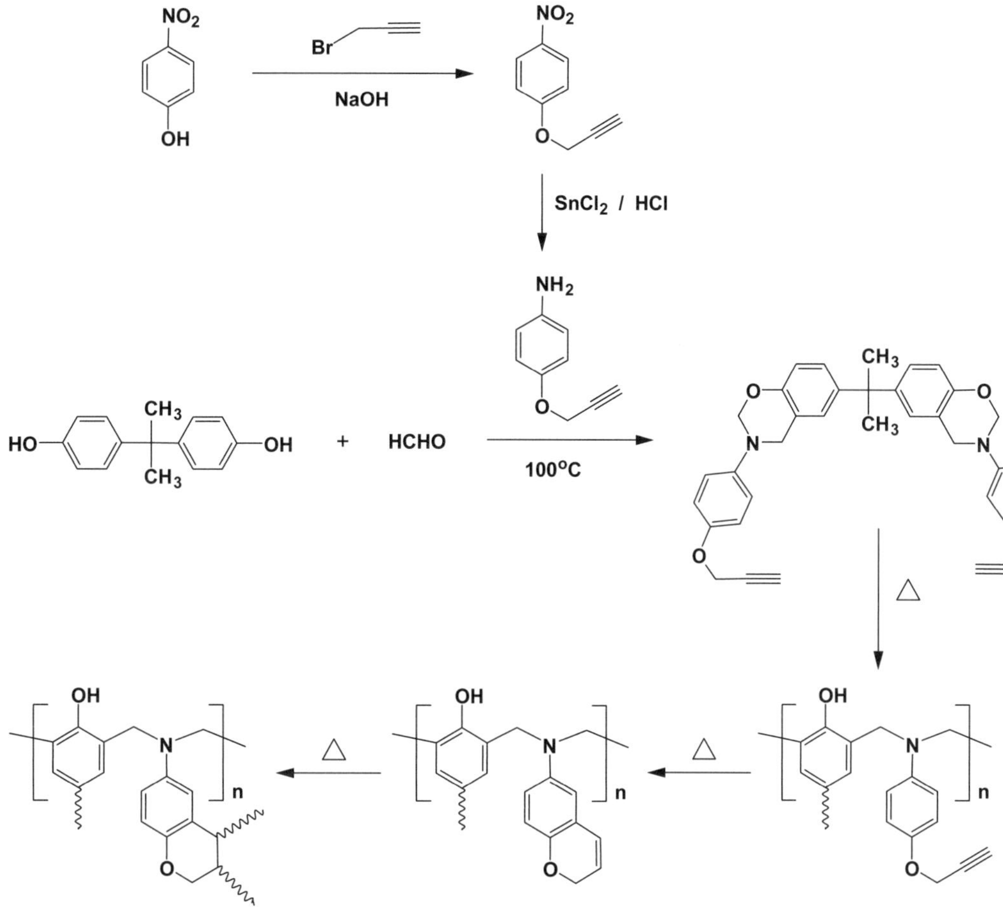

Figure 3.58. Synthesis and thermal crosslinking of a bis-benzoxazine substituted with arylpropargyl ether groups.

3.11.8. Ring-Opening Polymerization of Methylenecyclopropane

It is interesting to note that methylenecyclopropane (MCP) can be used to prepare a new class of polyspirane in the presence of an appropriate metallocene catalyst (Figure 3.59).[97] NMR studies of the end groups of the polymer led to the conclusion that the mechanism of the polymerization involves coordinative intramolecular initiation. The presence of the cyclopropyl end groups suggests that the *zipping-up process* is initiated when a methylenecyclopropane insertion is followed by intramolecular ring-closing $R_2C{=}CH_2$ insertion, before β-alkyl shift ring-opening can occur, leading to sequential ring closure along the entire polymer chain.

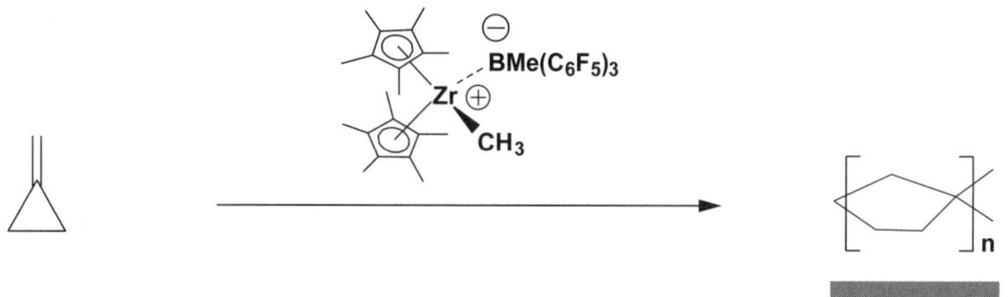

Polyspirane

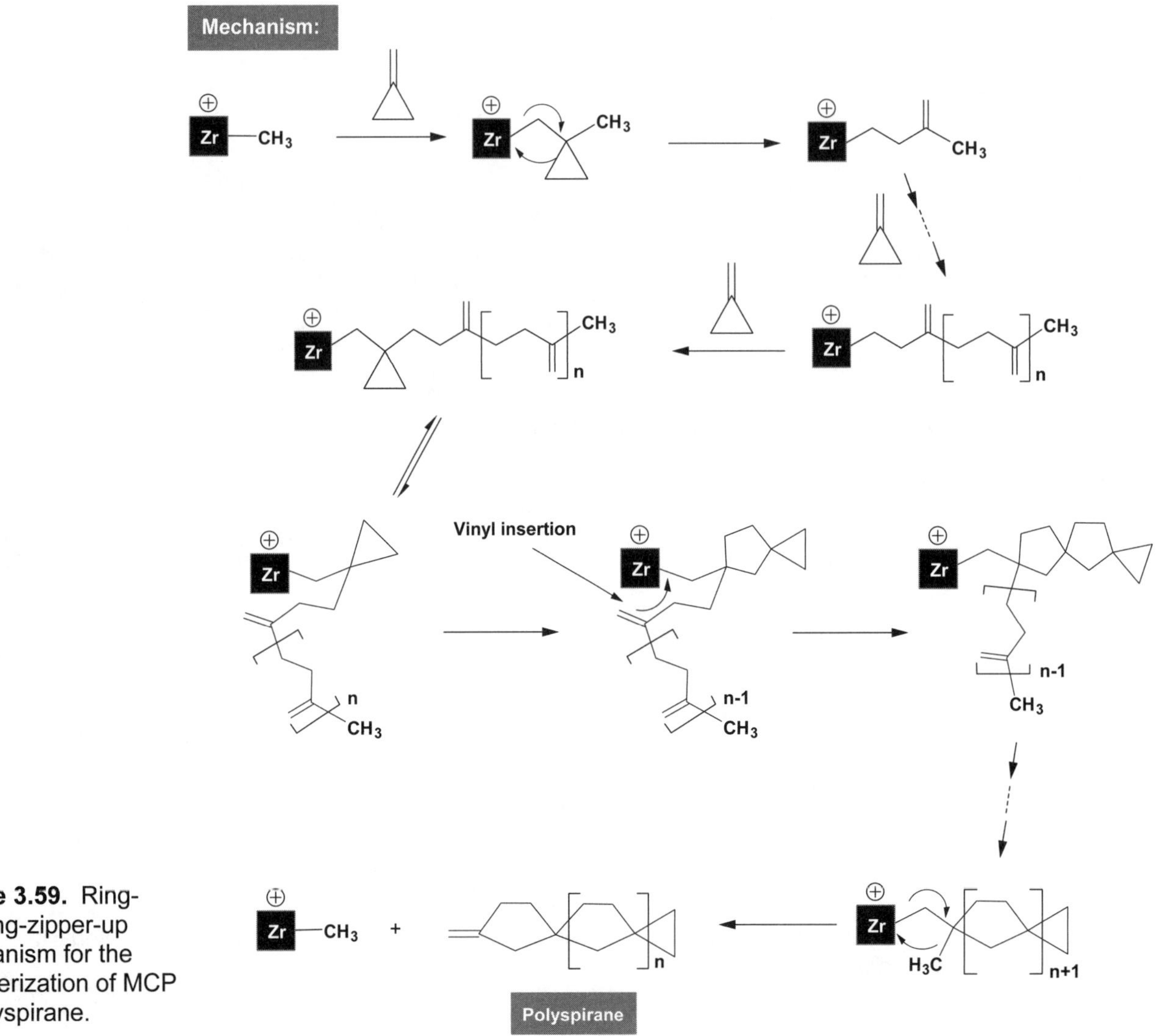

Figure 3.59. Ring-opening-zipper-up mechanism for the polymerization of MCP to polyspirane.

3.12. FUTURE OUTLOOK

In the past decade, the demand for engineering polymers has been growing at a slow pace, which is expected to continue because of vastly improved synthetic procedures for currently used polymers and the invention of new polymer blends. For example, the recent development of a green synthesis of bisphenol-A polycarbonate (a leading engineering polymer in terms of consumption) and metallocene and/or metathesis catalysts which assist synthesis of cycloolefin copolymers (COCs) and poly(methylpentene), offer superior quality products. Fundamental studies with a polymer blend containing 80% polycarbonate and 20% ABS indicate that ABS not only improves processability by reducing the melt viscosity of the product by a factor of 4 to 5, but also provides enhanced chemical resistance, especially attractive for automotive applications. Blends of polycarbonate with polyesters, viz., PET and PBT, are very popular in automotive exterior parts because they effectively combine toughness and impact strength of the polycarbonate with the crystallinity and inherent solvent resistance of polyesters.

The future of nylons, one of the major leaders in terms of usage, is also very promising. Currently, a major portion of nylons, mostly glass- or mineral-reinforced, go into engine compartments of U.S.-built cars. Nylon-PPO blends are increasingly popular for automobile fenders and will continue to expand its limit since all auto-manufacturers are shifting from metal to all-plastic automobile bodies. Semi-aromatic nylons, namely polyphthalamide, are becoming more attractive because of their superior dimensional stability at higher temperatures which are necessary for under-hood automotive components. Considerable progress has also been made in the area of matrix materials for thermosetting composites (e.g., polybenzoxazines, dicyanates, bismaleimides, etc.), but not yet taken up for full scale production. More research is required on bulk mechanical properties of the composites in order to evaluate their potential over traditional materials.

General Study Questions:

1. Bisphenol-A, BPA, is an important monomer in the polymer industry, especially in the manufacture of polycarbonate. BPA is commercially manufactured by acid catalyzed condensation of phenol with acetone. Write the mechanism of the reaction. How would you prepare the following bisphenol monomers from readily available starting materials? Comment on the properties of the polymers derived from these monomers.

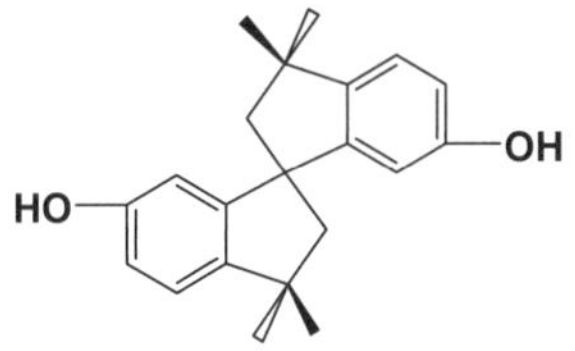

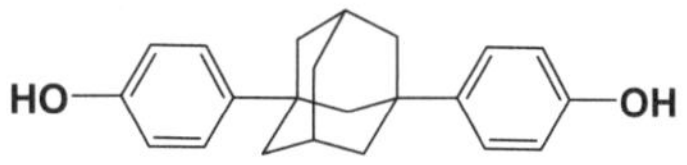

HO OH HO OH

2. When the following monomer is used in lieu of BPA, the resulting polycarbonate displays improved ductility and toughness due to the lower molecular cross-sectional area of the polymer chain and packing length compared to PC. Starting from benzene, suggest a feasible synthetic route to prepare this monomer.

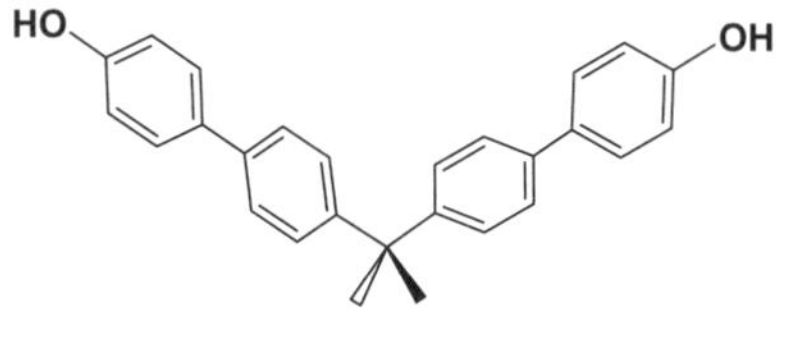

HO OH

3. In 1999, Dow Chemical Co. introduced polyhydroxy amino ether (PHAE) with the tradename Blox®, a thermoplastic product obtained by reaction of the diglycidyl ether of bisphenol-A with an equivalent amount of 2-aminoethanol. The high cohesive energy density of PHAE offers outstanding gas barrier properties against oxygen and carbon dioxide, including good mechanical properties, optical clarity, and excellent melt strength and adhesion to many substrates. Write the structure of the polymer and propose a few possible applications.
4. Using the synthesis of bisphenol-A as a guideline, outline a strategy for the synthesis of tetrakis(4-hydroxyphenyl)ethane, a monomer for the preparation of a high-performance epoxy compound, tetraglycidyl ether of tetrakis(4-hydroxyphenyl)ethane, TGEPE.

5. Interpret the thermal analysis data obtained from the following series of alternating copolymers of CO and α-olefins.

Copolymer	T_g (°C)	T_m (°C)
1-Hexene-CO	20	55
1-Heptene-CO	25	-10
1-Octene-CO	35	Not detected
1-Dodecene-CO	60	Not detected
1-Hexadecene-CO	Not detected	15
1-Octadecene-CO	Not detected	20
1-Icosene-CO	Not detected	30

6. Write the intermediate products (**A** through **J**) in the synthesis of the highly active zirconocene shown below, which can produce PMP with a low polydispersity index (~1.95) and high isotactic structures, [*mmmm*] ~ 92.5%.

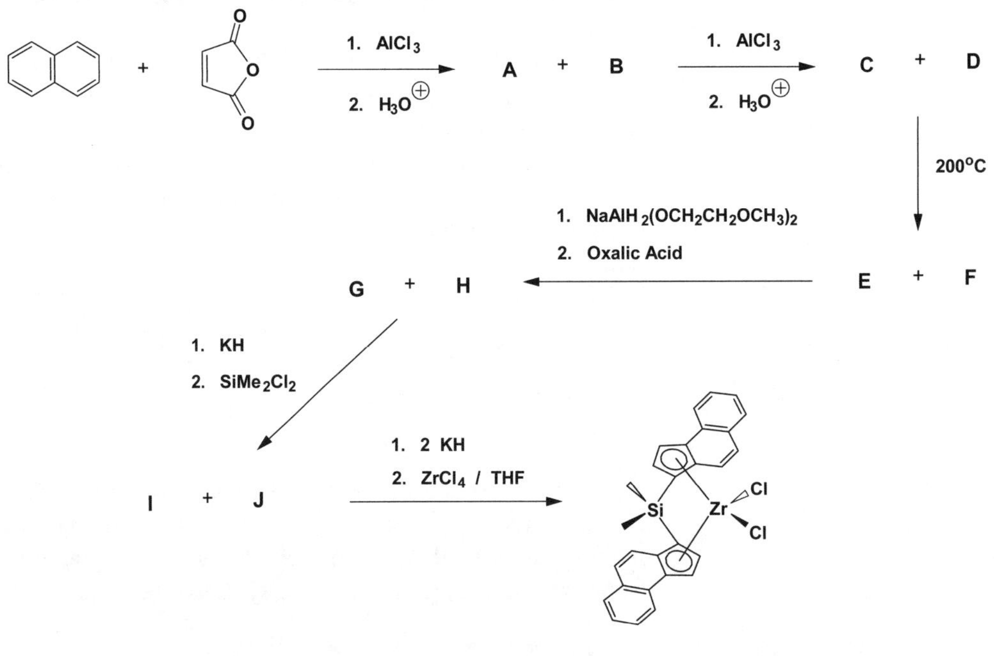

Naphthalene + maleic anhydride —(1. $AlCl_3$; 2. $H_3O^{\oplus}$)→ **A** + **B** —(1. $AlCl_3$; 2. $H_3O^{\oplus}$)→ **C** + **D** —(200°C)→ **E** + **F** —(1. $NaAlH_2(OCH_2CH_2OCH_3)_2$; 2. Oxalic Acid)→ **G** + **H** —(1. KH; 2. $SiMe_2Cl_2$)→ **I** + **J** —(1. 2 KH; 2. $ZrCl_4$ / THF)→ Me_2Si-bridged bis(benz[e]indenyl) $ZrCl_2$

7. Dow Chemical developed the following diglycidyl derivative, which exhibits nematic liquid crystalline behavior, to achieve a novel liquid crystalline thermoset via a conventional epoxy curing method. Propose a practical synthetic scheme, starting with any compounds containing no more than six carbon atoms.

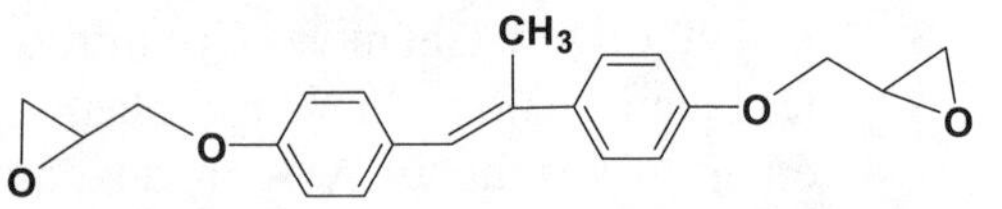

(Structure: glycidyl ether–O–C_6H_4–CH=C(CH_3)–C_6H_4–O–glycidyl ether)

8. Nylon-6,6 and nylon-6 are isomers that share the same empirical formula ($C_6H_{11}NO$), density, refractive index and many other properties, such as thermal behavior between the T_g and T_m windows that are important in fiber melt-spinning and drawing and in fiber-to-fabric processing. However, their softening and melting temperatures are quite different (nylon-6 softens at 170°C and melts at 220°C whereas the same properties for nylon 6,6 are 235°C and 260°C, respectively). Explain.

9. Shown below is a synthetic scheme for the preparation of a liquid-crystalline (LC) thermoset. Identify the intermediates, including the structure of the LC thermoset.

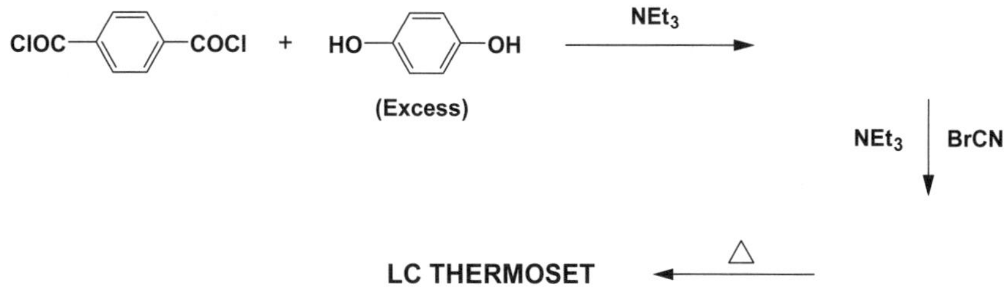

ClOC–C₆H₄–COCl + HO–C₆H₄–OH (Excess) $\xrightarrow{NEt_3}$; NEt_3 / BrCN ; Δ → LC THERMOSET

10. The rigid and flexible segments in the following polymers are perfect for displaying thermotropic liquid crystalline properties. Suggest a smart synthetic route for each, using compounds containing no more than six carbon atoms.

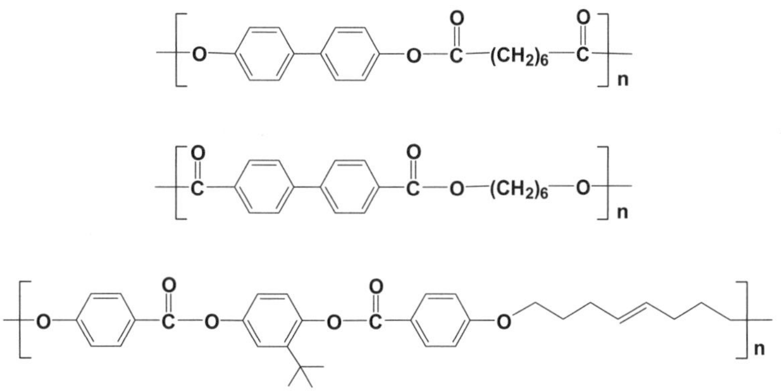

$[\!-O-C_6H_4-C_6H_4-O-C(=O)-(CH_2)_6-C(=O)-]_n$

$[\!-C(=O)-C_6H_4-C_6H_4-C(=O)-O-(CH_2)_6-O-]_n$

$[\!-O-C_6H_4-C(=O)-O-C_6H_3(tBu)-O-C(=O)-C_6H_4-O-CH_2CH_2CH_2CH=CHCH_2CH_2CH_2-]_n$

11. Write the structures of the intermediate products and polymer that is expected at the end of the reaction sequence shown below. Comment on the physical and thermal properties of this polymer with respect to a commercially available polymer belonging to the same family.

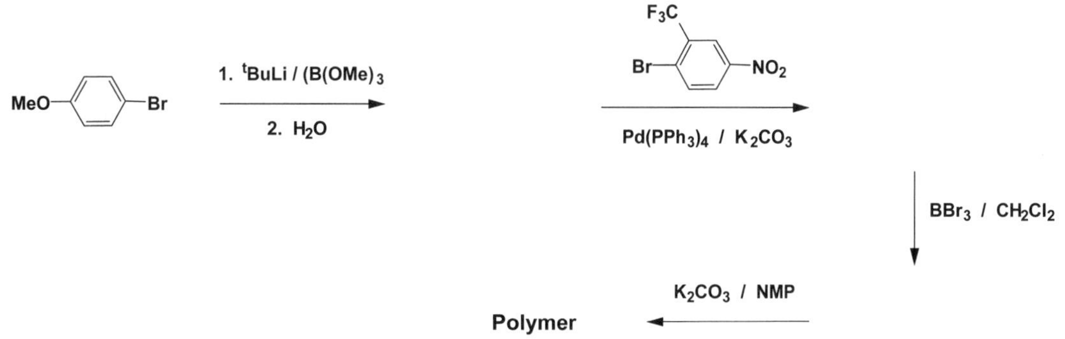

MeO–C₆H₄–Br $\xrightarrow{1.\ {}^tBuLi / (B(OMe)_3)\quad 2.\ H_2O}$; Br–C₆H₃(CF₃)–NO₂, $Pd(PPh_3)_4$ / K_2CO_3 ; BBr_3 / CH_2Cl_2 ; K_2CO_3 / NMP → Polymer

12. Identify the structures of the intermediates and the polymer obtained at the end of the following synthetic scheme.

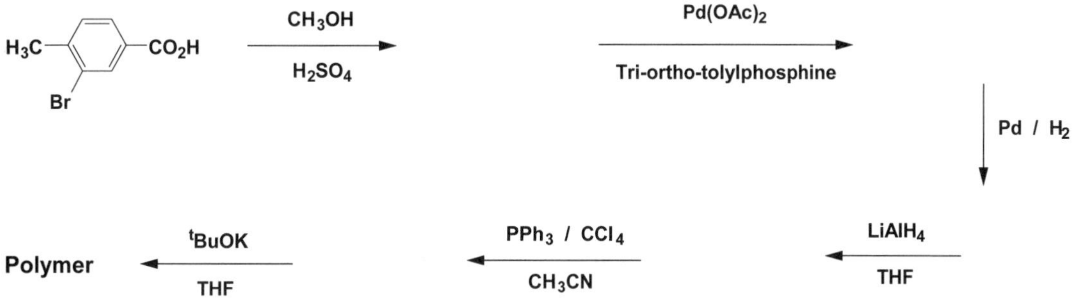

H_3C–C₆H₃(Br)–CO_2H $\xrightarrow{CH_3OH / H_2SO_4}$; $Pd(OAc)_2$ / Tri-ortho-tolylphosphine ; Pd / H_2 ; $LiAlH_4$ / THF ; PPh_3 / CCl_4, CH_3CN ; ${}^tBuOK$ / THF → Polymer

Advanced Study Questions:

13. The following scheme depicts the synthesis of an aromatic polyether starting with monomer **K** in the presence of an initiator **L** via a chain-growth polycondensation reaction (nucleophilic site propagation)! Identify all the missing intermediates.

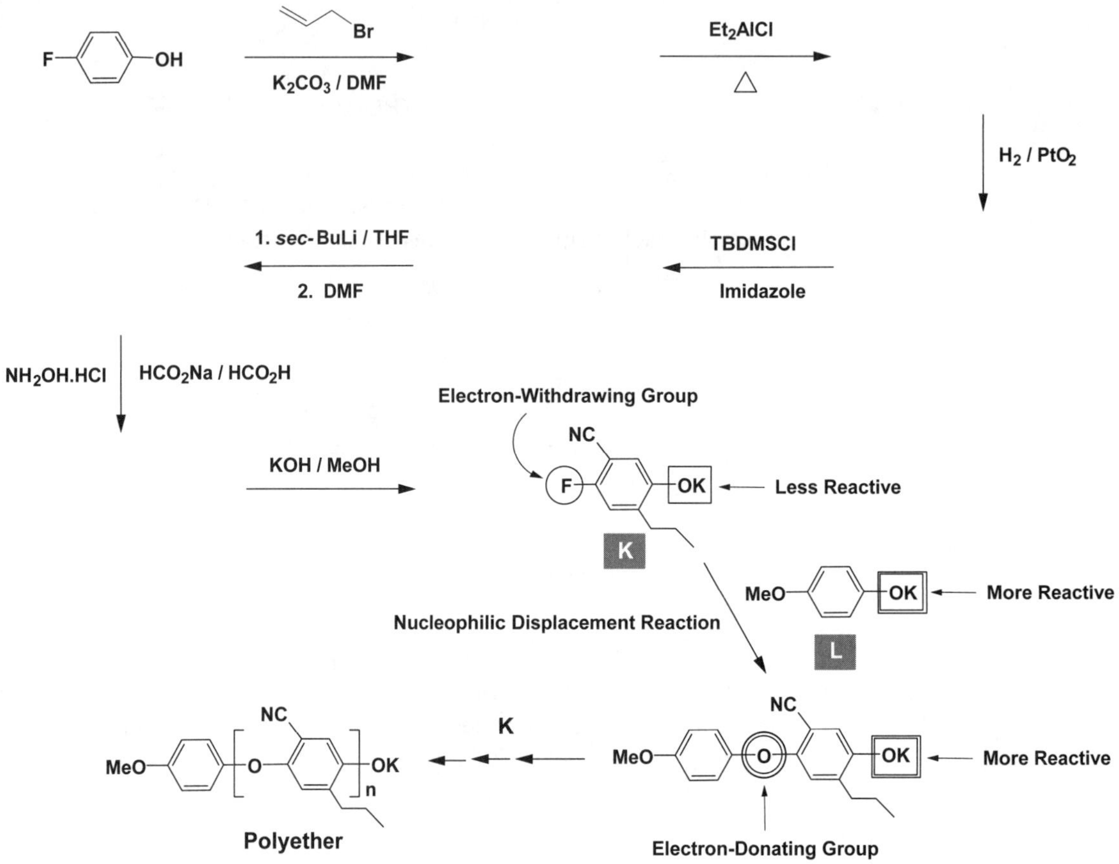

F–C6H4–OH; Br (allyl bromide), K_2CO_3 / DMF; Et_2AlCl, Δ; H_2 / PtO_2; TBDMSCl, Imidazole; 1. *sec*-BuLi / THF, 2. DMF; $NH_2OH.HCl$, HCO_2Na / HCO_2H; KOH / MeOH

Electron-Withdrawing Group

NC, F, OK ← Less Reactive

K

MeO, OK ← More Reactive

L

Nucleophilic Displacement Reaction

NC, MeO, O, OK ← More Reactive

Electron-Donating Group

K

NC, MeO, O, OK, n

Polyether

14. Decafluorobiphenyl is now a very popular monomer for the preparation of semi-fluorinated polymers. Complete the following synthetic scheme.

O, O; CuCl / AcOH; $Na_2S_2O_4$; K_2CO_3 / DMAc; F_5, F_5

Semi-fluorinated Polymer

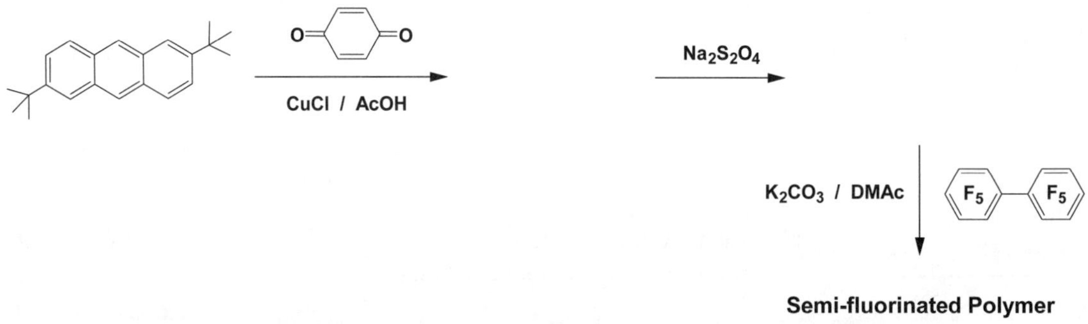

15. Mention two significant attributes of the each of the following polymers (for example, PC is noted for its high impact resistance and optical transparency): (a) ABS, (b) Nylon-6,6, (c) POM; (d) PMMA, (e) SBS, (f) PVC, (g) PET, and (h) PMMI.

16. The polymer obtained by the following synthetic scheme exhibits a number of desirable properties, such as low-water absorption, good mechanical properties and high thermal stability (decomposition temperature ~415°C and especially, very low dielectric constant (low-κ). These characteristics are valuable in the semiconductor

industry for providing insulation for next generation microprocessor and memory devices. Write the structure of the polymer including all intermediates.

CH_3CN

1. NaH / DMF
2. Me_2SO_4

Grubbs Catalyst (2nd Gen.)

Low-κ Polymer

References for Chapter-3:

1. *Handbook of Polycarbonate Science and Technology,* LeGrand, D. G.; Bendler, J. T., Eds., Marcel Dekker, New York, 2000.
2. Jones, A. A., *Macromolecules*, **18**, 902 (1985).
3. Sung, Y. J.; Chen, C. L.; Su, A. C., *Macromolecules*, **24**, 6123 (1991).
4. Henrichs, P. M.; Luss, H. R.; Scaringe, R. P., *Macromolecules*, **22**, 2731 (1989).
5. Wimberger-Friedl, R.; Hut, M. G. T.; Schoo, H. F. M., *Macromolecules*, **29**, 5453 (1996).
6. Liu, J.; Yee, A. F., *Macromolecules*, **31**, 7865 (1998).
7. Li, X.; Yee, A. F., *Macromolecules*, **36**, 9411 (2003).
8. Li, X.; Yee, A. F., *Macromolecules*, **36**, 9421 (2003).
9. Lloyd, J. B. F.; Ongley, P. A., *Tetrahedron*, **21**, 245 (1965).
10. Upshaw, T. A.; Stille, J. K.; Droske, J. P., *Macromolecules*, **24**, 2143 (1991).
11. Marks, M. J.; Sekinger, J. K., *Macromolecules*, **27**, 4106 (1994).
12. Marks, M. J.; Erskine, J. S.; McCrery, D. A., *Macromolecules*, **27**, 4114 (1994).
13. Crespy, D.; Landfester, K., *Macromolecules*, **38**, 6882 (2005).
14. Coates, G. W. *Chem. Rev.,* **100**, 1223 (2000).
15. Tritto, I.; Boggioni, L.; Jansen, J. C.; Thorshaug, K.; Sacchi, M. C.; Ferro, D. R., *Macromolecules*, **35**, 616 (2002).
16. Tritto, I.; Boggioni, L.; Zampa, C.; Ferro, D. R., *Macromolecules*, **38**, 9910 (2005).
17. Thorshaug, K.; Mendichi, R.; Boggioni, L.; Tritto, I.; Trinkle, S.; Friedrich, C.; Mulhaupt, R., *Macromolecules*, **35**, 2903 (2002).
18. Tritto, I.; Marestin, C.; Boggioni, L.; Sacchi, M. C.; Brintzinger, H.-H.; Ferro, D. R., *Macromolecules*, **34**, 5770 (2001).
19. Matsuzaki, K.; Masamoto, J., *Ind. Eng. Chem. Res.,* **37**, 1729 (1998).
20. Nagahara, H.; Kagawa, K.; Hamanaka, K.; Yoshida, K.; Iwaisako, T.; Masamoto, J., *Ind. Eng. Chem. Res.,* **39**, 2275 (2000).
21. Basko, M.; Kubisa, P.; Penczek, S.; Moreau, M.; Vairon, J.-P., *Macromolecules*, **33**, 294 (2000).
22. Basko, M.; Kubisa, P., *Macromolecules*, **35**, 8948 (2002).

23. Basko, M.; Kubisa, P., *J. Polym. Sci. Part A, Polym. Chem.,* **42**, 1189 (2004).
24. Drent, E.; Budzelaar, P. H. M., *Chem. Rev.,* **96**, 663 (1996).
25. Sen, A., *Acc. Chem. Res.,* **26**, 303 (1993).
26. Rix, F. C.; Brookhart, M.; White, P. S., *J. Am. Chem. Soc.,* **118**, 4746 (1996).
27. Margl, P.; Ziegler, T., *Organometallics*, **15**, 5519 (1996).
28. Hearley, A. K.; Nowack, R. J.; Rieger, B., *Organometallics*, **24**, 2755 (2005).
29. Fujita, T.; Nakano, K.; Yamashita, M.; Nozaki, K., *J. Am. Chem. Soc.,* **128**, 1968 (2006).
30. Nozaki, K.; Sato, N.; Takaya, H., *J. Am. Chem. Soc.,* **117**, 9911 (1995).
31. Yuan, J.-C.; Lu, S.-J., *Organometallics*, **20**, 2697 (2001).
32. Cowie, J. M. G.; Harris, S.; Gomez Ribelles, J. L.; Meseguer, J. M.; Romero, F.; Torregrosa, C., *Macromolecules*, **32**, 4430 (1999).
33. Kapellen, K. K.; Mistele, C. D.; DeSimone, J. M., *Macromolecules*, **29**, 495 1996).
34. Zhong, Y.; Abrams, C. F.; Lim, P. K., *Ind. Eng. Chem. Res.,* **34**, 1529 (1995).
35. Oyaizu, K.; Kumaki, Y.; Saito, K.; Tsuchida, E., *Macromolecules*, **33**, 5766 (2000).
36. Ikeda, R.; Tanaka, H.; Uyama, H.; Kobayashi, S., *Macromolecules*, **33**, 6648 (2000).
37. Photo obtained from Wikipedia. Source: http://en.wikipedia.org/wiki/Surface-mount_technology.
38. Barclay, G. G.; Ober, C. K.; Papathomas, K. I.; Wang, D. W., *Macromolecules*, **25**, 2947 (1992).
39. Xu, G.; Cheng, D., *Macromolecules*, **34**, 2040 (2001).
40. Stehling, U.; Diebold, J.; Kirsten, R.; Roell, W.; Brintzinger, H. H.; Juengling, S.; Muelhaupt, R.; Langhauser, F., *Organometallics*, **13**, 964 (1994).
41. Irwin, L. J.; Miller, S. A., *J. Am. Chem. Soc.,* **127**, 9972 (2005).
42. Hubbard, P.; Brittain, W. J.; Simonsick, W. J., Jr.; Ross, C. W. III, *Macromolecules*, **29**, 8304 (1996).
43. Gorham, W., *J. Polym. Sci. A-1*, **4**, 3027 (1966).
44. Fortin, J. B.; Lu, T.-M., *Chem. Mater.,* **14**, 1945 (2002).
45. Schafer, O.; Greiner, A., *Macromolecules*, **29**, 6074 (1996).
46. Lahann, J.; Langer, R., *Macromolecules*, **35**, 4380 (2002).
47. Herrera-Alonso, M.; McCarthy, T. J., *Langmuir*, **20**, 9184 (2004).
48. Chen, H.-Y.; Elkasabi, Y.; Lahann, J., *J. Am. Chem. Soc.,* **128**, 374 (2006).
49. Dolbier, W. R., Jr.; Rong, X. X.; Xu, Y.; Beach, W. F., *J. Org. Chem.,* **62**, 7500 (1997).
50. Dolbier, W. R., Jr.; Duan, J.-X.; Roche, A. J., *Org. Lett.,* **2**, 1867 (2000).
51. Amii, H.; Hatamoto, Y.; Seo, M.; Uneyama, K., *J. Org. Chem.,* **66**, 7216 (2001).
52. Gilch, H. G.; Wheelwright, W. L., *J. Polym. Sci., Part A-1*, **4**, 1337 (1966).
53. Brink-Spalink, F.; Greiner, A., *Macromolecules*, **35**, 3315 (2002).
54. Beck, J. B.; Kokil, A.; Ray, D.; Rowan, S. J.; Weder, C., *Macromolecules*, **35**, 590 (2002).
55. Hahn, S. F., *J. Polym. Sci., Part A: Polym. Chem.,* **30**, 397 (1992).
56. Marshall, A. R.; Bunz, U. H. F., *Macromolecules*, **34**, 4688 (2001).
57. Ricks, H. L.; Choudry, U. H.; Marshall, A. R.; Bunz, U. H. F., *Macromolecules*, **36**, 1424 (2003).
58. Knapton, D.; Rowan, S. J.; Weder, C., *Macromolecules*, **39**, 651 (2006).
59. Knapton, D.; Iyer, P. K.; Rowan, S. J.; Weder, C., *Macromolecules*, **39**, 4069 (2006).
60. Kelsey, D. R.; Scardino, B. M.; Grebowicz, J. S.; Chuah, H. H., *Macromolecules*, **33**, 5810 (2000).

61. Jones, J. R.; Liotta, C. L.; Collard, D. M.; Schiraldi, D. A., *Macromolecules*, **32**, 5786 (1999).
62. Jones, J. R.; Liotta, C. L.; Collard, D. M.; Schiraldi, D. A., *Macromolecules*, **33**, 1640 (2000).
63. Hibbs, M. R.; Vargas, M.; Holtzclaw, J.; Rich, W.; Collard, D. M.; Schiraldi, D. A., *Macromolecules*, **36**, 7543 (2003).
64. Miyatake, K.; Oyaizu, K.; Tsuchida, E.; Hay, A. S., *Macromolecules*, **34**, 2065 (2001).
65. Lu, J.; Miyatake, K.; Hlil, A. R.; Hay, A. S., *Macromolecules*, **34**, 5860 (2001).
66. Wang, L.; Meng, Y. Z.; Wang, S. J.; Shang, X. Y.; Li, L.; Hay, A. S., *Macromolecules*, **37**, 3151 (2004).
67. Shaikh, A. A. G.; Hlil, A. R.; Shaikh, P. A.; Hay, A. S., *Macromolecules*, **35**, 8728 (2002).
68. Kwock, E. W.; Baird, T.; Miller, T. M. Jr., *Macromolecules*, **26**, 2935 (1993).
69. Deck, P. A.; Maiorana, C. R., *Macromolecules*, **34**, 9 (2001).
70. Smith, D. W.; Chen, S.; Kumar, S. M.; Ballato, J.; Topping, C.; Shah, H. V.; Foulger, S. H., *Adv. Mater.,* **14**, 1585 (2002).
71. Jin, J.; Smith, D. W., Jr.; Glasser, S.; Perahia, D.; Foulger, S. H.; Ballato, J.; Kang, S. W.; Kumar, S., *Macromolecules*, **39**, 4646 (2006).
72. Ghim, J.; Shim, H.-S.; Shin, B. G.; Park, J.-H.; Hwang, J.-T.; Chun, C.; Oh, S.-H.; Kim, J.-J.; Kim, D.-Y., *Macromolecules*, **38**, 8278 (2005).
73. Spraul, B. K.; Suresh, S.; Jin, J.; Smith, D. W. Jr., *J. Am. Chem. Soc.,* **128**, 7055 (2006).
74. Jin, J.; Smith, D. W. Jr.; Topping, C. M.; Suresh, S.; Chen, S.; Foulger, S. H.; Rice, N.; Nebo, J.; Mojazza, B. H., *Macromolecules*, **36**, 9000 (2003).
75. Huang, X.; Lu, G.; Peng, D.; Zhang, S.; Qing, F., *Macromolecules*, **38**, 7299 (2005).
76. Benito, J. M.; de Jesus, E.; de la Mata, F. J.; Flores, J. C.; Gomez, R., *Organometallics*, **25**, 3045 (2006).
77. Bartolini, S.; Carfagna, C.; Musco, A., *Macromol. Rapid Commun.* **16**, 9 (1995).
78. Brookhart, M.; Wagner, M. I.; Balavoine, G. G. A.; Haddou, H. A., *J. Am. Chem. Soc.,* **116**, 3641 (1994).
79. Carfagna, C.; Gatti, G.; Martini, D.; Pettinari, C., *Organometallics*, **20**, 2175 (2001).
80. Zhang, S.-W.; Kaneko, T.; Takahashi, S., *Macromolecules*, **33**, 6930 (2002).
81. Okuyama, K.; Sugiyama, J.; Nagahata, R.; Asai, M.; Ueda, M.; Takeuchi, K., *Macromolecules*, **36**, 6953 (2003).
82. Okuyama, K.; Sugiyama, J.; Nagahata, R.; Asai, M.; Ueda, M.; Takeuchi, K. J., *Mol. Catal. A: Chem.,* **21**, 203 (2003).
83. Darensbourg, D. J.; Holtcamp, M. W.; Struck, G. E.; Zimmer, M. S.; Niezgoda, S. A.; Rainey, P.; Robertson, J. B.; Draper, J. D.; Reibenspies, J. H., *J. Am. Chem. Soc.,* **121**, 107 (1999).
84. Koning, C.; Wildson, J.; Parton, R.; Plum, B.; Steeman, P.; Darensbourg, D. J., *Polymer,* **42**, 3995 (2001).
85. Darensbourg, D. J.; Rodgers, J. L.; Fang, C. C., *Inorg. Chem.,* **42**, 4498 (2003).
86. Mang, S.; Cooper, A. I.; Colclough, M. E.; Chauhan, N.; Holmes, A. B., *Macromolecules*, **33**, 303 (2003).
87. Super, M.; Berluche, E.; Costello, C.; Beckman, E., *Macromolecules*, **30**, 368 (1997).
88. Ishihara, K.; Ohara, S.; Yamamoto, H., *Macromolecules*, **33**, 3511 (2000).
89. Ning, X.; Ishida, H., *J. Polym. Sci., Polym. Chem. Ed.,* **32**, 1121 (1994).
90. Ishida, H.; Sanders, D. P., *Macromolecules*, **33**, 8149 (2000).

91. Subrayan, R. P.; Jones, F. N., *Chem. Mater.,* **10**, 3506 (1998).
92. Wirasate, S.; Dhumrongvaraporn, S.; Allen, D. J.; Ishida, H., *J. Appl. Polym. Sci.,* **70**, 1299 (1998).
93. Dunkers, J. P.; Zarate, A.; Ishida, H., *J. Phys. Chem.,* **100**, 13514 (1996).
94. Ishida, H.; Low, H. Y., *Macromolecules*, **30**, 1099 (1997).
95. Agag, T.; Takeichi, T., *Macromolecules*, **34**, 7257 (2001).
96. Agag, T.; Takeichi, T., *Macromolecules*, **36**, 6010 (2003).
97. Jia, L.; Yang, X.; Seyam, A. M.; Albert, I. D. L.; Fu, P.-F.; Yang, S.; Marks, T. J., *J. Am. Chem. Soc.,* **118**, 7900 (1996).

The majority of high-performance polymers are being developed to meet the demand for lighter, yet comparable or superior properties to the metals or ceramics now used in the aerospace industry.[1]

CHAPTER-4

HIGH-PERFORMANCE POLYMERS

High-performance polymers are classified on the basis of a temperature resistance >150°C. In addition, they possess superior mechanical strength and chemical resistance compared to that of the engineering polymers. Most high-performance polymers are reinforced by fibers and/or filled with internal antifriction lubricants, such as silicone oil. The strongest motivation for exploring high-performance polymers was provided by the aerospace industry, which emphasized the need for lighter, thermostable, stronger and durable structural components for airplanes and spacecraft. Indeed, the success of space and communication satellite programs was an affirmation of the ability of high-performance matrix polymers, including novel polymer fibers, to outperform conventional materials. For example, weight savings by use of high-performance polymer composites over aluminum is about 30% and savings of over $100,000 for each kilogram reduction in weight of aerospace vehicles in favor of high-performance polymers.

4.1. POLY(PHENYLENE SULFIDE)S

Poly(*p*-phenylene sulfide), PPS, also known as Ryton® (Chevron Phillips Chemicals) and Procon® (Toyobo, Japan), is the best-known member of this family and is highly regarded in the field of injection molding as a rapidly growing heat-resistant polymer with very stable dielectric and insulating properties, including high stiffness and good retention of mechanical properties at elevated temperatures. PPS possesses excellent chemical resistance (second to PTFE) and is almost insoluble in organic solvents up to 200°C, but can be gradually dissolved by treatment with methyl triflate in triflic acid.[2] The polymer is only affected by strong mineral acids like concentrated sulfuric and nitric acid or strong oxidizing environments. PPS is a semi-crystalline polymer with 40 – 60% crystallinity and melts at 285°C, provides a T_g of 90°C and exhibits inherent flame resistance which is described by the high *limiting oxygen index* (LOI) of 45% (see Appendix-VIII for comparison with other polymers). Since it is injection moldable, the major applications include thick-walled to delicate electrical/electronic and automotive parts, and industrial hot gas and liquid process filtration housings. PPS is also useful in powder coating technology, which involves spraying of aqueous slurries of PPS, followed by baking at elevated temperatures to obtain a tough, coalesced coating. Consequently, a significant amount of PPS goes into specialty coatings that require both heat and chemical resistance. PPS can be reinforced with fibers (glass, carbon, Kevlar, etc.) to as high as 40 wt.% to obtain composites with extremely high strength to weight ratios with maximum heat resistance (>250°C), which have great importance in the aircraft, military hardware, and sporting equipment industries.

PPS is manufactured industrially by step-growth polymerization of *p*-dichlorobenzene (PCB) and sodium sulfide in a polar solvent, such as N-methyl-2-pyrrolidinone (NMP) (Figure 4.1) under high temperature and high pressure conditions. The polymerization, however, displays significant deviations from classic step-growth polymerization behavior.[3] Thus, at incomplete conversions, polymer (or oligomer) yields and molecular weights are higher than expected, and perfect 1:1 stoichiometric monomer ratios are not required to achieve high molecular weight polymer. In fact, greater molar excess of DCP over sodium sulfide is required. The polymer isolated by this method is a linear material with modest molecular weight (M_w = 15,000 – 20,000) and a few percent of disulfide linkages, which is primarily used for coating applications. For other uses, this low molecular weight polymer must be subjected to a heat treatment operation under oxygen (or air) prior to molding and/or fabrication in order to improve mechanical and thermal properties. This thermal step, although called curing, does not produce thermosetting materials and goes through a series of complex reactions leading to chain extension, partial crosslinking (thermal and oxidative) and formation of biphenyl units via oxygen uptake, followed by loss of SO_2.[4] PPS is customarily cured in the air at 260°C for molding precure, and at 370°C for coatings. It is important to note that PPS is the only commercial polymer which is melt processable and can be made electrically conducting by doping with an oxidant, such as arsenic pentafluoride (see Chapter-5 for further discussion).[5]

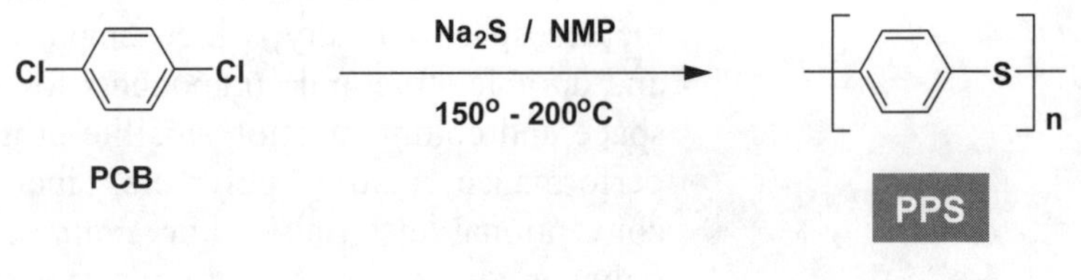

Na_2S / NMP
150° - 200°C
PCB
PPS

Figure 4.1. Commercial synthesis of PPS.

Several methods have been developed recently to improve synthetic and processing aspects of PPS. For example, acid-induced self-polymerization of methyl 4-(phenylthio)phenyl sulfoxide (MPTO) leads to a very high molecular weight PPS (M_w ~ 200,000) at ambient temperature and pressure, thus eliminating the need for thermal pre-curing (chain extension) which yields a slightly darkened product (Figure 4.2).[6,7] The mechanism of polymerization involves protonation of the sulfoxide group of MPTO, followed by an electrophilic reaction with the activated aromatic thioether end of MPTO, leading to a soluble precursor of PPS, poly(phenylenesulfonium) salt (PPSS). Since polymerization proceeds in protic acid (e.g., trifluoromethanesulfonic acid) homogeneously, the polymerization produces high molecular weight PPSS, which is also soluble in common solvents, such as formic acid and dimethyl sulfoxide, and can be converted into PPS by reaction with a nucleophile (pyridine or halide ion). The monomer, MPTO, is prepared by condensation of methyl phenyl sulfoxide with thioanisole, followed by dealkylation with pyridine and oxidation with 70% nitric acid.

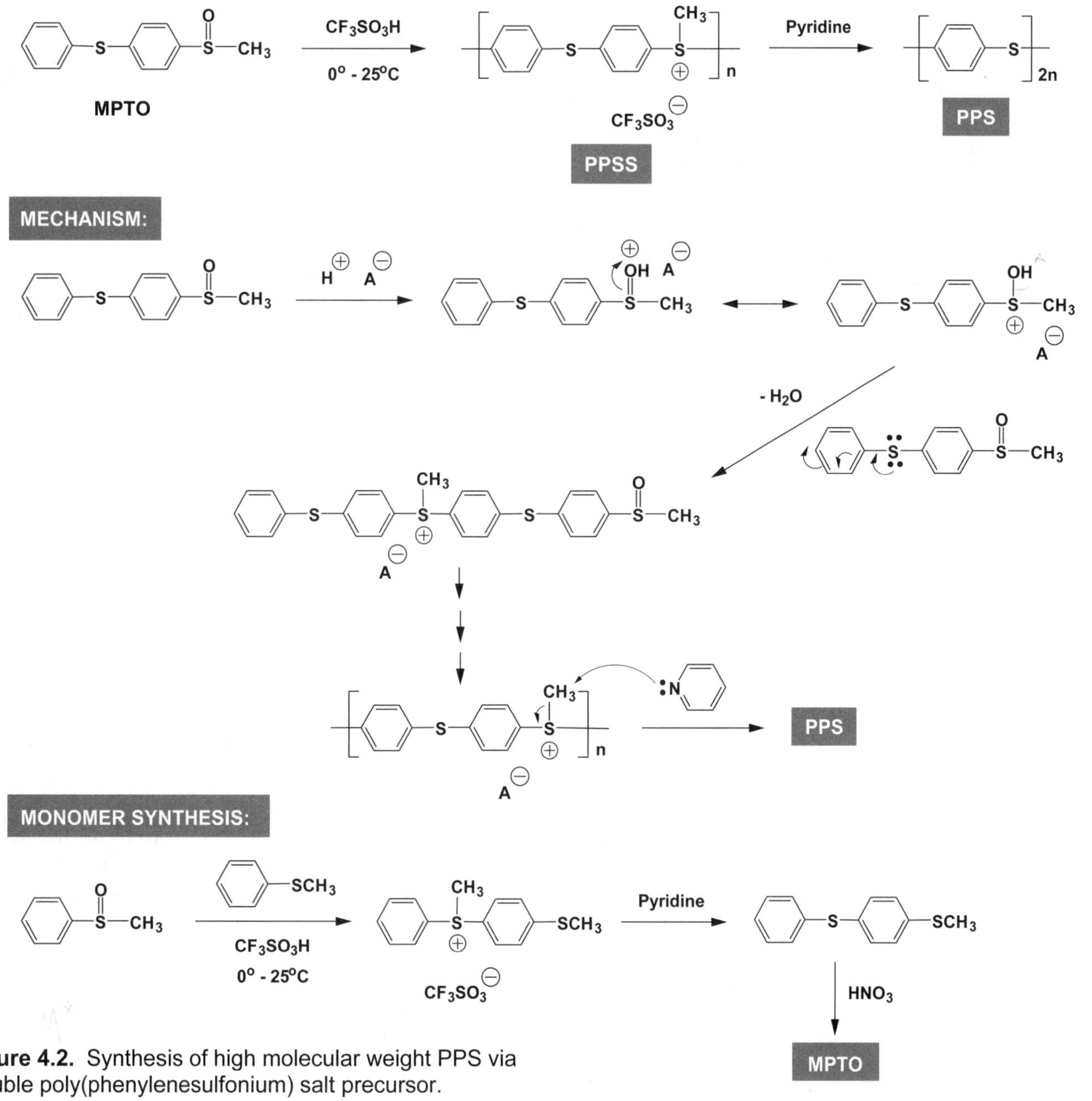

Figure 4.2. Synthesis of high molecular weight PPS via soluble poly(phenylenesulfonium) salt precursor.

The aforementioned methodology is a versatile process which has led, for the first time, to the synthesis of high molecular weight linear perfluorinated PPS (FPPS)[8] and poly(phenylene sulfide-phenyleneamine) (PPSA)[9], a hybrid structure of PPS and polyaniline (PANI) (Figure 4.3). FPPS displays superior thermal properties (T_m ~ 375°C), but PPSA shows lower electronic conductivity upon doping (1.4 S/cm with ferric chloride) compared to doped PPS and PANI, presumably because of the highly amorphous character resulting from its more irregular repeating unit and hydrogen bonding. Surprisingly, PPSA exhibits good thermal stability (stable up to 380°C) and possesses a T_g of ~150°C.

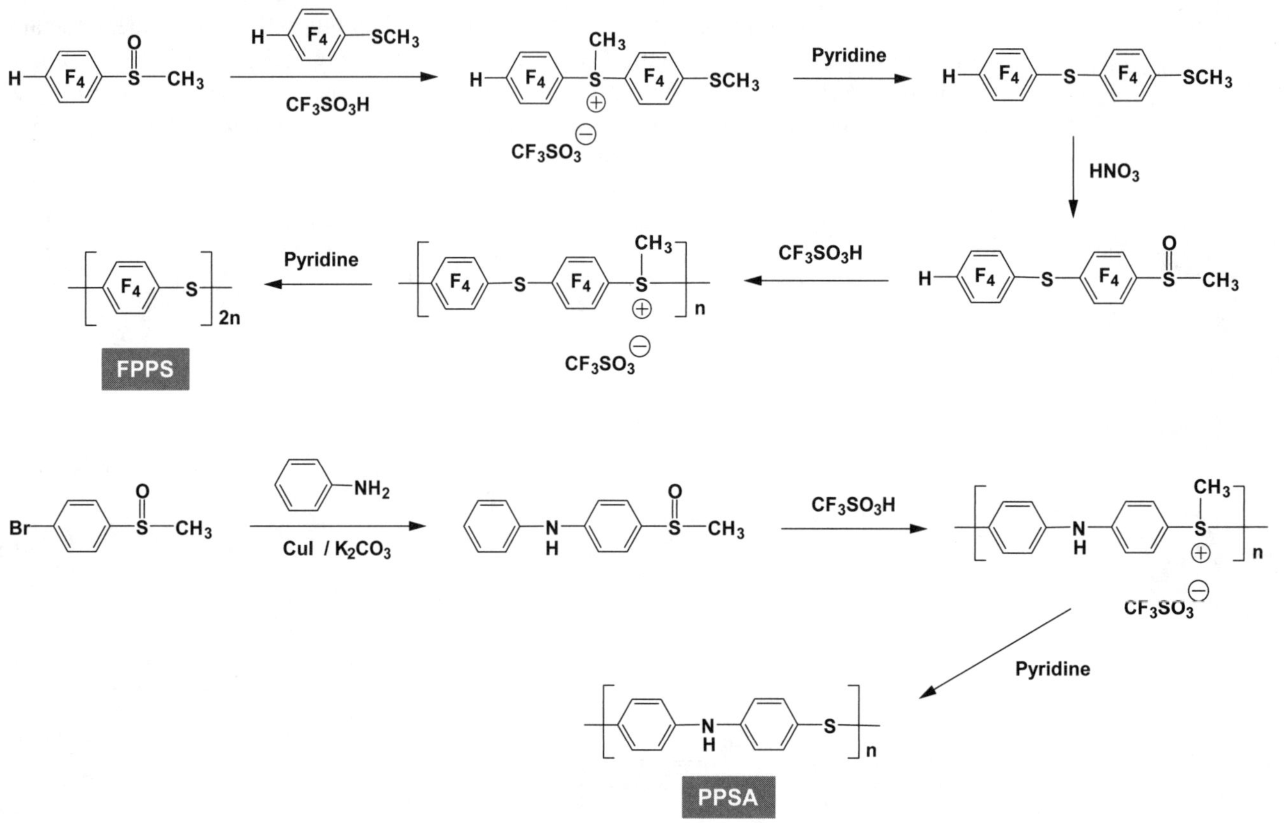

Figure 4.3. Synthesis of PPS analogs, FPPS and PPSA.

Another recently developed method is the thermal *ring-opening polymerization* (ROP) of cyclic disulfide oligomers in the presence of a dihalo aromatic compound (Figure 4.4).[10,11] The reaction is believed to proceed via a typical free-radical *ipso*-substitution. At high temperatures, disulfide linkages in cyclic disulfide oligomers are degraded to thiyl radicals, which *ipso*-substitute the halogen atom of the dihalo compound to form diaryl sulfide linkages and halogen radicals. These radicals eventually combine to form free halogen molecules that must be destroyed (specifically, bromine molecules from dibromo compounds) to avoid side reactions by using potassium iodide as a reductant. Cyclic disulfide oligomers are readily prepared by catalytic oxidation of arenedithiols in the presence of a mixture of tertiary amine and a copper salt under high dilution conditions.[12] Thus, this ROP provides flexibility to incorporate other aromatic residues in the PPS backbone by selection of appropriate aromatic residues, Ar_1 and Ar_2.

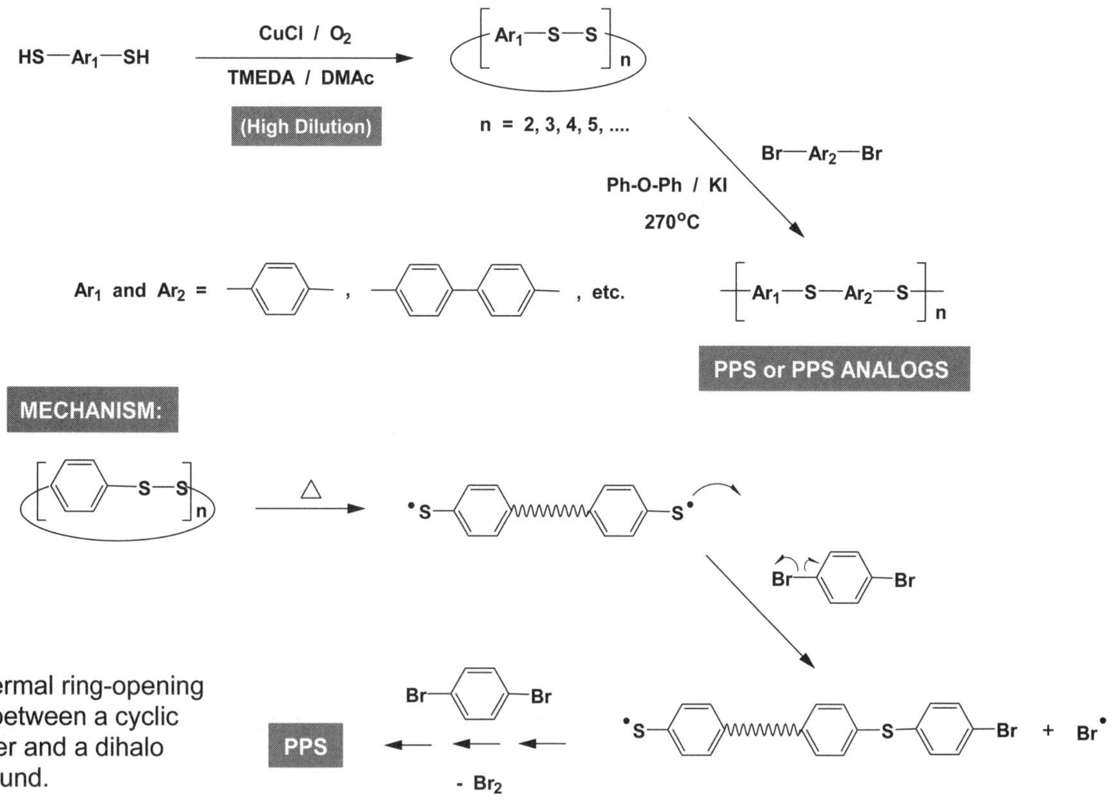

Figure 4.4. Thermal ring-opening polymerization between a cyclic disulfide oligomer and a dihalo aromatic compound.

4.2. AROMATIC POLYSULFONES

These polymers are characterized by the presence of the *para*-linked diphenylsulfone moiety as part of the repeat unit. Poly(*p*-phenylene sulfone), $PPSO_2$, the simplest member of this family, is a highly crystalline (>85%) material and has no commercial significance because it is practically insoluble in any solvent and does not melt before decomposition (~500°C). Consequently, all commercially available aromatic polysulfones are ether derivatives of $PPSO_2$. Depending on the chemical structure, aromatic polyethersulfones are usually prepared either by polysulfonation or polyetherification routes. Radel®-H (Solvay Advanced Polymers) polyethersulfone (PES) is manufactured by polysulfonation of diphenyl ether with the disulfonylchloride of diphenyl ether in the presence of a catalytic amount of $FeCl_3$ (Figure 4.5). PES can also be made by self-polysulfonation of 4-chlorophenyldiphenylether. This single-monomer route provides more *para*-linked repeat units (i.e., more linear backbone) and is preferred for PES with higher *heat-distortion temperature* (HDT). The properties of PES are similar to those of nylons except for higher service temperature (180°C). It is resistant to most chemicals and may be extruded or injection molded to close tolerances. Applications are as a replacement for glass for medical needs and food handling, circuit boards, general electrical components, and car parts requiring good mechanical properties and dimensional stability. PES offers unique properties, such as the ability to easily create porous filaments or flat sheet from stable solutions that allow it to be used in micro and ultra filtration and reverse osmosis membranes. These membranes have applications ranging from artificial kidneys for blood purification to wastewater recovery, as well as food and beverage processing. In addition, PES is used to create water purification membranes that filter harmful bacteria spores, such as cryptosporidium from municipal drinking water.

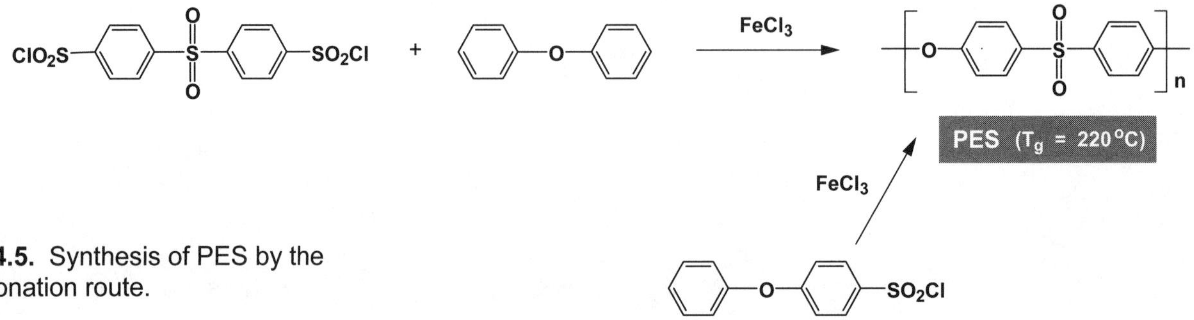

PES (T_g = 220°C)

Figure 4.5. Synthesis of PES by the polysulfonation route.

Radel®-R (Solvay Advanced Polymers) polyphenylsulfone (PPSF) is manufactured by polyetherification of 4,4'-dichlorodiphenyl sulfone (DCPS) with the disodium salt of 4,4'-dihydroxybiphenyl (Figure 4.6). The driving force towards formation of high molecular weight polymer is the facile nucleophilic aromatic displacement (S_NAr) of halogens, which are highly activated by the strong electron-withdrawing sulfone group. It is interesting to note that the rate of polymerization depends on the leaving group in the order of F >> Cl > Br > I, despite the fact that the bond strengths for carbon-halogen bonds decrease in the same order. This is explained by the greater electronegativity of the fluorine atom which allows it to inductively withdraw electron density from the activated carbon, thereby further activating it to nucleophilic attack, as well as stabilizing the intermediate. Steric effects may also play a role in the increase in rate. A smaller atom on the activated carbon allows greater access to that carbon for the incoming nucleophile. However, from an economic standpoint, DCPS is used for all commercial polysulfones. Recently, an alternate approach to PPSF has been developed involving nickel-catalyzed coupling of aryl dihalide, obtained by nucleophilic displacement between DCPS and the potassium salt of *p*-chlorophenol.[13] PPSF stands out as one of the best in medical applications, requiring repeated sterilization or uncompromising toughness. With its high heat deflection temperature of 210°C, it can withstand continuous exposure to heat and still absorb a tremendous impact without deflecting or breaking. Moreover, its chemical resistance surpasses that of most amorphous polymers. PPSF can be injection molded, vacuum formed or machined. Current applications include a wide assortment of medical trays and containers as well as surgical instruments.

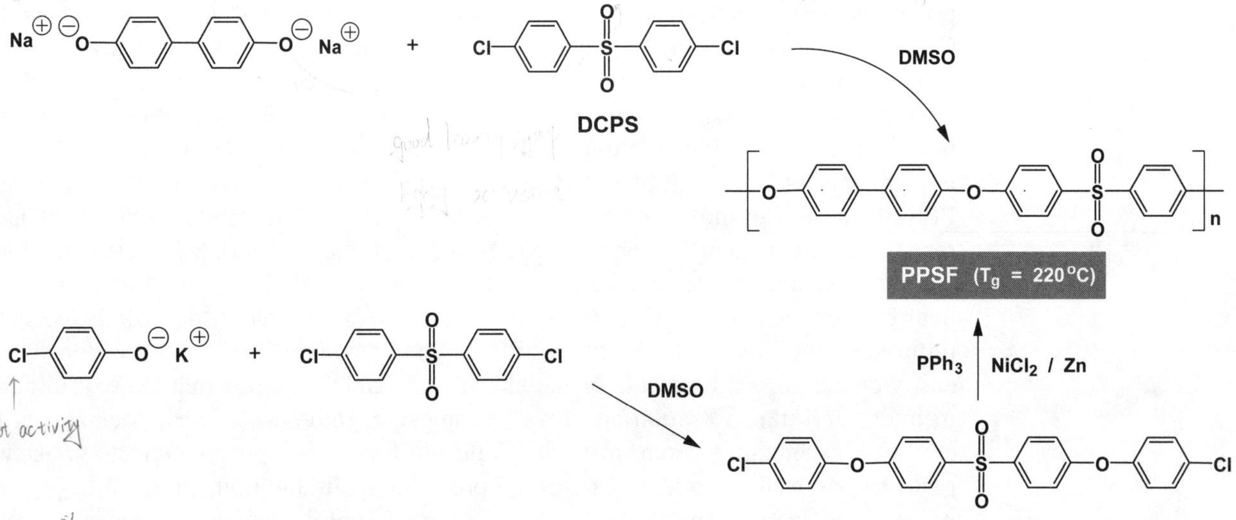

DCPS

PPSF (T_g = 220°C)

Figure 4.6. Synthesis of PPSF by the polyetherification route.

Udel® (Solvay Advanced Polymers) or Ultrason®-S (BASF) polysulfone (PSF), composed of phenylene units linked by three different chemical groups-isopropylidene, ether and sulfone, is also manufactured by the polyetherification route involving 4,4'-dichlorodiphenyl sulfone and the disodium salt of bisphenol-A (Figure 4.7). Each of the three linkages imparts specific properties to the polymer, such as chemical resistance, melt processability, temperature resistance and impact strength. Like polycarbonate, PSF is clear, strong, non-toxic and extremely tough. PSF is resistant to acids, bases, aqueous solutions, aliphatic hydrocarbons and alcohols. It has properties similar to nylon, but are retained up to 180°C compared with 120°C for nylon, which greatly expands the range of applications. Optical clarity is good and its moisture absorption lower than nylon. Applications are as a replacement for glass for medical needs and chemistry equipment, circuit boards, electrical/electronic components and automotive parts. PSF is also widely used as a membrane material or membrane support for liquid separation processes, such as ultrafiltration or reverse osmosis.

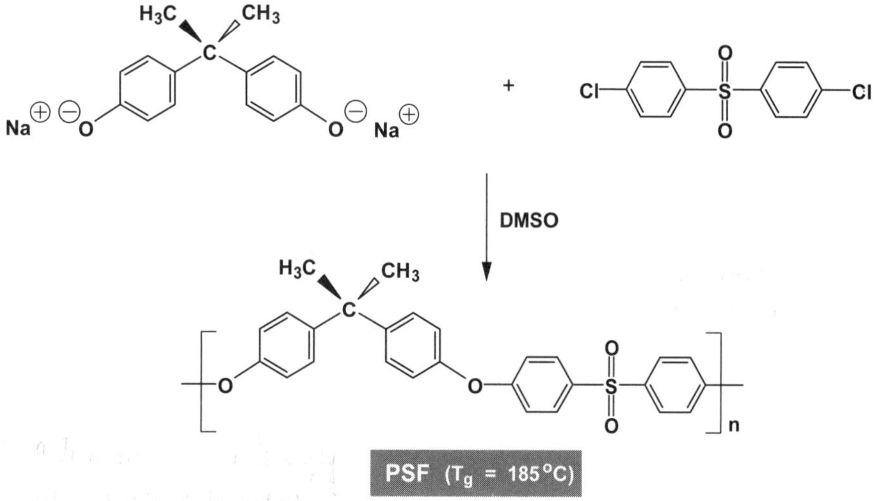

H_3C CH_3 C $Na^{\oplus}$ $^{\ominus}O$ $O^{\ominus}$ $Na^{\oplus}$ + Cl S O O Cl

DMSO

H_3C CH_3 C O O S O O n

PSF (T_g = 185°C)

Figure 4.7. Synthesis of PSF by the polyetherification route.

In recent years, PSF has been the subject of intensive research for both gas separation and fuel cell *proton conducting membranes* (PCMs). PSF is the first membrane introduced for commercial gas separation because of its overall combination of relatively high permselectivities and adequate permeabilities to various gases (e.g., H_2, CO_2, O_2, N_2, CH_4, etc), as well as its good mechanical properties and fiber spinning qualities. Studies indicate that the gas permeation behavior is mainly affected by the packing density and segmental motion of the polymer chain.[14,15] Typically, chain rigidity results in increased permselectivity but lower permeability, whereas greater free volume gives higher permeability but lower selectivity. To achieve simultaneously higher permeability and selectivity, chain stiffness should be coupled with an increase in interchain separation. On this basis, a variety of PSF analogs have been prepared, mostly by post-modification of PSF (Figure 4.8). Gas permeabilities have been shown to be significantly improved by introducing bulky groups, such as trialkylsilyl and hexafluoro-2-propyl.[16-18] For example, when trimethylsilyl (TMS) groups are introduced at sites *ortho* to the ether linkage, the oxygen permeability increased almost 7-fold with only a marginal decrease in selectivity compared with that of the unmodified polysulfone. Finally, it is important to note that hexafluoroisopropylpolysulfone (6FPSF) is more permeable to many gases than PSF and shows less than tradeoff behavior in permselectivity because hexafluoroisopropylidene groups sterically hinder both bond rotation and intersegmental packing, which is further inhibited by intermolecular repulsive forces between fluorine atoms that have high electron density.[19]

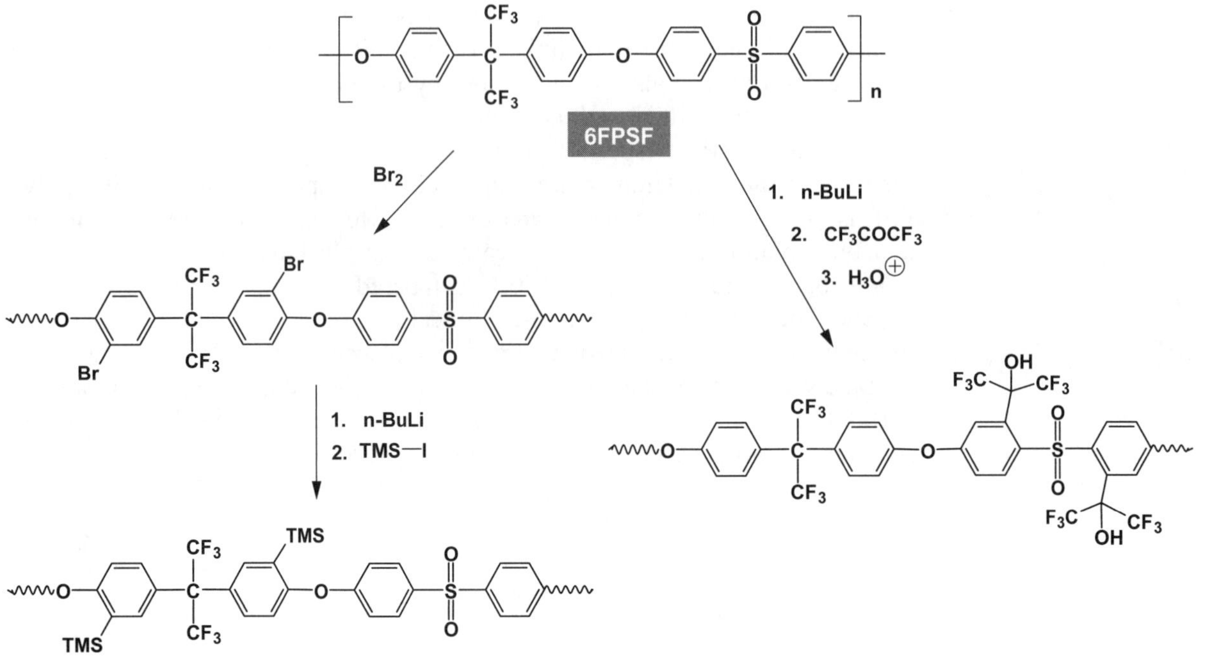

Figure 4.8. Post-modified aromatic polysulfones for gas separation membrane applications.

The thermal and gas separation properties can also be improved by incorporating adamantyl groups in the aromatic polysulfones.[20,21] These compounds were prepared by polyetherification of a more reactive dihalide, 4,4'-difluorodiphenyl sulfone (DFDS), with an appropriate adamantine moiety containing diphenol, in the presence of K_2CO_3 (Figure 4.9). Interestingly, the polymer containing the adamantane moiety as the part of the polymer backbone exhibits lower T_g compared to the polymers with pendent adamantyl moieties. It is important to stress that the presence of this group has a negligible effect on the inherent thermal stability of the aromatic polysulfones (all display thermal stability >450°C), but has strong influence in elevating T_g (~100°C for the polymer containing a pendent adamantyl group at the bridgehead position of bisphenol).

Aromatic polysulfone-based PCMs for *direct methanol fuel cells* (DMFCs) are attractive because they comply with most of the demanding requirements, such as proton conductivity higher than 0.01 S/cm, long-term stability under humidified and heated conditions, impermeability to hydrogen, methanol and oxygen, and good mechanical properties. Among the several polysulfones tested, FL-PSF, derived from the polyetherification of DFDS with 9,9'-bis(4-hydroxyphenyl)fluorene (BHF), is very promising (Figure 4.10).[22] FL-PSF can be regioselectively substituted with sulfonic acid groups to afford an ionomer, FL-PSFI, with an ion exchange capacity up to ~2.0 mequiv/g (see Chapter-5 for other important classes of PCMs). Moreover, FL-PSFI can be solution cast to a tough, flexible, ductile, and transparent membrane, which exhibits thermal stability with a decomposition temperature of ca. 250°C. The membrane exhibits outstanding stability to oxidation and hydrolysis, good mechanical properties (lower elongation and higher strength), and a proton conductivity of 0.2 S/cm at 140°C, including lower gas (H_2 and O_2) permeation. All of these properties of FL-PSFI are the best among the hydrocarbon based ionomers. Thus, FL-PSFI is a very promising electrolyte membrane for high-temperature DMFCs.

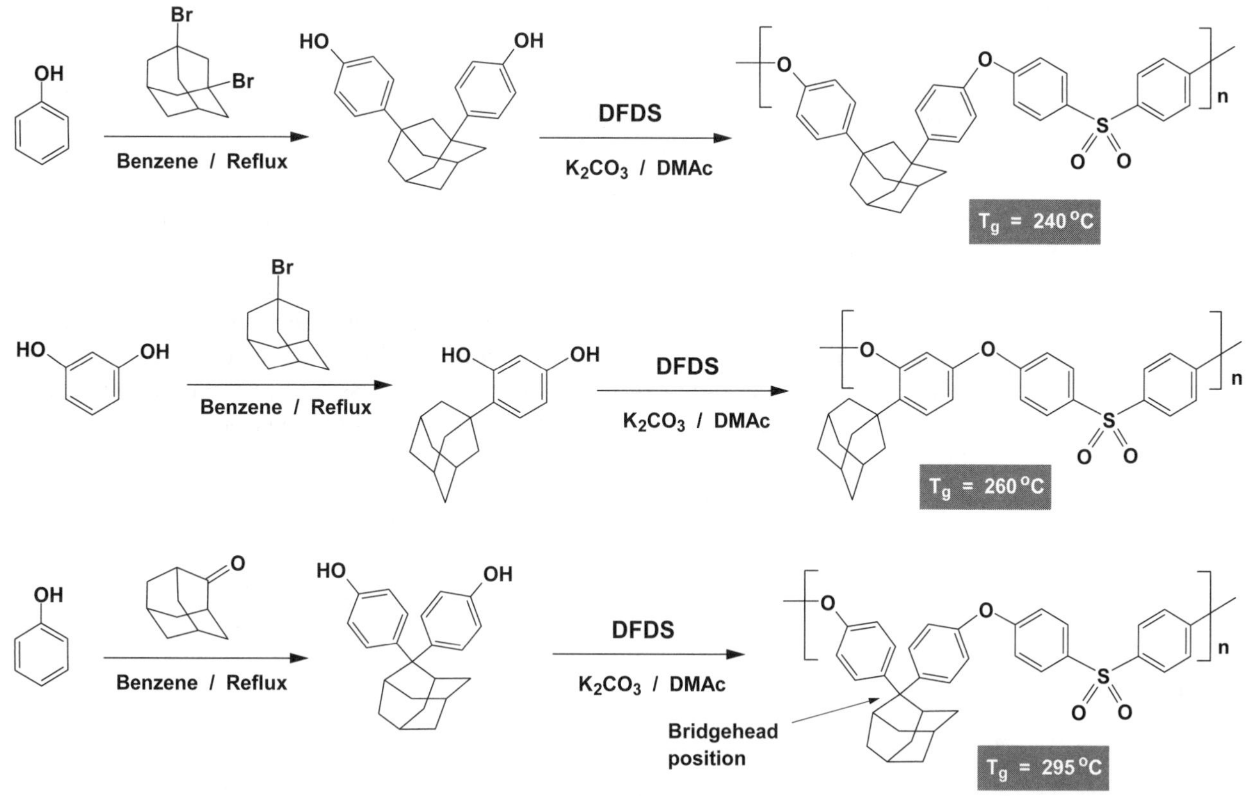

Figure 4.9. Synthesis of aromatic polysulfones containing adamantyl moieties.

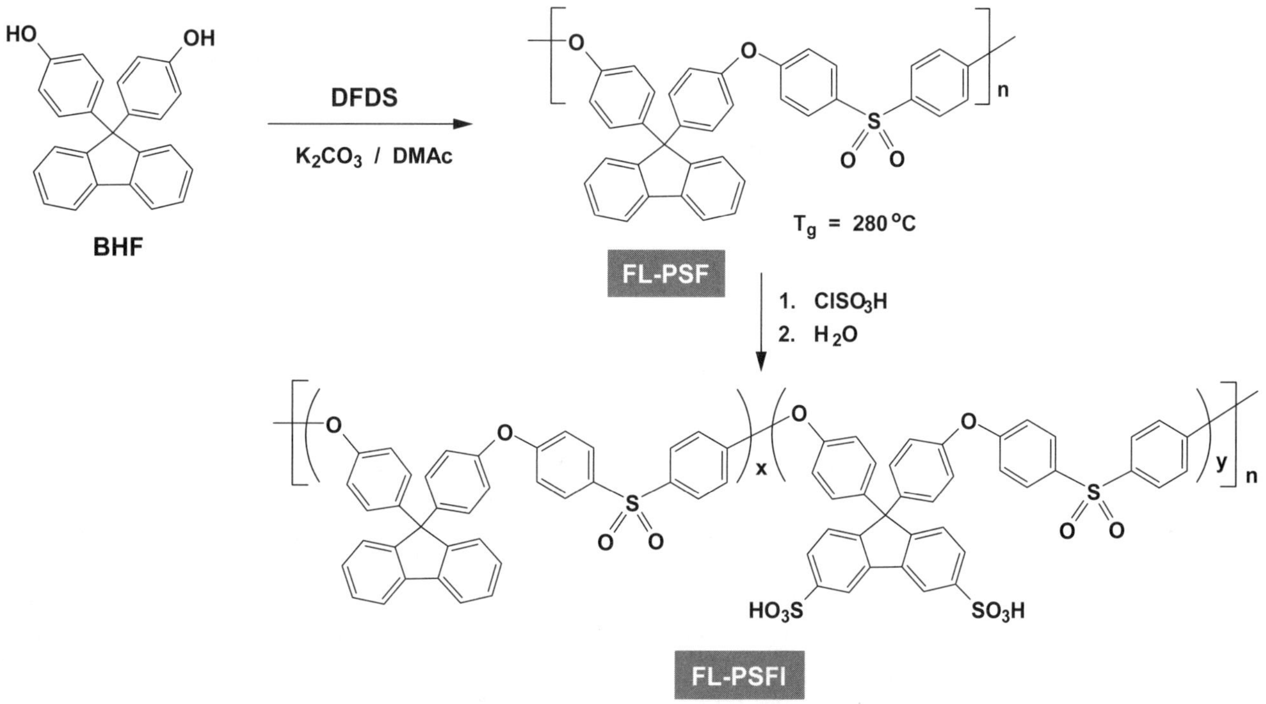

Figure 4.10. Synthesis of fluorenyl groups containing aromatic polysulfone for PCM applications.

4.3. AROMATIC POLYKETONES

Since the carbonyl moiety is a good electron-withdrawing group, the polyetherification (nucleophilic displacement) route used for polyethersulfones is also adapted for the synthesis of most commercial aromatic polyketones, viz., poly(ether ketone) (PEK), poly(ether ether ketone) (PEEK), poly(ether biphenyl ether ketone) (PEBEK) and poly(ether aryl ether ketone) (PEAEK) (Figure 4.11).[23,24] The most important member of this family is PEEK® (Victrex plc), a semicrystalline thermoplastic (T_g = 145°C and T_m = 340°C), which performs well at extremely high temperatures, 250°C long term and 300°C short term. This makes it a high strength alternative to fluoropolymers. Although having high T_m, PEEK is an injection moldable material (no decomposition below 400°C in air!) and can be reinforced with glass, mineral, and graphite fibers. It has one of the lightest strength to weight ratios and exhibits outstanding resistance to aggressive chemicals. Thus, PEEK offers chemical and water resistance comparable to PPS, but can sustain higher temperatures.

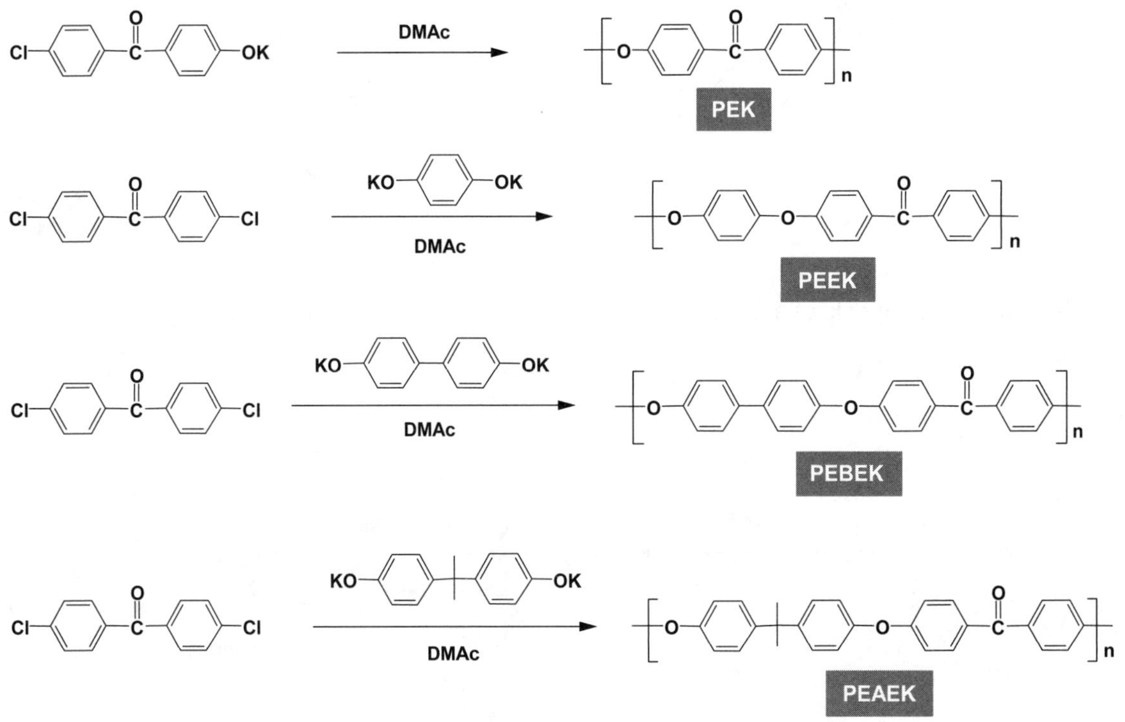

Figure 4.11. Aromatic polyketones by nucleophilic displacement.

Among recently developed aromatic polyketones, *iso*PEK (the simplest isomer of PEK that possesses a well-ordered microstructure of alternating *m*- and *p*-phenylene rings) and *iso*PEKEK (a companion polymer) are important (Figure 4.12) because of their ease of injection moldability.[25-27] They exhibit much lower T_ms than traditional PEK (T_g = 155°C and T_m = 355°C) due to a lesser degree of crystallinity, but show thermostability similar to PEK. The monomers are prepared by Friedel-Crafts acylation of fluorobenzene or phenol with *m*-hydroxybenzoic acid in the presence of the BF_3/HF catalyst system. N-Methylcaprolactam (NMC), which permits reaction temperatures up to 225°C, was found to be the best solvent for the S_NAr polymerization of the appropriate monomer(s).

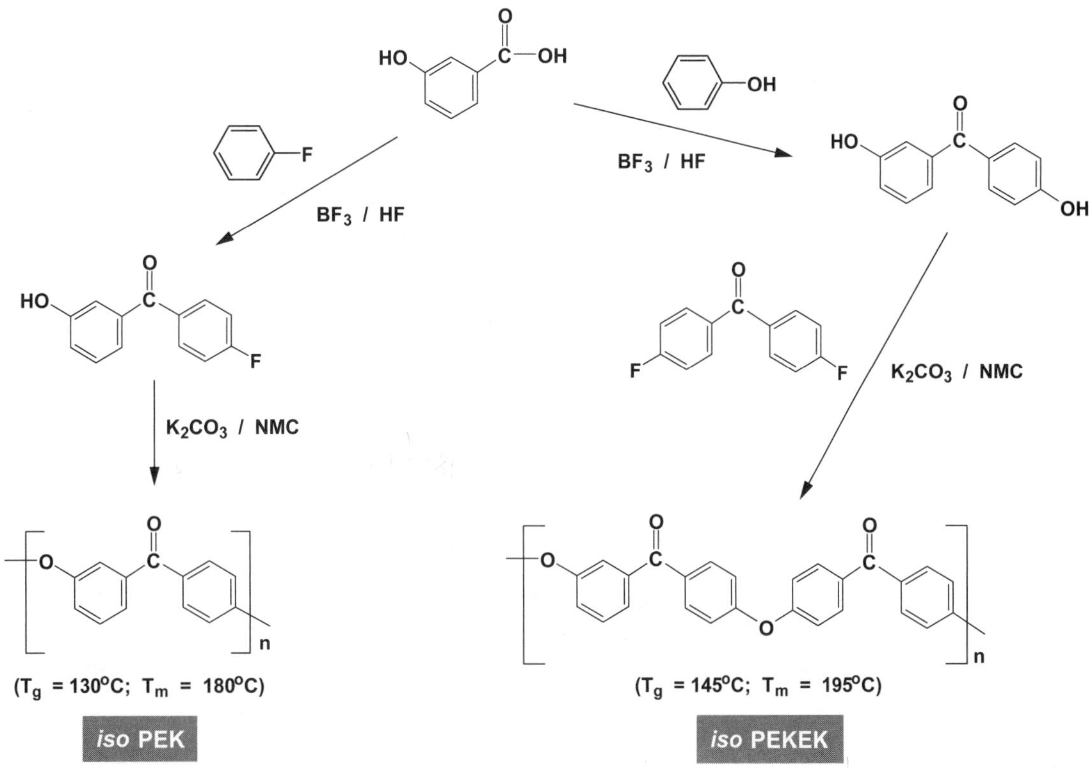

HO, C(=O)OH, OH, F, BF_3 / HF, BF_3 / HF, K_2CO_3 / NMC, K_2CO_3 / NMC, F, F, O, n

(T_g = 130°C; T_m = 180°C)

iso PEK

(T_g = 145°C; T_m = 195°C)

iso PEKEK

Figure 4.12. Synthesis of soluble and melt-processable PEK analogs.

Aromatic polyketones containing rigid moieties, such as 4,4'-biphenylene, in the polymer backbone have also been developed for applications under extreme conditions beyond the limits of traditional materials, such as PEK and PEEK. As shown in Figure 4.13, these polymers are prepared by both S_NAr and electrophilic substitution methods.[28-30] The latter employs trifluoromethanesulfonic acid for polycondensation of aromatic ether and carboxyl groups and is preferred when high molecular weight products are desired.[31-33] These polyketones are highly crystalline because of the ease of edge-to-face packing of laterally adjacent chains and exhibit very high T_m. The degree of crystallinity and T_m can be reduced significantly by introducing 2,6-naphthylene moieties along with 4,4'-biphenylene in the backbone. Very high boiling solvents, such as diphenyl sulfone (DPS) and N-cyclohexylpyrrolidone (NCP), are required for S_NAr reactions of these highly aromatic poly(ether ketone)s.

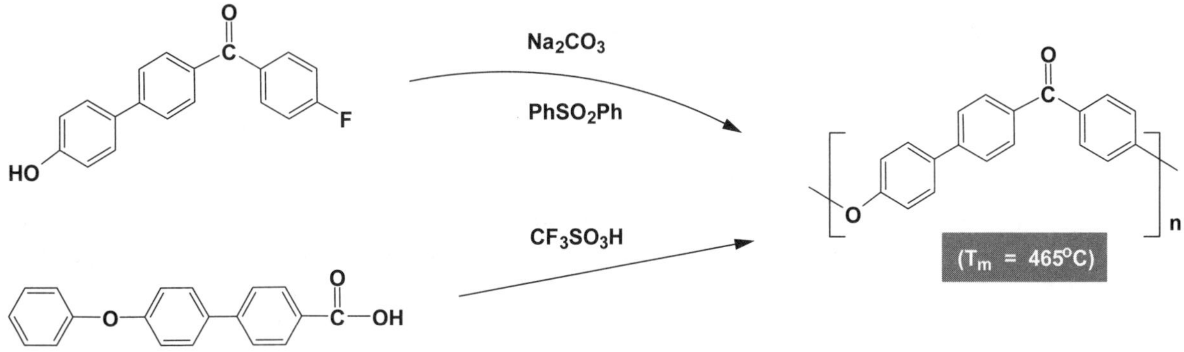

HO, F, Na_2CO_3, $PhSO_2Ph$, CF_3SO_3H, C(=O)OH, O, n

(T_m = 465°C)

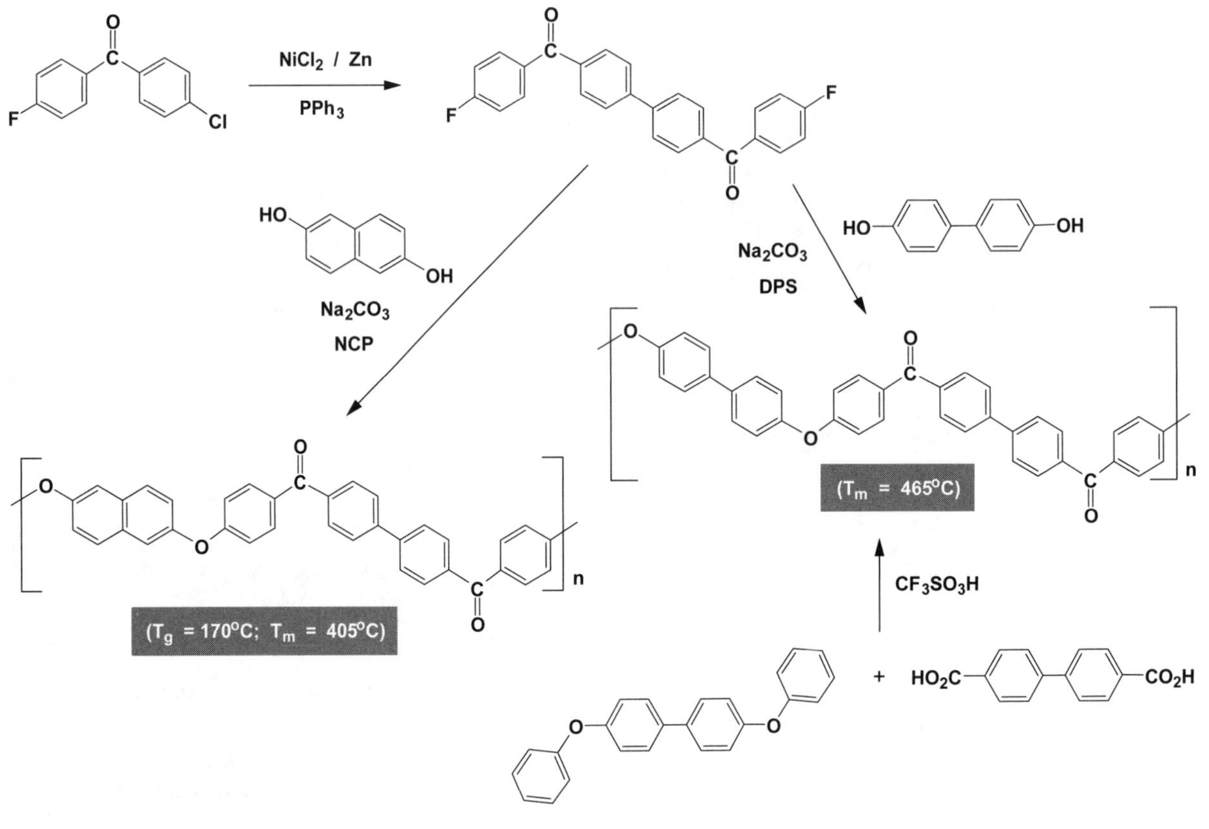

Figure 4.13. Synthesis of high-performance aromatic polyketones.

Wholly aromatic polyketones, devoid of any ether linkages in the backbone, represent a class of highly thermostable (>500°C) polymers. They are very difficult to prepare in high molecular weights by the conventional electrophilic substitution[32] or nickel-mediated aromatic coupling method because of their insolubility in the solvent of polymerization. Recently, a novel nucleophilic carbon-carbon bond-forming polymerization route has been described for the synthesis of these polyketones via soluble precursors derived from bis(α-aminonitrile)s under mild reaction conditions (Figure 4.14, next page).[33-36] Moreover, they can be prepared at moderate temperatures and in high yields. It is noteworthy that this methodology can also be used to obtain a variety of unique hybrids of aromatic polyketones, such as poly(arylene ketone sulfone)s, including poly(ether ketone)s bearing various sequences of ether and keto groups bridging together arylene rings with a proper selection of monomers.

4.4. LIQUID CRYSTALLINE POLYESTERS

In contrast to *polyarylates* (PARs), discussed in Chapter-3, *liquid crystalline polyesters* (LCPs) are wholly aromatic (i.e., do not have any functional groups in the main chain other than ester) and contain inherently rigid units, thereby forming a highly "extended chain" morphology. LCPs possess excellent physical properties, high mechanical strength, high impact resistance, outstanding thermal (upper use temperature of more than 250°C) and barrier properties, and good inherent flame retardant behavior. LCPs are virtually unaffected by most acids, bases, and solvents over a broad temperature

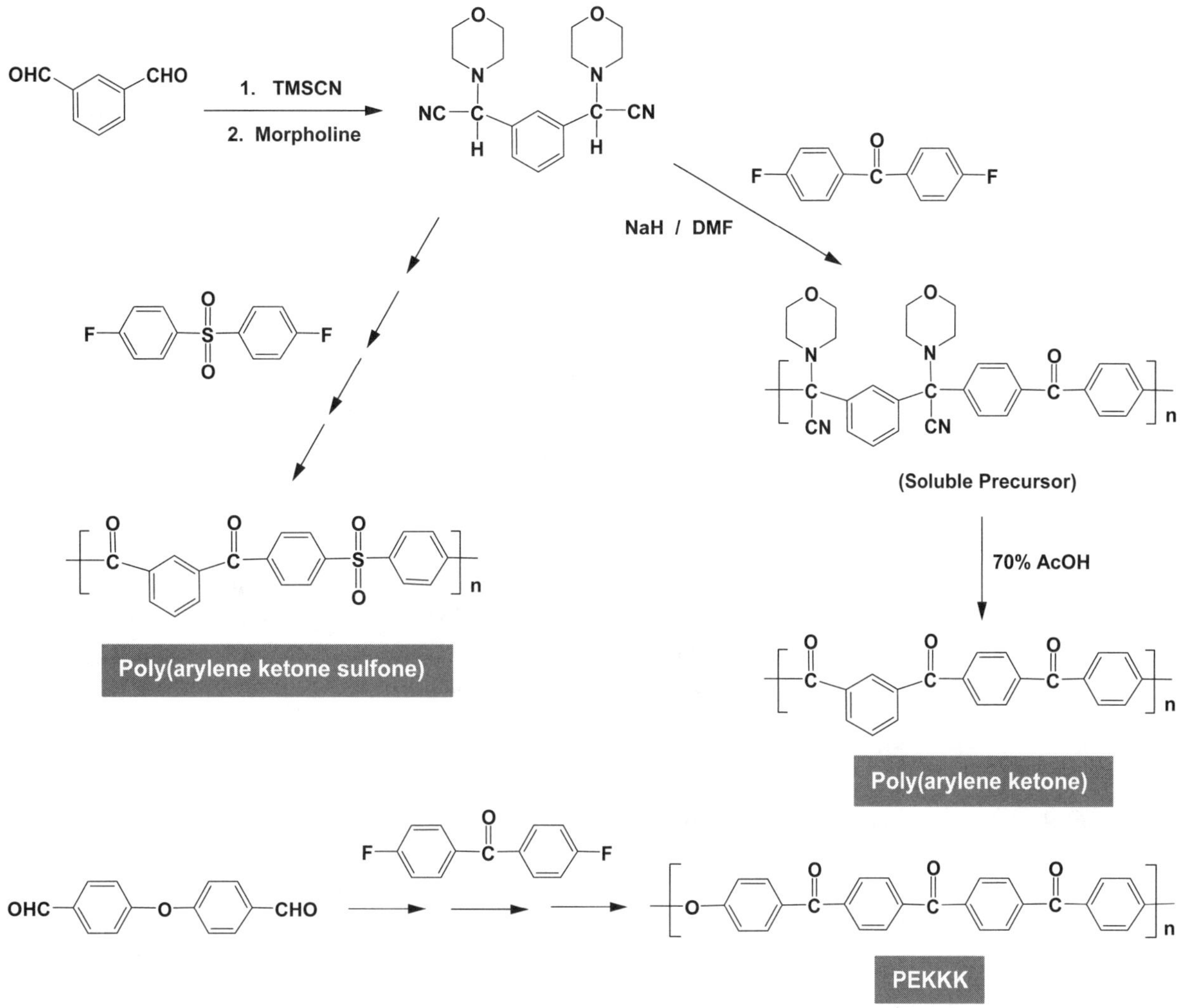

Figure 4.14. Synthesis of wholly aromatic polyketones and companions.

range. The unique feature of LCPs is that they exhibit low viscosity during processing and can be melt-spun into fibers with exceptional strength and rigidity, which are attributed to its highly anisotropic orientation of polymer chains (Figure 4.15). By contrast, in conventional polyesters, the molecular chains are random and flexible. Consequently, the fibers must be further oriented, generally through a combination of extrusion speed and post-spin drawing, to obtain higher tensile properties. The differences between LCP fiber and two other high-performance fibers, aramids (*vide infra*) and UHMWPE, are as follows: LCP fiber is thermotropic (forms liquid crystalline structure in melt), melts at a high temperature, and is melt-spun. Aramid fiber is lyotropic (forms liquid crystalline structure in solution), does not melt at high temperature, and is solvent-spun. UHMWPE fiber is gel-spun and melts at a low temperature. While the lyotropic aramids can be fabricated only into fibers or films, the thermotropic LCP can be made into a three-dimensional structure by conventional processing, such as injection molding. This makes thermotropic LCP a unique material for a wide range of applications. When considered pound for pound, LCP fibers are five times stronger than steel and ten times stronger than aluminum. Consequently, LCP fibers are used in air- and spacecraft technology, ocean exploration and development, electronic support structures, the recreation and leisure industry, safety materials, industrial applications, ropes and cables, composites, and protective garments.

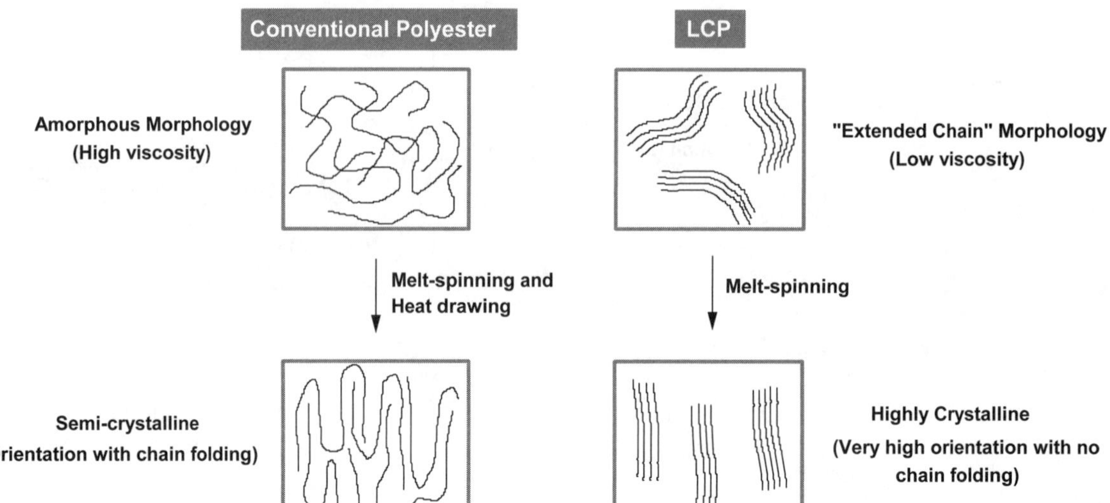

Figure 4.15. Schematic of molecular chain structures in LCP and conventional polyester fibers.

LCPs, such as Vectra® (Ticona, formerly Celanese) and Xydar® (Solvay Advanced Polymers) are produced through an ion-free polycondensation process involving a variety of aromatic hydroxy acids, diacid and dihydroxy monomers (Figure 4.16). This makes LCPs especially suited for applications in the electronics sector (e.g., connecting parts in fiber optics, telecommunication and medical devices, cell phone battery housing), where ion concentrations of less than 5 ppm are desired. Moreover, LCP films have a lower dielectric constant and loss factor over the functional frequency range of 1 kHz to 45 GHz with negligible moisture effects compared to commonly used polyimide films. Circuits built using LCP as the base substrate can have metal trace signal lines placed closer together without crosstalk, resulting in more densely packed circuits. In order to obtain polymers with high molecular weights, the monomers must be acetylated (to improve reactivity) either *in situ* or before conducting the polycondensation reaction. The most common acetylated monomers are *p*-acetoxybenzoic acid (ABA), 6-acetoxy-2-naphthoic acid (ANA) and 4,4'-bis-acetoxybiphenyl (ABP). While terephthalic acid (TPA) is one of the major constituents in most LCP formulations (e.g., Xydar), isophthalic acid (IPA) or *m*-acetoxybenzoic acid (mABA) is often employed to modify LCP properties. The introduction of *meta* linkages (kinks) into the polymer backbone reduces the regularity of the polymer chain, thus offering processing advantages due to lowering of melting temperature.[37] However, the *meta* linkage also has a detrimental effect on the stability of the LC phase behavior if its content exceeds a certain percentage.

ABA + ANA

- AcOH (Vacuum) 250 - 300°C

Vectra®

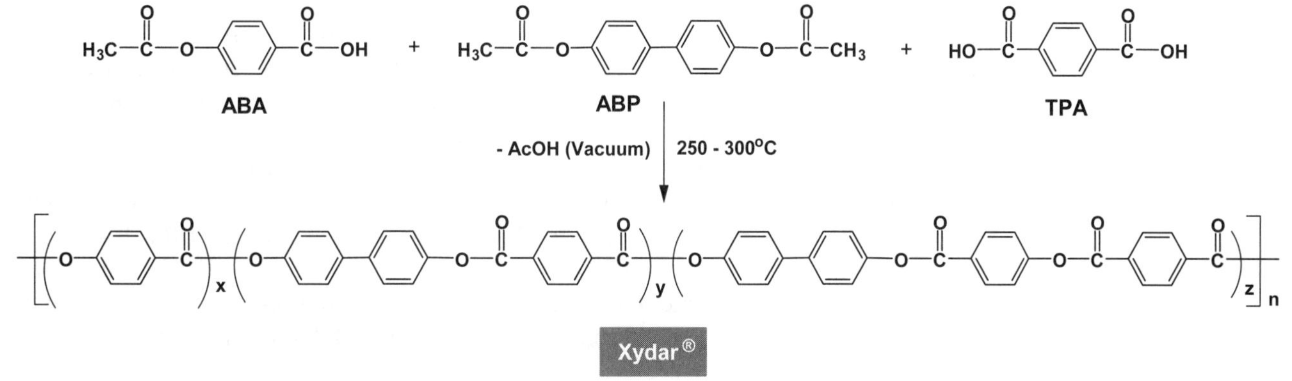

Figure 4.16. Synthesis of representative commercial LCPs.

The introduction of pendent groups to the LCP backbone is another important factor in improving melt processability. The effect of both rigid side-rod and flexible side chain on LCP properties has been investigated. Among the side-rod monomers, 2,5-diphenyl-1,4-diacetoxybenzene (DPAB) and 3,3'-diphenyl-4,4'-diacetoxybiphenyl (DPDB) are important (Figure 4.17).[38-40] The resulting LCPs exhibit good thermal stability, lower dielectric constants compared with their parent polymers, and liquid crystallinity up to a maximum side-rod concentration of 20 mol%. The degree of crystallinity of LCPs, however, decreases with the increase in side-rod concentration. The reduction in dielectric constant may be attributed to a lower degree of crystallinity and less dense packing structure of the polymer caused by the presence of side-rods.

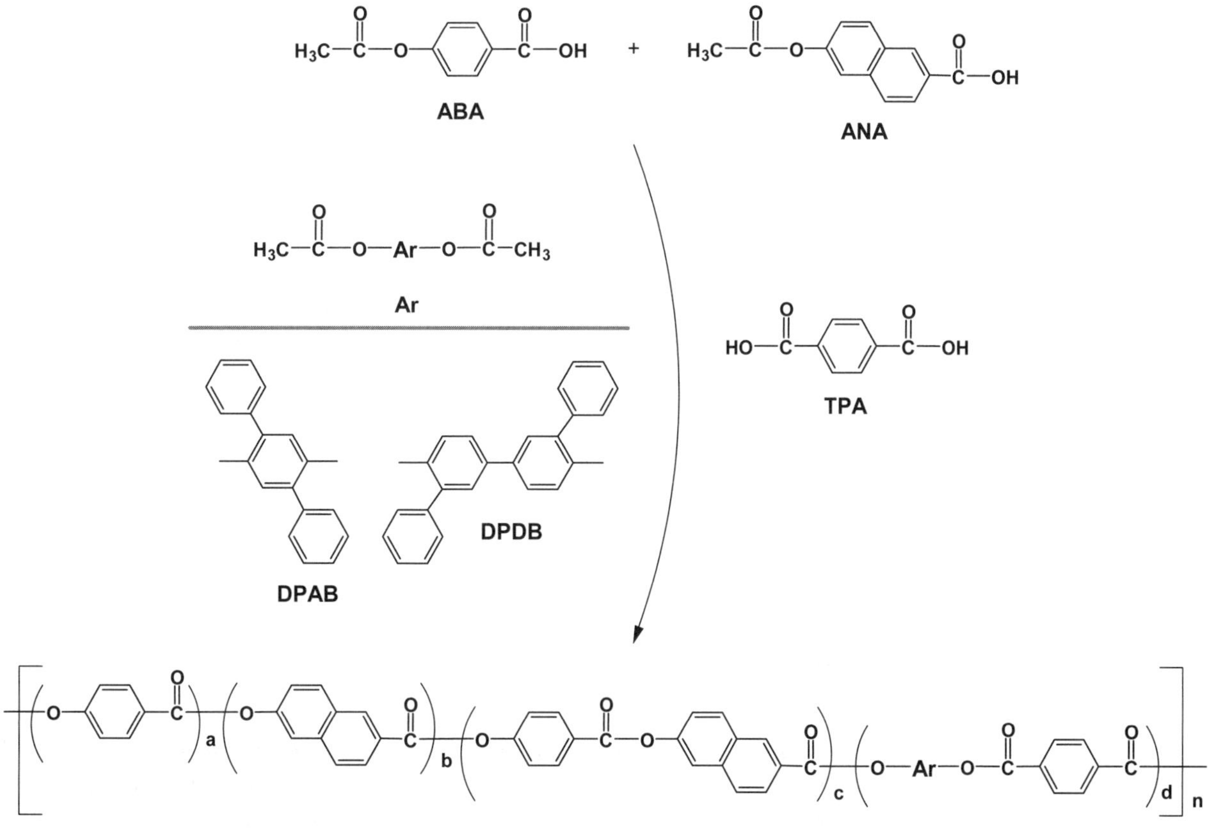

Figure 4.17. Synthesis of rigid side rods containing LCPs.

The effect of flexible side chains (especially long chain alkoxy and alkyl) on both diphenol and dicarboxylic acid monomers has been studied extensively.[41-43] In general, the flexible side chains containing LCPs (often called *"hairy-rod" polymers*) are soluble in common organic solvents, but exhibit significantly lower liquid crystalline transition temperatures and poor modulus at temperatures above 150°C. The introduction of oligophenylene (terphenylene or quinquephenylene) segments, which increase rigidity in the polymer backbone, seems to improve overall properties. The oligophenylene monomers may be prepared either by palladium-mediated coupling of the 1,4-dibromo compound with an appropriate hydroxyl-protected Grignard complex or by Suzuki-type coupling between a diboronic acid and a hydroxyl-protected bromo compound (Figure 4.18). The benzyl protective group is easily removed by catalytic reduction with hydrogen.

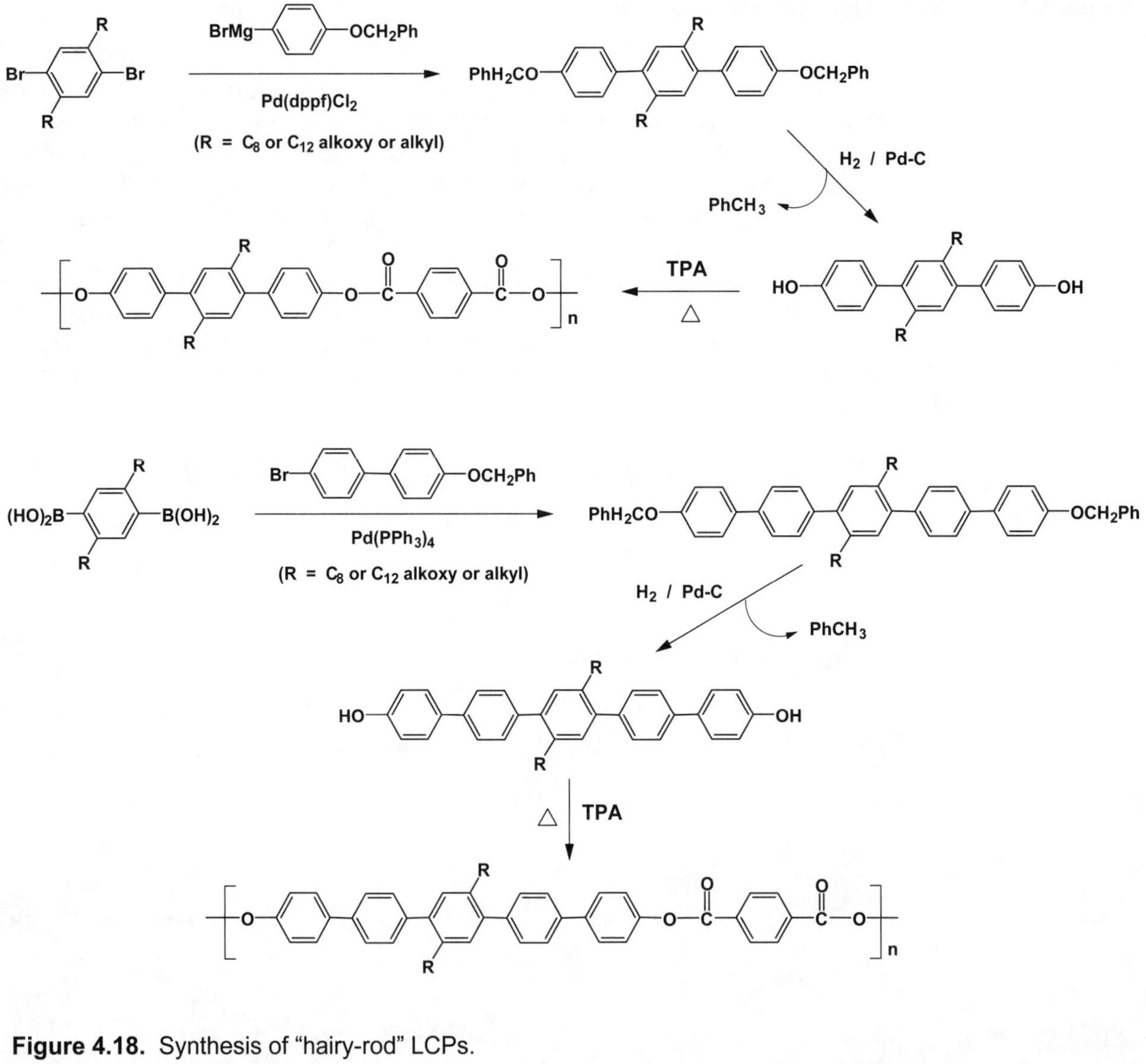

Figure 4.18. Synthesis of "hairy-rod" LCPs.

A recent study indicates that the incorporation of ionic groups into LCPs is a promising approach for improving compressive (and transverse) properties without sacrificing tensile properties.[44-46] It is well known that strong ionic interactions (bonds) between polymer chains can significantly enhance mechanical properties, as demonstrated for polyethylene ionomer, Surlyn® (see Chapter-2). In ionic polymers, polymer chains are ionically crosslinked through nondirectional strong ionic bonds, but are thermally labile. Thus, unlike chemically crosslinked polymers, they melt upon heating and re-form upon cooling. The introduction of ~1 mol% of ionic groups, e.g., sodium sulfonate, into LCP chains, using sodium 5-sulfoisophthalate (SSI) as co-monomer and the same amount of *p*-diacetoxybenzene (DAB) to balance the extra carboxyl group of the SSI monomer, is adequate for superior mechanical properties (Figure 4.19). Moreover, the melt of the resulting ionic LCP exhibits extensive birefringence and nematic mesophase textures over a wide temperature range, without showing a transition to an isotropic phase to at least 380°C. Unlike conventional flexible ionomers whose T_g increase with ionic content, the ionic LCPs show a relatively constant T_g below 10 mol % ionic content. This behavior is considered to be a result of the competition between two opposing factors: a "kinked" structure that reduces the rigidity of the polymer backbone chains, and an ionic interaction that restricts the segmental mobility of the polymer chain. Thus, the advantages of thermal lability and reprocessability can be used to develop novel polymeric materials whose intermolecular interactions can be reinforced via ionic bonds.

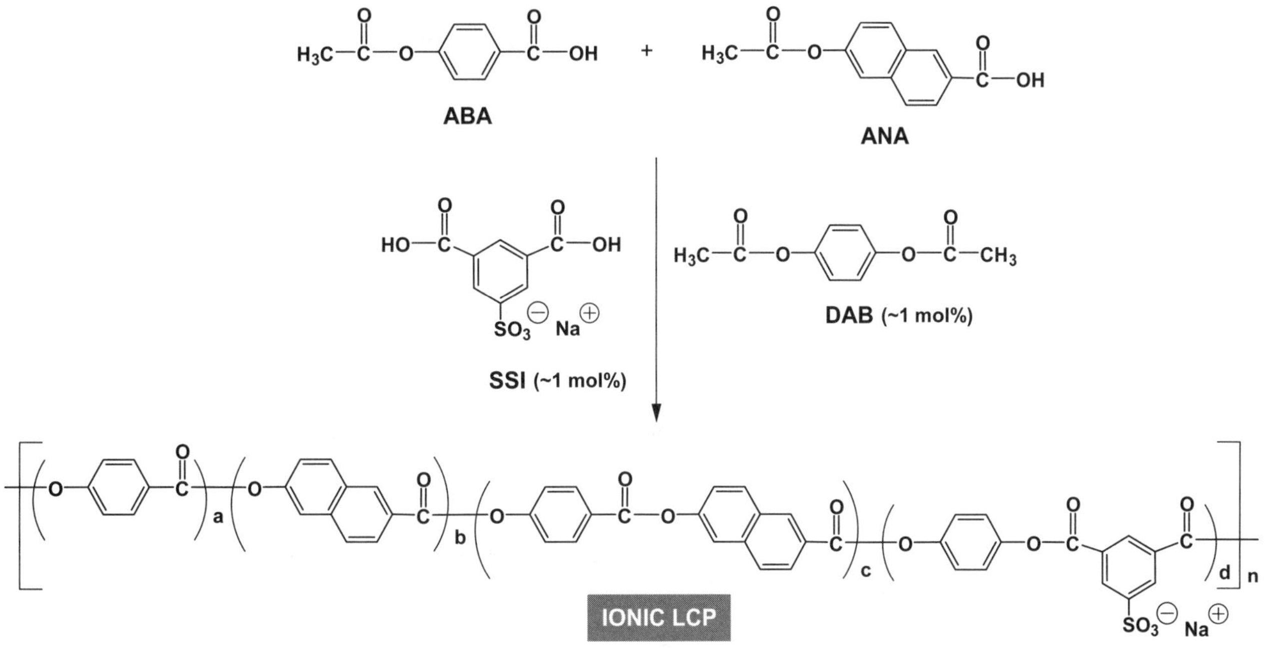

Figure 4.19. Synthesis of an ionic LCP.

4.5. AROMATIC POLYAMIDES

Aromatic polyamides are commonly termed "aramids". The most important commercial aramids are Nomex® [poly(*m*-phenylene isophthalamide) from DuPont], Kevlar® [poly(*p*-phenylene terephthalamide) from DuPont] and Tecnora® [copoly(*p*-phenylene/3,4'-diphenyl ether terephthalamide) from Teijin Chemicals]. As mentioned in Chapter-3 under nylons, aramids cannot be obtained in high molecular weights by the melt method because of the low reactivity of aromatic amines. They are prepared by the solution condensation method in polar organic solvents, usually from diamines and very reactive species such as acid chlorides. Indeed, Nomex is produced by polymerization of isophthaloyl chloride and *m*-phenylenediamine in dimethylacetamide (DMAc) with 5% lithium chloride (Figure 4.20). The reaction must be carried out in the temperature range of -40 to 0°C to avoid undesirable side reactions, such as acylation of diamine and *trans*-amidification by the amide solvent, which cause stoichiometric imbalance leading to low molecular weight products. Nomex is manufactured in both fiber and sheet forms and is used as a fabric wherever resistance from heat and flame is required. A Nomex hood is a common piece of firefighting equipment. It is placed on the head on top of a firefighter's face mask, which supplies air inside a smoke filled environment. The hood protects the portions of the head not covered by the helmet and face mask from the intense heat of the fire. Race car drivers commonly use a similar hood to protect them in the event a fire engulfs their car. Nomex has been adapted to a wide variety of uses, including machinery and circuitry for its insulation.

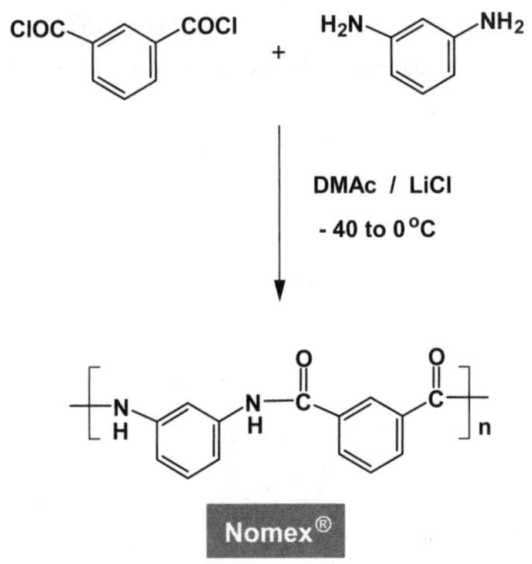

ClOC–C6H4–COCl + H2N–C6H4–NH2

DMAc / LiCl

- 40 to 0°C

Nomex®

Figure 4.20. Synthesis of Nomex.

Kevlar is less soluble in amide solvent and is prepared by polymerization of terephthaloyl chloride and *p*-phenylenediamine in a solvent mixture of hexamethylphosphoramide (HMPA) and N-methylpyrrolidinone (NMP), often in the presence of $CaCl_2$, which forms a soluble complex with the polymer, thus permitting high molecular weight products. The *p*-phenylene rings in Kevlar cause the bonds between the NH and the CO units to be highly resistant to rotation. As a result, the connecting bonds on both side of amide group are formed almost exclusively in the *trans*-configuration, which allows for perfectly straight polymer chains with a parallel orientation (Figure 4.21). This is in contrast to nylons, such as nylon-6,6, where the connecting bonds on both side of amide group are found in both the *trans*- and *cis*-configurations. The *trans*-configuration enables polymer chains to line up in an almost linear fashion, whereas the *cis*-configuration causes the fiber path to change direction. Kevlar derives its strength from intra-molecular hydrogen bonds and phenyl stacking interactions between aromatic moieties in neighboring strands. The strength of Kevlar fiber is five times that of steel, weight for weight. Kevlar is very heat resistant and decomposes above 400°C without melting. It is usually used in bulletproof vests, in extreme sports equipment, and for composite aircraft construction. It is also employed as a replacement for steel cords in car tires, fire suits, and as an asbestos replacement.

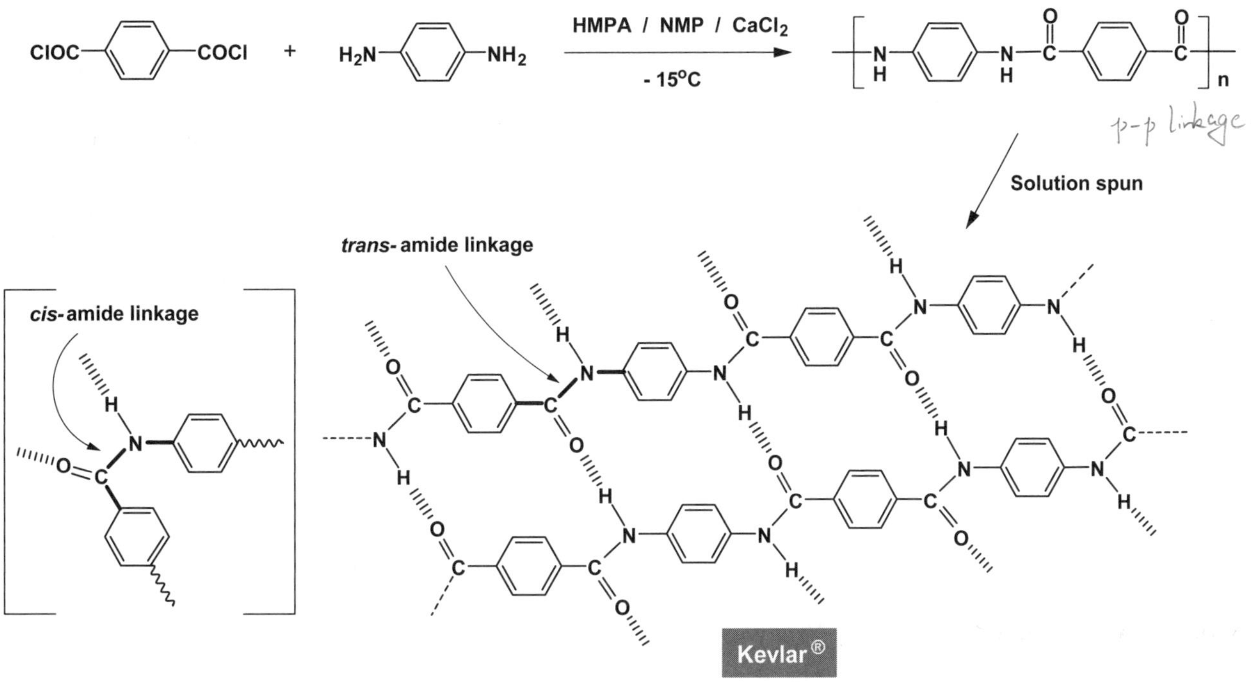

Figure 4.21. Synthesis of Kevlar.

Technora®, a newer member of the aramid family (introduced in 1987 by Teijin Aramid), is prepared using the 1:1 copolyterephthalamide of 3,4'-diaminodiphenyl ether (DAPE) and *p*-phenylenediamine (Figure 4.22).[47] Unlike Kevlar, which exhibits an anisotropic phase in sulfuric acid solution, Technora forms an isotropic solution that becomes anisotropic during shear alignment of the spinning process. Technora fibers display a slightly lower tenacity and tensile modulus compared to Kevlar, but offer greater processing flexibility. It is important to note that most aramids melt with decomposition. Consequently, they are solution-spun (from sulfuric acid solution) through a spinnerette located in a coagulation bath containing cold water. The fiber formed is then drawn to increase molecular orientation in the direction of stretch, tenacity, and modulus. However, both Nomex and Technora are melt processable because of the presence of *m*-phenylene rings in the polymer backbone, which facilitates the formation of more *cis*-amide linkages, leading to a lower degree of crystallinity and lesser interchain hydrogen bonds than Kevlar.

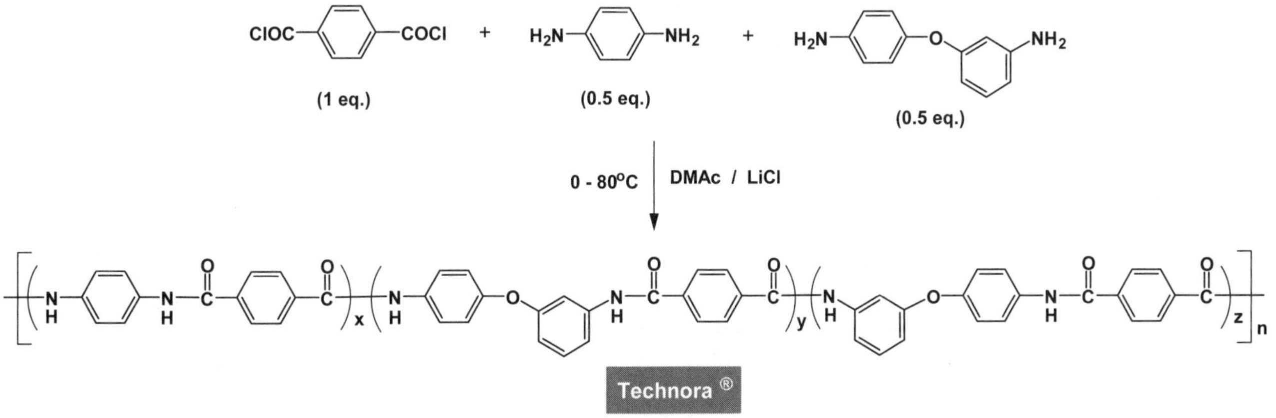

Figure 4.22. Synthesis of Technora.

In past years, more robust and high temperature and chemical resistant aramids have been prepared by using specifically designed aromatic diamines or dicarboxylic acids. Most contain *meta-* or *para-*linked aromatic rings or fused aromatic rings, including pendent heterocyclic or phenyl rings. The example shown in Figure 4.23 is a typical synthetic strategy for the preparation of a diamine containing a pendent heterocyclic moiety, which is well-known for improving thermal stability. The resulting aramid exhibits superior properties compared to that of the unmodified polymer, such as a lower softening temperature, ~10% improvement in thermal stability and marked enhancement in hydrophobicity.[48] Please see the following section on aromatic polyimides, since they are also prepared from diamine and problems at the end of the chapter for more examples of novel diamines.

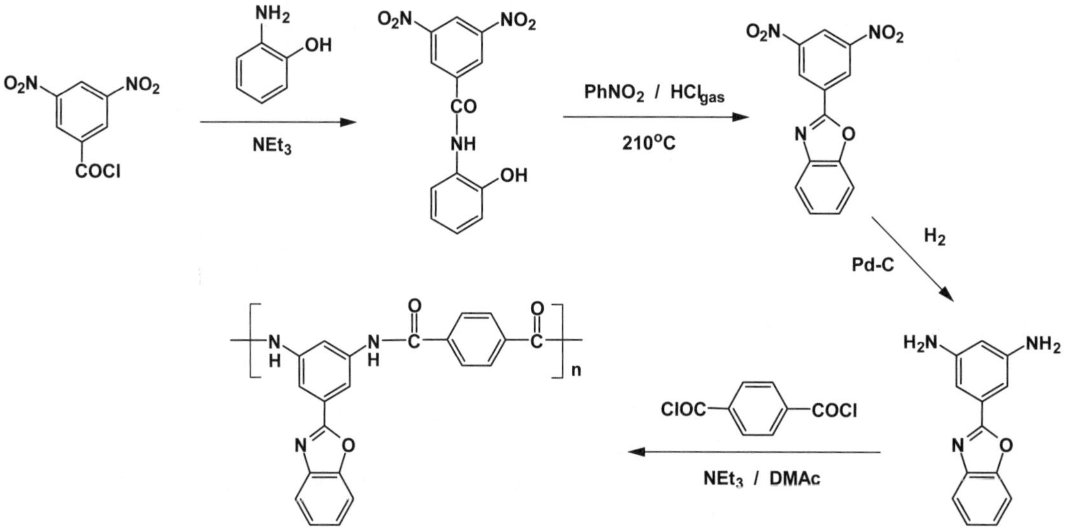

NH2
OH
O2N NO2
COCl
NEt3
O2N NO2
CO
NH
OH
PhNO2 / HClgas
210°C
O2N NO2
N O
H2
Pd-C
H2N NH2
N O
ClOC COCl
NEt3 / DMAc
N H
N H
O
C
O
C
n
N O

Figure 4.23. Synthesis of an aromatic polyamide containing pendent heterocyclic moieties.

By contrast, the scheme depicted in Figure 4.24 is more versatile and offers, if desirable, access to both diamine and diacid with an identical aromatic residue (nonlinear terphenylene moiety) containing a pendent phenyl ring. As expected, the molecular design permits high solubility of the resulting aramid in common organic solvents, without considerable influence on its thermal stability. The approach involves well-known chemistry of a perylium salt, which readily reacts with a condensing agent, such as sodium acetate, in the presence of acetic anhydride. The perylium salt is formed by reaction between an aromatic aldehyde and acetophenone in the presence of $BF_3 \bullet Et_2O$.

4.6. POLYIMIDES

Polyimides (PIMs) are distinguished from other high-performance polymers by the solubility of the poly(amic acid) precursor, which can be cast into uniform films and quantitatively converted to the polyimide. They are very attractive to various scientific communities because of their ease of synthesis, broad spectrum properties (high thermal stability, superior mechanical strength, wide chemical resistance, excellent adhesion to a variety of substrates, relatively low dielectric constants, etc.) and monomeric tailorability for specific applications. Besides the aromatic imide functionality, most

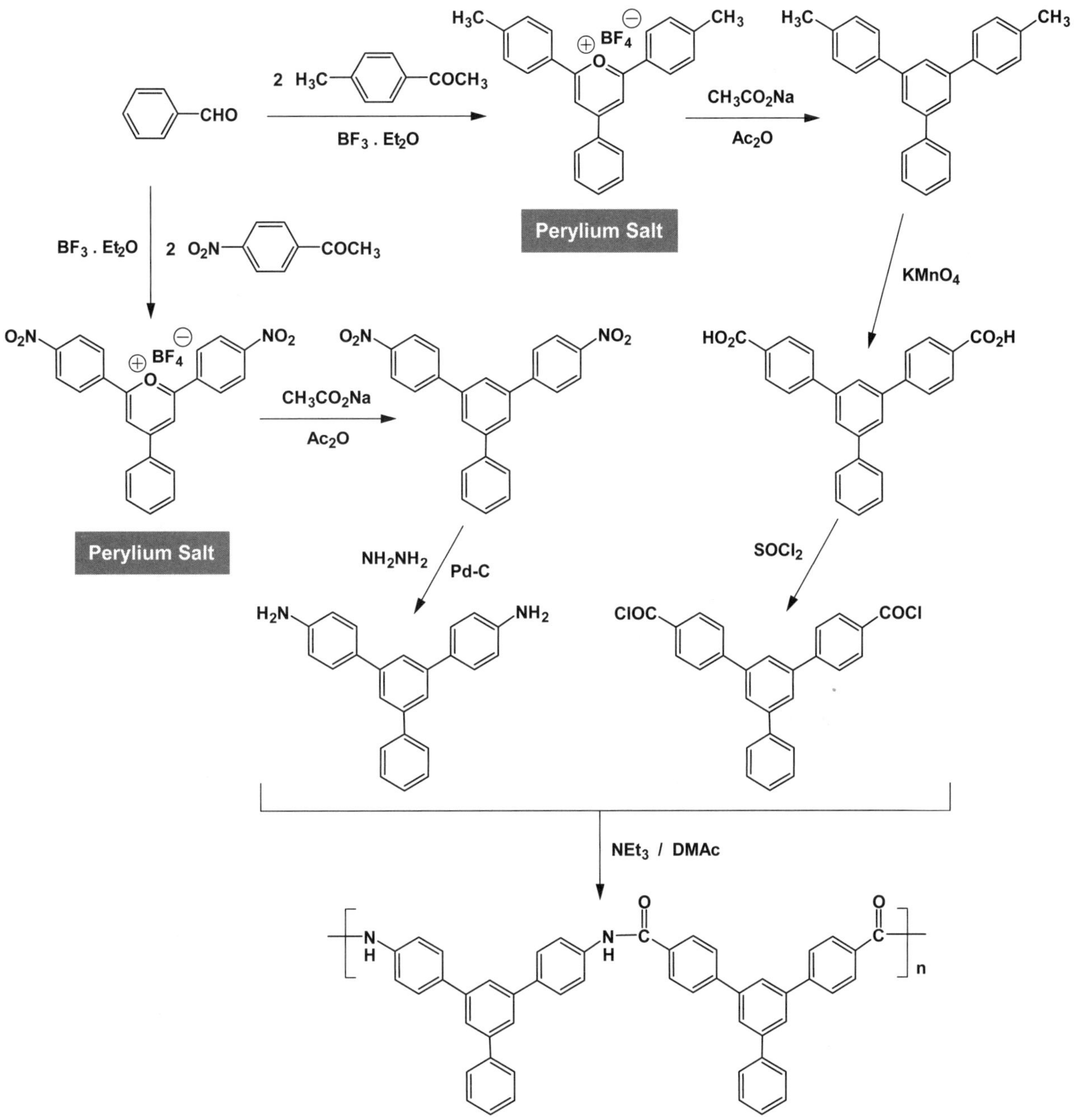

Perylium Salt

Perylium Salt

Figure 4.24. Synthesis of an aromatic polyamide containing pendent phenyl rings.

commercial polyimides contain ether linkages in the backbone for improved solubility in common organic solvents and melt processability. The most common brand names for PIM include Kapton® (DuPont), Ultem® (General Electric), P84® (Degussa Corporation) and the newcomer, Aurum® (Mitsui Chemicals). In general, aromatic polyimides are prepared via a two-step process involving the synthesis of a processable poly(amic acid) precursor and an intramolecular ring closure to the polyimide. The imidization step is usually carried out in a solid state, thermally induced cyclization reaction. Thus, Kapton is obtained by polycondensation of pyrromellitic dianhydride (PMDA) and 4,4'-oxydianiline (ODA) in a polar organic solvent at room temperature to yield the processable precursor, poly(amic acid), which is completely imidized on heating at 150°C (Figure 4.25). Kapton is extensively used in a wide variety of applications, such as substrates for flexible printed circuits, transformer and capacitor insulation and high-performance composites. Kapton has more than 40 years of proven performance as the flexible material of choice in applications involving very high, (400°C) or very low (-265°C) temperature extremes.

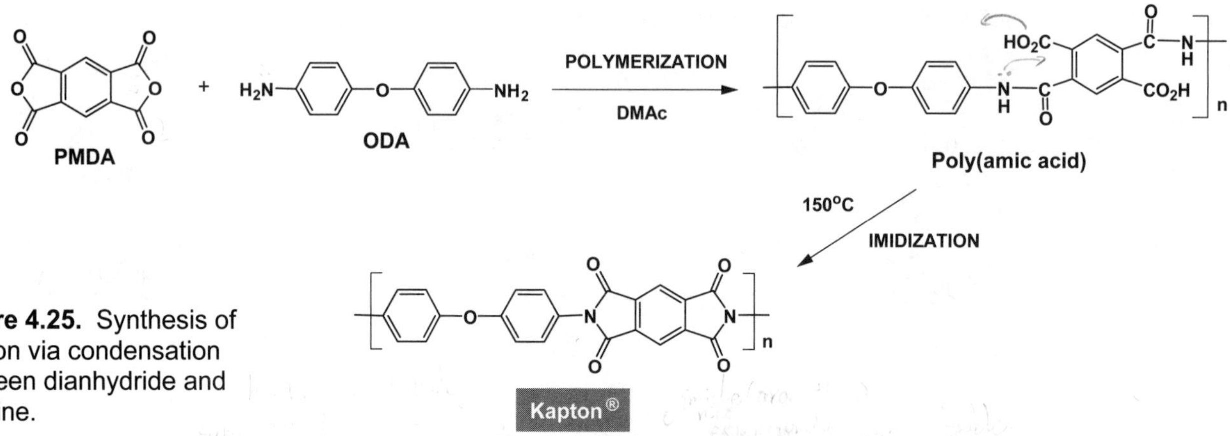

Figure 4.25. Synthesis of Kapton via condensation between dianhydride and diamine.

Ultem was designed to meet the need for high-performance polymers that could be readily fabricated by standard plastics extrusion and injection molding processes. The incorporation of such properties in PIM is possible by placing ether linkages between two imide moieties. Indeed, Ultem is an amorphous thermoplastic available in both extruded bars and as pellets for injection molding. It can be filled with as much as 30 percent glass. Glass filled Ultem displays excellent property retention and resistance to environmental stress. The polymer can be further reinforced with conductive fibers, or plated, for electromagnetic interference (EMI) resistance. Ultem performs in operating environments of up to 175°C long term and 200°C short term. PIMs like Ultem are best prepared by "nitro-displacement" polymerization between a bisnitrophthalimide and a biphenoxide (Figure 4.26). The driving force toward high molecular weight polymer is the labile nature of nitro groups in bisnitrophthalimide, which are highly activated for nucleophilic displacement by the two electron-withdrawing imide carbonyl groups. Bisnitrophthalimides are readily obtained by conventional condensation of 4-nitrophthalic anhydride with an appropriate diamine. It is important to note that while 3-nitrophthalic anhydride may also be used to produce PIMs, favorable thermal properties are sacrificed (e.g., lower T_g and T_m due to the greater zig-zag nature of the polymer structure).

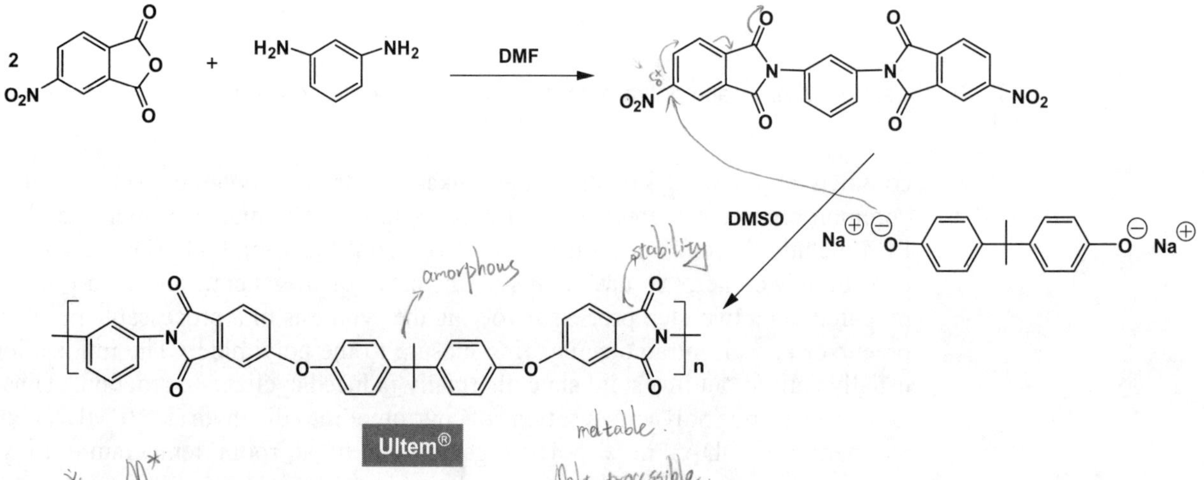

Figure 4.26. Synthesis of Ultem via nitro-displacement route.

Polymer P84 is manufactured by reaction of an aromatic dianhydride and a mixture of aromatic diisocyanates.[50,51] The material obtained is very pure because the only by-product is carbon dioxide (Figure 4.27). The reactants in the production of P84 are 1 equivalent of 3,3'4,4'-benzophenone tetracarboxylic dianhydride (BTDA), 0.8 equivalent of tolylene-2,4-diisocyanate (TDI) and 0.2 equivalent of 4,4'-methylenebis(phenyl isocyanate) (MDI). P84 is amorphous, probably because of the random copolymerization and unsymmetrically substituted methyl groups, which prevent crystallization by reducing inter-chain interactions. The polymrt is non-melting, and starts to carbonize above 375°C, with a T_g of 315°C. Despite the non-melting aromatic and halogen-free structure, it is classified as non-flammable, with a limiting oxygen index (LOI) of 38%. P84 can be used at temperatures up to 260°C in air. It is stable against most common organic solvents like alcohols, ethers, halogenated hydrocarbons or ethers. P84 fiber, with a unique trilobal cross-section, provides outstanding surface-to-volume ratios, exceptional temperature resistance and good chemical resistance for fire-protective clothing, as well as for garment reinforcement. However, because of the low modulus and high elongation, P84 fiber is not destined for typical "reinforcing" applications as are *p*-aramid or carbon fibers.

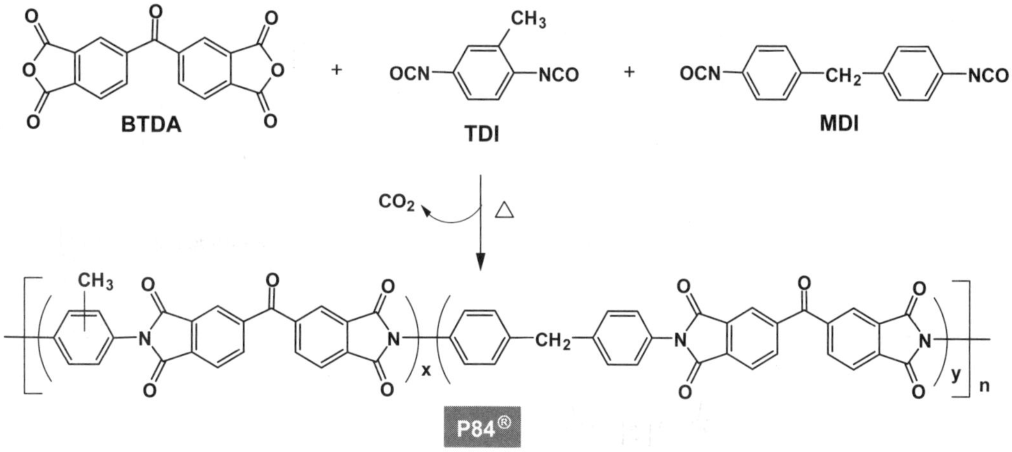

Figure 4.27. Synthesis of P84 via condensation between dianhydride and diisocyanate.

Similar to Kapton, Aurum is prepared by condensation of dianhydride with diamine (Figure 4.28). The balance between meta-phenylene and biphenylene linkages make Aurum an easy melt processable and recyclable thermoplastic polyimide. It is designed to withstand high-loads and high velocities at temperatures exceeding 250°C and can be injection-molded into complex shapes to tight and consistent tolerances using standard equipment. Aurum is utilized in a variety of other demanding applications, such as high pressure-velocity (PV) automotive transmission thrust washers and oil seal rings, wear and friction components for business machinery, jet engine components, power tool parts, and high purity components for semiconductor handling and manufacturing equipment.

In the past and currently, several attempts have been made to synthesize new types of PIMs, that exhibit superior thermal and mechanical properties and are soluble in at least a few solvents. Consequently, a variety of novel dianhydrides and diamines have been developed. *Nitro-displacement reaction* of N-substituted 4-nitrophthalimide or 4-nitrophthalonitrile with a diphenoxide by a three-step sequence is one of the most convenient routes for the preparation of dianhydrides (Figure 4.29).[52-55] In addition to flexible ether linkages, this methodology permits incorporation of *ortho/meta-*

phenylene, biphenylene, kink diphenylmethylene or fused aromatic linkage, and a bulky group between anhydride moieties. In general, PIMs with 4,4'-biphenylene linkages exhibit superior thermal stability and, with kink diphenylmethylene, marked enhancement in solubility.

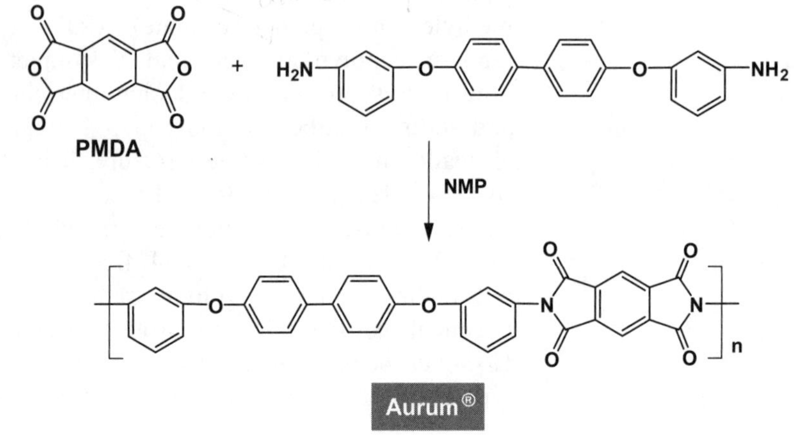

PMDA

NMP

Aurum®

Figure 4.28. Synthesis of Aurum.

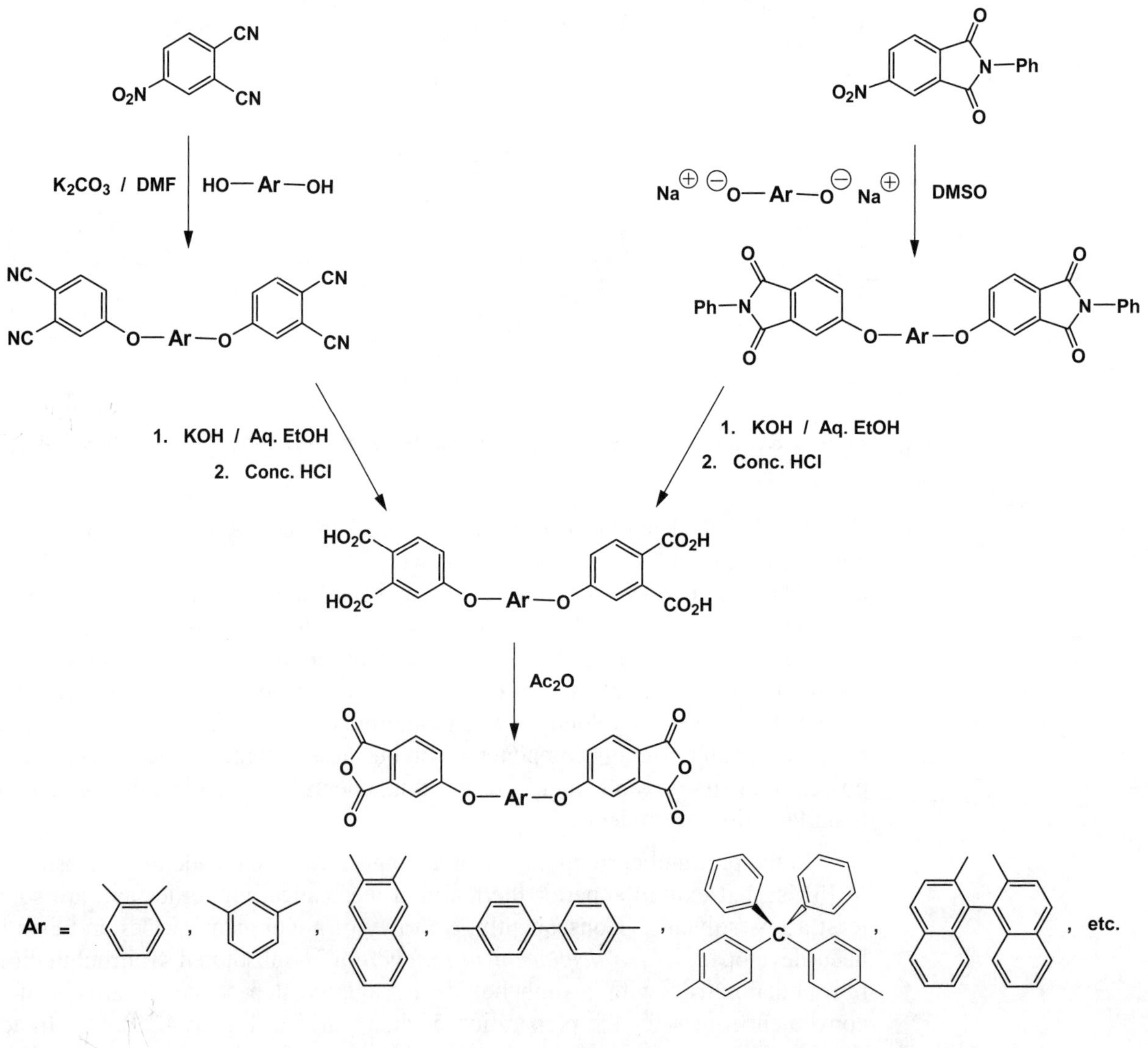

K_2CO_3 / DMF HO—Ar—OH

$Na^{\oplus}$ $^{\ominus}$O—Ar—O$^{\ominus}$ $Na^{\oplus}$ DMSO

1. KOH / Aq. EtOH
2. Conc. HCl

1. KOH / Aq. EtOH
2. Conc. HCl

Ac_2O

Ar = , , , , , , etc.

Figure 4.29. Synthesis of aromatic bis(ether anhydride)s via nitro-displacement reaction.

Aromatic dianhydrides containing no ether linkage have also been thoroughly investigated. The most important ones are the analogs of PMDA, a dianhydride employed for the manufacture of Kapton. A trifluoromethylated analog, P6FDA, was introduced for superior interlayer dielectrics in electronic devices, such as integrated circuits. Indeed, the polyimide prepared from P6FDA exhibits highly favorable properties compared to Kapton, such as a low dielectric constant, low water absorption, a low refractive index and a high optical transparency, with good solubility in common organic solvents.[56] The four-step synthesis, starting from 1,2,4,5-tetramethylbenzene (durene), depicted in Figure 4.30, produces good yields in each step. However, P6FDA polymer, despite having fluorine atoms, shows a lower polymer decomposition temperature (480°C vs. 570°C for Kapton), which may be accounted for by lack of chain rigidity. By contrast, the polymer obtained from the phenylated analog, PPMDA, prepared by a similar route (Figure 4.30)[57], also displayed good organo-solubility, but thermal stability comparable to that of Kapton.

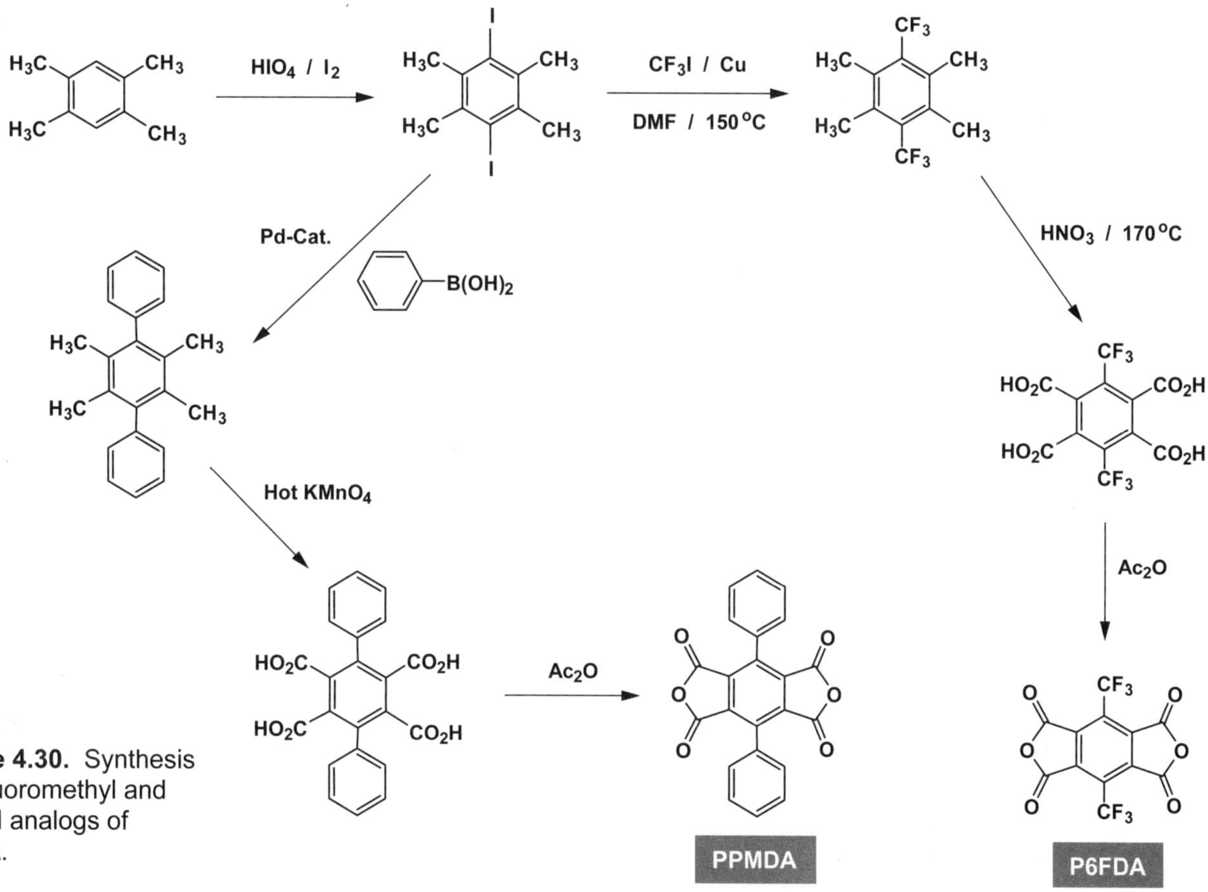

Figure 4.30. Synthesis of trifluoromethyl and phenyl analogs of PMDA.

Synthesis of *mellophanic dianhydride* (MPDA), an isomer of PMDA, and its phenylated analog, PMPDA, has also been conducted as part of studies on isomerism in polymers and the effect of bent, but still rigid dianhydride functionality on properties of highly aromatic polyimides. MPDA can be prepared by various routes.[58,59] One method providing a modest yield involves a Diels-Alder reaction of 1,3-cyclohexadiene with maleic anhydride, followed by oxidation with nitric acid, aromatization with bromine, and dehydration with acetic anhydride (Figure 4.31). PMPDA can be synthesized in four steps from diethyl 1,3-acetonedicarboxylate and benzil, following the scheme in Figure 4.31.[60,61] An alternative approach involves the Diels-Alder reaction of the cyclone obtained in the first step with inexpensive maleic anhydride, followed by aromatization with bromine, hydrolysis, and dehydration. Unlike PMDA and other commercially available dianhydrides, the polymerization of MPDA or PMPDA with a diamine in polar organic solvent, such as NMP, is complicated because of the reaction of the acid or amide functionality of amic acid (resulting from the reaction between one anhydride group and an amino group) with the other anhydride group. Consequently, the polymerization results in low molecular weight along with crosslinked product. However, this problem does not arise if the polymerization is conducted in *m*-cresol. This solvent effect can be attributed to the fact that water is miscible with NMP, but not with *m*-cresol. The water formed during the reaction in NMP can effectively interfere with imidization or hydrolyze the amic acid intermediate. Polymers derived with MPDA or PMPDA are organosoluble and highly amorphous or have a low degree of crystallinity, but are slightly less thermostable than those obtained from PMDA.

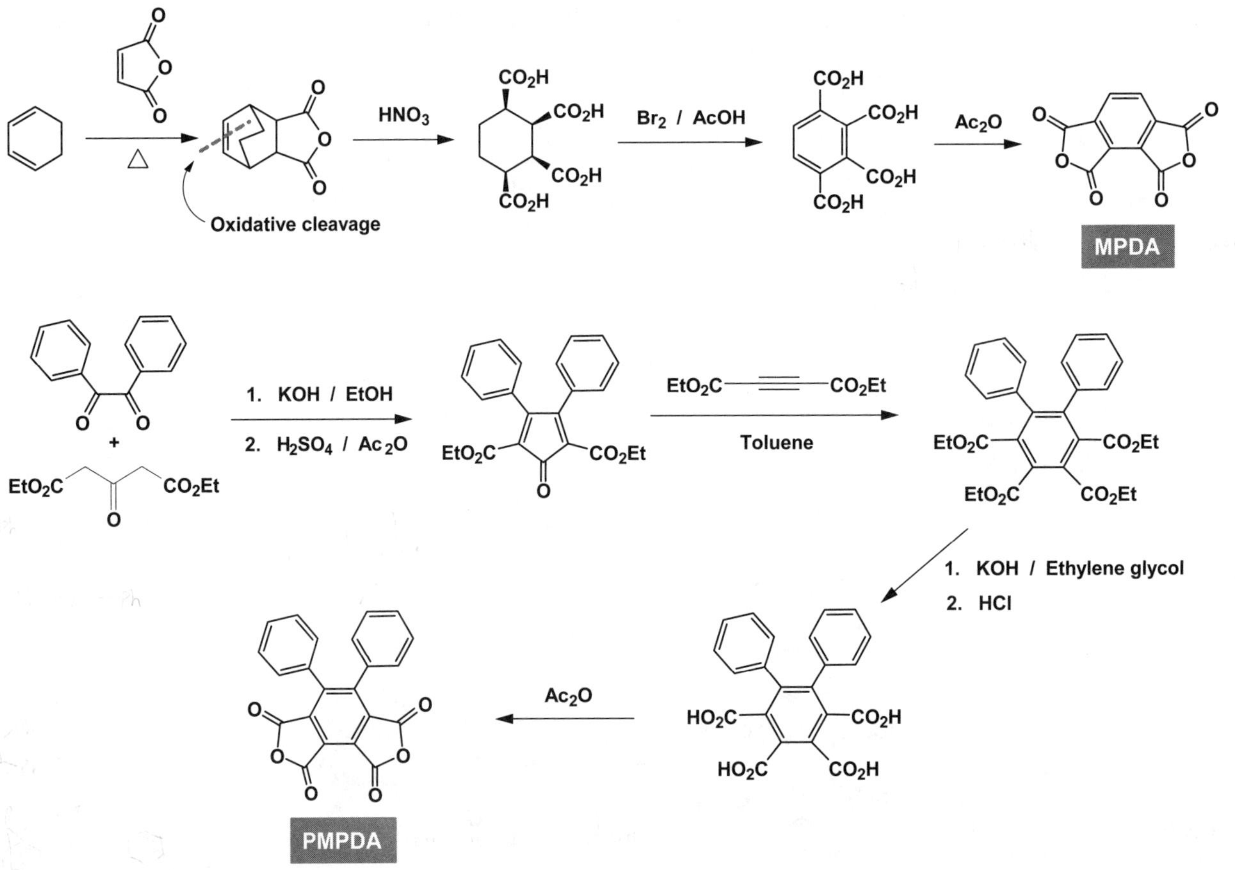

Figure 4.31. Synthesis of MPDA and its diphenyl analog.

Aromatic dianhydrides in which the phthalic anhydride moieties are connected through a single bond (e.g., biphenyltetracarboxylic dianhydride, BPDA[62-65], and its phenylated analog, PBPDA[66]) or a 1,4-phenylene linkage (e.g., terphenyltetracarboxylic dianhydride, TPDA[67]) represent another extensively studied class of compounds. They are prepared via Suzuki-type or Ni-catalyzed coupling reactions (Figure 4.32). The resulting polymers are soluble in common organic solvents with a slight compromise in thermal stability when compared with Kapton. The polymer obtained from PBPDA exhibits very high oxygen permeability, which is attributed to a higher free-volume resulting from a *t*-butylphenyl group substituted non-coplanar twisted biphenyl unit.

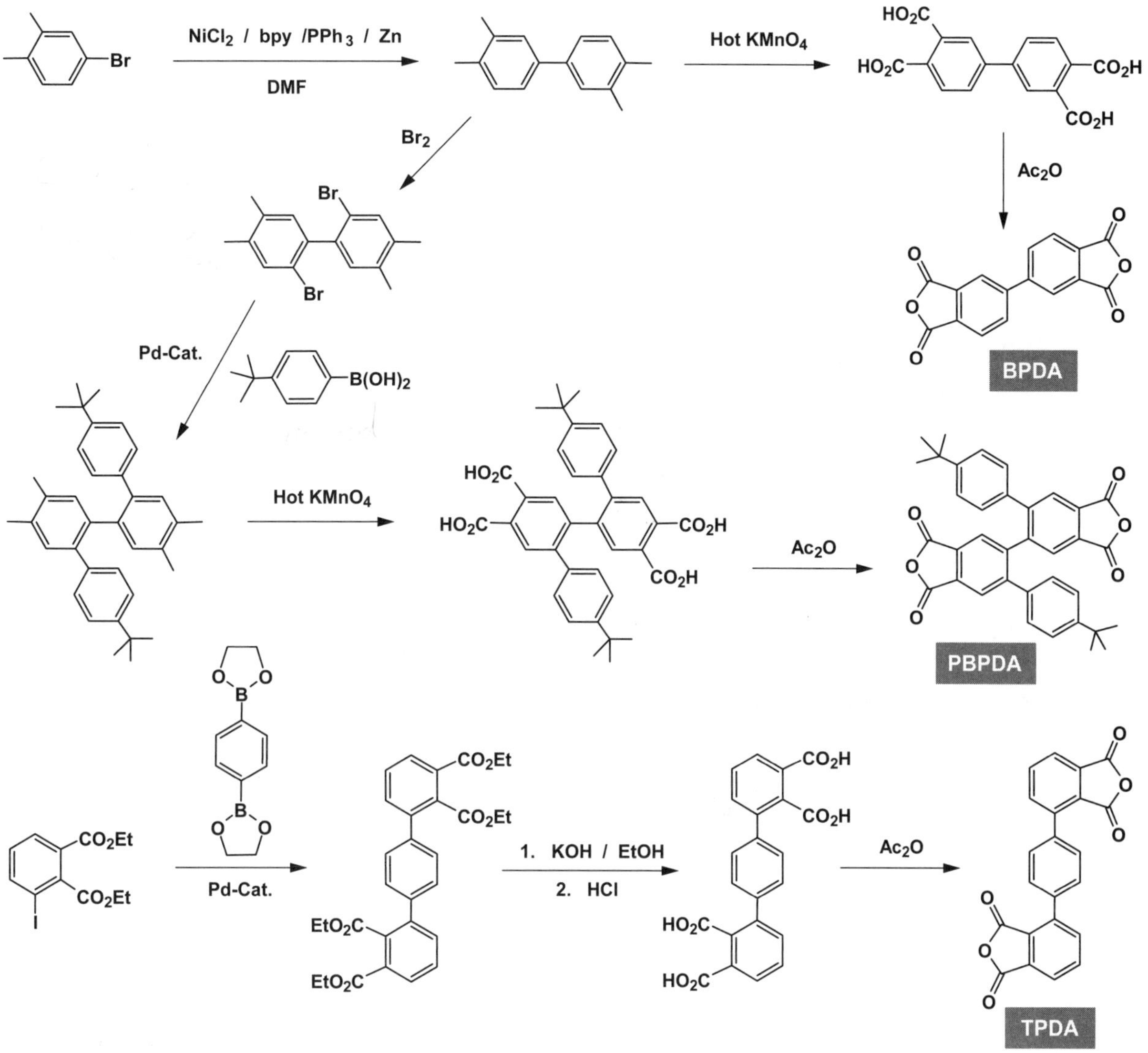

Figure 4.32. Synthesis of dianhydrides via coupling reactions.

Synthesis of novel diamines used to prepare polyimides with specific properties has also been thoroughly investigated (see preceding section, aromatic polyamides, for examples). For instance, polyimides derived from aromatic diamines containing an alicyclic ring provides an especially low dielectric constant and high moisture resistance, including very good thermal and mechanical properties.[68-74] These diamines are prepared by acid catalyzed condensation of an alicyclic carbonyl compound and aniline (Figure 4.33). In some cases, they are best prepared via the bisphenol derivative of the alicyclic moiety (see Figure 4.9), followed by etherification and introduction of nitro groups which are reduced to amino groups.

Another approach to increase the solubility of rigid-rod polyimides is by incorporation of a fully aromatic bulky non-coplanar group (such as naphthyl, which possesses the combination of bulkiness, rigidity and heat resistance) in the polymer backbone.[75] Figure 4.34 shows an example of a diamine consisting of two naphthyl groups at the 2,2'-positions of biphenyl, perfectly suited for disruption of the crystal packing and reduction of intermolecular interactions, leading to enhanced solubility of the polyimide, without sacrificing thermal stability. The four-step synthetic scheme involves nitration of biphenyl, followed by iodination, Suzuki-type coupling with 1-naphthylboronic acid and finally, reduction of the dinitro compound in a polar organic solvent in the presence ammonium formate and 10% Pd/C.

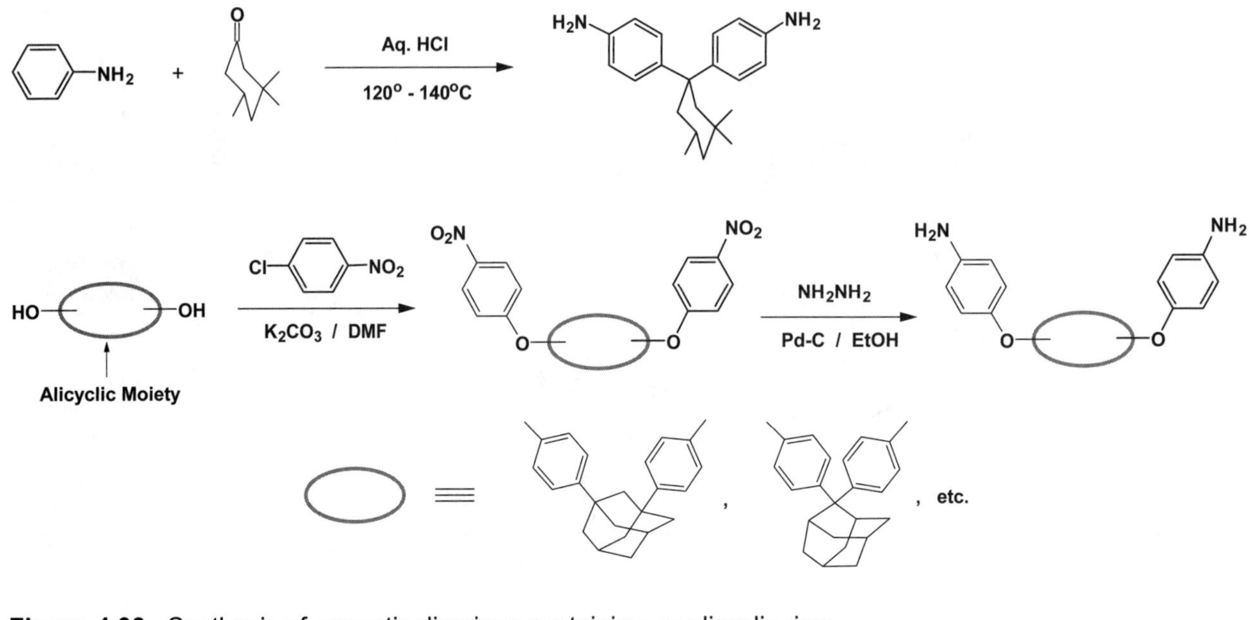

Figure 4.33. Synthesis of aromatic diamines containing an alicyclic ring.

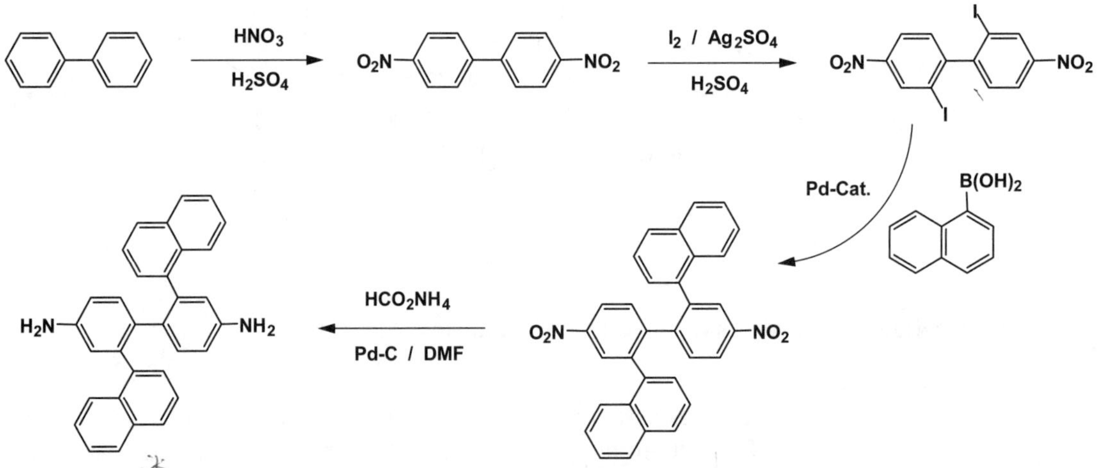

Figure 4.34. Synthesis of a non-coplanar naphthalene-biphenyldiamine.

4.7. POLY(AMIDE IMIDE)S

Poly(amide imide)s, PAIs, represent a family of hybrid polyimides that, unlike Kapton, are soluble in many polar organic solvents. The best known PAI is Torlon® (Solvay Advanced Polymers), which has exceptional strength at high temperatures and, like a thermoplastic, can be processed by standard methods, such as injection molding, extrusion and compression molding. Torlon is also very wear and friction resistant, which makes it an ideal material for mechanical retention components, such as anti-decoupling springs and contact retention springs. The injection moldable material is non-conductive and operates at temperatures up to 250°C. Torlon is also a major player in coating applications, due to its outstanding surface adhesion to a multitude of materials, including metals and polytetrafluoroethylene. Similar to polyimides, Torlon is manufactured by a two-step polycondensation of 4-(chloroformyl)phthalic anhydride (commonly called trimellitic anhydride chloride, TMAC) and ODA (Figure 4.35). In the first step, pyridine or triethylamine is used as an HCl acceptor to obtain a high molecular weight poly(amide amic acid). In the subsequent step, acetic anhydride and pyridine are added to effect imidization. Since Torlon is organo-soluble or melt processable, it is isolated as a fully imidized product. TMAC is usually prepared by treating trimellitic anhydride or trimellitic acid with thionyl chloride. Torlon is also attractive for gas separation and reverse osmosis membranes because of its high temperature resistance and water selectivity. In a recent study, a series of Torlon analogs have been prepared by replacing 10 to 40 mol% of ODA with a oligo(dimethylsiloxane) containing diamine co-monomer to obtain membranes with superior oxygen permeation behavior.[76,77]

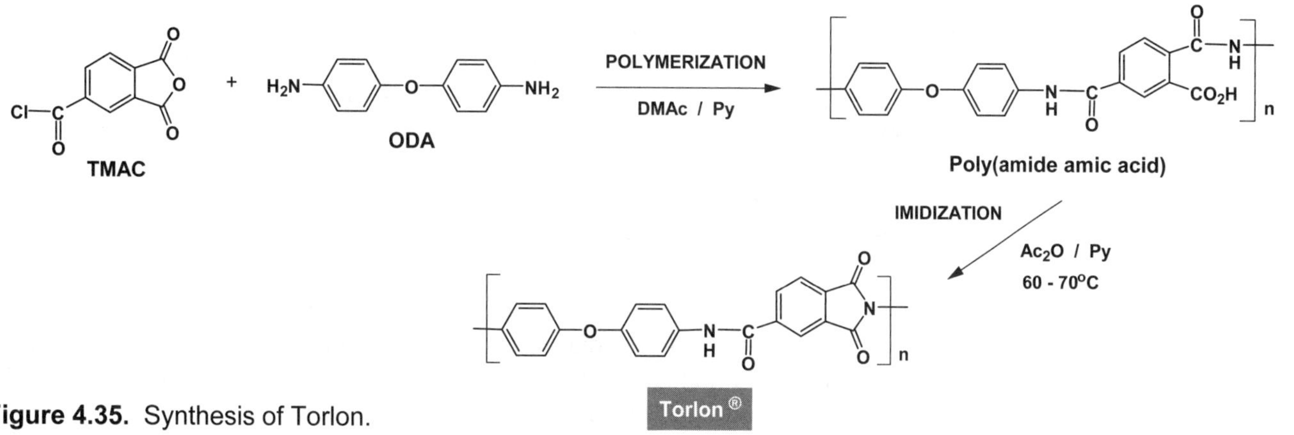

TMAC + ODA → POLYMERIZATION (DMAc / Py) → Poly(amide amic acid) → IMIDIZATION (Ac_2O / Py, 60 - 70°C) → Torlon®

Figure 4.35. Synthesis of Torlon.

PAIs can also be prepared by condensation of a dicarboxylic acid containing phthalimide moieties with a diamine under Yamazaki reaction conditions, using triphenyl phosphite (TPP) and pyridine as condensing agents (Figure 4.36).[78-80] If specific properties are desired, a special feature of this methodology is that a second amine can also be placed in the polymer backbone. The diacid monomers are readily prepared by reaction of trimellitic anhydride (TMA) with a diamine in refluxing glacial acetic acid solution. The PAIs obtained by this method are also soluble in polar organic solvents and exhibit excellent thermal and mechanical properties.

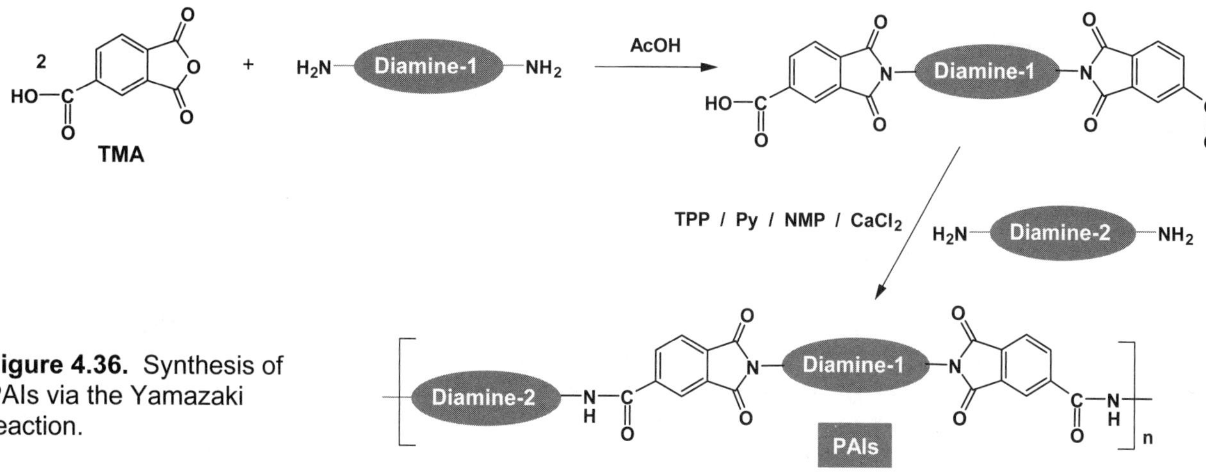

2 TMA + H_2N–Diamine-1–NH_2 → AcOH → diacid; + H_2N–Diamine-2–NH_2 → TPP / Py / NMP / $CaCl_2$ → PAIs

Figure 4.36. Synthesis of PAIs via the Yamazaki reaction.

4.8. RIGID-ROD AROMATIC HETEROCYCLIC POLYMERS

The wholly aromatic *p*-phenylene-heterocyclic rigid-rod containing polymers exhibit many exceptional properties, such as being the most thermally and thermooxidatively stable organic polymer known (>500°C), unusual resistance to organic solvents and excellent mechanical properties. These features are due to their densely packed (highly ordered morphology) and perfectly aligned straight chain structure (catenation angles of nearly 180°). Moreover, they exhibit interesting electrical and nonlinear optical (NLO) properties originating from their π-conjugated backbone (see Chapter-5).[81,82] The development of these polymers is believed to be a spin-off of ladder polymers (*vide infra*), when it was concluded that a rigid linear molecular geometry is more important than the ladder structure in order to improve on DuPont's Kevlar. Poly(*p*-phenylene-2,6-benzobisthiazole) (*trans*-PBZT), poly(*p*-phenylene-2,6-benzobisoxazole) (*cis*-PBO) and poly[2,6-diimidazo(4,5-b:4',5'-e)pyridinylene-1,4-(2,5-dihydroxy)phenylene] (PIPD) are the most prominent members of this family. Poly[2,2'-(*m*-phenylene)-5,5'-dibenzimidazole] (PBI), although a slight compromise of overall properties because of the *meta*-phenylene linkage in the repeat unit, is also regarded as a useful member, since it is derived from inexpensive starting materials. The major application of these polymers is as high strength and high modulus synthetic polymeric fibers required for the aerospace industry.

4.8.1. Polybenzothiazoles

The most important member of this class is *trans*-PBZT (or PBZT), prepared commercially by reaction of 2,5-diamino-1,4-benzenedithiol dihydrochloride (DABT) with terephthalic acid (TPA) in polyphosphoric acid (PPAc) (Figure 4.37). The benzothiazole ring structure is formed by condensation of a carboxylic acid with an *o*-aminothiophenol. The feature of this synthesis is that water is the only by-product and the solution formed after polymerization exhibits lyotropic behavior (characteristic of the nematic mesophase), which can be used directly as the dope for spinning into fibers using the dry jet-wet spinning technique. The spun fibers consist of highly ordered bundles of ~20 linear polymer chains in which the phenyl ring is about 20° out of plane of the benzothiazole moiety. The overall axial molecular orientation can be significantly improved to ~400 polymer chains per bundle by heat treatment above 300°C.

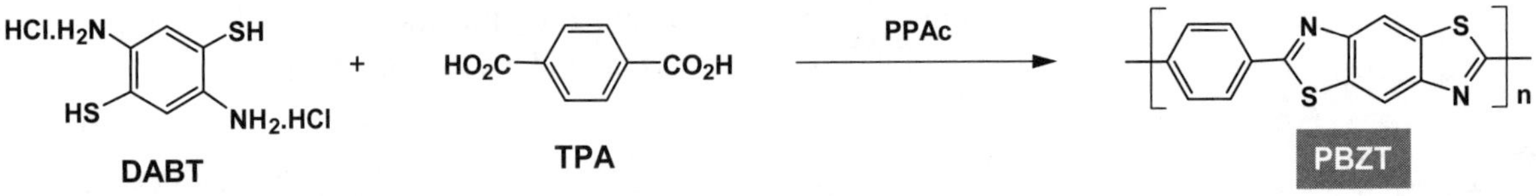

Figure 4.37. Commercial synthesis of PBZT.

Once PBZT is isolated as a solid material after polymerization, it is insoluble in common organic solvents because of this highly ordered rigid structure. Thus, the application of PBZTs, especially in the area of electronics, where spin-coated thin films are desirable, is hindered. Although the solubilization of aromatic heterocyclic rigid-rod polymers can be accomplished by means of complex formation with Lewis acids (e.g., $AlCl_3$, $FeCl_3$) in aprotic organic solvents such as nitroalkanes and nitrobenzene, the complete removal of Lewis acids after processing is very difficult.[83] A more desirable approach is the preparation of the polymer via a soluble precursor, which after processing, will lead to a polymer with high purity. Figure 4.38 describes such an approach for the synthesis of PBZT and its analogs via thermal cyclization of aromatic polyamides containing pendent (cyanoethyl)thio groups.[84] The monomer, DAST-CET, is readily prepared by reaction of the standard monomer DAST with 3-bromopropionitrile in the presence of a phase-transfer catalyst, cetyltrimethylammonium chloride (CTMAC). The PBZTs obtained from the precursor polyamides show excellent thermal properties comparable to those of PBZTs prepared by solution polycondensation in PPA.

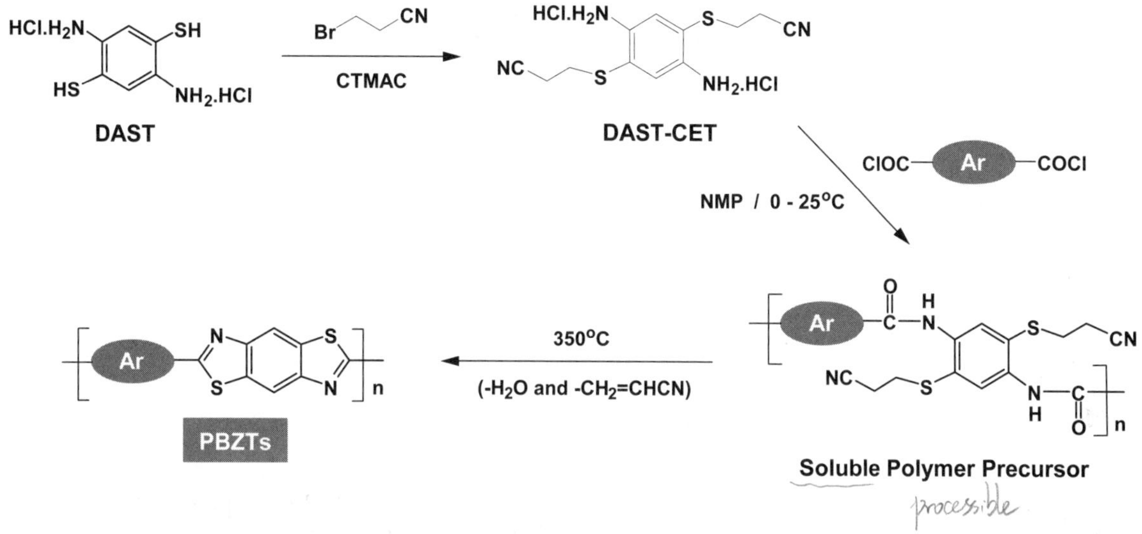

Figure 4.38. Synthesis of PBZTs via the soluble precursor route.

PBZT has now been established as a strong candidate for high-performance of nanostructured conducting fibers used in embedded sensors, electromagnetic shielding, and smart structures. Such fibers are fabricated by depositing silver nanoparticles *in-situ* into a polymer template structure, creating an interpenetrating silver network parallel to the fiber axis.[85] Spatial control is achieved through precise fiber swelling and infiltration of the silver precursor and reducing agents. Silver infiltrated PBZT fibers exhibit electronic conductivities exceeding 10^4 S/cm. The Ag/PBZT composite fiber also maintains the high strength of the polymer (Table 4.1). Tests have revealed an approximate 200-fold increase in strength and a 50% reduction in weight compared to current aerospace signal wire cores.

Table 4.1. Structure and Property Enhancement of an Ag/PBZT Fiber[86]

Fiber	Modulus (GPa)	Strength (MPa)	Strain (%)	Conductivity (S/cm)
PBZT	95	900	2.0	$10^{-12} - 10^{-14}$
Ag/PBZT	52	1050	3.3	2.5×10^4
Ag	76	55	60.0	6.3×10^5

4.8.2. Polybenzoxazoles

The most important member of this class is PBO, a new entry to the high performance organic fibers market. The only product thus far, is Zylon® PBO fiber (a product of Toyobo, Japan), which has the highest tensile strength (almost double that of Kevlar fiber) among high-performance fibers. Zylon is projected as the next generation super fiber as it possesses very high strength, 100°C higher decomposition temperature than Kevlar fiber, and, by far, the highest LOI (limiting oxygen index = 68) among organic super fibers (Table 4.2). Its high modulus and LOI make it an excellent candidate for fiber-reinforced composites, multilayer circuit boards, athletic equipment, thermal shields, fire-resistant safety and protective clothing, and ballistic applications. PBO is prepared by reaction of 4,6-diamino-1,3-benzenediol dihydrochloride (DADO) with terephthalic acid in PPAc. PBO forms a lyotropic solution after polymerization and is processed into fibers similar to PBZT.

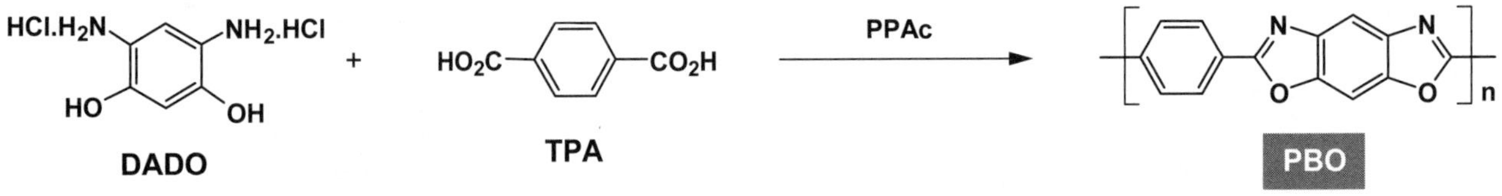

Figure 4.39. Commercial synthesis of PBO.

Table 4.2. Properties Comparison of Thermostable Organic Fibers

Polymer	Density (g/cm³)	Tenacity (gpd)[a]	Tensile Strength (MPa)	Elongation (%)	Moisture Regain (%)	Abrasion Resistance	LOI (%)	Melt/ (Decomposition) Temperature (°C)
Polyester (Dacron®)	1.38	3	55	25	0.4	Good	17	260
UHMWPE (Spectra® or Dyneema®)	0.97	34	2861	3.5	0.0	Good	18	155
Aramid (Nomex®)	1.38	5	621	22	6.5	Excellent	28	(400)
Aramid (Kevlar®)	1.45	25	2930	2.4	4.5	Good	29	(550)
Polyimide (P-84®)	1.41	4	462	25	3.0	Excellent	38	375
PBI (Celazole®)	1.43	3	345	28	15.0	Excellent	40	(550)
LCP (Vectra®)	1.39	26	172	3.5	0.1	Excellent	30	330
PBO (Zylon®)	1.54	41	5654	3.5	2.0	Good	68	(650)

[a]gpd = gram per denier

Processable PBOs have also been prepared by intramolecular thermal conversion of polyimides containing pendent hydroxyl groups *ortho* to the heterocyclic imide nitrogen (Figure 4.40).[87] The strategy involves synthesis of a soluble hydroxypolyamic acid precursor by reaction of a dianhydride and a *bis*-*o*-aminophenol. The processed polyamic acid film is then subjected to a series of heat treatments to obtain PBO films. Thorough studies with model compounds indicate that imidization of hydroxypolyamic acid to hydroxypolyimide occurs at an early stage of heating by the elimination of water. Subsequently, the hydroxyl group participates in ring-opening of an adjacent imide ring to form a carboxypolybenzoxazole intermediate, which, on further heating, undergoes complete decarboxylation to a solvent-resistant thermostable PBO film. PBOs can also be obtained by thermal cyclodehydration of poly(*o*-hydroxy amides) at 250°C in vacuo.[88]

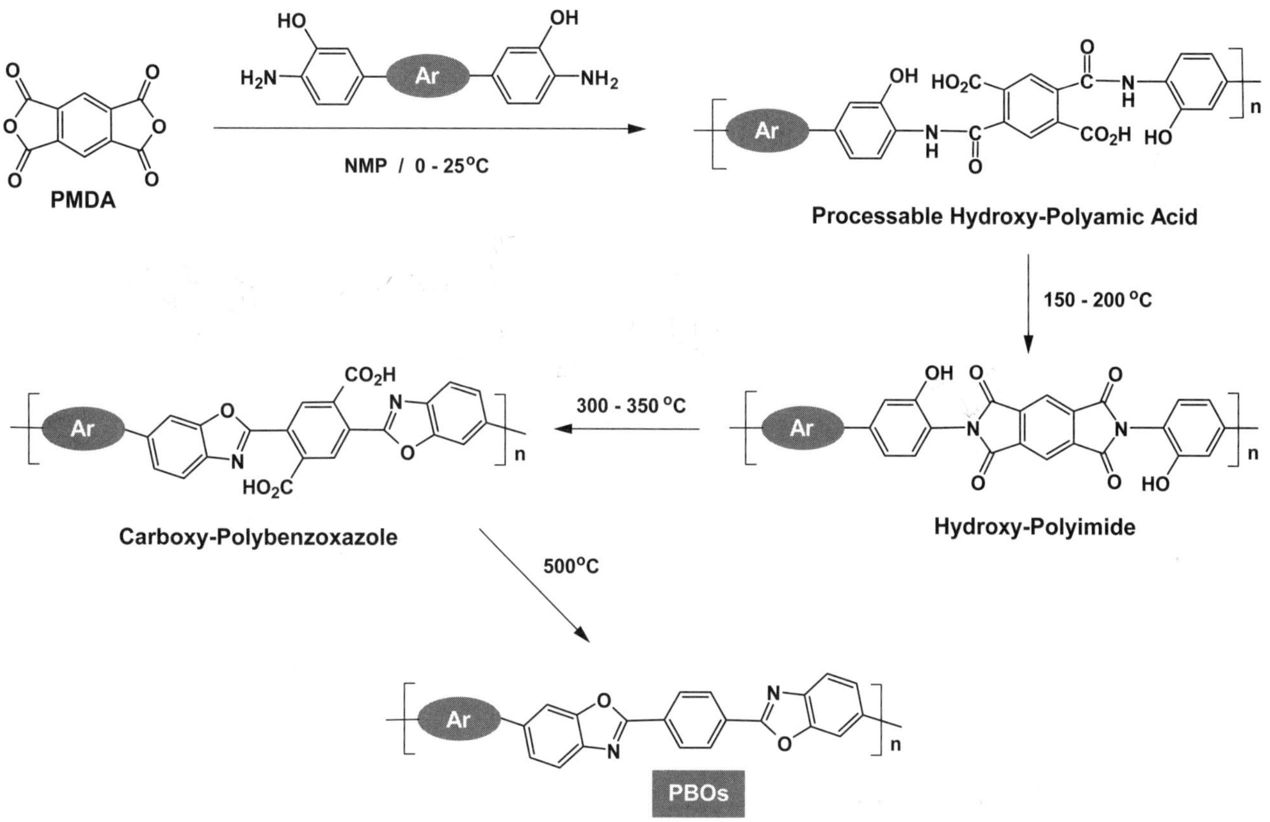

PMDA

NMP / 0 - 25°C

Processable Hydroxy-Polyamic Acid

150 - 200 °C

Hydroxy-Polyimide

300 - 350 °C

Carboxy-Polybenzoxazole

500°C

PBOs

Figure 4.40. Synthesis of PBOs by thermal conversion of polyimides containing pendent hydroxyl groups.

4.8.3. Polybenzimidazoles

The most important member of this class is PBI, which is a very appealing material to high-tech industries, such as semiconductor, aircraft and aerospace companies, because of their superior diverse properties. These include (i) high maximum allowable service temperature in air (300°C continuously, going up to 500°C for short periods of time), (ii) excellent retention of mechanical strength, stiffness and creep resistance over a wide range of temperatures, (iii) extremely low coefficient of linear thermal expansion up to 250°C, (iv) excellent wear and frictional behavior, (v) inherent low flammability, (vi) good electrical insulating and dielectric properties, (vii) low outgassing in vacuum (dry material), (viii) high ionic purity level, and (ix) excellent resistance against high energy radiation. In 1983, Hoechst Celanese began commercial production of PBI fiber, Celazole®, which finds applications in firefighters' gear, industrial protective clothing, fire-blocking layers for aircraft seats, high temperature filtration fabrics, and other high-performance products. The polymerization of PBI is carried out by condensation of 3,3',4,4'-tetraaminobiphenyl (TABI) with diphenyl isophthalate (DPIP) in PPAc (Figure 4.41). Unlike the aforementioned rigid-rod polymers containing heterocyclic rings, PBI is soluble in some solvents, including sulfuric acid, DMAc, DMF and DMSO. About 23 weight/weight concentration of PBI in DMAc is usually used for the production of solution spun fibers.

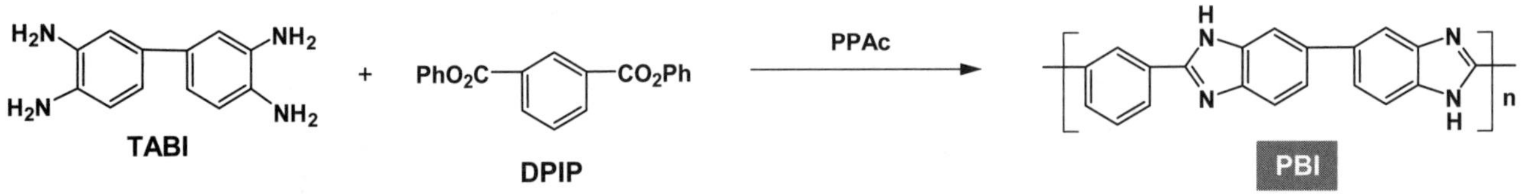

TABI + DPIP —PPAc→ PBI

Figure 4.41. Commercial synthesis of PBI.

4.8.4. Hydroxylated Polybenzimidazole

This polymer, better known as poly(pyridobisimidazole) (PIPD), was developed by Akzo Nobel with recent commercial production by Magellan Systems under the M5® trademark. M5 is prepared by reaction of 2,3,5,6-tetraaminopyridine (TAPY) with 2,5-dihydroxyterephthalic acid (DHTPA) in PPAc (Figure 4.42). It has extraordinary potential for use in armor systems for personnel and vehicles, flame and thermal protection, as well as in lightweight high performance structural composites. Based on initial tests, it is estimated that fragmentation-protective armor systems made of M5 will reduce the areal density of the ballistic component of these systems by approximately 40-60% compared with Kevlar fabric at the same level of protection. Potential defense applications of M5 include fragmentation vests and helmets, composites for use in conjunction with ceramic materials for small arms protection, and structural composites for vehicles and aircraft.

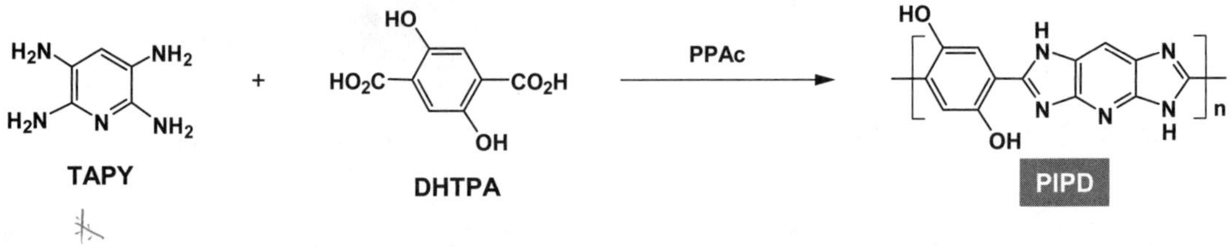

TAPY + DHTPA —PPAc→ PIPD

Figure 4.42. Commercial synthesis of PIPD.

M5 is a unique rigid-rod polymer which features hydrogen bonds in both the 'x' and 'y' directions ('z' representing the rod-like polymer chain direction). The effect of the bi-directional hydrogen bonding is to connect the M5 molecules into a 3-dimensional or "honeycomb" network (Figure 4.43). Fiber physics theory projects that a well-oriented fiber with M5's molecular structure will have a combination of mechanical properties that are far superior to that of any other fiber on the market today. Preliminary data and ongoing empirical testing of M5 provide an ever-growing body of evidence in support of the theoretical projections.

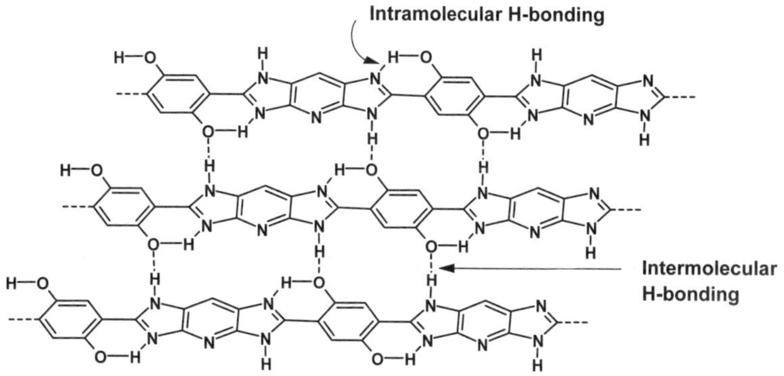

Figure 4.43. Hydrogen bonding in M5 fiber. Note the bi-directional, hydrogen-bonded network between the molecules.

4.9. AROMATIC LADDER POLYMERS

The concept of aromatic ladder or double-stranded polymers originated in the late 1960s in order to obtain polymers with exceptionally high thermal stability (>500°C), because such polymers have two independent strands of bonds tied together regularly without merging to a single or double bond or crossing each other like a spiro connection.[89] Consequently, breakdown of polymer chains does not occur easily, resulting in their retention of thermal and mechanical properties at higher temperatures. Shortly thereafter, attention was diverted to the aforementioned aromatic heterocyclic ring containing rigid-rod polymers because of their all-around performance, which finally led to the triumph of DuPont's Kevlar. Nevertheless, the initiative resulted in a few important aromatic ladder polymers, such as poly(benzobisimidazo benzophenanthroline), BBL, which are still used for very high temperature coating applications in the aerospace industry. In the early 1990s, the focus on aromatic ladder polymers was revived, but this time, to develop a new class of electronic and optical materials, utilizing their extended π-conjugation.[90]

The classical synthetic routes to ladder polymers involve ring-forming condensation (or cycloaddition) reactions of multifunctional monomers or cyclization of a functionalized single-strand precursor polymer. One of the first and most studied ladder polymer is BBL, which was prepared by ring-forming condensation of 1,4,5,8-naphthalenetetracarboxylic acid (NTCA) and 1,2,4,5-tetraaminobenzene (TAB) in polyphosphoric acid (Figure 4.44).[91] BBL in completely soluble in methanesulfonic acid and can be cast into thin films, which exhibit a high degree of crystallinity and very high thermal stability (<10 wt.% loss at 600°C in air and <5 wt.% loss at 700°C in nitrogen). Since BBL possesses a near-planar conformation and extended π-orbital overlap, it displays a semiconductor band gap of 1.8 eV. In addition, the electron rich nitrogen and oxygen heteroatoms in BBL give rise to excellent electron-accepting properties, including reversible n-type doping to high dc conductivity, the ability to accept up to 2 electrons per repeat unit, and a high field-effect mobility of electrons (i.e., electron transport can be as facile as hole transport). This set of attractive properties has established BBL as a promising material for field-effect transistors, photoluminescence, and third-order nonlinear optical (NLO) applications.[92,93]

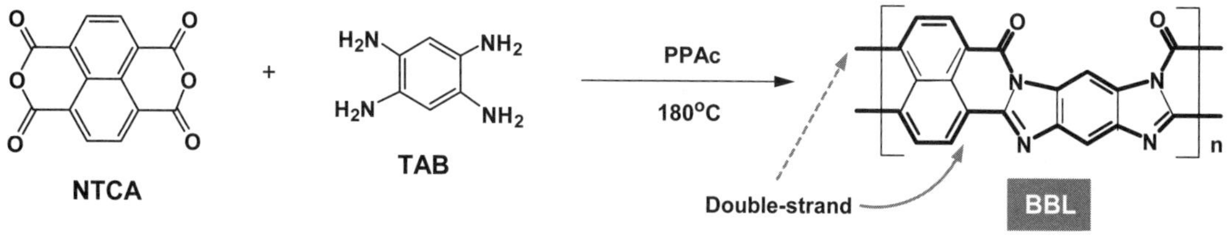

Figure 4.44. Synthesis of BBL.

Aromatic ladder poly(*p*-phenylene)s, LPPPs, which have near planar aromatic rings (<1° twist angle between consecutive phenyl rings), are another class of materials developed for electronic and photonic applications. Unlike poly(*p*-phenylene) (PPP), which is highly insoluble in common organic solvents and has a 23° twist between consecutive phenyl rings due to *ortho*-hydrogen interactions, LPPPs are organosoluble. It is important to note that alkyl group-substituted PPPs, in which consecutive aryl rings are even further out of plane, are soluble in organic solvents, but display poor electronic and optical properties due to the plummeting of the extended π-conjugation. LPPPs are best prepared via cyclization of a functionalized single-strand precursor polymer. As depicted in Figure 4.45, a PPP precursor containing well-positioned keto groups is achieved via a palladium-mediated Suzuki-type cross-coupling reaction.[94,95] Subsequently, the keto groups react with methyllithium and the resulting tertiary alcohol is cyclized to LPPPs, which exhibit excellent solubility and processabilty into thin films and layers, including a steep, vibronically structured absorption band (λ_{max} ca. 446 nm at 2.78 eV), a mirror-symmetrical blue photoluminescence (PL), and a very small Stokes loss (≥150 cm^{-1}). This chemistry can also be extended to obtain LPPPs containing conjugated 2,6- or 1,5-naphthylene building blocks for the purpose of further optical tuning of the absorption and emission bands of the ladder polymers. For instance, the 2,6-naphthylene-linked ladder polymer (2,6-NLP) exhibits an intense blue PL, while the 1,5-NLP shows a red shift of the absorption band, leading to a blue-green PL.

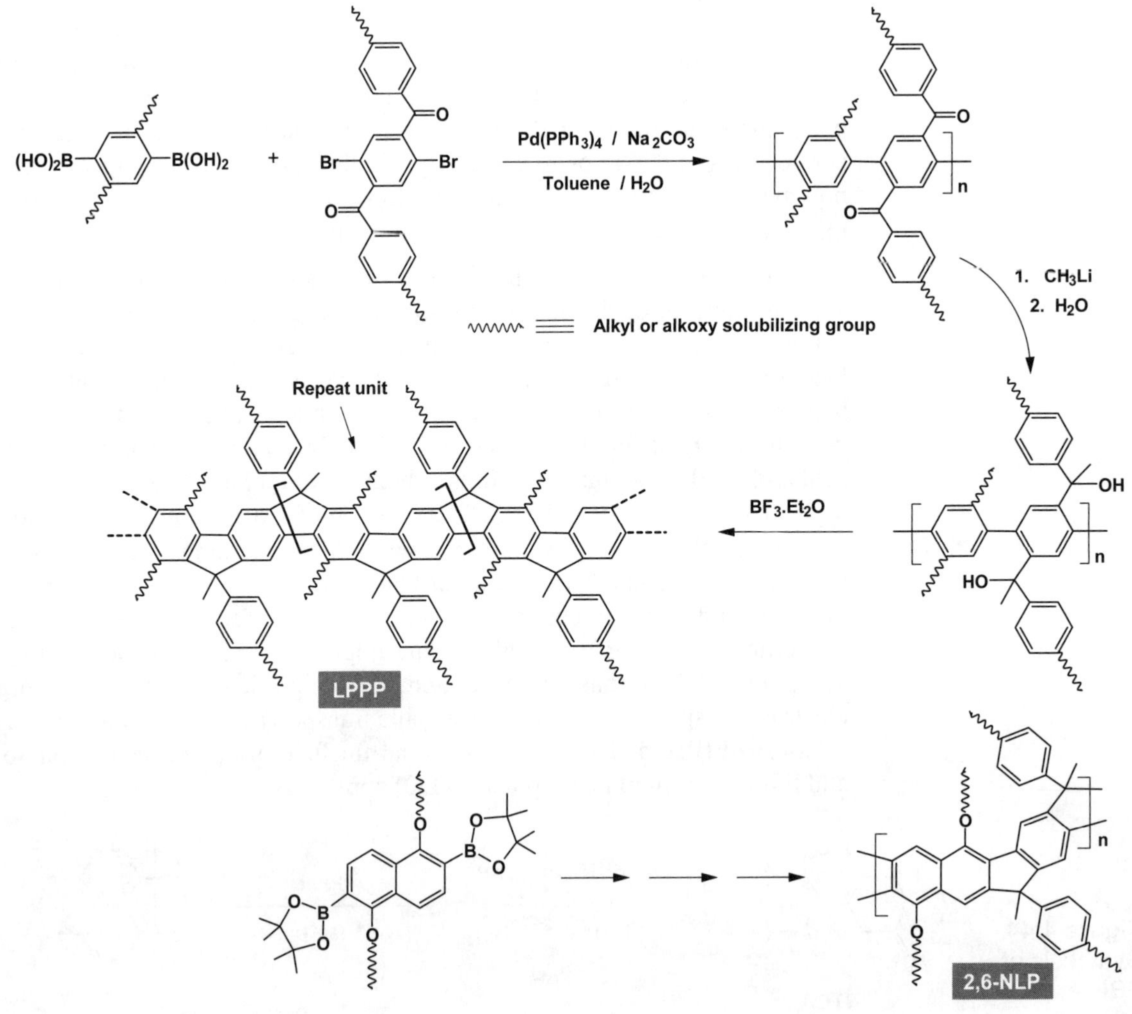

$(HO)_2B$ B$(OH)_2$ + Br Br O O $Pd(PPh_3)_4$ / Na_2CO_3 Toluene / H_2O n

1. CH_3Li 2. H_2O

Alkyl or alkoxy solubilizing group

Repeat unit

$BF_3.Et_2O$ OH HO n

LPPP

O B O O B O O O n

2,6-NLP

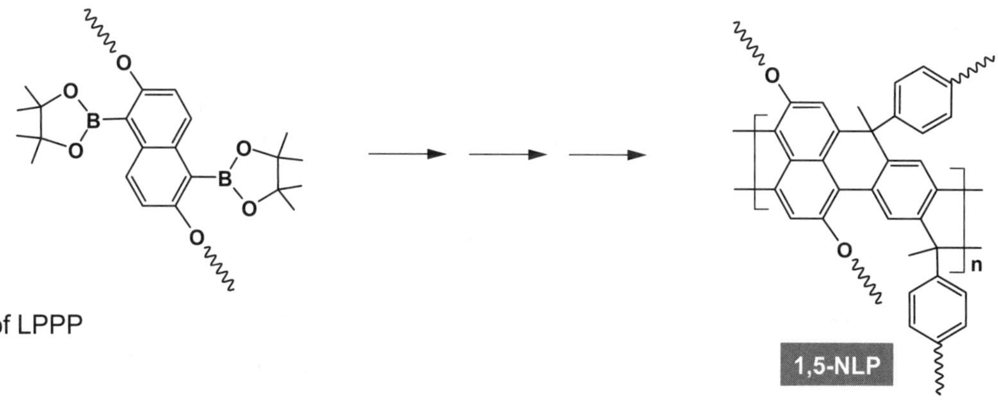

Figure 4.45. Synthesis of LPPP and related analogs.

Cyclization of a functionalized single-strand precursor polymer can also be used to prepare LPPPs containing heterocyclic rings, provided proper functional groups are present in the starting monomers (Figure 4.46).[96] Thus, an imine-bridged ladder polymer, Im-LPPP, results from Pd(0)-catalyzed coupling of a BOC protected diamino arylbis(boronic ester) with keto groups bearing aryl dibromide, followed by exposure of the resulting substituted PPP to trifluoroacetic acid, which promotes condensation between keto and amino groups, thus forcing aryl rings into planarity. As expected, Im-LPPP is organosoluble, film formable, and exhibits enormous bathochromic shifts of 210-240 nm compared to that of nonplanar alkyl group-substituted PPPs, indicating greatly enhanced degrees of extended conjugation.

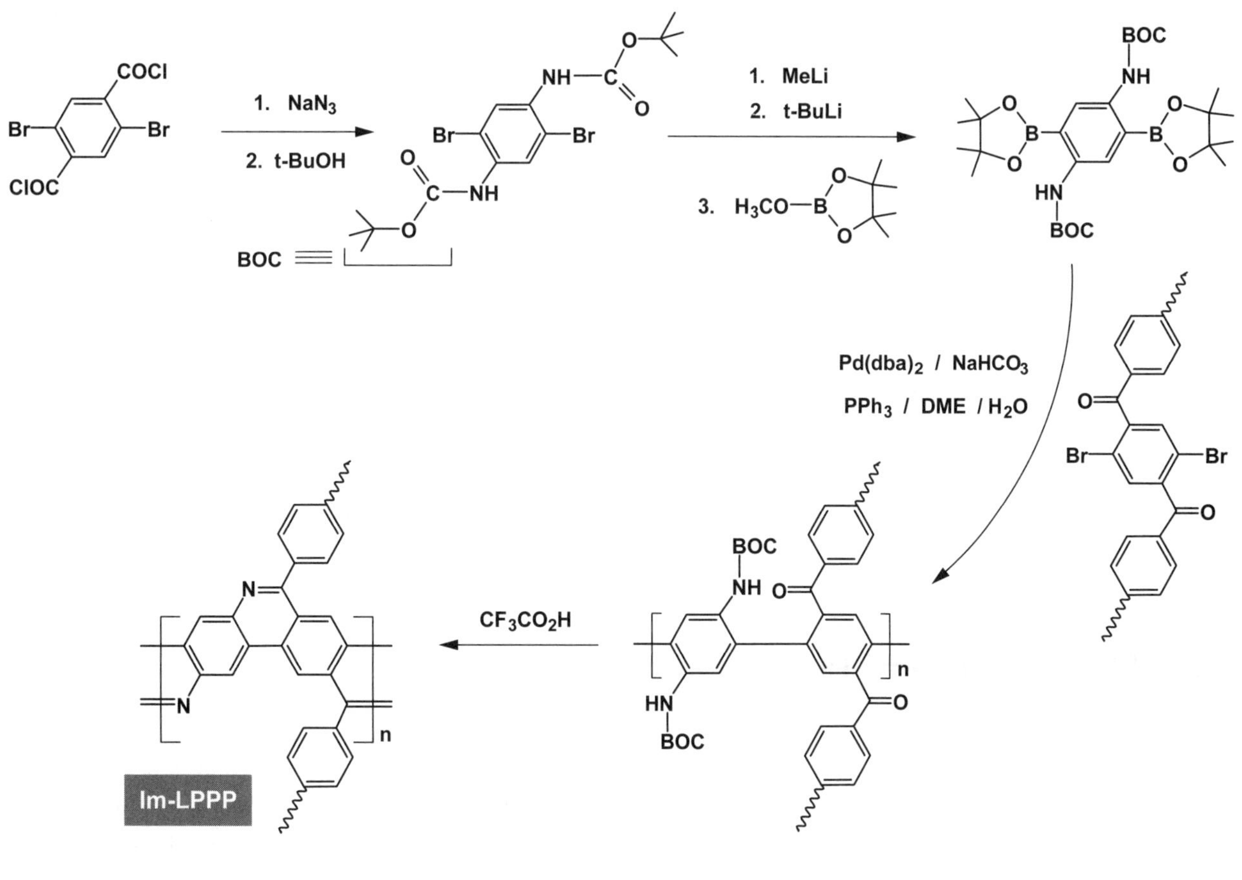

Figure 4.46. Synthesis of LPPP containing heterocyclic rings.

Another class of newly developed ladder polymer is poly(iptycene)s, which contain rigid three-dimensional (similar to a paddlewheel configuration with D_{3h} symmetry) "iptycene" units in the polymer backbone.[97-99] The term iptycene is used to describe a family of organic molecules that contain a number of arene units joined together to form the bridges of [2.2.2] bicyclic ring systems. They are best prepared via step-growth [4 + 2] Diels-Alder (DA) cycloaddition polymerization of an AB-type monomer containing anthracene or a higher acene (serving as the diene) and a benzo-fused endoxide functionality (as the dienoplile). Figure 4.47 outlines the synthesis of a representative monomer, 1,4-epoxy-5,12-dialkyloxy-1,4-dihydrotetracene (EDDT), which is obtained in good yield via a four-step synthetic scheme involving classical DA chemistry. The scheme also permits incorporation of solubilizing groups, such as alkyl, in the polymer backbone. The *oxo*-bridged adduct ladder polymer can be successfully converted to more aromatic poly(iptycene) by thermal dehydration in the presence of pyridinium *p*-toluenesulfonate and acetic anhydride. Poly(iptycene)s possesses high degrees of internal free volume, good mechanical and thermal properties and low dielectric constants, leading to potential applications in material and supramolecular chemistry.

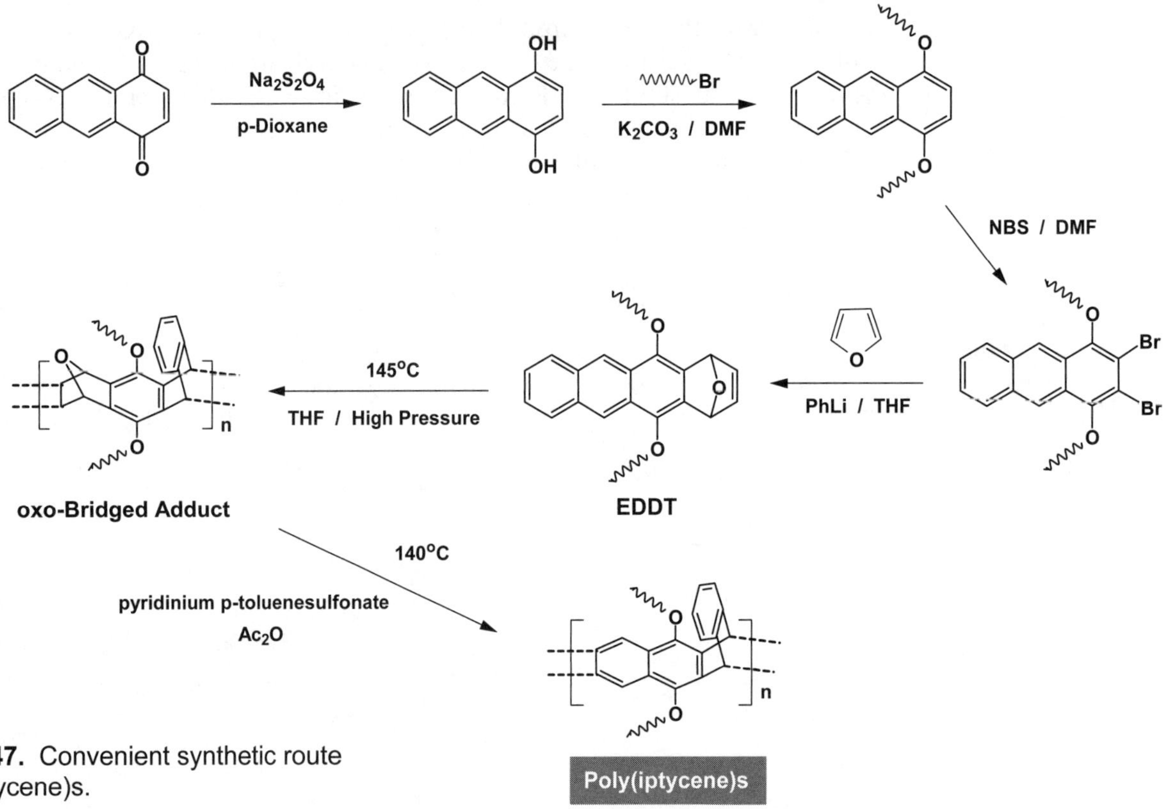

$Na_2S_2O_4$ / p-Dioxane; Br / K_2CO_3 / DMF; NBS / DMF; PhLi / THF; 145°C, THF / High Pressure; 140°C, pyridinium p-toluenesulfonate, Ac_2O

oxo-Bridged Adduct

EDDT

Poly(iptycene)s

Figure 4.47. Convenient synthetic route to poly(iptycene)s.

4.10. PERFLUOROALIPHATIC POLYMERS

Polyperfluoroolefins, with very high fluorine content, exhibit a unique combination of desirable physical and chemical properties. These include outstanding thermal stability and chemical resistance, low dissipation factor, excellent weatherability, low water absorptivity, good resistance to oxidation and ageing, low flammability, and very interesting surface properties (Table 4.3). Despite the high cost, their excellent performance allow use in numerous high end applications ranging from surfactants, optical fibers, aerospace, microelectronics, biomaterials, coatings, to membranes for fuel cells (see Chapter-5). In addition, some members, especially poly(vinylidene fluoride) (PVDF) and poly(vinylidiene fluoride-*co*-trifluoroethylene), P(VDF-TrFE), exhibit high dielectric constants and large electromechanical responses, and have received considerable attention in many applications, such as transducers, actuators, sensors, and capacitors. The synthesis of most polyperfluoroolefins is best accomplished through aqueous emulsion polymerization of fluorovinyl monomer in the presence of an inorganic peroxy initiator, such as ammonium persulfate. The polymerization also employs high pressure (50-1,500 psi) and perfluorooctanoic acid ammonium salt (PFOA) as an emulsifier to obtain desired emulsion characteristics with the monomer. The molecular weight of the polymer is controlled by the ratio of initiator to monomer or by using a chain-transfer agent, such as carbon tetrachloride. The polymer obtained by this technique possesses an average particle size of 100-300 nm.

Table 4.3. Important Properties of Major Perfluoroaliphatic Polymers

Polymer	Trade Name	Density (g/cm^3)	Refractive Index	Visible Light Transmission (%)	Upper Service Temperature[a] (°C)	T_m (°C)	Limiting Oxygen Index (%)
PTFE	Teflon	2.18	1.352	Opaque	260	330	>95
PVDF	Kynar	1.77	1.420	88	130	175	43
PCTFE	Aclar	2.08	1.425	90	130	220	100
FEP	Teflon-FEP	2.15	1.343	96	200	260	>95
PFA	Teflon-PFA	2.13	1.350	93	260	305	>95
ETFE	Tefzel	1.74	1.403	95	150	270	31
ECTFE	Halar	1.68	1.447	Opaque	160	255	60

[a] Stable for 20,000 h.

Polytetrafluoroethylene (PTFE)

PTFE, commercially introduced in 1947 under the trademark Teflon® (DuPont), was the first fluorinated polyolefin developed. Unlike some other fluoropolymers, the carbon chain in Teflon is completely surrounded or wrapped by fluorine atoms so that nothing can get at it to react with it. Moreover, the carbon-fluorine bond is exceptionally strong, and the fluorine atoms shield the vulnerable carbon chain (Figure 4.48). This unusual structure gives Teflon its unique properties and makes it useful in the chemical and food industries to coat vessels and make them resistant to almost everything which might otherwise corrode them. Owing to the extremely low surface tensions of fluoroaliphatic compounds, PTFE possesses remarkable non-stick properties (extreme slipperiness), which is the basis for its most familiar uses in non-stick kitchen and garden utensils. For the same reason, it can also be used in low-friction bearings. PTFE is manufactured by free-radical polymerization of tetrafluoroethylene (TFE) (Figure 4.48). PTFE is not melt-processable because of the strength of the attractions between the chains, but can be processed by sintering of powders/paste through extrusion and compression molding. PTFE can be glass filled for increased strength and rigidity. PTFE possesses an outstanding working temperature range of –270°C to 260°C and is used in a broad range of applications, including gasketing, pump parts, electrical components, bearings, and anti-stick applications.

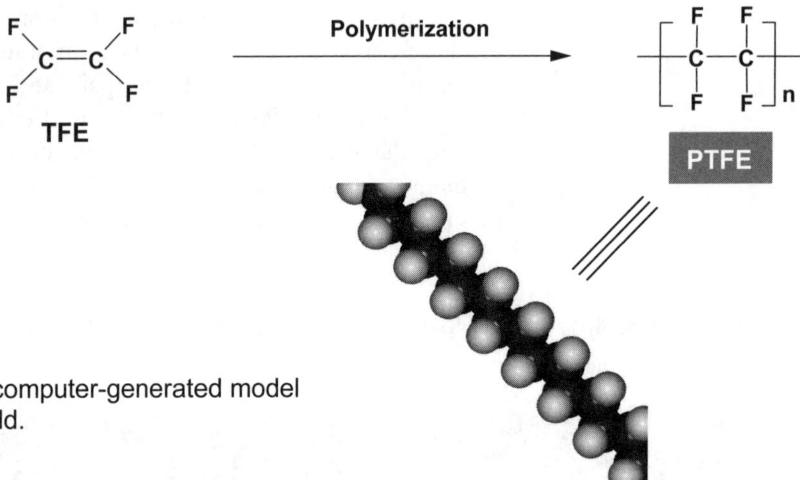

Figure 4.48. Synthesis of PTFE and its computer-generated model structure showing the fluorine atoms shield.

Poly(vinylidene fluoride) (PVDF)

PVDF, known by various brand names, such as Kynar® (Arkema) and Solef® (Solvay), has the characteristic stability of fluoropolymers when exposed to harsh thermal, chemical, and ultraviolet environments, while the alternating CH_2 and CF_2 groups along the polymer chain provide a unique polarity that influences its solubility and electrical properties. PVDF is manufactured by free-radical polymerization of vinylidene fluoride, which can be partially replaced with some co-monomers, such as hexafluoropropylene and trifluoroethylene, to produce useful copolymers (Figure 4.49). For instance, poly(vinylidene fluoride-*co*-hexafluoropropylene), P(VDF-HFP), commercially known as Viton® (DuPont), is an excellent fluoroelastomer, while poly(vinylidene fluoride-*co*-trifluoroethylene), P(VDF-TrFE), has been the subject of recent scientific study as an efficient *piezoelectric material* because of its conspicuous effects on crystal morphologies related to dielectric properties, such as generation of electrical polarization in response to mechanical stress or converse effect: mechanical deformation upon application of an electrical charge or signal. PVDF is readily melt-processed by standard methods of extrusion, injection or compression molding. At elevated temperatures, PVDF can be dissolved in polar solvents, such as DMF. This selective solubility is advantageous in the preparation of corrosion-resistant coatings for chemical process equipment and long-life architectural finishes on building panels. PVDF components are used extensively in the high purity semiconductor market (low extractable values), pulp and paper industry (chemically resistant to halogens and acids), nuclear waste processing (radiation and hot acid applications), the general chemical processing industry (chemical and temperature applications), and water treatment membrane (industrial and potable water use). PVDF also meets specifications for the food and pharmaceutical processing industries and has also gained success in the battery sector as binders for cathodes and anodes in lithium-ion technology, and as battery separators in lithium-ion polymer technology.

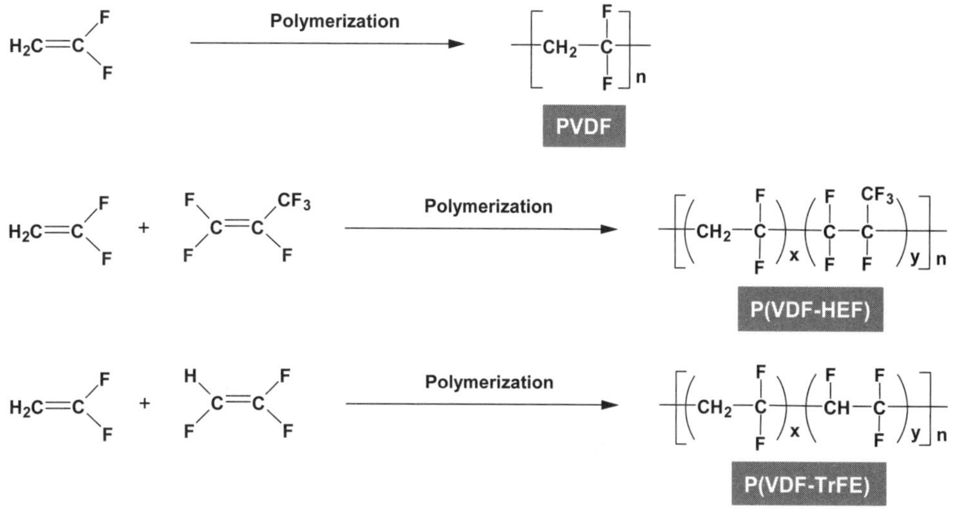

Figure 4.49. Synthesis of PVDF and its notable copolymers.

Polychlorotrifluoroethylene (PCTFE)

This homopolymer is used extensively in pharmaceutical packaging and industrial applications for its chemical and moisture resistant properties. PCTFE film has a very high clarity, contains no plasticizers, is chemically resistant, and possess a very low coefficient of friction. The most common brand is Aclar® (Honeywell). It is interesting to note that PCTFE, which differs from PTFE in that one fluorine atom in every repeat unit is replaced with one chlorine atom, exhibits drastically lower thermal properties compared to PTFE, but displays the best fire-resistance properties (deforms in a flame, but does not burn) among the perfluoropolymers (Table 4.3). Recently, it was demonstrated that the secondary chlorine atoms in PCTFE are much more reactive than those in PVC with respect to radical generation under atom-transfer radical polymerization (ATRP) conditions.[100] This observation resulted in the preparation of a variety of well-defined graft copolymers of PCTFE or its copolymer, P(VDF-*co*-CTFE) via the "grafting-from" approach (see Figure 2.125 in Chapter-2) An important feature of such a graft copolymer is that it uses *tert*-butyl acrylate (^{t}BA) as the grafting monomer. The resulting graft copolymer, e.g., P(VDF-*co*-CTFE)-*g*-P^{t}BA, can be easily converted to an amphiphilic graft copolymer with poly(acrylic acid) (PAA) side chains by hydrolysis of poly(tert-butyl acrylate) (P^{t}BA) side chains (Figure 4.50). This type of amphiphilic polymer is attractive for novel high-performance filtration membranes with engineered surface properties.

Fluorinated Ethylene-Propylene (FEP) Copolymer

FEP, a random copolymer of tetrafluoroethylene (TFE) and hexafluoropropylene (HFP), was developed by DuPont as a melt-processable Teflon (Teflon® FEP), which, unlike virgin PTFE, can be processed by normal plastic methods (Figure 4.51). The copolymerization lowers the melting point of PTFE from 330°C to about 260°C. With the same benefits of PTFE, FEP has a lower maximum operating temperature (200°C). The structure of FEP looks very similar to PTFE, except for random placement of pendent trifluoromethyl groups, which markedly reduce the degree of crystallinity (70 vs 98% for PTFE). The principal large scale applications of FEP include coaxial cable, pipes and fittings, and antistatic conveyer belts and roll covers. Interestingly, FEP is highly transparent to visible light (96% vs opaque for PTFE, see Table 4.3) coupled with its light weight and excellent weatherability, making FEP films attractive for solar collector windows.

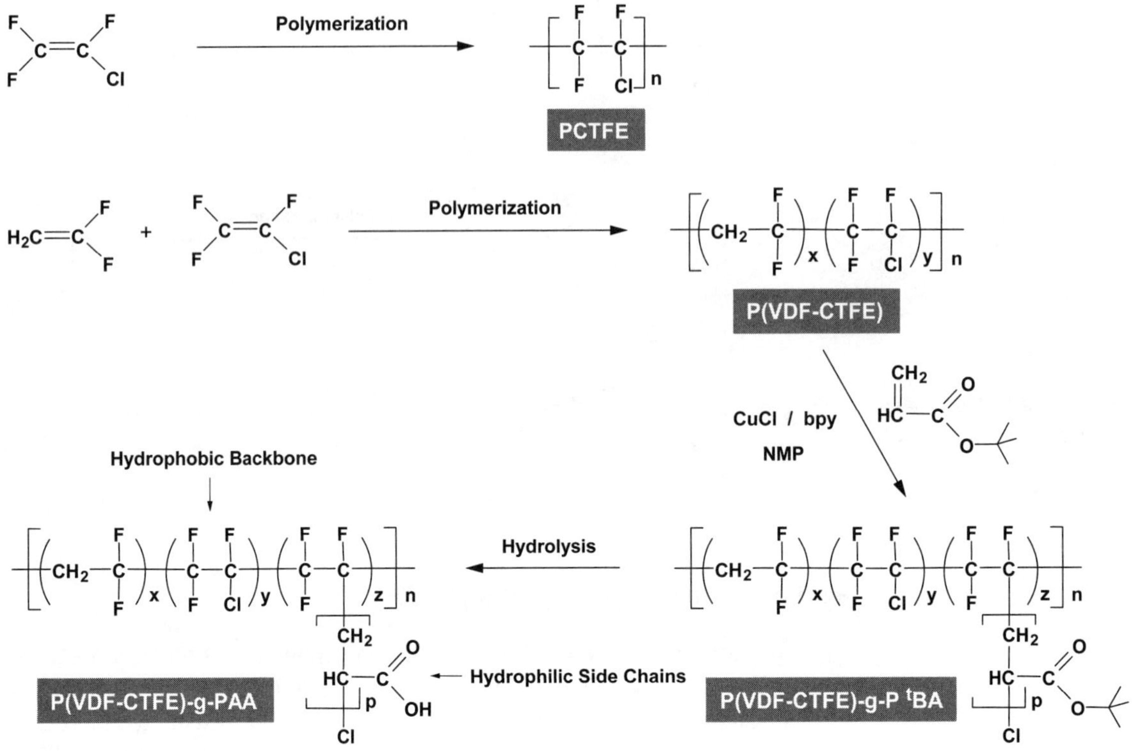

Figure 4.40. Synthesis of PCTFE and PCTFE-based amphiphilic graft copolymer.

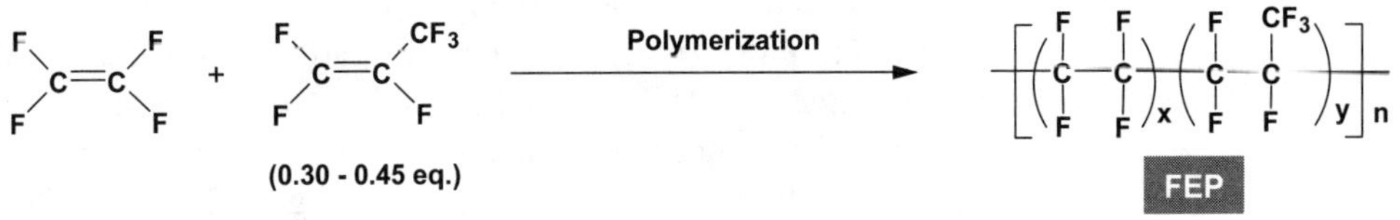

Figure 4.51. Synthesis of FEP.

Perfluorovinyl ether-Tetrafluoroethylene (PFA) Copolymer

In contrast to FEP, only a small amount of perfluorovinyl ether monomer (e.g., heptafluoropropyl trifluorovinyl ether) is required for reduced crystallinity (~60%) and desired toughness of PFA (Figure 4.52). PFA was developed by DuPont (Teflon® PFA) as a high temperature Teflon with a maximum operating temperature of 260°C, while maintaining properties similar to those of other fluoropolymers. However, this added temperature resistance significantly increases the cost because of the higher price of the perfluorovinyl ether monomer. PFA is colorless and its thin films are transparent. PFA is a melt-processable thermoplastic with chemical resistance similar to PTFE.

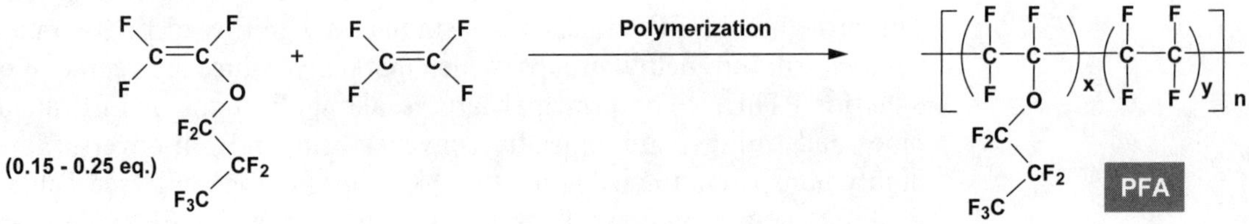

Figure 4.52. Synthesis of PFA.

Ethylene-Tetrafluoroethylene (ETFE) Copolymer

ETFE (Tefzel®, DuPont) is a less expensive tough Teflon with a hardness similar to nylon, but higher than virgin PTFE and FEP. The improvement in stiffness is paid for by reduced chemical resistance and operating temperature (170°C). ETFE, made from a 1:1 mole ratio of monomers, consists of a nearly 1:1 alternating structure, isomeric with PVDF, but with a higher melting point (270°C) and a lower dielectric loss (Figure 4.53). ETFE is semi-crystalline (~60%) and its thin films exhibit good transparency (Table 4.3). The major application of this polymer is in insulating and jacketing low voltage power wiring for mass transport systems.

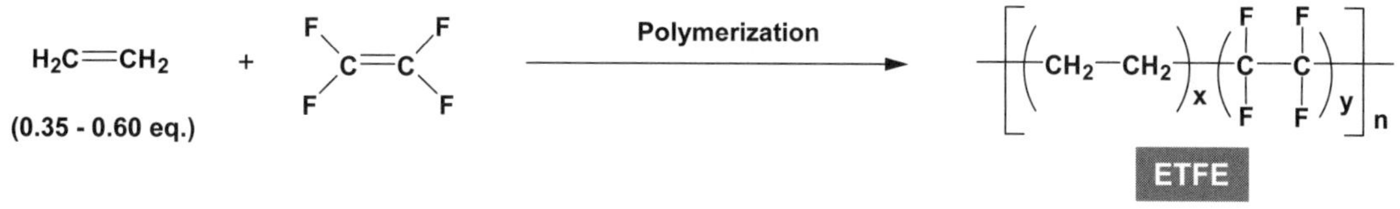

$H_2C{=}CH_2$ (0.35 - 0.60 eq.) + $F_2C{=}CF_2$ —Polymerization→ $-[(CH_2-CH_2)_x(CF_2-CF_2)_y]_n-$ ETFE

Figure 4.53. Synthesis of ETFE.

Ethylene-Chlorotrifluoroethylene (ECTFE) Copolymer

This is a tough fluoroplastic with properties similar to ETFE. ECTFE film provides by far the highest abrasion resistance and the highest dielectric strength of any fluoropolymer film. Consequently, its major use is in wire and cable insulation. ECTFE, prepared from an equimolar proportion of monomers, exhibits a melting point of 255°C with a chemical composition near perfect alternating linking of each monomer (Figure 4.54). The polymer is melt-processable and the most common brand name is Halar® (Solvay). ECTFE withstands continuous exposure to extreme temperatures and maintains excellent mechanical properties across the entire range from cryogenic temperatures to 180°C. It exhibits excellent electrical properties and chemical resistance and is unaffected by solvents at 120°C.

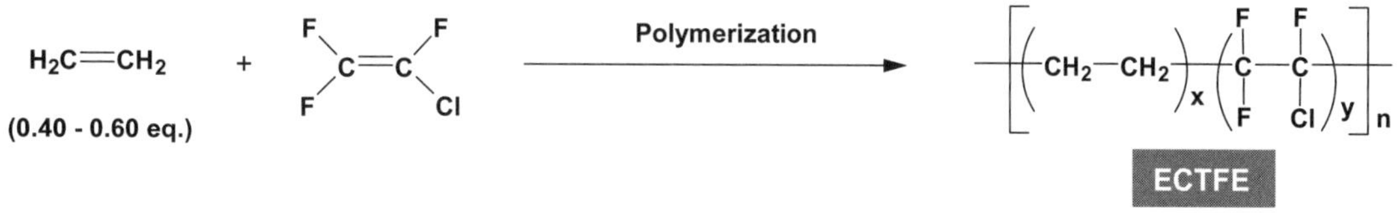

$H_2C{=}CH_2$ (0.40 - 0.60 eq.) + $F_2C{=}CFCl$ —Polymerization→ $-[(CH_2-CH_2)_x(CF_2-CFCl)_y]_n-$ ECTFE

Figure 4.54. Synthesis of ECTFE.

Highly Amorphous Perfluoropolymers

Unlike the aforementioned perfluoropolymers, these polymers, e.g., Cytop® (Asahi Glass Co., Japan) and Teflon® AF (DuPont), contain alicyclic fluoroether rings and are highly amorphous with high optical transparency. Cytop is manufactured by cyclopolymerization of an open chain perfluorodivinyl ether monomer, 1,1,2,4,4,5,5,6,7,7-decafluoro-3-oxa-1,6-heptadiene, DFOHD, which can also be copolymerized with a small proportion of TFE for property adjustment.[101] By contrast, Teflon AF is prepared by copolymerization of a cyclic monomer, 2,2-bistrifluoromethyl-

4,5-difluoro-1,3-dioxole, BDDO, with TFE (Figure 4.55). These polymers are prepared for a wide range of innovative optical applications because of their high optical clarity and their much lower refractive indices (1.295 to 1.355) than competing materials, such as PMMA (1.492) and PC (1.584). This makes these amorphous fluoropolymers suitable for optical technology products, such as waveguides, optical filters, fiber gratings and a wide range of optical devices. Most importantly, since these polymers contain no hydrogen, they show excellent near-infrared transparency and exhibit negligible absorption losses at the most important telecommunication wavelengths. Thus, they are attractive for specialty *plastic optical fiber* (POF) applications in the near-infrared region where PMMA is unsuitable due to strong absorption of carbon-hydrogen bonds.[102]

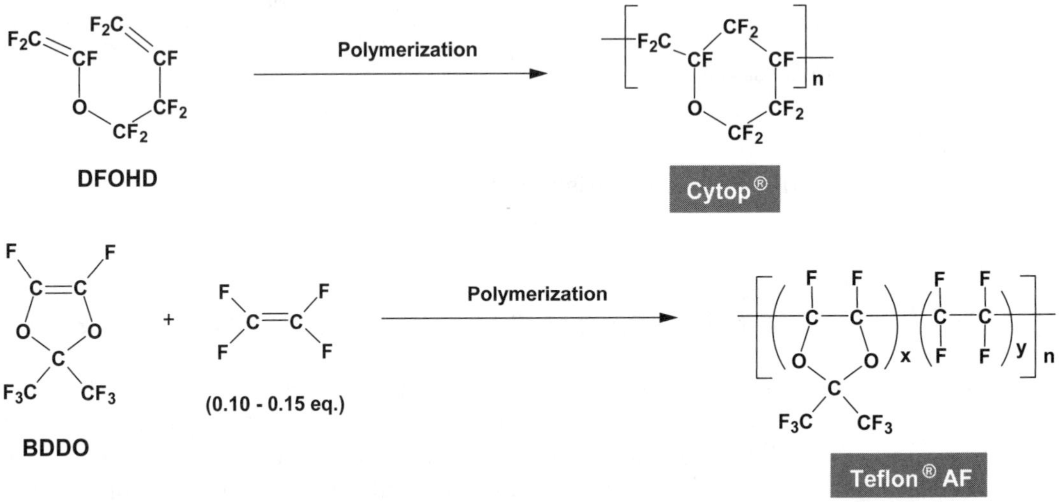

DFOHD — Polymerization → Cytop®

BDDO + $F_2C{=}CF_2$ (0.10 - 0.15 eq.) — Polymerization → Teflon® AF

Properties	Cytop®	Teflon® AF	PMMA	SiO_2
T_g (°C)	110	160	100	1125
Density (g/cm^3)	1.426	1.782	1.195	2.198
Refractive Index	1.342	1.291	1.498	1.463
Visible Transparency (%)	96	96	93	>99

Figure 4.55. Synthesis of important amorphous perfluoropolymers and their property comparison with competitors.

4.11. RECENT ADVANCES IN HIGH-PERFORMANCE POLYMERS

In the past decade, a variety of novel monomers, including new polymerization techniques, have been developed to obtain high-performance polymers with properties superior to those in use in existing technology. The following are some notable examples which highlight recent advances in the area of high-performance polymers.

New Synthetic Routes to Aramids and Poly(amide imide)s

In past years, several unconventional synthetic routes to high molecular weight aramids have been developed. Palladium-catalyzed carbonylation and condensation of diiodoaromatics with aromatic diamines is considered one of the most versatile methods because of its tolerance of a wide range of functional groups (Figure 4.56).[103] The polymerization is conducted in common polar aprotic solvents in the presence of a hindered base, such as 1,8-diazabicyclo[5.4.0]undec-7-ene (DBU). Moreover, this method offers potential advantages, such as the elimination of corrosive, hydrolytically sensitive acid chlorides and the availability of a variety of bishalogenated monomers. The mechanism of the reaction involves oxidative addition of a coordinatively unsaturated Pd(0) complex to an iodo compound to give the Pd(II) aryl intermediate, followed by CO insertion into the aryl-palladium bond to form an acyl complex. Subsequent attack by an amino group of the diamine leads to the formation of an aromatic amide linkage and regeneration of the active Pd(0) catalyst. This methodology can also be extended to poly(amide imide)s (PAIs) by using the phthalimide moiety containing diiodo compounds.[104]

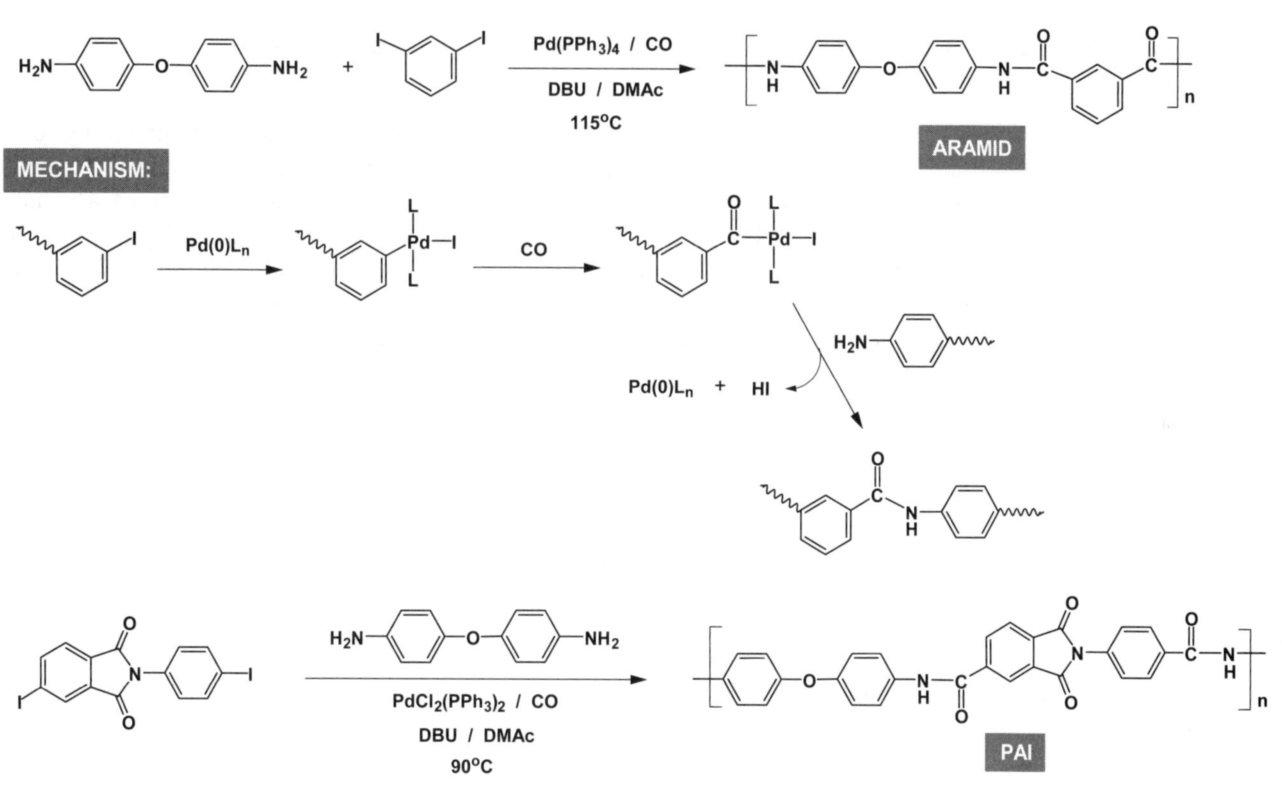

H_2N NH_2 + I I — $Pd(PPh_3)_4$ / CO, DBU / DMAc, 115°C → ARAMID

MECHANISM:

Pd(0)L_n → Pd—I (L, L) — CO → C—Pd—I ; H_2N ; Pd(0)L_n + HI

H_2N NH_2 — $PdCl_2(PPh_3)_2$ / CO, DBU / DMAc, 90°C → PAI

Figure 4.56. Synthesis of aramids and poly(amide imide)s by palladium-catalyzed carbonylation and mechanism of the condensation between diiodoaromatics and aromatic diamines.

The synthesis of aramids has also been efficiently performed by dissolving an aromatic diamine in DMAc, followed by addition of TMSCl to form a silylated diamine (Figure 4.57).[105,106] Subsequent addition of a stoichiometric amount of aromatic diacid chloride to the reaction mixture affords high molecular weight aramids in excellent yields because N-trimethylsilylated aromatic amines are far more reactive than the corresponding unsubstituted amines toward acid chlorides. This polymerization can also be carried out by reaction between separately prepared silylated diamine and diacid chloride. However, the *in situ* silylation method has additional advantages. First, since TMSCl reacts very readily with water, its presence in the solution ensures that small amounts of water will not destroy the moisture-sensitive acid chloride. Second, the handling of silylated diamines is highly simplified, allowing the polyamidation reaction to be carried out without special glassware and sophisticated operation, just as a classical low-temperature polyamidation.

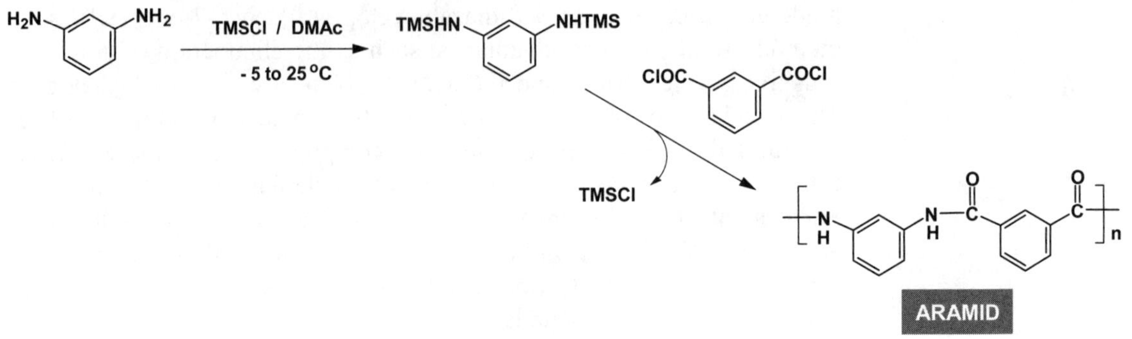

Figure 4.57. Synthesis of aramids by *in situ* silylation of aromatic diamine.

Very recently, high molecular weight aramids have been prepared by direct amidification of diamine and diacid monomers in high boiling solvent mixtures, such as *m*-terphenyl (MTP) and N-butyl-2-pyrrolidinone (NBP) in the presence of a catalyst, 3,4,5-trifluorophenylboronic acid (Figure 4.58).[107] The mechanism of polymerization involves formation of an active (aryloxy)boron complex by condensation of the catalyst with the acid functional group, followed by nucleophilic attack by the amine to form an amide linkage, with recovery of the catalyst (see Figure 3.56 in Chapter-3 for mechanism).

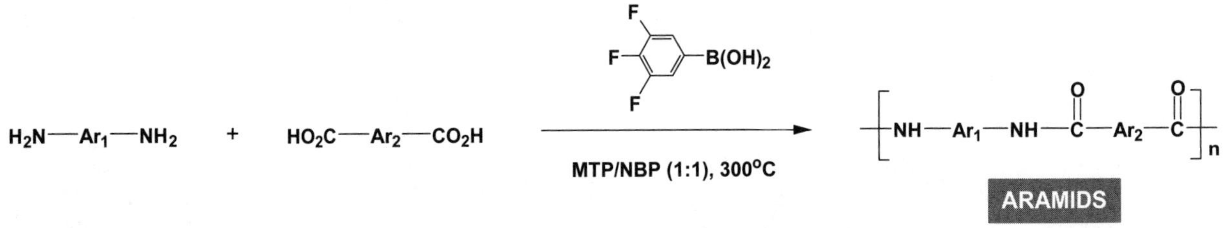

Figure 4.58. Synthesis of aramids by arylboronic acid catalyzed polycondensation of diamine and diacid monomers.

Poly(thioether thioether ketone) (PTTK)

In contrast to the commercial success of PPS and PEEK, the thioether linkages containing aromatic polyketones, such as poly(thioether thioether ketone) (PTTK), did not receive much attention because the dithiophenol monomers are prone to oxidize to sulfonic acids during nucleophilic displacement polymerization with 4,4'-difluorobenzophenone (DFBP). These thioether compounds are also difficult to obtain in high purity and possess an unpleasant odor. Recent success using masked dithiophenol monomers, such as 1,4-bis(N,N'-dimethyl-S-carbamoyl)phenylene (DMSC) has gained significant interest in thioether analogs of aromatic polyketones (Figure 4.59).[108,109] The masked monomers, which release bis-thiophenolate ions *in situ* in the presence of a mixture of $CsCO_3$ and $CaCO_3$, are readily prepared in high purity from the corresponding diphenols via the Newman-Karnes reaction[110] and do not have an unpleasant odor. The interesting feature of aromatic polyketones containing thioether linkages is that they exhibit a thermal stability similar to those of their ether analogues, but possess significantly lower T_m, which is attractive from a processing standpoint.

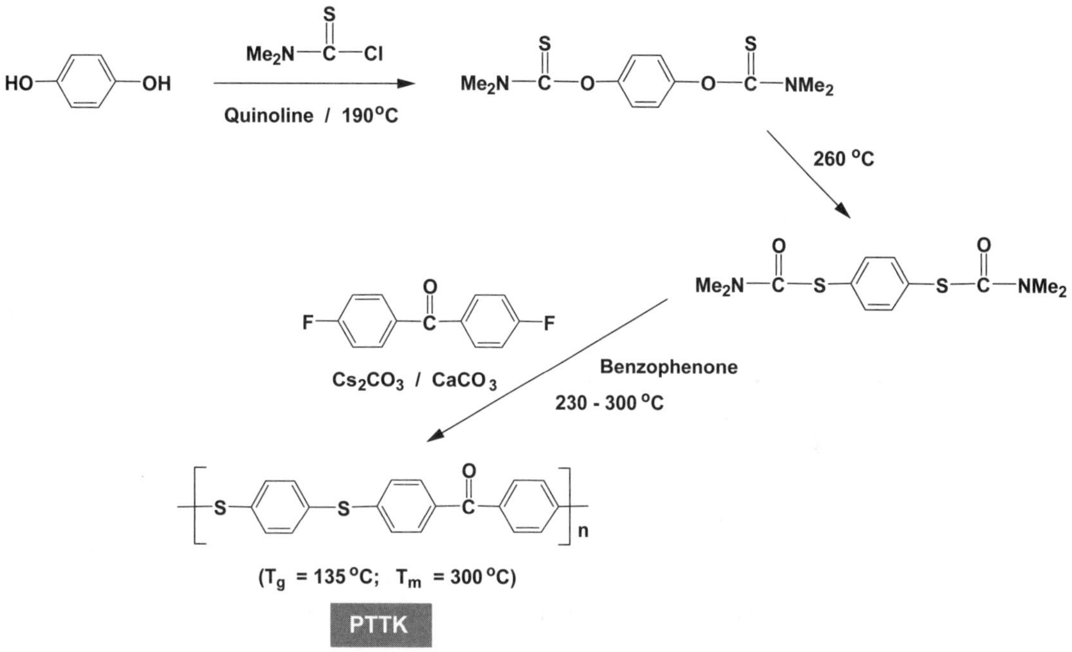

HO–C6H4–OH → [Me2N–C(=S)–Cl; Quinoline / 190°C] → Me2N–C(=S)–O–C6H4–O–C(=S)–NMe2 → [260 °C] → Me2N–C(=O)–S–C6H4–S–C(=O)–NMe2 → [F–C6H4–C(=O)–C6H4–F; Cs_2CO_3 / $CaCO_3$; Benzophenone; 230 - 300 °C] → [–S–C6H4–S–C6H4–C(=O)–C6H4–]n

(T_g = 135 °C; T_m = 300 °C)

PTTK

Figure 4.59. Synthesis of a thioether analog of PEEK.

Self-Assembled Polyimide

Polyimides are extensively used as dielectric and encapsulation materials in the microelectronics industry. New materials with improved dielectric, mechanical, and physicochemical properties are required for the realization of integrated circuit (IC) chips containing ultra-high resolution (submicron) electronic features. Therefore, the design and synthesis of novel polyimides with superior properties remain of great interest. The most common methods for improving these properties of polyimides have included the use of perfluoro monomers and/or the incorporation of pendent fluoro- or perfluoroalkyl groups. A fresh approach, depicted in Figure 4.60, is the preparation of a self-assembled polyimide, which consists of a semi-rigid fluorinated polyimide (F-PIM) backbone with nearly monodispersed poly(pentafluorostyrene) (F-PS) brushes.[111] The key to the synthetic strategy is the preparation of a diamine monomer, 2,4-diaminophenyl-2-bromoisobutyrate (DABB) containing an initiating species suitable for atom transfer radical polymerization (ATRP). DABB can be prepared by reaction of 2,4-dinitrophenol with 2-bromoisobutyric acid, followed by reduction of the resulting nitro compound. The comb-shaped polymer, obtained by ATRP of pentafluorostyrene monomer using F-PIM macroinitiator, was shown to self-assemble into ordered arrays on a hydrophobic surface consisting of aligned and uniformly spaced rigid rods 20-30 nm in length and 4-6 nm in lateral dimension. In addition to good solution processability and unique macromolecular architecture, the (F-PIM)-*cb*-(F-PS) copolymer exhibits good thermal stability, improved mechanical properties over those of the F-PS homopolymer, and very low dielectric constant (~2.1).

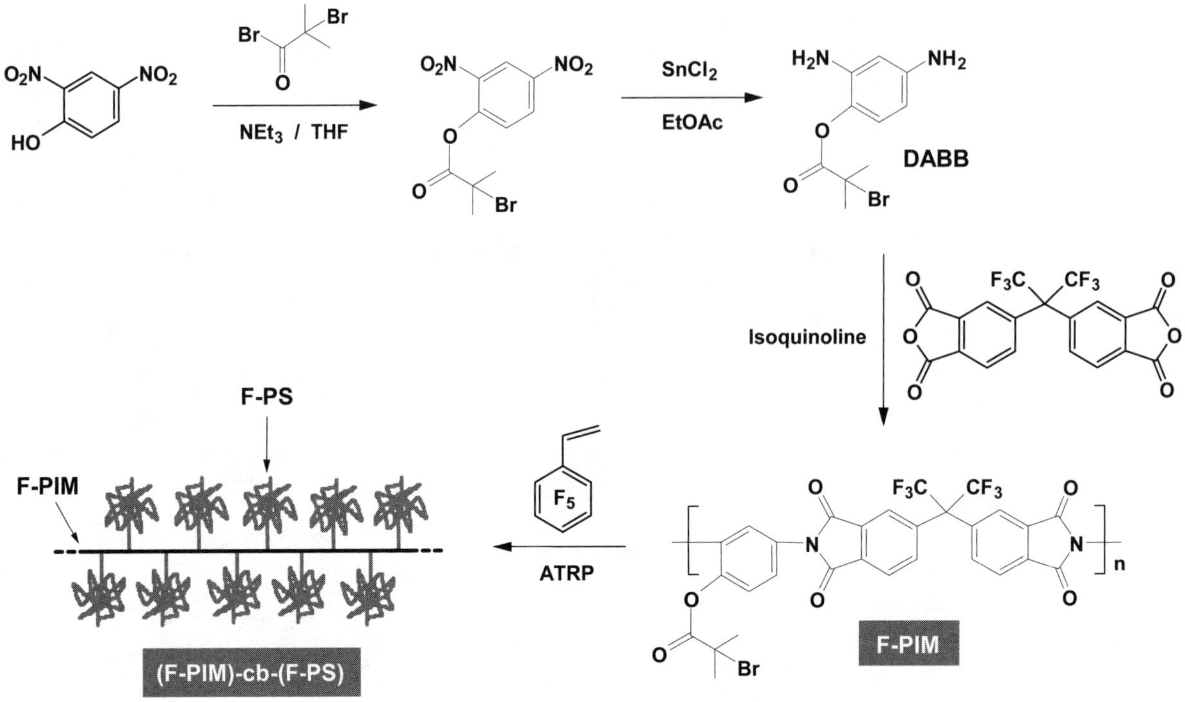

Figure 4.60. Synthesis of a comb-shaped self-assembled polyimide.

Phthalazinone Containing Polymers

Recently developed polymers containing phthalazinone and bisphthalazinone moieties, e.g., PPZ and PBPZ, have emerged as a new class of heterocyclic ring containing high-performance polymers (Figure 4.61).[112,113] The most used monomer for PPZs is 1,2-dihydro-4-(4-hydroxyphenyl)(2H)-phthalazin-1-one (PZ), in which the NH group behaves like the phenolic OH group. Consequently, nucleophilic displacement polymerization (*vide supra*) of PZ with activated dihalo compounds leads to polymers with both ether and N-C linkages. Bisphthalazinone (BPZ) monomers are readily prepared in two steps from an aromatic dianhydride via Friedel-Crafts reaction with benzene followed by treatment of the diacid mixture with hydrazine. Thus, the polymerization of BPZ with activated dihalo compounds will form only an N-C bond between the monomers. Both PPZs and PBPZs exhibit high T_gs and excellent thermostabilities.

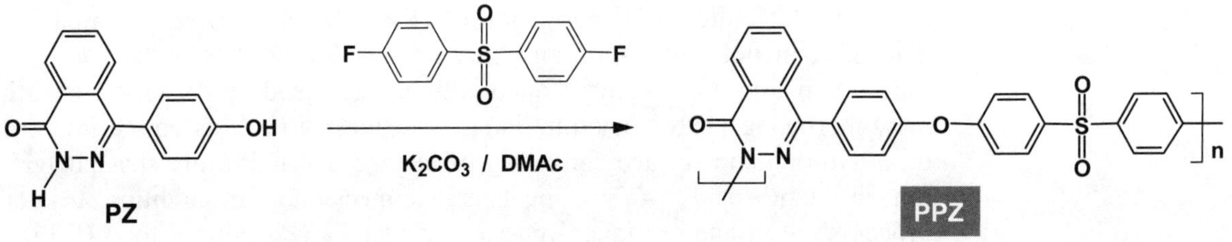

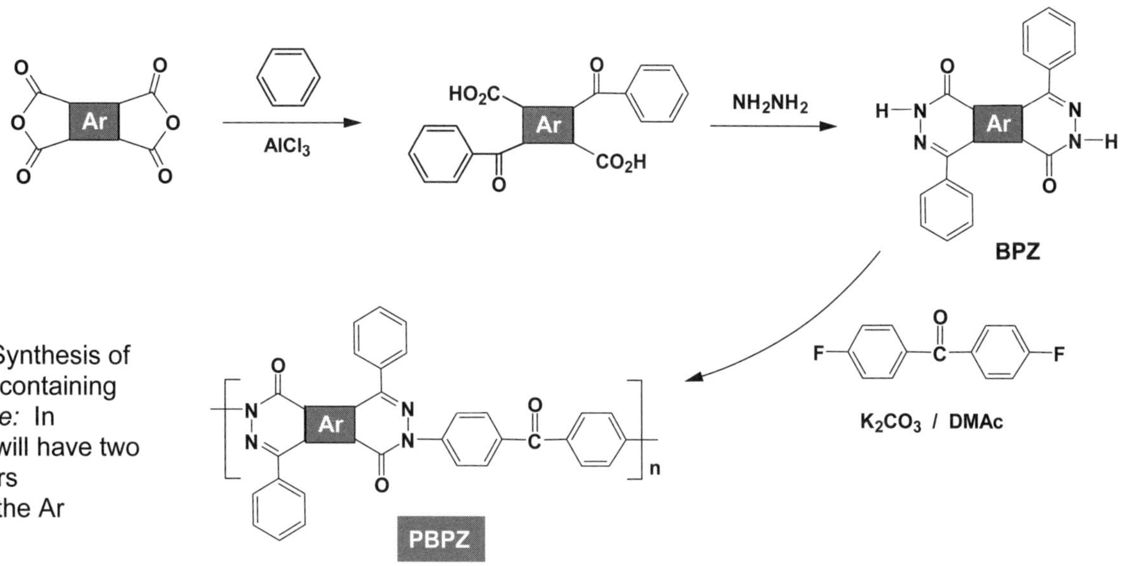

Figure 4.61. Synthesis of phthalazinone containing polymers. *Note:* In practice, BPZ will have two or more isomers depending on the Ar moiety.

Nickel-Catalyzed Coupling Polymerization

Nickel-catalyzed carbon-carbon coupling of aromatic dihalides or bistriflates has been a very popular method to synthesize π-conjugated polymers, such as poly(*p*-phenylene) and polythiophene (see Chapter-5).[114-117] The polymerization reaction is so mild that it permits the presence of certain functional groups, such as ester, on the monomers, leading to polymers with enhanced solubility. Recently, this methodology has been extended to synthesize a variety of high-performance polymers, viz., poly(arylene ether sulfone)s, poly(arylene ether ketone)s and poly(arylene phosphine oxide)s.[118-121] It is noteworthy that with proper selection of monomers, this method can be used to prepare high-performance polymers, which are identical or similar to those obtained by electrophilic (Friedel-Crafts) or aromatic nucleophilic substitution reactions. Figure 4.62 demonstrates the simplicity of this method through the synthesis of two quite different representative polymers. The first member belongs to the family of aromatic poly(ether ketone)s, while the second is a new high-performance polymer containing the hexafluoroisopropylidene, [$C(CF_3)_2$] moiety, but contains no ether linkages.[122] As shown by other hexafluoroisopropylidene group containing polymers, this new polymer, poly[{1,1'-biphenyl}-4,4'-diyl{2,2,2-trifluoro-1-(trifluoromethyl) ethylidene}] (PDTFE), is soluble in common organic solvents, and has a high T_g (255°C) and negligible weight loss below 500°C.

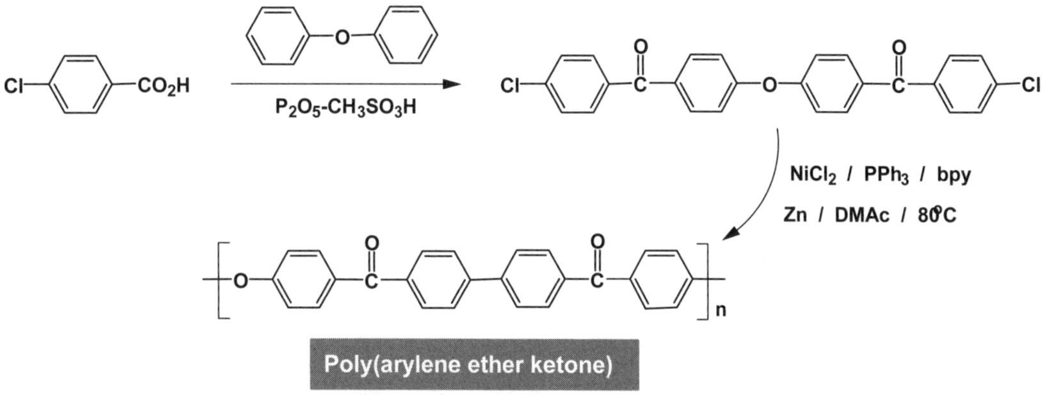

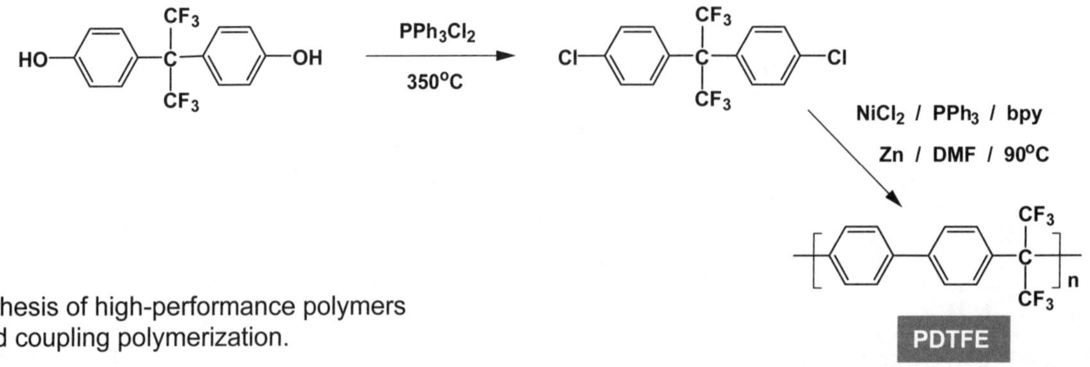

Figure 4.62. Synthesis of high-performance polymers by nickel-catalyzed coupling polymerization.

Superacid-Catalyzed Polycondensation

Superacid-catalyzed polycondensation between a monomer containing 1,2-dicarbonyl groups, such as acenaphthenequinone and isatin, and an aromatic hydrocarbon, has recently opened new possibilities for Friedel-Crafts polymer chemistry.[123-125] The mechanism of polymerization involves superelectrophilic activation of the 1,2-dicarbonyl compounds in the presence of a Brønsted superacid, trifluoromethanesulfonic acid (TFSA), often in conjunction with a mixture of methanesulfonic acid (MSA) and trifluoroacetic acid (TFA), acting as both solvent and a medium for generation of electrophilic species (Figure 4.63). Most importantly, the polymerization is conducted at ambient temperature and pressure. Only one of the two carbonyl groups of the 1,2-dicarbonyl compound participates in the polymerization, leading to a new class of polyetherketones. The polymers obtained are soluble in common organic solvents, such as chloroform, and exhibit high T_gs with no thermal decomposition below 500°C. It is noteworthy that polymers with similar structures may be prepared via aromatic nucleophilic displacement or Friedel-Crafts aromatic electrophilic substitution reactions, but the synthetic flexibility is limited or requires multiple steps to obtain the desired monomers. Thus, this one-pot preparative method starting from readily available reagents provides a new approach to aromatic polymers with promising properties, such as thermal stability and processability.

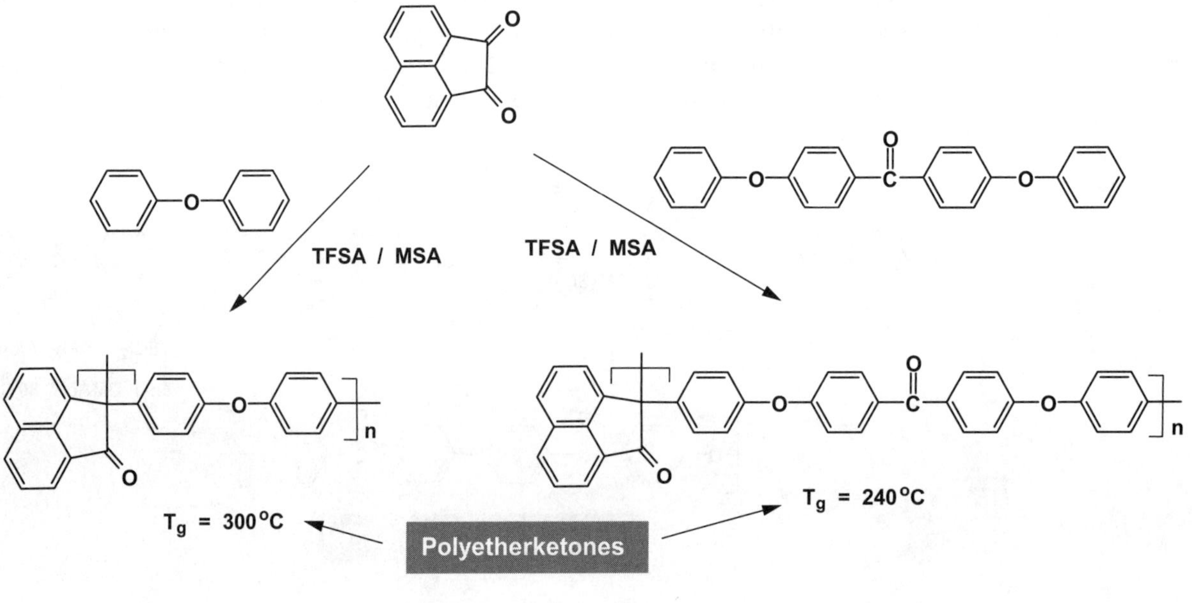

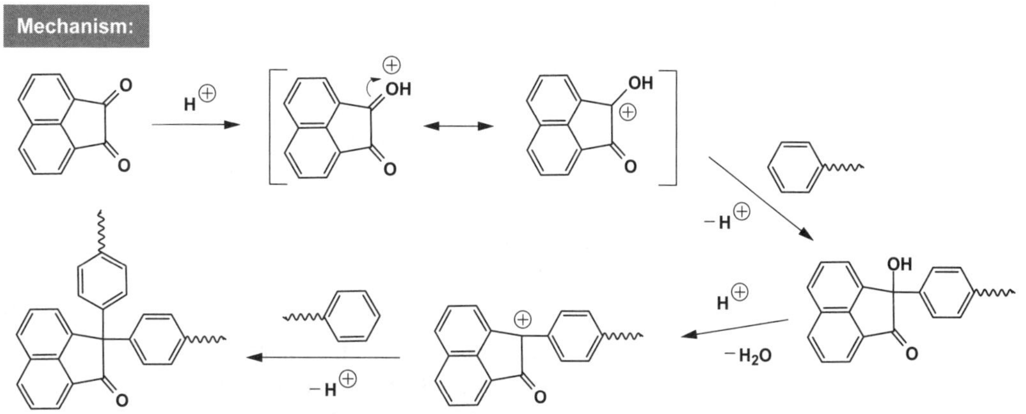

Mechanism:

Figure 4.63. Polymerization of acenaphthenequinone with aromatic ethers via superelectrophilic activation of the former.

Perfluorocyclobutane Aryl Ether Polymers

Polymers containing perfluorocyclobutane (PFCB) moieties have recently attracted the attention of a number of scientific communities because they exhibit properties similar to those of conventional fluoropolymers. These include high thermal/oxidative stability, low dielectric constant, low moisture absorption, low surface energy, high chemical resistance, optical transparency, improved processability, and good thermo-mechanical properties. The PFCB aryl ethers, such as PFCB-PH, PFCB-NP and PFCB-TP, are prepared by step-growth 2+2 cycloaddition polymerization of di-functional trifluorovinyl ether monomer in bulk or solution at about 150°C, without any initiator or catalyst (Figure 4.64).[126-129] The monomers are readily prepared in two steps via fluoroalkylation of a bisphenol compound with $BrCF_2CF_2Br$, followed by Zn-mediated elimination. Interestingly, the polymer with terphenyl moieties in the polymer backbone, PFCB-TP, exhibits a thermotropic nematic mesophase as characterized by polarized optical microscopy.[130] Thus, this methodology offers a unique approach to liquid crystalline polymers because of their availability via condensate-free thermal polymerization of appropriate PFCB monomers.

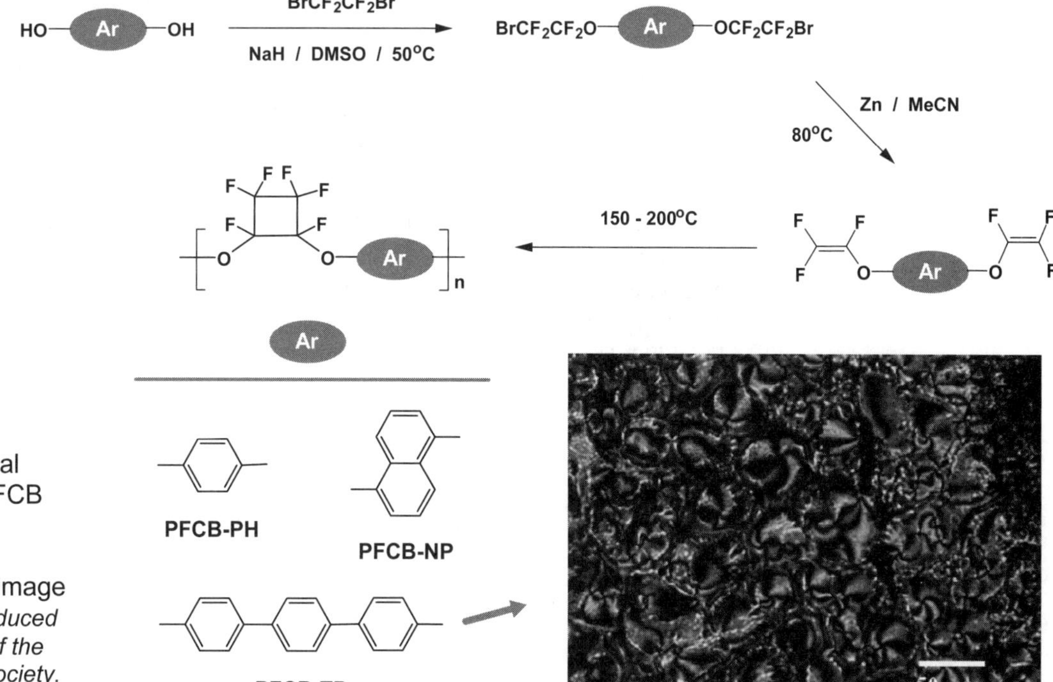

Figure 4.64. General synthetic route to PFCB aryl ether polymers. Below is a polarized optical microscopic image of PFCB-TP. *Reproduced with kind permission of the American Chemical Society.*

4.12. FUTURE OUTLOOK

As with engineering polymers, high-performance polymers are expected to grow at a slower rate, although there are new applications in the automobile and electronic sectors. In particular, the use of PPS (Ryton®) will continue to dominate, owing to its easy melt processability by injection molding and newer methods which provide access to improved PPS and its derivatives. The ready availability of fibers and films, such as those obtained from PBO (Zylon®), P84® and M5®, are also expected to accelerate the evaluation of these materials for specific applications.

Major growth is inevitable with aromatic liquid crystalline polyesters (LCPs) because of their excellent processing characteristics, physical and chemical properties, and mechanical strength. Besides applications in high density electronic and medical devices, interest of LCPs in the area of polymer blends is very promising. This is indicated by the vast amount of studies on the structure-property-application relationships in LCP/ general-purpose thermoplastics blends. The easier processing and improved engineering performances of the specifically designed LCP/polymer blends may counter the economic outlay of using relatively expensive LCPs.

Fluorinated polyolefins are also expected to maintain the steady consumption of the past fifty years. In conclusion, with continuing rapid progress in the science, engineering, and technology of materials and their processing, high-performance polymers are expected to provide significant advances in the foreseeable future.

General Study Questions:

1. Write the names and structures of three commercially available polymers that use bisphenol-A as a monomer. What differences in properties (e.g., T_g, percent crystallinity, PDT, and toughness) would you expect if the bisphenol-A monomer were replaced by *p*-hydroquinone?
2. The following macromolecular synthetic scheme involves the Ni(0)-mediated Yamamoto-type polycondensation (reductive aryl-aryl coupling) of a bistriflate monomer using a catalyst system consisting of bis(1,5-cyclooctadiene) nickel(0), 2,2'-bipyridyl, and free 1,5-cyclooctadiene (COD) in toluene/DMF mixtures. Establish the structure of the polymer.

OH

\+

O

$H^{\oplus}$

$(CF_3SO_2)_2O$

Pyridine

$Ni(COD)_2$

Polymer

3. In past years, a variety of aromatic polysulfones have been synthesized by nucleophilic displacement step-growth polymerization of 4,4'-dichlorodiphenyl sulfone with the disodium salt of a biphenol in order to tailor T_g. Based on the factors affecting T_g discussed in Chapter-1, match each repeat unit structure in the left-hand column with the appropriate T_g value in the right-hand column.

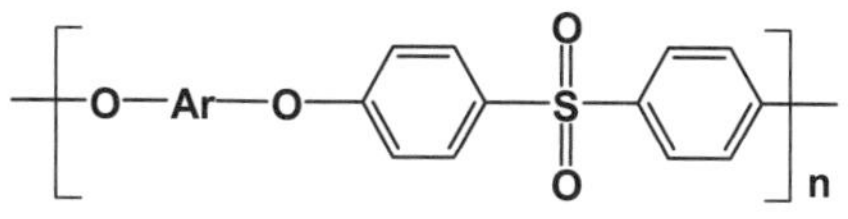

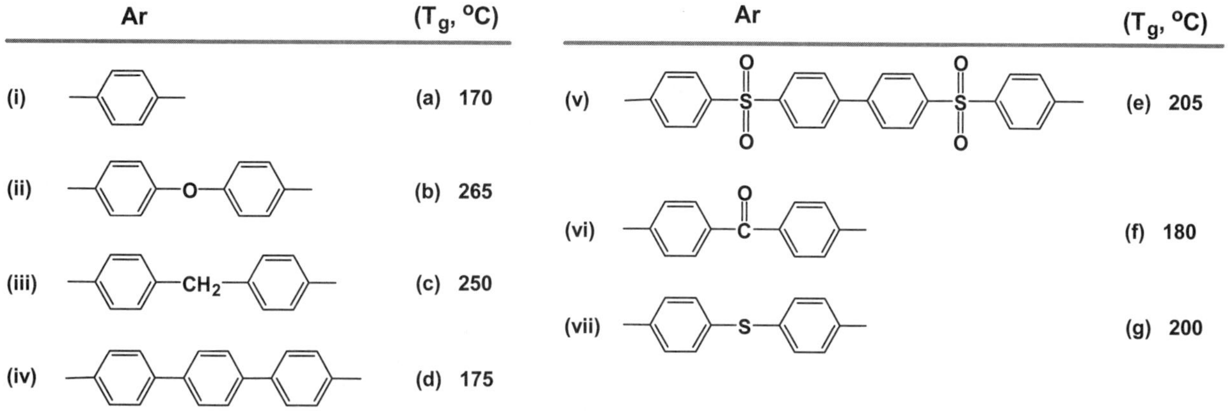

	Ar	(T_g, °C)		Ar	(T_g, °C)
(i)		(a) 170	(v)		(e) 205
(ii)	–O–	(b) 265	(vi)	C=O	(f) 180
(iii)	CH_2	(c) 250	(vii)	S	(g) 200
(iv)		(d) 175			

4. Similar to 4-nitrophthalonitrile, tetrafluorophthalonitrile undergoes nucleophilic displacement with phenoxide ion. With this clue, identify the structure of the perfluorinated polymer obtained by the following reaction scheme. Besides thermal stability, the special feature of this polymer is high transparency (i.e., low optical loss) at wavelengths of optical communication (WOC), 1.0 – 1.7 μm, because the wavelength of the fundamental stretching vibration of the C-F bond is about 2.8 times larger than that of the C-H bond. Polymers of this type are used as media for transmitting near-infrared light in optical communication devices as the waveguide in optoelectronic integrated circuits and in multi-chip interconnections.

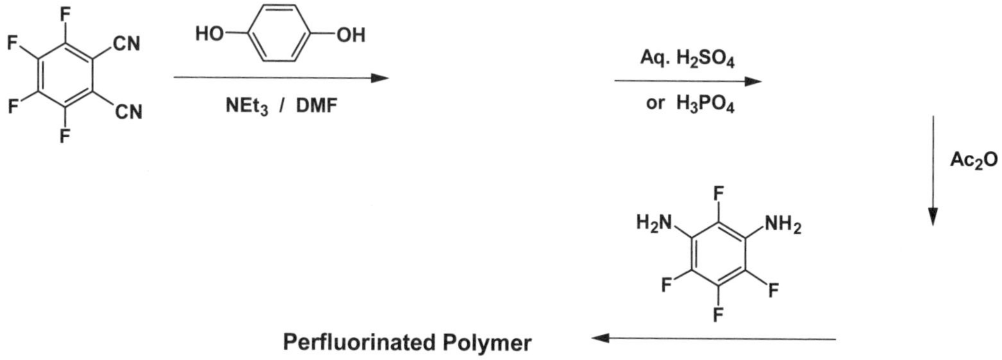

HO–C₆H₄–OH, NEt_3 / DMF; Aq. H_2SO_4 or H_3PO_4; Ac_2O; H_2N–C_6F_3–NH_2 → **Perfluorinated Polymer**

5. What are the primary chemical structural requirements that you should keep in mind in designing polymers with the following properties: (a) a melt processable thermoplastic with thermal stability in excess of 350°C, (b) a crosslinked rubber composite that can withstand prolonged exposure to sunlight, and (c) a melt processable, highly transparent thermoplastic capable of withstanding 100°C for a prolonged time. Write the chemical structure of a representative example from each category. Outline a synthetic strategy for the synthesis of each polymer.

6. Write the chemical structures of PC, Udel-PSF and Ultem-PI. Why do they possess excellent impact resistance?

7. Starting with adamantane and any compounds containing no more than six carbon atoms, synthesize the following polymer. What specific properties are expected of the polymer due to incorporation of adamantyl groups.

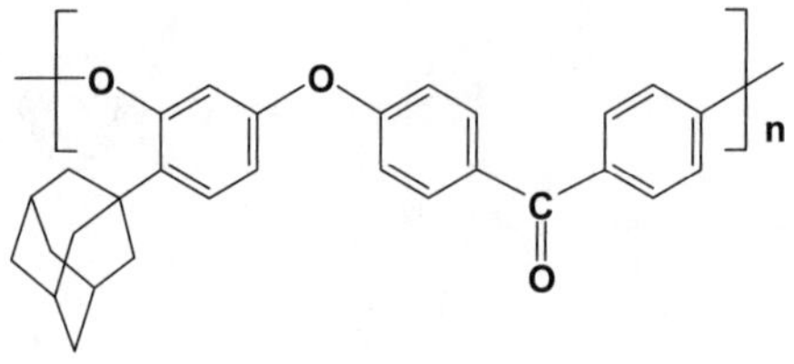

8. Write the structure of the polymer obtained by the polycondensation of the following monomer with 1,4-hydroquinone in the presence K_2CO_3 in DMAc. Compare the T_g of this polymer with that of PEBEK (see Section 4.3). Outline a synthetic strategy for this monomer using compounds with no more than seven carbon atoms.

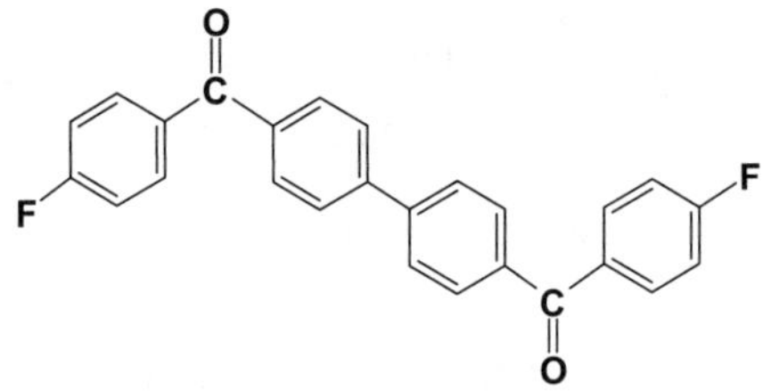

9. Complete the following reaction scheme for the synthesis of a high T_g polymer via nickel-mediated aromatic coupling polymerization.

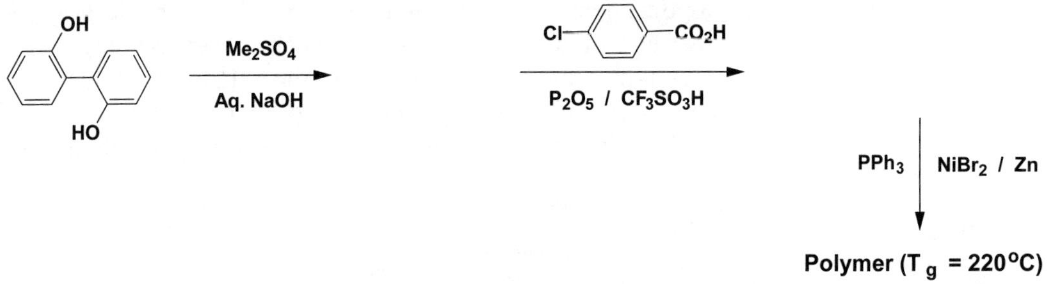

Me$_2$SO$_4$ / Aq. NaOH; Cl–C$_6$H$_4$–CO$_2$H, P$_2$O$_5$ / CF$_3$SO$_3$H; PPh$_3$, NiBr$_2$ / Zn

Polymer (T_g = 220°C)

10. Identify the target polymer in the sequence below which exhibits a T_g of 190°C and shows no thermal decomposition below 500°C! Write the structures of the intermediate compounds.

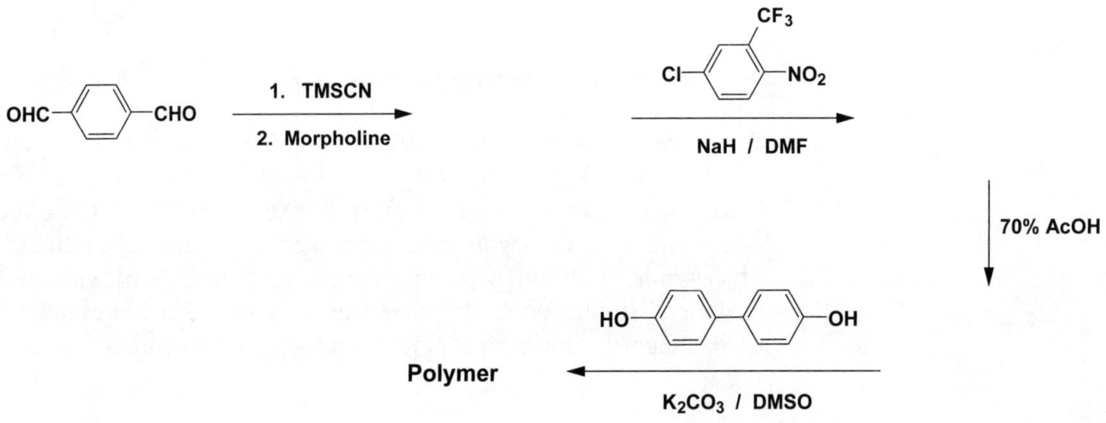

OHC–C$_6$H$_4$–CHO; 1. TMSCN 2. Morpholine; Cl–C$_6$H$_3$(CF$_3$)–NO$_2$, NaH / DMF; 70% AcOH; HO–C$_6$H$_4$–C$_6$H$_4$–OH, K$_2$CO$_3$ / DMSO; Polymer

11. The following is the scheme for the synthesis of a polymer containing pendent functional groups. Identify the structure of the polymer. How would you utilize the functional groups to create new features in the polymer? Explain the basis of your choice.

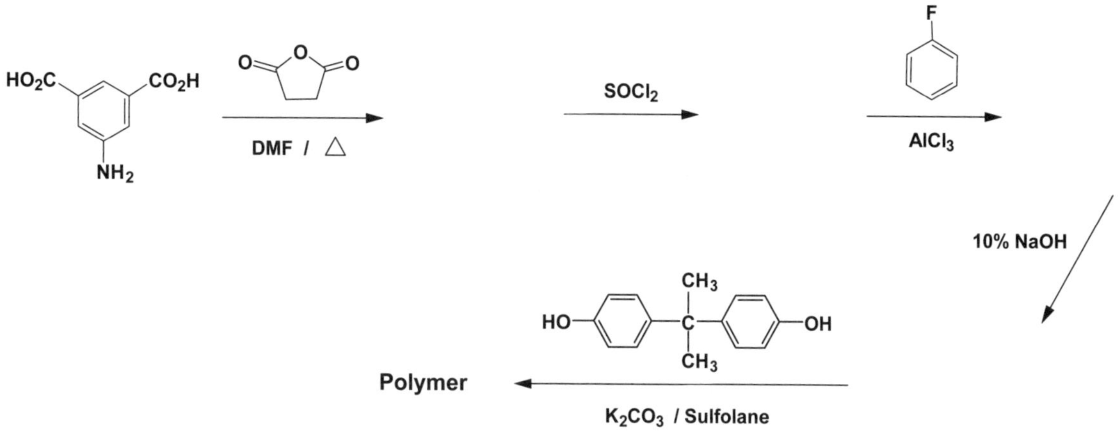

HO_2C CO_2H NH_2 — DMF / △ — $SOCl_2$ — F — $AlCl_3$ — 10% NaOH — HO CH_3 C CH_3 OH — K_2CO_3 / Sulfolane — Polymer

12. The following polymer exhibits thermotropic liquid crystalline behavior (hexagonal columnar phase) via interactions between the rigid rod-like main chains and flexible side chains. Identify the dicarboxylic acid monomer and lay out a feasible synthetic plan starting from hydroquinone.

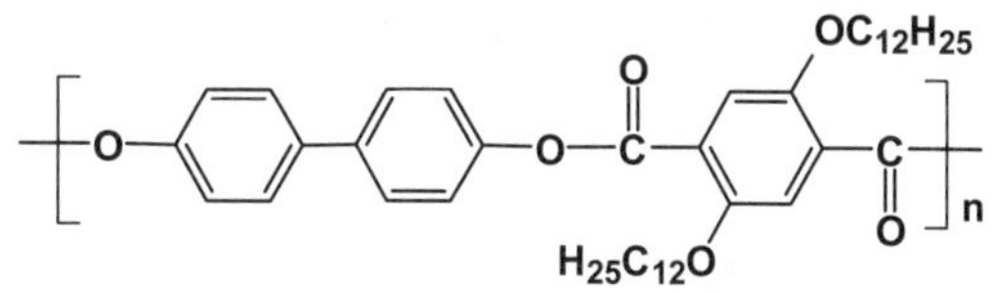

O O C $OC_{12}H_{25}$ $H_{25}C_{12}O$ C O n

13. Identify the structure of the polymer at the end of the reaction scheme shown below.

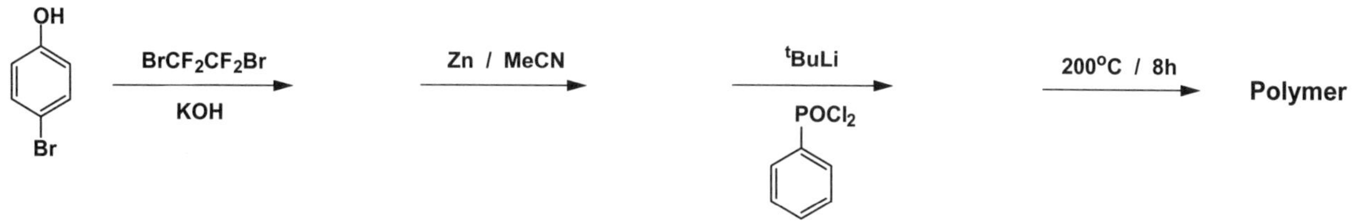

OH Br — $BrCF_2CF_2Br$ / KOH — Zn / MeCN — ^tBuLi / $POCl_2$ (phenyl) — 200°C / 8h — Polymer

Advanced Study Questions:

14. Identify the structures of the following rigid-rod polyamides and the intermediates. It is important to note that both polymerization reactions, (a) and (b), have been carried out by either direct polycondensation of dicarboxylic acid and diamine monomers or by a monomer containing both dicarboxylic acid and diamine groups in NMP containing dissolved $CaCl_2$ (or LiCl) using triphenyl phosphite (or triphenyl phosphate) and pyridine as condensing agents.

(a) $HO_2C-C_6H_4-CHO$ → ($C_6H_5COCH_3$; $BF_3 . Et_2O$) → ($NaO_2CH_2C-C_6H_4-NO_2$; Ac_2O) → (NH_2NH_2 / Pd-C) → ($P(OPh)_3$ / Py; DMAc / LiCl) → Rigid-rod Polyamide

(b) $H_2N-C_6H_3(CH_3)-C_6H_3(CH_3)-NH_2$ → (1. $NaNO_2$ / HCl; 2. H_2O /△) → ($F-C_6H_4-CN$; K_2CO_3 / DMF) → (KOH / Isopropanol; Aq. H_2O_2) → ($H_2N-C_6H_4-NH_2$; $P(OPh)_3$ / Py; NMP / $CaCl_2$) → Rigid-rod Polyamide

15. There have been considerable efforts to synthesize organo-soluble aramids by the introduction of bulky substituents or solubilizing linkages along the polymer chain. The following are the few selected monomers (I-IV) developed towards this goal. Devise a convenient synthetic route for each monomer.

I: $H_2N-C_6H_4-O-C_6H_4-C(CF_3)_2-C_6H_4-O-C_6H_4-NH_2$

II: 9,9-bis(4-aminophenyl)fluorene (H_2N, NH_2)

III: H_2N … NH_2 (phenyl-substituted oligophenylene diamine)

IV: $H_2N-C_6H_4-O-C_6H_4-C(C_6H_5)_2-C_6H_4-O-C_6H_4-NH_2$

16. The following is a straightforward synthesis of an aromatic poly(amine-amide) bearing pendent N-phenylcarbazole units. Besides high thermal stability and film forming characteristics, this polymer exhibits reversible electrochemical behavior, which make it potentially useful for the applications in dynamic electrochromic and electroluminescence devices. Identify the structure of the polymer and the intermediates.

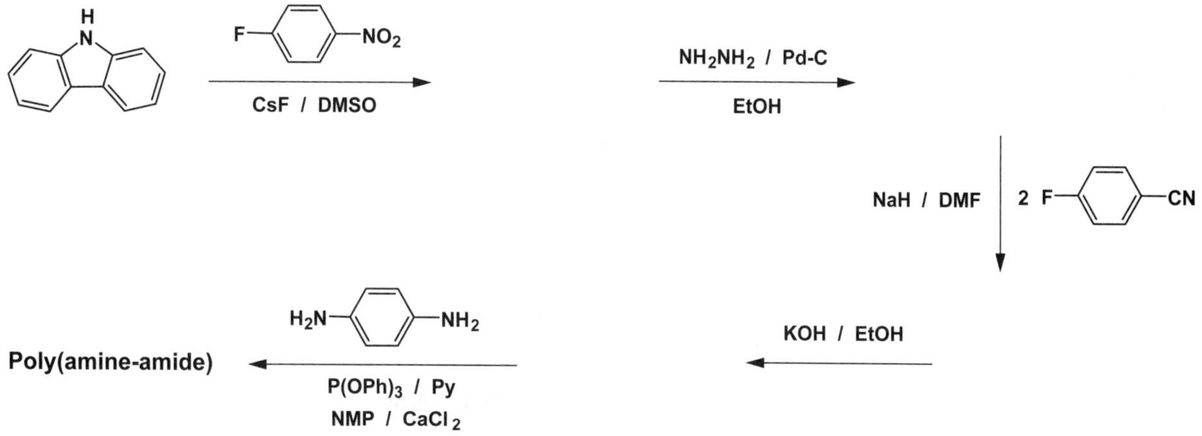

H N (carbazole) — $F-C_6H_4-NO_2$, CsF / DMSO → ; NH_2NH_2 / Pd-C, EtOH → ; NaH / DMF, 2 $F-C_6H_4-CN$ → ; KOH / EtOH → ; $H_2N-C_6H_4-NH_2$, $P(OPh)_3$ / Py, NMP / $CaCl_2$ → Poly(amine-amide)

17. Kapton®, in its imidized form, is insoluble in common organic solvents because of its highly rigid polymer backbone structure. By contrast, the following Kapton analog exhibits high solubility without affecting thermal performance. Identify the structure of the analog and provide two reasons for the marked improvement in solubility.

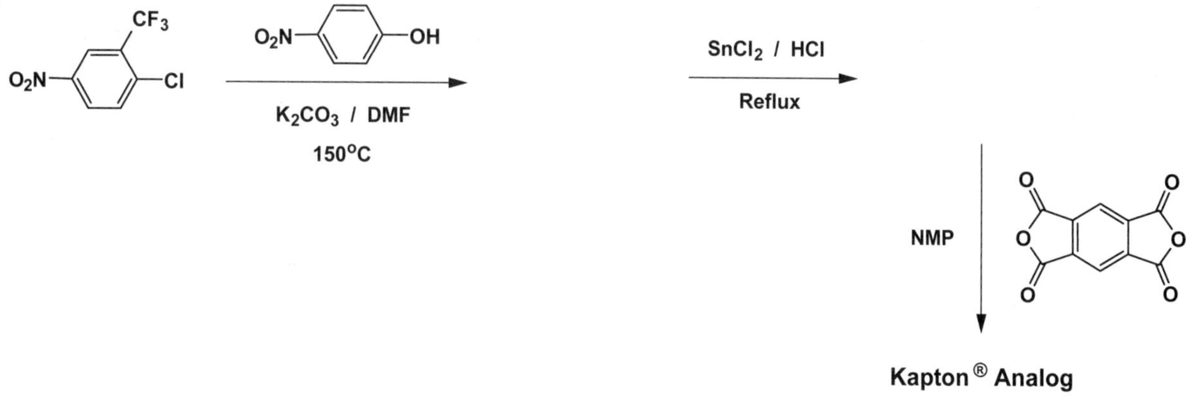

CF_3, O_2N, Cl (substituted benzene) — $O_2N-C_6H_4-OH$, K_2CO_3 / DMF, 150°C → ; $SnCl_2$ / HCl, Reflux → ; NMP, pyromellitic dianhydride → Kapton® Analog

18. Identify the structure of the polymer obtained by the following synthetic scheme.

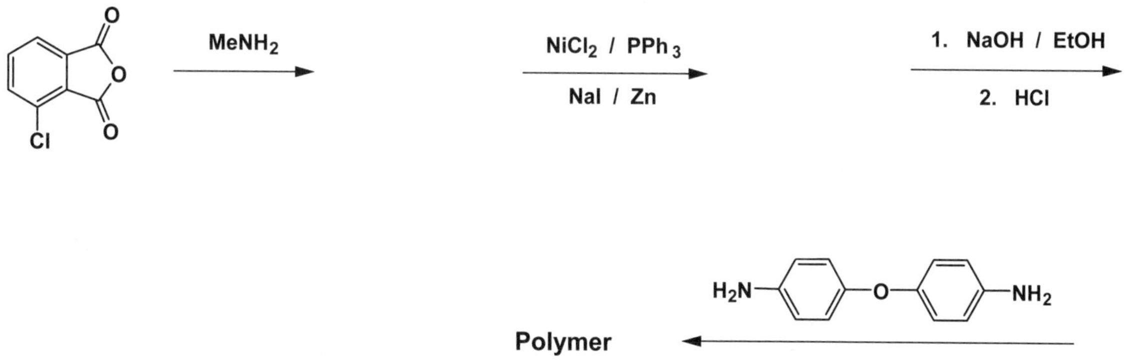

3-chlorophthalic anhydride (O, O, O, Cl) — $MeNH_2$ → ; $NiCl_2$ / PPh_3, NaI / Zn → ; 1. NaOH / EtOH, 2. HCl → ; Ac_2O → ; $H_2N-C_6H_4-O-C_6H_4-NH_2$ → Polymer

19. The polymer resulting from the following scheme belongs to the category of high-performance polymers. Identify the structure of the polymer.

HO_2C, CO_2H (5-tert-butylisophthalic acid) — $SOCl_2$ → ; Br (bromobenzene), $AlCl_3$ / 60 °C → ; $H_2N-C_6H_4-NH_2$, NaO^tBu / 165 °C, Pd-Cat. / DMAc → Polymer

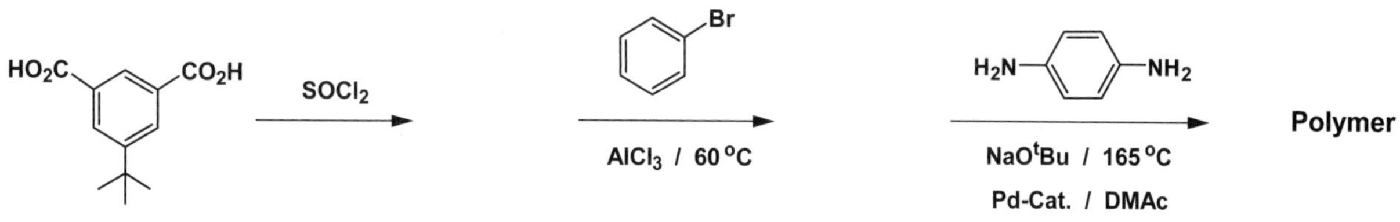

20. Identify the structure of the polymer obtained by the following scheme.

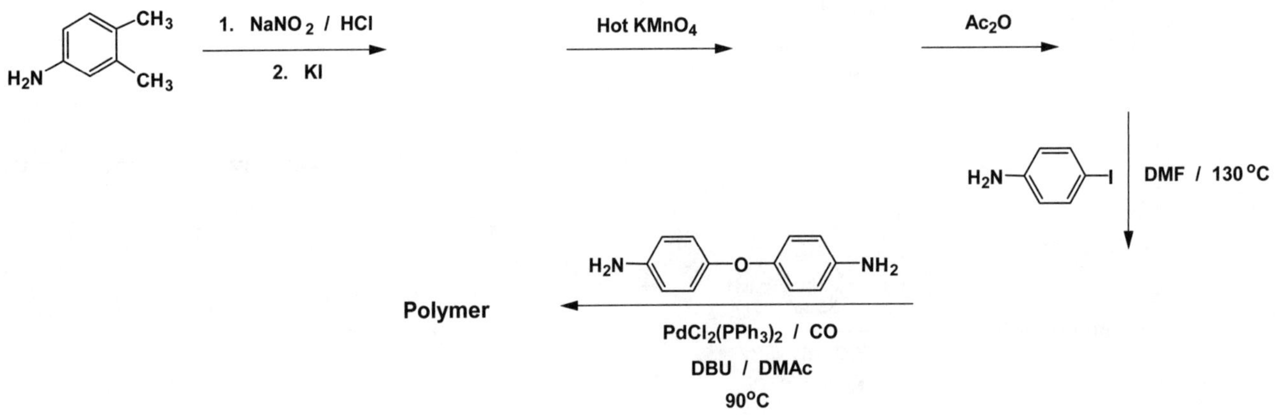

1. $NaNO_2$ / HCl
2. KI

Hot $KMnO_4$

Ac_2O

$H_2N-C_6H_4-I$ DMF / 130 °C

$H_2N-C_6H_4-O-C_6H_4-NH_2$

Polymer

$PdCl_2(PPh_3)_2$ / CO
DBU / DMAc
90°C

21. Identify the structure of the polymer obtained by the scheme below.

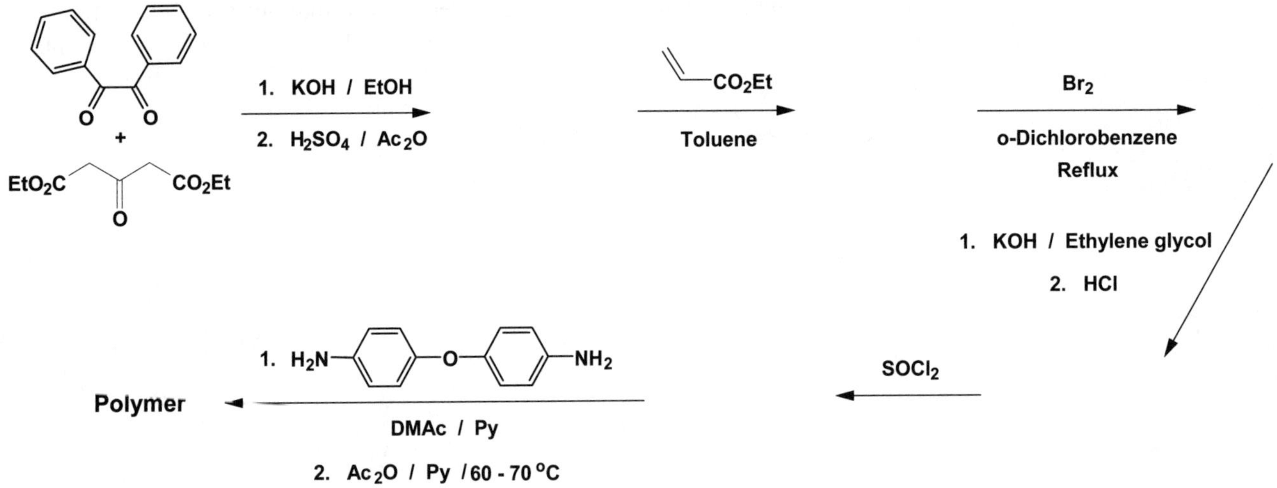

+

EtO_2C CO_2Et

1. KOH / EtOH
2. H_2SO_4 / Ac_2O

CO_2Et
Toluene

Br_2
o-Dichlorobenzene
Reflux

1. KOH / Ethylene glycol
2. HCl

$SOCl_2$

Polymer

1. $H_2N-C_6H_4-O-C_6H_4-NH_2$
DMAc / Py
2. Ac_2O / Py / 60 - 70 °C

22. As an alternative approach to organosoluble polybenzoxazoles (PBOs), the following dicarboxylic acid containing a *p*-terphenylene unit has been prepared. Identify the structures of all intermediates.

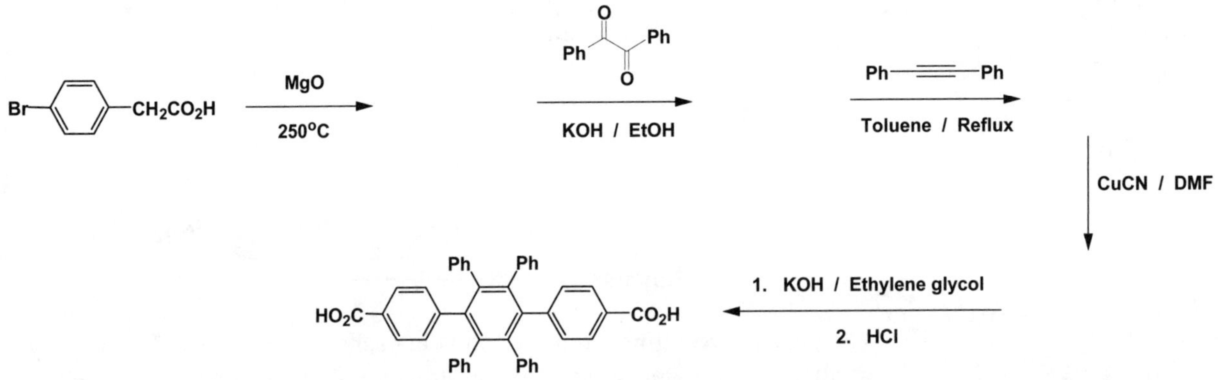

Br-C_6H_4-CH_2CO_2H

MgO
250°C

Ph Ph
KOH / EtOH

Ph—≡—Ph
Toluene / Reflux

CuCN / DMF

1. KOH / Ethylene glycol
2. HCl

Ph Ph
HO_2C CO_2H
Ph Ph

23. The scheme below provides a ladder polymer containing iptycene units. Identify the structure of the polymer. Comment on any special feature that this polymer may exhibit.

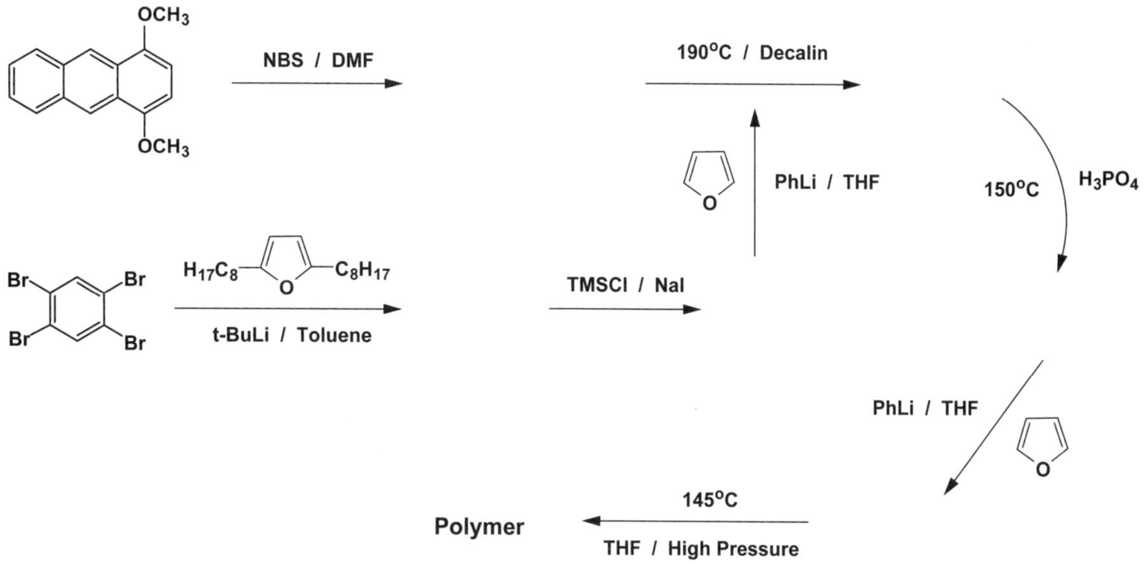

24. The four perfluorocyclobutane (PFCB) aryl ether polymers depicted below possess an isomeric repeat unit. A differential scanning calorimetry (DSC) experiment recorded their T_g values as: 106, 110, 117 and 144°C. Assuming they have almost identical degrees of polymerization, assign the T_g values to the respective polymers, including a reasonable explanation.

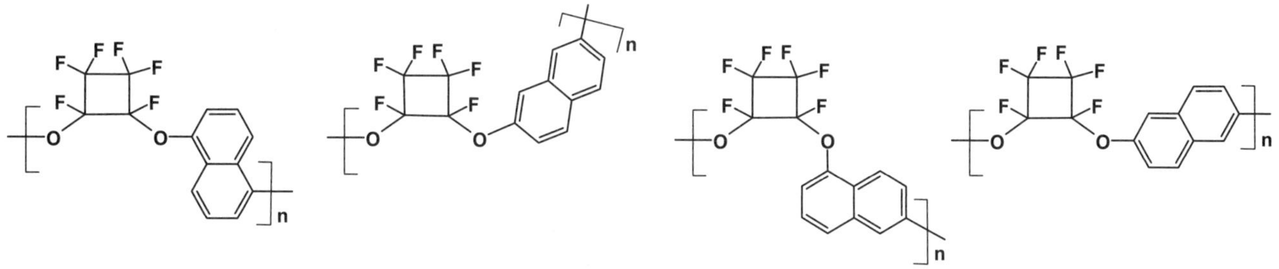

25. The monomer shown below can be used to prepare a perfluorocyclobutane (PFCB) aryl ether polymer suitable for low loss optical waveguides. Suggest a synthetic strategy to obtain this monomer from readily available starting materials.

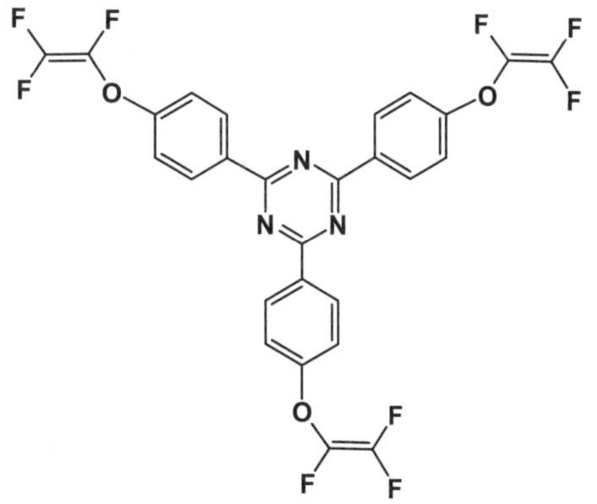

26. While the dianhydride monomers of the following polyimides are commercially available, the diamine monomers require multi-step synthetic schemes. For each monomer, suggest a convenient preparative route using readily available starting materials containing no more than six carbon atoms. Also, name one appropriate application of each polyimide.

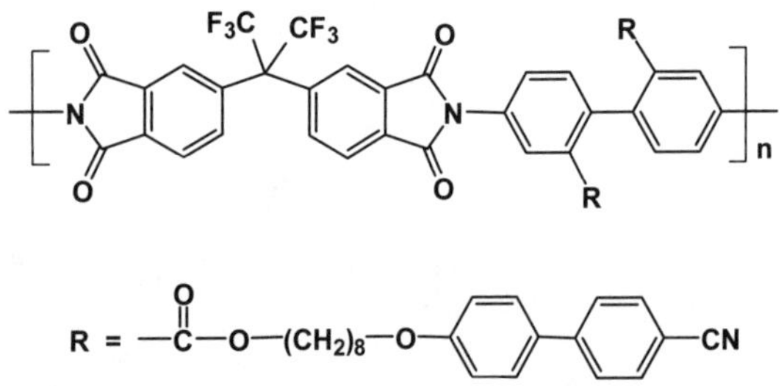

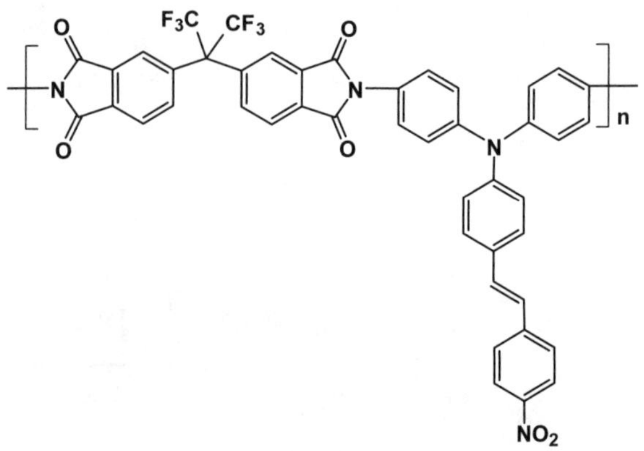

27. How would you prepare the following diamine from readily available starting materials? Comment on the effect on polymer properties when using this monomer.

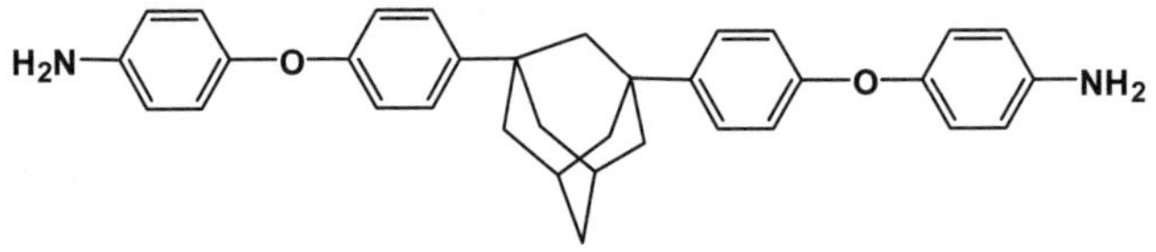

References for Chapter-4:

1. *High Performance Polymers,* Fink, J. K., William Andrew, Norwich, NY (2008).
2. Miyatake, K.; Endo, K.; Tsuchida, E., *Macromolecules*, **32**, 8786 (1999).
3. Fahey, D. R.; Hensley, H. D.; Ash, C. E.; Senn, D. R., *Macromolecules*, **30**, 387 (1997).
4. Hawkins, R. T., *Macromolecules*, **9**, 189 (1976).
5. Rabolt, J. F.; Clarke, T. C.; Kanazawa, K. K.; Reynolds, J. R.; Street, G. B., *J. Chem. Soc. Chem. Commun.,* 347 (1980).
6. Tsuchida, E.; Shouji, E.; Yamamoto, K., *Macromolecules*, **26**, 7144 (1993).
7. Haryono, A.; Yamamoto, K.; Shouji, E.; Tsuchida, E., *Macromolecules*, **31**, 1202 (1998).
8. Miyatake, K.; Yamamoto, K.; Yokoi, Y.; Tsuchida, E., *Macromolecules*, **31**, 403 (1998).
9. Leuninger, J.; Wang, C.; Soczka-Guth, T.; Enkelmann, V.; Pakula, T.; Mullen, K., *Macromolecules*, **31**, 1720 (1998).
10. Ding, Y.; Hay, A. S., *Macromolecules*, **29**, 4811 (1996).
11. Ding, Y.; Hay, A. S., *Macromolecules*, **30**, 2527 (1997).
12. Ding, Y.; Hay, A. S., *Macromolecules*, **29**, 6386 (1996).
13. Colon, I.; Kelsey, D. R., *J. Org. Chem.,* **51**, 2627 (1986).
14. Pixton, M. R.; Paul, D. R., *Macromolecules*, **28**, 8277 (1995).
15. Kim, I.-W.; Lee, K. J.; Jho, J. Y.; Park, H. C.; Won, J.; Kang, Y. S.; Guiver, M. D.; Robertson, G. P.; Dai, Y., *Macromolecules*, **34**, 2908 (2001).

16. Dai, Y.; Guiver, M. D.; Robertson, G. P.; Kang, Y. S.; Lee, K. J., *Macromolecules*, **36**, 6807 (2003).
17. Dai, Y.; Guiver, M. D.; Robertson, G. P.; Kang, Y. S., *Macromolecules*, **38**, 9670 (2005).
18. Ghosal, K.; Chern, R. T.; Freeman, B. D.; Daly, W. H.; Negulescu, I. I., *Macromolecules*, **29**, 4360 (1996).
19. Dai, Y.; Guiver, M. D.; Robertson, G. P.; Kang, Y. S.; Lee, K. J.; Jho, J. Y., *Macromolecules*, **37**, 1403 (2004).
20. Pixton, M. R.; Paul, D. R., *Polymer*, **36**, 3165 (1995).
21. Mathias, L. J.; Lewis, C. M.; Wiegel, K. N., *Macromolecules*, **30**, 5970 (1997).
22. Chikashige, Y.; Chikyu, Y.; Miyatake, K.; Watanabe, M., *Macromolecules*, **38**, 7121 (2005).
23. Bender, T. P.; Burt, R. A.; Hamer, G. K.; DeVisser, C.; Smith, P. F.; Saban, M., *Org. Process Res. Dev.,* **6**, 714 (2002).
24. Hergenrother, P. M.; Jensen, B. J.; Havens, S. J., *Polymer*, **29**, 358 (1988).
25. Teasley, M. F.; Hsiao, B. S., *Macromolecules*, **29**, 6432 (1996).
26. Bai, S. J.; Dotrong, M.; Soloski, E. J.; Evers, R. C., *J. Polym. Sci., Part B: Polym. Phys.,* **29**, 119 (1991).
27. R. S. Irwin, W. Sweeny, K. H. Gardner, C. R. Gochanour, M. Weinberg *Macromolecules*, **22**, 1065 (1989).
28. Colquhoun, H. M.; Dudman, C. C.; Blundell, D. J.; Bunn, A.; Mackenzie, P. D.; McGrail, P. T.; Nield, E.; Rose, J. B.; Williams, D. J., *Macromolecules*, **26**, 107 (1993).
29. Aldred, P. L.; Colquhoun, H. M.; Williams, D. J.; Blundell, D. J., *Macromolecules*, **35**, 9420 (2002).
30. Colquhoun, H. M.; Aldred, P. L.; Zhu, Z.; Williams, D. J., *Macromolecules*, **36**, 6416 (2003).
31. Colquhoun, H. M.; Lewis, D. F., *Polymer*, **29**, 1902 (1988).
32. Yonezawa, N.; Miyata, S.; Nakamura, T.; Mori, S.; Ueha, Y.; Katakai, R., *Macromolecules*, **26**, 5262 (1993).
33. Iyoda, M.; Otsuka, H.; Sato, K.; Nisato, N.; Oda, M., *Bull. Chem. Soc. Jpn.,* **63**, 80 (1990).
34. Yang, J.; Tyberg, C. S.; Gibson, H. W., *Macromolecules*, **32**, 8259 (1999).
35. Yang, J.; Gibson, H. W., *Macromolecules*, **30**, 5629 (1997).
36. Pandya, A.; Yang, J.; Gibson, H. W., *Macromolecules*, **27**, 1367 (1994).
37. He, C.; Lu, Z.; Zhao, L.; Chung, T-S., *J. Polym. Sci. Part A: Polym. Chem.,* **39**, 1242 (2001).
38. Bhowmik, P. K.; Han, H., *Macromolecules*, **26**, 5287 (1993).
39. Bhowmik, P. K.; Atkins, E. D. T.; Lenz, R. W.; Han, H., *Macromolecules*, **29**, 1910 (1996).
40. Kakali, F.; Kallitsis, J. K., *Macromolecules*, **29**, 4759 (1996).
41. Kakali, F.; Kallitsis, J.; Pakula, T.; Wegner, G., *Macromolecules*, **31**, 6190 (1998).
42. Andrikopoulos, K.; Vlassopoulos, D.; Voyiatzis, G. A.; Yiannopoulos, Y. D.; Kamitsos, E. I., *Macromolecules*, **31**, 5465 (1998).
43. Matsui, M.; Yamane, Y.; Kuroki, S.; Ando, I.; Fu, K.; Watanabe, J., *Ind. Eng. Chem. Res.,* **44**, 8694 (2005).
44. Xue, Y.; Hara, M., *Macromolecules*, **30**, 3803 (1997).
45. Xue, Y.; Hara, M.; Yoon, H. N., *Macromolecules*, **31**, 7806 (1998).

46. Xue, Y.; Hara, M.; Yoon, H., *Macromolecules*, **34**, 844 (2001).
47. Matsuda, H.; Asakura, T.; Nakagawa, Y., *Macromolecules*, **36**, 6160 (2003).
48. Mikroyannidis, J. A., *Macromolecules*, **28**, 5177 (1995).
49. Spiliopoulos, I. K.; Mikroyannidis, J. A., *Macromolecules*, **31**, 1236 (1998).
50. Meyers, R. A., *J. Polym. Sci. Part A-1*, **7**, 2757 (1969).
51. Kakimoto, M-A.; Akiyama, R.; Negi, Y. S.; Imai, Y., *J. Polym. Chem. Part:A, Polym. Chem.*, **26**, 99 (1988).
52. Liaw, D.-J.; Liaw, B.-Y.; Hsu, P.-N.; Hwang, C.-Y., *Chem. Mater.*, **13**, 1811 (2001).
53. Eastmond, G. C.; Paprotny, J.; Irwin, R. S., *Macromolecules*, **29**, 1382 (1996).
54. Mi, Q.; Gao, L.; Ding, M., *Macromolecules*, **29**, 5758 (1996).
55. Hsiao, S.-H.; Yang, C.-P.; Chu, K.-Y., *Macromolecules*, **30**, 165 (1997).
56. Matsuura, T.; Ishizawa, M.; Hasuda, Y.; Nishi S., *Macromolecules*, **25**, 3540 (1992).
57. Giesa, R.; Keller, U.; Eiselt, P.; Schmidt, H.-W., *J. Polym. Sci., Part A: Polym. Chem.*, **31**, 141 (1993).
58. Fang, X.; Yang, Z.; Zhang, S.; Gao, L.; Ding, M., *Macromolecules*, **35**, 8708 (2002).
59. Masaaki, T., *Bull. Chem. Soc. Jpn.*, **41**, 265 (1968).
60. Wang, Z. Y.; Qi, Y., *Macromolecules*, **27**, 625 (1994).
61. Wang, Z. Y.; Qi, Y., *Macromolecules*, **28**, 4207 (1995).
62. Hasegawa, M.; Sensui, N.; Shindo, Y.; Yokota, R., *Macromolecules*, **32**, 387 (1999).
63. Rozhanskii, I.; Okuyama, K.; Goto, K., *Polymer*, **41**, 7057 (2000).
64. Tong, Y.; Huang, W.; Luo, J.; Ding, M., *J. Polym. Sci. Part: A. Polym. Chem.*, **37**, 1425 (1999).
65. Gao, C.; Zhang, S.; Gao, L.; Ding, M., *Macromolecules*, **36**, 5559 (2003).
66. Kim, H.-S.; Kim, Y.-H.; Ahn, S.-K.; Kwon, S.-K., *Macromolecules*, **36**, 2327 (2003).
67. Walsh, C. J.; Mandal, B. K., *Chem. Mater.*, **13**, 2472 (2001).
68. Yi, M. H.; Huang, W.; Jin, M. Y.; Choi, K.-Y., *Macromolecules*, **30**, 5606 (1997).
69. Hsiao, S.-H.; Li, C.-T., *Macromolecules*, **31**, 7213 (1998).
70. Chern, Y.-T.; Shiue, H.-C., *Macromolecules*, **30**, 4646 (1997).
71. Chern, Y.-T., *Macromolecules*, **31**, 1898 (1998).
72. Chern, Y.-T.; Shiue, H.-C., *Macromolecules*, **30**, 5766 (1997).
73. Chern, Y.-T., *Macromolecules*, **31**, 5837 (1998).
74. Chern, Y.-T.; Shiue, H.-C., *Chem. Mater.*, **10**, 210 (1998).
75. Liaw, D.-J.; Chang, F.-C.; Leung, M.; Chou, M.-Y.; Muellen, K., *Macromolecules*, **38**, 4024 (2005).
76. Ha, S. Y.; Park, H. B.; Lee, Y. M., *Macromolecules*, **32**, 2394 (1999).
77. Ha, S. Y.; Oh, B-K.; Lee, Y. M., *Polymer*, **36**, 3549 (1995).
78. Yamazaki, N.; Matsumoto, M.; Higashi, F., *J. Polym. Sci., Polym. Chem. Ed.*, **13**, 1373 (1975).
79. Liaw, D.-J.; Hsu, P.-N.; Chen, W.-H.; Lin, S.-L., *Macromolecules*, **35**, 4669 (2002).
80. Chern, Y-T.; Chung, W-H., *Macromol. Chem. Phys.*, **197**, 1171 (1996).
81. DePra, P. A.; Gaudiello, J. G.; Marks, T. J., *Macromolecules*, **21**, 2295 (1988).

82. Rao, D. N.; Swiatkiewicz, J.; Chopra, P.; Ghoshal, S. K.; Prasad, P. N., *Appl. Phys. Lett.,* **48**, 1187 (1986).
83. Jenekhe, S. A.; Johnson, P. O.; Agrawal, A. K., *Macromolecules*, **22**, 3216 (1989).
84. Hattori, T.; Kagawa, K.; Kakimoto, M.; Imai Y., *Macromolecules*, **26**, 4089 (1993).
85. Kelly, P. A.; O'Connor, J. J., *J. Biomechanics*, **34**, 1599 (2001).
86. Craig, B. D.; Lane, R. A., *AMPTIAC*, **8**, 22 (2004).
87. Tullos, G. L.; Powers, J. M.; Jeskey, S. J.; Mathias, L. J., *Macromolecules*, **32**, 3598 (1999).
88. Maruyama, Y.; Oishi, Y.; Kakimoto, M.; Imai, Y., *Macromolecules*, **21**, 2305 (1988).
89. Schlüter, A-D., *Adv. Mater.,* **3**, 282 (1991).
90. Scherf, U.; Müllen, K., *Makromol. Chem., Rapid Commun.,* **12**, 489 (1991).
91. Arnold, F. E.; Van Deusen, R. L., *Macromolecules*, **2**, 497 (1969).
92. Babel, A.; Jenekhe, S. A., *J. Am. Chem. Soc.,* **125**, 13656 (2003).
93. Alam, M. M.; Jenekhe, S. A., *J. Phys. Chem. B.,* **106**, 11172 (2002).
94. Forster, M.; Annan, K. O.; Scherf, U., *Macromolecules*, **32**, 3159 (1999).
95. Nehls, B. S.; Fuldner, S.; Preis, E.; Farrell, T.; Scherf, U., *Macromolecules*, **38**, 687 (2005).
96. Lamba, J. J. S.; Tour, J. M., *J. Am. Chem. Soc.,* **116**, 11723 (1994).
97. Perepichka, D. F.; Bendikov, M.; Meng, H.; Wudl, F., *J. Am. Chem. Soc.,* **125**, 10190 (2003).
98. Thomas, S. W., III; Long, T. M.; Pate, B. D.; Kline, S. R.; Thomas, E. L.; Swager, T. M., *J. Am. Chem. Soc.,* **127**, 17976 (2005).
99. Chen, Z.; Amara, J. P.; Thomas, S. W., III; Swager, T. M., *Macromolecules*, **39**, 3202 (2006).
100. Zhang, M.; Russell, T. P., *Macromolecules*, **39**, 3531 (2006).
101. Yang, Z.-Y.; Feiring, A. E.; Smart, B. E., *J. Am. Chem. Soc.,* **116**, 4135 (1994).
102. Mikes, F.; Yang, Y.; Teraoka, I.; Ishigure, T.; Koike, Y.; Okamoto, Y., *Macromolecules*, **38**, 4237 (2005).
103. Perry, R. J.; Turner, S. R.; Blevins, R. W., *Macromolecules*, **26**, 1509 (1993).
104. Perry, R. J.; Turner, S. R.; Blevins, R. W., *Macromolecules*, **27**, 4058 (1994).
105. Oishi, Y.; Kakimoto, M.; Imai, Y., *Macromolecules*, **20**, 703 (1987).
106. Lozano, A. E.; de Abajo, J.; de la Campa, J. G., *Macromolecules*, **30**, 2507 (1997).
107. Ishihara, K.; Ohara, S.; Yamamoto, H., *Macromolecules*, **33**, 3511 (2000).
108. Ding, Y.; Hay, A. S., *Macromolecules*, **31**, 2690 (1998).
109. Ding, Y.; Hlil, A. R.; Hay, A. S.; Tsuchida, E.; Miyatake, K., *Macromolecules*, **32**, 315 (1999).
110. Newman, M. S.; Karnes, H. A., *J. Org. Chem.,* **31**, 3980 (1966).
111. Fu, G. D.; Kang, E. T.; Neoh, K. G.; Lin, C. C.; Liaw, D. J., *Macromolecules*, **38**, 7593 (2005).
112. Yoshida, S.; Hay, A. S., *Macromolecules*, **28**, 2579 (1995).
113. Wang, S. J.; Meng, Y. Z.; Hlil, A. R.; Hay, A. S., *Macromolecules*, **37**, 60 (2004)
114. Ueda, M.; Miyaji, Y.; Ito, T.; Oba, Y.; Sone, T., *Macromolecules*, **24**, 2694 (1991).
115. Percec, V.; Okita, S.; Weiss, R., *Macromolecules*, **25**, 1816 (1992).
116. Percec, V.; Zhao, M.; Bae, J.-Y.; Hill, D. H., *Macromolecules*, **29**, 3727 (1996).

117. Grob, M. C.; Feiring, A. E.; Auman, B. C.; Percec, V.; Zhao, M.; Hill, D. H., *Macromolecules*, **29**, 7284 (1996).
118. Ueda, M.; Ichikawa, F., *Macromolecules*, **23**, 926 (1990).
119. Ueda, M.; Ito, T., *Polym. J.,* **23**, 297 (1991).
120. Ghassemi, H.; McGrath, J. E., *Polymer*, **38**, 3139 (1997).
121. Colon, I.; Kwiatkowski, G. T., *J. Polym. Sci. Part-A: Polym. Chem.,* **28**, 367 (1990).
122. Wang, J.; Sheares, V. V., *Macromolecules*, **31**, 6769 (1998).
123. Zolotukhin, M. G.; Fomine, S.; Lazo, L. M.; Salcedo, R.; Sansores, L. E.; Cedillo, G. G.; Colquhoun, H. M.; Fernandez-G., J. M.; Khalizov, A. F., *Macromolecules*, **38**, 6005 (2005).
124. Zolotukhin, M. G.; Fomina, L.; Salcedo, R.; Sansores, L. E.; Colquhoun, H. M.; Khalilov, L. M., *Macromolecules*, **37**, 5140 (2004).
125. Colquhoun, H. M.; Zolotukhin, M. G.; Khalilov, L. M.; Dzhemilev, U. M., *Macromolecules*, **34**, 1122 (2001).
126. Huang, X.; Lu, G.; Peng, D.; Zhang, S.; Qing, F., *Macromolecules*, **38**, 7299 (2005).
127. Wong, S.; Ma, H.; Jen, A. K.-Y.; Barto, R.; Frank, C. W., *Macromolecules*, **37**, 5578 (2004).
128. Spraul, B. K.; Suresh, S.; Glaser, S.; Perahia, D.; Ballato, J.; Smith, D. W., Jr., *J. Am. Chem. Soc.,* **126**, 12772 (2004).
129. Ghim, J.; Lee, D.-S.; Shin, B. G.; Vak, D.; Yi, D. K.; Kim, M.-J.; Shim, H.-S.; Kim, J.-J.; Kim, D.-Y., *Macromolecules*, **37**, 5724 (2004).
130. Jin, J.; Smith, D. W., Jr.; Glasser, S.; Perahia, D.; Foulger, S. H.; Ballato, J.; Kang, S. W.; Kumar, S., *Macromolecules*, **39**, 4646 (2006).

Dendritic polymers, recently added as the fourth member to the family of polymer architecture, have been emerging as one of the promising classes of materials for diverse applications ranging from nanotechnology to drug delivery. A tree with roots can be viewed as an excellent natural motif to describe a dendritic structure.[1]

CHAPTER-5

SPECIAL-PURPOSE POLYMERS

Special-purpose polymers represent a unique class of polymers that are consumed in very small volume and possess certain specific attributes or have its own unique benefits and applications. This chapter will highlight the most important members with special emphasis on their recent advances, including key strategies to synthesize these materials.

5.1. CONDUCTING POLYMERS

In general, polymers that conduct electricity or have resistivity comparable to that of graphite (10^{-5} S/cm) may be called conducting polymers. Although the use of these polymers as antistatic coatings or films dates back to 1930, the birth of a new era of conducting polymers began in the early 1970s when Shirakawa *et al.* reported that the oxidation of *trans*-polyacetylene films with iodine vapor increased the conductivity of the films by seven orders of magnitude relative to that of unoxidized films at room temperature.[2-4] Since then, this field has expanded rapidly by the synthesis of a variety of conducting polymers and a thorough investigation of intrinsic electrical, optical, thermal, and mechanical properties.[5-10] This area is now at the forefront of several new, important and far-reaching technologies and is one of the leading topics in polymer science, as evident by the recognition of the 2000 Nobel Chemistry prize, which was awarded to Shirakawa, Heeger and MacDiarmid. It is important to emphasize that this new generation of conducting polymers, which possess extended π-conjugation, is completely different from the early conducting polymers, which are merely a physical mixture of a nonconductive polymer with a conducting material, such as a metal or carbon powder distributed in a polymer matrix.

At present, the field of conducting polymers is very broad. Polymers capable of conducting ions (proton or metal ion) are also included under the umbrella. Based on the conduction mechanism, recently developed conducting polymers may be divided into electron-conducting (where mainly electronic excitations move), and ion-conducting (especially movement of lithium ions) and proton-conducting (movement of protons). As shown in the classification chart below, very recently conceived redox and hybrid polymers may be included under electron-conducting polymers because they involve electron transport, but do not necessarily require extended π-conjugation.

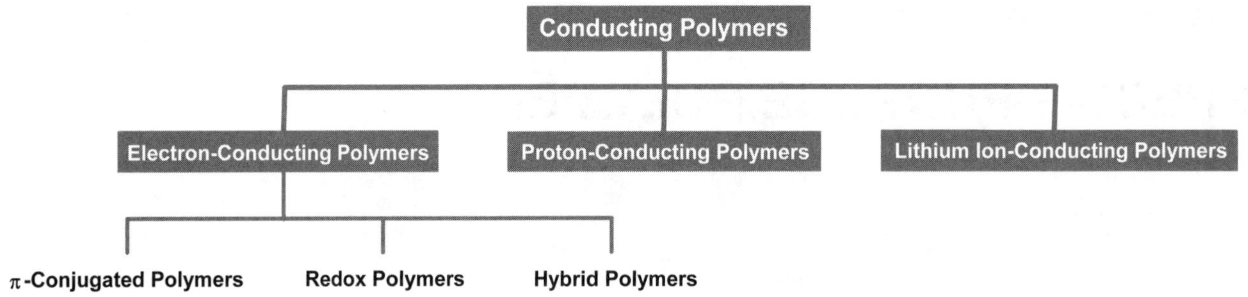

5.1.1. Electron-Conducting Polymers

This class of polymers has received much attention because of their versatility in methods of preparation, high anisotropy of electrical conduction, and non-metallic temperature dependence of conductivity. The following sections provide brief descriptions of each category with a few representative examples.

5.1.1.1. π-Conjugated Polymers

The most important members of this family are polyacetylenes, polydiacetylenes, polyanilines, polypyrroles, polythiophenes, polyphenylenes, polyphenylenevinylenes and polyphenyleneethynylenes. What differentiates these polymers from other insulating polymers, such as PE, PP and PMMA, is their extended π-conjugation, which allows mobility of charge along polymer chains via a rearrangement of double bonds. It should be noted that aromatic polymers, such as polyesters, polyimides, and polyamides, have π-electrons, but they are all insulating, since they lack extended π-conjugation. π-Conjugated polymers are also called *intrinsically conducting polymers* (ICPs), because they do not require any conducting fillers, such as metal or carbon particles to impart conductivity. The properties of ICPs depend strongly on the main chain structure, substituents, and molecular dopants. Most ICPs can be switched reversibly between conductive and nonconductive states, with the result that their conductivities can span an enormous range. This switching is accomplished through oxidation-reduction (redox) chemistry, since the conductivity is sensitive to the degree of oxidation of the polymer backbone. Conducting polymers have been actively investigated for applications in electrochromic devices, rechargeable batteries, and chemical and biological sensors because of several unique properties, such as electrical conductivity, optical nonlinearity and photoconductivity.

5.1.1.1a. Polyacetylenes

As mentioned earlier, the first ICP synthesized was polyacetylene (PAC) (note that PA usually refers to polyamide). Shirakawa's method involves purging of acetylene gas at pressures ranging from a few Torr to one atmosphere over a concentrated solution of a modified Ziegler-Natta catalyst system, $Ti(O^nBu)_4$-$Al(Et)_3$.[2-4] As shown in Figure 5.1, the microstructure of the polymer can be altered by adjusting the polymerization conditions. The PAC films prepared by this method typically contain residues of the catalyst, which is difficult to wash out completely. This approach was subsequently improved by various groups to obtain superior PAC films.[11-13] For example, highly oriented *trans*-PAC films can be obtained directly through an anisotropic reaction field, which is produced by macroscopically oriented nematic liquid crystals used as the polymerization solvent. A much more complicated, but elegant method, comprising several synthetic steps, was developed by Feast *et al.* (better known as the Durham

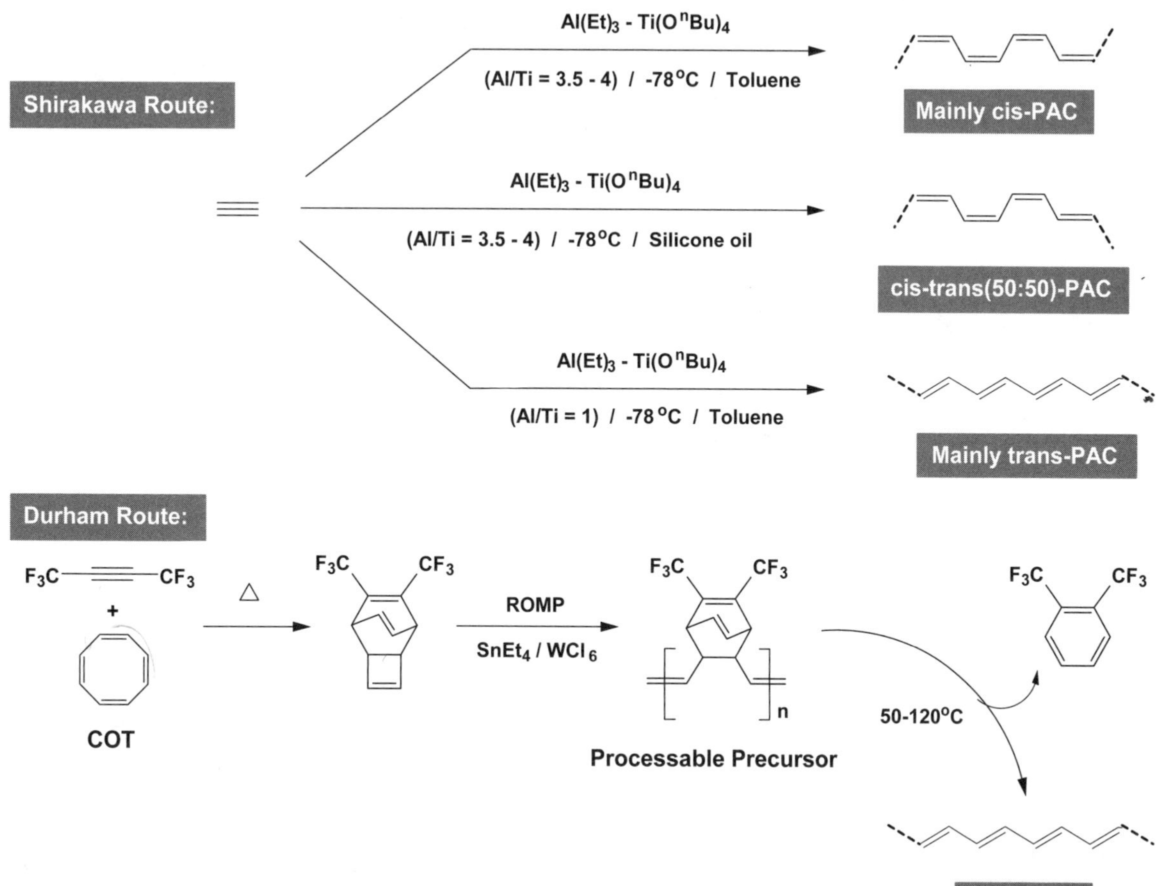

Figure 5.1. Early preparative methods for PAC.

route, named after the British university).[14,15] This route employs ring-opening metathesis polymerization (ROMP) of a cyclobutene monomer using Schrock's molybdenum catalyst system to prepare an acetone-soluble precursor polymer that is then converted to intractable PAC by thermolysis. The monomer was prepared by thermal reaction of hexafluorobut-2-yne with 1,3,5,7-cyclooctatetraene (COT). The resulting PAC samples are free of any contaminants, and can be oriented and used in the preparation of devices. PAC, which is oxygen sensitive and insoluble in all solvents, can be doped with iodine or AsF_5 to produce highly conducting (10^5 S/cm) material.

Recent important methods for PAC include the ROMP of COT and the direct polymerization of acetylene in the presence of a specific Grubbs catalyst system at ambient temperature (Figure 5.2). The former approach also offers soluble telechelic polyenes with up to 20 double bonds by using a *chain-transfer agent* (CTA) in conjunction with COT.[16,17] Thus far, the latter approach has only been successful when a more reactive Grubbs catalyst containing 3-bromopyridine ligands is used.[18] This method can be used to prepare free-standing *trans*-riched PAC thin films simply by dipping the substrate (e.g., glass plate) in the catalyst solution, followed by exposure to acetylene. It should be noted that care must be taken when selecting a ROMP catalyst. If too active, the catalyst can metathesize the unstrained olefinic bonds in the growing polymer chain (a process analogous to intramolecular "back-biting" in free-radical polymerization of ethylene, but here the process involves elimination of benzene), leading to a low molecular weight product with broad molecular weight distribution (i.e., high polydispersity index).

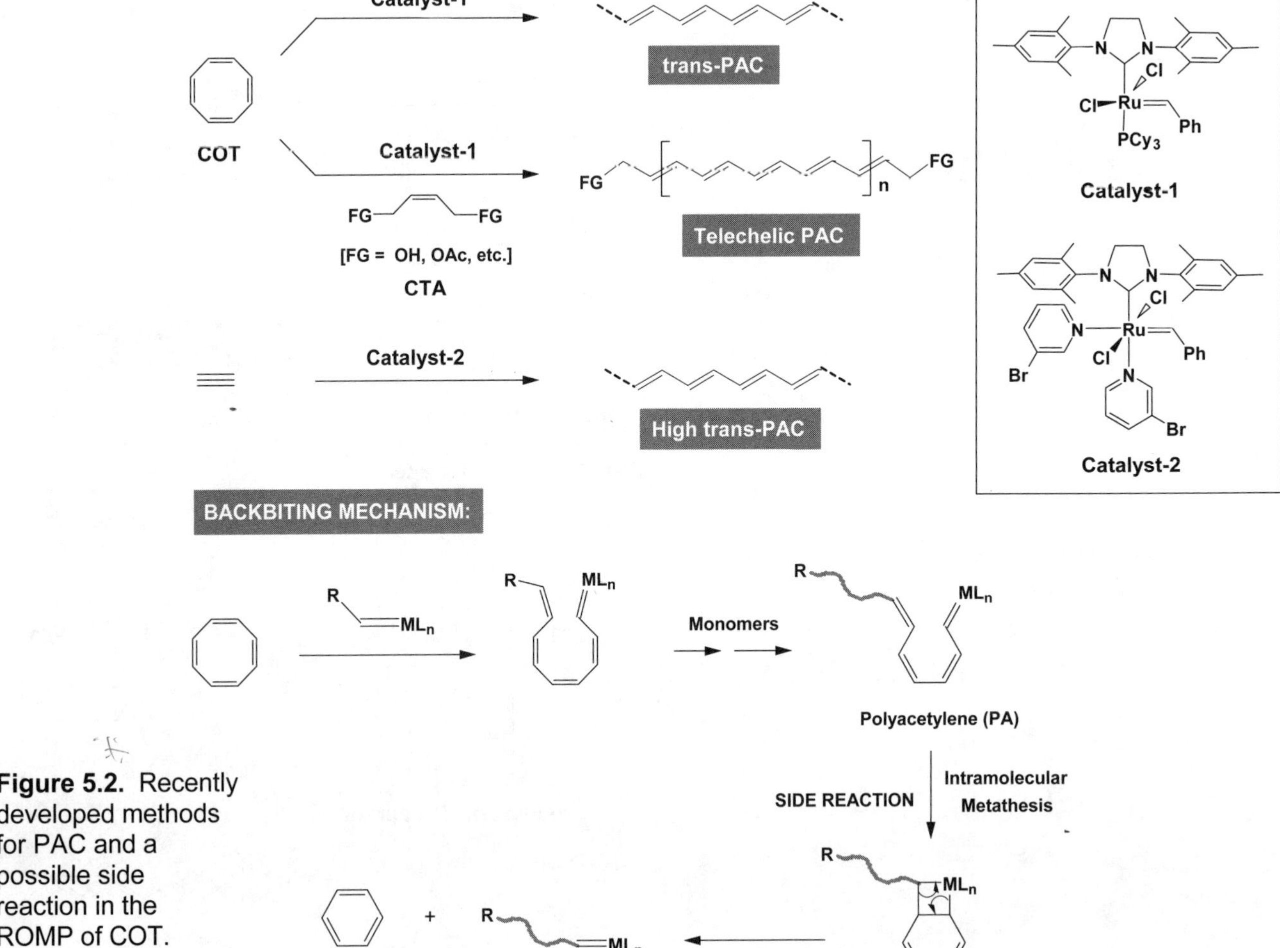

Figure 5.2. Recently developed methods for PAC and a possible side reaction in the ROMP of COT.

In past decades, substantial efforts have also been dedicated to substituted PACs to obtain superior materials with highly oriented polymer chains and/or pendent groups capable of introducing novel properties, such as electro-optic activity, photonic responsiveness, and biological compatibility.[19] Substituted PACs are generally soluble in common organic solvents and are fairly air stable. It is important to note that both the pendant and backbone segments play an important role in tailoring polymer properties. For example, the former perturbs the electronic conjugation of the latter, resulting in a drop in conductivity, while the latter influences the molecular alignment of the former, leading to a well-defined conformation. Thus, proper structural design may tune the backbone-pendant interplay into harmony and synergy, generating new substituted PACs with unique properties. Figure 5.3 describes the synthesis of two representative examples in which both substituted PACs (S-PAC_1 and S-PAC_2) exhibit liquid crystalline (LC) properties. The preparation of S-PAC_1 involves esterification of 4-ethynylbenzoic acid (EBA) with L- or D-alanine decyl ester in the presence of N,N'-dicyclohexylcarbodiimide (DCC), followed by polymerization of the resulting substituted phenylacetylene monomer with a Rh-catalyst, $[Rh(nbd)Cl]_2$ (nbd: 2,5-norbornadiene).[20-23] While Rh-catalysts are monomer specific, Schrock-type molybdenum carbenes, such as $Mo(CHR)(NAr)(OR')_2$, are more versatile and very effective for most mono-substituted acetylenes, including the cholesteryl moiety-containing monomer for S-PAC_2 (Figure 5.3).[24,25] It is worth mentioning that S-PAC_1, which does not contain any pendent mesogens, forms well-defined lyotropic cholesteric LCs resulting from the main-chain stiffness with a macromolecular helicity. By contrast, S-PAC_2, exhibits a mesophase of the smectic-A type owing to the mesogenic pendants (cholesteryl groups) covalently bonded to the main chain. As emphasized in Chapter-1 (Figure 1.71), 1,6-heptadiyne and its homologues of substituted acetylenes are very interesting examples of substituted acetylenes, which can be susceptible to the ring-forming metathesis polymerization (RFMP) to give a new class of substituted polyacetylenes.[26]

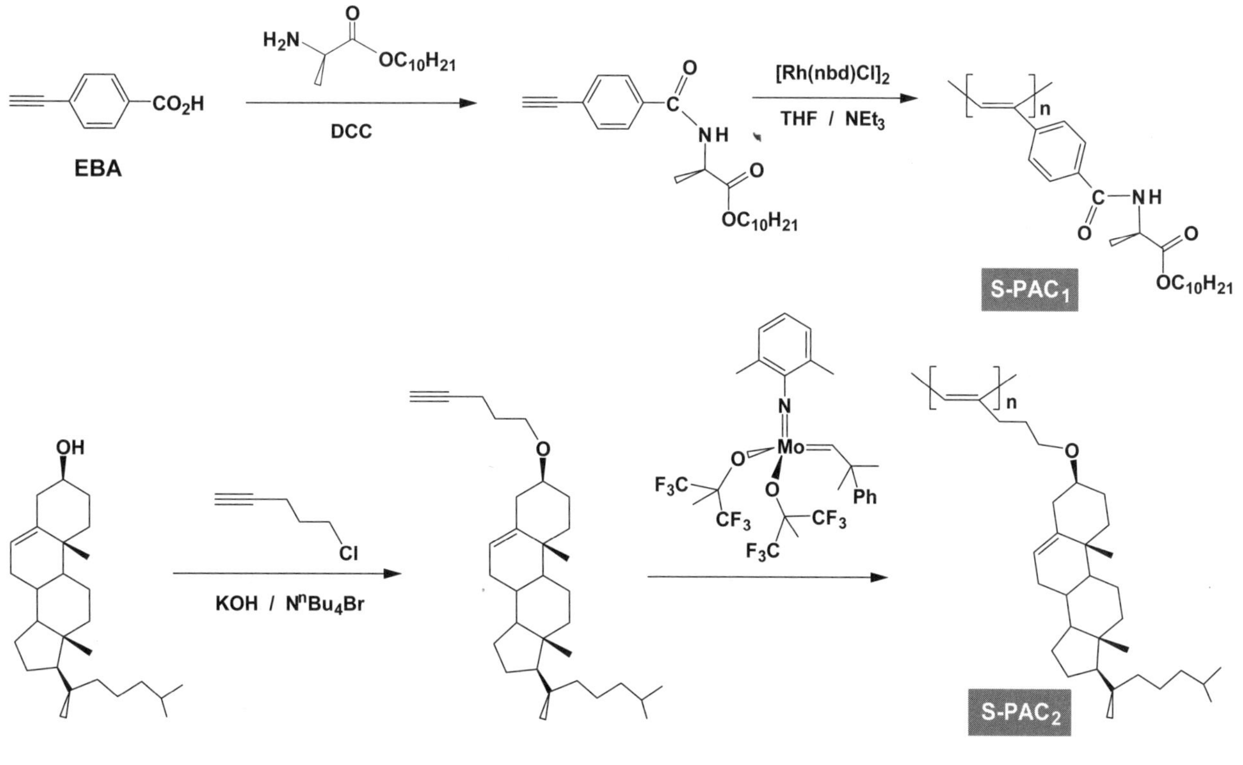

Figure 5.3. Synthesis of liquid crystalline PACs.

5.1.1.1b. Polydiacetylenes

The interest in *polydiacetylenes* (PDACs) arises from the highly conjugated ene-yne backbone and tailored side chains that lead to intriguing optical and electronic properties suitable for many potential applications, such as nonlinear optical materials, ultrathin photoresists, biomimetic liposome for drug delivery or vesicles for biosensing, and chemical sensors. As mentioned previously (Figure 1.92 in Chapter-1), the preorganization or topochemical requirement of the diacetylene (DA) monomers is essential for a successful 1,4-polymerization. The major disadvantage of PDACs lies in their preparation, which, for a given polymer, requires two major steps, the preparation of DA monomers and the organization of the monomers in the solid state for a topochemically controlled polymerization. Since, for most applications, it is desirable to have PDACs in the form of films, the second step is especially challenging. The generally accepted requirement for topotactic polymerization to occur is that DA molecules pack with their molecular axis at an angle of 45° to the stacking direction and the stacking repeat distance be ≤5 Å, corresponding to a perpendicular distance of 3.5 Å between the molecules. In some cases, this topochemically controlled polymerization of DAs can be conducted in the crystal of the monomer, thus giving rare examples of macroscopic polymer single crystals.[27]

The oxidative homocoupling of mono-substituted acetylenes, using copper salts, continues to be the favorite route to symmetrical DAs (Figure 5.4).[28] An alternate methodology involves Stille coupling between 4-di(tributylstannyl)-1,3-butadiyne and a halo compound in the presence of a Pd-catalyst in toluene.[29]

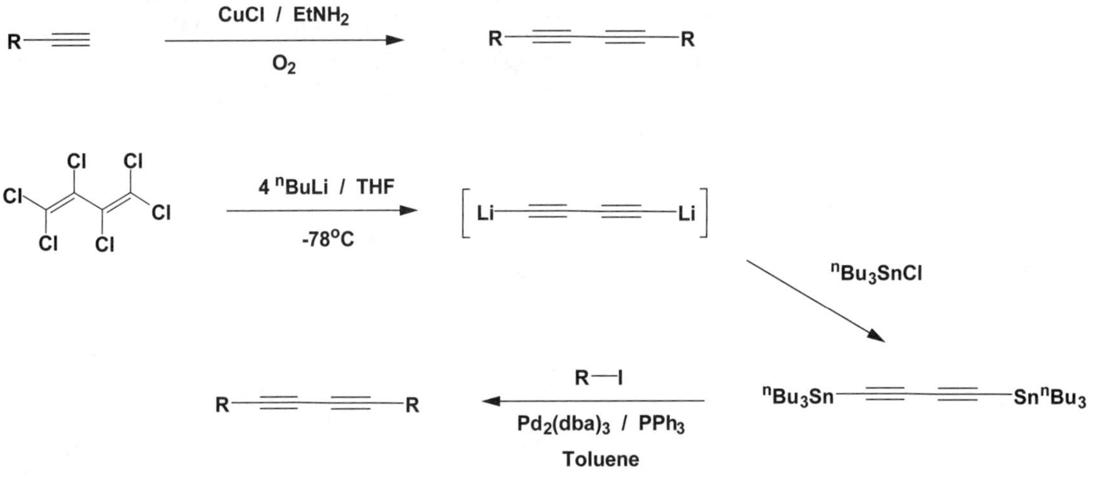

Figure 5.4. General synthetic routes to symmetrical DA monomers.

By contrast, the synthesis of unsymmetrical DAs is commonly carried out via the Cadiot-Chodkiewicz reaction, which involves copper-catalyzed coupling between a mono-substituted acetylene and a mono-substituted bromoacetylene (Figure 5.5).[30] A recently developed method, *"pair"-selective synthesis*, seems to be more effective as the process produces high yields and does not form undesired homocoupling diynes.[31] This method involves two steps: Pd-catalyzed yne-ene coupling of an ethynylzinc bromide with (E)-chloroiodoethylene and subsequent coupling of the resulting arylenyne derivative with a halo compound. Both methodologies can also be employed to prepare symmetrical DAs.

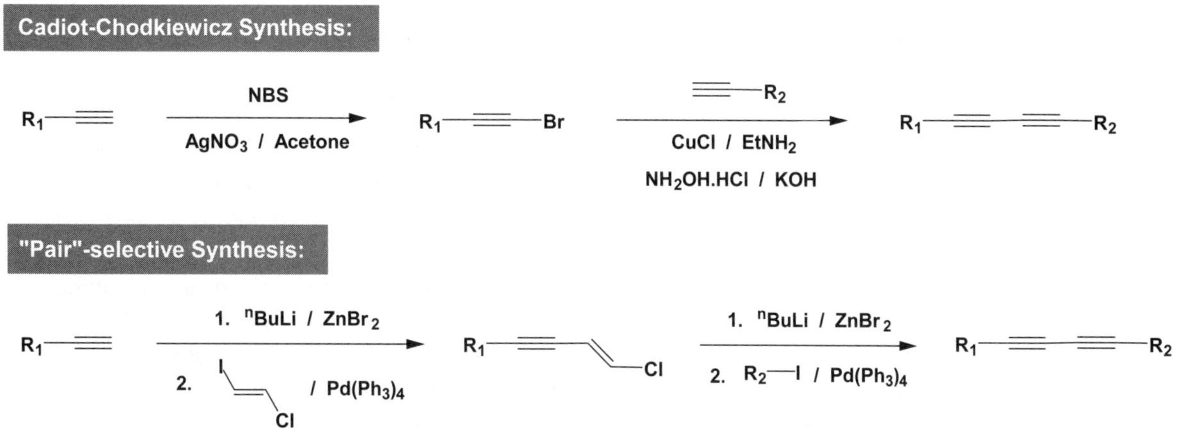

Cadiot-Chodkiewicz Synthesis:

"Pair"-selective Synthesis:

Figure 5.5. Common synthetic routes to unsymmetrical DA monomers.

Research in *topochemical polymerizations* has recently been reinvigorated by concepts borrowed from crystal engineering and supramolecular chemistry (see Chapter-1).[32-37] For example, monomers with molecular arrangements suitable for polymerization have been prepared as self-assembled films by spin-coating of monomer solutions to a variety of substrates. Figure 5.6 illustrates a synthon of such a diacetylene monomer, which contains a phthalimido group providing necessary intermolecular π–π anchoring, leading to preferential unidirectional stacking of diacetylene moieties.[38]

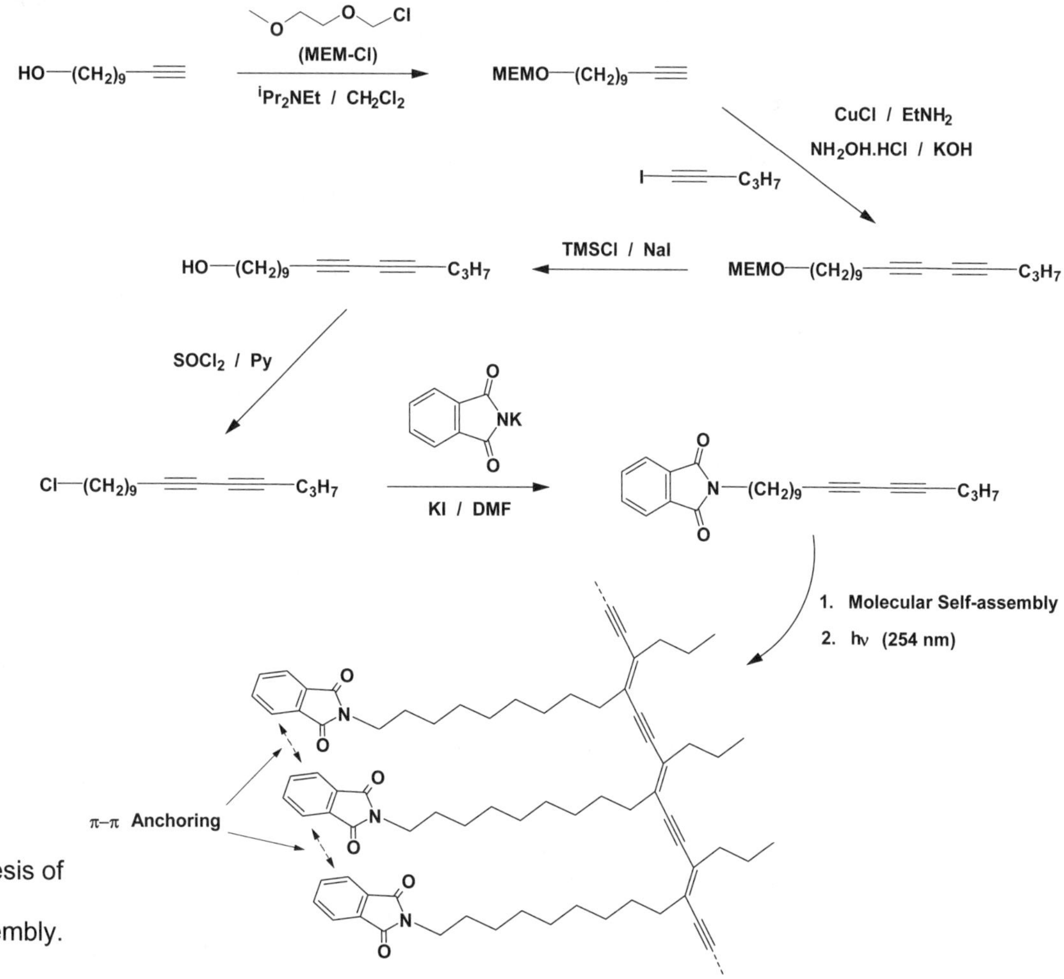

Figure 5.6. Synthesis of a PDAC film via molecular self-assembly.

The Cadiot-Chodkiewicz reaction between a 2-methoxyethoxymethyl (MEM)-ether protected acetylene and an alkyl-substituted haloacetylene has been used to prepare the unsymmetrical diacetylene compound. Subsequent deprotection of the MEM group by TMSCl and conversion of –OH to –Cl sets the stage for attachment of the phthalimido group by nucleophilic displacement reaction with potassium phthalimide.

Another example is commercially available 10,12-pentacosadiynoic acid (PCDA) lipid monomer, which readily assembles in aqueous media to form closely packed liposomes capable of undergoing polymerization upon UV irradiation, leading to PDAC liposome vesicles.[39] Consequently, this monomer has received much attention to develop PDAC-based sensors for the detection of biologically important species, such as influenza virus.[40] The unique applicability of PDACs as chemosensors derives from the fact that these supramolecules undergo a blue to red visible color change in response to a variety of environmental perturbations, such as temperature, pH, and ligand-receptor interactions. Although it is not clear why, it has been widely accepted that color change is associated with a conformational change or distortion of the polymer backbone. The synthesis of an amine-terminated diacetylene monomer, PCDA-NH_2, is a significant step-forward in fabricating film sensors (Figure 5.7, next page).[41,42] The monomer is readily prepared by reaction between the succinimidyl ester of PCDA and 2,2'-(ethylenedioxy)diethylamine. The PCDA-NH_2 liposomes can be immobilized onto the aldehyde-modified glass substrate via formation of imine linkings. After UV irradiation, the immobilized liposomes turned into blue-colored vesicles with a maximum absorption wavelength at around 640 nm. Although some aggregates of the vesicles exist, the SEM images show clean formation of the monolayers of the immobilized PDAC vesicles. The average diameter of the round-shaped immobilized vesicles is found to be approximately 60 nm.

5.1.1.1c. Polyanilines

Among the family of conjugated polymers, *polyaniline* (PANI) has been extensively investigated due to its (i) superior air and moisture stability, (ii) tunable electrical and optical properties, and (iii) very simple acid/base doping/dedoping chemistry. PANI is also attractive in many applications, e.g., sensors, electro-optics, light-emitting diodes, rechargeable batteries and antistatic coatings, and is readily prepared chemically or electrochemically by oxidative polymerization of aniline. The electrochemical synthesis generally yields a PANI film on the anode, while chemical polymerization can make PANI in bulk quantities. The classical chemical synthesis of PANI is carried out in solution using aniline, an oxidant (e.g., ammonium persulfate), and a strong doping acid (e.g., HCl) in either aqueous or organic solvents.

It is generally accepted that PANI is a mixed oxidation state polymer composed of reduced benzenoid units and oxidized quinoid units.[43] Figure 5.8 shows the general structure of PANI (with an average oxidation state 1-x) along with three important oxidation states: (i) the completely reduced leucoemeraldine base (**LEB**) state, where 1-x = 0, (ii) the completely oxidized pernigraniline base (**PNB**) state, where 1-x = 1, and (iii) the half-oxidized (1-x = 0.5) emeraldine base (**EB**) state composed of an alternating sequence of two benzenoid units and one quinoid unit. Unlike most other polyaromatics, the fully oxidized state in PANI (i.e., PNB) is not conducting, as are all the others too! PANI becomes conducting when the moderately oxidized states, in particular, EB, are doped with protonic acids (HA) to yield the emeraldine salt (**ES**) form, which shows a dc conductivity in the metallic regime (ca. 1~5 S/cm). The conducting ES can also be obtained through a redox-doping process under acidic conditions from its corresponding reduced LEB form or oxidised PNB form by either a chemical (e.g., iodine) or an electrochemical step, but the resulting conductivity is lower

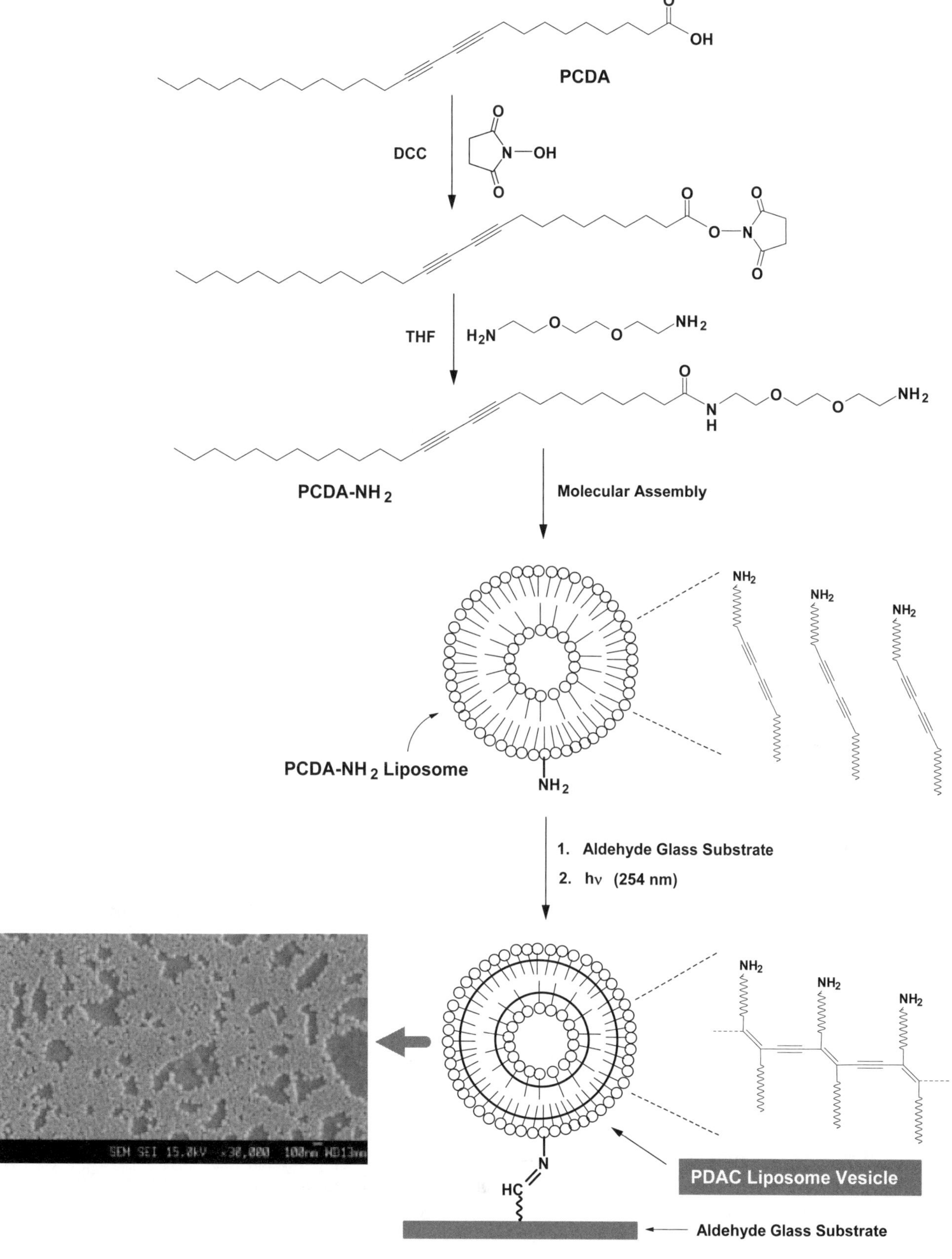

Figure 5.7. Synthesis of immobilized polydiacetylene liposome vesicles (shown with only one peripheral amino group for clarity). *SEM image is reproduced with kind permission of the Wiley-VCH Verlag GmbH & Co. KGaA.*

than that obtained via protonic acid doping. Nevertheless, the non-redox doping process is different from the redox doping in that it does not involve the addition or removal of electrons from the polymer backbone. Instead, the imine nitrogen atoms of the polymer are protonated to give a polaronic form where both spin and charge are delocalized along the entire polymer backbone. Both the redox and non-redox doping processes are reversible. The conductive ES form can be converted back to its corresponding insulating base forms if the conditions change, either physically (for non-redox doping) or electrochemically (for redox-doping).

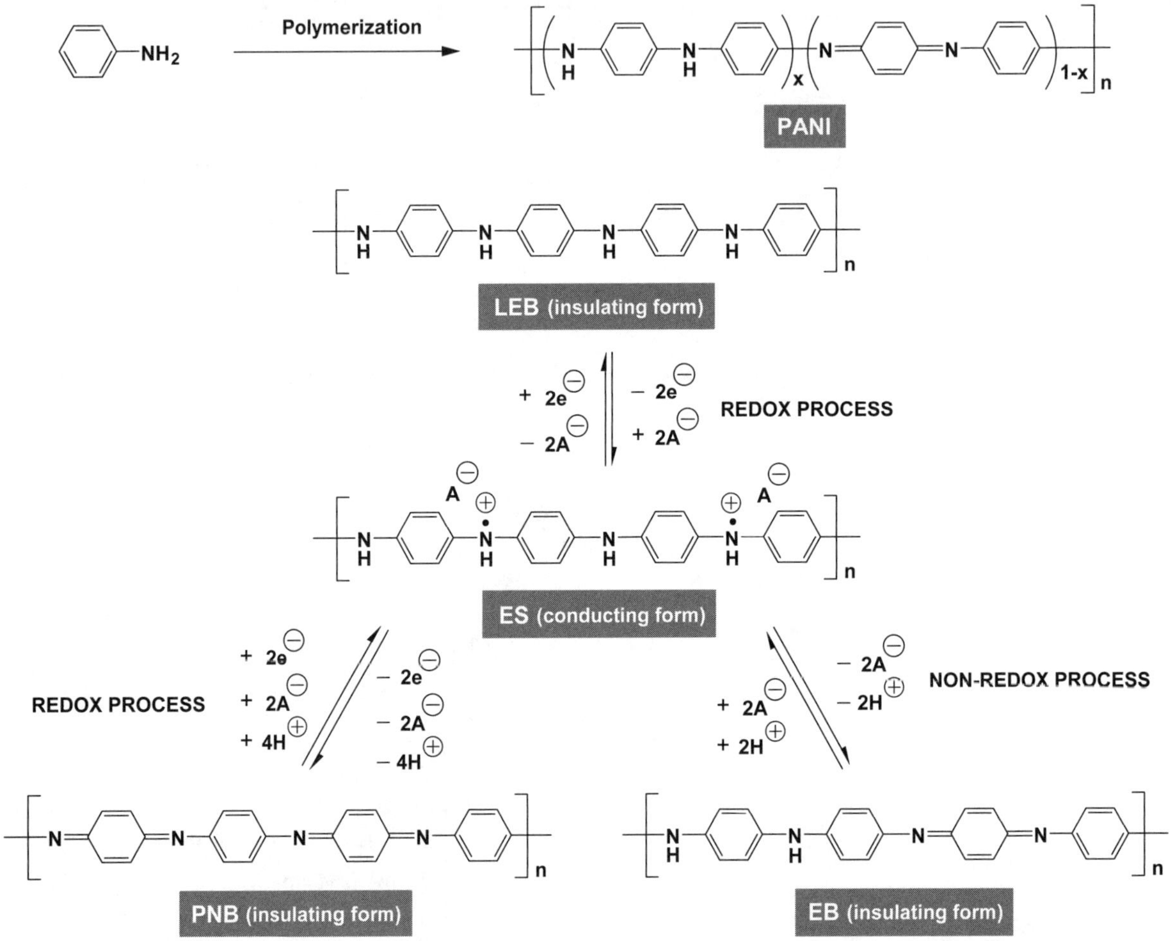

NH2 — Polymerization → PANI

LEB (insulating form)

+ 2e⁻ − 2A⁻ / − 2e⁻ + 2A⁻ REDOX PROCESS

ES (conducting form)

REDOX PROCESS + 2e⁻ + 2A⁻ + 4H⁺ / − 2e⁻ − 2A⁻ − 4H⁺

− 2A⁻ − 2H⁺ / + 2A⁻ + 2H⁺ NON-REDOX PROCESS

PNB (insulating form)

EB (insulating form)

Figure 5.8. General structure of PANI, including its three normally found oxidation states.

Whether PANI is synthesized electrochemically or chemically, it is generally believed that there is a close similarity in their polymerization mechanism.[44] In both cases, the polymerization process proceeds via the formation of the radical cation by an electron transfer from the 2s energy level of the aniline nitrogen atom (Figure 5.9). The aniline radical cation generated has several resonance contributing structures (**A**-**D**), in which **C** is the more reactive one due to its important substituent inductive effect and its absence of steric hindrance. A dimer **E** is readily formed by "head to tail" reaction. Subsequently, **E** is oxidized to a new radical cation dimer **F**, which can react with either the radical cation monomer or with the radical cation dimer to form a trimer (**G**) or a tetramer (**H**), respectively. Thus, PANI is formed upon continuation of this process. It is important to emphasize that *para* coupling is not exclusive; very low degree of radical cation coupling through the *ortho* position (i.e., with **B** or **D**) also occurs simultaneously.

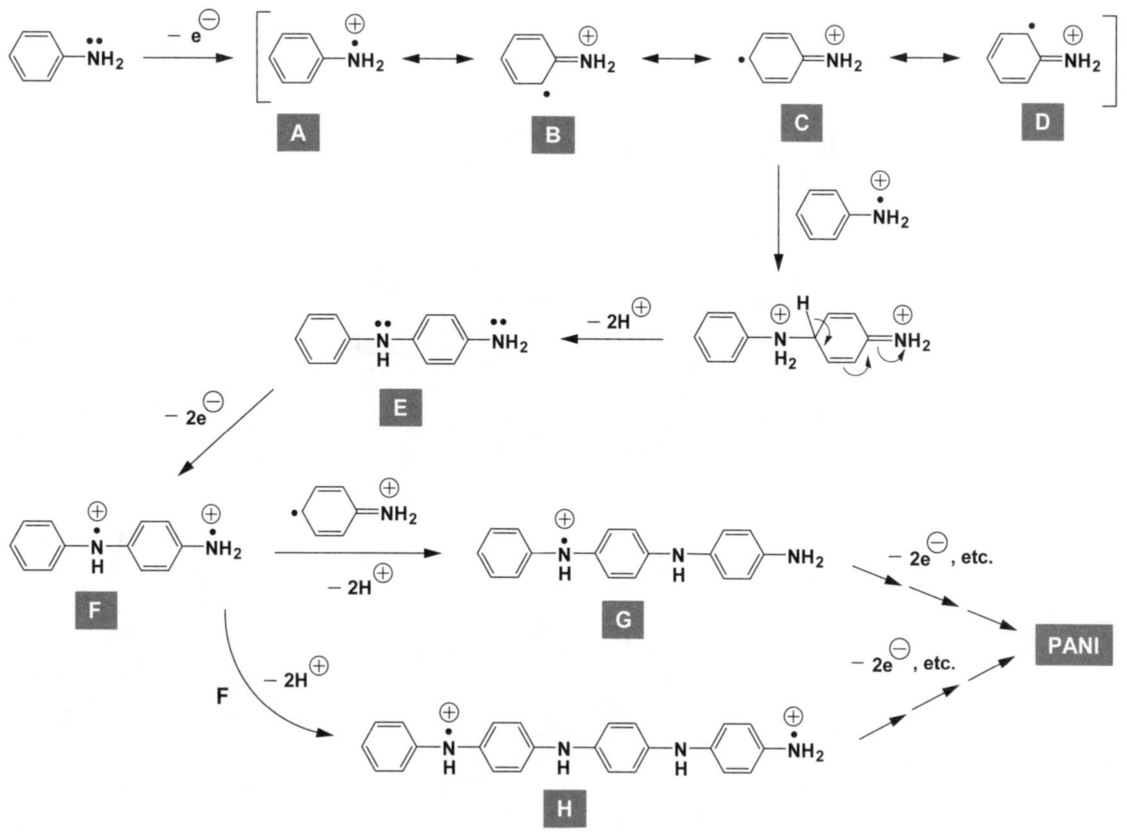

Figure 5.9. One possible pathway for the oxidation of aniline to yield PANI.

In the past decade, there has been considerable progress in the preparation of processable PANI. A new approach involves inverse emulsion polymerization of aniline in the presence of benzoyl peroxide as oxidizing agent, toluene-2-propanol-water as the solvent system, and dodecylbenzenesulfonic acid (DBSA) as the dopant/surfactant.[45] The resulting PANI-DBSA is completely soluble in common organic solvents, such as chloroform and a 2:1 mixture of toluene and 2-propanol. When redissolved in these solvents, the polymer can be spin-, drop-, or dip-coated on metallic or glass substrates with very good adhesion, and exhibits very good electrochromic reversibility and conductivity. The amount of DBSA in the feed strongly influences the morphology of the polymer, but the other properties, such as conductivity and solubility are not much affected. The change in morphology (from fibrillar to porous network type, Figures 5.10a, b and d) is attributed to the change in conformation of the polymer due to the change in the mole ratio of DBSA to aniline. At higher DBSA to aniline mole ratios, PANI prefers compact film morphology (Figure 5.10c). The interesting feature of this method is that the polymer suspension obtained during synthesis can also be used directly for practical applications.

There has also been increased interest in synthesizing processable chiral PANI (C-PANI) films because of their potential applications as surface-modified electrodes, chiral recognition, and chemical and biological sensors. These films are readily prepared, for example, by chemical doping of EB with optically active camphorsulfonic acid (CSA) in a polar solvent, such as NMP, and by electrochemical polymerization of aniline in the presence of either (+) or (-) CSA in an aqueous medium.[46,47] 3D macroporous materials comprising C-PANI composites have also been prepared by the *"template-guided synthesis"*.[48,49] These macroporous materials are attractive for filling of the column, opening the possibility for large-scale chiral separation.

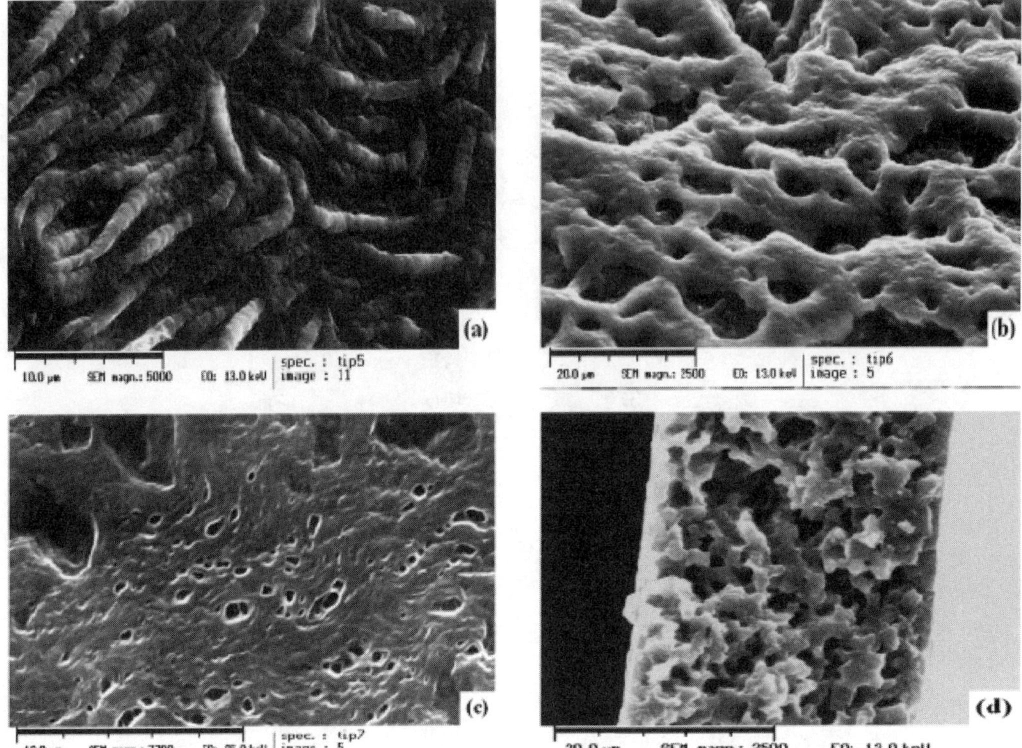

Figure 5.10. SEM micrographs of PANI-DBSA at (a) 5:1, (b) 7:1, and (c) 10:1 feed ratios of DBSA to aniline. (d) Cross-sectional view of image (b). *Reproduced with kind permission of the American Chemical Society.*

The synthesis of substituted poly(aniline)s, S-PANIs, is also of great interest for a variety of applications ranging from electronics to sensors. S-PANIs are prepared typically via oxidative polymerization of the corresponding monomer. However, in many cases the monomer is either too difficult to oxidize or sensitive to oxidative or acidic conditions. An alternate strategy is the use of a monomer containing a reactive functional group to synthesize a precursor polymer that subsequently can be modified to obtain the desired polymer. An excellent example is the use of poly(aniline boronic acid) (PABA) as the precursor because the pendent boronic acid groups can be transformed under mild conditions to a wide range of groups, such as hydroxyl and halogen (Figure 5.11).[50-52] It is important to note that PABA exhibits unique self-doping properties through the formation of four-coordinated boronate species in the presence of fluoride ions and is emerging as a unique material for the detection of oxidized and reduced forms of nucleotides.[53]

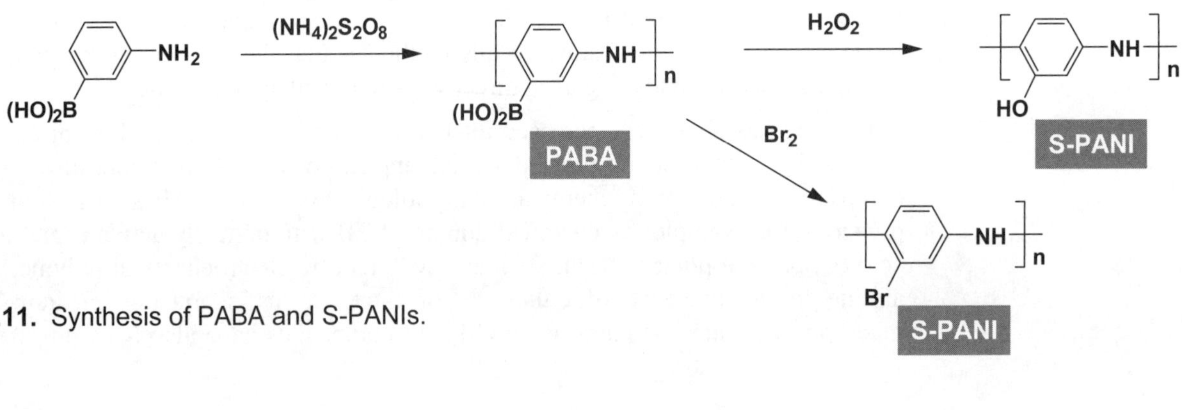

NH_2 / $(HO)_2B$ —$(NH_4)_2S_2O_8$→ PABA —H_2O_2→ S-PANI (HO); PABA —Br_2→ S-PANI (Br)

Figure 5.11. Synthesis of PABA and S-PANIs.

5.1.1.1d. Polypyrroles

A significant portion of recent research on conducting polymers has also been devoted to *polypyrrole* (PPy) and its derivatives, because of their good electrical conductivity, excellent environmental stability, and versatility of synthesis. The stability of PPy in air at ambient conditions or in an inert atmosphere at high temperatures comes from its lower oxidation potential and has led to its use in commercial applications, such as electrolytic capacitors, conducting powder, conducting coating, and electronic noses.[54] PPy and its analogs are best prepared by electrochemical polymerization of pyrrole or its derivatives, although the chemical oxidation process is also used. Electrochemical preparation of PPy has been widely conducted because of the formation of a free-standing film on the electrode surface (see Figure 1.94 in Chapter-1 for the mechanism of electrochemical polymerization). One of the advantages of electrochemical polymerization (EP) is that the instantaneous growth rate of the PPy film is proportional to the current, thus allowing control over the thickness of the film.

Chemical oxidative polymerization of pyrrole has the advantage of shorter reaction times and large-scale production of PPy powders referred to as "pyrrole black". The most used oxidant is $FeCl_3$, because of its faster rate of polymerization and production of PPy powder with conductivity as high as 10^2 S/cm, which is comparable to that of electrochemically-prepared PPy (Figure 5.12). A reactant mole ratio of 4:1 ($FeCl_3$/pyrrole) in diethyl ether was found to be optimal in obtaining high conductivity, suggesting that the oxidant plays dual roles as an initiator and dopant to induce the oxidative polymerization and to increase the level of conductivity. Pyrrole black is an intractable, insoluble, brittle solid, but products with usable mechanical properties can be made by blending PPy with another polymer, such as PMMA, PC and PS (Figure 5.12). The blends, which are often referred to as conductive PPy composites, are generally prepared by impregnation of pyrrole monomer into a host polymer dispersed with an oxidant, e.g., $FeCl_3$, followed by in situ polymerization.[55]

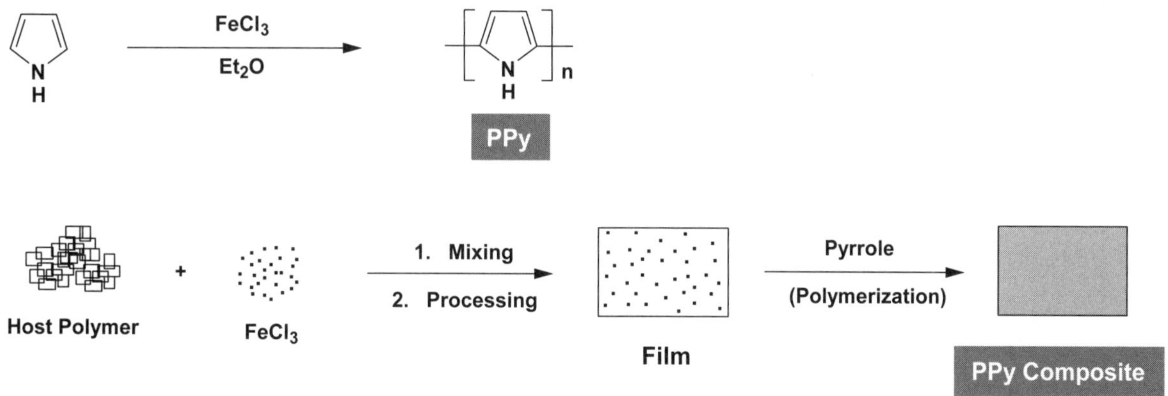

Figure 5.12. Chemical oxidative synthesis of PPy.

In recent years, many substituted pyrrole monomers have been studied for obtaining polymers with novel and/or improved properties. In particular, 3,4-disubstituted alkoxypyrroles and alkylthiopyrroles are very promising because substituents at the 3- and 4-positions of pyrrole prevent the undesirable α-β coupling, which interrupts the conjugation along the polymer chains leading to lower conductivity, but also because substitution plays an important role for the electrical and electrooptical properties of the polymers.[56] Moreover, these substituents lower the oxidation potential of the monomers and stabilize the oxidized form of the polymers. However, steric hindrance between neighboring β-substituted monomer units in the polymer chain, which prevents good conjugation, should not be ignored. For example, poly(3,4-dimethylpyrrole) possesses a lower conjugation length and lower electrical conductivity than PPy itself. Recent studies concluded that steric hindrance between alkylenedioxy-substituted monomer units in the polymer chain is not as severe as in the case of 3,4-alkyl-substituted monomers. Indeed, poly(3,4-ethylenedioxypyrrole), PEDOP, exhibits one of the lowest half wave potentials ($E_{1/2}$) for p-type doping of any conjugated polymer reported thus far. In addition, PEDOP switches between a bright red neutral form and a highly transmissive blue-gray doped/conducting form.[57] The synthesis of 3,4-di-substituted pyrroles, especially 3,4-alkylenedioxypyrroles is usually very challenging since the 2- and 5-positions of pyrrole are electron-rich and possess high reactivity.[58-62] However, with proper protection of the 1, 2, and 5 positions (Figure 5.13), the monomer, 3,4-ethylenedioxypyrrole (EDOP), has been prepared, although in low yield, through a multi-step synthetic scheme.[57]

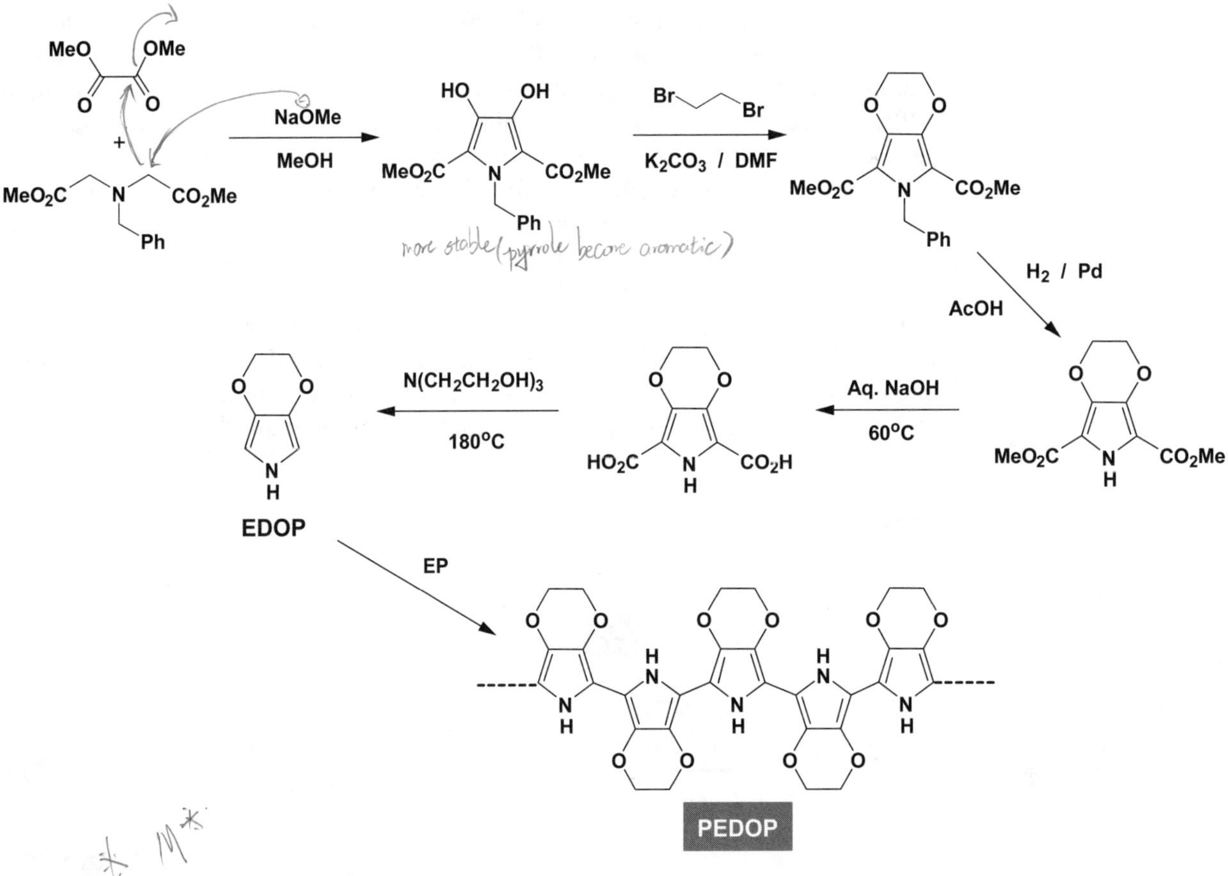

Figure 5.13. Synthesis of PEDOP.

Very recently, a new approach has gained access to 3,4-di-substituted alkylthiopyrroles, including 3,4-ethylenedithiopyrrole (EDSP), the thioether analog of EDOP (Figure 5.14).[63,64] The construction of the pyrrole ring was achieved via a nonclassical pyrrole synthesis, involving preparation of 4,5-bis-(bromomethyl)-1,3-dithiol-2-thione followed by cyclization using sodium tosylamide.[65-68] It is important to note that this route produces a very good yield of the monomer, EDSP, and offers an electrochemically synthesized polymer, PEDSP, with conductivity of ~140 S/cm.

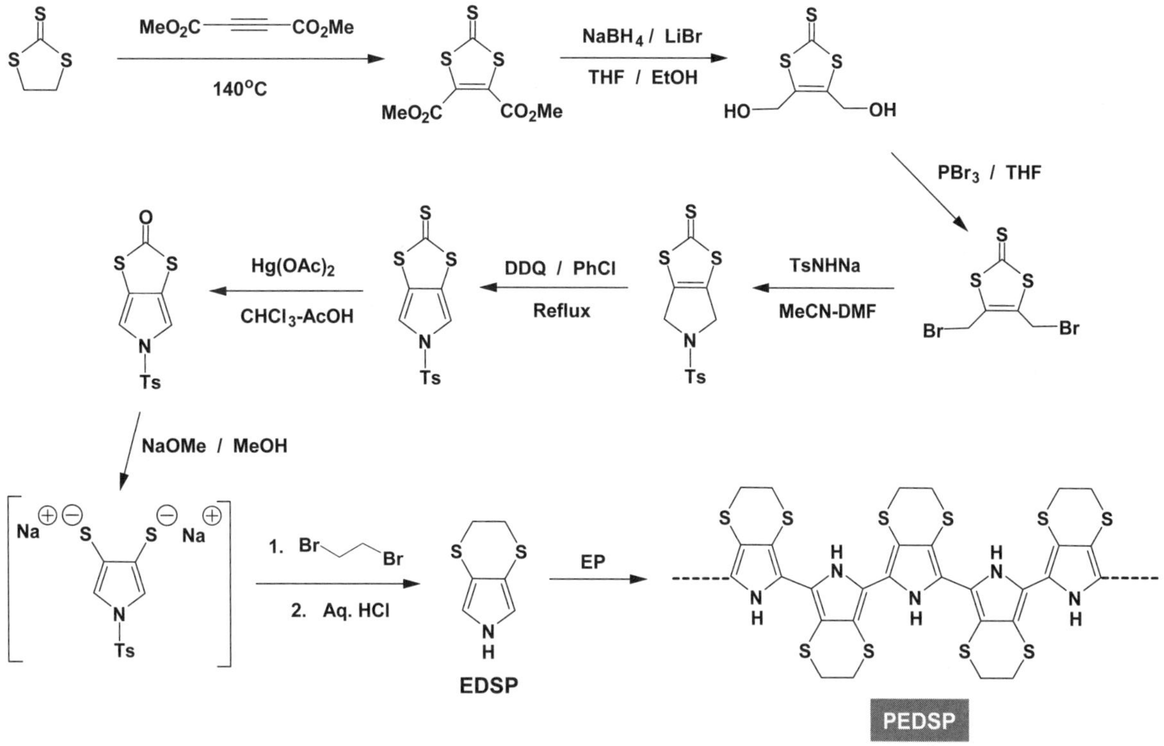

Figure 5.14. Synthesis of PEDSP.

5.1.1.1e. Polythiophenes

Unlike pyrrole, thiophene monomer does not polymerize under the conditions of chemical oxidative polymerization with $FeCl_3$ as an oxidant. However, it can be polymerized effectively under electrochemical conditions to produce *polythiophene* (PTh) on the anode surface (see Figure 1.94 in Chapter-1 for the EP mechanism). During the past twenty years, the study of PTh analogs, especially 3,4-di-substituted PTh, has intensified because of well-established thiophene chemistry and ease of polymerization under both chemical oxidative and electrochemical conditions leading to well-defined polymeric materials with superior conductivity and/or optical properties.[69,70] Similar to the PPy system, the polyalkylenedioxythiophenes, such as PEDOT (Figure 5.15), exhibit excellent conductivity. For example, the polymer obtained by chemical oxidation of 3,4-ethylenedioxythiophene (EDOT) exhibits a conductivity of 20 S/cm while the same via EP results in 200 S/cm. The extended π-systems of these materials produce very interesting properties that are useful for both static and dynamic applications. Static applications rely on the intrinsic conductivity of the materials along with their ease of processing. A good example is the commercially available poly(3,4-ethylenedioxythiophene)-poly(styrene sulfonate) (PEDOT-PSS, Baytron®, Bayer AG), which was initially developed for antistatic applications in the photographic industry because it is virtually transparent (thin layer) and colorless, prevents electrostatic discharges during film rewinding, and reduces dust buildup on the negatives after processing (Figure 5.15).[71] PEDOT-PSS is prepared by oxidative polymerization of EDOT in aqueous medium in the presence of an aqueous polyelectrolyte (usually PSS) using $Na_2S_2O_8$ as an oxidant. Currently, the polymer films prepared by electrochemical polymerization of EDOT and related analogs are attractive for many applications, e.g., primers for electrostatic spray coating of plastics, hole-injecting layers on ITO substrates for organic electroluminescent devices, etc. By contrast, the dynamic applications utilize changes in the conductive and optical properties, resulting either from application of electric potentials or from environmental stimuli. Among the many dynamic applications, field-effect transistors, electroluminescent devices, solar cells, nonlinear optical (NLO) devices, sensors and diodes are important.

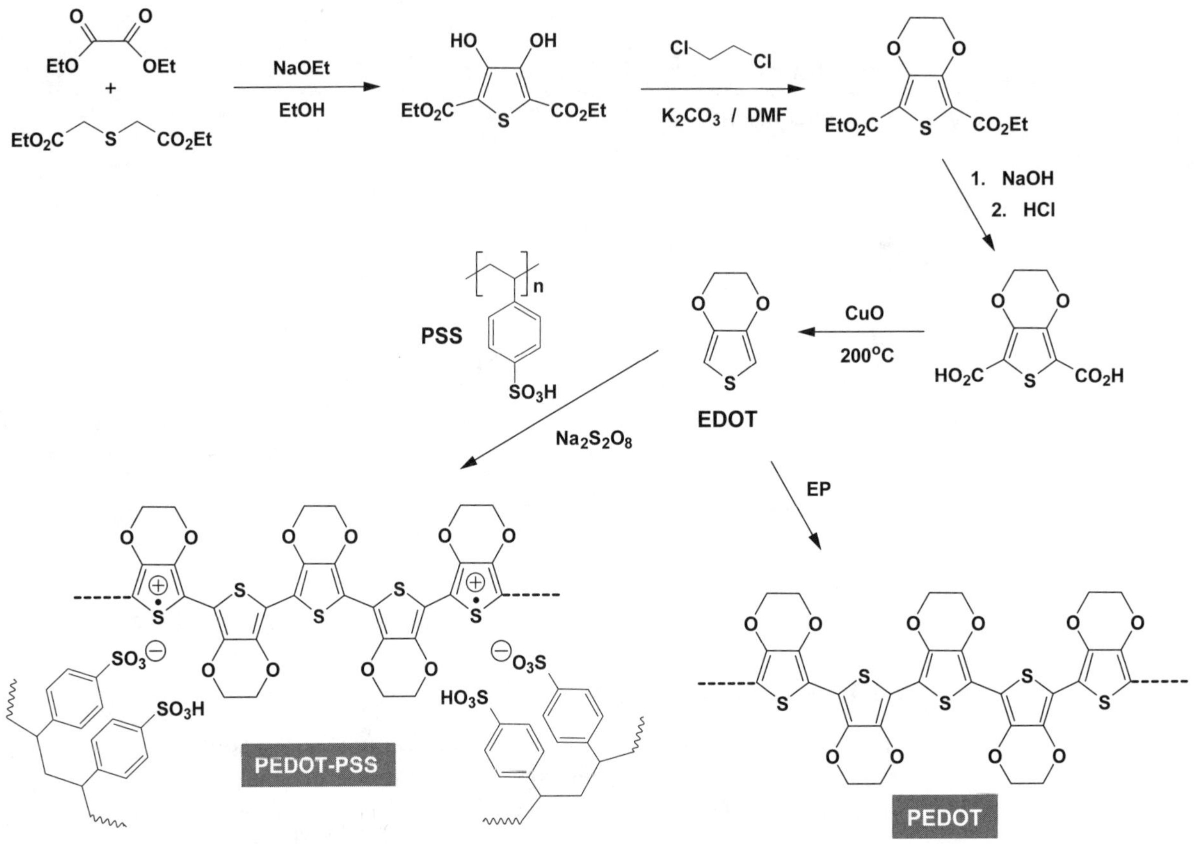

Figure 5.15. Synthesis of notable PThs.

Another example of an extensively studied PTh analog is poly(3,4-ethylenedithiathiophene), PEDST.[72-76] In contrast to PEDOT, this polymer is completely soluble in NMP and partly soluble in THF, $CHCl_3$, and other common organic solvents, and offers an exceptional advantage from the standpoint of thin film processing. The doped polymer shows moderate conductivity (~0.4 S/cm) at room temperature, about 2-6 orders of magnitude higher than that of polythiophenes with linear alkylmercapto substituents on the thiophene ring. The dramatic enhancements in the conductivity of PEDST can be attributed to improved conjugation and better interchain contacts compared to, for example, poly[3,4-bis(ethylmarcapto)thiophene]. However, the observed conductivity of PEDST is much lower than that for PEDOT. Moreover, in contrast to PEDOT, this polymer is not optically transparent in the doped state. The first synthesis of the monomer, 3,4-ethylenedithiathiophene (EDST), involves monolithiation of 3,4-dibromothiophene, treatment with elemental sulfur, and repetition of the cycle to produce 3,4-thiophenedithiolate (Figure 5.16). However, for ease of purification, the dithiolate is converted to a purifiable thione derivative by treatment with CS_2, but with a very low overall yield. Subsequently, this method was modified by preparing the precursor 3,4-bis(isopropylthio)-thiophene (BITT), which generates 3,4-thiophenedithiolate upon treatment with sodium in pyridine.[73]

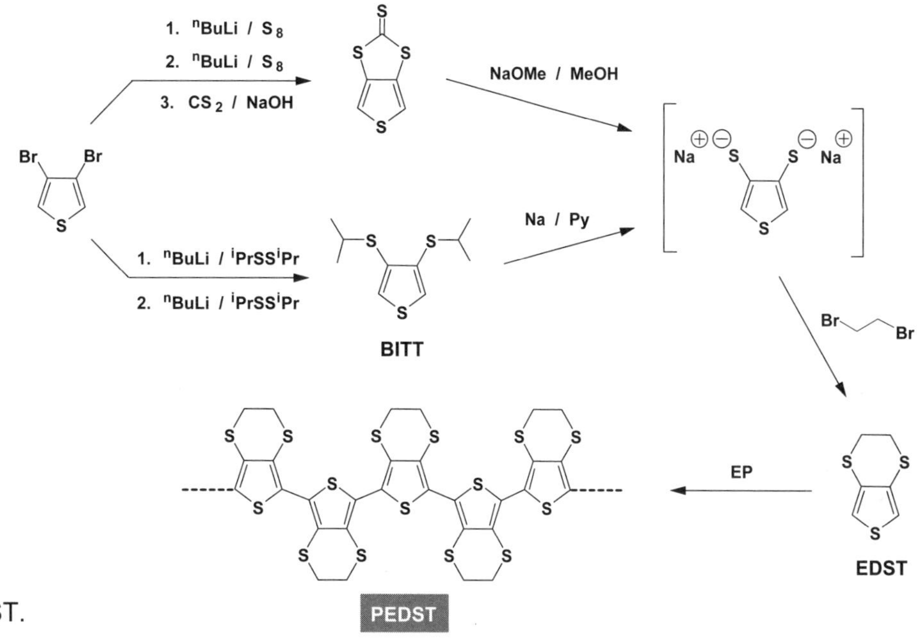

Figure 5.16. Synthesis of PEDST.

Polythiophenes containing pendent or main-chain crown ether functionalities have also been the subject of intense research because of their potential use in highly sensitive sensors (Figure 5.17).[77] Depending on the size of the crown ether ring (number of oxygen atoms), these polymers can be made ion-selective. For example, when an electrochemically polymerized thin film of PTh-P (a polythiophene chemically linked with a pendent crown-4 moiety) is exposed to solutions containing millimolar concentrations of alkali cations (viz., Li^+, Na^+, and K^+), the current which passes through the film at a fixed potential drops dramatically in solution of lithium ion, less so for sodium ion, and only slightly for potassium ion.[78] By contrast, PTh-M, with two adjacent thiophene rings tethered with an oligoethylene oxide chain, can be used to detect millimolar concentrations of alkali cations by monitoring their absorbance shifts (ionochromic effect) by UV-Vis spectroscopy. The magnitude of the hypsochromic shifts (46 nm for Li^+, 91 nm for Na^+ and 22 nm for K^+) is attributed to the ion-binding preferences of the corresponding crown ether, resulting from a twist in the conjugated polymer backbone induced by ion binding.[79]

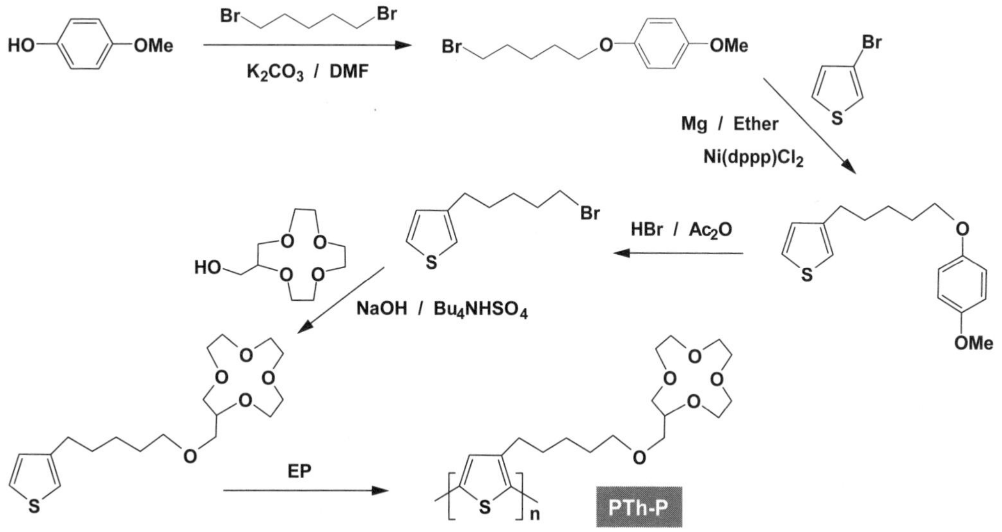

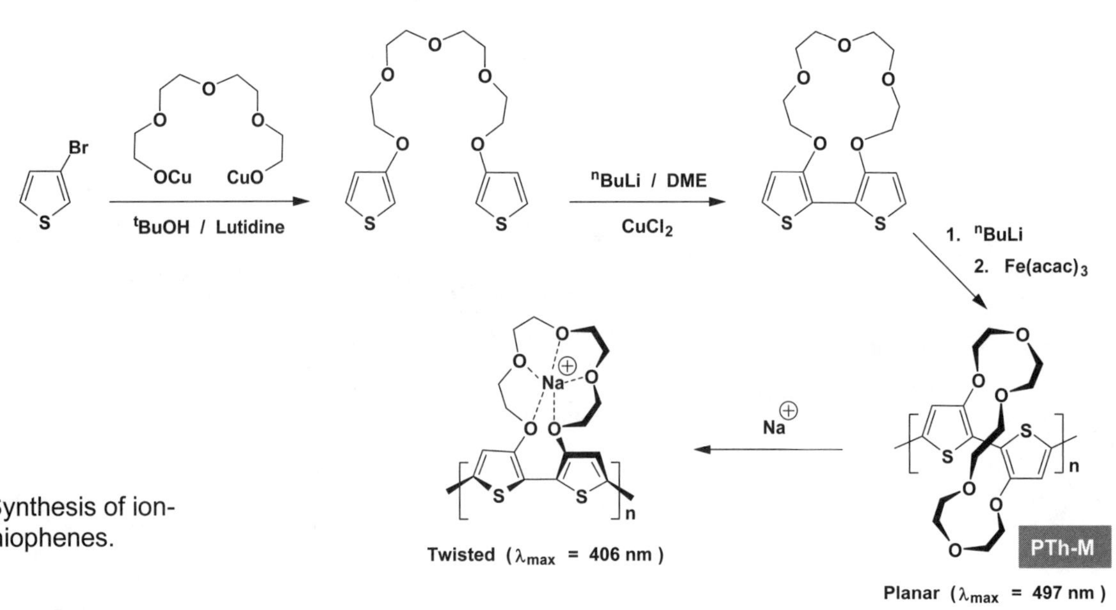

Figure 5.17. Synthesis of ion-selective polythiophenes.

5.1.1.1f. Polyphenylenes

Poly(p-phenylene), PPP, the simplest aromatic polymer containing only carbon and hydrogen, has been extensively investigated because of its rigid-rod-like structure, high mechanical strength, excellent thermal stability, and unique conducting and nonlinear optical properties.[80] The favored routes for the preparation of linear PPP include nickel(0)-mediated Yamamoto-type polycondensation (reductive aryl-aryl-coupling) of bishalides (bistriflates and bismesylates are also good starting materials) and palladium-catalyzed cross-coupling reaction between aryl bis(boronic ester) and dihaloarenes (Suzuki-coupling) (Figure 5.18).[81-84] Unfortunately, the rigid conjugated backbone largely responsible for the aforementioned properties also renders PPP insoluble and infusible. Only low molecular weight PPP (seven or less phenylene units) is soluble in common organic solvents, while the high molecular weight product is only sparingly soluble at elevated temperatures. Consequently, the most recent work has focused on the preparation of substituted PPP analogs to enhance the solubility and processability of PPP.

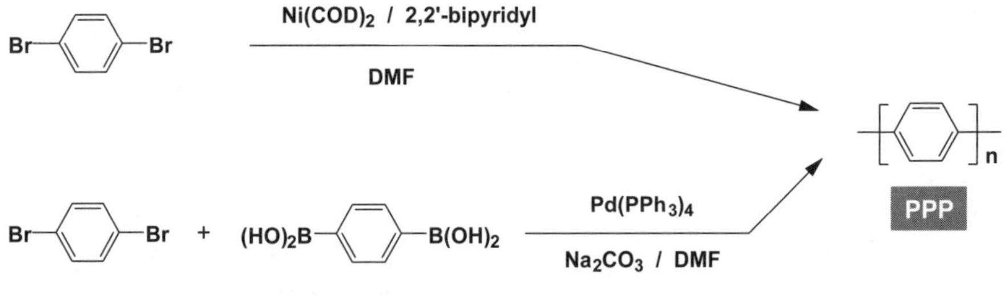

Figure 5.18. Common methods for the synthesis of linear PPP.

Suzuki coupling has attained greater importance and is potentially more versatile than the Yamamoto route, mainly because boronic acid derivatives are easy to handle and tolerant of a large variety of functional groups. Figure 5.19 describes a typical synthetic scheme for PPP with pendent aliphatic chains.[85] PPP can be made water soluble by proper selection of a pendent functional group at the terminal position of the side chain. Figure 5.19 also shows a classic synthetic strategy for the preparation of

PPP with pendent O-alkyl chains. Water solubility is enhanced by appropriate functional groups, such as tertiary amino, attached to the chains. The electronic absorption of the neutral polymer, N-PPP, can be altered by quaternization of tertiary amino groups with ethyl iodide. Thus, the fully quaternized polymer, Q-PPP, exhibits a blue shift, presumably due to intermolecular electrostatic repulsion of positive charges, leading to a lowest energy conformation where the torsional angle is increased.

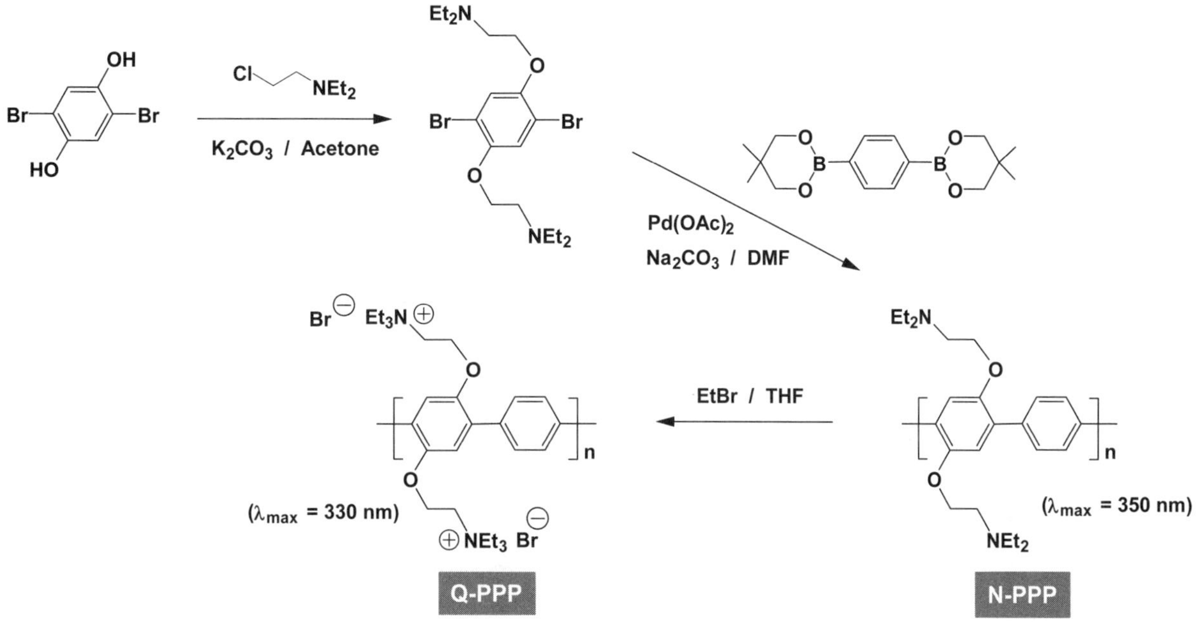

Figure 5.19. Synthesis of a representative substituted PPP analog.

5.1.1.1g. Poly(*p*-phenylene vinylene)s

Much of the early research on *poly(p-phenylene vinylene)*, PPV, was rather disappointing because of its poor conductivity, coupled with insolubility and infusibility. Interest in PPV was reawakened in 1990 when Friend *et al.* discovered that undoped PPV films, prepared via a soluble precursor polymer route, could be used as the light emitting layer in organic electroluminescent devices.[86] Subsequently, the chemistry of PPV (which has an average tilt angle of the phenyl ring relative to the chain axis of 7.7° compared to 9.2° for trans stilbene) and its derivatives, including other π-conjugated polymers (see the section light-emitting polymers, *vide infra*) has been the subject of intense research in both academia and industry. The precursor polymer method, often referred to as Wessling or sulfonium precursor route,[87] is still very attractive for the preparation of PPV because it produces a very high molecular weight product compared to direct methods, which are more suitable for substituted PPV. The methodology involves polymerization of the bis sulfonium salt with NaOH to produce a soluble polyelectrolyte (precursor polymer), which can be purified, processed into films and finally thermally converted to fully conjugated PPV (Figure 5.20). This method was modified later by several groups to improve the quality of films and/or for low temperature conversion in the final step.[88-91] For example, a modified route involving a soluble dithiocarbamate (DTC) precursor produces excellent quality polymer films and is very suitable for the preparation of π-extended PPV, such as poly(*p*-fluoranthene vinylene) (PFV).[92-94]

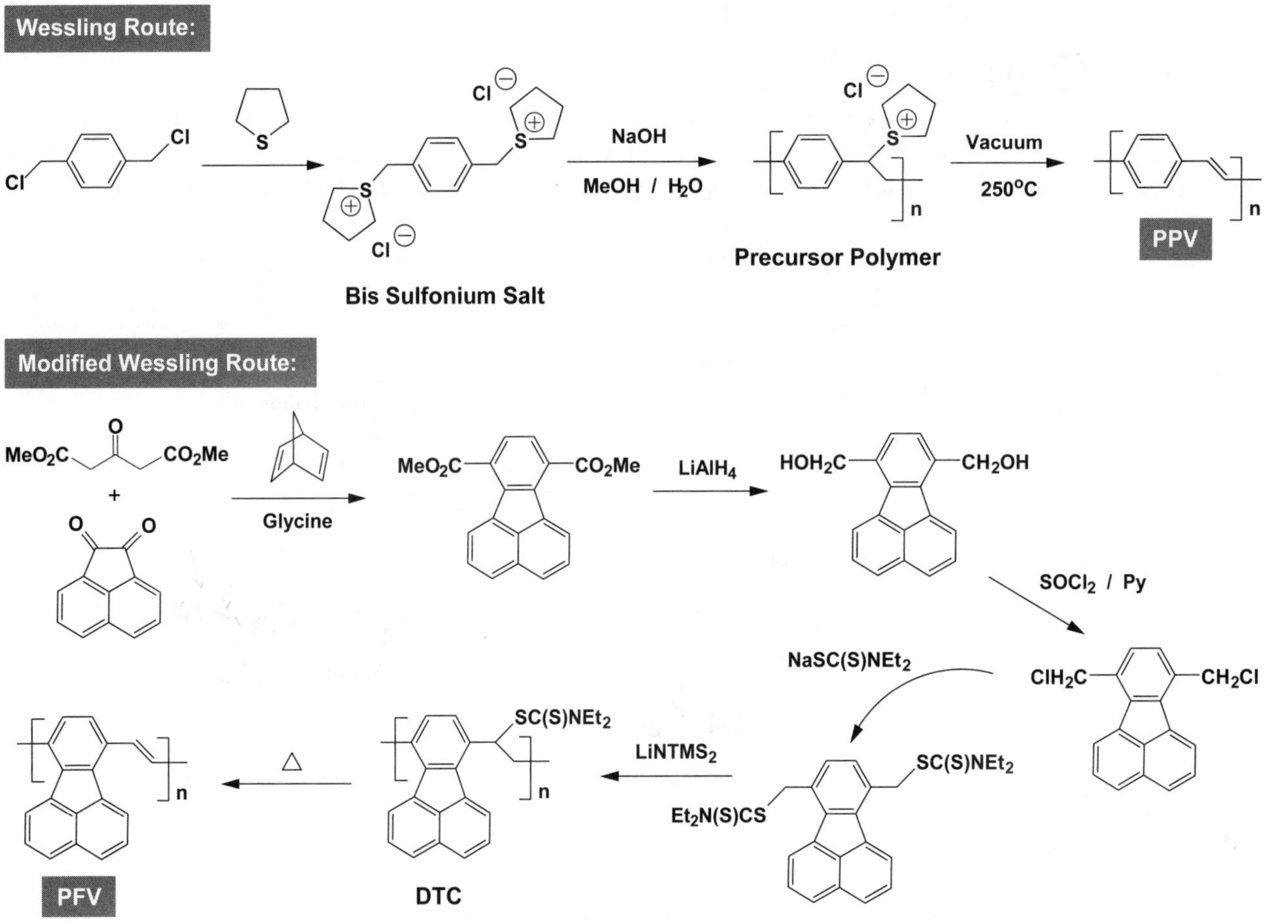

Figure 5.20. Synthesis of PPV and PFV via the precursor polymer route.

For substituted PPV analogs, S-PPV, the Horner-Wittig-Emmons (HWE) reaction is often chosen because of the straightforward monomer synthesis and formation of high molecular weight products.[95-97] Figure 5.21 outlines selected general synthetic strategies for the preparation of substituted dialdehyde and diphosphonic acid ester monomers. For ease of purification, the former is often prepared by introduction of one aldehyde group at a time following lithiation-DMF protocol with an aldehyde protection step in between. The latter is best prepared by reaction of triethyl phosphite with a bis-halomethyl compound.

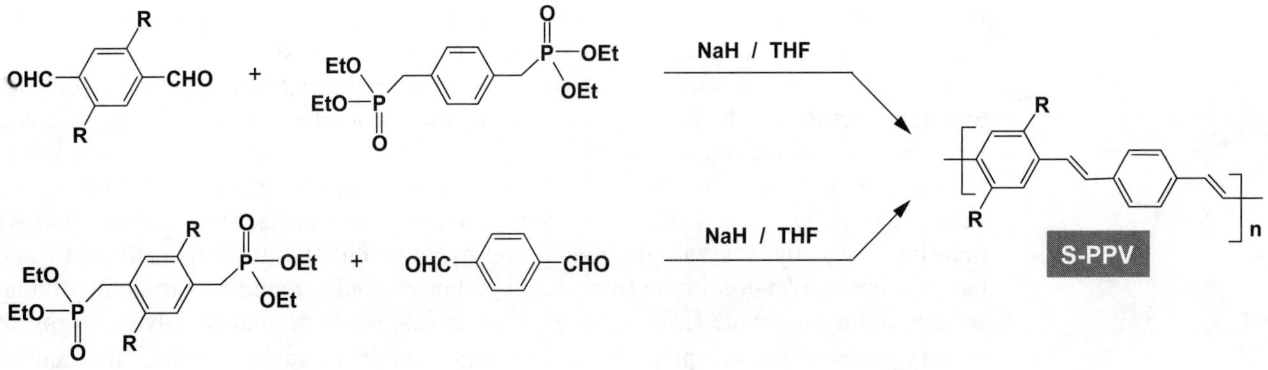

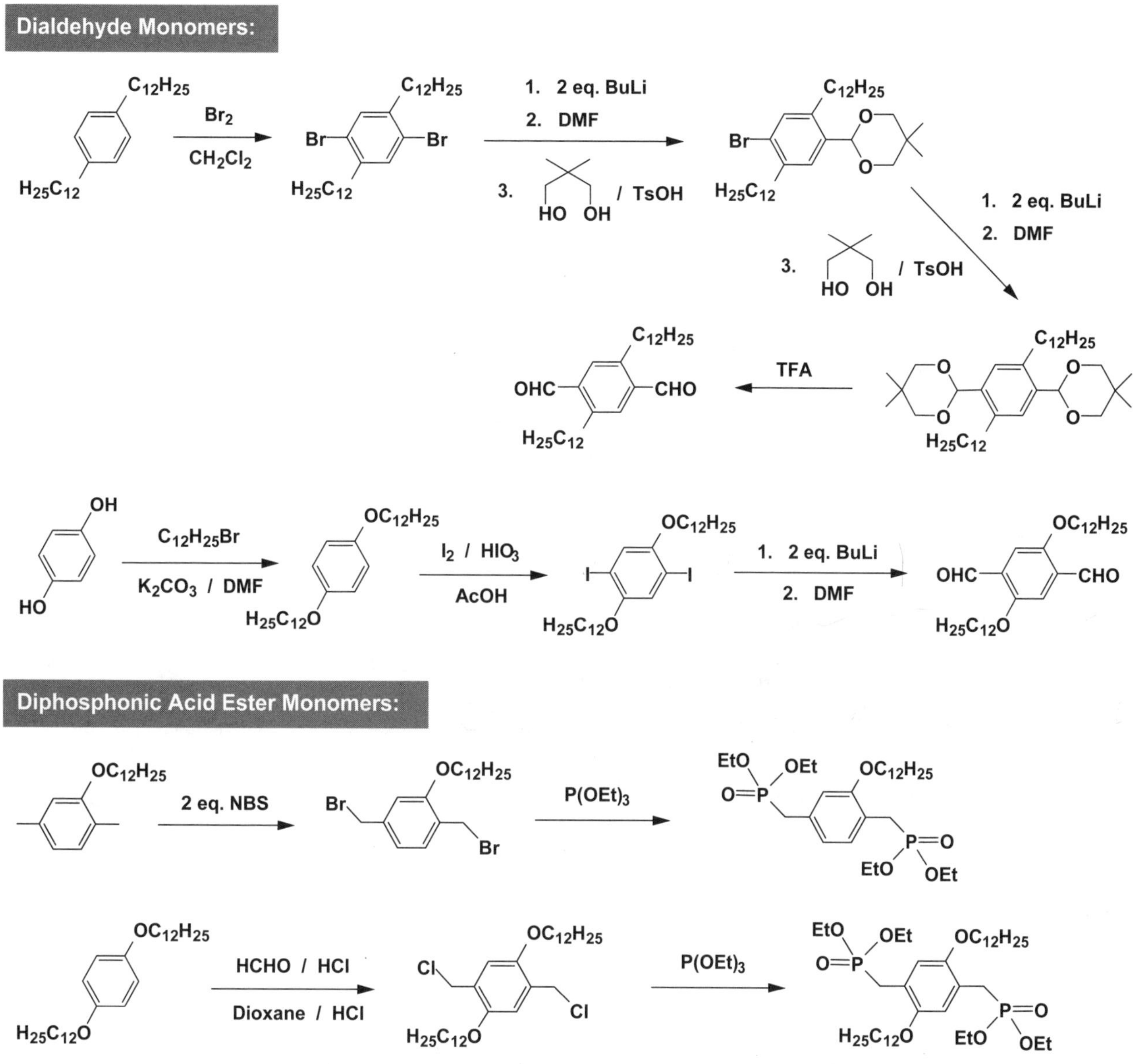

Dialdehyde Monomers:

Diphosphonic Acid Ester Monomers:

Figure 5.21. Synthesis of S-PPV by the HWE route.

Pd-catalyzed Heck reaction between *p*-divinylbenzene and aromatic dihalide has also been used to prepare S-PPV. This method permits incorporation of pendent reactive functional groups, such as amino (Figure 5.22).[98,99] Another seldom used approach, the Gilch route, involves the reaction of a α,α'-dihalo-*p*-xylene derivative with potassium *tert*-butoxide.[100,101] Recently, this method was applied to prepare a crown ether a containing PPV derivative, which exhibits very high luminance (yellow-green light, ~730 cd/m^2) when used in a traditional double layer LED device (Figure 5.22).[102] This polymer also can bind with alkali metal ions in solution. It was observed that the fluorescent intensity decreases as the molar ratio of K^+, Na^+ or Li^+ increases, compared with that in the absence of metal ions, making the polymer suitable for chemosensor applications. Interestingly, a dilute chloroform solution of this polymer with K^+ forms nanoribbons through supramolecular assembly. The length of the nanoribbons increases with an increase in the standing time of the solution.[103]

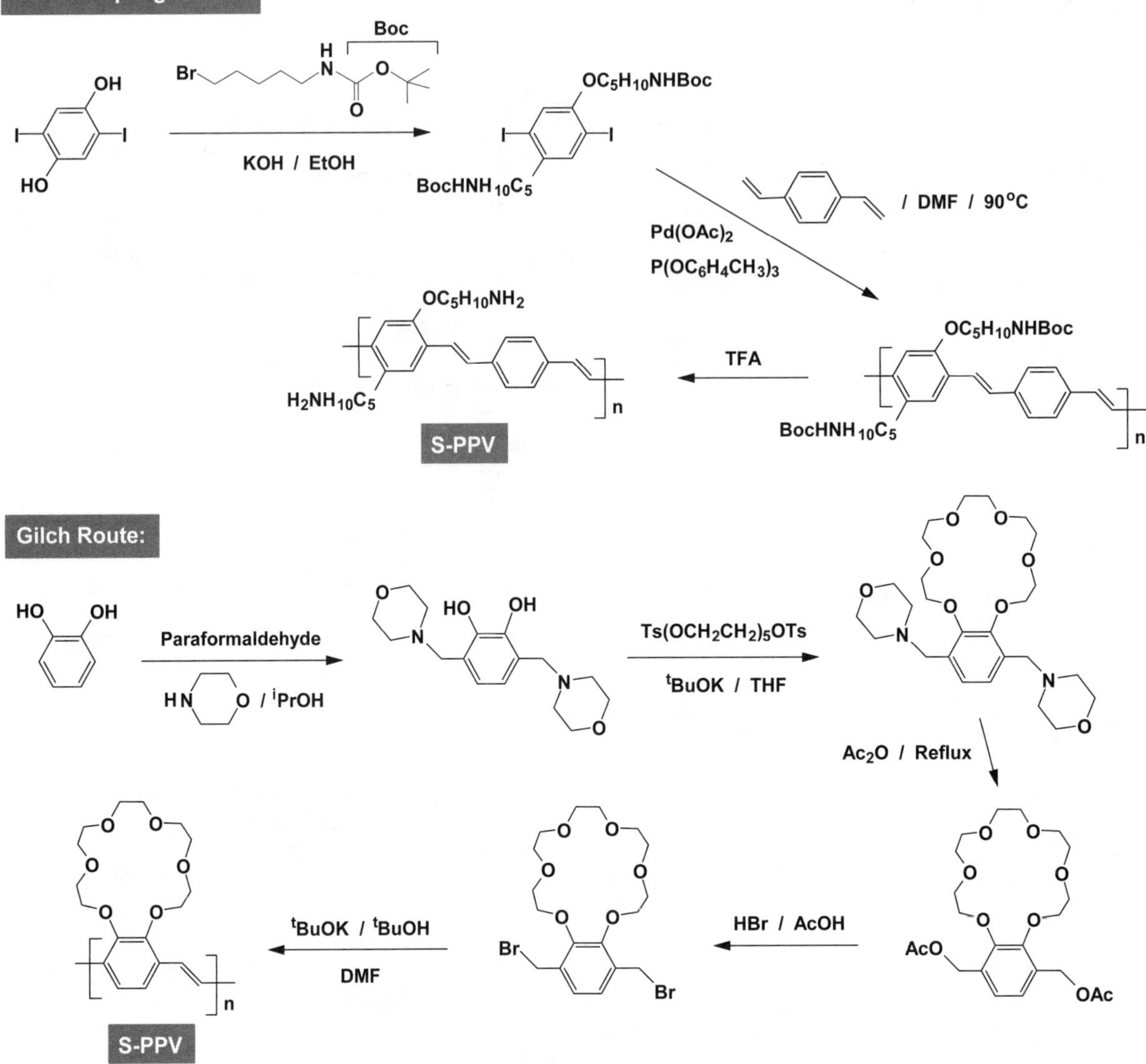

Figure 5.22. Other important approaches for the synthesis of S-PPV.

5.1.1.1h. Poly(*p*-phenylene ethynylene)s

Poly(p-phenylene ethynylene)(PPE) and its analogs are another class of polymers that have been extensively investigated as materials primarily for LED devices and recently, for land mine detection chemosensors. Similar to PPV, PPE, which contains alternate aromatic rings and a triple bond, is insoluble and infusible. Moreover, there has been no precursor polymer route developed to date that can lead to PPE films. Consequently, all studies conducted thus far involve the preparation of substituted-PPE (S-PPE).[104] The most powerful tool for S-PPE synthesis is Heck-Cassar-Sonogashira-coupling. This Pd-mediated reaction is commonly carried out between an aromatic bis-alkyne and a bis-iodo-substituted benzene (Figure 5.23).[105-107] It should be noted that bis-iodo monomers are more desirable than bis-bromo analogs for higher molecular weight products. Since the photoluminescence of these polymers is strongly influenced by intermolecular packing, a variety of pendent groups (non-ionic, ionic or amphiphilic) on one or both monomers have been synthesized to achieve solubility as well as other specific properties, such as effect of aggregation on the optical spectra of S-PPEs.[108,109]

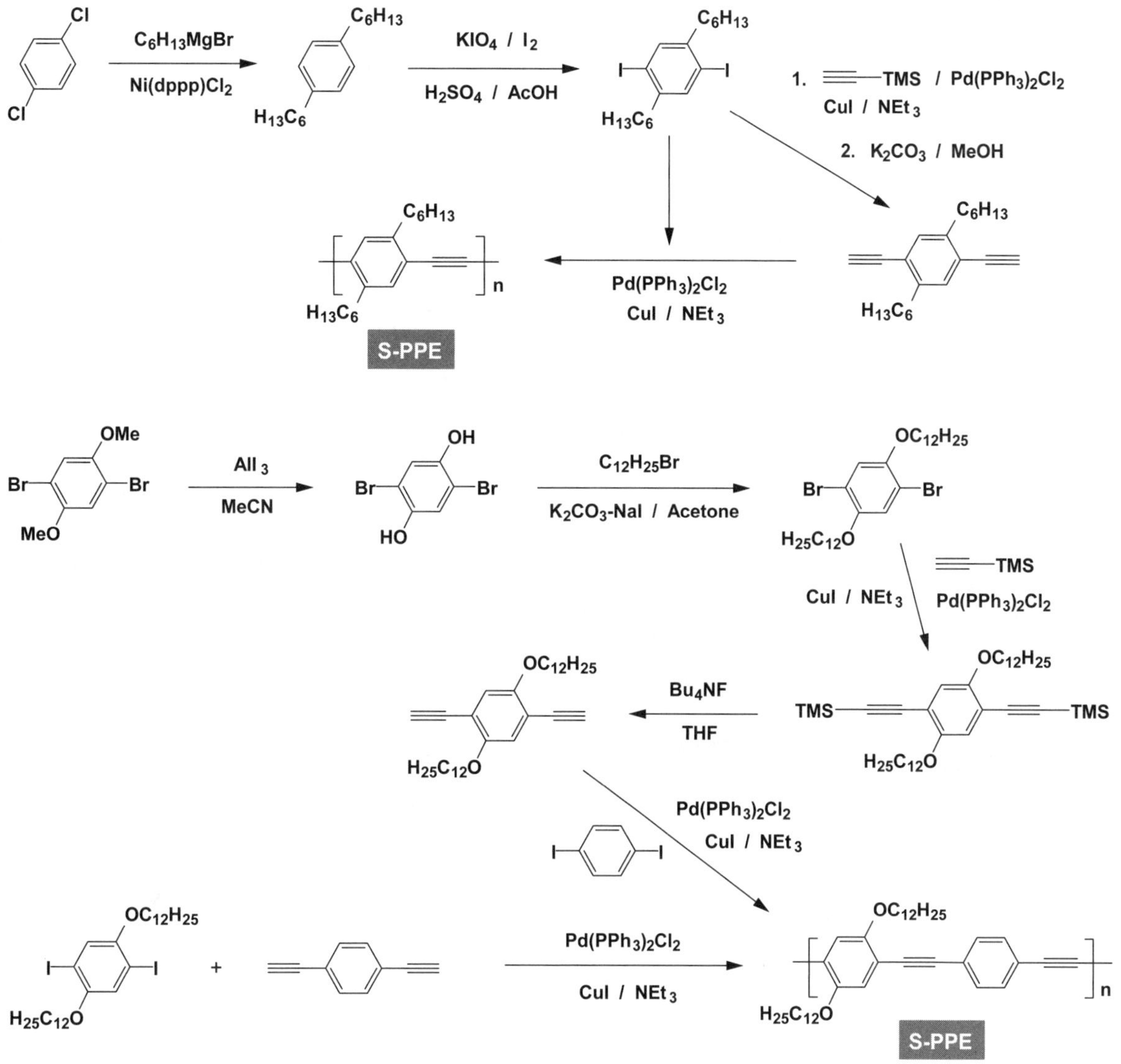

Figure 5.23. Synthesis of S-PPEs via Heck-Cassar-Sonogashira-coupling reaction.

S-PPEs have also been prepared from dialkylsubstituted methyl-capped bis-alkynes via alkyne metathesis polymerization in the presence of a catalytic amount of $Mo(CO)_6$ in 4-chlorophenol or *o*-dichlorobenzene (Figure 5.24).[110-112] Interestingly, the dialkylsubstituted PPEs (in contrast to dialkoxysubstituted PPE shown in Figure 5.23) form aggregates in the solid state or on addition of methanol to their solutions in chloroform, that resemble highly ordered Scheibe-type aggregates, found in low molecular weight merocyanine dyes.[113] Their occurrence in these S-PPEs suggest a well-defined and strong interaction of the polarizable π-clouds in the solid state.

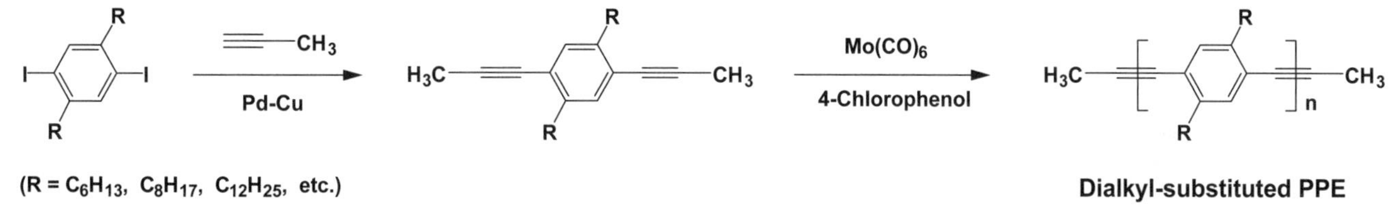

Figure 5.24. Synthesis of dialkylsubstituted PPEs via alkyne metathesis reaction.

Recent studies showed that among conducting polymers, PPEs are promising candidates for redox sensing of very low-level (less than parts per billion) nitroaromatic explosives. The property of nitroaromatics which is exploited in the detection schemes is their electron accepting capability. It is well known that substitution of the electron-withdrawing nitro groups on the aromatic ring lowers the energy of the empty π* orbitals, thereby making these compounds good electron acceptors. Indeed, reduction potentials become more favorable (less negative) as nitro substitution increases, viz., nitrobenzene (-1.15 V), 2,4-dinitrotoluene (DNT, -0.9 V), and 2,4,6-trinitrotoluene (TNT, -0.7 V), *versus* normal hydrogen electrode (NHE). Since conducting polymers are good electron donors and have enhanced delocalized π* excited states, they experience an efficient electron-transfer fluorescence quenching process in the presence of an electron deficient analyte, which acts as an electron acceptor for photoexcited electrons of the polymer.[114] Figure 5.25 is a schematic diagram of the electron-transfer mechanism, including the synthesis of a promising PPE derivative (S-PPE-IP) in which pentiptycene modules are incorporated into the PPE main chain. This polymer, which can be casted into thin films that exhibit high fluorescence, is especially suitable for the detection of TNT.[115-117] The synthesis of the bis-alkyne monomer involves the Diels-Alder reaction of benzoquinone with an excess of anthracene, followed by nucleophilic reaction of the resulting extended quinone to LiC≡CTMS to produce a mixture of two diols. Subsequent TMS deprotection and aromatization lead to the desired diethynylated pentiptycene monomer.

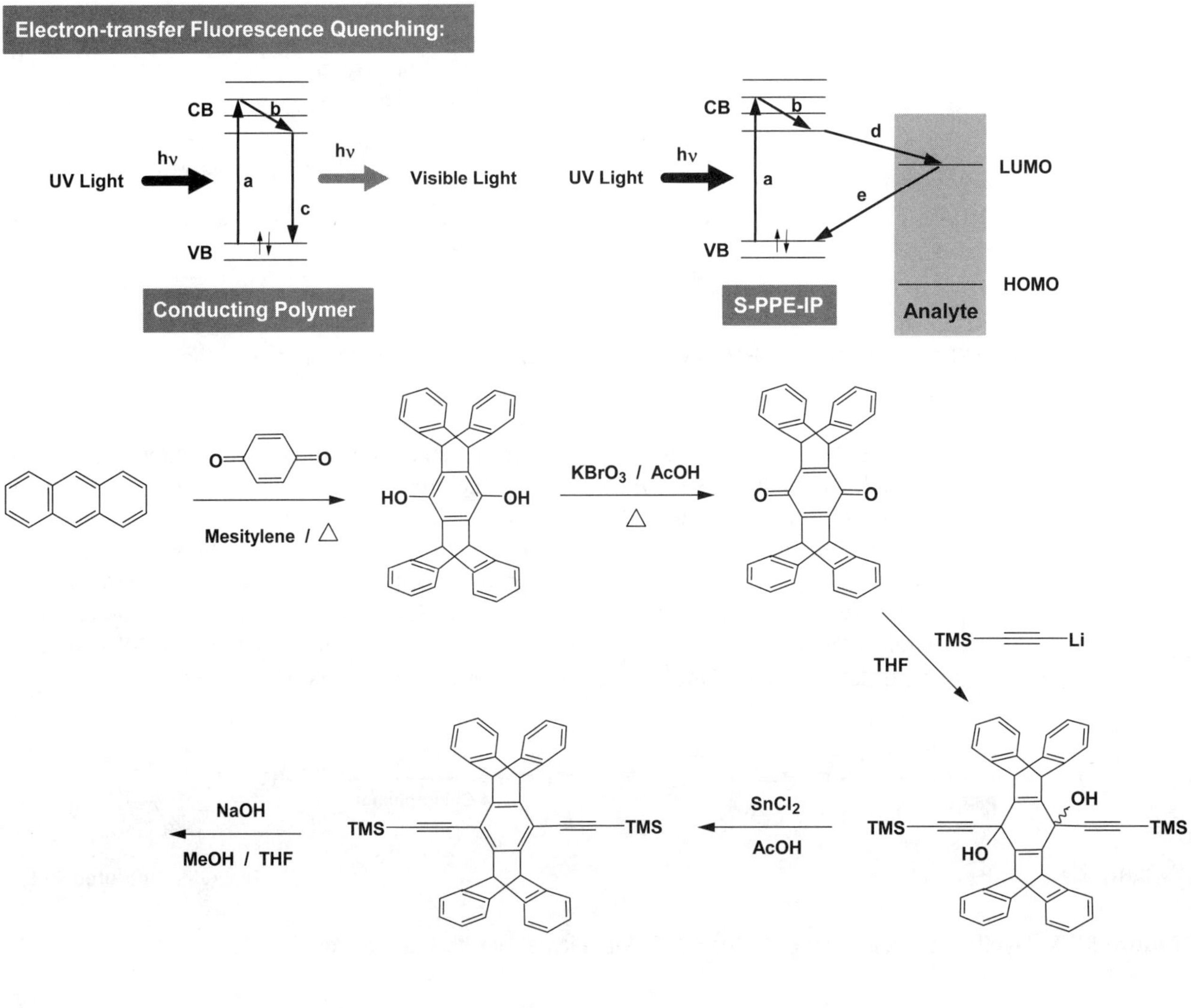

Electron-transfer Fluorescence Quenching:

UV Light
hν
CB
VB
a
b
c
hν
Visible Light
Conducting Polymer
UV Light
hν
CB
VB
a
b
d
e
LUMO
HOMO
S-PPE-IP
Analyte
O
O
Mesitylene / △
HO
OH
$KBrO_3$ / AcOH
△
O
O
TMS
Li
THF
TMS
TMS
OH
HO
$SnCl_2$
AcOH
TMS
TMS
NaOH
MeOH / THF

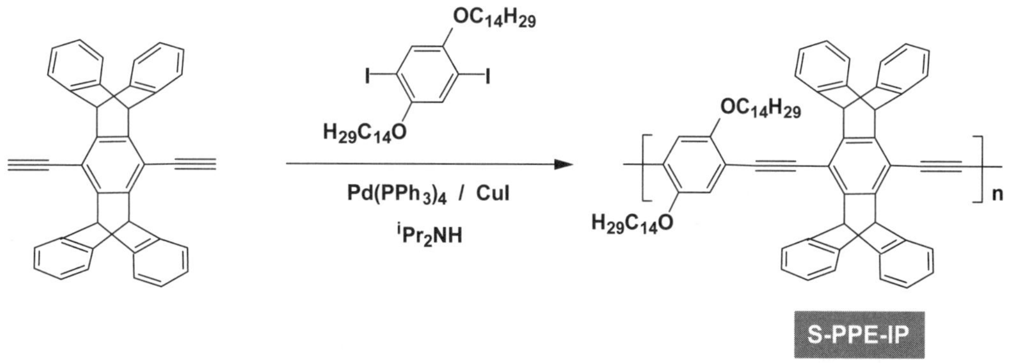

Figure 5.25. Top: Schematic diagram of electron-transfer quenching mechanism (a = excitation of an electron, b = non-radiative decay, c = fluorescence, d = electron-transfer quenching, and e = back electron transfer) *(With kind permission of The Royal Society of Chemistry, Ref. 114).* Below: Synthesis of a pentiptycene-containing PPE.

5.1.1.2. Redox Polymers

In contrast to π-conjugated polymers, *redox polymers* are localized state conductors and usually consist of redox-active species, such as ferrocene and osmium bipyridyl complex, connected by a covalent or coordinate bond to an electrochemically inactive (non-π-conjugating) polymer backbone. The widespread interest in these polymers has been spurred by their applicability to the area of chemically modified electrodes. Figure 5.26 depicts a simple strategy to attach an osmium-pyridine based redox species pendant to a polymer chain, such as poly(allyl)amine (PAA).[118] Osmium complexes have been the choice as redox species because of their well-known stability and their standard potential of 0.2-0.4 V (vs. SCE), which make them suitable for practically any electrode surface. This redox polymer, which can be coated onto electrodes by drop casting or spin-coating, is an excellent material for robust glucose and lactate biosensors.[119,120] The electron transport in this type of polymer occurs via a process of sequential electron self-exchange between neighboring redox species. This process is termed electron hopping and the conductivity of such a material is called *redox conductivity*. Since electroneutrality in the film must be maintained, the generation of charge at the electrode and the motion of the charge throughout the polymer must be accompanied by the ingress and motion of counterions across the film or solution interface. This is an important consideration, since redox polymers can be regarded as mixed conductors, displaying both electronic and ionic conductivity.

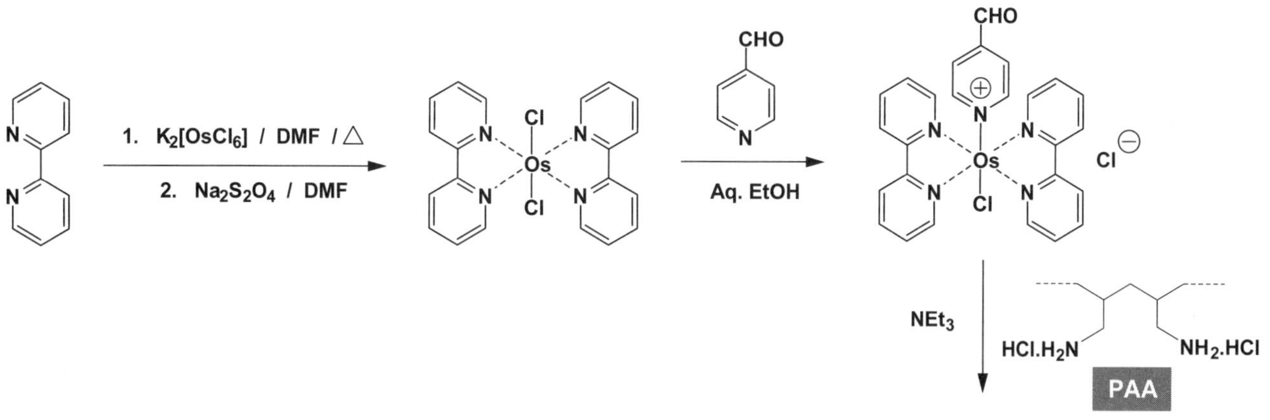

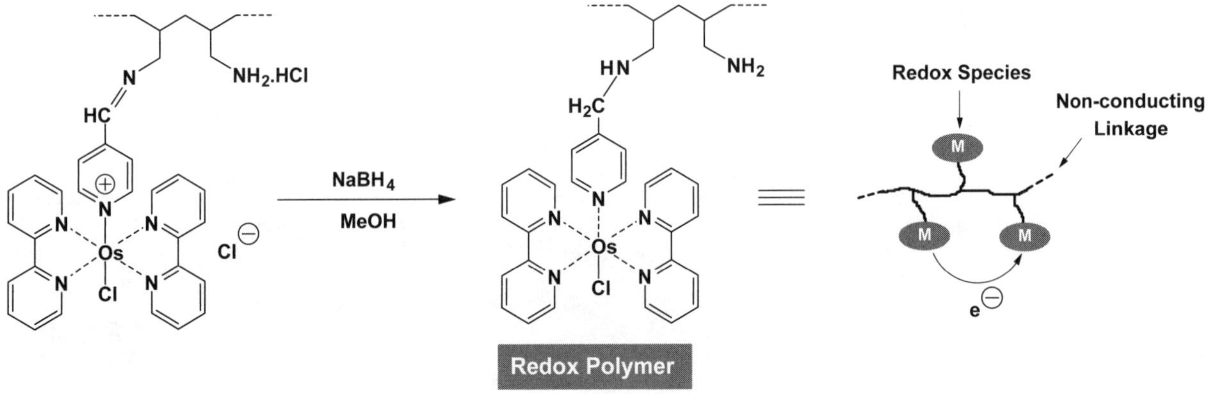

Figure 5.26. Synthesis of a representative redox polymer.

Redox polymers have also been prepared on electrode surfaces by electropolymerization of transition metal complexes with multiple polymerizable ligands, such as 4-vinyl-4'-methyl-2,2'-bipyridine (Figure 5.27).[121] One of the key advantages of this class of redox polymers is that the polymer coating can be precisely located on the electrode surface and the amount deposited can be controlled with high precision.

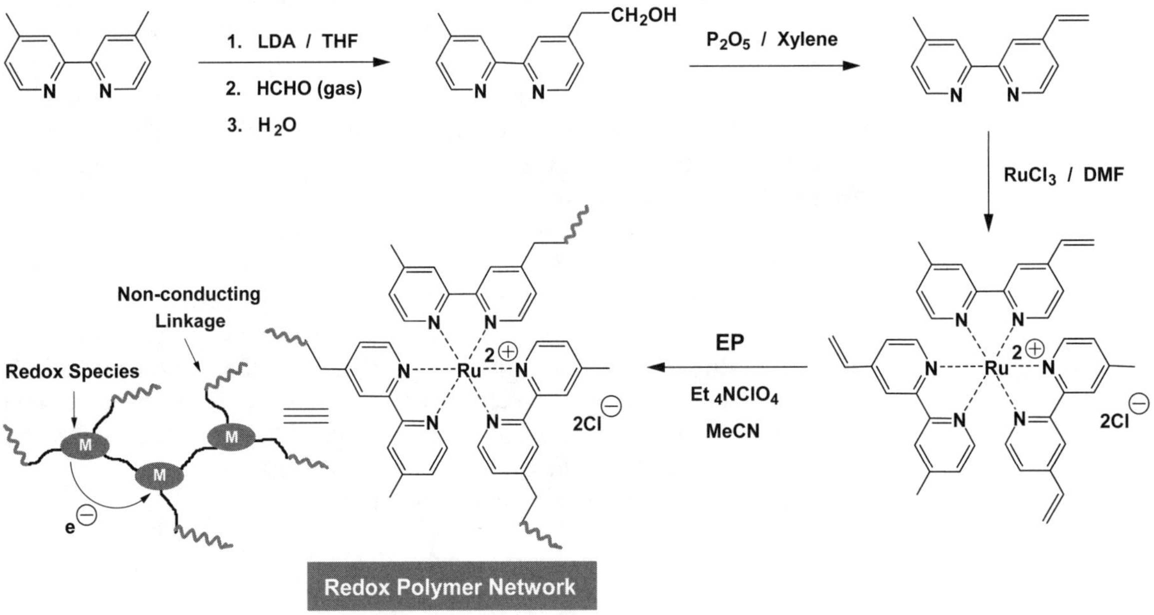

Figure 5.27. Synthesis of a representative redox polymer by the electropolymerization method.

5.1.1.3. Hybrid Polymers

This class of polymers has received a significant amount of attention in recent years because of the opportunity to combine the properties of conjugated and redox polymers as well as the optical properties of transition metal complexes (redox species).[122] As depicted in Figure 5.28, *hybrid polymers* can be divided into three major types. Type-I materials consist of metal centers tethered to the conjugated polymer backbone through a non-conducting linkage, such as an aliphatic chain. In this case, the polymer backbone acts primarily as a conductive support, and the properties of the metal center are essentially unchanged. In Type-II materials, the metal center and the conjugated polymer backbone are electronically coupled, often by use of a conjugated linker or by coordination to sites directly on the backbone, thus influencing each other's properties. In Type-III materials, the metal centers are located directly within the conjugated backbone. In this configuration, strong interaction between the metal center and the conjugated polymer bridge is possible.

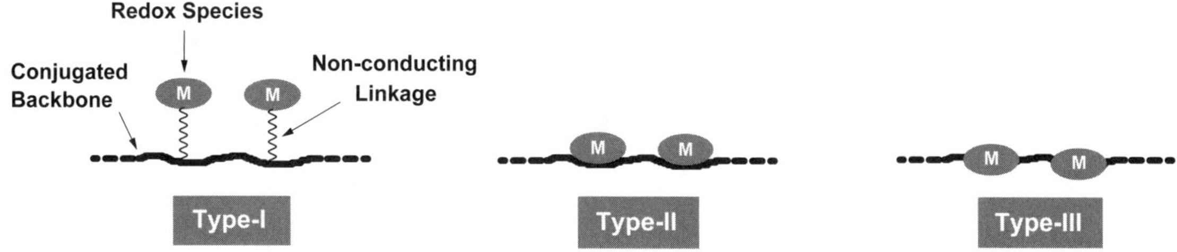

Figure 5.28. Schematic representation of three types of hybrid polymers.

Type-I polymers are normally prepared by linking a redox species to an electrochemically polymerizable monomer, such as pyrrole and thiophene.[123-127] A variety of redox species, such as ferrocene, metallo-porphyrins and metal bipyridyl complexes, have been examined. Figure 5.29 outlines the synthesis of an osmium-complex tethered pyrrole monomer, which upon electropolymerization in the presence of pyrrole deposits a copolymer film on the electrode surface suitable for oxygen-insensitive, reagentless glucose biosensors.[128]

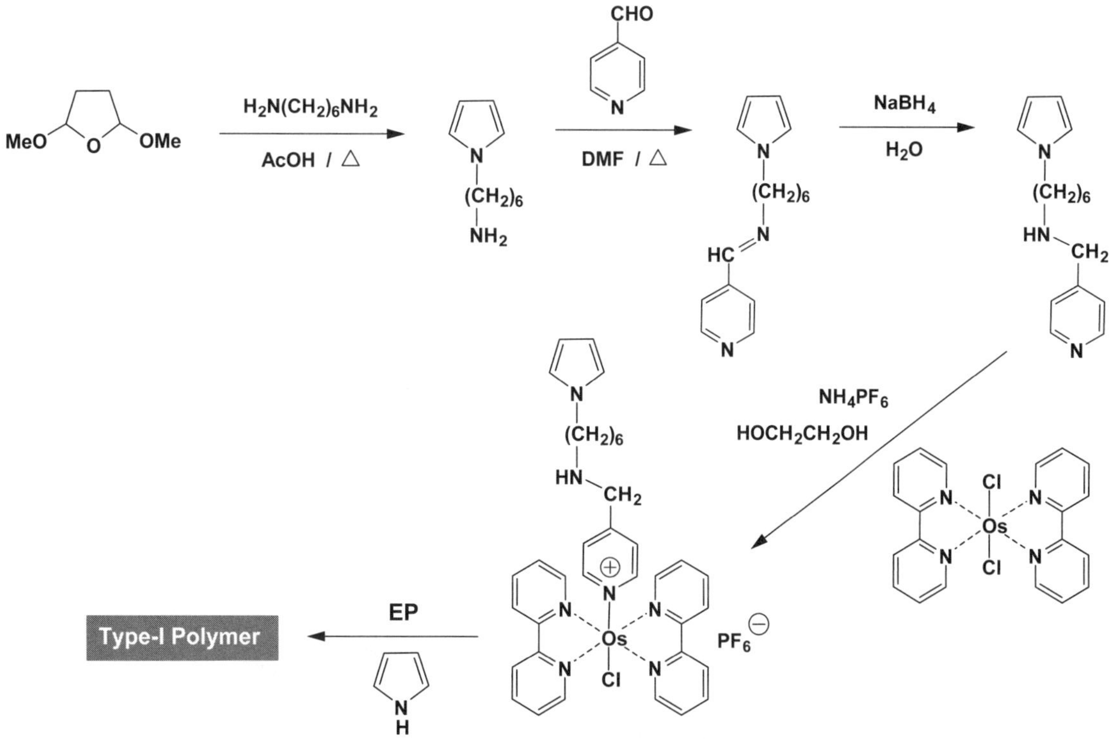

Figure 5.29. Synthesis of a representative Type-I hybrid polymer.

Type-II hybrid polymers have also been extensively investigated because of their unique conducting properties at the redox potential of the metal complex.[129-132] These materials are best prepared by electropolymerization of thiophene or pyrrole monomers π-linked with redox species. Figure 5.30 shows two well-studied examples. Both demonstrated that electron exchange between the redox species and the polymer backbone is efficient.

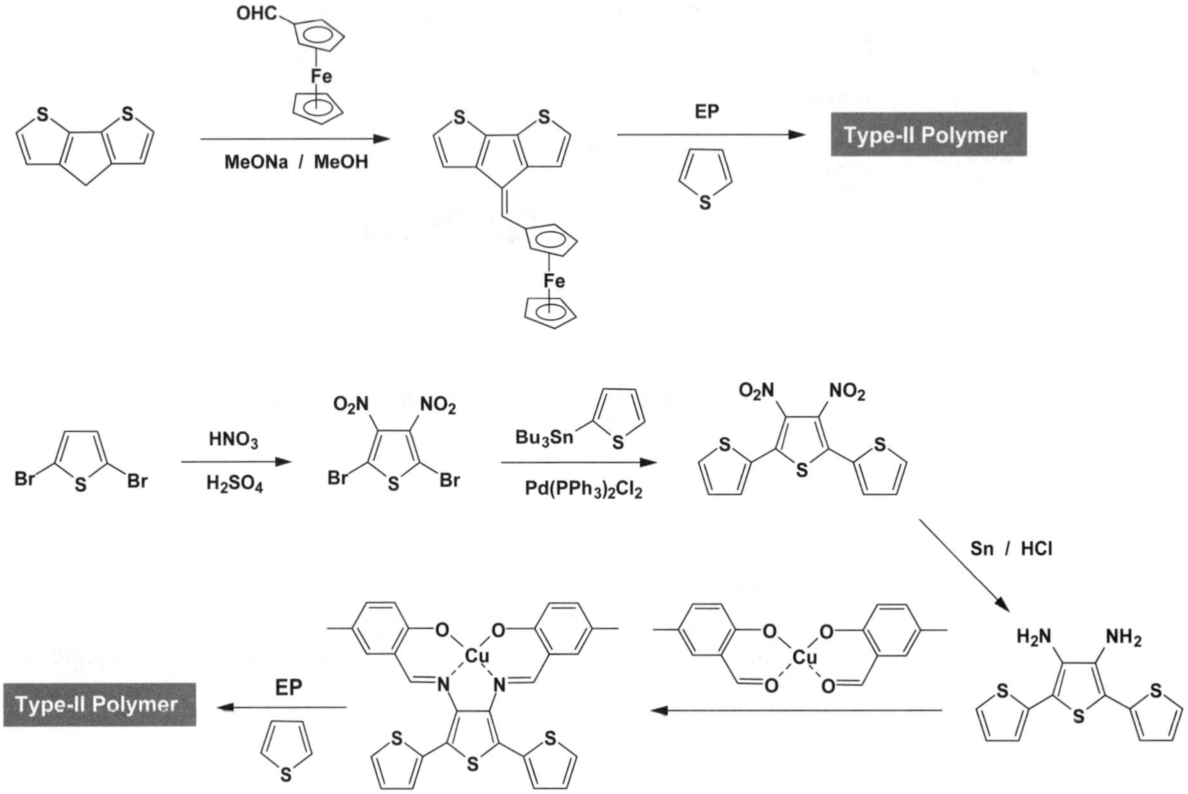

Figure 5.30. Synthesis of Type-II hybrid polymers with ferrocene or copper complex as redox species.

One of the most significant positive attributes of using conducting backbones to electronically "wire" or link redox centers (Type-II and III materials) is an increased rate of charge transport which, in conjugated systems, are up to two orders of magnitude greater than comparable non-conjugated analogs. Figure 5.31 illustrates (with a Type-III polymer) three possible mechanisms by which electron-transfer may occur between immobilized metal centers in a polymer film: (**A**) outer-sphere electron-transfer between metal centers (electron hopping), as observed in conventional redox polymers, (**B**) electron-transfer via a superexchange pathway (non-resonant superexchange), and (**C**) mediated by charge carriers on conjugated linkers or polymer backbones (which essentially is resonant superexchange, or electron hopping).[133]

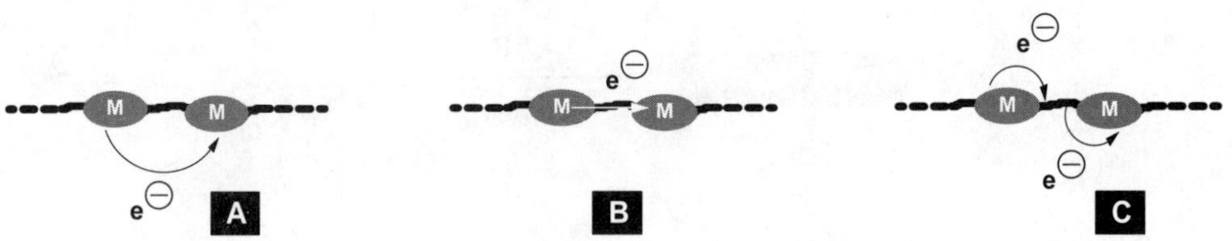

Figure 5.31. Schematic illustration of electron transfer pathways in Type-III hybrid polymers.

Type-III hybrid polymers have been the subject of recent research because of their superior semiconducting properties that can be conveniently tuned via coordination of ligands to the metal center.[134-137] For example, the salen-based polymer films of Co derivatives show an interesting, albeit irreversible, decrease in polymer conductivity in response to pyridine (Figure 5.32). This effect is believed to result from an interaction between the Co centers and the Lewis base. This class of polymers also exhibits a marked dependence of conductivity on interchain spacing, which is dependent on the bulkiness of the bridging diimine group. Thus, larger diamine groups in this series of polymers result in a drop in conductivity. Polythiophene hybrid materials containing ferrocenyl and Ru and Os bis-terpyridine complexes represent other notable Type-III materials.

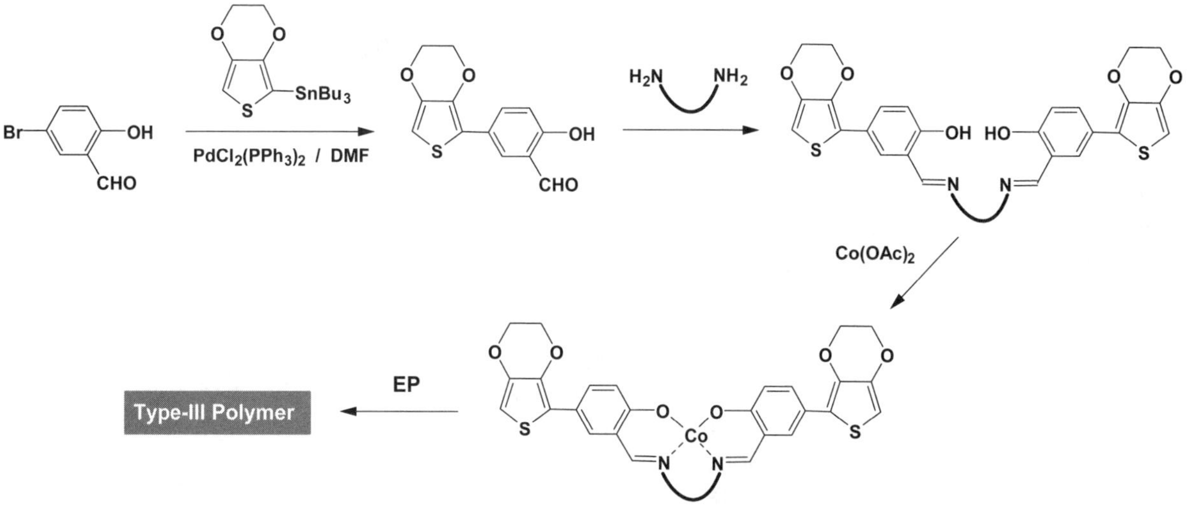

Figure 5.32. Synthesis of a representative Type-III hybrid polymer.

5.1.2. Proton-Conducting Polymers

Proton-conducting polymers are one of the key components in *polymer electrolyte fuel cells* (PEFCs) and *direct methanol fuel cells* (DMFCs), which electrochemically convert energy from renewable sources with practically no pollutant emissions. Among the various types of fuel cells currently under investigation, these fuel cells are the choice of most of the automotive industries, due to its high power density (i.e., low weight) and low relative cost (when compared to solid oxide fuel cells), and possible use of air as the oxidant. In these fuel cells, an electric current is produced through the catalyzed (viz., Pt or Pt/Ru alloy) oxidation of a fuel, such as H_2(g) and CH_3OH(aq) at the anode to produce protons, which are transported and consumed through a reductive reaction with oxygen at the cathode, forming water (Figure 5.33). The proton-conducting polymer, commonly referred to as *polymer electrolyte membrane* (PEM), functions in the important capacity as the electrolyte medium for proton transport and as the separator of both the electrodes and the fuel and oxygen. Among the PEMs currently available, Nafion® (DuPont) and various sulfonated high-performance aromatic polymers have been subjected to considerable characterization and testing for fuel cell applications.[138,139] Although Nafion, a free-radical initiated copolymer of tetrafluoroethylene (TFE) and perfluorinated vinyl ether containing a perfluorosulfonic acid group, has been the prototypical PEM for PEFCs involving hydrogen gas as the feed, its high manufacturing cost and permeability to methanol limit practical utilization in commercial fuel cells. When methanol is directly used as fuel, as for DMFCs, Nafion suffers from a high crossover rate of methanol through the membrane, leading to low efficiency of the fuel cells. Moreover, Nafion membranes are restricted to operating temperature below 90°C, due to insufficient proton conductivity under low humidity conditions.

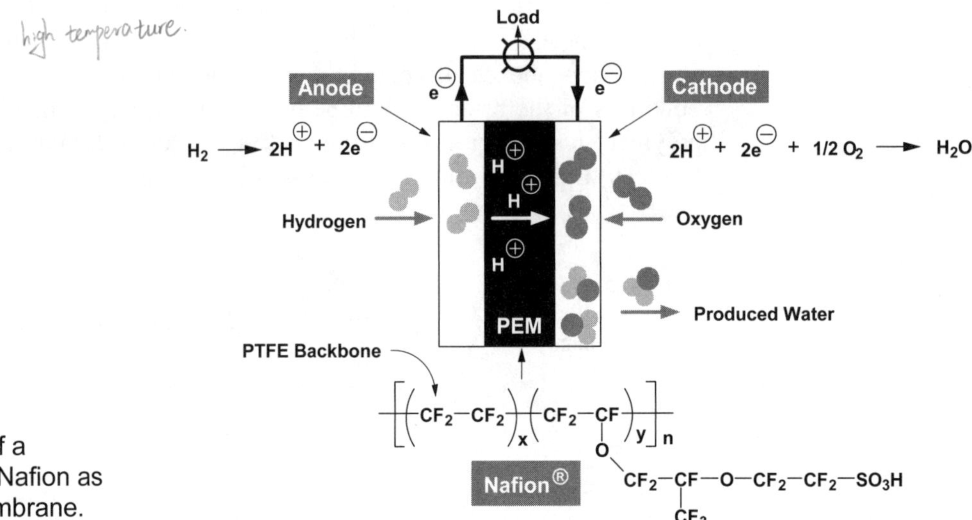

Figure 5.33. Schematic of a hydrogen/air fuel cell with Nafion as the proton-conducting membrane.

Hydrated Nafion is believed to have a microstructure morphology consisting of a cluster network where the polymer ions and the absorbed water exist in spherical domains. They are separated from the poly(tetrafluoroethylene) (PTFE) matrix. The three dimensional structure is composed of 1 nm wide channels that interconnect spherical clusters, creating a matrix of inverted micelles. The size of the spherical domains grows in size from 2.5 nm to 4 nm as the water absorbed increases (Figure 5.34a). At low hydration levels, such as at temperatures above 90°C, the pores between sulfonic acid clusters are thought to collapse due to low water content in the membrane, resulting in a drop in ionic conductivity. At high hydration, Nafion exhibits high conductivity (~0.2 S/cm) because the pores become open and the sulfonic acid clusters are truly interconnected. As a result of this rather complex morphology, various theories seek to describe how protons are transported within the membrane. One possibility is illustrated in Figure 5.34b. In this case, protons are conducted through small, water filled pores within the membrane by "hopping" from one sulfonic acid site to the next. Thus, the key element in this transport mechanism is the presence of water. Indeed, without exception, the ability of current state-of-the-art polymer membrane materials to conduct protons is proportional to the level of hydration of the membrane.

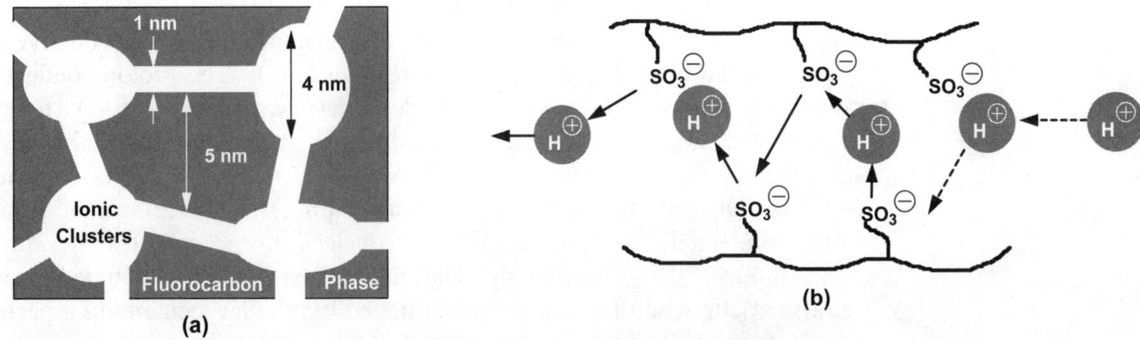

Figure 5.34. (a) Generally accepted morphology of hydrated Nafion. (b) A conceptual diagram of proton transport in a Nafion membrane.

In addition to water management in a PEM, several other key parameters, especially mechanical strength and dimensional stability of membranes in a hydrated state at intermediate temperatures (80-130°C), must be satisfied to enhance the efficiency of fuel cells. Another critical effect associated with a low operational temperature is the reduced tolerance of a platinum electrode to fuel impurities, viz., CO in the hydrogen stream. This poisoning effect has been shown to be very temperature-dependent (CO adsorption on the electrode surface is more pronounced at lower temperatures). For example, at 80°C, the typical operational temperature of a PEFC, a CO content as low as 20 ppm in the fuel stream will result in significant loss in cell performance. Consequently, very pure hydrogen is needed for operation of PEFCs. This shortcoming can be solved or avoided by developing alternative membranes which operate at temperatures higher than 100°C, because at higher temperatures the CO tolerance is markedly improved (e.g., 10-20 ppm of CO at 80°C, to 1,000 ppm at 130°C). This high CO tolerance makes it possible for a fuel cell to use hydrogen directly from a simple reformer, such as a water-gas-shift reactor.

In the past decade, a variety of high-performance polymers as the base skeleton have been tested for PEMs.[140-143] Among these, poly(arylene ether sulfone)s, Udel-PEM and BHF-PEM, are especially attractive because of their outstanding hydrolytic stability. The introduction of sulfonic acid groups in a commercial poly(ether sulfone), such as Udel®, is normally conducted by a directed lithiation method[144], which, in contrast to the traditional chlorosulfonation method[145], requires no chlorinated hydrocarbon solvents (Figure 5.35). Moreover, the chlorosulfonation route is limited to poly(ether sulfone)s

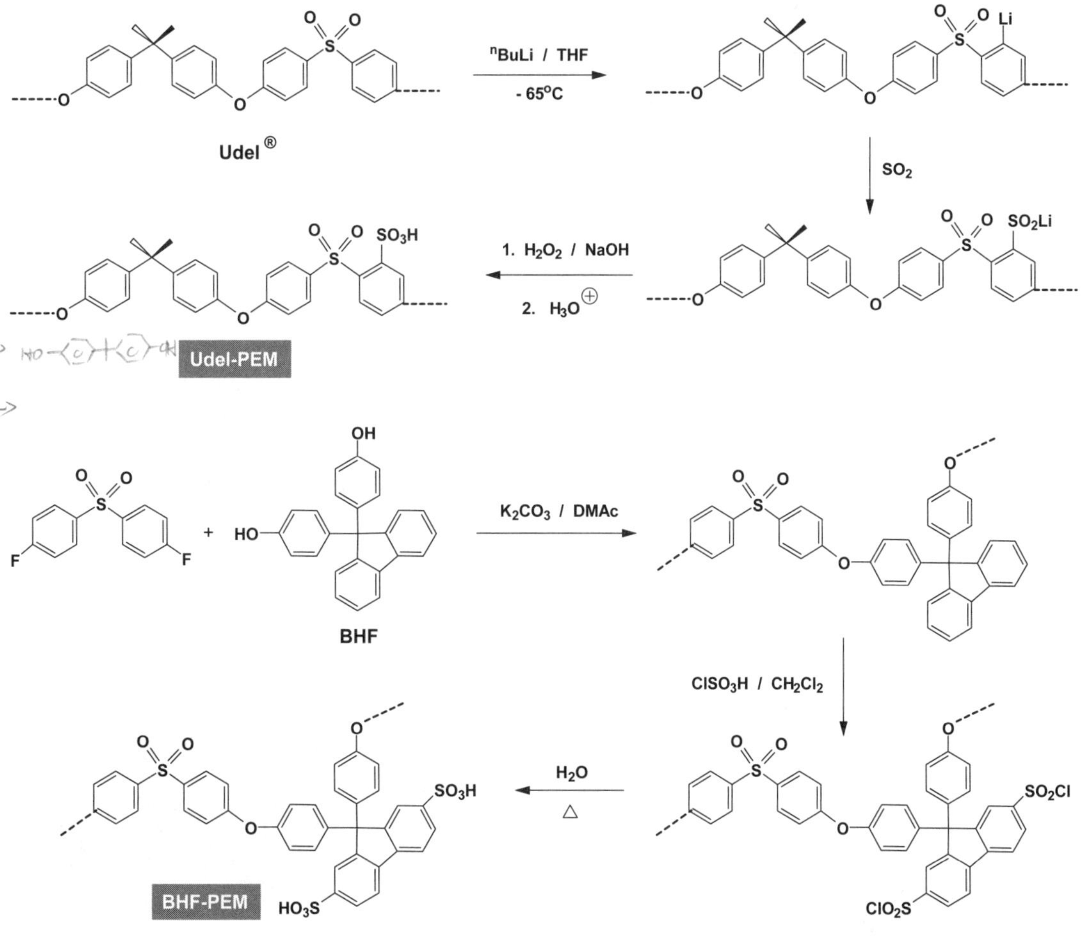

Udel®

^nBuLi / THF

- 65°C

SO_2

1. H_2O_2 / NaOH

2. $H_3O^{\oplus}$

Udel-PEM

BHF

K_2CO_3 / DMAc

$ClSO_3H$ / CH_2Cl_2

H_2O

Δ

BHF-PEM

Figure 5.35. Common sulfonation methods for the preparation of poly(arylene ether sulfone)-based PEMs.

that are made from monomers containing activated aromatic rings, such as 9,9'-bis(4-hydroxyphenyl)fluorene (BHF). Under dry conditions, the PEMs obtained by both methods are stable up to 250°C without any thermal transitions and decomposition. Under wet conditions at 140°C and 100% RH, they also do not show any hydrolytic degradation for 700 h. It is worth mentioning that the BHF-PEM exhibits comparable proton-conducting properties to Nafion with the highest proton conductivity (0.2 S/cm) obtained at 140°C and 100% RH. In addition, this PEM is very stable mechanically at 85°C and 93% RH and keeps its strength even at 120°C. Hydrogen and oxygen permeability of this PEM is also much lower than that of Nafion under a wide range of conditions (40-120°C and 0-90% RH).

5.1.3. Lithium Ion-Conducting Polymers

Unlike fuel cells, which produce energy, batteries store energy. *Lithium ion-conducting polymers* are projected as the most desirable electrolyte system for lithium-ion rechargeable batteries (often called "*lithium polymer battery*" when the electrolyte is made of a lithium ion-conducting polymer) to satisfy the ever-growing need for high energy density power sources in automotive industries, portable devices and aerospace applications. The major advantage of the lithium-ion battery is its high energy density compared to other types of battery, such as nickel cadmium (Ni-Cd) and nickel metal hydride (Ni-MH). Lithium has several unique properties: it is light and has the lowest redox potential (i.e., largest negative electrode potential) of all metals (-3.04 vs. Standard Hydrogen Electrode), which gives the lithium-ion battery a high energy density and a high working voltage compared, for example, to a Ni-MH battery. However, lithium metal reacts violently with air and moisture, which can make its use hazardous. Consequently, materials that can host lithium ions in their structure are used as electrodes in these batteries. Thus, lithium ions are employed as "energy carriers" and move from the anode across the electrolyte to the cathode during battery discharge and vice versa as the battery is recharged. Li-ion has been termed a "rocking chair" or "swing" battery system, since the cell reactions essentially transport lithium ions from one electrode to the other and back again (Figure 5.36). During charge, the lithium ions from the lithium cobalt oxide (Li_yCoO_2) or lithium vanadium oxide ($Li_yV_3O_8$) cathode migrate to the carbon/graphite anode where they are intercalated. On discharge, the ions reverse direction, leave the carbon and reenter the cathode structure. Although Li-ion is used to designate the cell chemistry, there is no lithium metal in the cell. Lithium refers to the Li^+ ions intercalated into the crystal structure of the carbon and cobalt oxide active materials and the ions of the electrolyte that transport current during cell operation.

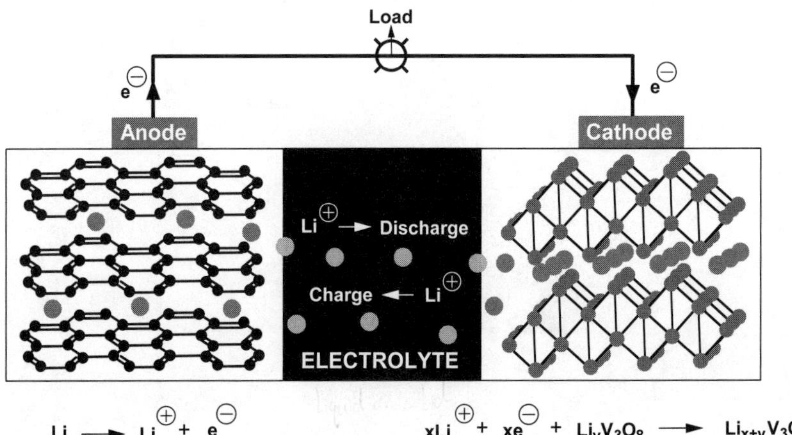

Figure 5.36. Schematic illustration of a lithium polymer battery.

With an emphasis on lithium-ion batteries, the field of polymer electrolytes has gone through three stages; dry solid systems, polymer gels, and polymer composites.[146-148] The "dry systems", commonly known as *solid polymer electrolytes* (SPEs), use a polymer host as the solid solvent and do not include any organic liquids. Usually, SPEs are obtained by dissolving a low lattice energy lithium salt, such as $LiN(SO_2CF_3)_2$, in a poly(ethylene oxide) (PEO)-based material. The main advantages of PEO as a host are its chemical, mechanical and electrochemical stabilities, since it contains only strong unstrained C-O, C-C, and C-H bonds. PEO is very flexible (T_g = -65°C) because of the presence of swivel ether linkages and the repeat unit, $-CH_2CH_2O-$, provides just the right spacing for maximum solvation, which decreases the energy of coordination with lithium ion. PEO electrolyte behaves like a rubbery material, due to the presence of sufficient interchain entanglement, and contains both crystalline and amorphous regions. Lithium ion conduction is believed to occur in the amorphous phase via diffusion which occurs through a complex mechanism involving the PEO segmental mobility (Figure 5.37).[149] The "*polymer gels*", also called "*gel electrolytes*", are prepared by trapping a large volume (50-80%) of liquid electrolyte (e.g., 1M $LiN(SO_2CF_3)_2$ in a high boiling solvent, viz., ethylene carbonate or γ-butyrolactone) in a polymer matrix, such as poly(vinylidine fluoride) (PVDF) and poly(acrylonitrile) (PAN).[150,151] In contrast, the "*polymer composites*" are obtained by incorporating electrochemically inert high surface area inorganic solids (e.g., 10-30 wt.% of ZrO_2, TiO_2, Al_2O_3 or hydrophobic fumed silica) in a "dry solid polymer" or "polymer gel" system as a means to increase mechanical stability of the polymer.

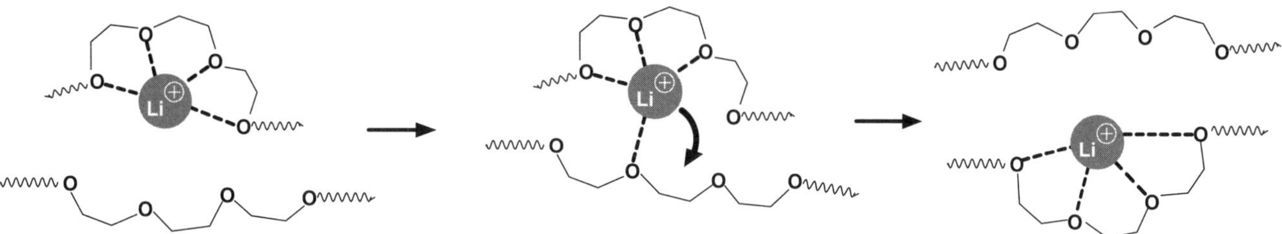

Figure 5.37. Schematic representation of lithium ion migration associated with the segmental mobility of the PEO chains.

One of the important properties of a solid polymer electrolyte relating to its development activity is the ionic conductivity. For an amorphous SPE, the relationship between temperature and conductivity (**σ**) is best represented by the *Vogel-Tammann-Fulcher (VTF) equation*:

$$\sigma = AT^{1/2} \exp[E/(T-T_g)]$$

where, **A** is the pre-exponential factor, **T** is the temperature of measurement, $\mathbf{T_g}$ is the glass transition temperature of the polymer electrolyte, and **E** is the activation energy which can be evaluated either from the configurational entropy theory or the free-volume theory, and hence relates to the segmental motion of polymer chains. The ionic conductivity is usually measured by AC impedance techniques.[152]

Another important property of the SPE is the *lithium ion transference number* (t_{Li+}), which ideally should be unity for lithium battery applications. A value of t_{Li+} lower than 1 leads to polarization of the electrolyte with an increase in resistivity. Both ionic conductivity and t_{Li+} are important in choosing a polymer electrolyte for a practical lithium polymer battery. SPEs presently suffer from poor ionic conductivities (~10^{-5} S/cm at 20°C) compared to the aprotic liquid electrolytes currently used in Li-ion batteries (>10 x 10^{-3} S/cm). However, SPEs are much safer than "polymer gels", due to the absence of any organic solvent which can cause environmental and/or fire hazards. It is noteworthy that although higher conductivities are preferable, 1000-fold increases are not essential, as a thin-film electrochemical cell configuration can largely compensate for these lower values. Good ionic conductivity (~10^{-3} S/cm) is essential to ensure that a battery system is capable of delivering usable amounts of power at a high rate. In the past, a variety of polymer systems containing PEO segments in the backbone or as a pendant (comb-type) have been synthesized to achieve improved SPE properties.[153-158] Figure 5.38 outlines the synthetic strategy of a few such polymers, SPEs 1-4, which exhibit reduced crystallinity even in the presence of high concentrations of lithium salts.

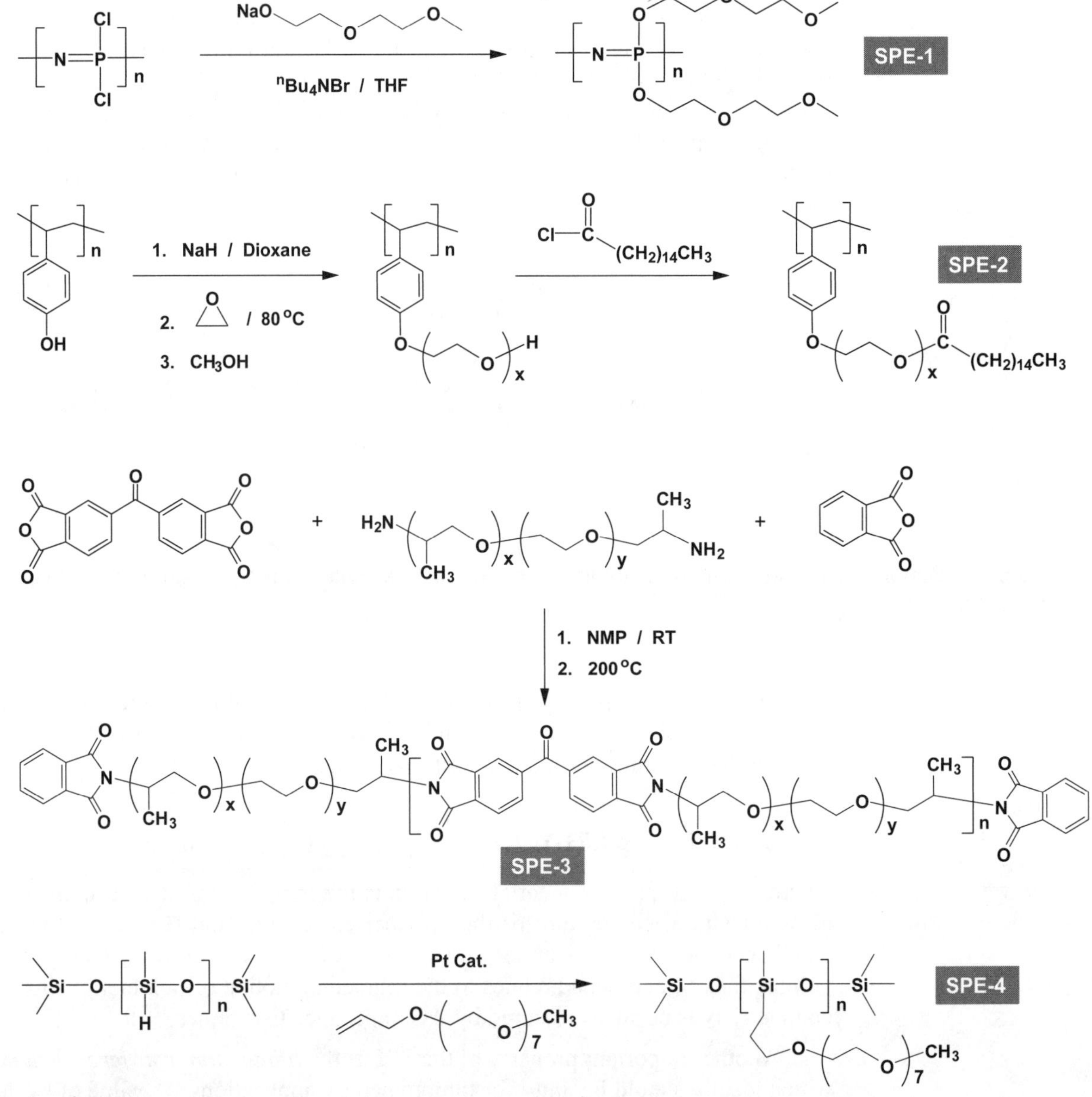

Figure 5.38. Synthesis of selected PEO-based polymers for superior SPEs.

Recent research efforts have been dedicated to the synthesis of SPEs containing a covalently linked lithium salt, better known as "single-ion conductors" (SICs), because of the transport of only lithium ions (Figure 5.39).[159-162] The important advantage of single-ion conductors is that they do not exhibit a "cell polarization" problem, a property associated with typical SPEs containing bi-ion salts, such as $LiN(SO_2CF_3)_2$. During discharge in bi-ion salt-based SPEs, mobile anions and cations migrate toward the oppositely charged electrodes, thereby polarizing the electrolyte and increasing its resistivity. Recharging the cell then requires more energy, time, and a greater electrochemical potential.

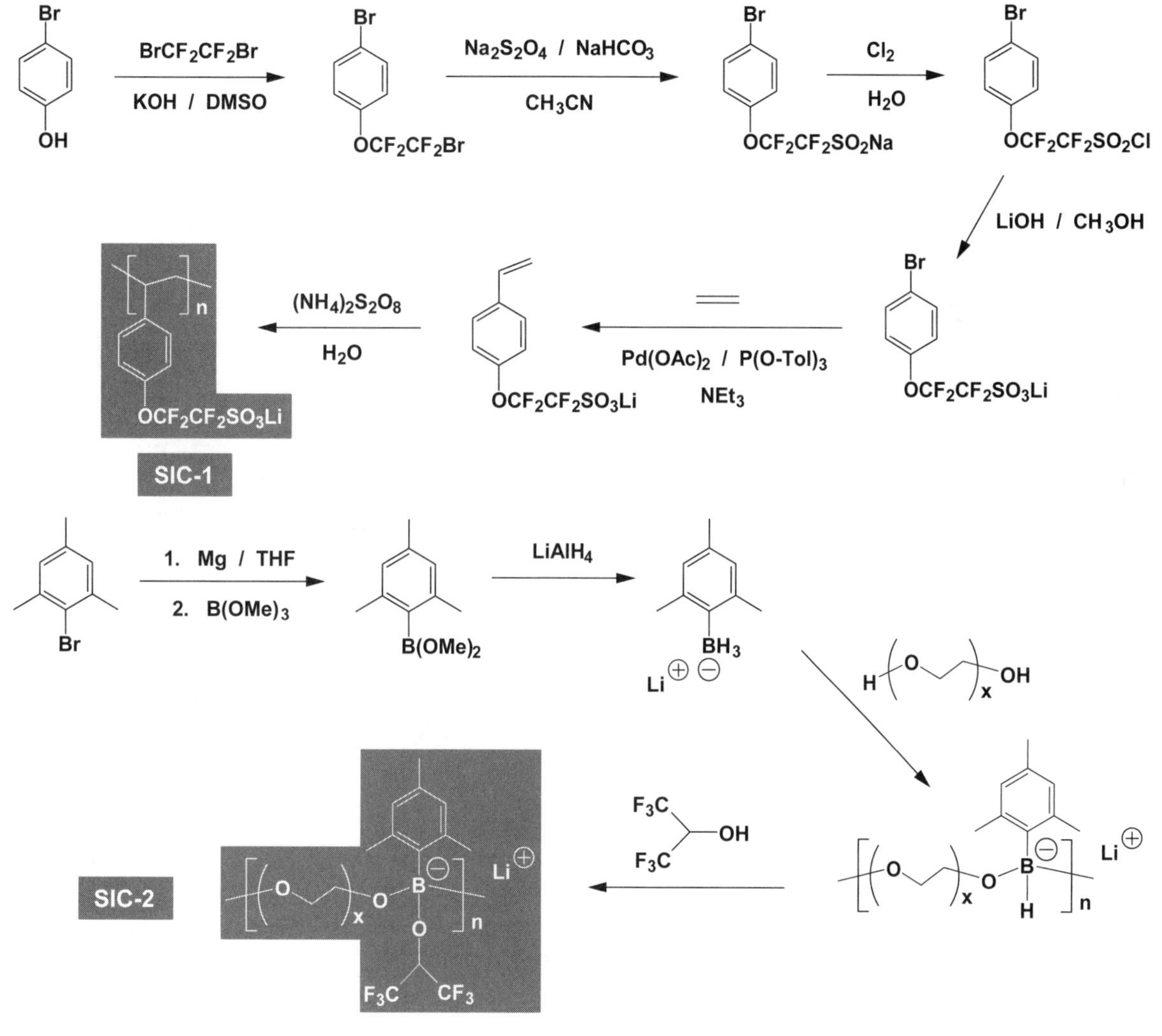

Figure 5.39. Synthesis of single-ion conducting SPEs.

5.2. LIGHT-EMITTING POLYMERS

As mentioned earlier, since the discovery in 1990 that *poly(phenylene vinylene)*(PPV) could be used as the light emitting layer in organic electroluminescent devices (alternatively called *light-emitting diodes*, LEDs), other π-conjugated polymers, viz., *polyfluorene* (PFL), *poly(p-phenylene)* (PPP), *polythiophene* (PTh), *polycarbazole*

(PCBz), and their derivatives, have been thoroughly investigated to obtain three basic colors (red, green and blue) with high luminescence efficiency and tunable emission, long lifetimes, and color purity.[163-171] Among the *light-emitting polymers* (LEPs, also called *electroluminescent polymers*), PFLs have emerged as the most promising materials, due to their emission at wavelengths spanning the entire visible spectrum, high fluorescence efficiency, and good thermal stability. PFLs exhibit interesting and unique chemical and physical properties because they contain a rigid planar biphenyl unit and facile substitution at the remote C_9 position can improve the solubility and processabililty of polymers without significantly increasing the steric interactions in the polymer backbone. *Polymer light-emitting diodes* (PLEDs) are especially attractive for patterned light sources and flat panel displays, including low-power-consumption white light illumination. As outlined in Figure 5.40, PFL derivatives with a wide range of light-emitting properties can be obtained by proper selection of monomers. For example, a red-LEP is obtained when the backbone consists of alternating fluorene and 2-pyran-4-ylidenemalononitrile moieties, while a green-LEP results from fluorene containing 4,4-diphenyldithienosilole units.

CHO Br NC CN O Piperidine / MeCN NC CN O Br Br FLB-1 or 2 Pd(PPh3)4 K2CO3 NC CN O n H17C8 C8H17 Red LEP

Br Br S S Br Br 2 eq. nBuLi / Et2O Me3SiCl Br Me3Si S S SiMe3 Br 2 eq. nBuLi / Et2O Ph2SiCl2 Ph Ph Si Me3Si S S SiMe3 Br2 / Et2O Ph Ph Si Br S S Br FLB-1 or 2 / FLBr Pd(PPh3)4 / K2CO3 Ph Ph Si S S x y n H17C8 C8H17 H17C8 C8H17 Green LEP

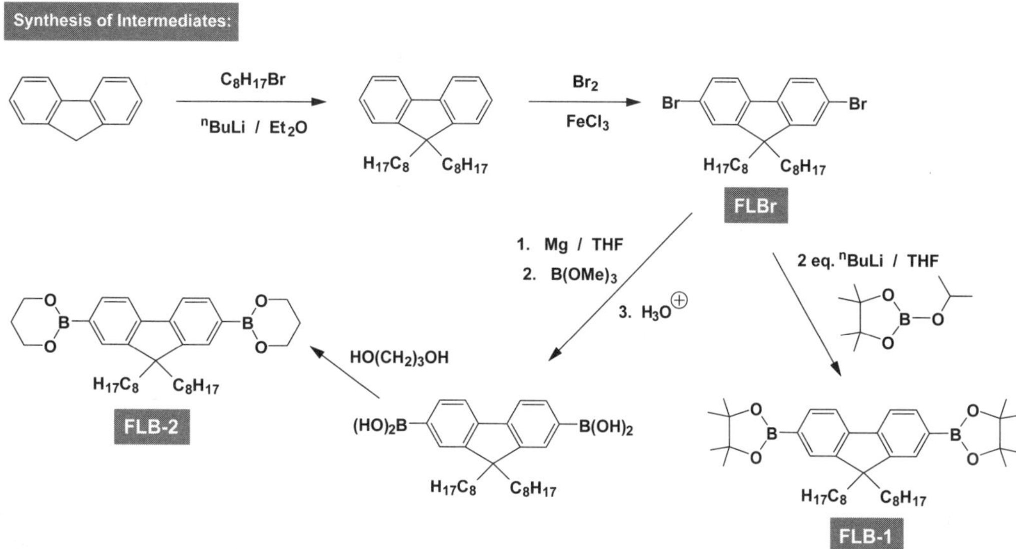

Figure 5.40. General synthetic methodologies for PFL-based LEPs.

In general, PFL copolymers are prepared by Suzuki-type coupling reactions and homopolymers by nickel-mediated Yamamoto-type polycondensation.[172-174] Solubility, oxidative stability, low turn-on voltage, and color tunability (especially blue emission) are desirable properties for conjugated polymers used in LEDs. Moreover, good thermal stability is needed because heat is generated when current passes through the device. Figure 5.41 shows more examples of PFL-based LEPs, which exhibit blue light emission. It is important to note that recent research has focused more on blue-emitting materials with a longer conjugation length, using ladder-type PFL (LPFL) or PFL-containing dibenzosilole building blocks, such as PFL-DBS, due to superior sensitivity to the human eye, excellent color purity, and high photoluminescence efficiency and thermal stability.

CO_2Me Br
$(HO)_2B$ $B(OH)_2$
$Pd(PPh_3)_4$
K_2CO_3
CO_2Me MeO_2C
$H_{17}C_8$ C_8H_{17}
1. PhLi
2. $H_3O^{\oplus}$
Ph Ph Ph Ph
Ph OH HO Ph
$BF_3.OEt_2$
$CuBr_2.Al_2O_3$
Br Br
$Ni(COD)_2$ / 2,2'-bipyridyl
DMF
n
LPFL

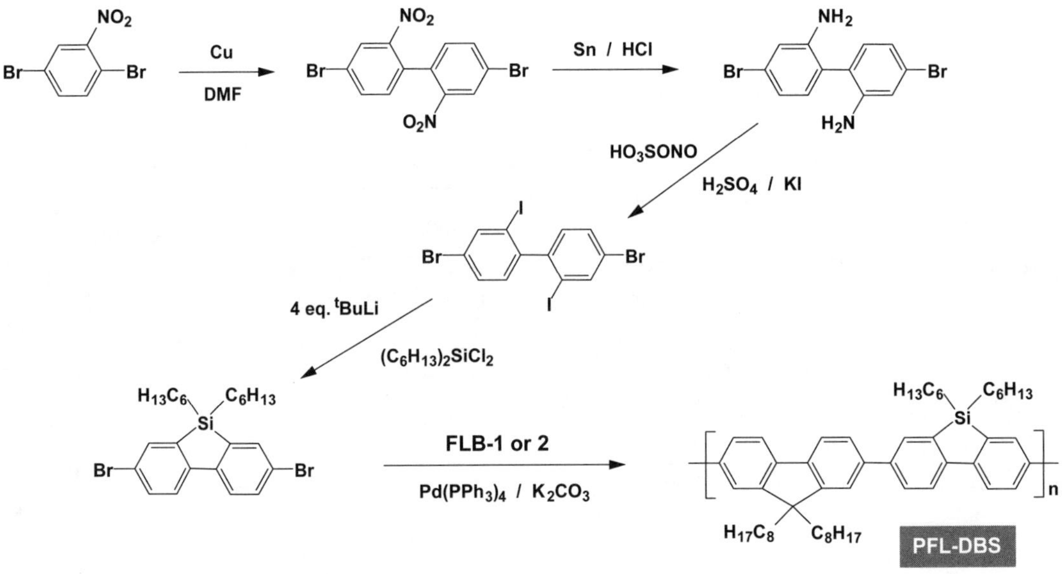

Figure 5.41. Synthetic strategies to blue-light emitting PFLs.

LEPs containing alternating fluorene and divinylbenzene moieties have also been explored. The common synthetic route involves Wittig polycondensation of fluorene bisaldehyde (FLBA) with bisphosphonium salt (Figure 5.42). This methodology allows tuning of light emitting color by placing proper functional groups on the bisphosphonium salt monomer. For example, the presence of trimethylsilyl electron-donating substituents blue-shifts the emission maximum peak compared to that of alkoxy substitutents.[175] It is noteworthy that LEPs containing pendent fluorene moieties are also excellent candidates for efficient blue emission.[176]

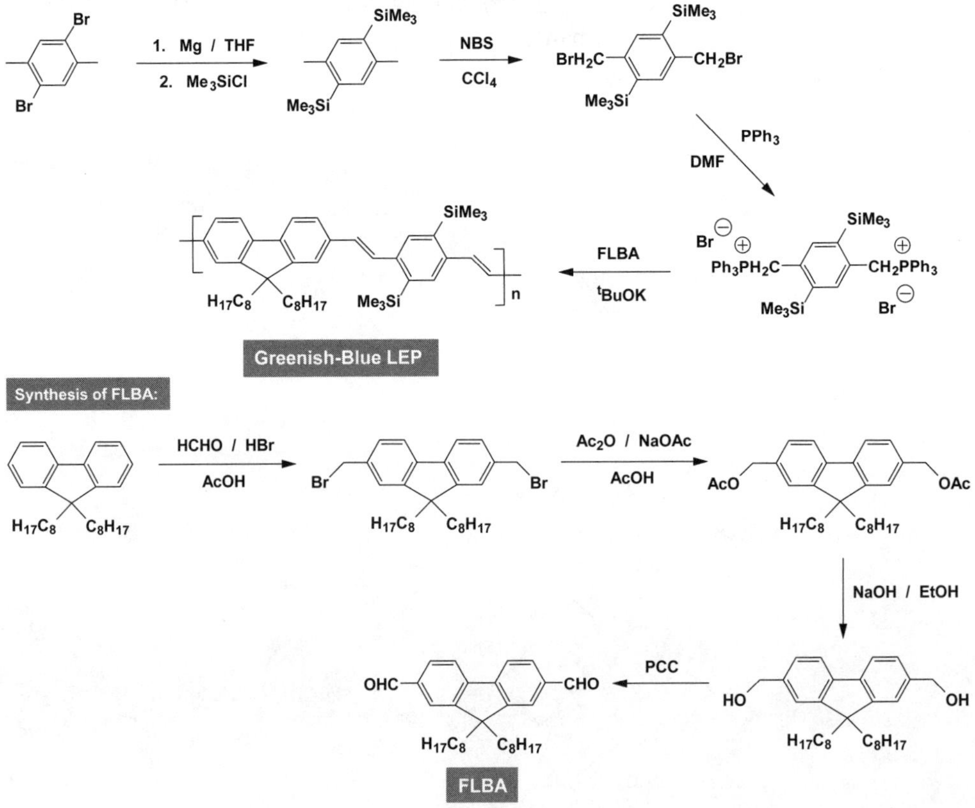

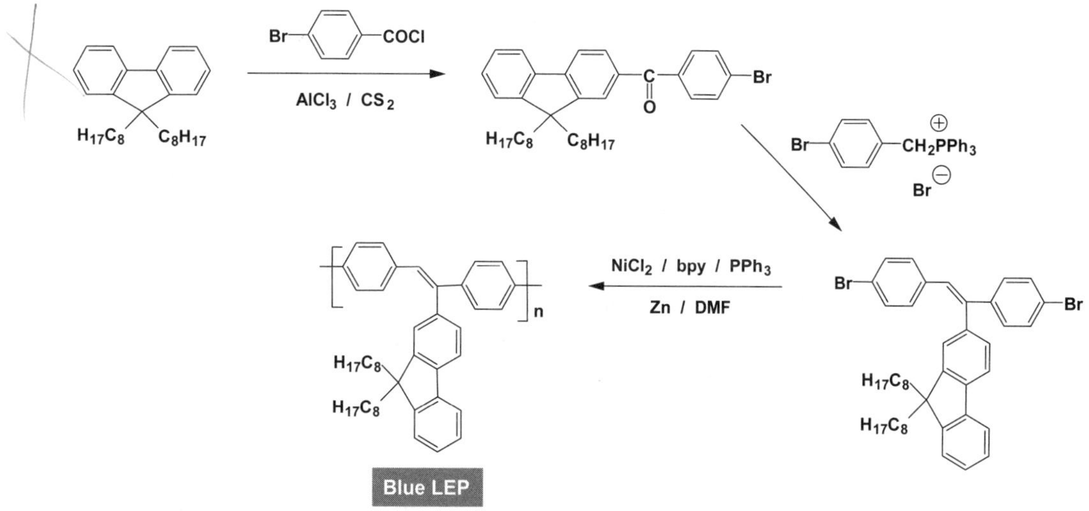

Figure 5.42. Synthesis of PFL-PPV hybrid LEPs.

Recently, a series of new LEPs containing alternating fluorene and divinylbenzene moieties have been prepared by Knoevenagel condensation of a bis-cyanomethyl fluorene with a variety of aromatic bis-aldehydes.[177-179] These polymers were found to be predominantly in the *trans* configuration, exhibit good thermal stability and solubility in common organic solvents, and display a range of colors depending on the backbone structure and conformation (Figure 5.43). The fabricated light-emitting devices showed very good performance in terms of turn-on voltage (wherein visible emission is first noticeable to the naked eye in normal ambient lighting conditions), electroluminescence, and lifetime properties. For example, the polymer obtained with isophthalaldehyde possesses a low turn-on voltage of 2.4 V, while the polymer with terephthalaldehyde exhibits electroluminescence greater than 3000 cd/m^2.

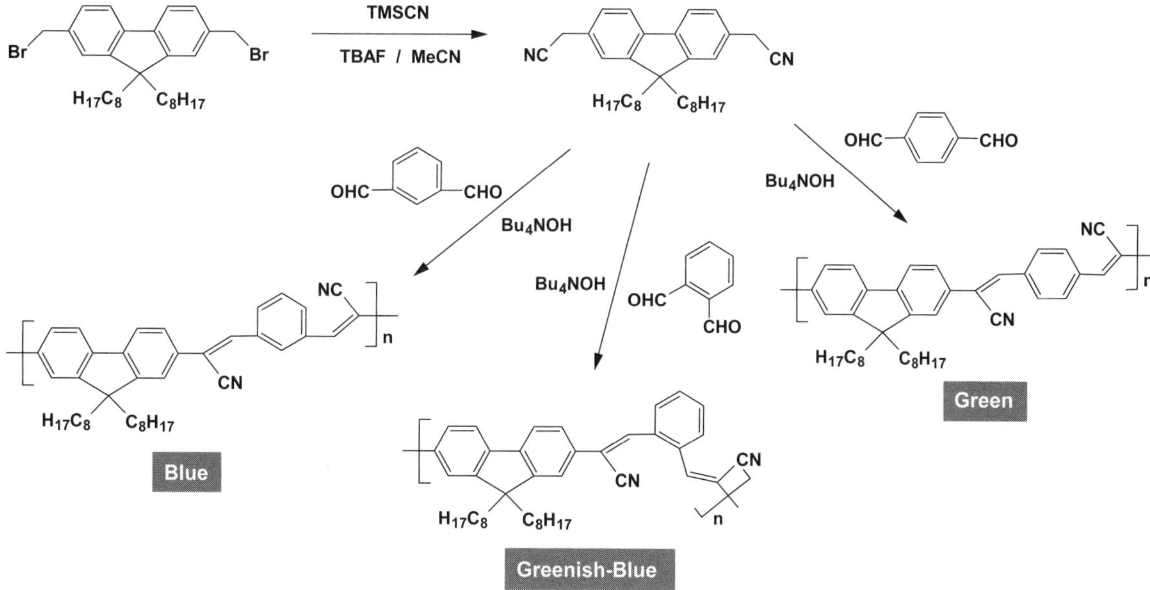

Figure 5.43. Synthesis of a new class of fluorene-containing polymers including the color of emission light.

5.3. NONLINEAR OPTICAL POLYMERS

Traditional optically transparent polymers, such as PS, PMMA and PC, are called linear optical polymers because their primary optical parameters, such as refractive index and absorption coefficient, do not vary significantly with the change in intensity of light, similar to ordinary glass. By contrast, the optical parameters of *nonlinear optical* (NLO) *polymers* are intensity dependent (i.e., refractive index or absorption coefficient can be tuned by changing the intensity of light) especially when subjected to an intense electromagnetic field, such as that due to an intense laser pulse, which causes the polarization (**P**) of the medium that can be expressed in a power series of the field strength (**E**) according to the equation:

$$\mathbf{P} = \chi^{(1)} \cdot \mathbf{E} + \chi^{(2)} : \mathbf{EE} + \chi^{(3)} \vdots\, \mathbf{EEE} + \cdots$$

where $\chi^{(1)}$ is the linear optical susceptibility, $\chi^{(2)}$ the second-order NLO susceptibility and $\chi^{(3)}$ the third-order NLO susceptibility. Higher order susceptibilities are of very little practical interest because of their greatly diminished strength. Thus, depending on the molecular compositions of the NLO polymers, second-order and/or third-order NLO properties can be significantly prominent for practical devices.

In the past decade, the *second-order NLO polymers* have generated significant attention because of their fortuitous combination of exceptional optical qualities, low cost, and ease of fabrication into thin films leading to electro-optic (EO) devices, such as EO modulators, for applications in ultra-high speed information transmission and processing. Most current commercial EO modulators take advantage of solid-state crystals, such as $LiNbO_3$ (EO coefficient ~30 pm/V), and have switching voltages typically in the range of 3-5 V. Unfortunately, broadband amplifiers are required to drive such modulators, thus limiting bandwidth considerably. It is important to note that crystal-based EO modulators have physically limited bandwidths at approximately 40 GHz. This is a material limitation primarily because of very high dielectric constant (ε ~29), which cannot be bypassed. In contrast, polymer-based EO modulators offer potential advantages of large bandwidths and low switching voltages. This is because NLO polymers have very low dielectric constants (ε ~2-6), which, given traveling wave modulator geometries, permit the electromagnetic waves at optical and microwave frequencies to propagate with nearly equal phase velocities. Moreover, NLO polymers offer the promise of exceptionally high EO coefficient (**r** >100 pm/V), which is a very important factor in reducing the switching voltage and is directly related to the change in the index of refraction (**Δn**) by the equation:

$$\Delta n = -\frac{n^3}{2} rE$$

where **n** is the optical index of refraction of the polymer.

Typically, the second-order NLO polymers are prepared by incorporating specifically designed dipolar donor-π-acceptor (**D**-π-**A**) chromophore molecules (also called NLO-phores) in a glassy polymer.[180] In such molecules, the donor and acceptor groups provide the requisite ground-state charge asymmetry, whereas the π-conjugation bridge offers a pathway for the ultra-fast redistribution of electric charges under an intense laser pulse. Figure 5.44 depicts various strategies (guest-host, side-chain, main-chain, crosslinked and self-assembled systems) to incorporate NLO-phores into a polymer matrix. It is important to emphasize that the molecular origin of optical nonlinearity is due to electrical polarization of a NLO-phore as it interacts with electromagnetic radiation. These interactions may change the frequency, phase, polarization, or path of the incident light. However, it is essential that the NLO-phores be organized in the polymer film in a non-centrosymmetric fashion (i.e., the polymer film must have a bulk anisotropy), because the centrosymmetry tends to cancel the individual molecular contribution to $\chi^{(2)}$, resulting in a zero bulk non-linearity. After thin film processing, all systems except the self-assembled systems, produce centrosymmetric films due to random molecular orientations of the NLO-phores. Thus, their alignment and retention in a noncentrosymmetric state for an indefinite period remain a major challenge in developing efficient second-order NLO polymers. According to the following equation, the second-order NLO susceptibility, $\chi^{(2)}$, may also be improved by increasing the number of NLO-phores in the polymeric matrix:

$$\chi^{(2)}_{333} = NF\beta_{zzz} \langle \cos^3\theta \rangle$$

where **N** is the number of NLO-phores, **F** is a dimensionless combined field factor of the electric and electromagnetic fields, β_{zzz} is a tensor element of molecular hyperpolarizability (also called *first hyperpolarizability*) along the dipole axis, and θ (often described as a measure of noncentrosymmetry) is the average orientation angle between the film normal and the dipole axes.

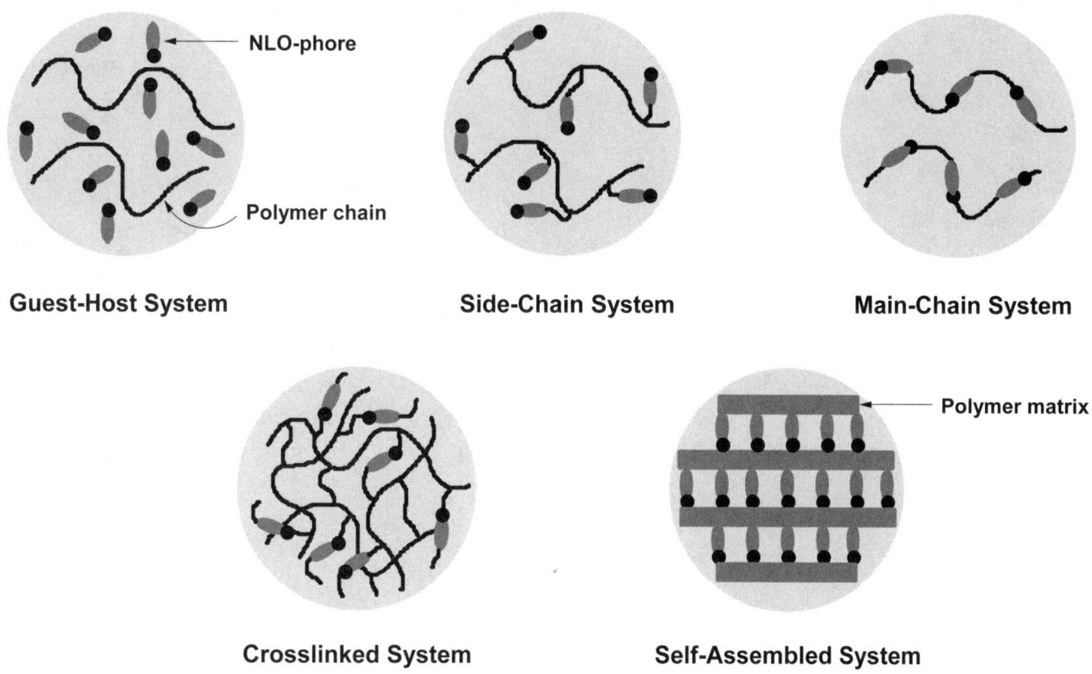

Figure 5.44. Schematics of important types of NLO polymers.

The most widely used technique to impart non-centrosymmetry in a polymer film is electric field poling, a technique by which an electric field (~hundreds of volts per micron thick film) is applied across the polymer film while the film is heated to near its glass transition temperature (T_g), as it sits on a grounded conductor. Generally, the EO coefficient increases linearly with poling field until a saturation condition is established. The degree of alignment is proportional to

$$\mu E / kT$$

where μ is the ground state dipole moment of the chromophore, **E** is the applied electric field, **k** is Boltzmann's constant, and T is the poling temperature. There are several problems with this technique. First, the polymer must be heated to high temperatures (usually, near T_g of the polymer) where thermal disordering of the chromophores works against the torque of the electric field and may damage the surface of the film, causing defects. Second, after the electric field is removed, the torque is gone and thermal vibration tends to destroy the molecular alignment, leading back to centrosymmetric (disordered) film. Consequently, the widespread applications of a second-order NLO polymer require synergistic improvement of the following primary aspects: large molecular hyperpolarizability and high concentrations of NLO-phores, effective dipolar alignment, and superior temporal stability. The use of high-T_g polymers, such as polyimides and polyquinolines, is considered to be effective in restraining the relaxation of the noncentrosymmetric NLO-phore alignment induced by the electric field. Figure 5.45 outlines representative examples of such polymers, which exhibit good optical nonlinearity and fair temporal stability of the poled films.[181-187]

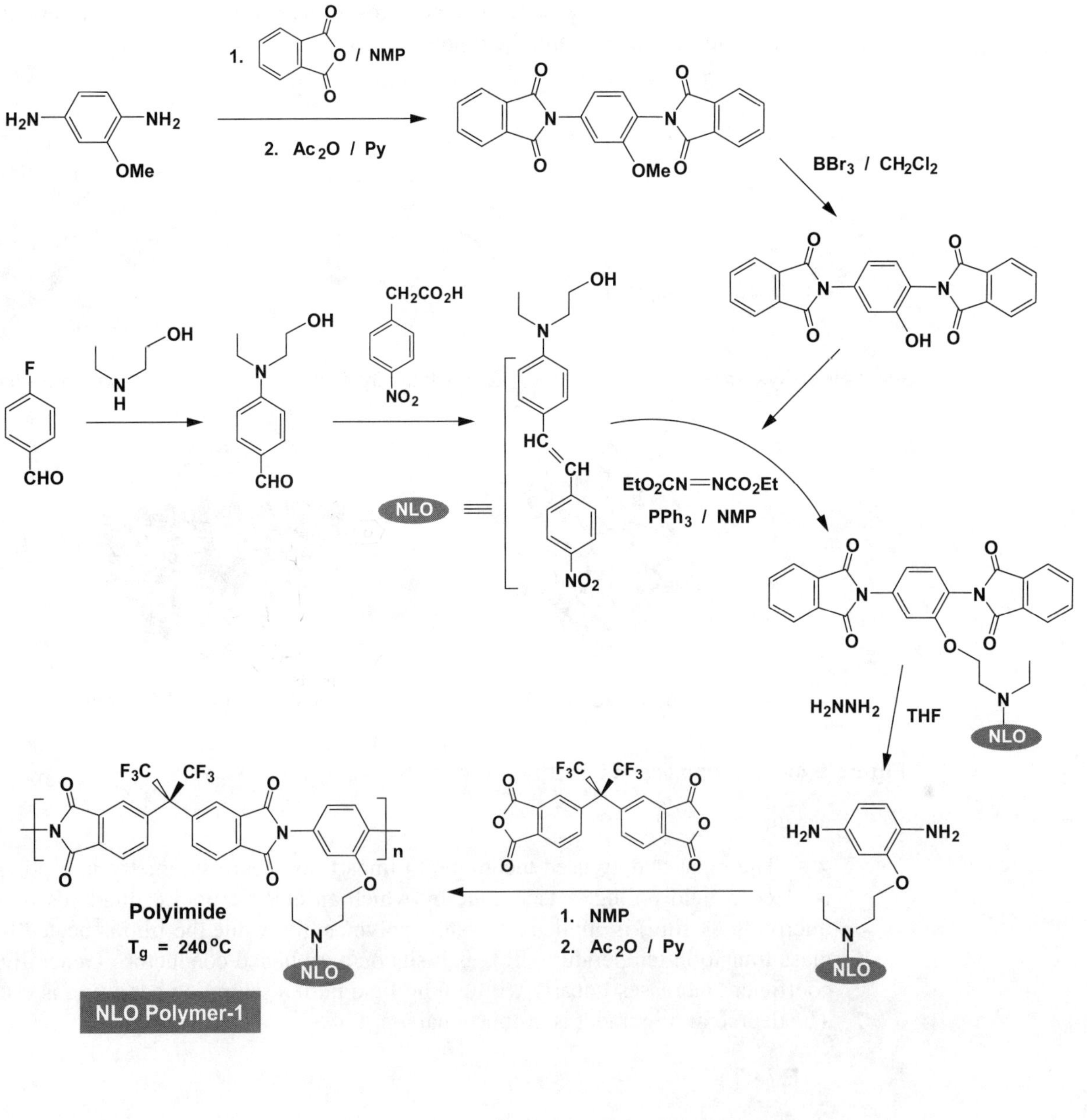

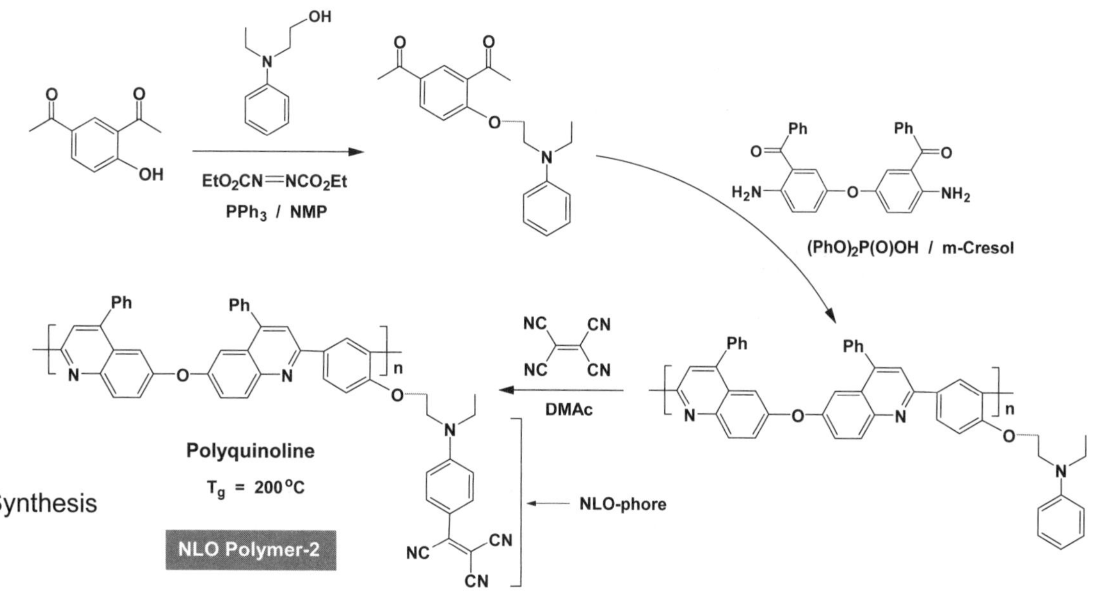

Figure 5.45. Synthesis of high T_g NLO polymers.

Another commonly employed method to circumvent this temporal stability problem is to covalently attach chromophores onto a polymer backbone and then harden the resulting material with a subsequent crosslinking reaction (Figure 5.46).[188-190] A variety of crosslinking approaches have been adopted to vitrify the aligned NLO-phores. The most common methods include (i) addition of a diisocyanate compound to an NLO polymer containing pendent hydroxyl groups to yield urethane linkages,[191] (ii) self thermal reaction of pendent benzocyclobutenone (BCBO) moieties via a reactive vinylketene intermediate, which undergoes intermolecular [4+2] cycloaddition, followed by a 1,5-hydrogen shift in the dimer[192,193] and (iii) thermal [2+2] cyclodimerization of trifluorovinyl ether (TFVE)-substituted arenes to form fluorinated cyclobutyl rings.[194,195] The crosslinked systems offer better results by maintaining some reasonable polar order for some years, but relaxation of poled alignment cannot be completely halted.

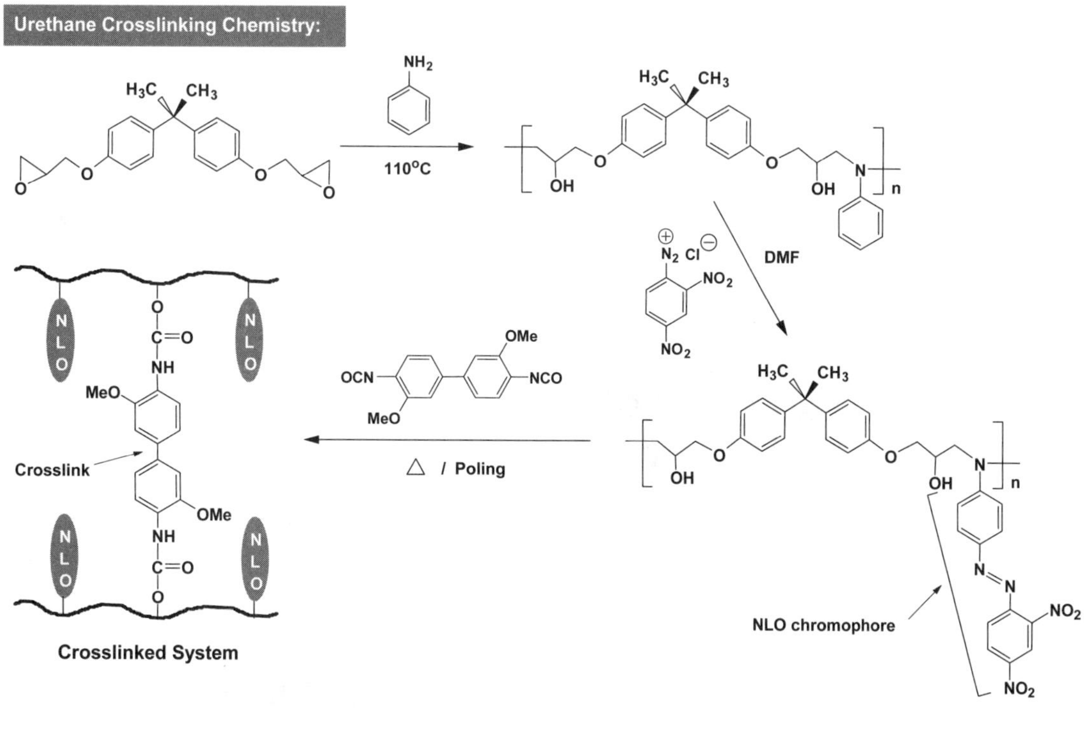

BCBO Crosslinking Chemistry:

150-200°C

TFVE Crosslinking Chemistry:

150-200°C

Figure 5.46. Synthesis of a crosslinked system, including other crosslink chemistry used to develop second-order NLO polymers.

Therefore, what is needed is a technique to "freeze" the molecular orientation of the NLO chromophores (Figure 5.47). Self-assembled films seem to be a viable solution because, unlike poled polymers, they tend to have an intrinsic molecular dipolar alignment that does not decay with time, thereby eliminating the need for electric field poling.[196] However, this protocol poses a major synthetic challenge to construct noncentrosymmetric molecular systems containing efficient NLO-phores in desired concentrations.

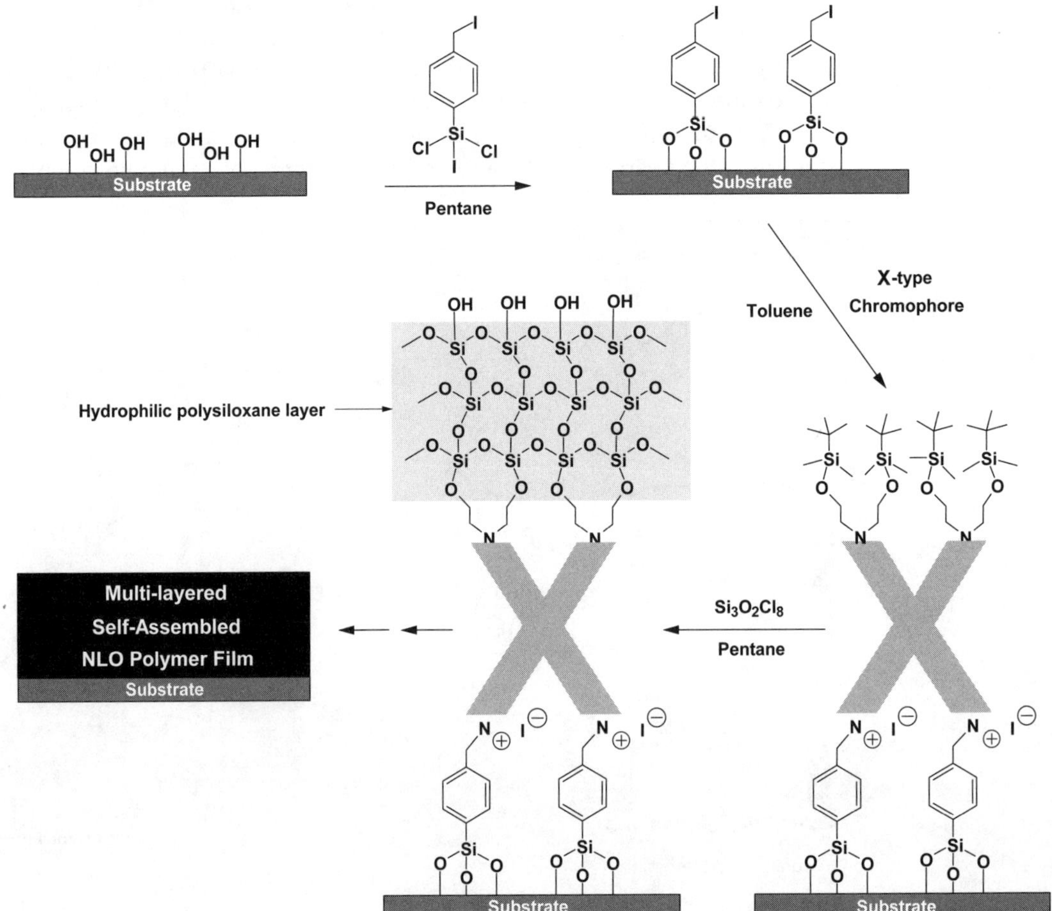

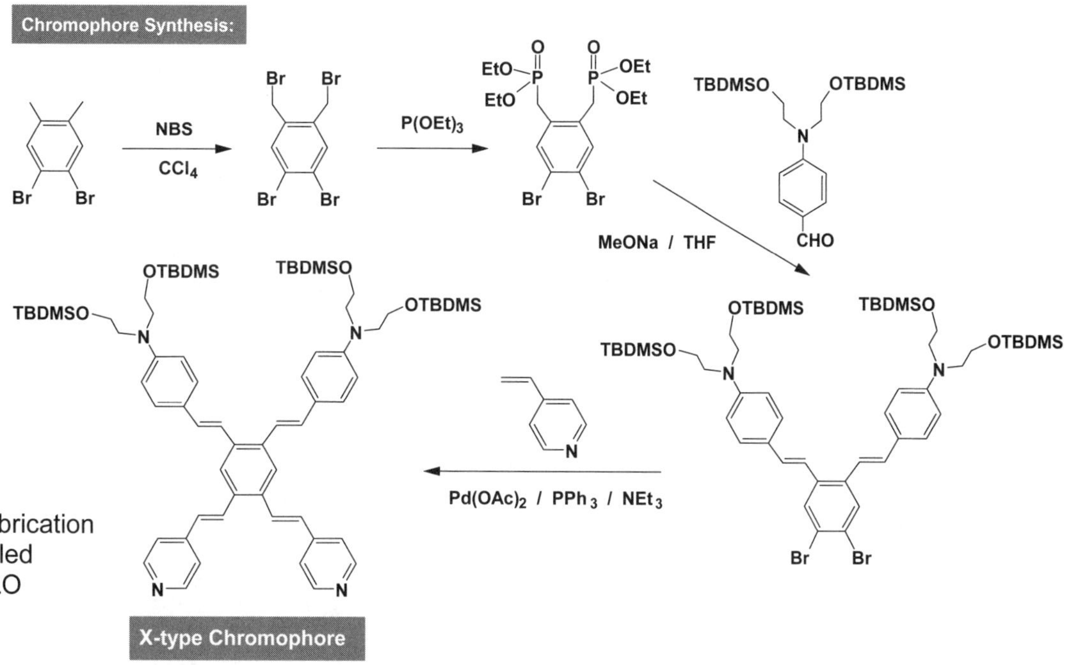

Chromophore Synthesis:

NBS / CCl_4 → P(OEt)$_3$ → MeONa / THF → Pd(OAc)$_2$ / PPh$_3$ / NEt$_3$

X-type Chromophore

Figure 5.47. Fabrication of a self-assembled second-order NLO polymer film.

The synthesis of NLO-phores with very high β, along with thermal stability, transparency and processability, is another important challenge in realizing practical second-order NLO polymers. As mentioned earlier, an NLO-phore consists of three segments: electron donor, π-bridge, and acceptor. Most studies used substituted anilines as the donor system because of its stability and good electron-donating ability. The acceptor portion of the molecule originally studied contained a nitrophenyl ring, but was soon replaced by a variety of structures with better electron-withdrawing ability and overall stability, such as tricyanovinyldihydrofuran. Efficient π-bridge systems include open-chain and ring-locked polyenes and various heterocyclic moieties. In general, the heterocyclic or aromatic systems exhibit superior thermal and photochemical stability, while the polyene systems display exceptionally higher β (Table 5.1).[197-208]

Table 5.1. Structure-property Relationships of NLO-phores[a]

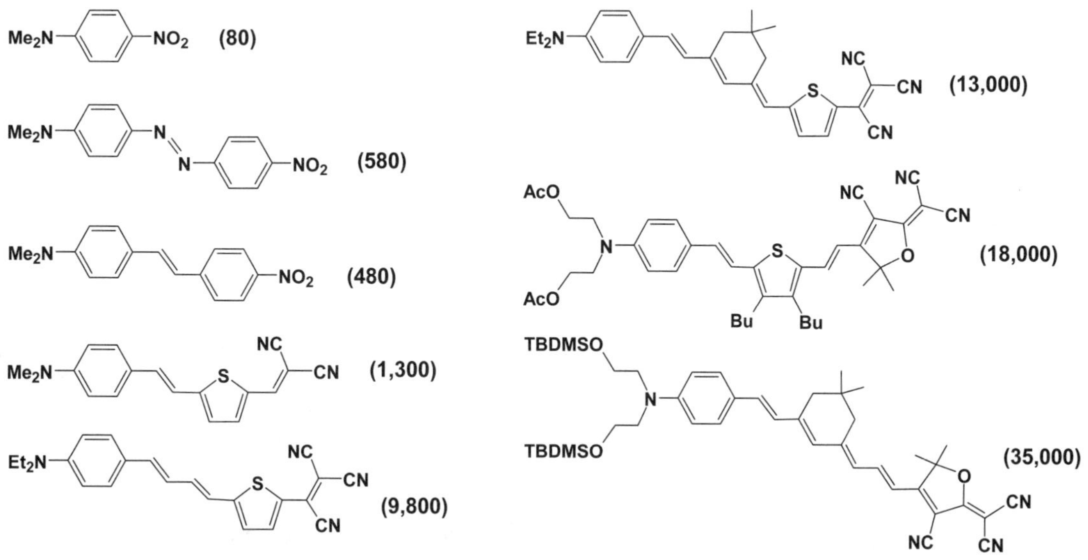

(80) (580) (480) (1,300) (9,800) (13,000) (18,000) (35,000)

[a]Numbers in parentheses indicate their μβ values (@1.9 mm, x 10^{-48} esu).

Indeed, a guest-host type poled polymer film was recently prepared by mixing a high concentration (45 wt.%) of a suitable polyene-based chromophore with PMMA to achieve an EO coefficient in excess of 250 pm/V at the measuring wavelength of 1.31 μm (Figure 5.48).[209] However, besides the relatively lower thermal stability compared to that of aromatic π-bridge systems, another common problem associated with polyenes is the formation of centrosymmetric aggregates when used in high concentrations. This issue may be eliminated by introducing bulky substituents (linked through the donor, acceptor and/or π-bridge segments), which not only reduce dipole-dipole interactions between chromophores, but also improve chromophore solubility.

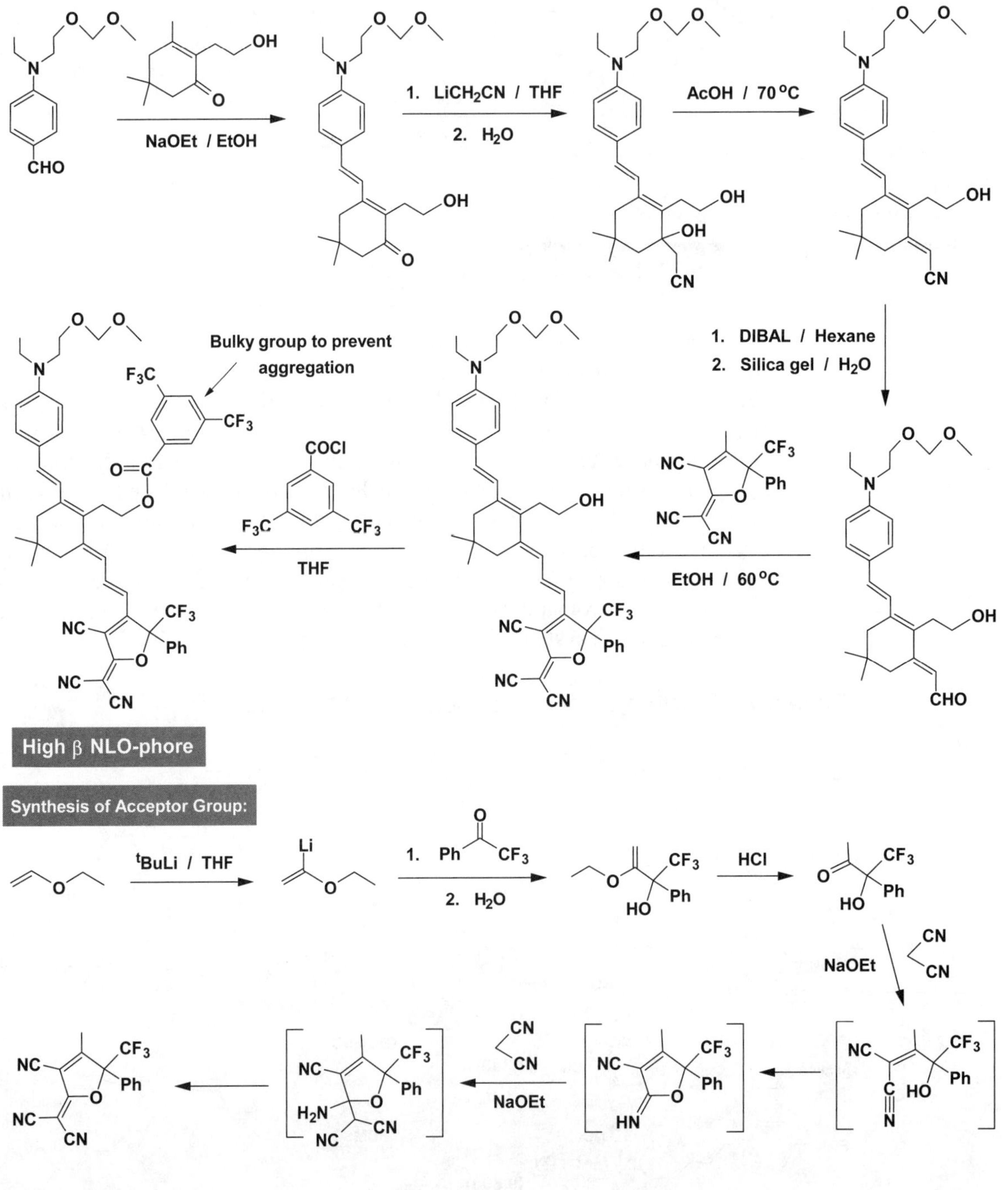

Figure 5.48. Synthesis of a highly effective polyene-based NLO-phore.

Despite the significant advances that have been made in understanding the chemical basis for second-order NLO effects, the same level of success has not been achieved for *third-order NLO effects*, even though, unlike second-order NLO polymers, they do not require bulk non-centrosymmetry, but are heavily dependent on the effective π-conjugation length of the polymer. Consequently, fully π-conjugated polymers have been the subject of extensive investigation for third-order NLO studies. However, the number of nuclei over which the π-orbital electrons are delocalized is limited in these polymers due to bond length alternation. The most promising and well-studied third-order NLO polymers are *trans*-polyacetylene (PAC) and poly(diacetylene *para*-toluenesulfonate) (PDAC-PTS) (Figure 5.49).[210,211] PAC exhibits one of the highest measured $\chi^{(3)}$ values (which depends on the second hyperpolarizability, γ) for third-order NLO polymers, but is air-sensitive and insoluble (*vide supra*). By contrast, PDAC-PTS is thermally stable to ~180°C and is less prone to optically induced thermal effects. In addition to a fast response time (10^{-14} s), a high NLO response, and a high damage threshold (50 Gw/cm^2), PDAC-PTS can be processed into waveguide structures for device applications and is one of the very few polymers that have been shown to meet the standard figure of merit for optical switching devices. Very recently, low molecular weight polymethines (PMEs), in which the C-C bonds along the polyene backbone exhibit essentially equivalent lengths, have attracted much attention because of their very high $\chi^{(3)}$ values, which can be optimized through the correct combination of donor and acceptor substitution.[212] It is generally accepted that the magnitude of $\chi^{(3)}$ in third-order NLO polymers should be improved to near 10^{-8} esu for practical applications involving all-optical computing and signal processing. In particular, an increase in the rate of telecommunication by at least 3 orders of magnitude is expected. Moreover, the availability of high-frequency laser beams produced by *third harmonic generation* (THG) processes will lead to tremendous progress in atomic and molecular physics and chemistry.

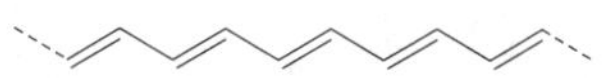

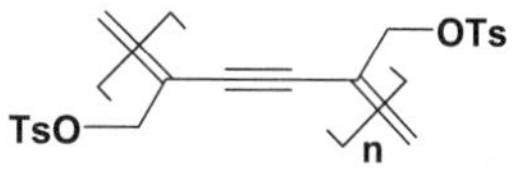

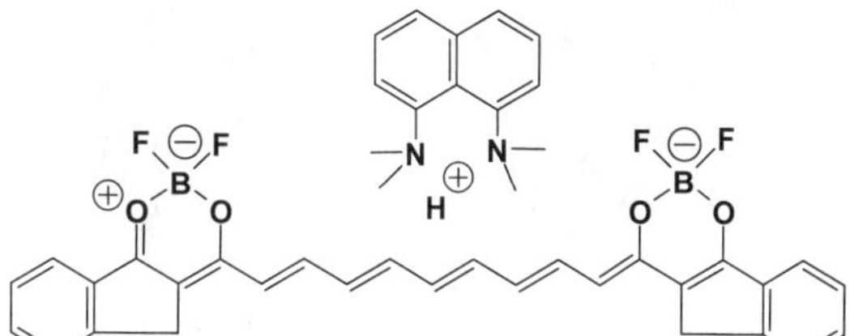

Figure 5.49. Structures of effective third-order NLO polymers.

5.4. LIQUID CRYSTALLINE POLYMERS

The liquid crystal phase is a thermodynamically stable state of matter and possesses properties of both the crystalline solid state (i.e., exhibits three-dimensional order) and the isotropic (disordered) liquid state. Formation of liquid crystalline (LC) states by low molar mass compounds has been known since Reinitzer's discovery in 1888 that cholesteryl benzoate melted on heating to form a turbid fluid which then appeared to melt again into a transparent phase at higher temperatures.[213] The LC states in synthetic polymers were first recorded by Elliot and Ambrose in 1950 for poly(γ-benzyl-L-glutamate) in chloroform solution.[214] However, scientific and industrial interest in *liquid crystalline polymers* (LCPs) was not spawned until the discovery of LC states of aramids, such as poly(*p*-phenylene terephthalamide) (Kevlar®) and poly(benzamide), in sulfuric acid solution by DuPont in the 1970s. More recent (1984) commercialization of aromatic co-polyesters (e.g., Xydar® and Vectra®) that form LC states in melt, sparked unabated growth in the field of LCPs. *Note: In industry, the word LCPs is used primarily to define liquid crystalline polyesters discussed in Section 4.4 of Chapter-4. In this section, for clarity, we will use the word LCPs to refer to any liquid crystalline polymers.* Considerable attention to the study of structure-property-application relationships in LCP/polymer blends due to the addition of relatively small amounts of thermotropic LCPs into commercial thermoplastics, has been shown to improve processing by marked reduction of the melt viscosity, including superior mechanical properties of the finished products.

There are four types of liquid crystalline phases: *nematic*, *cholesteric* (also called chiral nematic), *smectic*, and *discotic* (Figure 5.50). Nematic describes a liquid crystalline phase with only one-dimensional long range ordering; it possesses long-range orientational order (molecular alignment) but only short-range positional order (spatial ordering). A cholesteric is very similar to a nematic, but it is periodically twisted along the axis perpendicular to the long-range order axis. A smectic phase characterizes two-dimensional order (smectic A: the molecular orientation is perpendicular to the layers; smectic C: tilted). A discotic phase can occur when disc-like liquid crystalline molecules align in columns (discotic nematic: molecules possess some orientational order, but no positional order; discotic columnar: local columnar stacking with nematic arrangement of the columns).

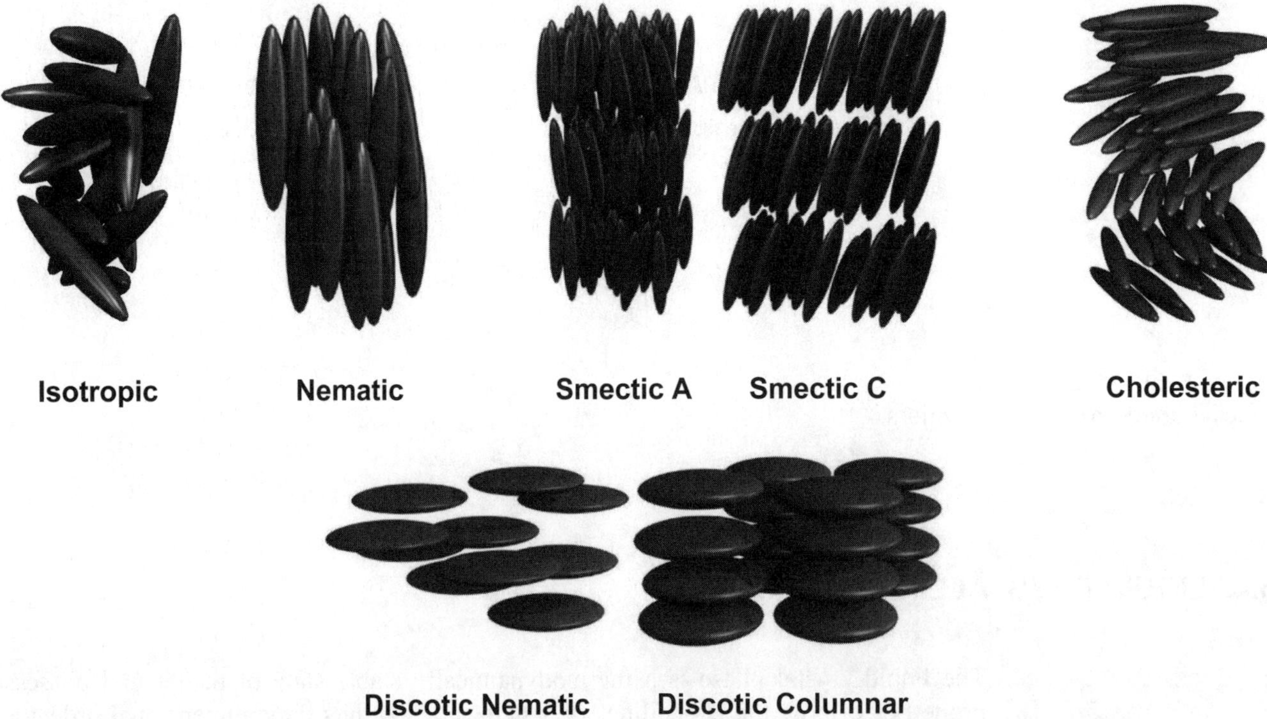

Figure 5.50. Schematics of isotropic and LC phases. *Courtesy: Professor Christopher J. Barrett and Dr. Kevin G. Yager, McGill University, Montreal, Canada.*

In polymeric systems, LC order originates from nonflexible repeat units, called mesogenic units, which can have either a rod, disc, or lathe-like structure. While the earlier work was carried out on small molecule mesogens, it was found that these could be incorporated into polymeric structures with retention of the LC phase. Consequently, a variety of LCPs with structures ranging from rigid main chain, flexible spacer main chain, side chain to discotic have been developed. As cited above, LC order can exist in either solution or melts. LC transition in solution is a function of concentration and temperature and is referred to as *lyotropic* systems. Since concentration is fixed, melts are only temperature sensitive and are referred to as *thermotropics*. The LC phase in thermotropic systems exists between the crystalline melting point, T_m (or in the case where no crystalline state exists, the glass transition temperature, T_g), and the upper transition temperature where the fluid reverts to an isotropic liquid, $T_{LC \rightarrow i}$. *Amphotropic* LCPs, which represent a less well-known class, are those which exhibit an LC phase in both the melt and in solution.[215-217] Among these, the thermotropic LCPs are the most studied class. Polarized light microscopy is the simplest method for the characterization of thermotropic LCPs, because the appearance of a particular "texture" of the melt is usually dependent on the structure of the mesophase (Figure 5.51). However, it should be emphasized that these LCPs can take minutes or hours to show recognizable textures because of higher melt viscosity compared to that of low molar mass LC compounds.[218] In general, threaded *Schlieren* (German: schliere ~ streak) texture is typical for nematic and discotic, with focal-conic or fan-shaped texture for smectic, and "oily streaks" or parallel disclinations for cholesteric LCPs.

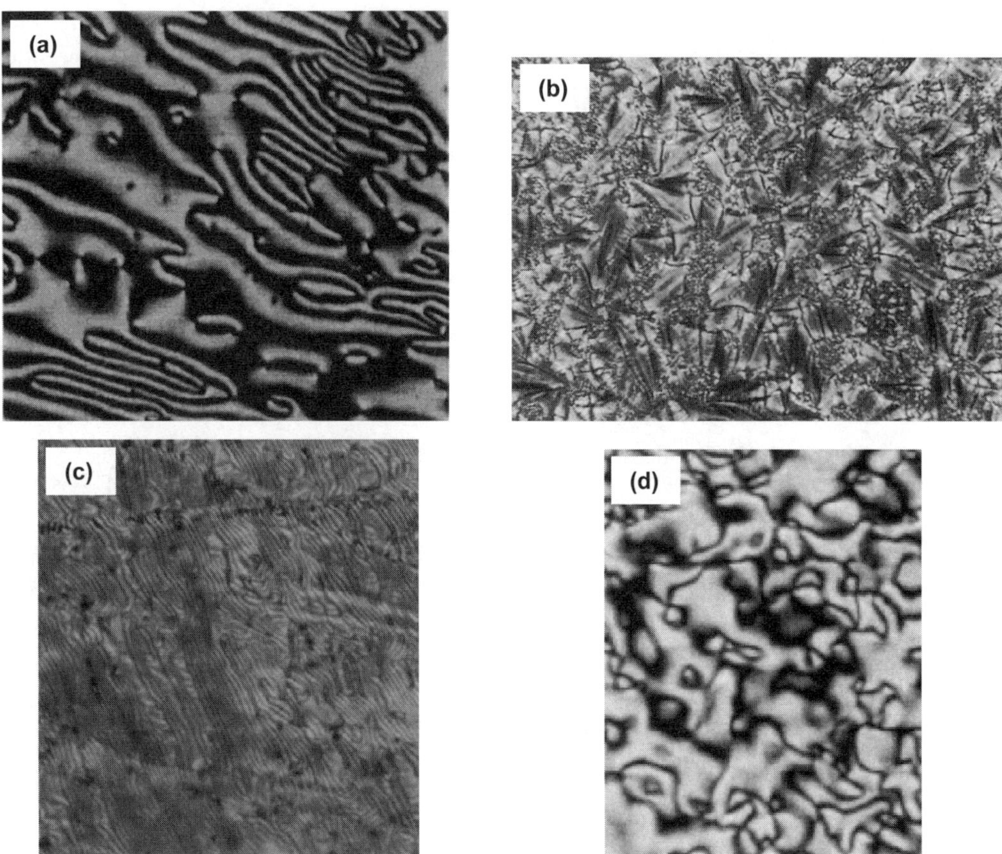

Figure 5.51. Representative optical microscopic pictures of (a) nematic[219], (b) smectic[220] (c) cholesteric[221] and (d) discotic[222] LCPs. *Reproduced with kind permission of the American Chemical Society (a and d) and Springer-Science and Business Media (b and c).*

Other commonly used techniques for the characterization of thermotropic LCPs include differential scanning calorimetry and wide angle X-ray diffraction (WAXD). The former provides all the transition (melting, isotropization and crystallization) temperatures, including a measure of the heats and entropies of each transition. The latter is more accurate for confirmation of the LC state because optical microscopy cannot always be relied upon to produce an unambiguous determination of the type of mesophase present. In WAXD, nematic structures show a diffuse ring diffraction pattern at 4-5 Å, which arises from the interchain spacings. By contrast, smectic structures produce both diffuse rings at 4-5 Å and sharp rings at a distance generally, but not necessarily, equal to the repeat length of the monomer unit.

From a synthetic standpoint, LCPs can be classified into two major groups, the so-called main-chain and side-chain types, depending on whether the mesogenic units are in the main or side chain, respectively. Kevlar®, Xydar® and Vectra®, which do not contain any aliphatic flexible segments, are examples of main-chain LCPs (see Chapter-4 for their syntheses). It should be noted that LC phases can also be observed in main-chain polymers containing aliphatic flexible segments. *Polybibenzoates* (PBBs), which display high tensile strength and improved toughness and are suitable for injection molding, represent another important class of main-chain LCPs (Figure 5.52).[223-225] In contrast, the mesogenic groups in side-chain LCPs must be connected to an aliphatic flexible segment. In these polymers, the flexible polymer backbone has a strong tendency to adopt a random, coiled conformation, while arrangement of the mesogenic units can result in an LC phase. When the mesogenic units are pendent to the polymer backbone directly (i.e., no flexible spacer) the dynamics of the backbone usually dominate the tendency for the mesogenic groups to orient anisotropically. Consequently, mesomorphic behavior is not observed for side-chain polymers in which the mesogens are not separated by aliphatic flexible segments. Side-chain LCPs have considerable potential, much of which is yet to be realized, in areas such as instance flexible displays, sensors, optical information storage and nonlinear optics, where the properties of facile alignment and the ability to scatter light from the fine textures formed are particularly useful.

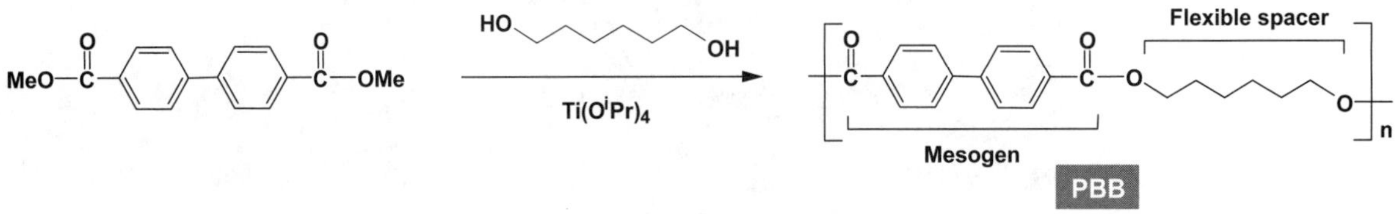

Figure 5.52. Synthesis of a representative main-chain LCP.

Side-chain LCPs have been prepared via a number of approaches.[226-233] The most common routes involve either free-radical polymerization of an acrylate monomer or by grafting a vinyl terminated monomer onto a polysiloxane (Figure 5.53). Both methods allow opportunities to incorporate a variety of mesogens, including disc-shaped mesogens, such as multi-substituted benzenes[234-236] and hexa(alkoxy)triphenylenes[237,238], and metal-containing mesogens[239,240], such as ferrocene. Depending on the structure and shape of mesogen, a side-chain LCP can exhibit a variety of mesomorphic characteristics. For example, the acrylate polymer bearing the pentakis(methylphenylethynyl)benzene mesogen with a flexible undecanoxy spacer exhibits a discotic columnar phase at lower temperatures and a discotic nematic phase at higher temperatures. This type of polymer is especially attractive as compensation layers in LCD technology and for one-dimensional electronic conduction. Metal-containing LCPs have also shown significant interest because of their unique magnetic, optical and electronic properties (the example shown below displays smectic C phase at lower temperatures and a smectic A phase at higher temperatures).

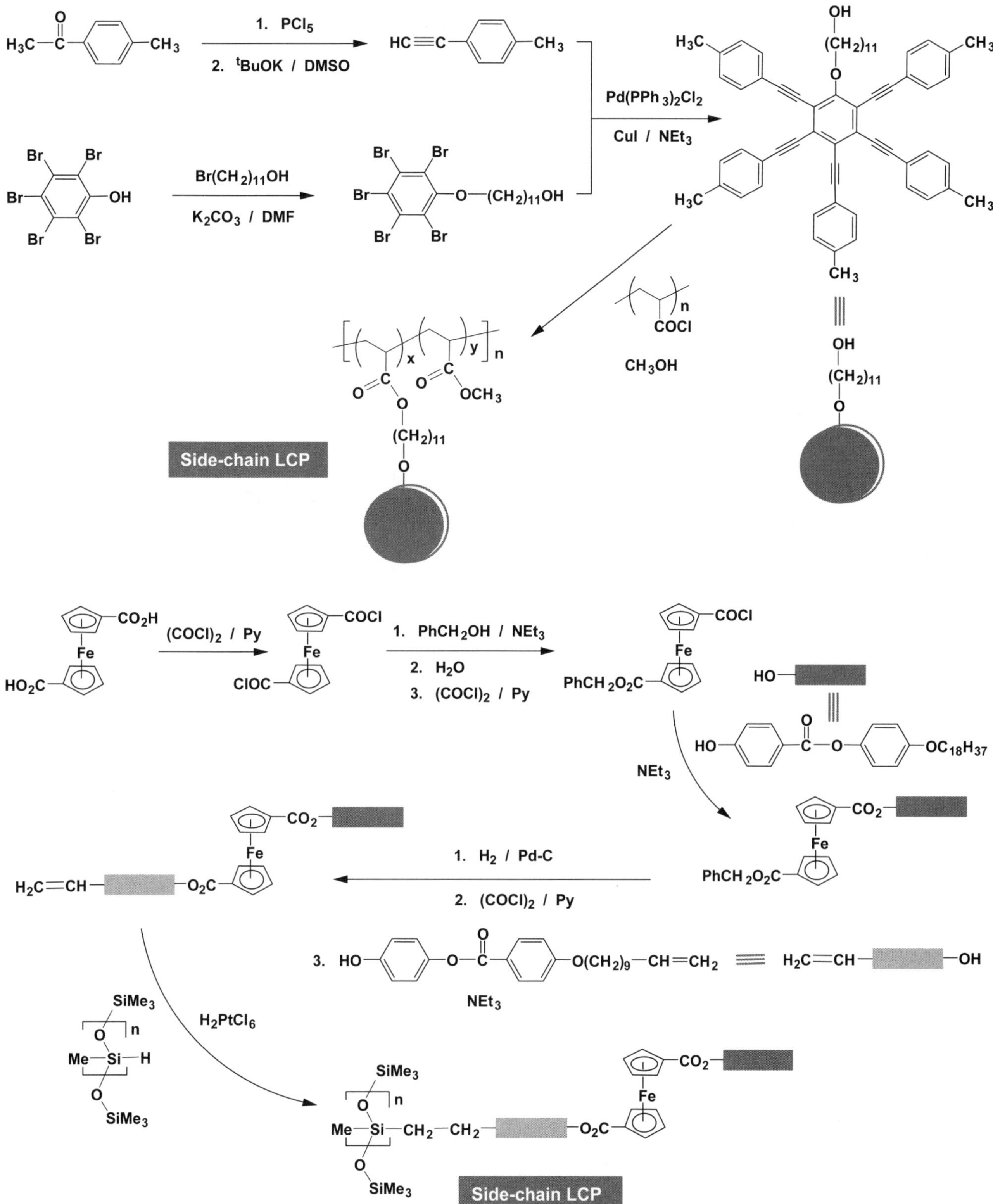

Figure 5.53. Common synthetic routes to side-chain LCPs.

Acyclic diene methathesis (ADMET) polymerization of vinyl terminated monomers with built-in mesogenic units is another approach for the synthesis of both main-chain and side-chain LCPs (Figure 5.54).[241,242] The advantage of this approach lies in the fact that reasonably high molecular weight polymers can be prepared at a low temperature under very mild conditions. Therefore, it can be envisaged that one may be able to synthesize LCPs containing functional groups that do not interfere with the metathesis catalyst activity. Moreover, since these LCPs contain double bonds along their backbones they are crosslinkable or vulcanizable.

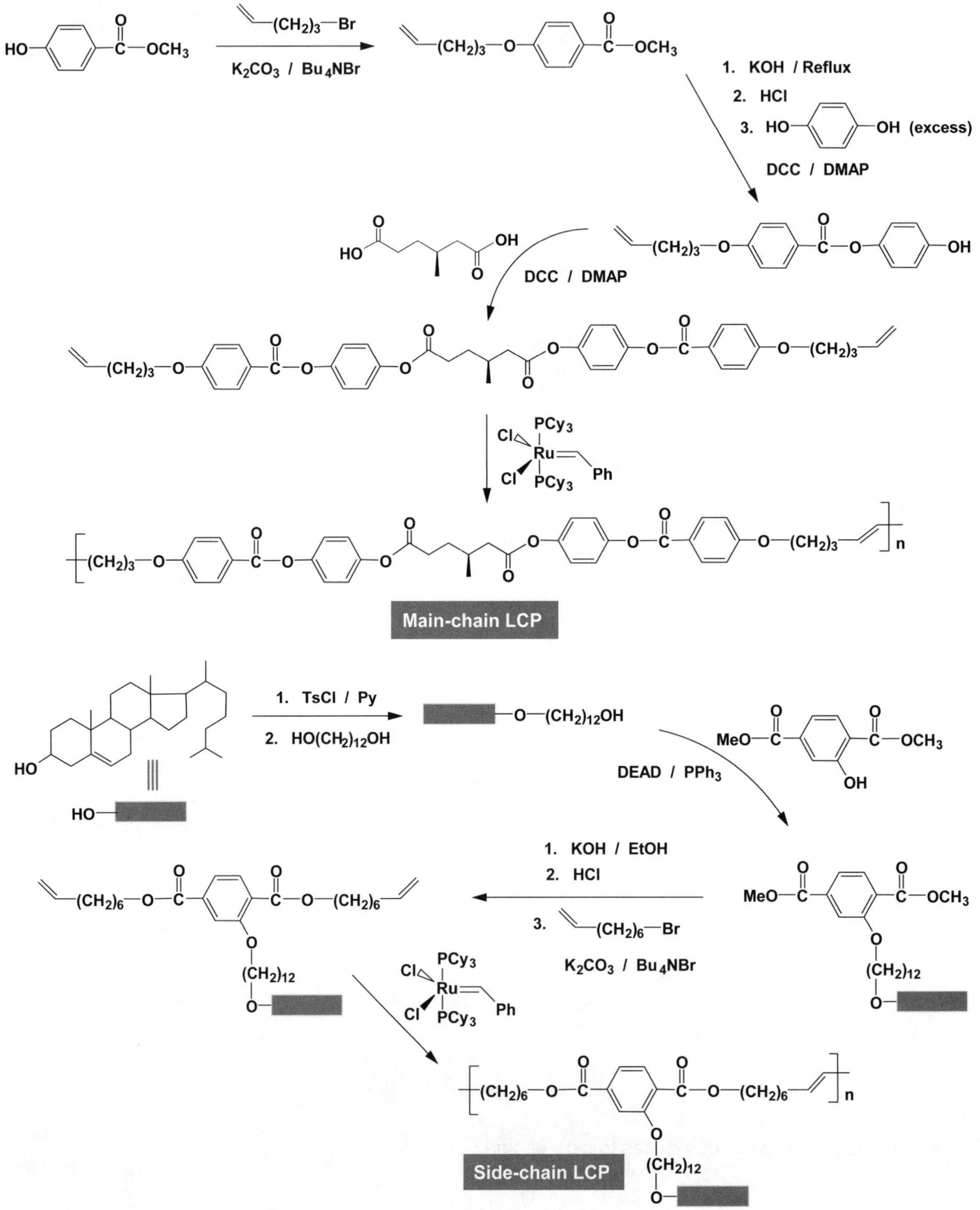

Figure 5.54. Synthesis of LCPs via ADMET polymerization.

5.5. INORGANIC POLYMERS

Polymers whose main molecular backbone contain no carbon atoms (composed solely of elements such as phosphorus, nitrogen, silicon, and transition metals) or possess few carbon atoms, along with these elements, are classified as *inorganic polymers*. Polysiloxanes or silicones in which the backbone is comprised of alternating silicon and oxygen atoms, represent the most well-developed class of inorganic polymers. Introduced commercially in 1943, polysiloxanes exhibit a number of useful properties, such as flexibility, permeability to gases, very low glass transition temperature, and low surface energy, which make them very attractive for general-purpose applications (see Chapter-2 for synthesis and elaborate discussion). In the past two decades, there has been a growing interest in the synthesis of other inorganic polymers, due to a strong demand for materials with properties that are difficult or impossible to achieve with conventional organic polymers. This section will focus only on the most promising examples, viz., polyphosphazenes, polysilanes, polycarbosilanes and polycarboranes.

5.5.1. Polyphosphazenes

Polyphosphazenes are the most important class of inorganic polymers since the commercialization of the silicones. While the polymer backbone of polyphosphazenes is composed of alternating phosphorus and nitrogen atoms, the two side groups, linked to each phosphorus atom, can be organic, inorganic, or organometallic. They are conveniently prepared by a route, developed by Allcock and co-workers, which involves ring-opening polymerization of hexachlorocyclotriphosphazene, HCPH, followed by macromolecular substitution of chlorine atoms of the resulting poly(dichlorophosphazene), PDCP, with a desired nucleophile or a combination of nucleophiles (Figure 5.55).[243-249] Unlike the parent polymer, PDCP, which is unstable in air or moisture due to high reactivity of phosphorus-chlorine bonds, the polyphosphazenes are oxidatively, thermally and hydrolytically stable and exhibit a range of attractive properties originating from the backbone and/or side groups. For example, polyphosphazenes have unusual backbone flexibility (T_g = -105°C when the side groups are *n*-butoxy, -85°C for ethoxy), which arises from the torsional and angular freedom of the phosphorus-nitrogen skeletal system. The conjugated double bonds in polyphosphazenes are made up of dπ-pπ bonds which, unlike carbon-carbon double bonds, do not impose severe conformational restrictions on the polymer backbone, since any one of the five phosphorous 3d orbitals can π bond to the nitrogen p-orbitals. In other words, the torsional freedom of the backbone bonds results from continuous orbital overlap switching of the π-orbital on each nitrogen from one phosphorus d-orbital to another. Moreover, wide bond angles at nitrogen, the presence of side groups on every other skeletal atom, and the strong tendency to form a *cis-trans*-planar conformation leading to the arrangement that places the side groups as far away as possible from each other, contribute towards unusual backbone flexibility.

Another unique feature of polyphosphazene chemistry is the ability to fine tune the properties of the polymers, spanning from fire resistant elastomers to biocompatible polymers, by judicious selection of appropriate side groups. For example, poly[bis(methoxyethoxyethoxy)phosphazene], MEEP, which has a T_g near -85°C, is an excellent host polymer for lithium ion conducting polymer electrolytes. By contrast, when the side groups are introduced by sequential or simultaneous reactions of PDCP with two different types of fluoroalkoxides, the resulting polyphosphazene becomes a commercially important elastomer, better known as *phosphonitrilic fluoroelastomer*

(PNF), exhibiting useful properties, such as low T_g (-60°C), nonflammability, and resistance to hydrocarbon solvents, oils, and hydraulic fluids. Besides alkoxides, PDCP reacts with aryloxide or aliphatic and aromatic amines to produce useful polyphosphazenes, such as poly[bis(phenyloxy)phosphazene], PHP, and poly[bis(phenylamino)phosphazene], PAP (Figure 5.55). These derivatives usually exhibit high T_gs because of bulky side groups and/or inter- and intramolecular hydrogen bonding. Consequently, PHP is a microcrystalline thermoplastic material, whereas PAP is a glassy thermoplastic.

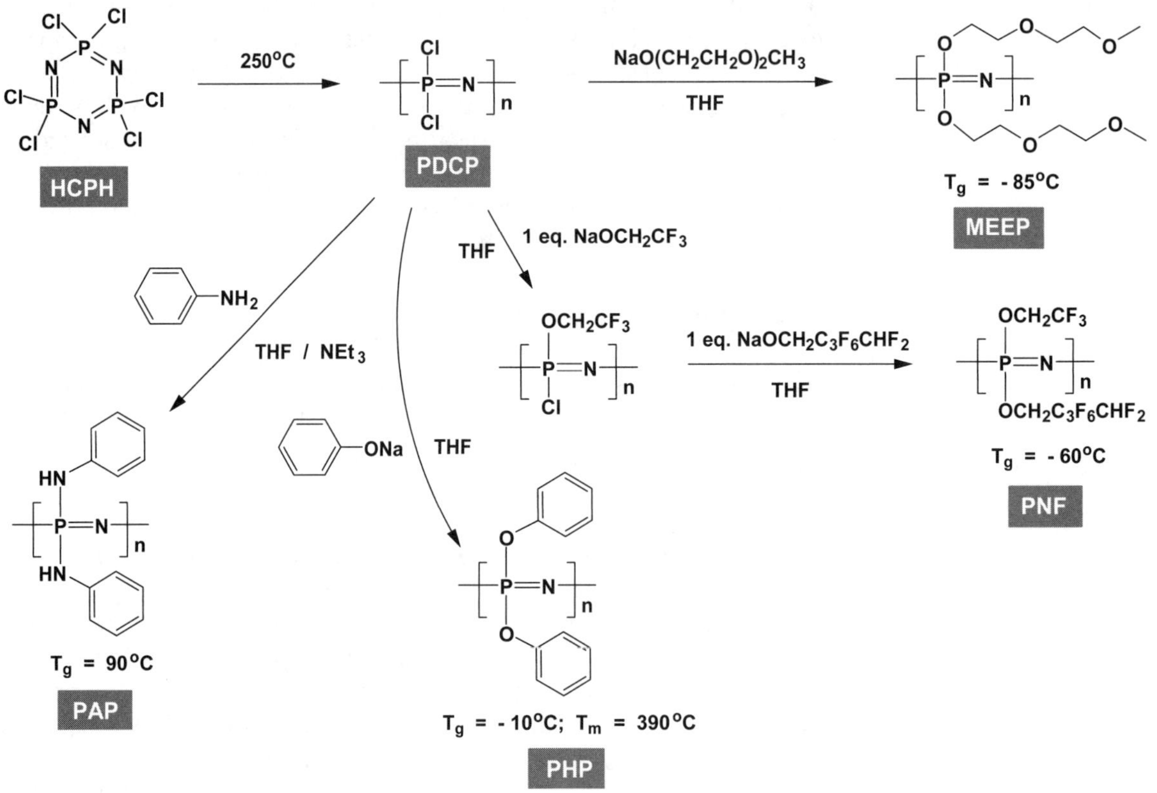

HCPH; 250°C; PDCP; $NaO(CH_2CH_2O)_2CH_3$; THF; T_g = - 85°C; MEEP; THF; 1 eq. $NaOCH_2CF_3$; OCH_2CF_3; 1 eq. $NaOCH_2C_3F_6CHF_2$; THF; $OCH_2C_3F_6CHF_2$; T_g = - 60°C; PNF; NH_2; THF / NEt_3; ONa; THF; T_g = 90°C; PAP; T_g = - 10°C; T_m = 390°C; PHP

Figure 5.55. The most common synthetic route to polyphosphazenes.

Polyphosphazenes containing side group functionalities have also been extensively studied. They can be synthesized by proper selection of nucleophiles or by post-functionalization of aryloxy substituted polyphosphazenes (Figure 5.56). For example, a very promising class of biodegradable polyphosphazenes, poly[bis(ethyl alanato)phosphazene] (ALP) and poly[(ethyl alanato)$_1$ (ethyl glycinato)$_1$ phosphazene] (AGP), are obtained by reaction of PDCP with amino acid esters.[250-253] They have potential for a variety of applications, such as controlled drug delivery matrices, tissue-engineering scaffolds, membranes, and bone-type composites. In these polymers, the types and ratios of co-substituents affect properties, such as molecular weight, T_g, and hydrophobicity, which in turn, influence degradation rate and tensile strength. For instance, a combination of alanine ethyl ester units with glycine ethyl ester side units leads to a drastic increase in the hydrolysis rate and also increases surface hydrophilicity.

Sulfonated polyphosphazenes (SP-1 and SP-2) are also under consideration as a low cost substitute for Nafion® in the area of proton-exchange membranes for fuel cells.[254-256] Two general approaches are available for the synthesis of polyphosphazenes with sulfonated aryloxy side groups (Figure 5.56).[257] The first involves the preparation of phosphazenes with unsubstituted aryloxy (or arylamino) side groups, followed by sulfonation. The alternative is the direct use of aryl oxide, alkoxide, or arylamine already bearing a terminal sulfonic acid or sulfonate group.

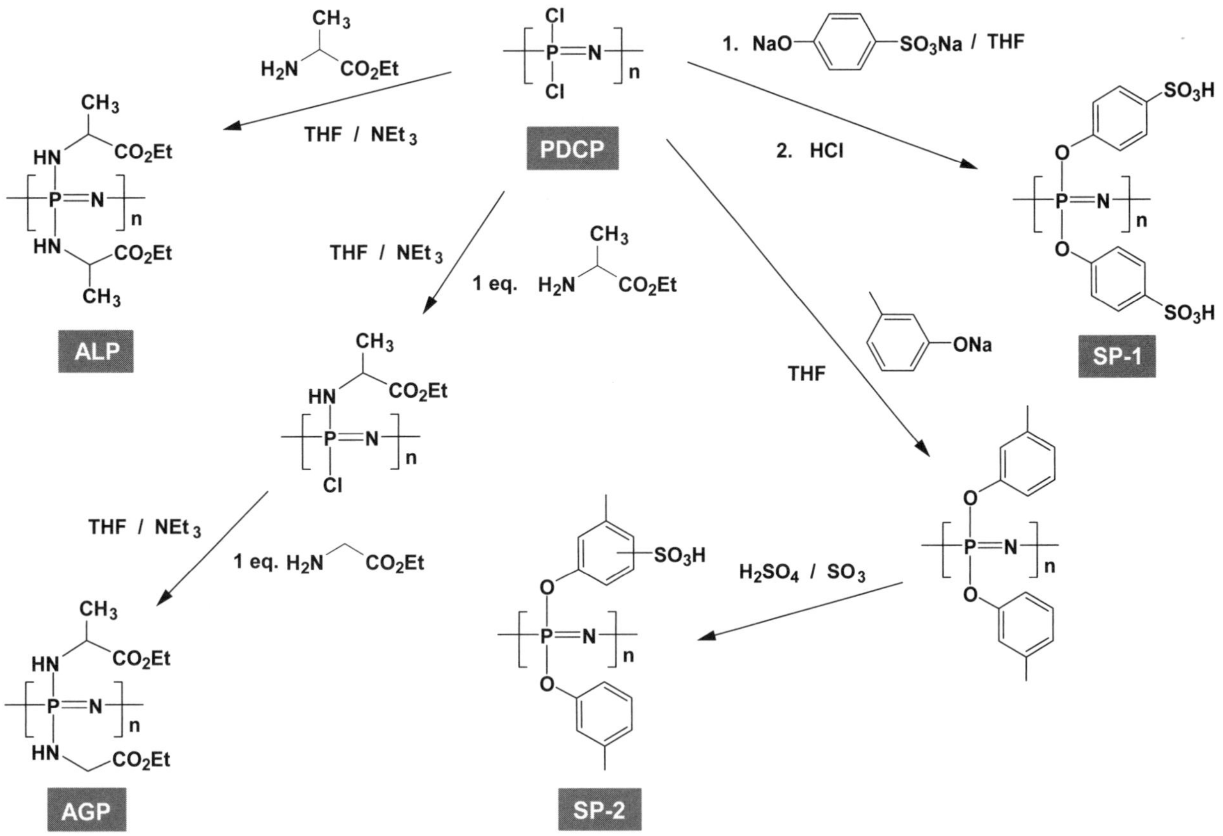

Figure 5.56. Synthesis of functionalized polyphosphazenes.

Polyphosphazenes with P-C bonded alkyl or aryl side groups are also an important class of materials. They cannot be prepared by reaction of organometallic reagents (e.g., RMgX or RLi) with PDCP, which results instead in either incomplete substitution under mild conditions or undesired reactions, such as chain cleavage and/or cross-linking under more vigorous condition. As outlined in Figure 5.57, the P-C analogs (DMP, CPP and FPP) are best prepared by thermal self-condensation polymerization of N-silylphosphoranimine monomers (e.g., SPM and SPP) containing the desired side groups and two leaving groups (trimethylsilyl and trifluoroethoxy).[258-260] These monomers are readily synthesized from either PCl_3 or $PhPCl_2$ in a straightforward, three-step sequence. Similar to the PDCP route, the post-functionalization of P-C bonded polyphosphazenes has also been performed to prepare interesting derivatives. For example, polyphosphazenes bearing carboxylic, alcohol or ester groups can be obtained by deprotonation of methyl groups with ^{n}BuLi followed by treatment with a desired nucleophile.

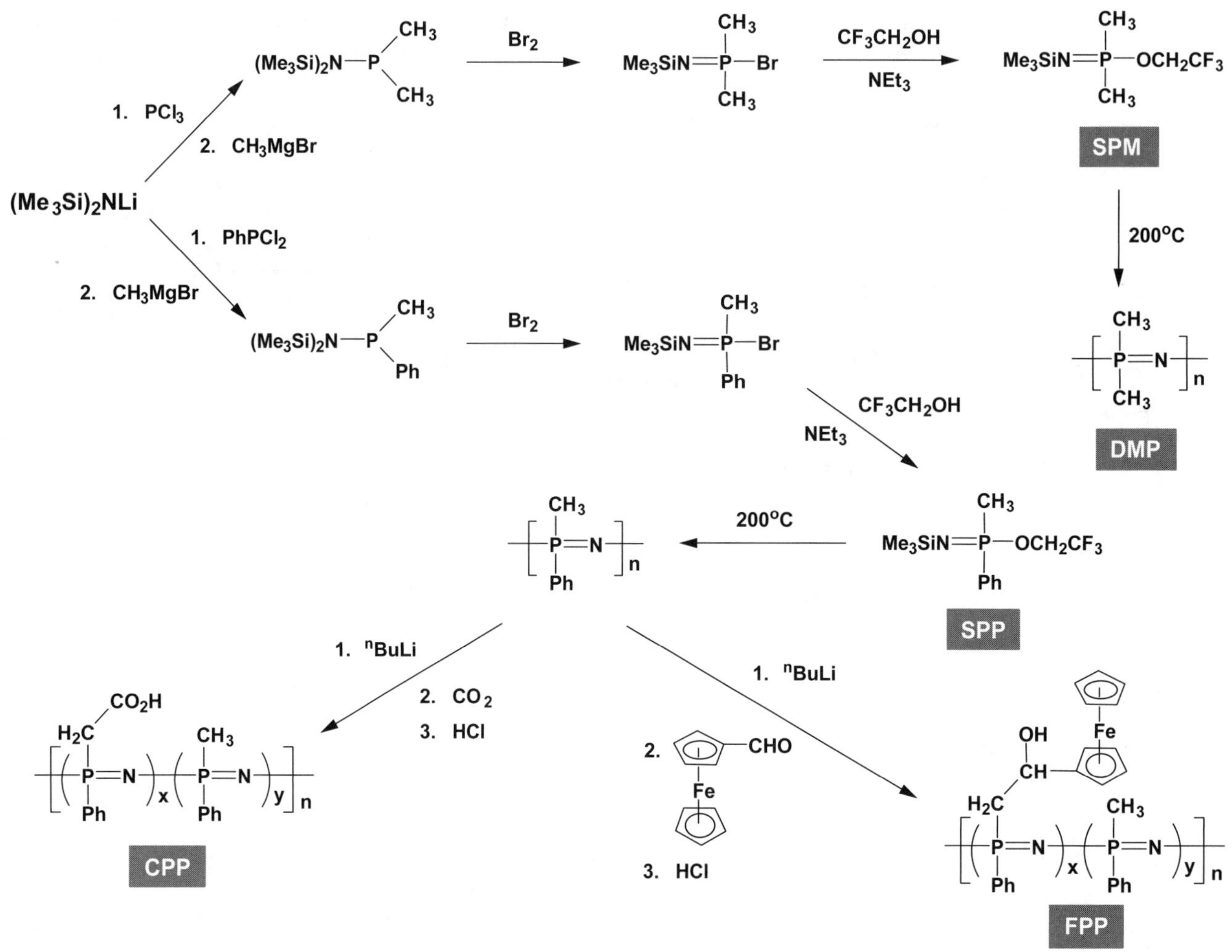

Figure 5.57. Synthesis of P-C bonded polyphosphazenes.

5.5.2. Polysilanes

Polysilanes possess a continuous backbone of silicon atoms with two organic substituents on each silicon atom. One of the most remarkable features of polysilanes is their unique optical properties, including long wavelength UV absorption which intensifies as the degree of polymerization increases. This is associated with delocalization of σ electrons, a phenomenon which is virtually absent in carbon chemistry. Unlike C-C σ bonds, Si-Si σ bonds are more diffuse because they are constructed from higher energy 3s and 3p atomic orbitals, resulting in significant interactions between adjacent Si-Si σ bonds along the polysilane chain, a situation analogous to that for the π bonds in conjugated polymers, such as polyacetylene. Similar to conjugated polymers, polysilanes also display appreciable electronic conductivity, especially after doping with AsF_5. For example, doped poly(methylphenylsilane) (PMPS) exhibits a conductivity of 0.5 S/cm (Figure 5.58).

Polysilanes (e.g., PMPS and FMPS) are usually prepared by reductive condensation of dichlorosilanes with alkali or alkali earth metals (Wurtz-type coupling).[261,262] This heterogeneous polymerization process (i.e., reaction occurs only on the metal surface) is rather complicated because the polysilanes obtained show polymodal molecular weight distribution, and is postulated to involve both silyl radicals and silyl anions as reactive intermediates (Figure 5.58). This method is limited to nonfunctional alkyl and/or aryl side groups, due to the use of metal. An alternative route to polysilanes (e.g., HPPS-1 and HPPS-2) is Group-4 metallocene-catalyzed dehydrogenative coupling of primary hydrosilanes (Figure 5.58).[263,264] Although this method produces low molecular weight products, the presence of reactive Si-H functionalities on the polysilane backbone permits the preparation of novel polysilane derivatives with new side groups via H_2PtCl_6-catalyzed hydrosilation reaction and free-radical reaction or after conversion to Si-Cl groups by treatment with CCl_4 or N-chlorosuccinimide (NCS).[265-268]

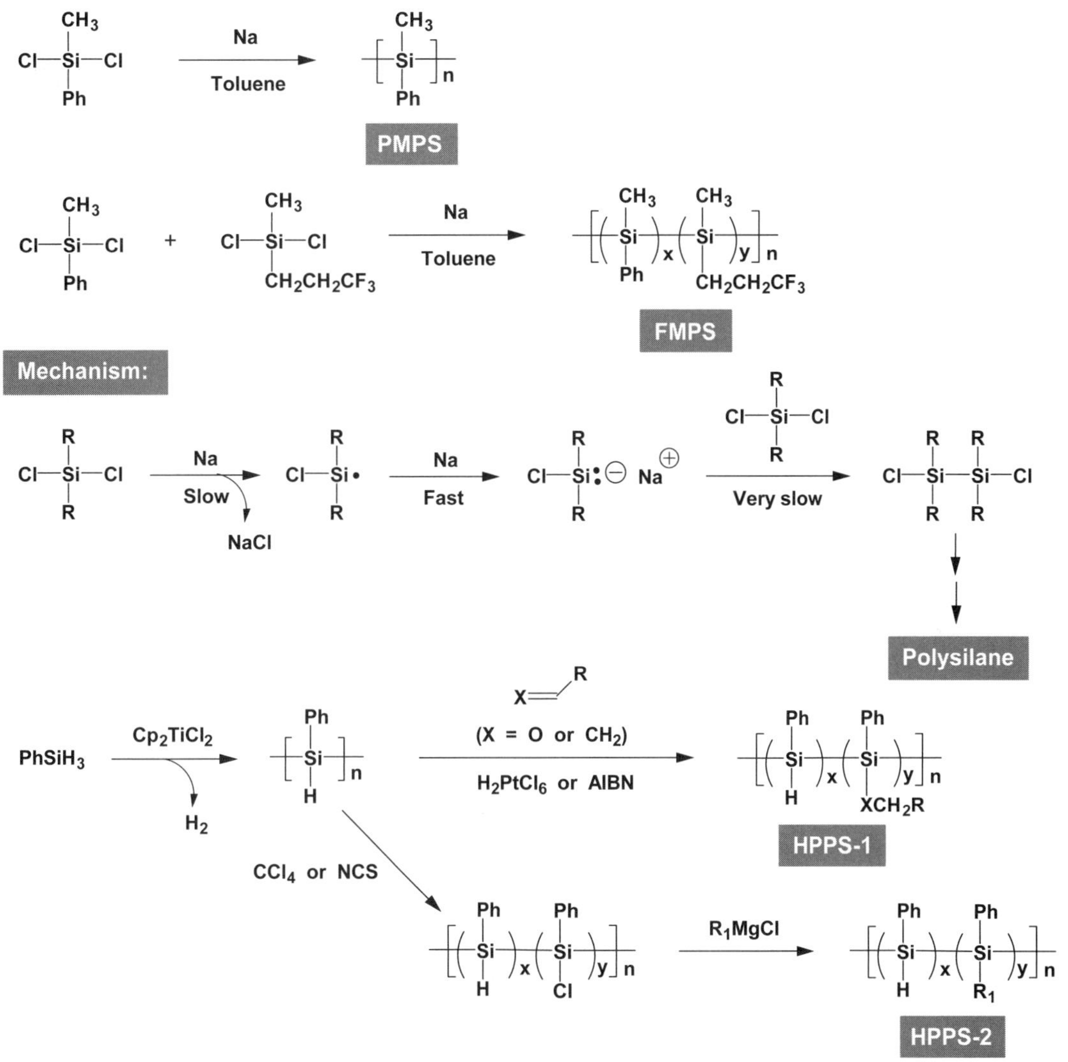

Figure 5.58. Common synthetic routes to polysilanes, including the mechanism of Wurtz-type coupling reaction.

Another new class of polysilanes that has been the subject of extensive study is polysiloles. The most studied member of this family is poly[1,1-(2,3,4,5-tetraphenylsilole)] (PTPS), which has a continuous Si-Si backbone formed by linking tetraphenylsilole rings through the ring silicon atom (Figure 5.59). The monomer unit, silole, is a five-membered silacycle, which may be viewed structurally as a cyclopentadiene derivative with its carbon bridge replaced by a silicon atom. PTPS has been synthesized by Wurtz-type polycondensation (lithium metal in THF) of dichlorotetraphenylsilole or by catalytic dehydrocoupling of dihydrosilole in the presence of H_2PtCl_6, $RhCl(PPh_3)_3$ or $Pd(PPh_3)_4$ in toluene (Figure 5.59).[269-272] Although both methods produce low molecular weight products, the resulting polymer can be cast into a thin film from solution. PTMS is highly photoluminescent (absorbs and emits at 370 nm and 510 nm, respectively, vs. 320 nm and 340 nm for polysilanes) and is very attractive in such areas as light emitting diodes and ultra-sensitive chemical sensors for nitroaromatics. For example, PTPS has about a 370% better quenching efficiency with TNT than organic pentiptycene-derived polymer (see Figure 5.25 for more discussion).[273] Characteristic features of PTPS include a low reduction potential and a low-lying LUMO, due to σ^*-π^* conjugation arising from the interaction between the σ^* orbital of the silicon and the π^* orbital of the butadiene moiety of the five-membered ring. In addition, PTPS exhibits σ-σ^* delocalization of the conjugated electrons along the Si-Si backbone. This electron delocalization in PTPS provides one means of amplification, because interaction of an analyte molecule at any position along the polymer chain quenches an excited state or exciton delocalized along the chain.

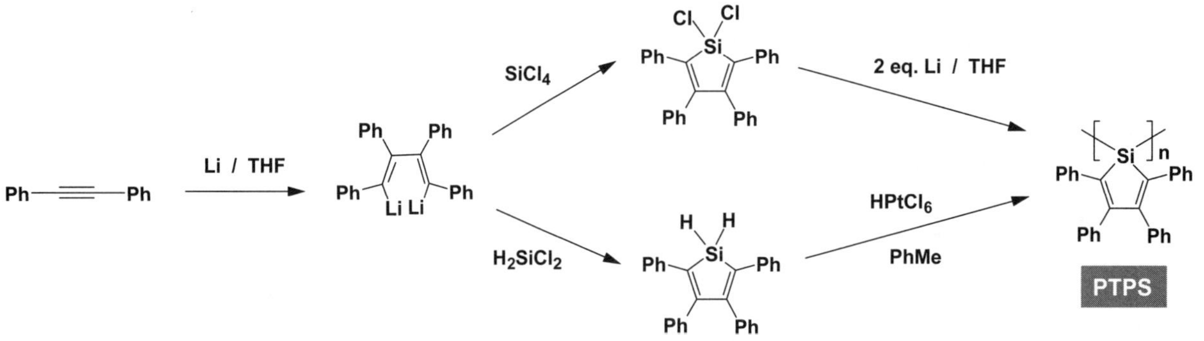

Figure 5.59. Common synthetic approaches to PTPS.

5.5.3. Polycarbosilanes

Polycarbosilanes, which contain alternating $-SiR_2-$ and an organic bridge in the backbone structure, exhibit many of the characteristics of polysiloxanes, in particular, low T_gs and ease of structural modification through R side groups. However, they also provide some of the more useful features of certain organic polymers, such as high thermal stability in inert atmospheres and resistance to attack by strong base and acids, due to the essentially non-polar character of the silicon and carbon-containing polymer backbone. While the side groups are usually selected from alkyl, aryl or alkoxy, the organic bridge can vary widely from methylene to arylene, alkenylene or metal-containing aromatics, such as ferrocene. Poly(silylenemethylene)s, $-[SiR_2(CH_2)]_n-$ (PSM), which can be regarded as carbon analogs of polysiloxanes, are the simplest and most investigated among polycarbosilanes because of their promise as precursors for silicon carbide (SiC) ceramic materials (Figure 5.60). The best way to access a variety of the simplest polycarbosilanes is Pt-complex catalyzed ring-opening polymerization of the corresponding substituted 1,3-disilacyclobutane monomers.[274-276] This methodology can also be employed to prepare poly(silaethylene) (PSE), poly(silapropylene) (PSP) and poly(silastyrene) (PSS) by reduction of the corresponding chloro-substituted polymers.

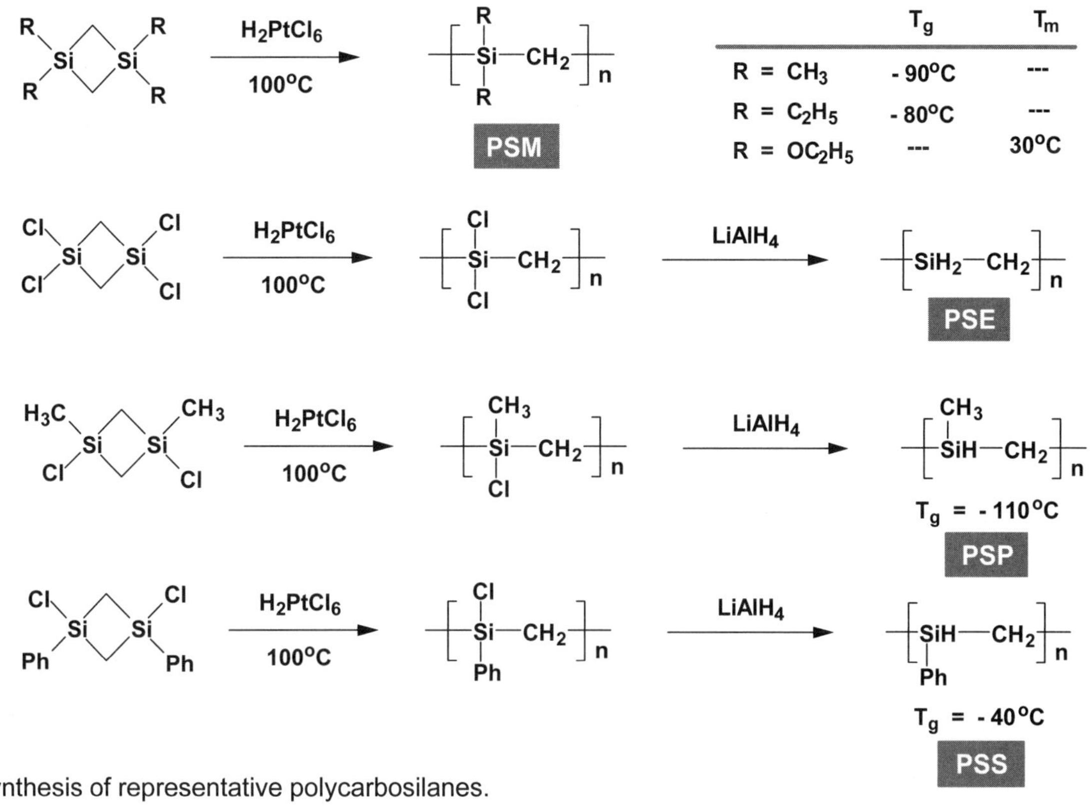

Figure 5.60. Synthesis of representative polycarbosilanes.

Polycarbosilanes with unsaturated or aromatic bridges between silicon atoms have also been prepared for various applications (Figure 5.61, next page). For example, poly(dimethylsilylenevinylene) (PDSV) can be melt-spun into fibers, which, on thermal treatment at 1300°C in an inert atmosphere, produce high yields of ceramic materials.[277] Polycarbosilanes with alkyne bridges were prepared for conducting and nonlinear optical properties. Although success in achieving good conductivity was not accomplished with poly(dimethylsilyleneethynylene) (PDSE), the poly(dimethylsilylene diethynylene) (PDSD) displayed conductivity in the range 10^{-5} to 10^{-3} S/cm after oxidation with $FeCl_3$.[278,279] Polymers containing an aromatic ring, such as poly(dimethylsilylene-*p*-phenylene) (PDSP), usually exhibit very high thermal stability (no decomposition even at 400°C).

In recent years, there has been enormous interest in the design and synthesis of metal-containing polycarbosilanes to develop materials with superior redox, magnetic, optical, or catalytic properties. Most noteworthy are the well-defined high molecular weight poly(ferrocenylsilane)s (PFSs) prepared via ring-opening polymerization (ROP) of silicon-bridged [1]ferrocenophanes, which are readily obtained from the reaction of dilithoferrocene-tetramethylethylenediamine with dichloroorganosilanes (Figure 5.62).[280-283] Poly(ferrocenylsilane)s with alkoxy, aryloxy or amino substituents at silicon have also been synthesized via ROP of similarly substituted [1]ferrocenophane precursors, which can be accessed through nucleophilic substitution reactions on the $SiCl_2$-bridged [1]ferrocenophane.[284] The dimethyl derivative, poly(ferrocenyldimethyl silane), is an amber-colored, highly flexible (T_g = 30°C), film-forming semicrystlline thermoplastic. The ability of the iron atom in ferrocene to act as a freely rotating "molecular ball-bearing" may play a key role in generating the observed conformational flexibility. This polymer can also be melt-processed into various shapes above 150°C and used to prepare crystalline, nanoscale fibers (<1.5 μm diameter) by the electrospinning technique.[285] One of the most interesting properties of PFSs is the observation of two reversible oxidation waves spaced ca. 0.25 V apart in a 1:1 ratio in the cyclic voltammogram, which is indicative of electronic interactions between the iron atoms.[286] They also exhibit good electronic conductivity (10^{-3} to 10^{-4} S/cm) and interesting hole-transport properties. Consequently, the thin films of these polymers have attracted attention for applications in chemomechanical sensors, electrochromic materials, and electrode mediators, including variable refractive-index material.[287-289]

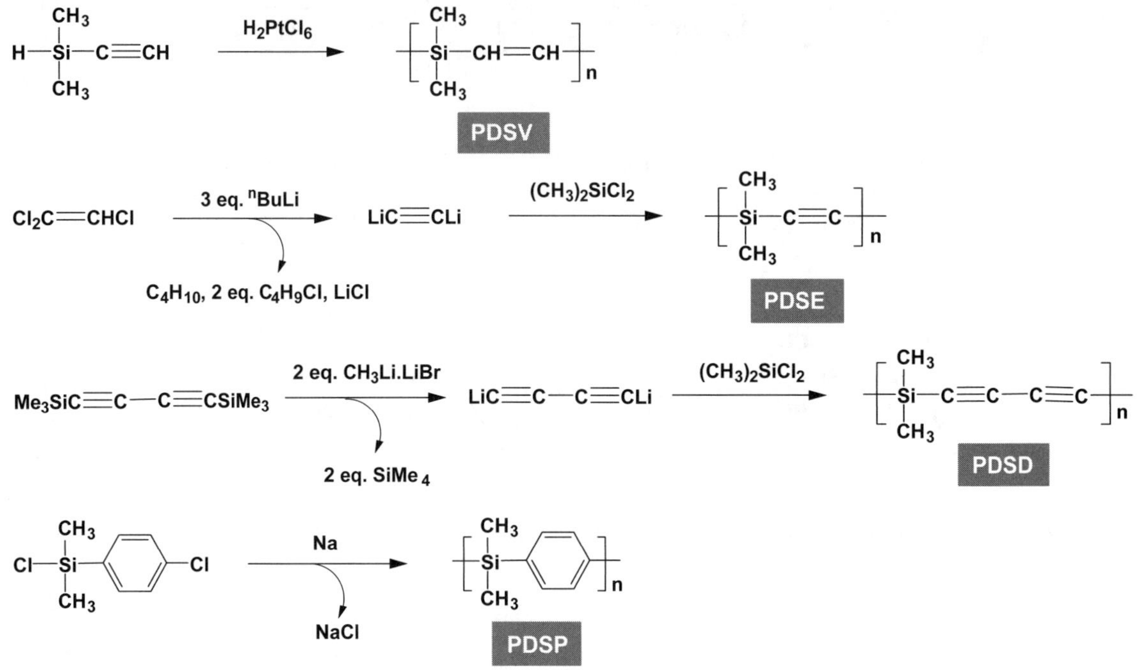

H_2PtCl_6
PDSV
3 eq. ^nBuLi
C_4H_{10}, 2 eq. C_4H_9Cl, LiCl
$(CH_3)_2SiCl_2$
PDSE
2 eq. $CH_3Li.LiBr$
2 eq. $SiMe_4$
$(CH_3)_2SiCl_2$
PDSD
Na
NaCl
PDSP

Figure 5.61. Synthesis of polycarbosilanes containing unsaturated organic bridges.

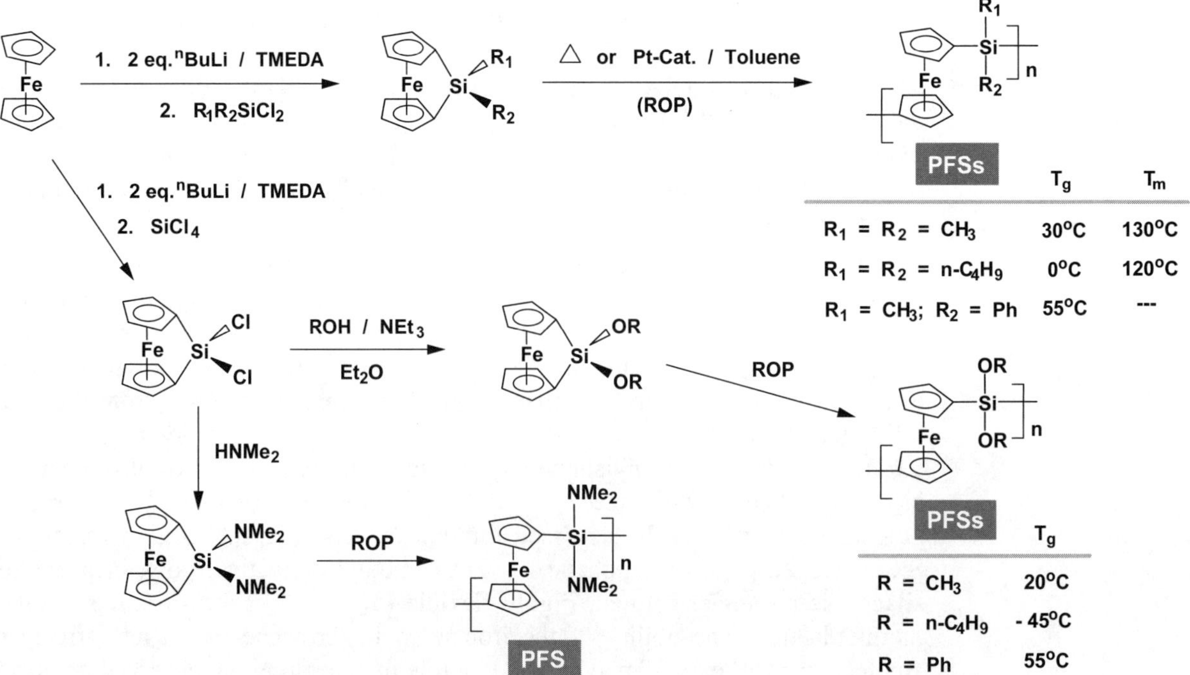

Figure 5.62. Synthesis of poly(ferrocenylsilane)s.

5.5.4. Polycarboranes

Polycarboranes, polymers containing a high proportion of icosahedral carborane units (especially *para*-carborane, 1,12-$C_2B_{10}H_{12}$, in which the two CH units are located at opposing sites on the closed cage pseudo-spherical surfaces) along with organic/inorganic segments, have been extensively studied primarily because of their very high thermo-oxidative stability in air (>500°C) and remarkable combustion and chemical resistance. The CH units of carborane possess weak protic acidity but strong enough to facilitate metallation by reactive metal alkyls, which offer access to carborane derivatives suitable for polymer reactions.[290,291] For example, catalytic polycondensation of the all-para bifunctional monomer, 1,12-bis(4-chlorophenyl)-1,12-dicarbadodecaborane, CPC, gave a rodlike poly(biphenylenecarborane), PBC (Figure 5.63).[292-294] This material showed no evidence of melting or softening up to 600°C, but it gave a well-defined x-ray powder diffraction pattern, suggesting that its intractability stems from a very high crystalline phase. Another example involves superacid catalyzed electrophilic polycondensation of a carborane-based monomer, 1,12-bis(4-phenoxyphenyl)-*para*-carborane (PPC), and an aromatic dicarboxylic acid, such as terephthalic acid (Figure 5.63).[295] The resulting *para*-carborane-containing polyetherketone (CPEK) is a semi-crystalline polymer and exhibits not only a very high T_g (~270°C) compared to commercial polyetherketones (~145°C, see Section 4.3 in Chapter-4) but also a weak melting transition at about 320°C.

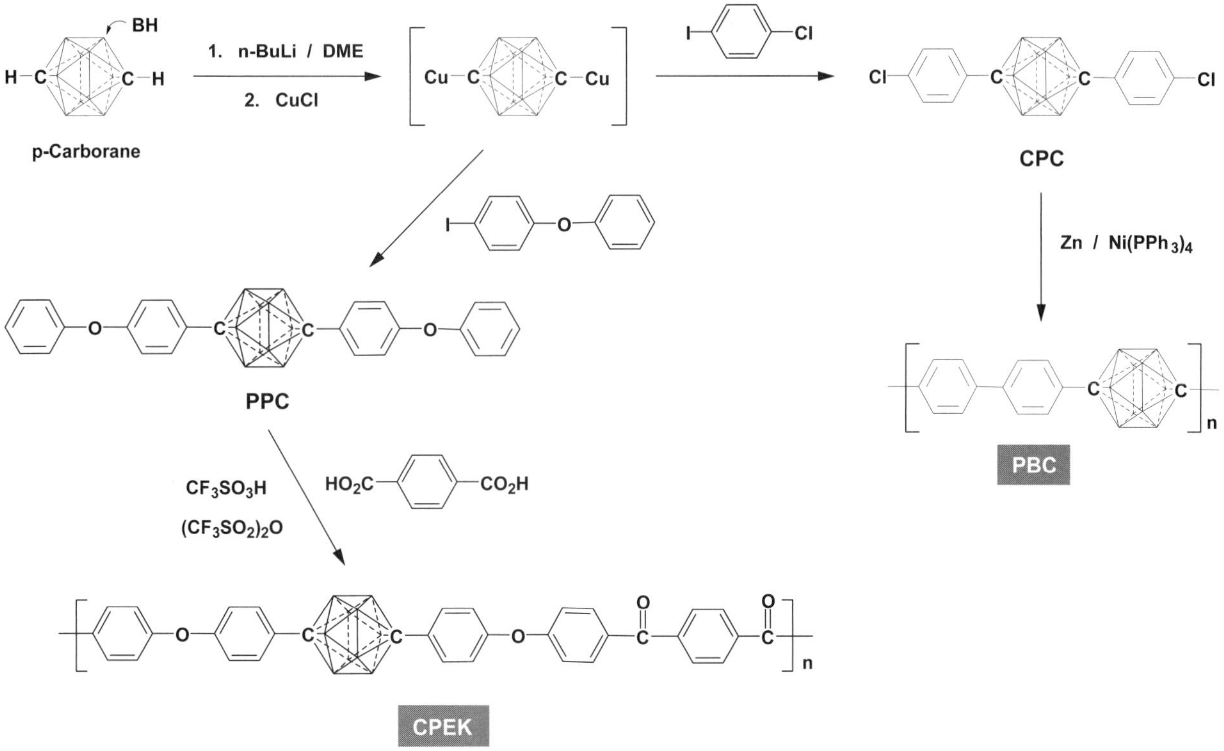

Figure 5.63. Synthesis of polycarboranes containing organic segments. *Note: BHs are omitted in the carborane unit for clarity.*

Inorganic/organic hybrid polymers containing *meta*-carborane (1,7-$C_2B_{10}H_{12}$, in which the two CH units are located at alternate sites) have also been extensively studied, especially to prepare high-temperature elastomeric materials suitable for sealing assemblies of landing gears for flight control and fuel systems, and for cable insulations in aerospace and defense industries. For example, poly-*m*-carboranylenesiloxanes, CPSI, are prepared by the ferric chloride-catalyzed copolymerization of dichloro- and dimethoxy-terminated monomers as shown in Figure 5.64.[296] Recently, this strategy has been extended to prepare polymeric precursors for ceramics and novel high-performance thermosetting materials. One approach involves a polycondensation reaction between dilithiobutadiyne (DLB), generated by reacting hexachlorobutadiene in THF with 4 eqiv of *n*-butyllithium at -78°C, and 1,7-bis(chlorotetramethyldisiloxy)-*m*-carborane (BCC).[297-299] The resulting polymer, PDSC, is soluble in most organic solvents, can be easily processed into shaped configurations and undergoes crosslinking upon heating over 150°C (Figure 5.64). Pyrolysis of the crosslinked PDSC to 1000°C produces a black solid ceramic material in 85% yield. Another approach involves the preparation of a vinyl group terminated *m*-carboranylenesiloxane monomer, VCS, which was used as a crosslinker for hydrosilation reaction with poly(methylhydrosiloxane), PMHS, elastomer (Figure 5.64).[300,301]

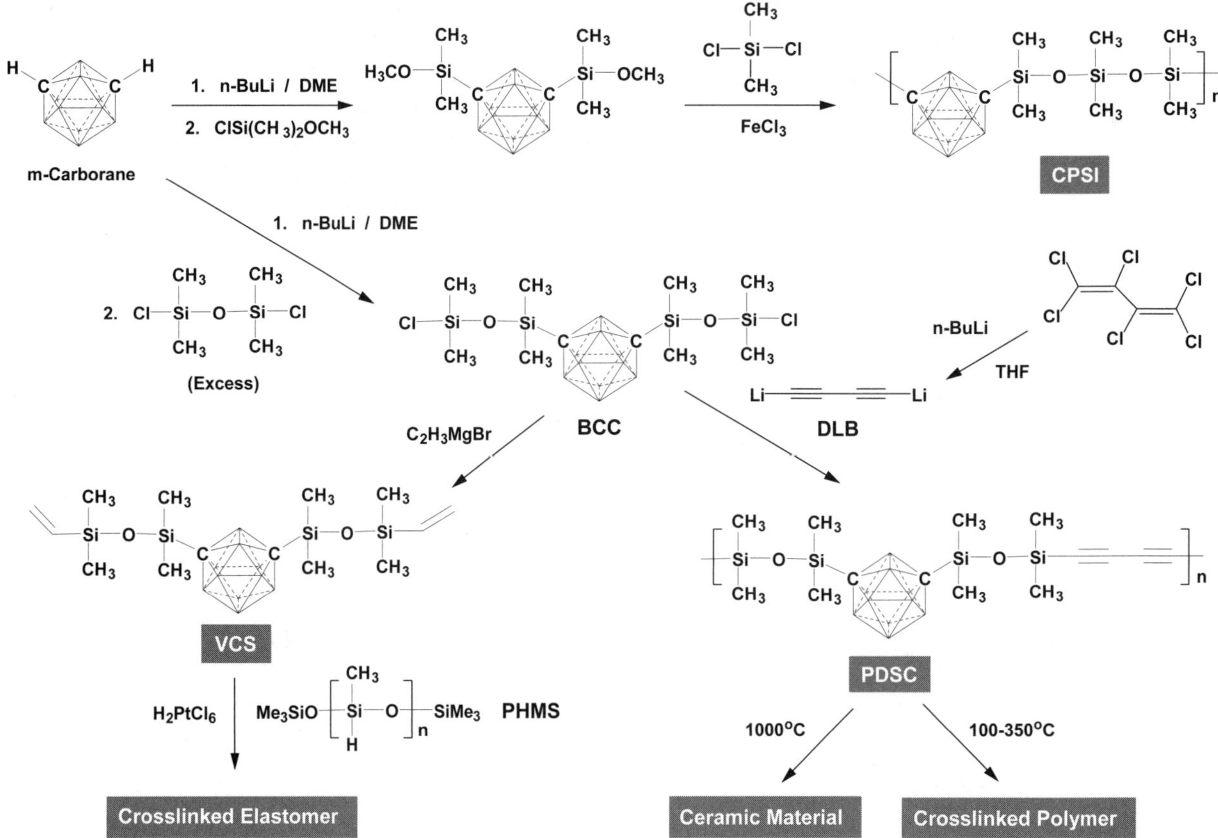

Figure 5.64. Synthesis of polycarboranes containing inorganic/organic segments.

5.6. DENDRITIC POLYMERS

As discussed in Chapter-1, dendritic polymers are regarded as a special class of highly branched macromolecules characterized by a tree-like architecture. In the past decade, the chemistry of dendritic polymers has been one of the most rapidly expanding fields in chemistry because of the opportunity to design novel materials, including nanomaterials, with greater structural control.[302-309] A variety of dendritic polymers have been prepared, which can be grouped into four major categories according to their architectural design (branching pattern) and/or degree of structural perfection: dendrimers, dendronized polymers, dendrigraft polymers, and hyperbranched polymers (schematic representations can be seen in Figure 1.13).

Dendrimers are highly uniform, three-dimensional, monodisperse polymers (M_w/M_n = 1.00-1.05) with a tree-like, spherical structure. By contrast, hyperbranched polymers exhibit polydispersity (M_w/M_n = 2-10) and irregularity in terms of branching and structure and they are not fully reacted at every repeating unit. Dendronized and dendrigraft polymers reside between these two extremes of structural control, frequently manifesting rather narrow polydispersities (M_w/M_n = 1.1-1.5) depending on their mode of preparation. Table 5.2 depicts some of the attractive features of each category. The following sections outline a few of several diverse synthetic methods used in designing and synthesizing dendritic polymers having unique and different properties compared to their linear analogues.

Table 5.2: Versatility of Dendritic Polymers in Comparison with Linear Polymers

Property	Linear Polymers	Dendrimers	Dendronized Polymers	Dendrigraft Polymers	Hyperbranched Polymers
Shape	Random coil	Dense sphere	Cylindrical	Star-like	Diffused sphere
Molecular weight distribution	Narrow to broad	Monodisperse	Very narrow	Narrow	Broad
Melt viscosity	High	Very low	Low	Low	Moderate
Intrinsic viscosity	High	Very low	Low	Low	Moderate to high
Solubility	Low	High	High	High	High
Crystallinity	High	Amorphous	Amorphous	Amorphous	Amorphous
Structural control	Low to moderate	Very high	Very high	high	Moderate
Synthetic steps	1-5	4-10	3-6	3-6	1-3
Cost	Very low	Very high	Moderate	Moderate	Very low

5.6.1. Dendrimers

Dendrimers are perfectly branched macromolecules in which each repeating unit has a branching point. The structure of a dendrimer consists of three domains: core, interior and shell (Figure 5.65). The interior is separated into layers called *generations*. The peripheral layer, called the *shell*, contains all the functional groups. The core of dendrimers is usually referred to as generation 0 (G_0), while each branched layer produced as a result of polymerization gives rise to subsequent generations. Dendrimers of lower generations (0, 1, and 2) have highly asymmetric shapes and possess more open structures compared with higher generation dendrimers. As the chains growing from the core molecule become longer and more branched (in the 4th and higher generations), dendrimers adopt a spherical shape. When a critical branched state is reached, dendrimers cannot grow because of a lack of space. This is called the "*starburst effect*".[310] Because of their molecular architecture, dendrimers show significantly different physical and chemical properties when compared to traditional linear polymers. For example, in solution, linear polymer chains exist as flexible coils, whereas the dendrimer structure resembles a tightly packed ball. This structure has a great impact on rheological properties such that dendrimer solutions have significantly lower viscosities than those of linear polymers. For linear polymers, the intrinsic viscosity increases continuously with molecular mass. By contrast, the intrinsic viscosity of dendrimers often goes through a maximum at the fourth generation and then begins to decline. An important difference between linear polymers and dendrimers is that in a dendrimer the many branches give rise to a very high number of terminal functional groups in each molecule, while a linear polymer molecule possesses only two terminal functional groups. The presence of a large number of chain ends in dendrimers is often responsible for high solubility and miscibility. For example, the solubility of dendritic polyesters are considerably higher than that of the analogous linear polyester. Thus, dendrimers have a unique combination of features, such as a compact spherical topology with diameters ranging from 1 nm to over 100 nm, the presence of internal cavities, and a large number of functional groups at the periphery. These remarkable features have led to a broad spectrum of applications, including microencapsulation, drug delivery, light harvesting, molecular recognition, and catalysis.

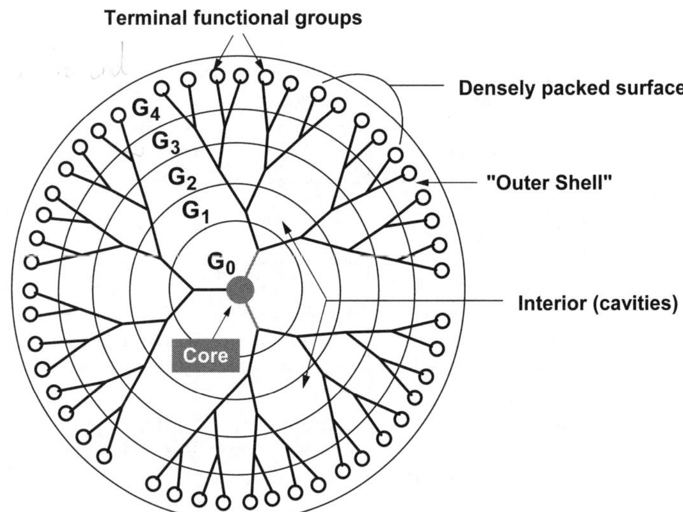

Figure 5.65. Schematic of a 4th generation dendrimer.

5.6.1.1. Synthesis of Dendrimers

Most syntheses of dendrimers involve repetitious alternation of a growth reaction and an activation reaction. Often, these reactions have to be performed at many sites on the same molecule simultaneously. Consequently, the reactions must be very "clean" and high yielding for the construction of large targets to be feasible. Most dendrimer synthetic schemes rely upon traditional reactions, such as the Williamson ether synthesis, or the Michael addition reaction, whilst others involve the use of modern techniques and chemistry, such as solid-phase synthesis, organo-transition-metal chemistry, organo-silicon chemistry, organo-phosphorus chemistry, or other contemporary organic methodologies. The choice of the growth reaction dictates the way in which branching is introduced into the dendrimer. Branching may either be present in the building blocks as is more often the case or it can be created as a function of the growth reaction. Although there are several approaches, dendrimers are conveniently prepared using either a divergent or a convergent approach by polycondensation of AB_n monomers using cycles of protection, condensation, and deprotection reactions. The fundamental difference between these two construction concepts are described below.

5.6.1.1a. The Divergent Approach

In a *divergent* or *"core-first" approach*, monomer addition starts from the core and proceeds towards the surface of the molecules (i.e., dendrimer grows outwards from a multifunctional core molecule). Thus, the core molecule reacts with monomer molecules containing one reactive and two dormant (masked) groups to give the first-generation dendrimer. The new periphery of the molecule is then activated (unmasking) for reaction with more monomers. The process is repeated for several generations to build a dendrimer, in a manner somewhat similar to that used in solid-phase synthesis of peptides or oligonucleotides (Figure 5.66). Since the reactive functionalities are in the periphery of the growing dendrimer and the reactivity of these groups is retained even at higher generations, the divergent approach is especially suitable for the production of large quantities of higher generation dendrimers. However, since the number of reactions to be performed on a single dendrimer molecule doubles with each generation, problems occur from incomplete and/or side reactions of the end groups, leading to structural defects. To prevent side reactions and to force reactions to completion, a large excess of reagents is required, which often causes difficulties in the purification of the final product, primarily due to physical entrapment of the reagent.

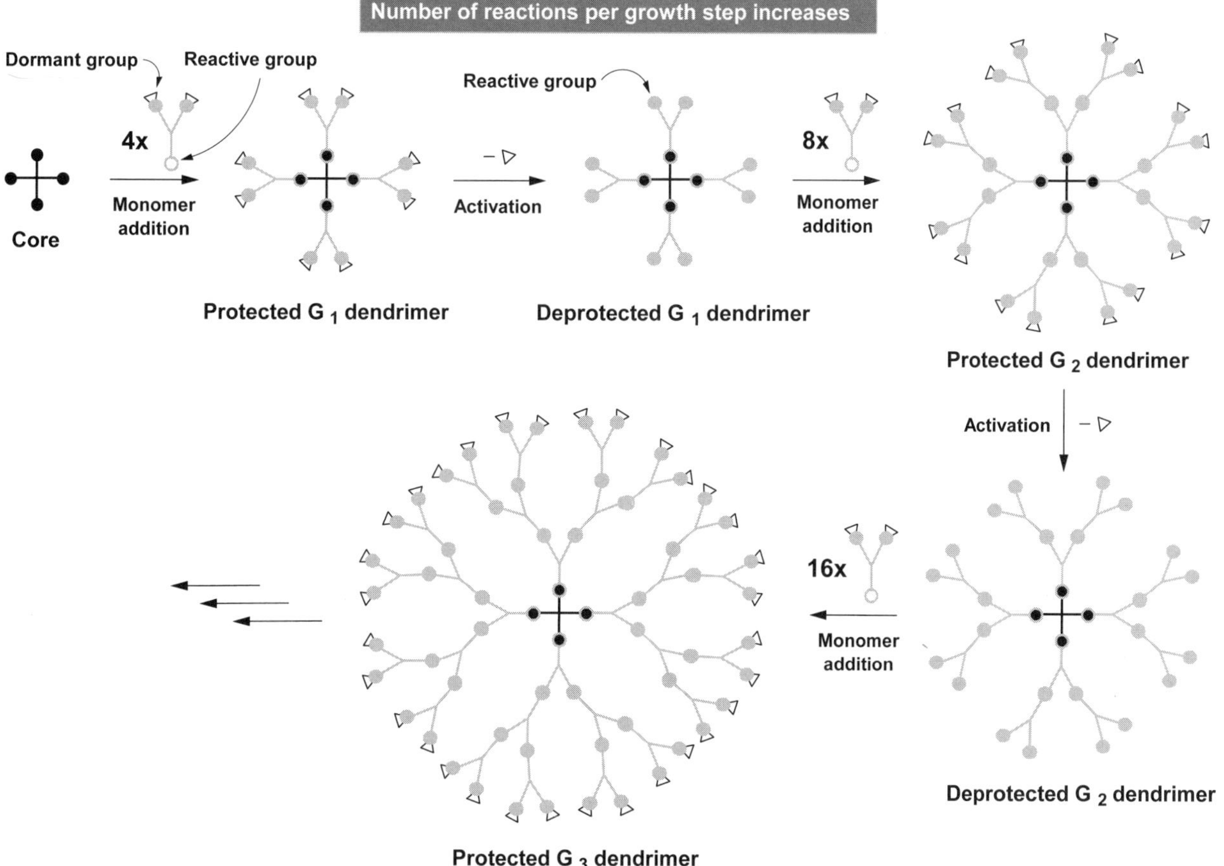

Figure 5.66. Schematic of the divergent approach for the synthesis of dendrimers.

Figures 5.67-5.70 outline routes to selected dendrimers prepared by the divergent approach. For example, the synthesis of polyphenylene dendrimers is based on two alternating reactions: (i) "growth step" - Diels-Alder cycloaddition between a cyclopentadienone bearing two tri-*iso*-propylsilyl (TiPS) protected ethynyl groups and the core, a compound with multiple ethynyl groups, such as 3,3',5,5'-tetraethynylbiphenyl, and (ii) "deprotection step" - the desilylation of the resulting TiPS capped alkyne, leading to a multi-functional ethynyl compound, which serves as the core for the next generation (Figure 5.67).[311] Dendritic poly(ethylene oxide)s were synthesized by combining the "living" anionic ring-opening polymerization of ethylene oxide with diphenylmethylpotassium (DPMK), followed by chain end functionalization (allylation)/branching (bis-hydroxylation) reactions of PEO chain ends (Figure 5.68).[312] The bis-hydroxylation of the allyl group was performed using OsO_4 and N-methylmorpholine-N-oxide (NMO). The synthesis of "biodendrimers" composed of glycerol and succinic acid has also been performed using a tetrafunctional core prepared by coupling succinic acid with *cis*-1,3-O-benzylideneglycerol (BGL) in the presence of N,N-dicyclohexylcarbodiimide (DCC) and 4-(dimethylamino)pyridinium 4-toluenesulfonate (DPTS), followed by removal of the benzylidene acetal group by hydrogenolysis (Figure 5.69).[313,314] The branching ligand, [2-(*cis*-1,3-O-benzylideneglycerol) succinic acid mono ester], BGL-SA, was prepared by treating BGL with succinic anhydride in pyridine. The preparation of commercially available poly(propyleneimine) (PPIM) and poly(amidoamine) (PAMAM) dendrimers consists of repeated double alkylation of the amino groups with acrylonitrile or methyl acrylate by ''Michael addition'', resulting in a branched alkyl chain structure, where each nitrogen atom of the amino groups serves as a branching point (Figure 5.70).[315,316] Subsequent reduction or aminolysis yields a new set of primary amines, which may then be double alkylated to provide further branching.

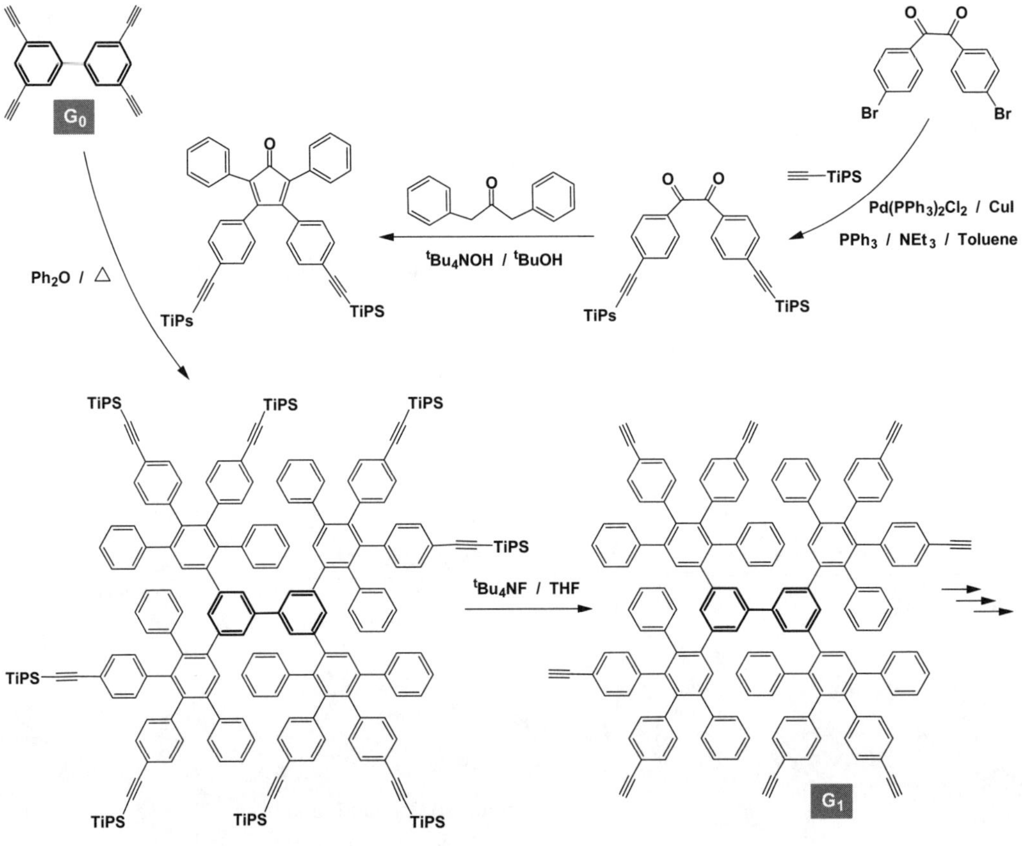

Figure 5.67. Divergent synthesis of polyphenylene dendrimers.

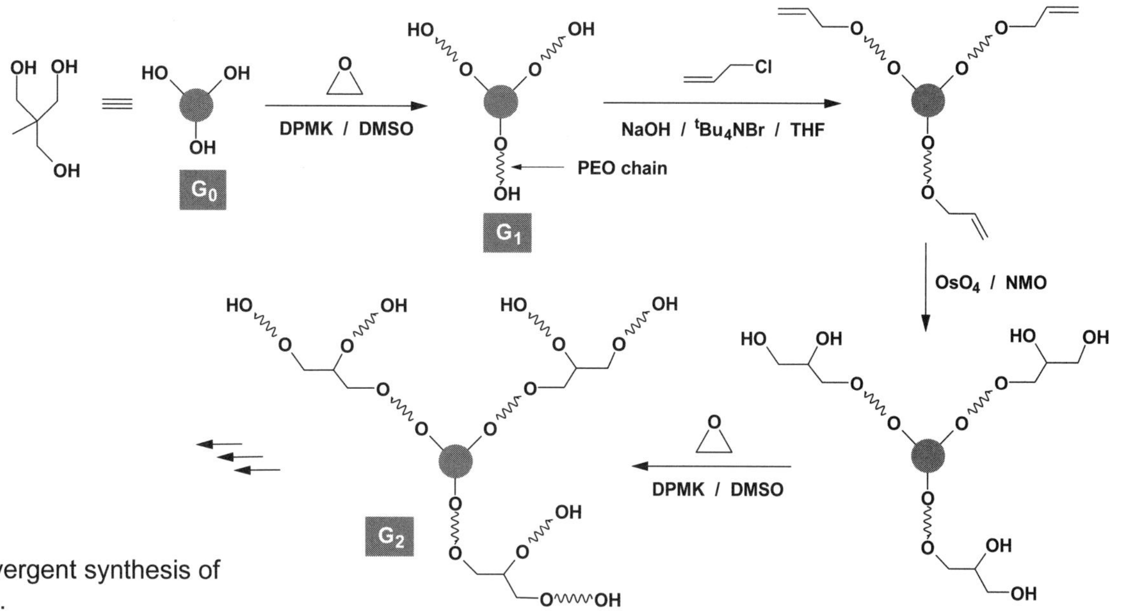

Figure 5.68. Divergent synthesis of PEO dendrimers.

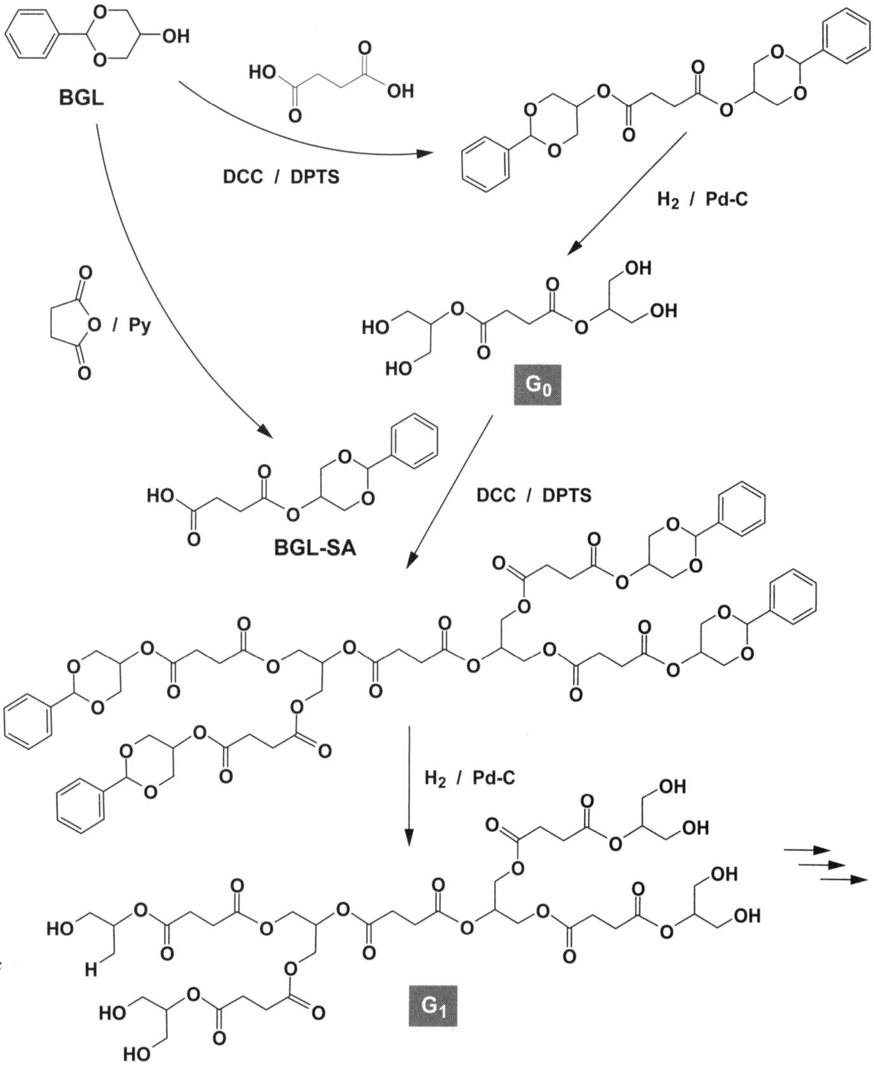

Figure 5.69. Divergent synthesis of poly(glycerol-succinic acid) dendrimers.

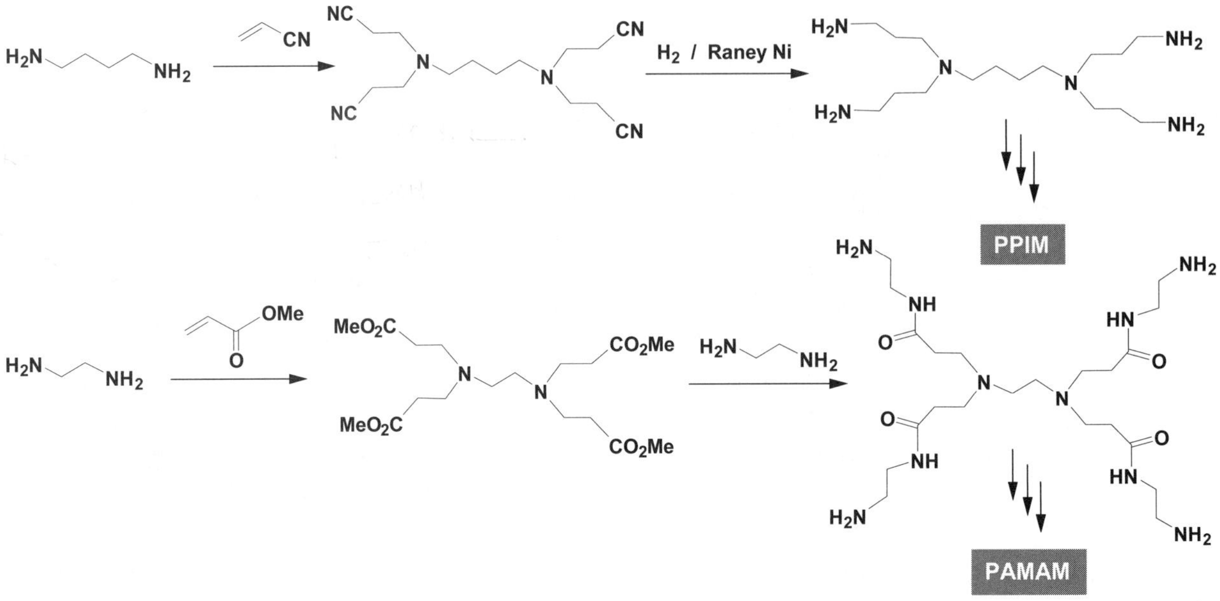

Figure 5.70. Divergent synthesis of commercially available PPIM and PAMAM dendrimers.

5.6.1.1b. The Convergent Approach

This strategy was developed as a response to the weaknesses of the divergent synthesis. In this methodology, dendritic cone-shaped fragments, often described as *dendrons*, are first synthesized starting from the chain ends on the "outside" using successive coupling reactions at a single reactive "focal" site. A few dendrons (usually 2-4) are then assembled via a final coupling reaction with a multifunctional core molecule into a spherical-shaped dendrimer (Figure 5.71).[317] This approach offers several advantages. Since the number of reactions to be performed in a particular molecule always remains the same (i.e., independent of the generation), it is relatively easy to purify the desired product and the occurrence of defects in the final product is minimized. Moreover, it becomes possible to introduce subtle engineering into the dendritic structure by precise placement of functionalities at the periphery of the macromolecule, including the construction of well-defined hybrid structures by using different dendrons (*vide infra*). However, this methodology is not suitable for the preparation of higher generation dendrimers because of the presence of a reactive functional group at the focal point of the dendron, which tends to get encapsulated (sterically crowded) at higher generations.

Figures 5.72 and 5.73 outline the synthesis of selected dendrimers by the convergent approach. For example, the most studied benzyl ether dendrimer (PBE) has been prepared from an unprotected AB_2 building block, 3,5-dihydroxybenzyl alcohol (DHBA), using thionyl chloride as an activating agent.[318,319] The dendrons thus obtained have also been employed successfully in the preparation of novel benzene-core dendrimers *via* alkyne cyclotetramerization (Figure 5.72).[320] Poly(benzyl ester) (PBET) dendrimers were synthesized *via* an "activated" monomer strategy involving reactions of two AB_2 orthogonal monomers, di-potassium salt of 5-(hydroxymethyl)isophthalic acid (PHPA) and 5-(chloromethyl)isophthalic acid (CMPA) (Figure 5.73).[321] Since these monomers are already activated with respect to reaction with one another and once incorporated into the monodendron, growth can continue without the need for further activation.

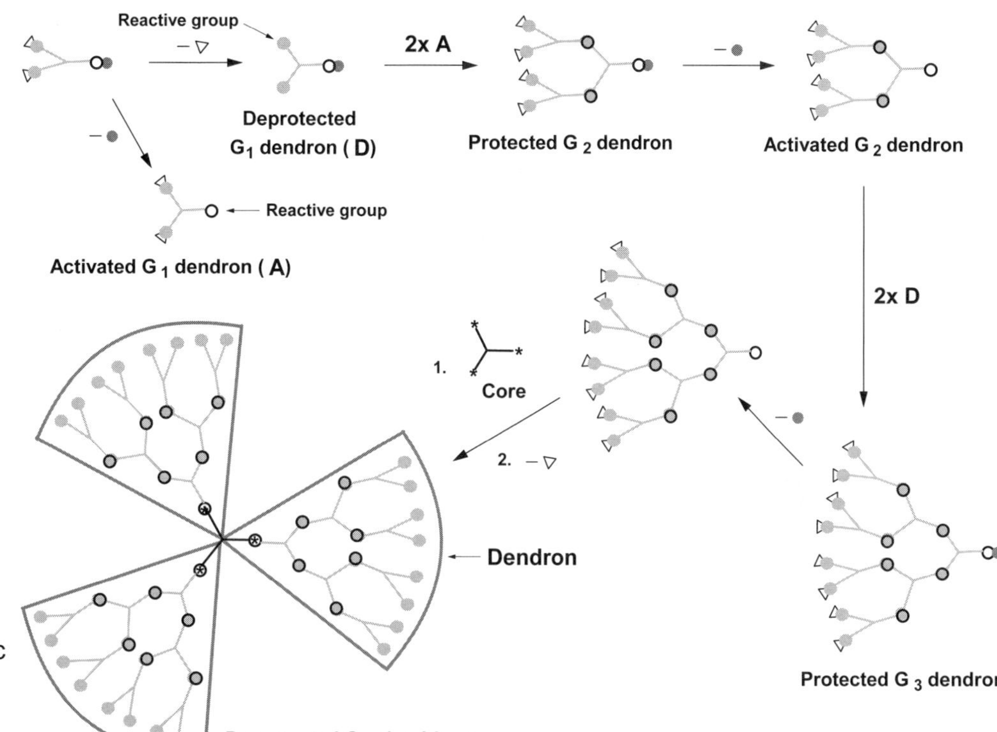

Figure 5.71. Schematic of the convergent approach for the synthesis of dendrimers.

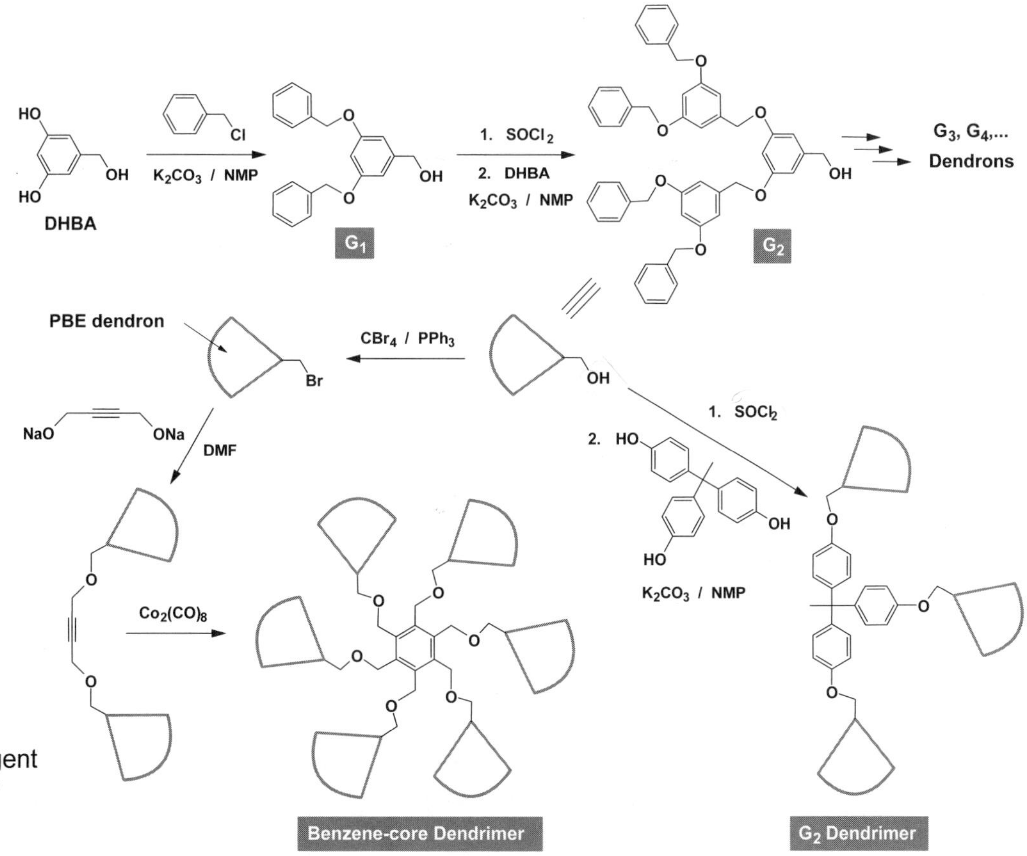

Figure 5.72. Convergent synthesis of aryl ether dendrimers.

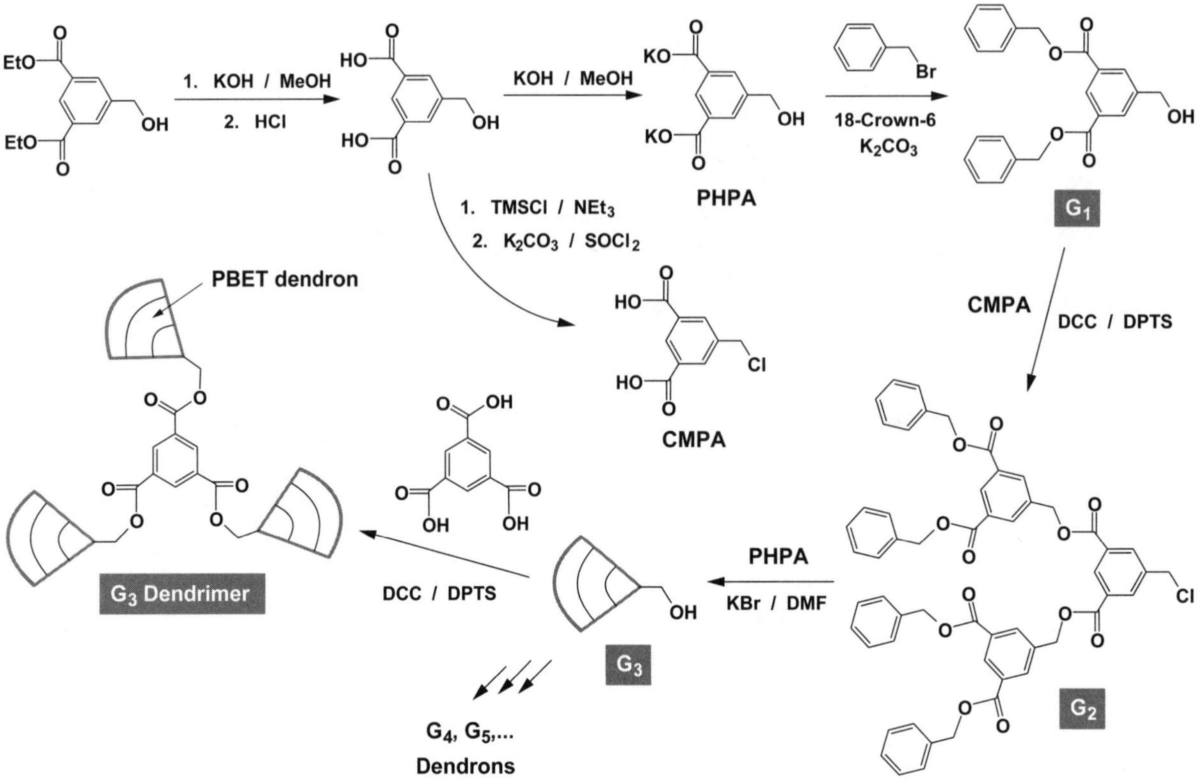

Figure 5.73. Convergent synthesis of benzyl ester dendrimers.

Dendrimers containing π-conjugated backbones have been prepared by the convergent approach. For example, phenylazomethine dendrimers were obtained up to the 4th generation via dehydration of an aromatic ketone with an aromatic amine (DABP) in the presence of titanium(IV) tetrachloride and 1,4-diazabicyclo[2.2.2]octane (DABCO), a more effective reagent system for irreversible dehydration compared with commonly used *p*-toluenesulfonic acid (Figure 5.74).[322,323] This methodology was later modified by introducing an additional oxidation step using 4,4'-methylenedianiline (MDA), in order to avoid undesirable dehydration between two molecules of DABP.[324] Since the dendrons can yield a reactive carbonyl group at the focal point, this strategy leads to one of a few dendrimers that contain metalloporphyrin (MTPP) at the core.[325-329] This class of dendrimers has been utilized as a mimic of enzymatic reactions and shape selective catalysis. Dendrimers containing substituted phenylene ethynylene building blocks were synthesized employing iterative chemistry involving Pd-catalyzed cross-coupling followed by "unmasking" of a diethyltriazene group to an iodo functionality using methyl iodide (Figure 5.75).[330,331] Dendritic poly(phenylene vinylene)s were also conveniently prepared by use of Horner-Wadsworth-Emmons and Heck coupling reactions to construct the vinylene linkages (Figure 5.76).[332]

The convergent approach was also very suitable for the preparation of high-performance dendrimers. For example, dendritic poly(aryl ether amide)s were synthesized by repeated condensation of an unprotected AB_2 building block, 3,5-bis(4-aminophenoxy)benzoic acid (APBA). Thionyl chloride was used to activate the acid at the focal point after each step (Figure 5.77).[333-335] Dendritic poly(ether ketone)s were prepared via aromatic nucleophilic displacement using 3,5-bis(4-fluorobenzoyl)anisole (FBA) as the building block (Figure 5.78).[336-338] Thus, the reaction of FBA with phenol gave the first-generation dendron. Next, after the methoxy group was converted to hydroxy by reaction with aluminum chloride, the resulting phenol functionality of the

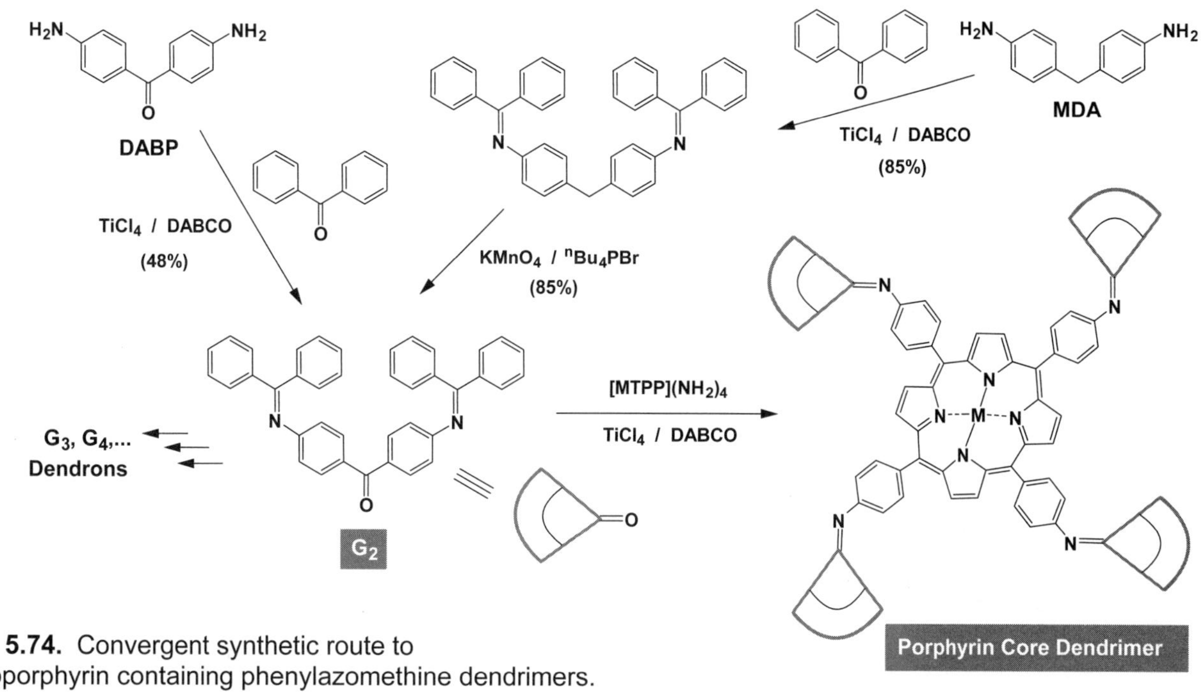

DABP
MDA
$TiCl_4$ / DABCO (48%)
$TiCl_4$ / DABCO (85%)
$KMnO_4$ / $^nBu_4PBr$ (85%)
$[MTPP](NH_2)_4$
$TiCl_4$ / DABCO
G_3, G_4,... Dendrons
G_2
Porphyrin Core Dendrimer

Figure 5.74. Convergent synthetic route to metalloporphyrin containing phenylazomethine dendrimers.

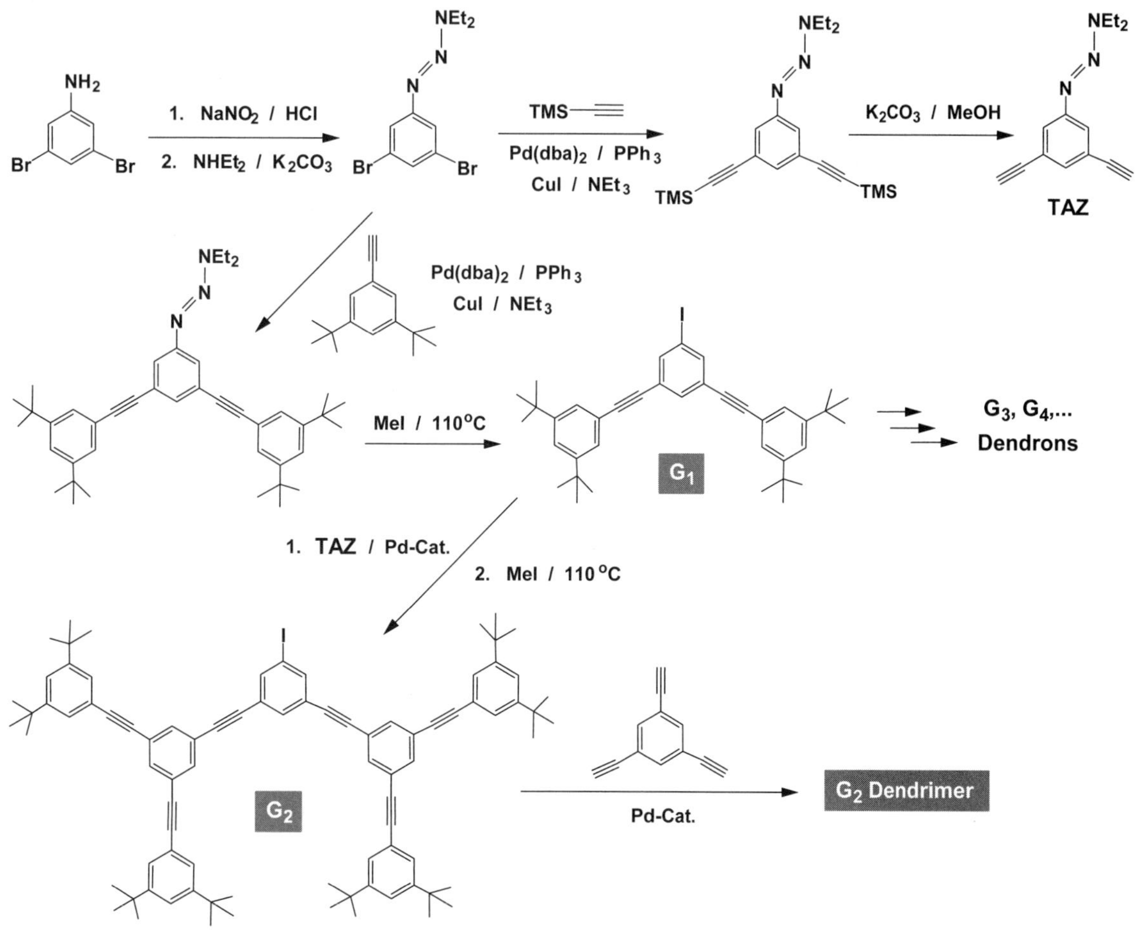

1. $NaNO_2$ / HCl
2. $NHEt_2$ / K_2CO_3
TMS
$Pd(dba)_2$ / PPh_3
CuI / NEt_3
K_2CO_3 / MeOH
TAZ
$Pd(dba)_2$ / PPh_3
CuI / NEt_3
MeI / 110°C
G_1
G_3, G_4,... Dendrons
1. TAZ / Pd-Cat.
2. MeI / 110°C
G_2
Pd-Cat.
G_2 Dendrimer

Figure 5.75. Convergent synthetic route to dendritic poly(phenylene ethynylene)s.

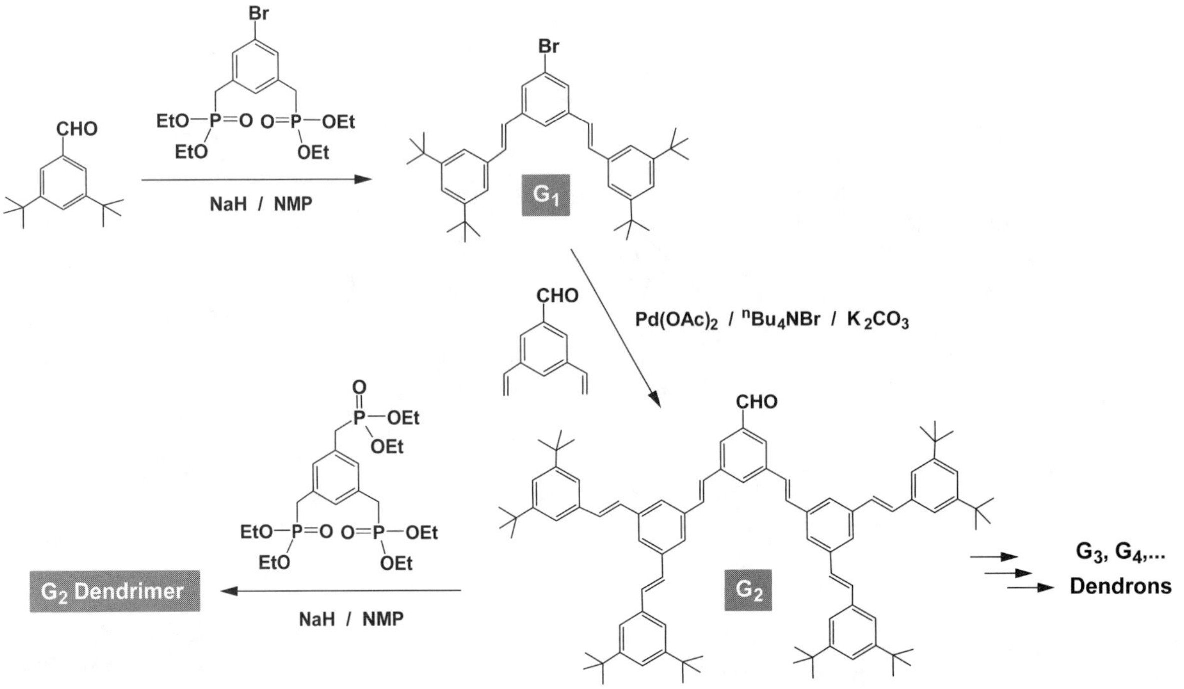

Figure 5.76. Convergent synthetic route to dendritic poly(phenylene vinylene)s.

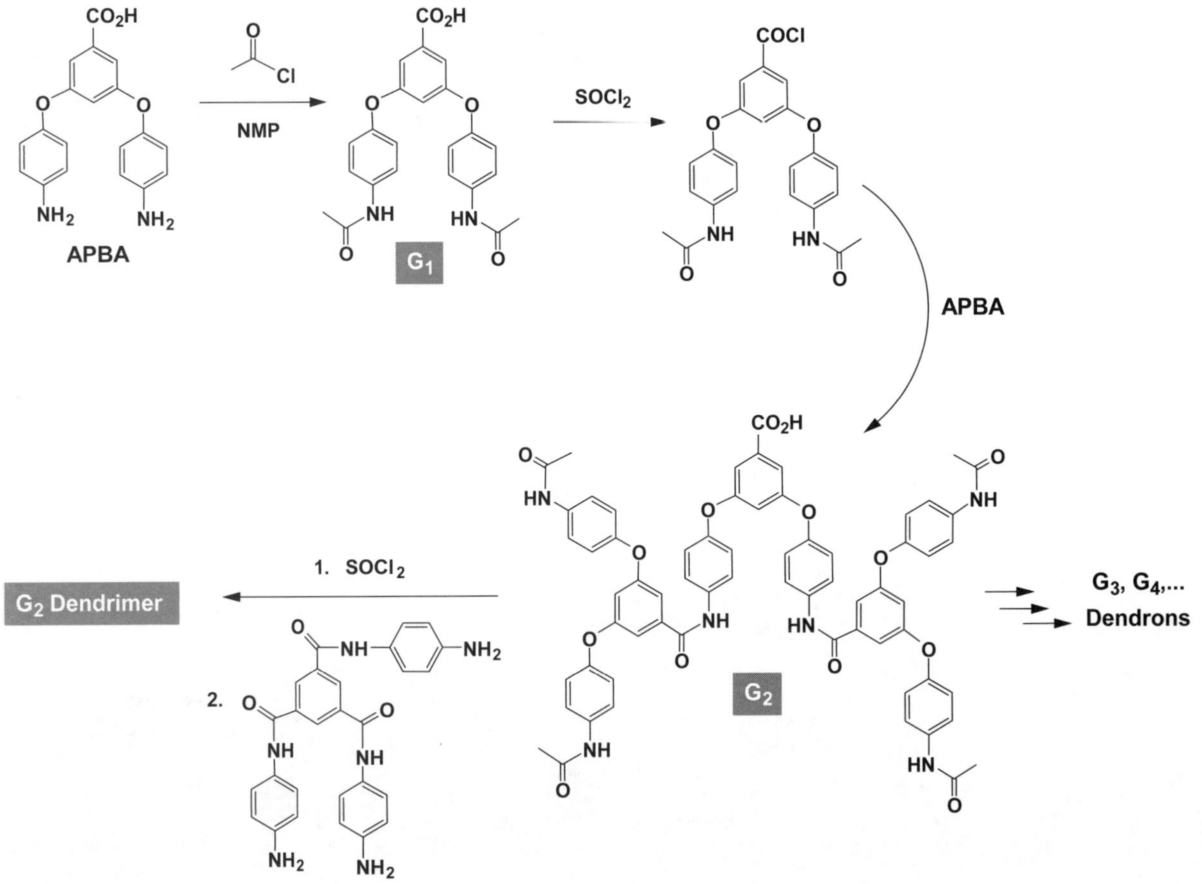

Figure 5.77. Convergent synthesis of dendritic poly(aryl ether amide)s.

first-generation dendron was allowed to react with FBA to yield the second-generation dendron, and so forth for higher generations. Dendritic poly(ether imide)s were obtained by using 1-(4-aminophenyl)-1,1-bis(4-hydroxyphenyl)ethane, APHE, as the building block (Figure 5.79).[339] Aromatic nucleophilic substitution of the building block with 3-nitro-N-phenylphthalimide led to a 1st generation dendron with an aminophenyl group at the focal point, which subsequently reacted with 3-nitrophthalic anhydride to yield the dendritic wedge containing an activated nitro group. The resulting nitro functionality reacted with the building block to give the second-generation dendron, which was then condensed with 3-nitrophthalic anhydride, followed by ring closure to re-form the phthalimide ring and restore a reactive nitro group. Through aromatic nucleophilic substitution, the dendritic wedges bearing an activated nitro group were coupled to the polyfunctional core, such as 1,1,1-tris(4-hydroxyphenyl)ethane (THPE), to form the dendritic macromolecules.

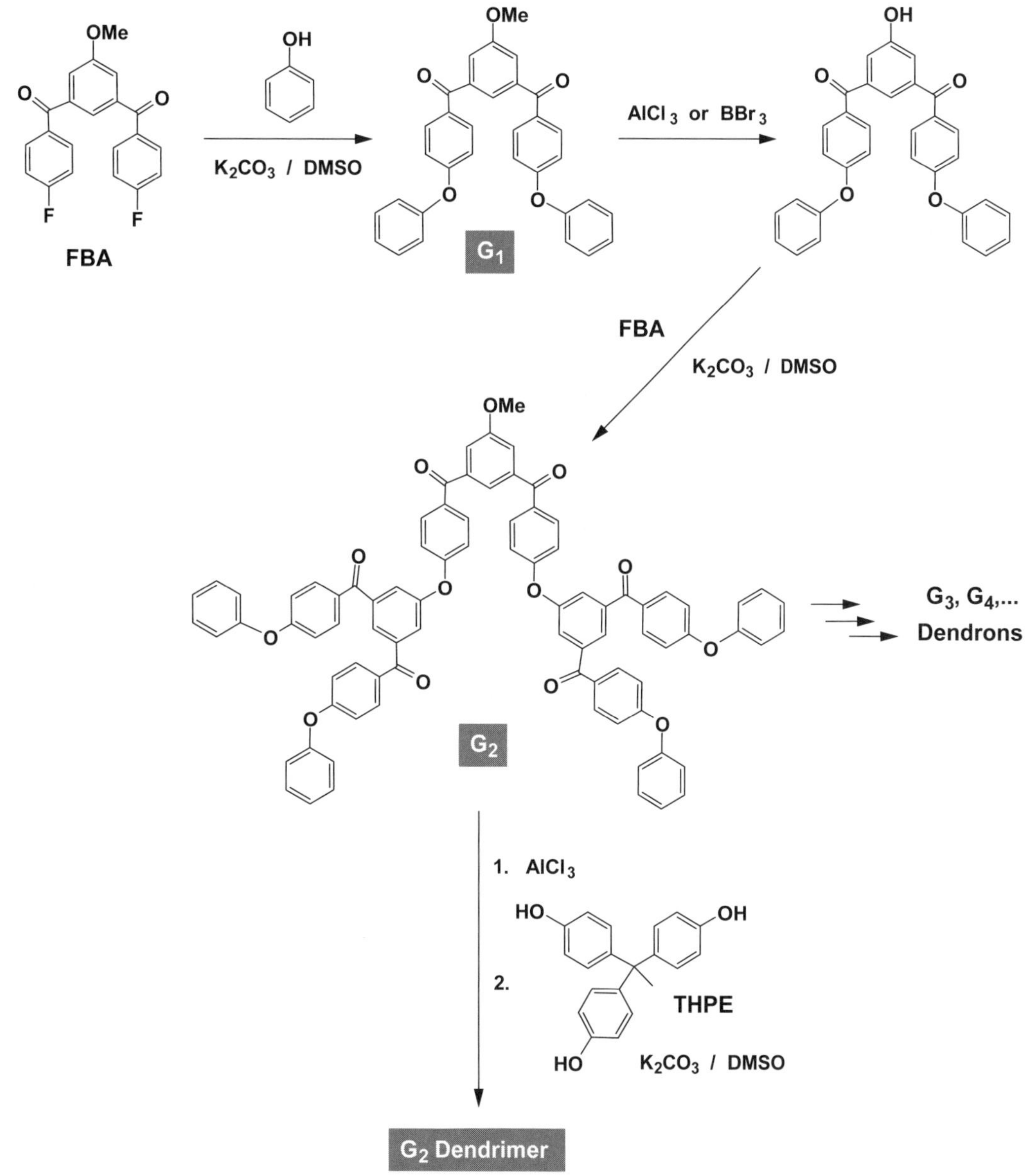

Figure 5.78. Convergent synthesis of dendritic poly(ether ketone)s.

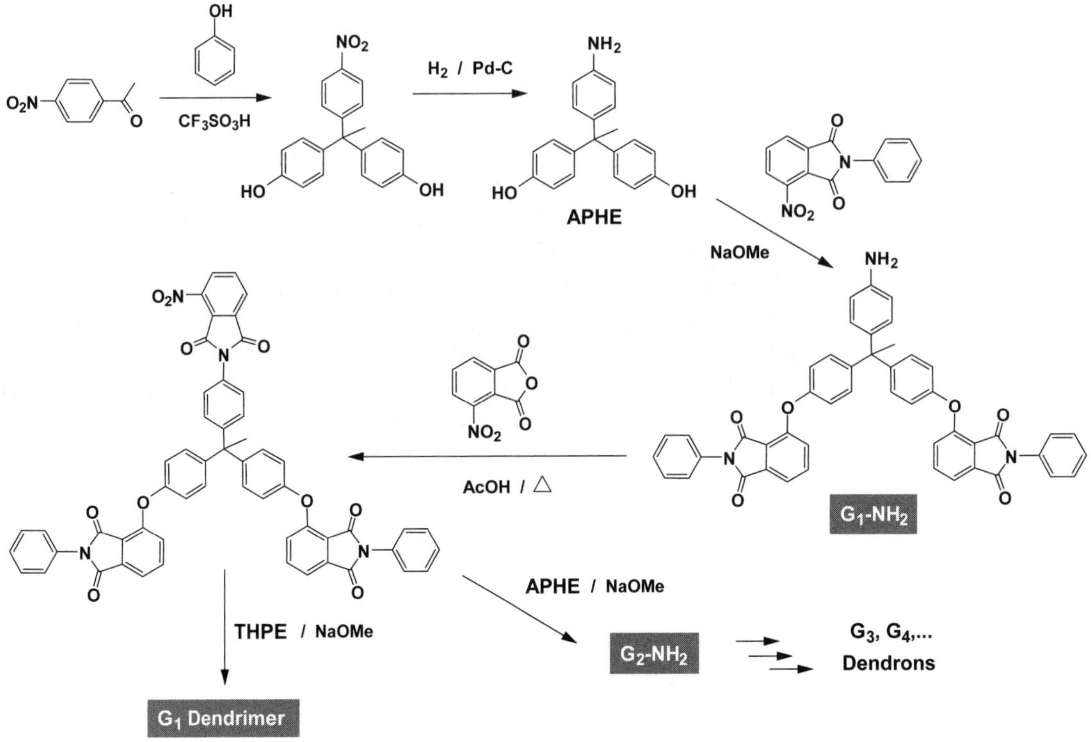

Figure 5.79. Convergent synthesis of dendritic poly(ether imide)s.

5.6.1.2. Dendritic Block Copolymers

Due to the three-dimensional globular nature of dendritic macromolecules, a number of different architectures can result in *dendritic block copolymers*. They may be classified into three categories: linear-dendritic block, dendritic segment-block and dendritic layer-block (Figure 5.80). Linear *dendritic-block* copolymers are similar to traditional block copolymers, but a linear and/or comb polymer block is connected to at least one dendritic (usually dendron) block, leading to AB diblock or ABA (or ABC) triblock.[340-345] The latter two classes are a well-defined specific group of dendrimers.[346-353] Dendritic *segment-block* copolymers are constructed with two or more dendrons of different constitutional building blocks while the dendritic *layer-block* copolymers consist of two or more concentric layers, which have different constitutional building blocks.

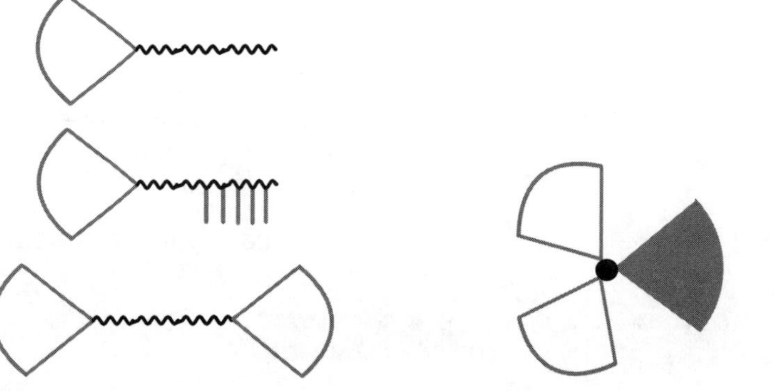

Linear dendritic-block **Dendritic Segment-block** **Dendritic Layer-block**

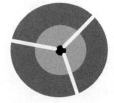

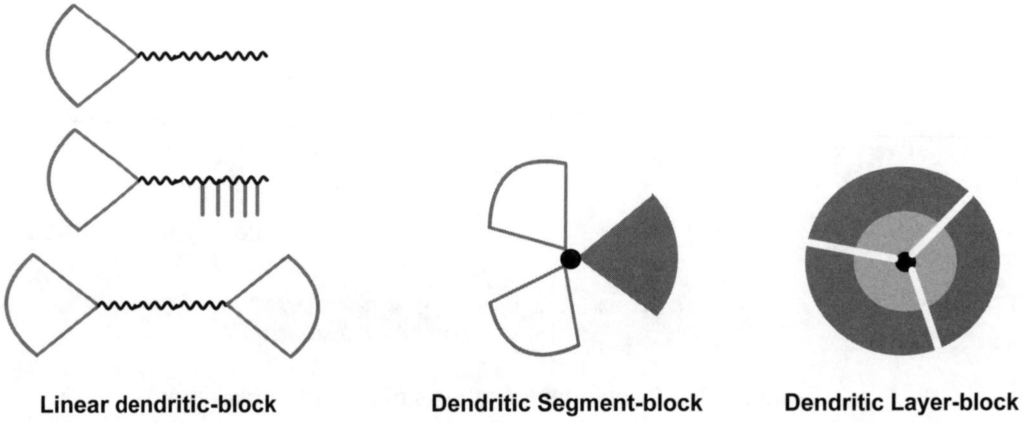

Figure 5.80. Schematic of major dendritic block copolymers.

Figure 5.81 outlines the synthesis of representative AB- and ABA-type linear dendritic-block copolymers. The AB-type can be constructed with poly(ethylene oxide) (PEO) as the linear block and poly(amidoamine) (PAMAM) or poly(benzyl ether) (PBE) as the dendritic block (*vide supra*).[340,341] This class of polymers exhibits interesting properties, e.g., PAMAM-based copolymer displays some degree of microphase segregation irrespective of the composition of the diblock. The ABA-type copolymers can be constructed by divergent growth of the A blocks from a difunction linear polymer B, or simply by connecting the linear polymer B with activated A dendrons.[341,342] For example, a new class of ampiphilic triblock copolymers in which the middle B block is a hydrophilic PEO segment, while the terminal hydrophobic A blocks are a dendritic carbosilane (PCS), has been prepared by the divergent approach by employing repeated hydrosilylation and alkylation.[342] These copolymers form micellar aggregates (mean diameters 170 and 190 nm for first- and second generation dendritic carbosilane blocks, respectively) in an aqueous phase.

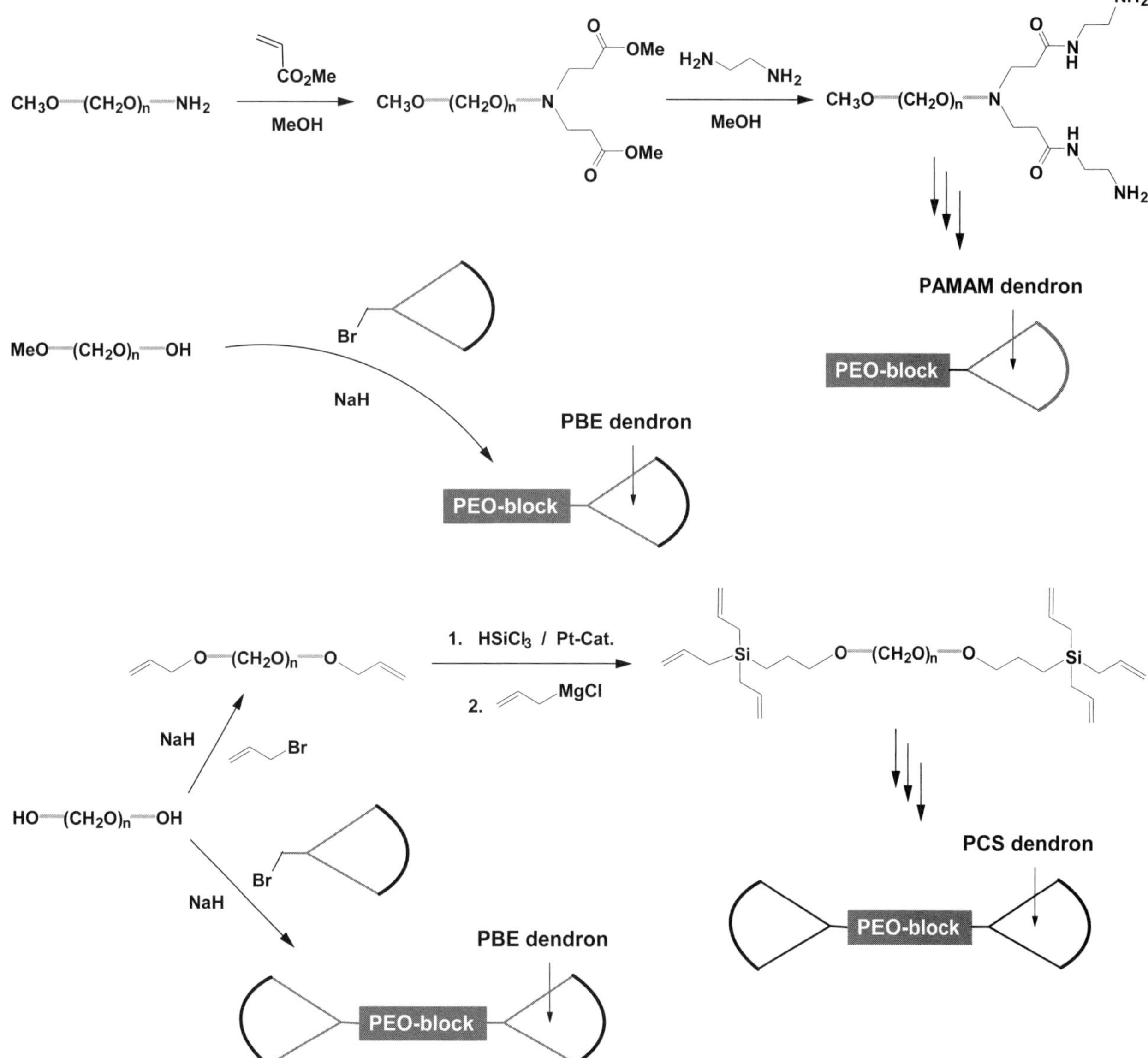

Figure 5.81. Synthesis of representative linear dendritic-block copolymers.

Dendritic segment-block copolymers are usually prepared by connecting different dendrons or dendrons containing different 'sub-dendrons' to a polyfunctional core.[346-348] Since the former approach yields statistical mixtures, the latter is preferred. Figure 5.82 outlines the step-wise preparation of a dendron containing two different sub-dendrons, PBE and poly(aryl ester) (PAE), following the chemistry discussed earlier in this section.[346]

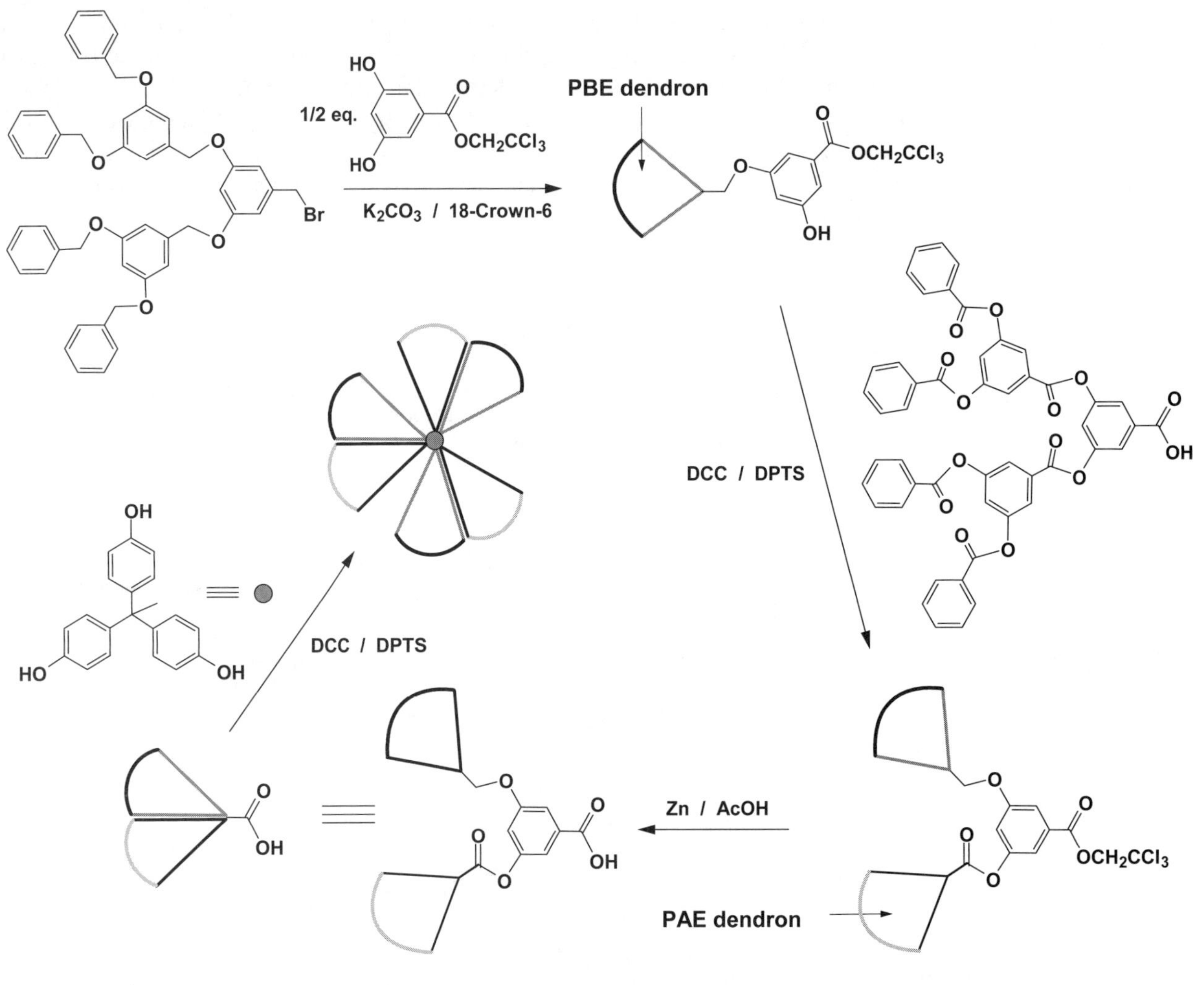

Figure 5.82. Synthesis of a representative dendritic segment-block copolymer.

Dendritic layer-block copolymers containing concentric layers around the central core have been obtained by both convergent and divergent approaches.[349-353] Figure 5.83 depicts the synthesis of dendron-containing layer blocks by judicious selection of reaction sequence, employing the aforementioned protocol.[346] Thus, linking the focal point of this dendron to a core leads to a dendritic layer-block copolymer. Figure 5.84 delineates a divergent strategy for the preparation of a tri-layer dendritic block copolymer in which a multifunctional core molecule was used as an initiator for the controlled ring-opening polymerization of ε-caprolactone to produce the poly(ε-caprolactone) (PCL) layer.[349,350] Subsequent covalent linking of a masked aliphatic ester-based dendron,[354] PDPA, through the terminal hydroxyl groups, produced the second layer, which after unmasking offered the opportunity to again grow PCL, the third terminal layer.

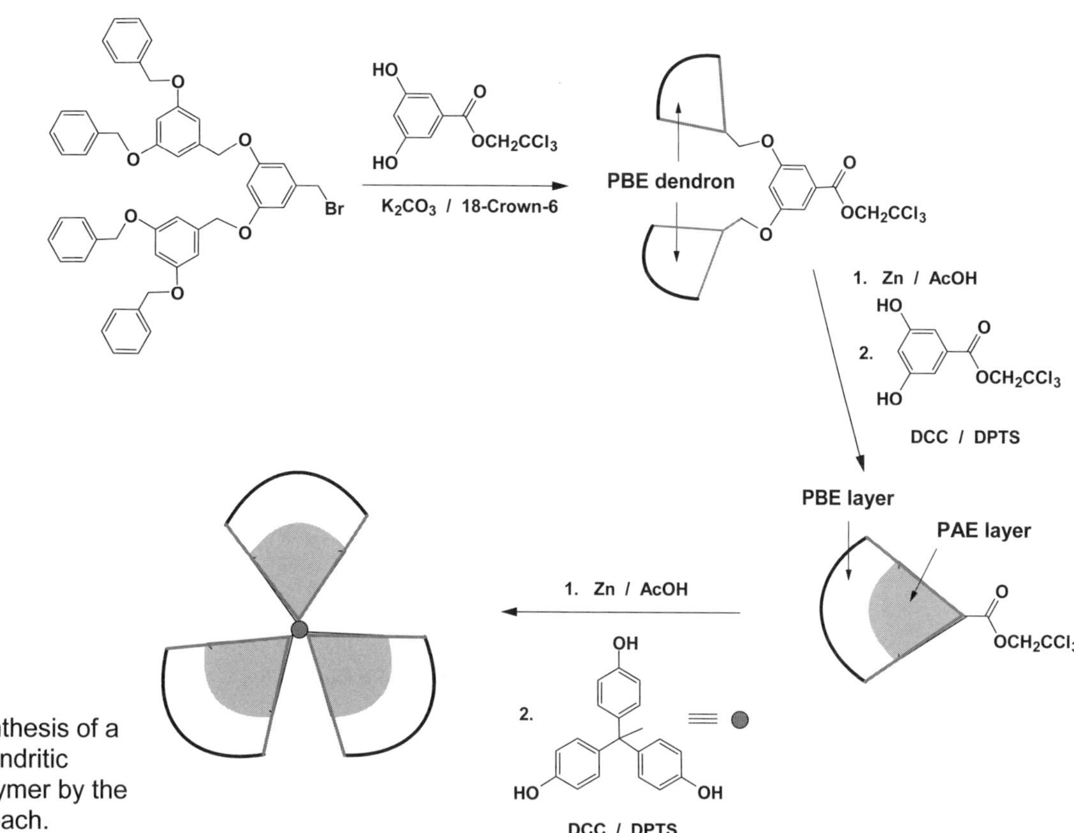

Figure 5.83. Synthesis of a representative dendritic layer-block copolymer by the convergent approach.

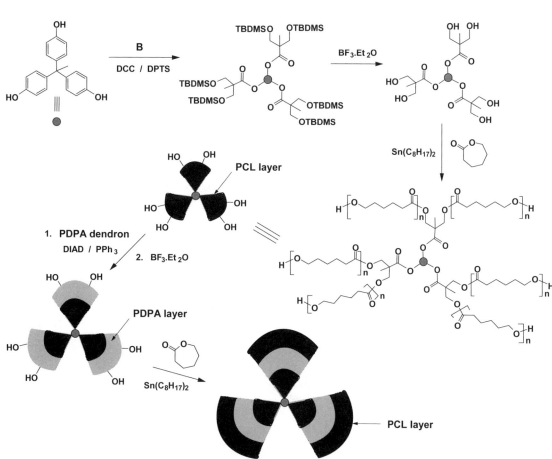

Figure 5.84. Synthesis of a representative dendritic layer-block copolymer by the divergent approach.

5.6.2. Dendronized Polymers

Dendronized polymers (often called "*denpols*") are linear dendritic polymers that have pendent dendrons in every repeat unit.[355-357] In these polymers, as the size of the dendron (i.e., the generation of the dendron) increases, the steric repulsion between neighboring dendrons increases (Figure 5.85).[358,359] Consequently, unlike dendrimers (which possess spherical shape), denpols with higher-generation dendrons (typically, third or fourth generation) form large molecular objects with a near-cylindrical/rod-like shape, which can have dimensions of 4-7 nm in diameter and 200-400 nm in length. The length and radial extent of these polymers may be controlled by the number of repeat units along the backbone and the generation of growth of the attached dendrons. This type of nanosized molecules with cylindrical shape is useful for building novel functional materials (such as scaffolds for drug delivery, DNA compaction and catalyst support), because of the high density of the functional groups at the periphery of the dendrons.

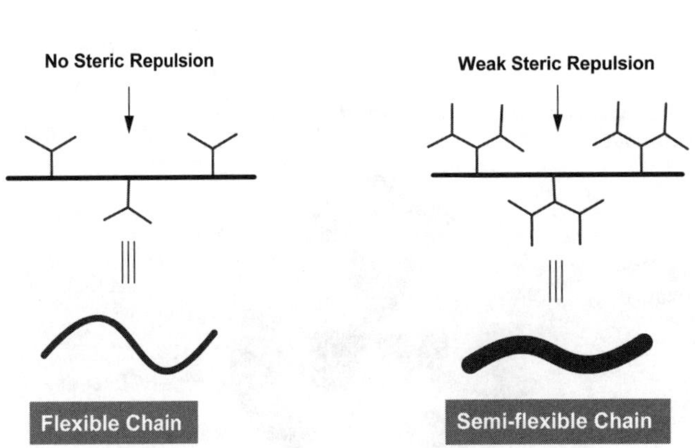

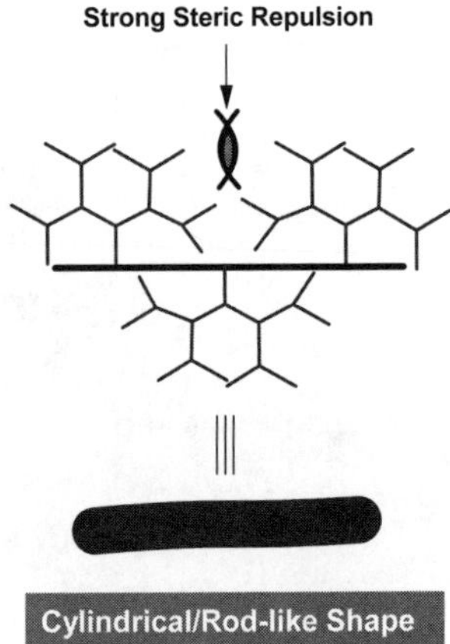

Figure 5.85. Schematic of the change of shape of dendronized polymers with the increase in size (generation) of dendrons.

As depicted in Figure 5.86, there are three synthetic approaches for the preparation of such "surface-decorated" type of cylindrical polymers: the "graft-to route", the "graft-from route" and the "macromonomer route". In the former two routes, a functionalized polymer is prepared first, followed by coupling of dendrons along the polymer chain. Thus, these two synthetic routes offer some synthetic freedom in terms of the dendrons, which can be achieved by divergent or convergent growth. The purification is usually simple since the dendronized polymers are easily isolated by precipitation. However, steric crowding of larger dendrons may prevent full coupling of the dendrons. By contrast, the macromonomer route involves the preparation of a polymerizable dendron monomer, followed by polymerization of the monomer. This approach is straightforward and popular since it offers accurate control over the dendritic side groups. However, steric hindrance may become a problem. Once the dendrons become too large, the polymerizable group may be "shielded" and inhibit polymerization, leading to a low molecular weight denpol or no product at all.

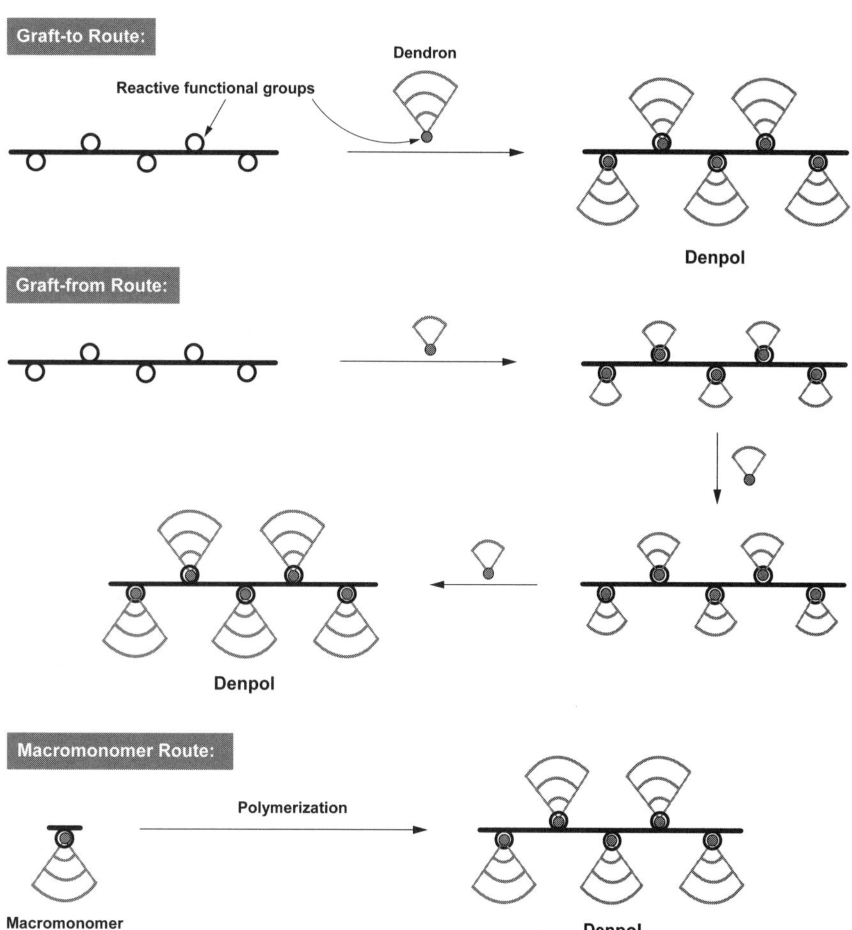

Figure 5.86. Schematic of the synthetic routes to denpols.

In the *graft-to strategy*, a linear polymer with reactive functional groups (one in every repeat unit) is required. One of the early examples utilized poly(*p*-phenylene)s (PPP-1 and PPP-2) containing pendent hydroxyl or iodo groups as the linear polymers, which were synthesized by a traditional palladium-catalyzed cross-coupling reaction (see the Section 5.1.1.1f).[360,361] The poly(*p*-phenylene)s were easily coupled with dendrons containing a single functional group at the focal point capable of reacting with the pendent functional groups on PPP (Figure 5.87).[362,363] The degree of coverage in this class of denpols (DEN-1 and DEN-2) was shown to be independent of the degree of polymerization, but decreases with increasing generation of the dendron.

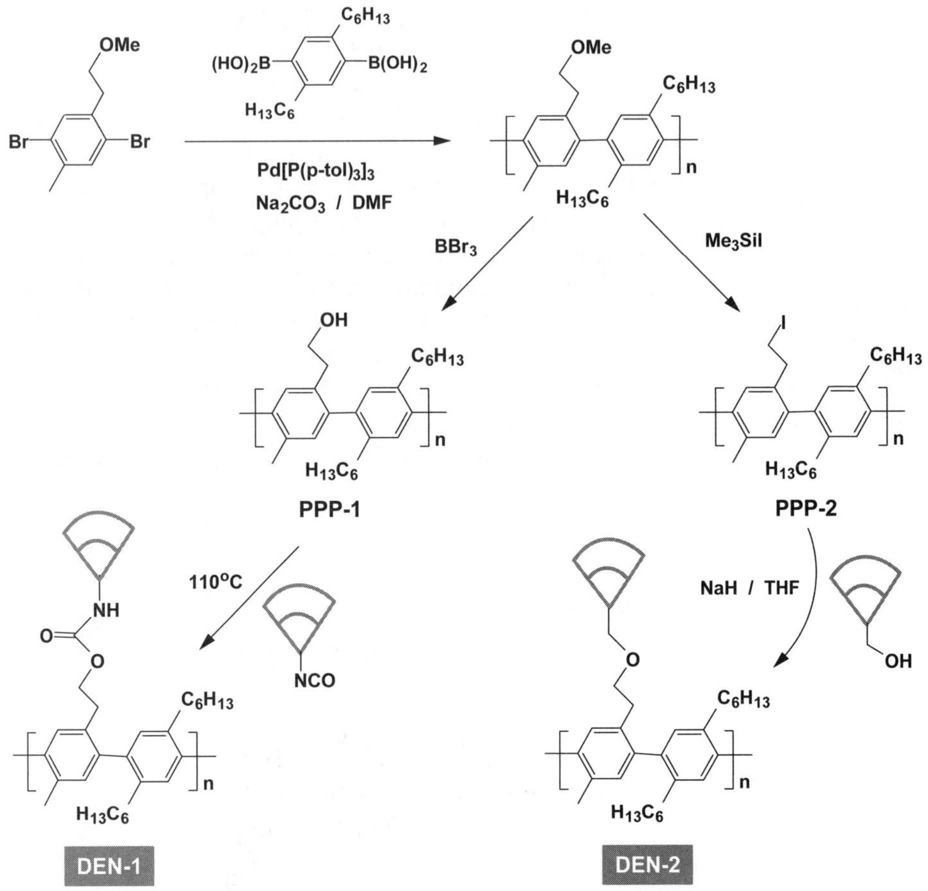

Figure 5.87. Synthesis of poly(*p*-phenylene)-based denpols by the graft-to approach.

Among the other denpols synthesized by this approach, the poly(vinyl acetylene)-based one, prepared via "*click chemistry* (reaction)" by Fréchet *et al.*, is especially important, because the Cu(I) catalyzed Huisgen 2+3 cycloaddition reaction between a terminal acetylene and an azide groups is highly efficient, and yet chemoselective (Figure 5.88).[364-367] Thus, poly(vinyl acetylene) (PVAC) reacted with poly(benzyl ether) (PBE, see Figure 5.72) dendron containing an azide group at the focal point to yield a series of denpols (e.g., DEN-3). The dendronization reaction was quantitative for G_1 and G_2 dendrons, while 98% for G_3 and no reaction for G_4. Other notable denpols include those derived from poly(ferrocenylsilane)s, which contain iron atoms in the main chain (see Figure 5.62 in the section of inorganic polymers).[368]

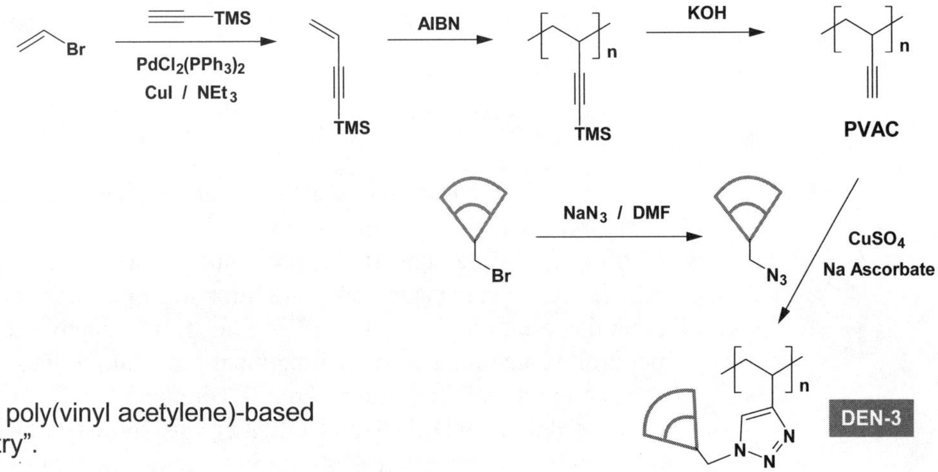

Figure 5.88. Synthesis of a poly(vinyl acetylene)-based denpol via the "click chemistry".

By contrast, dendronized polymers synthesized by the *graft-from route* typically involve the use of commercially available polymer-containing reactive functional groups, such as poly(ethylene imine) (PEI), poly(methylhydrosiloxane) (PMHS) and poly(*p*-hydroxystyrene) (PHS). PEI was converted to PAMAM-based denpols (e.g., DEN-4) by Michael addition of the amine to methyl acrylate and subsequent amide coupling with ethylene diamine (Figure 5.89).[369] PMHS-based denpols, such as DEN-5, were prepared via platinum catalyzed hydrosilylation chemistry, using an excess of allyltrichlorosilane, followed by reaction of the resulting chlorosilane functions with an allyl Grignard compound.[370,371] Most denpols by the graft-from approach can be readily prepared up to 2nd generation, albeit the requirement of large excess of reagents and longer reaction time. However, their yield and percent coverage are markedly reduced with the increase in generation. In most cases, the synthesis of 3rd generation denpol was unsuccessful. The denpols (e.g., DEN-6) obtained by divergent grafting of aliphatic polyester dendrons from PHS are somewhat remarkable, because unlike all others, it only requires a small excess of reagent to achieve quantitative growth, and it requires no means of purification other than a simple solvent extraction or precipitation (Figure 5.89).[372-374] The technique involves repetition of DMAP-catalyzed coupling between the benzylidene-protected anhydride derivative of 2,2-bis(hydroxymethyl)propionic acid (BAPA) and the hydroxyl groups of PHS, followed by a deprotection step involving palladium-catalyzed hydrogenation.

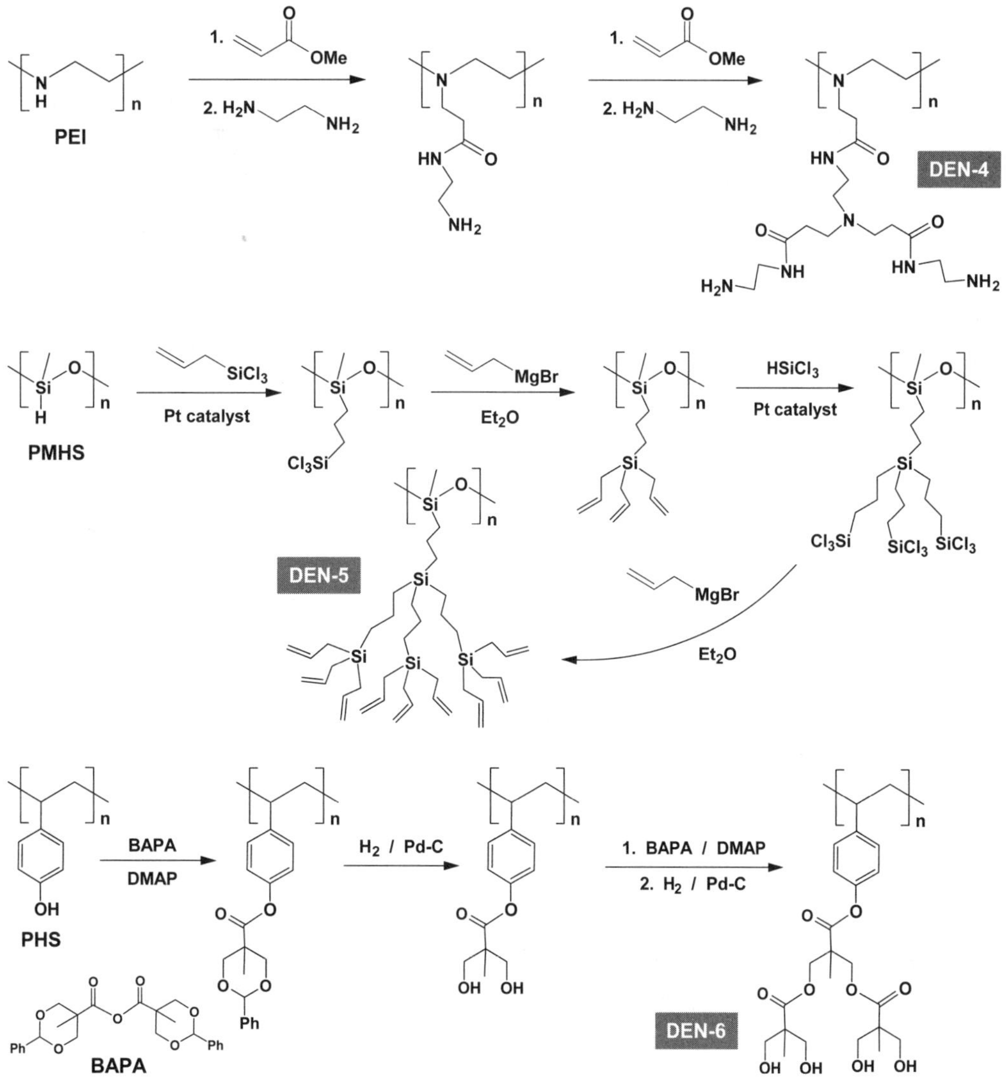

Figure 5.89. Synthesis of denpols via the graft-from approach.

As mentioned earlier, the "*macromonomer route*" has been very popular and that is due to ample opportunities to construct the linear polymer backbone using various chemistries involving both chain-growth and step-growth mechanisms (Figure 5.90). For example, several denpols were made by free-radical polymerization or controlled free-radical polymerization (e.g., ATRP) of dendrons bearing acryloyl or styryl group at the focal point.[375-380] Among these denpols, DEN-7, which are non-charged and water soluble and possess peripheral hydroxyl groups, are very promising for applications to critical areas, viz., biomineralization, drug delivery, and the entire complex of protein resistant materials.[375] Suzuki polycondensation between a dihalide carrying a dendron and a diboronic acid offers another new class of denpols (e.g., DEN-8 and DEN-9), which are electroactive because of the presence of continuous π-conjugation along the linear polymer backbone.[381-384] Palladium-catalyzed Heck coupling reaction between a dendron bearing dihalide and a divinyl compound (such as divinylbenzene) has also led to denpols with π-conjugated polymer backbone.[385] Ring-opening metathesis polymerization (ROMP) of norbornenyl-bearing dendrons in the presence of a Grubbs catalyst (see Chapter-1 for more discussion) is another attractive chemistry to prepare denpols (e.g., DEN-10 and DEN-11), since the relief of ring strain in the norbornenyl group results in a strong driving force for the polymerization.[386-389] Moreover, the pendent dendrons on these denpols are placed further apart along the backbone compared to the denpols derived from acryloyl or styryl macromonomers, resulting in a less sterically demanding environment.

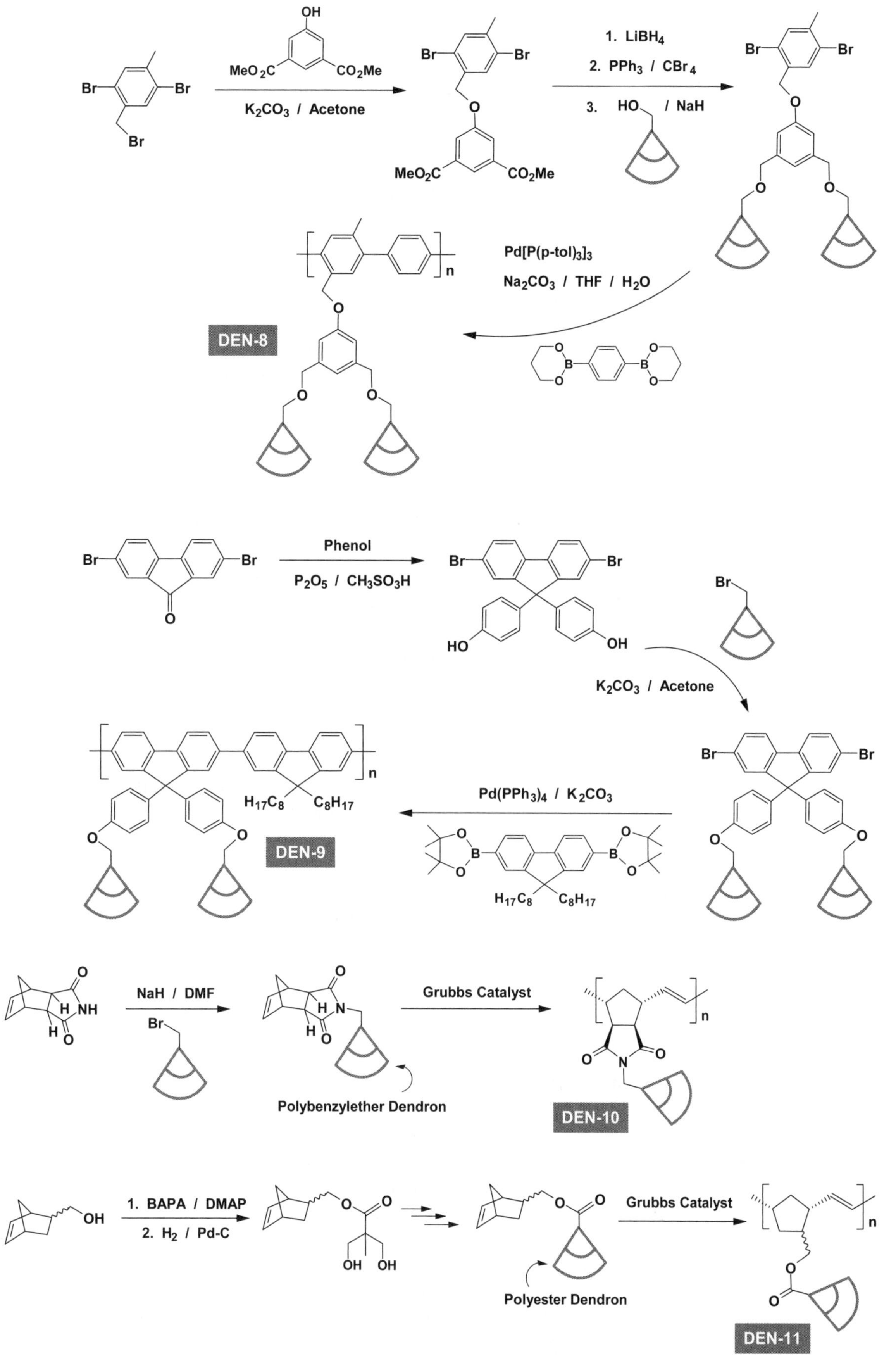

DEN-8

DEN-9

DEN-10

DEN-11

Figure 5.90. Synthesis of denpols via the macromonomer approach.

5.6.3. Dendrigraft Polymers

In contrast to dendrimers, *dendrigraft polymers* (also called *comb-burst* or *arborescent polymers*) are constructed around a linear polymer chain, to which branches and sub-branches consisting of homopolymer and/or copolymer blocks are randomly introduced.[390-392] It is important to emphasize that, unlike dendronized polymers, in these polymer branches are not present on every repeat unit or they are perfect dendron. Thus, dendrigraft polymers may be viewed as semi-controlled branched polymer architectures intermediate in terms of structure control between dendrimers and hyperbranched polymers (*vide infra*). Since these materials are prepared by linking macromolecular building blocks, a very high molecular weight is reached in a few cycles. In fact, dendrigraft technology is the fastest synthetic route for producing high molecular weight, low polydispersity polymers currently known. Moreover, each generation may be specifically tailored for properties by grafting chains of varying molecular weight or physical properties. The size of these polymers is typically 1-2 orders of magnitude larger (ranging from around 10 nm to a few hundred nanometers) than their dendritic counterparts.

5.6.3.1. Synthesis of Dendrigraft Polymers

In general, these materials are easier to synthesize than dendrimers and can be prepared by both divergent (core first) and convergent (arm first) approaches. The divergent strategy includes both *grafting onto* and *grafting from* methods, whereas a *grafting through* method, also developed, is a convergent technique (conceptually more closely related to the hyperbranched polymer syntheses).

5.6.3.1a. The Grafting onto Approach

The synthesis of *arborescent polystyrenes* is a classic example of this approach. The strategy involves successive reactions of chloromethylation and anionic grafting (Figure 5.91).[393] Thus, a linear polystyrene was chloromethylated under dilute solution conditions (to avoid intermolecular crosslinking reactions) to form a functionalized linear substrate, PS-CH_2Cl, which on coupling with living 1,1-diphenylethylene (DPE) unit capped polystyryllithium (PS-DPE) blocks leads to a comb-branched (G_0) polystyrene. Additional cycles of chloromethylation and coupling produce higher generation arborescent polystyrenes.

The grafting onto strategy has also been applied to synthesize *arborescent polybutadienes*.[394] The synthetic scheme relied on the anionic polymerization of 1,3-butadiene in hexane, yielding a polybutadiene (PB) microstructure with ca. 6% of pendent vinyl groups along the backbone (Figure 5.92). These vinyl groups were converted into reactive coupling sites by hydrosilylation with chlorodimethylsilane to produce the functional polymer, PB-DMSC. Thus, reaction of an excess of polybutadienyllithium (PBLi) with PB-DMSC affords a comb-branched (G_0) polymer. Repetition of the hydrosilylation and coupling reactions yielded higher generation arborescent polybutadienes. Apart from the aforementioned arborescent styrene and butadiene homopolymer syntheses, a variety of arborescent copolymers were also prepared by grafting poly(*tert*-butyl methacrylate)[395], polyisoprene[396,397], and poly(2-vinylpyridine)[398,399] macroanions onto arborescent polystyrene substrates, using variations of the basic schemes discussed above. These reactions broaden the range of physical properties observed and produce materials useful for a wider range of applications.

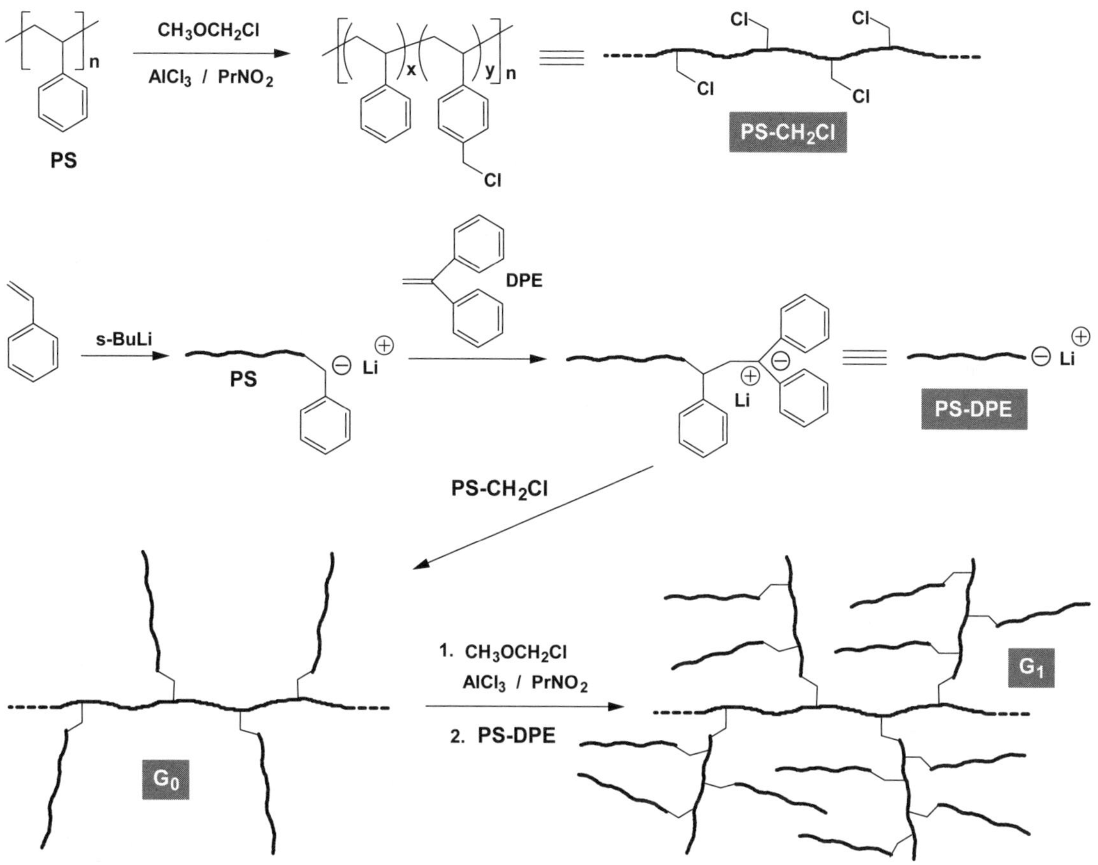

Figure 5.91. Synthesis of an arborescent polystyrene via the grafting onto approach.

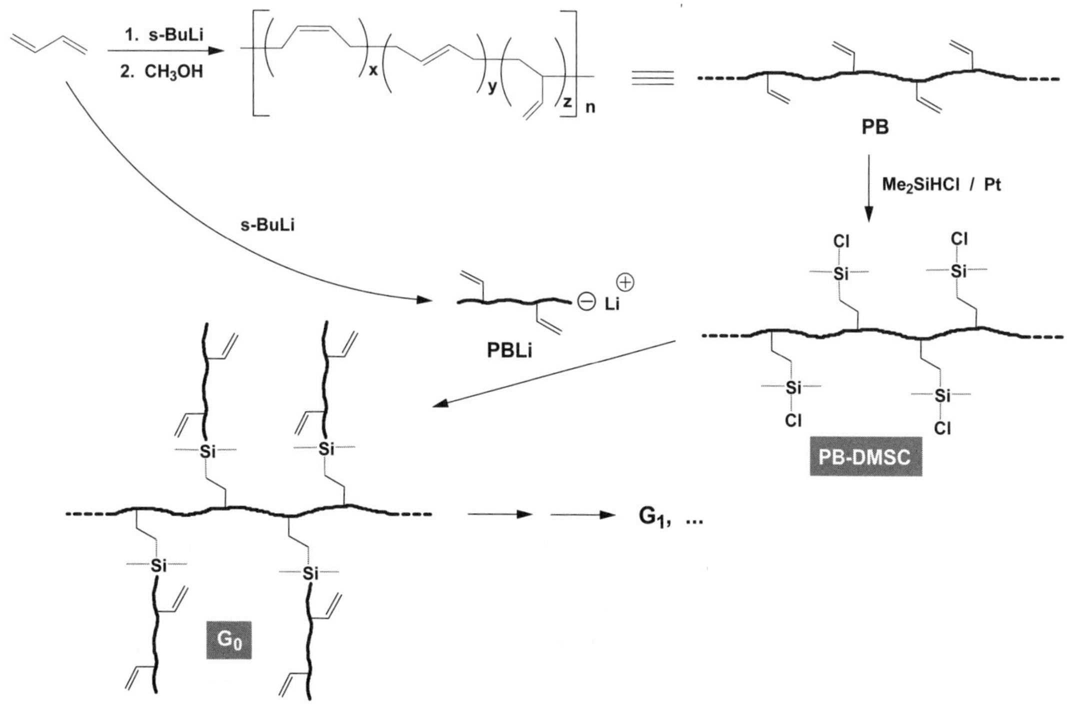

Figure 5.92. Synthesis of an arborescent polybutadiene via the grafting onto approach.

5.6.3.1b. The Grafting from Approach

This method has received less attention than the grafting onto approach, because it is often associated with side reactions leading to dendrigraft polymers, which are less perfect, difficult to characterize and possess broader molecular weight distribution (MWD). Nevertheless, this strategy has allowed the synthesis of novel macromolecular architectures inaccessible by other methods. An example of the grafting from approach is the preparation of arborescent copolymers, performed in a single pot, by anionic copolymerization of styrene with 1,3-diisopropenylbenzene (DIB) and activation of the pendent isopropenyl moieties of the resulting copolymer (PS-PDIB) with *sec*-butyllithium (Figure 5.93).[392] This strategy is made possible because the much lower reactivity of DIB than styrene in the anionic copolymerization reaction, which prevents gel (crosslinking) formation. Thus, arborescent polystyrene-*graft*-poly(*tert*-butyl methacrylate) copolymer (G_1) was obtained by addition of *tert*-butyl methacrylate (*t*-BMA) to activated G_0 polystyrene substrates.

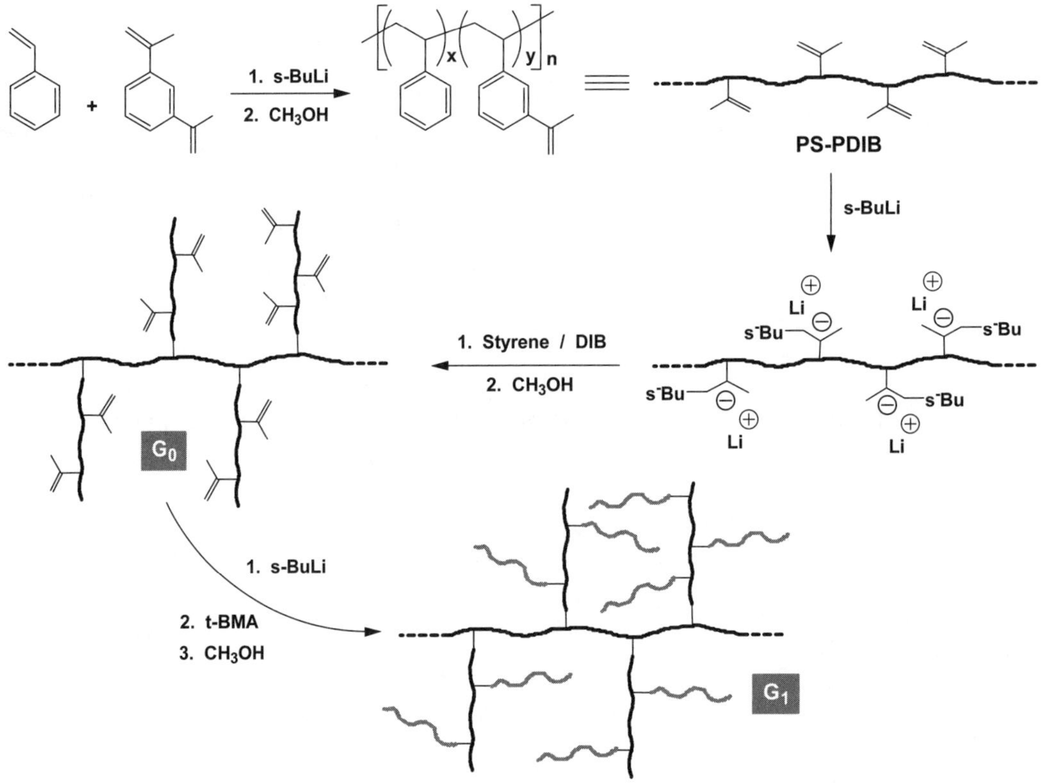

Figure 5.93. Synthesis of arborescent polystyrene-*graft*-poly(tert-butyl methacrylate) copolymers via the grafting from approach.

Although the graft from approach has limited opportunities in terms of molecular design, a number of dendrigraft polymers with unique architectures have been developed by combining the grafting onto and grafting from techniques. Figure 5.94 depicts an example of an amphiphilic arborescent copolymer consisting of a branched polystyrene core end-linked (outer shell) with poly(ethylene oxide) chains, synthesized by a hybrid approach.[400] The polystyrene core, serving as the grafting substrate, was synthesized by a variation of the grafting onto method described above (Figure 5.91) to introduce hydroxyl chain ends for polymerization with ethylene oxide. A bifunctional initiator, (6-lithiohexyl)acetaldehyde acetal (LHAA)[401], containing a protected hydroxyl functionality, was used to initiate the polymerization of styrene. Thus, the reaction of DPE-capped living polystyryl anions (AC-PS-DPE) with a chloromethylated G_0 polystyrene substrate (G_0-CH_2Cl), yielded a G_1 polymer end-terminated with acetal groups. Deprotection of the acetal functionalities with a small amount (0.1% v/v) of concentrated hydrochloric acid, followed by titration with potassium naphthalide and the addition of ethylene oxide, resulted in the amphiphilic copolymer (PS-*g*-PEO). Thus, by variation in the amount of ethylene oxide, one can control the thickness of the outer shell (hydrophilic polymer layer). Indeed, copolymers with poly(ethylene oxide) contents ranging from 19 to 66% by weight were achieved by this method.

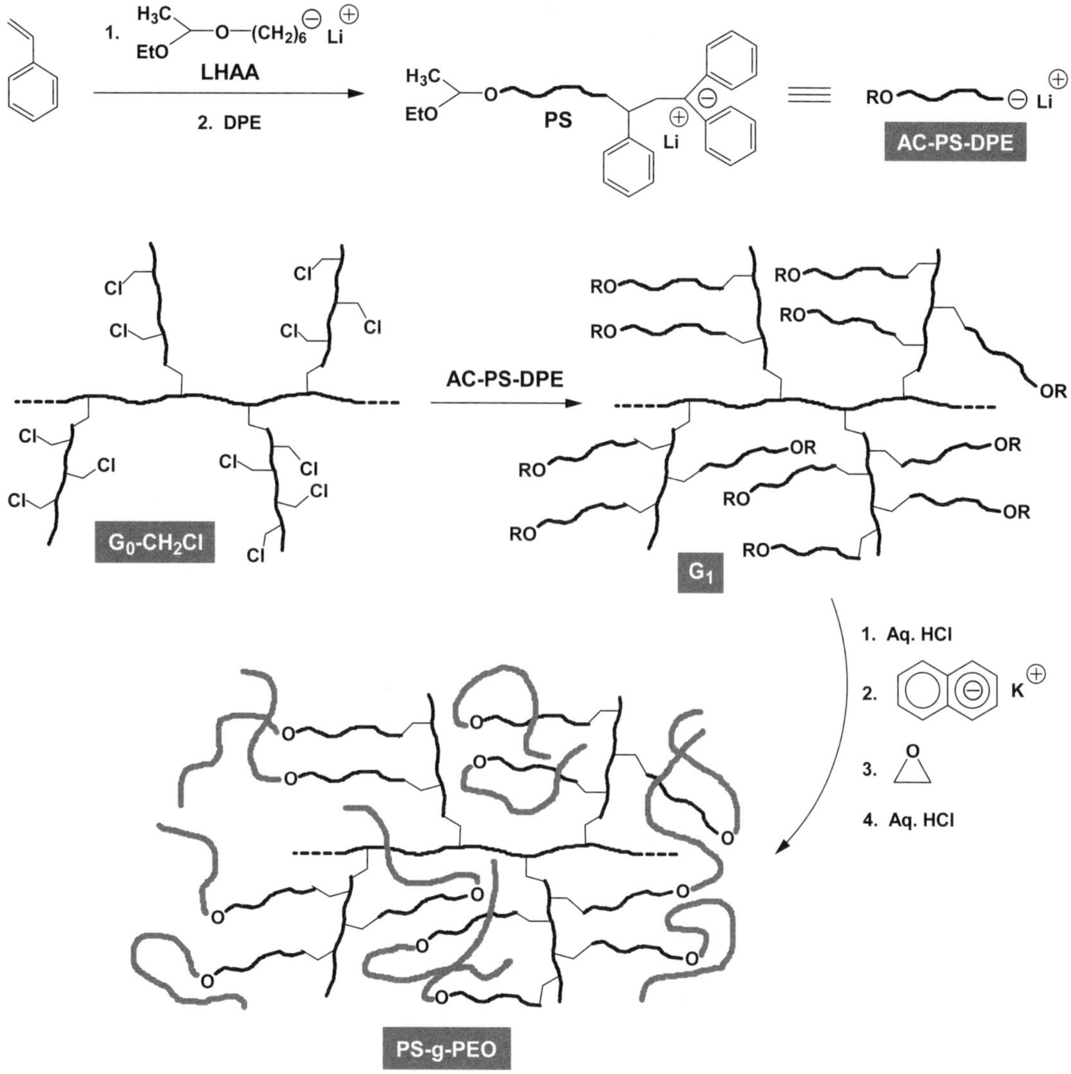

Figure 5.94. Synthesis of an amphiphilic arborescent polystyrene-*graft*-poly(ethylene oxide) copolymer.

Dendrigraft polymers based on poly(chloroethyl vinyl ether) (PCVE) and polystyrene macromolecular building blocks were also prepared by combining the aforementioned techniques (Figure 5.95).[402-405] Living cationic polymerization of 2-chloroethyl vinyl ether (CVE) in the presence of α-chloro(2-chloroethyl)ethyl ether (the HCl adduct of CVE) and zinc chloride was first used to obtain a linear PCVE backbone.[406] The anionic polymerization of styrene was then initiated with a lithioacetal compound, LAC, to generate polystyryllithium with a diethylacetal group at the chain end (DEA-PSLi). Thus, grafting of DEA-PSLi to the PCVE backbone generates a comb-branched structure (PCVE-PS). Subsequent treatment of the terminal diethylacetal and dimethylacetal groups of G_0 with trimethylsilyl iodide (TMSI) yields α-iodoether groups that can be activated with zinc chloride to initiate the cationic polymerization of a new aliquot of CVE. The resulting comb-branched copolymer, PCVE-PS-PCVE, can be subjected to further grafting with DEA-PSLi, and so on, to prepare the higher generation polymers. It is believed that the architecture obtained from the grafting process has branching points located only in the terminal (outer) portion of the side chains, rather than randomly distributed along the pendent PCVE chains. Variations in the architecture of the dendrigraft polymers are possible by controlling the length of the PCEVE and/or PS blocks, including the use of other monomers, such as 2-hydroxyethyl vinyl ether.[407]

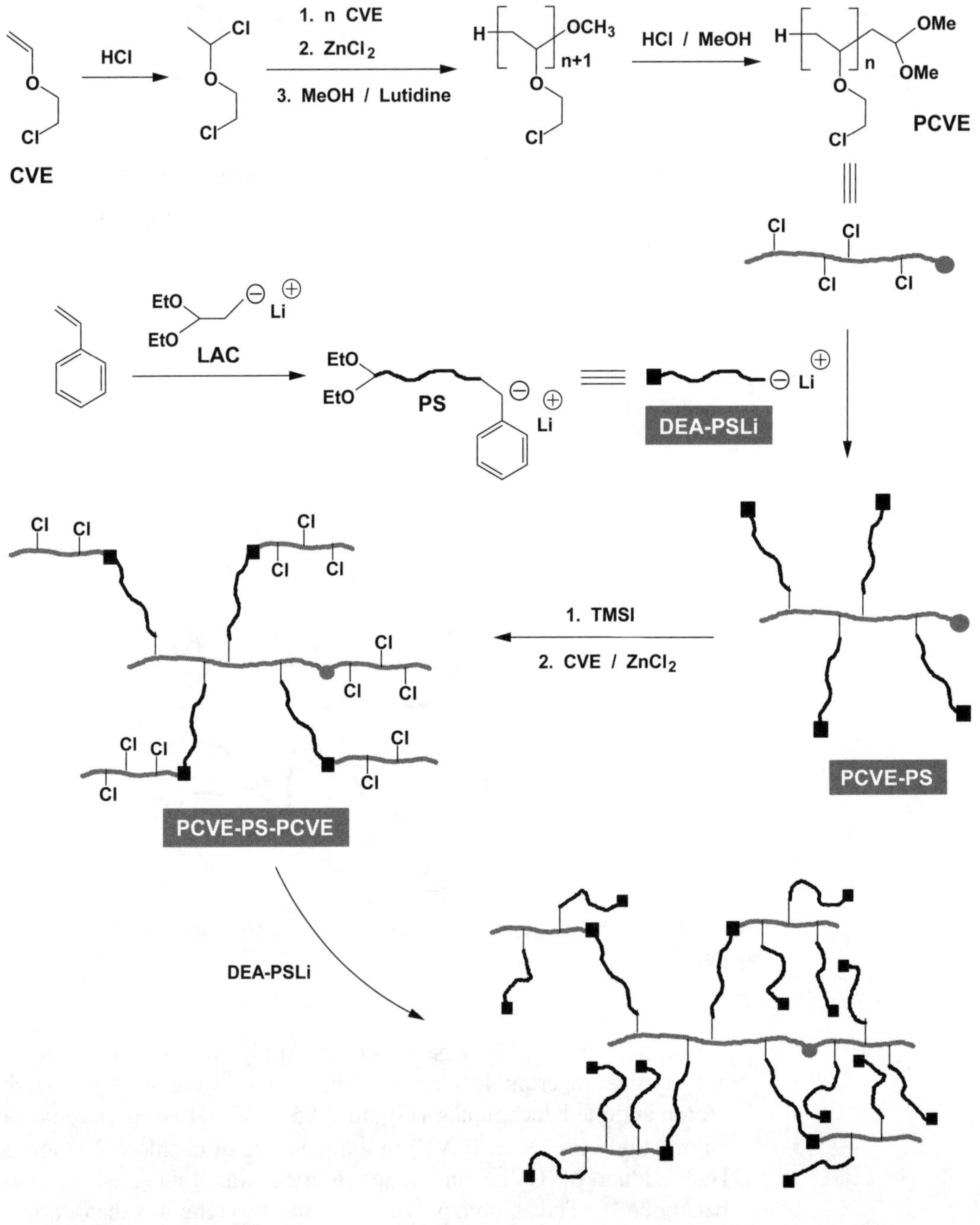

Figure 5.95. Synthesis of a dendrigraft polymer containing PCVE and PS blocks.

5.6.3.1c. The Grafting through Approach

This approach has less control and more complications than the aforementioned two approaches, resulting in only a few well developed schemes. Figure 5.96 depicts a strategy, a one-pot self-branching convergent synthetic scheme that relies on the *in situ* formation of macromonomers by reaction of living macroanions in the presence of a small amount of a bifunctional monomer, vinylbenzyl chloride (VBC) or 4-(chlorodimethylsilyl)styrene (CDMSS), carrying a polymerizable vinyl group and a chemical functionality capable of coupling with the living chains.[408,409] Since, the chloromethyl or chlorosilyl functionalities reacts with polystyryllithium at a faster rate than propagation through the vinyl group, the resulting macromonomers will always have a terminal vinyl group. Thus, when the bifunctional monomer and styrene (1:10 molar ratio) were added slowly to linear polystyryllithium living chains, randomly branched dendrigraft polymers (RB-DPS) with a narrow molecular weight distribution is produced. Another example involves convergent cationic polymerization of isobutylene in the presence of 4-(2-methoxyisopropyl)styrene, acting as the bifunctional monomer.[410]

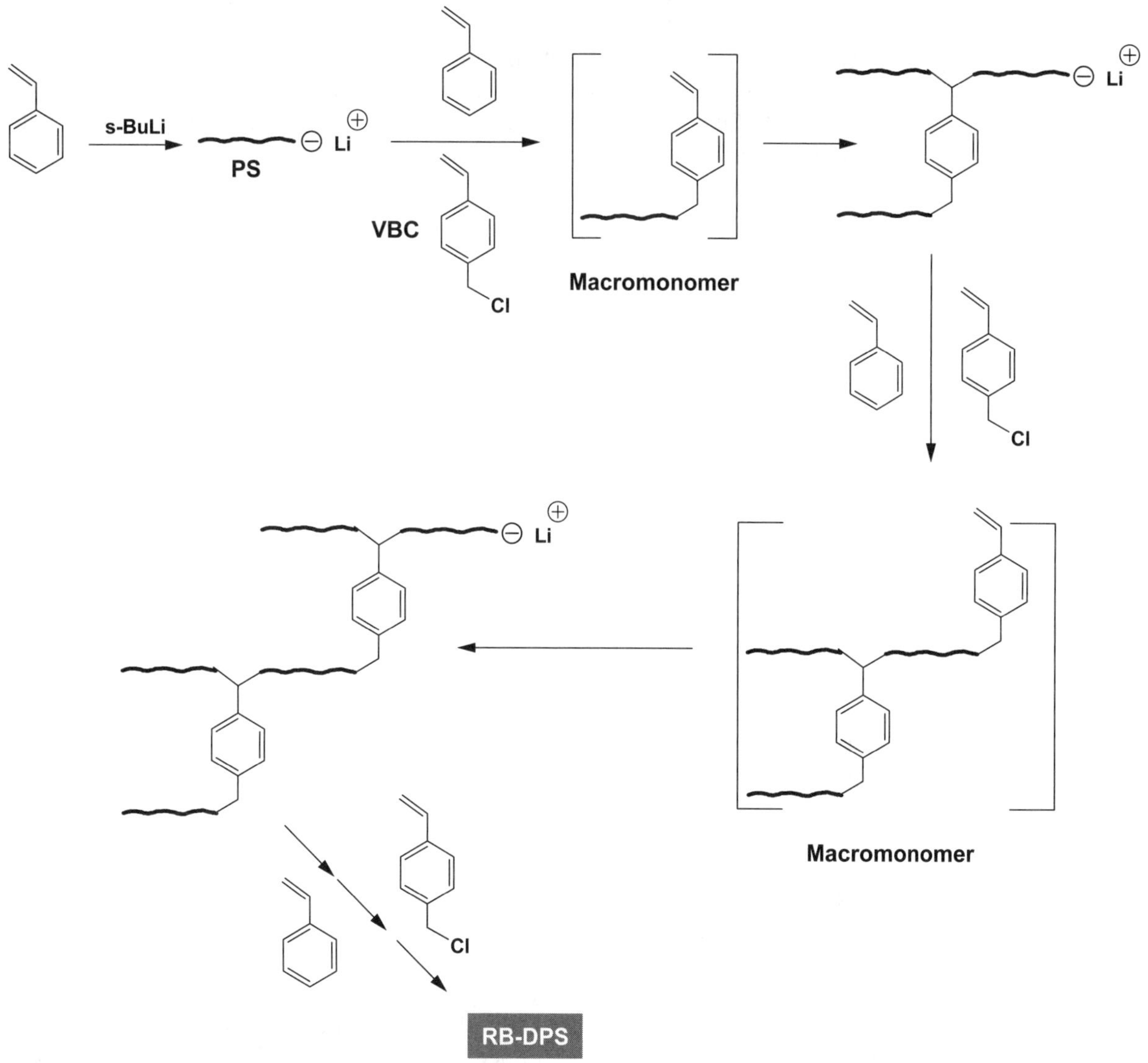

s-BuLi
PS
Li
VBC
Cl
Macromonomer
Li
Cl
Li
Macromonomer
Cl
RB-DPS

Figure 5.96. Synthesis of dendrigraft polystyrenes via the grafting through approach.

5.6.4. Hyperbranched polymers

Hyperbranched polymers possess dendritic branching, but the branches do not emanate from the central core, nor is the branching necessarily regular as it is in dendrimers. They are composed of terminal (**T**), linear (**L**) and dendritic (**D**) units, which are distinguished by the number of unreacted functional groups in the unit. The degree of branching (**DB**) is widely used as a parameter to indicate the architecture of hyperbranched polymers. The **DB** of hyperbranched polymers is given by

$$\mathrm{DB} = \frac{\text{(no. of dendritic units)} + \text{(no. of terminal units)}}{\text{total no. of units}} = \frac{D + T}{D + L + T}$$

The "one-pot" step-growth polymerization of $\mathbf{AB_x}$ ($\mathbf{x} \geq 2$ and **A** groups react exclusively with **B** groups) monomers is the most widely used pathway for the synthesis of hyperbranched polymers (Figure 5.97).[411,412] The $\mathbf{AB_2}$-type monomer is especially attractive because, despite the stoichiometric imbalance (double the amount of **B** compared with the **A** functionality), a high molecular weight polymer is achieved without the formation of crosslinking (gelation), owing to the presence of both functionalities in the same molecule. As per the theoretical prediction, direct polymerization of this type of monomer produces polymers with a highly branched, irregular structure possessing one unreacted **A** functional group and n+1 number of unreacted **B** functional groups at the chain ends of the polymers, where n is the degree of polymerization.[413]

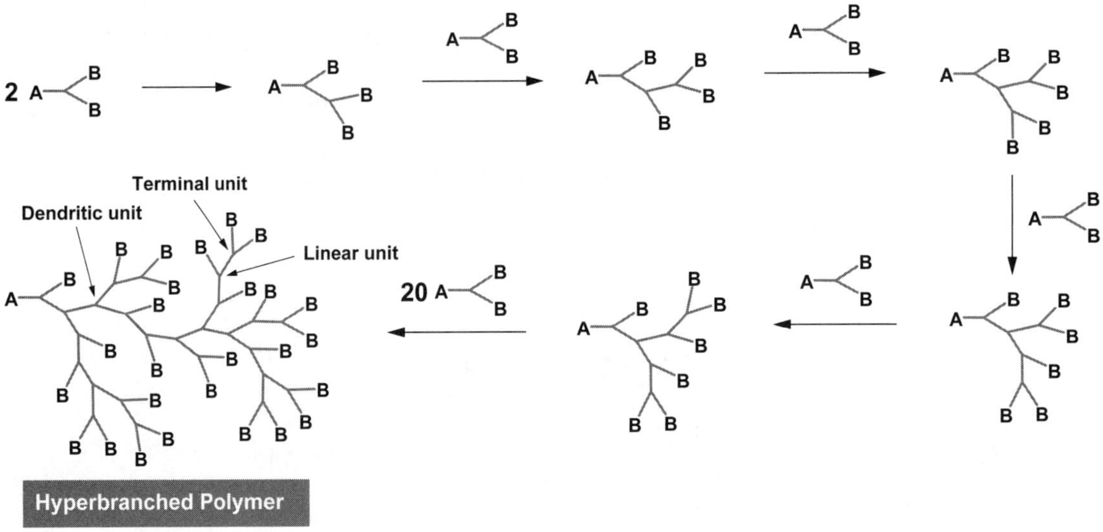

Figure 5.97. Schematic of the statistical growth of a hyperbranched polymer by self-polycondensation reaction of an $\mathbf{AB_2}$ monomer.

The polymerization involves a one-step reaction (usually condensation) where the monomer and suitable catalyst/initiator are mixed and heated to the required reaction temperature. Control over the branching process by this approach is limited, since molecular growth relies on random condensation reactions of multifunctional monomers and the formed oligomers. Typically, the polymerization leads to an extremely broad molecular weight distribution and a low DB around 0.5 compared to 1 for dendritic polymers. The monomers are either commercially available or readily prepared in one or two steps from inexpensive starting materials. Since hyperbranched polymers are easy to synthesize on a large scale, often at a reasonable cost, require little or no purification, and their properties are intermediate between those of dendrimers and linear polymers, they are attractive for large scale industrial applications, such as additives, powder coatings, high solid coatings, crosslinkers, catalysis, and delivery devices. It is important to mention that the hyperbranched polymers have also been prepared by condensation of A_2 + B_3 monomers (1:1 molar feed ratio) and other combinations, but the major problem associated with these systems is unavoidable gelation after a certain conversion level.[414,415] In the past decade, a variety of hyperbranched polymers, such as aromatic polyamides[416,417], poly(ether ketone)s[418-420], poly(phenylene sulfide)s[421], polyesters[422,423], including those containing heterocyclic rings, such as polyetherimides[424,425], have been synthesized by polycondensation of AB_2 type monomers (Figures 5.98 and 5.99). In most cases, these polymers displayed higher solubility compared to their linear analogs. For example, Polyamide-1 is highly soluble in polar aprotic solvents, such as NMP and DMF, while the linear analog is insoluble in these solvents.

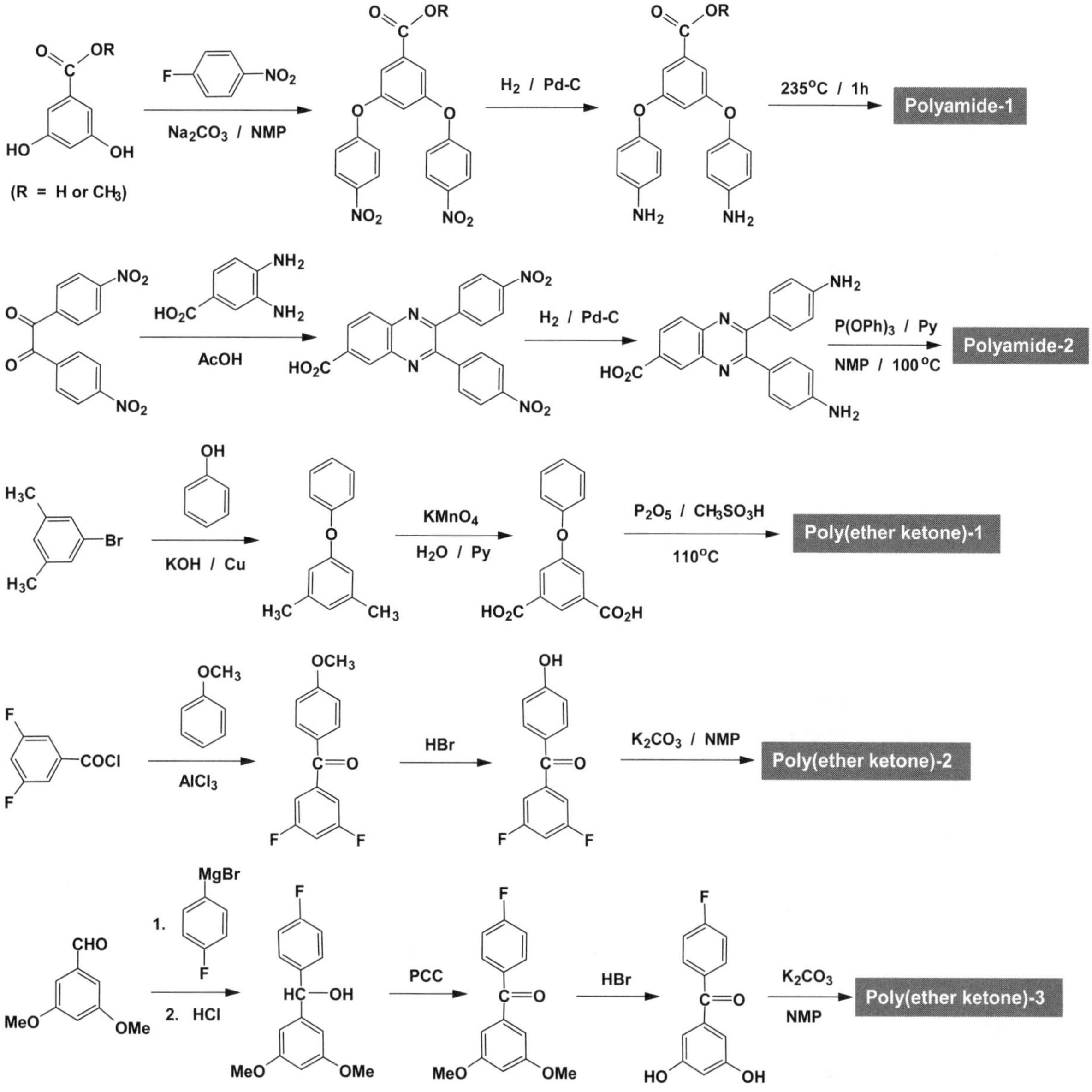

Figure 5.98. Synthesis of hyperbranched polyamides and poly(ether ketone)s via self-condensation of $\mathbf{AB_2}$ monomers.

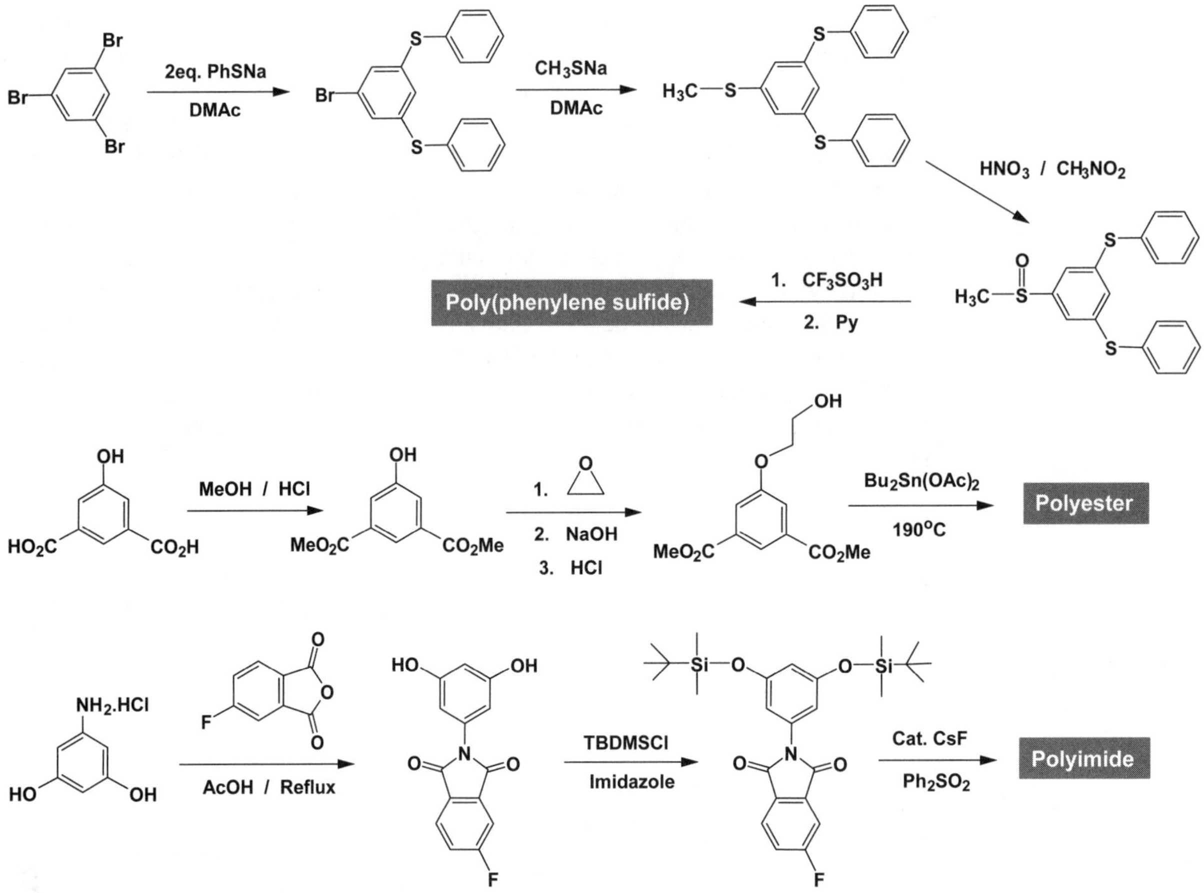

Poly(phenylene sulfide)

Polyester

Polyimide

Figure 5.99. Synthesis of hyperbranched poly(phenylene sulfide), polyester and polyimide via self-condensation of AB_2 monomers.

Among the unusual paths to prepare hyperbranched polymers, diyne polycyclotrimerization has received significant attention.[426,427] This method has been studied extensively using a variety of transtition metal catalysts, such as $TaCl_5$-$SnPh_4$. The transition-metal-mediated reaction, in general, is intolerant of functional groups and, thus, cannot be used to prepare polymers bearing functional groups. Moreover, the cyclization produces random mixtures of 1,2,4- and 1,3,5-trisubstituted benzenes, making the structures of the hyperbranched polymers irregular. This cyclization method has now been made very facile, yet effective, by using a simple base, such as piperidine.[428] The base-catalyzed diyne polycyclotrimerization is not only tolerant of functional groups, such as carbonyl, but produces perfect 1,3,5-regioregular substituents, including a high degree of branching. Figure 5.100 shows a base-catalyzed polymerization of bis(aroylacetylene) leading to a well-defined hyperbranched poly(aroylarylene), which resulted in an excellent photosensitive polymer (because of the presence of benzophenone moieties, see Appendix-I for radical crosslinking mechanism) and can be readily photocrosslinked to give photoresist patterns with nanometer resolutions. The mechanism of cyclization is believed to proceed via a ketoenamine (KEA) intermediate, which reacts further with two more aroylethynyl groups to give a dihydrobenzene (DHB). The piperidine moiety of DHB is eliminated by its reaction with another aroylethynyl group and aromatization gives a 1,3,5-trisubstituted benzene ring. Repetition of this cycle results in the formation of a high DB hyperbranched polymer of high molecular weight.

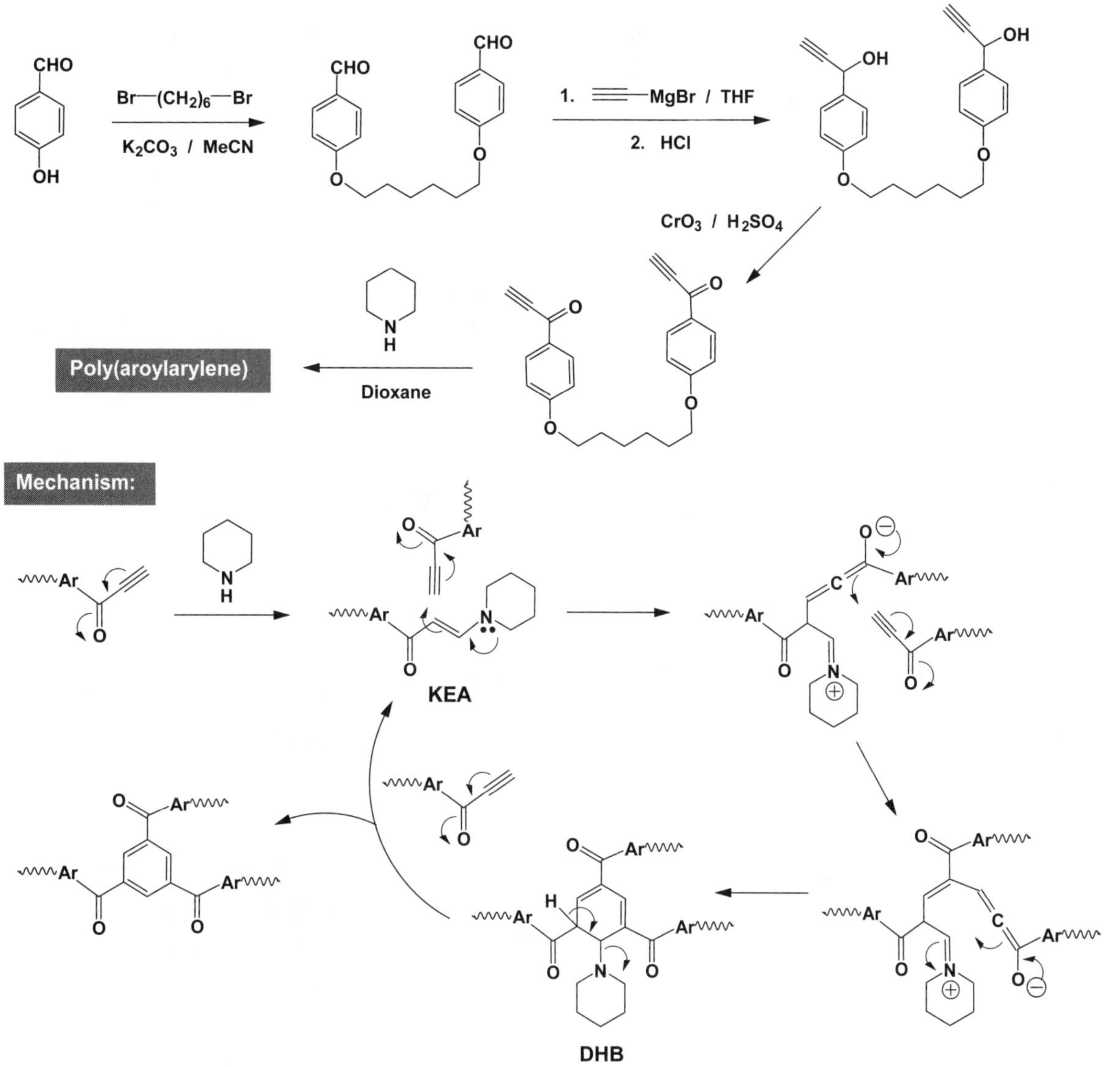

Figure 5.100. Synthesis of a hyperbranched poly(aroylarylene) via the diyne polycyclotrimerization method, including the mechanism of regioselective cyclization.

5.7. SUPRAMOLECULAR POLYMERS

In contrast to conventional covalent polymers, supramolecular polymers are arrays of low or high molar mass molecules (monomers) reversibly self-assembled through noncovalent interactions.[429-434] Various types of noncovalent interactions (viz., H-bonding, van der Waals interactions and metal-ion coordination) can be used for the preparation of supramolecular polymers. Among these, hydrogen bonding is important because of its unidirectional interaction and is associated with both synthetic and biological molecules. The H-bond involves a proton donor (**D**: C-H, O-H, N-H, F-H) and proton acceptor atom (**A**: O, N) with a separation distance of about 3Å. The binding energy of normal H-bonding is between 10 and 50 kJ/mol. Van der Waals interactions are the weakest among non-covalent interactions and their binding energy is about 0.1 to 1 kJ/mol. Van der Waals interactions include: induced dipoles, charge transfer (π-π stacking), dispersive or London attractions, and anisotropic attractions. Thus, according to the type of intermolecular interaction, supramolecular polymers can be divided into three main classes: *H-bonded polymers, coordination polymers, polymers by π-π stacking* (Figure 5.101). Since these interactions are weaker than covalent bonds, supramolecular polymers are thermodynamically less stable, kinetically more labile, and dynamically more flexible than covalent polymers. The preparation of supramolecular polymers is very simple because chain growth occurs upon mixing complementary monomers in solution or in the molten state. It should be noted that many examples of supramolecular polymers can be found in nature, such as nucleic acids, polypeptides and polysaccharides, all of which have H-bonding functional groups that play a critical role in biological processes and the formation of supramolecular structures.

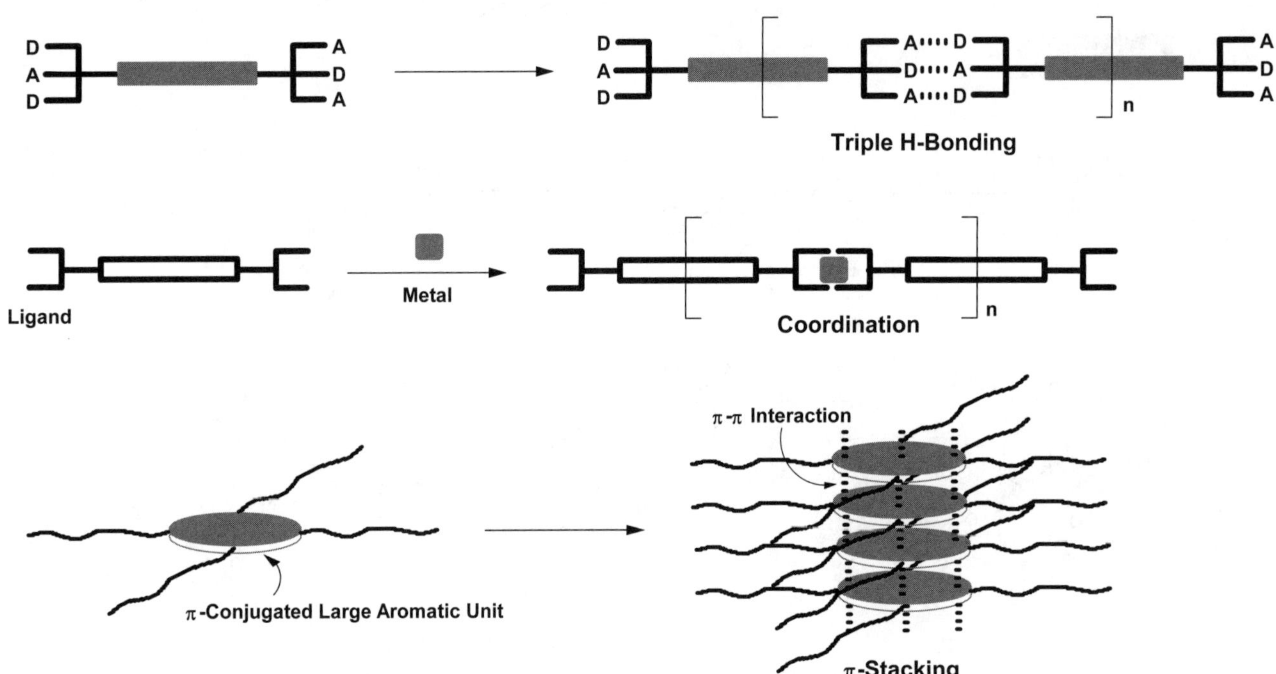

Figure 5.101. Schematics of the three major classes of supramolecular polymers.

Similar to conventional polymers, the architecture of supramolecular polymers can be main-chain, side-chain, branched or crosslinked, depending on the number and disposition of the interacting subunits. Main-chain supramolecular polymers can be homopolymers formed from monomers with two identical interacting groups or random copolymers with different interacting groups. Side-chain supramolecular polymers are formed when small molecules with a single interacting group are attached to complementary groups on the main chain of a traditional covalent polymer. When components for the preparation of supramolecular polymers contain three or more equivalent recognition groups and are mixed with linear associating species, branched (two-dimensional) and three-dimensional or crosslinked (networks or physical gels) supramolecular polymers are obtained. It is noteworthy that the area of supramolecular polymers, especially main-chain analogs, is now very attractive and stretches from molecular recognition in natural and artificial complexes to applications in new materials, in biology, chemical technologies, and medicine.

5.7.1. Supramolecular Polymers by H-Bonding

The most common noncovalent interaction in supramolecular polymer chemistry is hydrogen bonding. A variety of *hydrogen bonding motifs* containing multiple hydrogen bonds have been developed to obtain novel supramolecular polymeric materials.[435-443] It has been observed that not only the number of hydrogen bonds determines the stability of the assembly, but also the arrangement of the donor (**D**) and acceptor (**A**) sites plays a significant role.[444,445] For example, **ADA-DAD** motif exhibits an association constant of around 10^2 M^{-1} in chloroform, while this value is around 10^4 M^{-1} in complexes with a **ADD-DAA** motif, and for **DDD-AAA**, exceeding 10^5 M^{-1}. These differences in stability can be largely attributed to attractive and repulsive secondary interactions (Figure 5.102).[433] Stabilization arises from electrostatic attraction between positively and negatively polarized atoms in adjacent hydrogen bonds, whereas destabilization is likewise the result of electrostatic repulsions between two positively or negatively polarized atoms. Alternation of hydrogen bond donors and acceptors in the same functional group lowers the association constant and thus the overall binding Gibbs energy of a pair of molecules (repulsive secondary interactions). On the other hand, when a molecule consists of only donors and the corresponding partners only of acceptors, the secondary interactions are favorable, resulting in a much stronger hydrogen bonded complex (attractive secondary interactions).

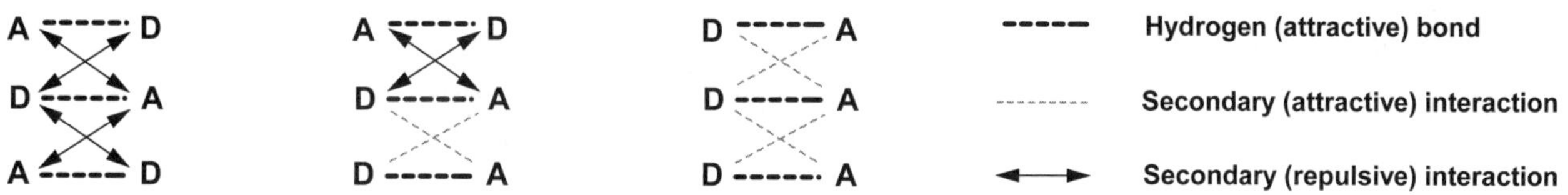

Figure 5.102. Interactions in different hydrogen bonding motifs.

The first example of a designed supramolecular polymer (**DAD-ADA** motif) was reported by Lehn et al. and was assembled from a 1:1 mixture of a difunctional uracil monomer and a difunctional 2,6-diacylaminopyridine monomer, which link alternatively through a *triple hydrogen-bonded array* (Figure 5.103).[446,447] The polymer displayed a highly ordered and remarkably stable (~220°C) liquid crystalline phase. The desired monomers were prepared by linking 6-hydroxymethyl uracil and 2,6-di-acetylamino-4-(hydroxyethyl)oxy-pyridine, respectively, on each end of a bis-acid chloride derivative of tartaric acid.

Another very attractive hydrogen bonding motif (**AADD-DDAA**) is ureidopyrimidone, which has self-complementary properties via *quadruple H-bonds* with an association constant of 6×10^7 M^{-1} in $CDCl_3$ (Figure 5.104).[448-453] Thus, it is possible to prepare very stable and long supramolecular homopolymers from bis-ureidopyrimidone monomers that cannot interact in an intramolecular fashion. The ureidopyrimidone unit was readily prepared by reaction between an isocytosine derivative with a commercially available diisocyanate compound. A convenient route to 6-substituted isocytosines involves condensation of β-keto esters with guanidine. This class of polymers exhibits most of the macroscopic properties of conventional high molecular weight covalent polymers, such as elasticity at room temperature and fibers can be drawn from the melt. Among the supramolecular polymers developed thus far, these polymers possess tremendous commercial importance, especially in the areas of thermoplastic elastomers, superglues, hotmelts and tunable polymeric materials.

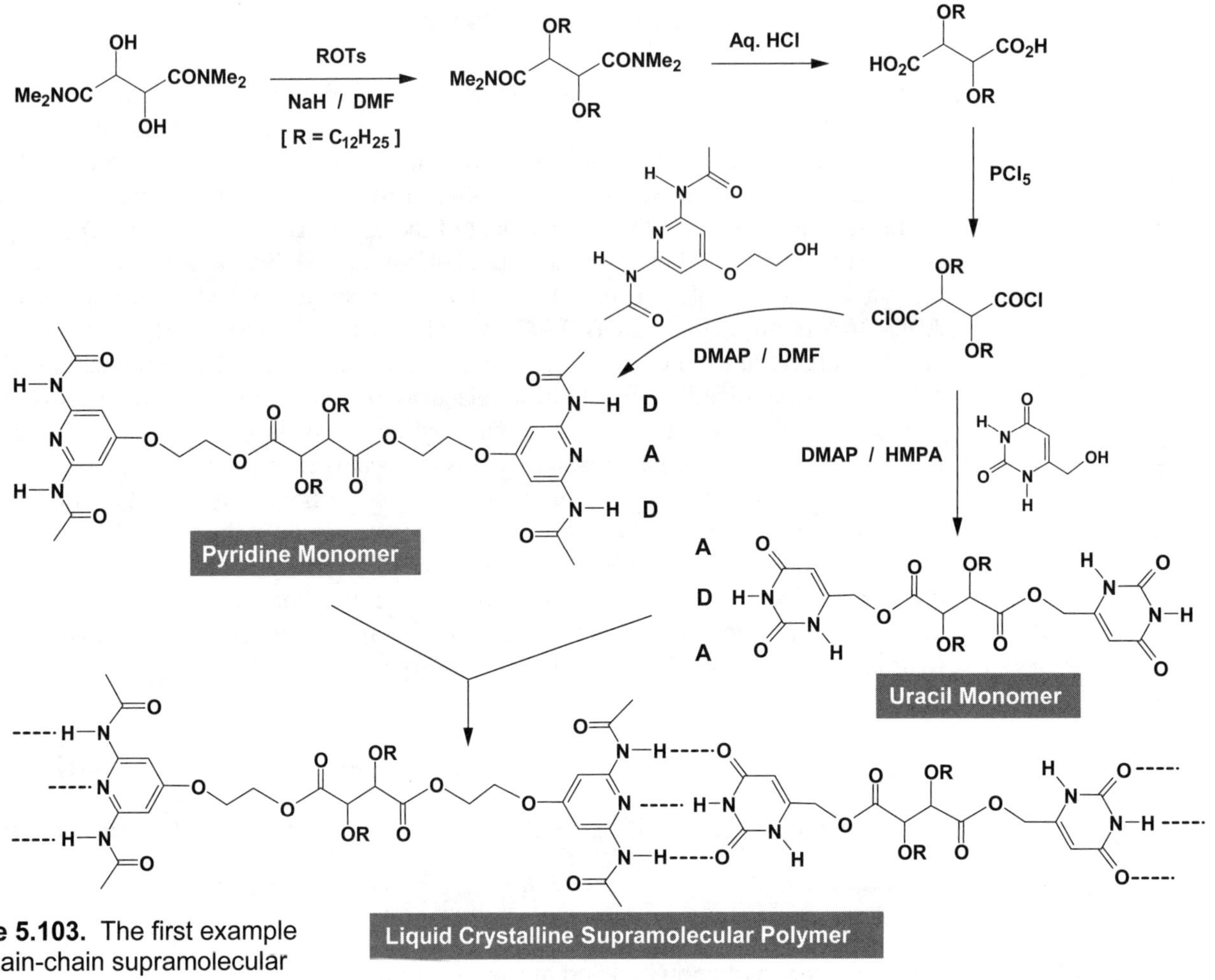

Figure 5.103. The first example of a main-chain supramolecular polymer.

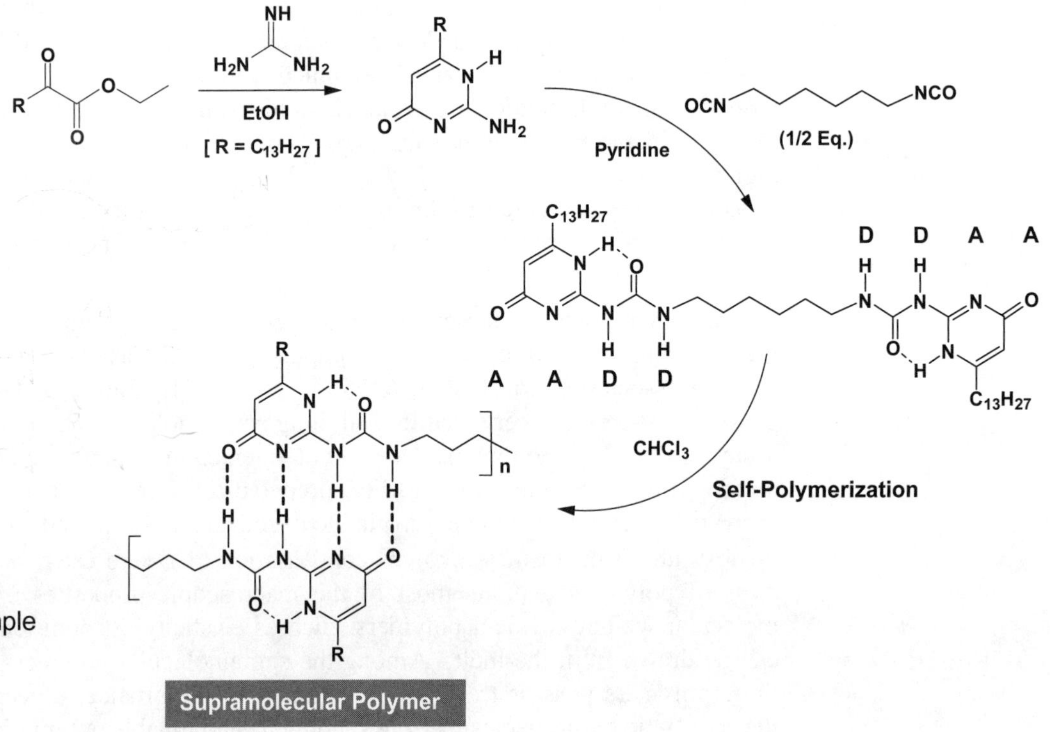

Figure 5.104. Example of a supramolecular polymer containing quadruple H-bonds.

5.7.2. Supramolecular Polymers by Metal-ion Coordination

The use of metal-ligand interactions offers another atractive method for the construction of metallo-supramolecular polymers because the coordination bond is highly directional, a wide range of easily functionalized ligands is available, and the interaction strength can be fine-tuned by choosing appropriate metal ions.[454-456] Besides reversibility of the metal coordination bonds, which allow improved control over the material properties or the construction of "smart" materials, the presence of a metal complex in the copolymer structure introduces additional electrochemical, photophysical, catalytic, and magnetic properties. Thus, these supramolecular polymers are useful as precursors for the generation of inorganic or hybrid structures, including the preparation of functional nanostructured materials. Moreover, supramolecular polymers containing metal ions, such as ruthenium(II), osmium(II), and iridium(II), possess special photophysical properties, and are useful for applications in solar cells and LEDs.

The chemistry of 2,2':6',2"-terpyridine (tpy) metal complexes is a particularly powerful tool for the construction of metallo-supramolecular architectures, since tpy ligands are able to form directed, stable, and inert, and under certain conditions, reversible complexes with a variety of metal ions. The three chelating pyridine units offer high binding constants. The formation of octahedral 2:1 ligand-metal complexes does not give rise to enantiomers as is the case for octahedral coordination by three phenanthroline or 2,2'-bipyridine ligands. Linear, cyclic and dendritic assemblies can be obtained utilizing the chemistry of tpy metal complexes. The first step toward the synthesis of such polymers is, of course, the attachment of tpy ligand to a polymer chain. Figure 5.105 depicts representative examples of tpy-terminated oligomers, which can be used to access interesting metallo-supramolecular dimers.[457-560] For example, tpy-functionalized polystyrene (PS-tpy) was achieved by reacting commercially available 4'-chloro-2,2':6',2"-terpyridine (Cl-tpy) with living polymeric carbanions synthesized by anionic polymerization of styrene. Alternatively, a tpy-terminated poly(ethylene oxide), PEO-tpy, can be prepared by a Williamson-type reaction of mono-methyl capped poly(ethylene oxide) with Cl-tpy. Ru(III) monocomplexes are obtained by heating a tpy oligomer with a 2-fold molar excess of $RuCl_3$. Biscomplexation is performed by heating each of the monocomplexes and tpy oligomer (1:1 molar ratio) in the presence of 3 equivalents of $AgBF_4$. It is important to note that PS-Ru-PEO block copolymer displays distinguished amphiphilic characteristics compared to that of the conalently bonded counterpart, PS-PEO (see Section 2.4.3 in Chapter-2). For example, the former was reported to form well-defined spherical micelles in water. Moreover, the primary micelles had a strong tendency to aggregate into large structures.[461,462]

Sec-BuLi

n-1

Li

n

Li

Cl

N

N

N

Cl-tpy

N

N

N

n

PS-tpy

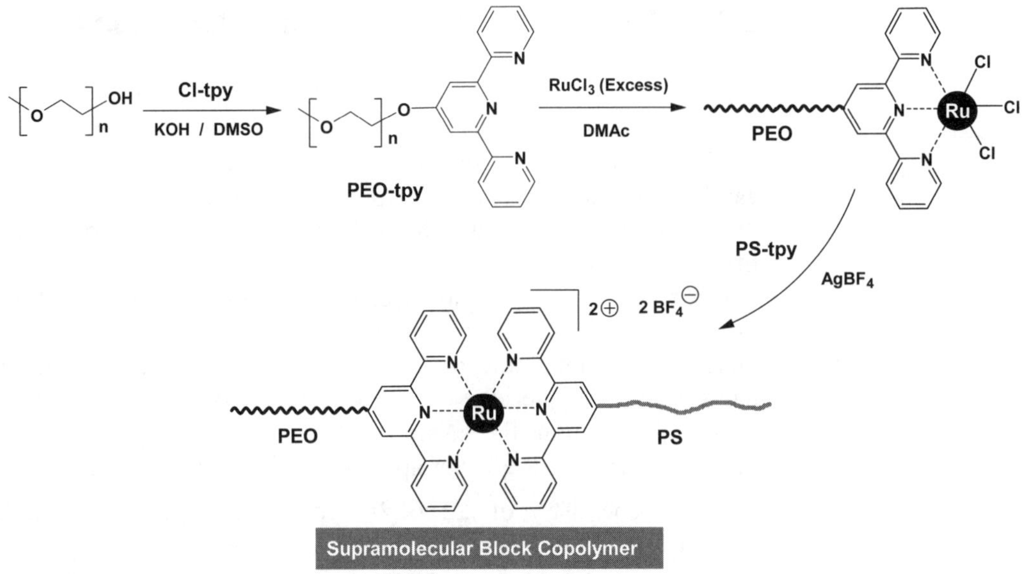

Figure 5.105. Synthesis of a representative metallo-supramolecular block copolymer.

Several tpy-based ditopic ligands have also been developed to prepare supramolecular polymers.[463-468] The total synthesis of two such ditopic ligands is shown in Figure 5.106. The coordination polymer derived from terphenyl-based ligand, TP-tpy$_2$, displayed a pronounced polyelectrolyte effect in a salt-free solution, while the oligo-*p*-phenylenevinylene-based ligand, OPV-tpy$_2$, forms a coordination polymer upon addition of Fe^{2+} ions. It is noteworthy that this methodology provides easy access to polymers for light-emitting diodes with electron and hole carrier mobilities of the order of 10^{-4} cm^2 V^{-1} s^{-1}.[469]

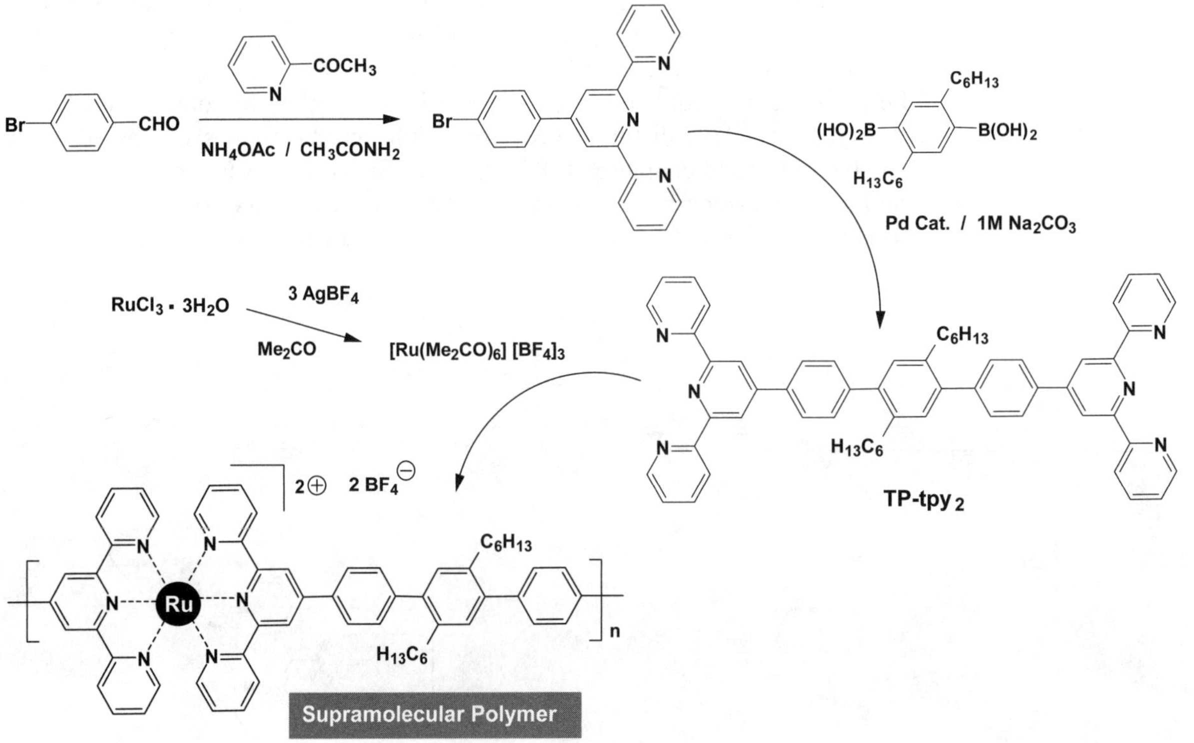

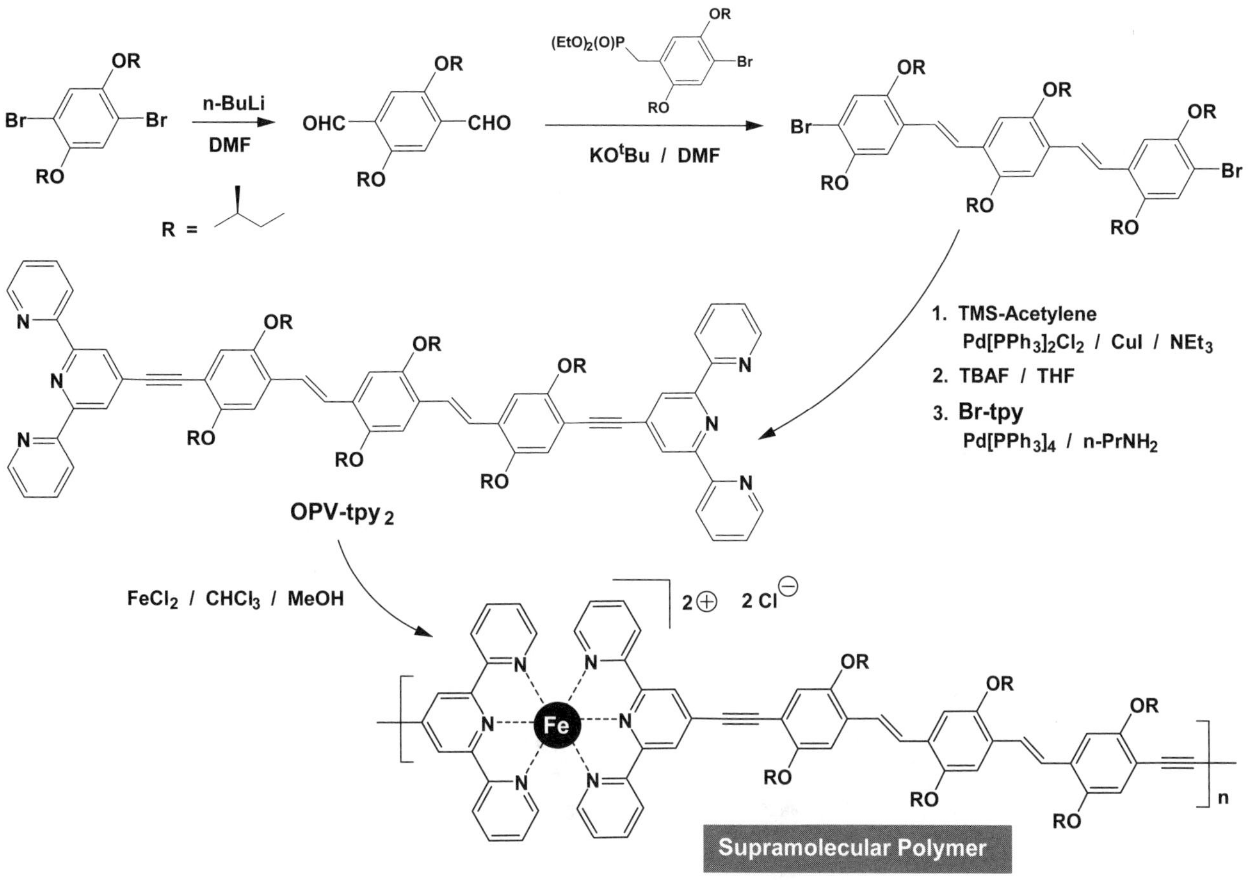

Figure 5.106. Synthesis of metallo-supramolecular polymers using ditopic tpy-ligands.

Another very important oligoether containing ditopic ligand, OEG-BIP, developed for the synthesis of photoactive mechanoresponsive gels, was obtained by reaction of 1,6-bis(*1'*-methylbenzimidazolyl)-4-hydroxypyridine (BIP-OH)[470] with diiodopentaethylene glycol under basic conditions (Figure 5.107).[471] The interesting feature of OEG-BIP is that it can form 2:1 metal complexes with transition metal ions (such as Co^{2+} and Zn^{2+}), but also forms 3:1 complexes with lanthanide ions (such as La^{3+} and Eu^{3+}). It should be noted that the latter complexes act as branching points and are responsible for gelation, when used in a small percentage to prepare the coordination polymer. Since the lanthanide complexes are less stable, the branching points open when the gel is heated or if mechanical stress is exerted by shaking, cause the gel to liquify. After cooling or leaving the sample motionless, a gel is reformed. The Eu^{3+}-based gels show the characteristic red luminescence of the complexed Eu^{3+} ion, which is sensitized by energy transfer from the ligand to the ion. If the Eu^{3+} complex is opened by heat or mechanical stress, the luminescence changes to blue, which is related to the ligand-centered emission.

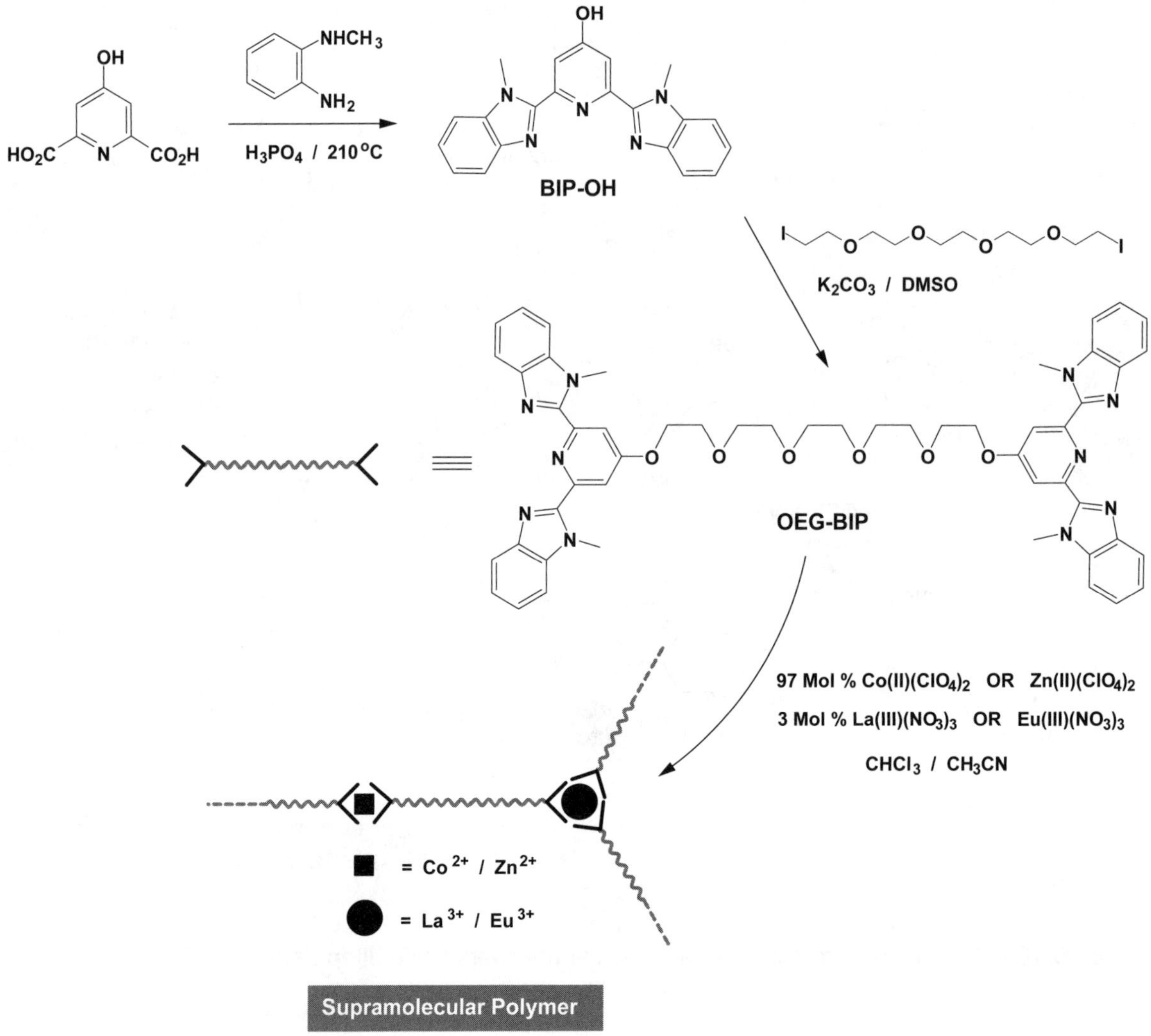

Figure 5.107. Synthesis of a supramolecular thermo- and mechanoresponsive gel.

5.7.3. Supramolecular Polymers by π-π Stacking

Discotic molecules, which have a disc-shaped planar aromatic core substituted with several flexible alkyl side-chains, have a tendency to form self-assembled supramolecular polymers. Because of the strong π-π (or arene-arene) interactions of their cores (ditopic structures), these molecules are prone to aggregate in solution or melt. The first example of discotics are triphenylene (TPH) derivatives, which are conveniently prepared by oxidative cyclotrimerization of dialkoxybenzenes by treatment with ferric chloride (Figure 5.108).[472-476] These molecules exhibit thermotropic liquid crystalline (LC) properties with columnar structures. Interest in triphenylene-based columnar LCs has intensified over recent years, not least because the supramolecular organization gives rise to a low-dimensional conduction pathway along the columns. Indeed, conductivity measurements reveal that reasonable charge carrier mobility ($\sim10^{-5}$ $m^2V^{-1}s^{-1}$) is observed in these materials, which make them suitable for plastic transistors and photovoltaics.

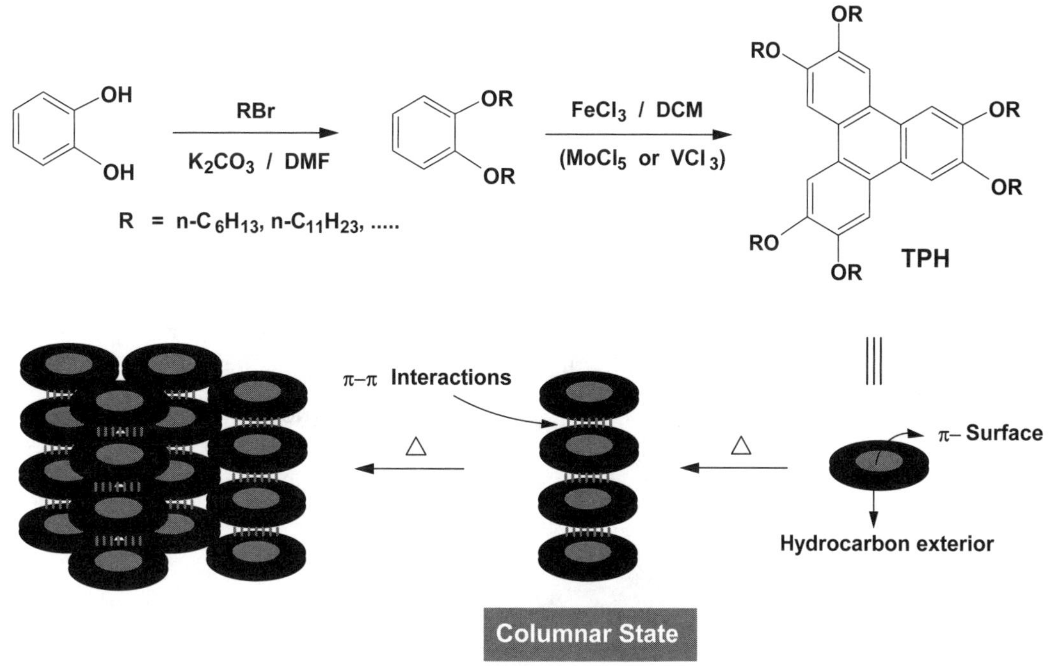

Figure 5.108. Synthetic route to triphenylene-based discotic liquid crystal molecules.

Another important class of discotics is hexa-*peri*-hexabenzocoronene (HBC) derivatives, which have graphite-like structure and are interesting because their large π-system, higher supramolecular order, high one-dimensional charge carrier mobilities (~0.7 $cm^2V^{-1}s^{-1}$) and easy solution processing. These materials can be used as an alternative to conjugated oligomers and polymers in the fields of organic field-effect transistors, and hole transporting layers in light-emitting diodes and photovoltaic cells. HBCs are conveniently prepared by cyclotrimerization of dialkyl tolanes (TOL) under the catalytic action of $Co_2(CO)_8$ followed by the oxidative cyclodehydrogenation of hexa(alkylphenyl)benzenes in the presence of $AlCl_3/Cu(CF_3SO_3)_2$ or $FeCl_3$ (Figure 5.109).[477,478] Specifically designed peripherally substituted phthalocyanines and porphyrins also form supramolecular assemblies through π-π interactions in both solution and melt.[479-481]

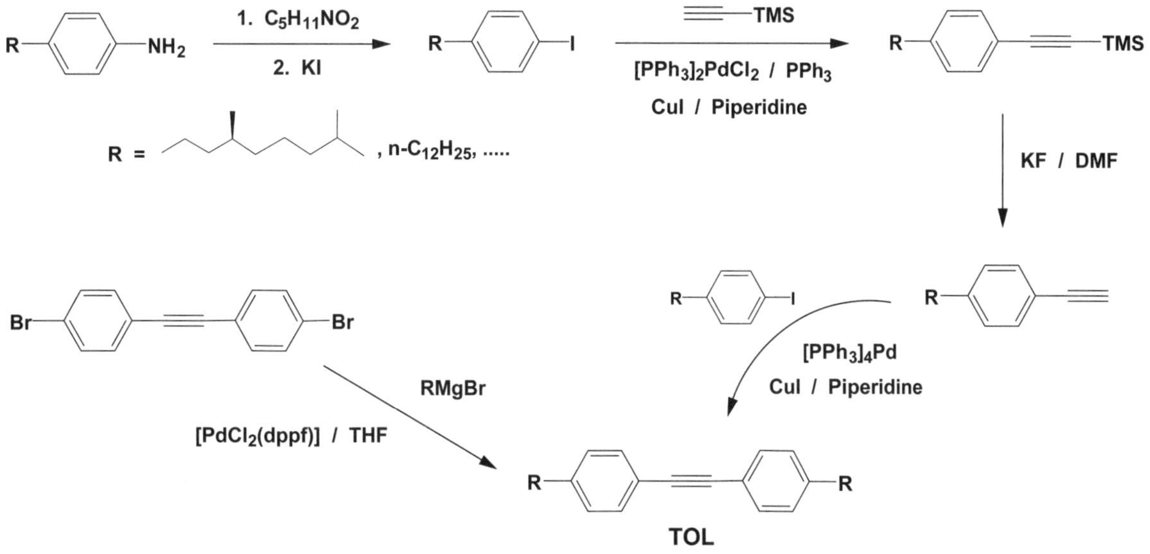

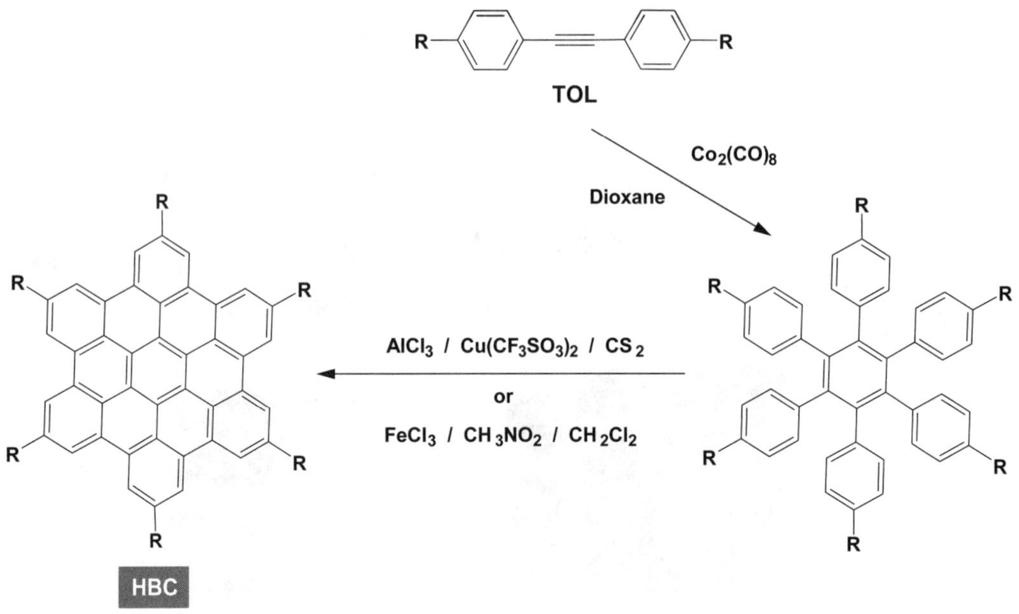

Figure 5.109. Synthetic route to HBC-based discotic liquid crystal molecules.

5.8. Future Outlook

Many of the specialty polymers discussed in this chapter are currently the focus of new emerging technologies and continue to be the dominant topic of research in both academia and industry. For example, over the past decade, extensive efforts have been made in establishing the fundamental relationship between nonlinear optical (NLO) response and chemical structure, and more applied efforts aimed at photonic and photoelectric device applications. Consequently, many new attractive NLO chromophores are now available, which, in turn, have resulted in major advances in electro-optic (EO) polymer modulator fabrication and have yielded a device with a very low switching voltage and a 40 GHz bandwidth!

The field of π-conjugated polymers has also developed rapidly and on different frontiers, including new and improved syntheses of known polymer topologies, understanding of structures and phase behavior in the bulk, thin films, LB assemblies, and tailoring of optical properties in solution and the solid state. For example, poly(*p*-phenylene ethynylene) (PPE) analogs display an array of properties attractive as chemosensors in land mine detection, as light-emitting devices, and in binary PPE/polyethylene mixtures as sheet polarizers in LC displays. After the success of poly(*p*-phenylene vinylene) (PPV) derivatives as the first commercial polymer light-emitting device (LED), polyfluorenes (PFLs) have now been identified as next-generation LEDs, because of their emission at wavelengths spanning the entire visible spectrum (i.e., tunable colors), high fluorescence efficiency, and good thermal stability.

Although dendritic polymers were discovered recently there are already proposed applications of materials based on polymers from this architectural class. Dendrimers pose an exciting possibility for chemists to create macromolecular structures with a specifically tailored function or several functions. An interesting example is as porogens for the production of nanoporous insulating materials. Such improved insulating materials are used to make better microchips needed in the fastest computers. The area where dendrimers are expected to have the most significant impact is in bio-

and nano technology. A good example is its application as contrasting agents for magnetic resonance imaging (MRI). Attachment of contrasting agents, such as gadolinium complexes, to a dendrimer scaffold enhance the resolution, since leakage of agent into the surrounding tissue is hindered. Other applications may be found in drug delivery and anti-HIV drugs. Because dendrimers are relatively expensive to produce, the applications will be in areas requiring small quantities. On the other hand, hyperbranched polymers are much cheaper and are produced in industrial quantities. The two foremost examples are Boltorn®, a polyester from Perstorp AB (Sweden) and Hybrane®, a polyester amide of DSM (Netherlands).

Supramolecular polymers is another area that will play a pivotal role in advancing polymer technology. Due to the advantages (viz., dynamic assembly and disassembly) of supramolecular polymers over conventional ones, many diverse applications are envisaged, including smart materials, self-healing materials, and functional materials with integrated dynamic functions, such as photo and electric properties, molecular sensoring, molecular information, or catalytic activities. Despite the short history of this field, supramolecular polymer materials derived from the ureidopyrimidone monomers offer strong promise for commercial success.

General Study Questions:

1. The following is the synthetic scheme to a poly(arylacetylene) that displays liquid crystalline properties. Identify the structure of the polymer.

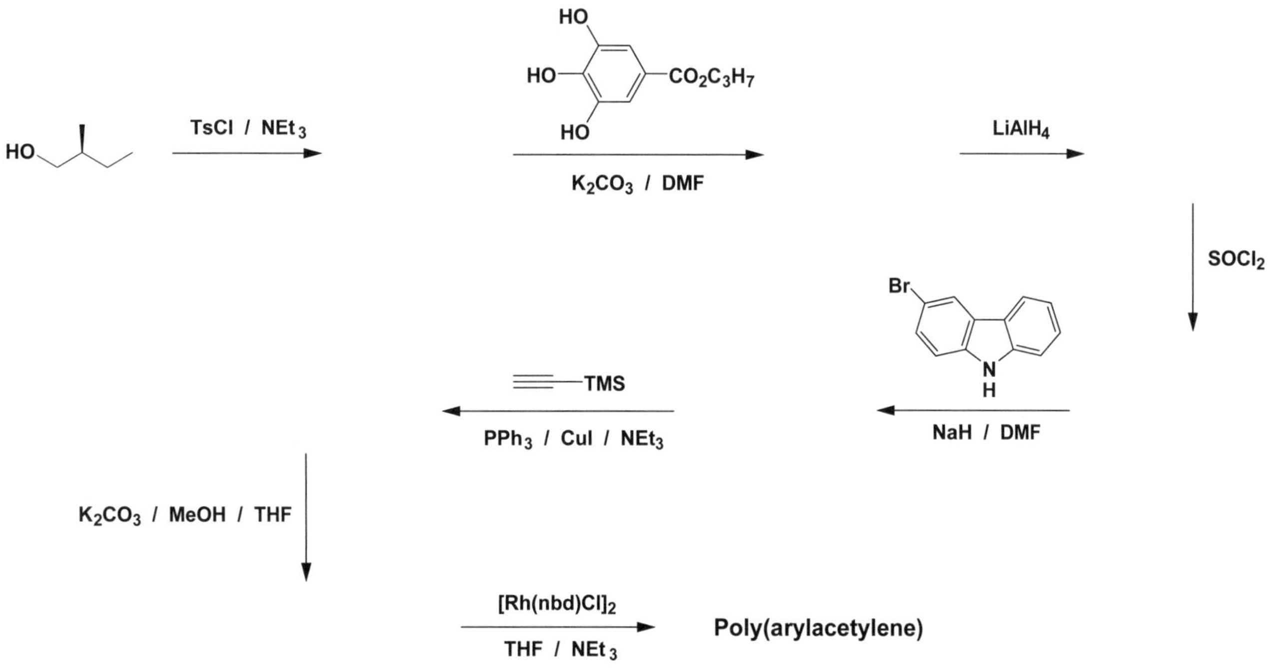

HO

HO — $CO_2C_3H_7$

HO

TsCl / NEt_3

K_2CO_3 / DMF

$LiAlH_4$

$SOCl_2$

Br

N H

NaH / DMF

TMS

PPh_3 / CuI / NEt_3

K_2CO_3 / MeOH / THF

$[Rh(nbd)Cl]_2$

THF / NEt_3

Poly(arylacetylene)

2. Symmetrical bithiophene systems are usually prepared by oxidative coupling of the lithiated monomer in the presence of $CuCl_2$. By contrast, the preferred route for unsymmetrical bithiophene systems is Stille coupling. Identify the bithiophene monomers **A** and **B**. It is important to note that the electrogenerated copolymers obtained from unsymmetrical bithiophene systems exhibit a band gap smaller than that of the two homopolymers, due to electronic and self-structuring effects leading to enhancement of planarity of the conjugated systems.

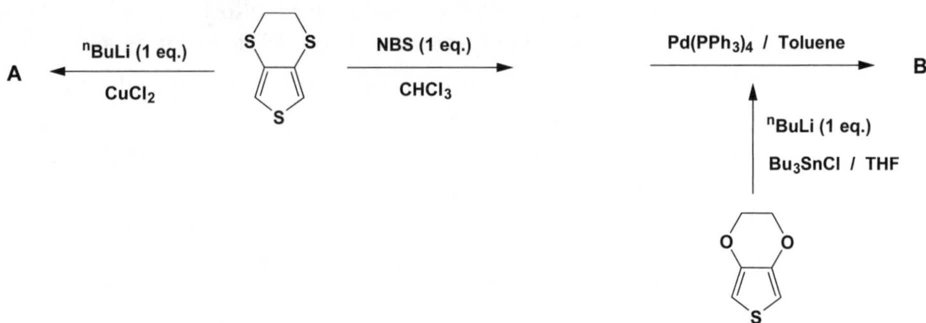

3. The following is the synthetic scheme to an unsymmetrical bithiophene, which on electrochemical polymerization, produces a low band-gap polymer. Identify the structure of the bithiophene.

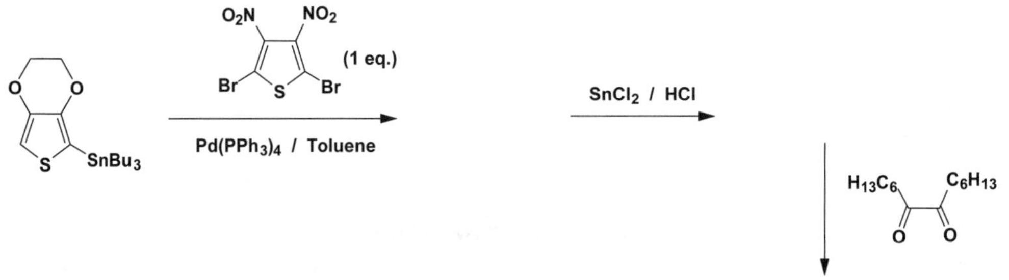

O O S $SnBu_3$ — O_2N, NO_2, Br, S, Br (1 eq.), $Pd(PPh_3)_4$ / Toluene → $SnCl_2$ / HCl → $H_{13}C_6$, C_6H_{13}, O, O → **Bithiophene**

4. One application of conjugated polymers is its use in organic field effect transistors (OFETs) as a low cost alternative to amorphous silicon technology. The following polymer is a very promising candidate for such an application. Identify the polymer.

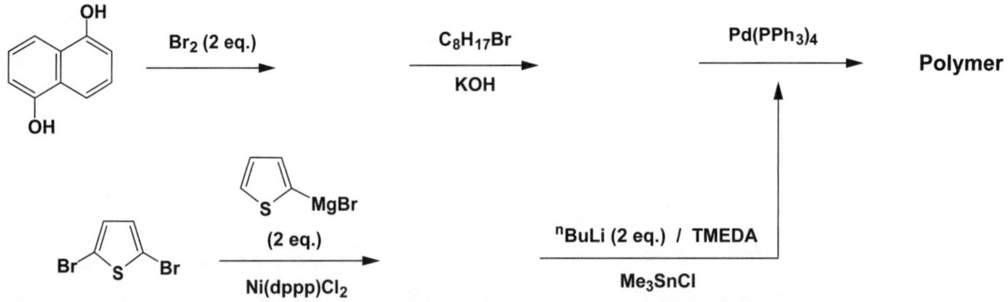

OH, OH — Br_2 (2 eq.) → $C_8H_{17}Br$ / KOH → $Pd(PPh_3)_4$ → **Polymer**

Br S Br — S MgBr (2 eq.), Ni(dppp)Cl_2 → ⁿBuLi (2 eq.) / TMEDA, Me_3SnCl ↑

5. The following scheme represents a classic synthetic approach for obtaining a new class of nonionic amphiphilic polymers, which exhibit an ionochromic effect in the presence of a base. Identify the structure of the polymer while ignoring the regioregularity during polymerization.

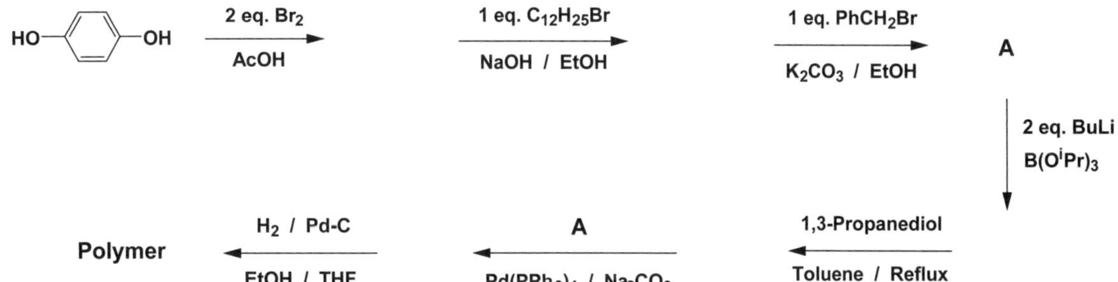

6. Identify the structure of the polythiophene derivative obtained after conducting the following synthetic scheme:

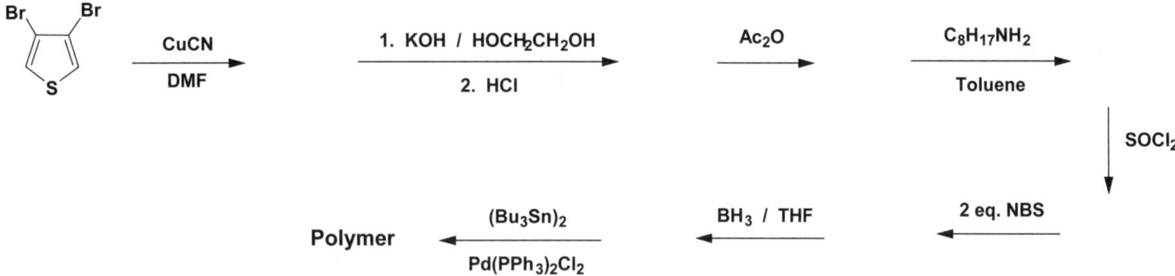

7. The polymer obtained by following the synthetic strategy below is sensitive to a large variety of metal ions because of the presence of pendent terpyridyl ligands and is useful in chemosensor applications. Identify the structure of the polymer.

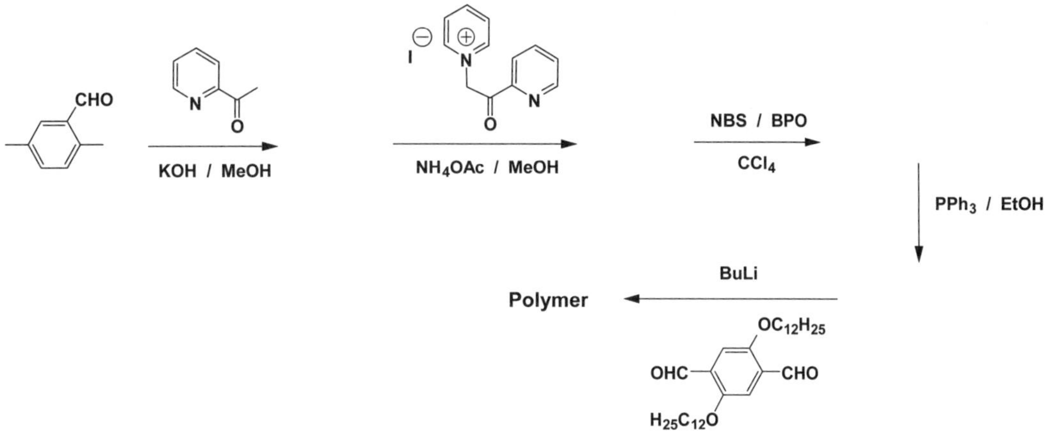

CHO
N
O
KOH / MeOH
I
N
N
O
NH_4OAc / MeOH
NBS / BPO
CCl_4
PPh_3 / EtOH
BuLi
Polymer
$OC_{12}H_{25}$
OHC
CHO
$H_{25}C_{12}O$

8. Redox polymers containing transition metal centers in the conjugated polymer backbone are an interesting class of materials. The presence of the metal significantly impacts the electronic conductivity and magnetic properties of such materials, leading to their application in electroluminescent devices, sensors, and storage devices. Identify the structure of the redox polymer.

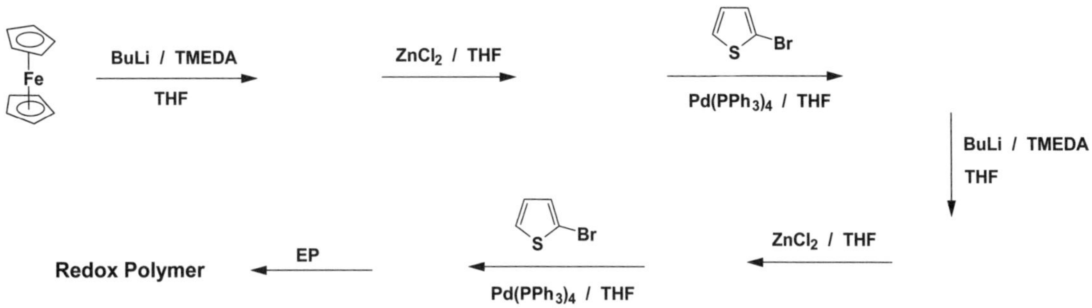

Fe
BuLi / TMEDA
THF
$ZnCl_2$ / THF
S
Br
$Pd(PPh_3)_4$ / THF
BuLi / TMEDA
THF
$ZnCl_2$ / THF
S
Br
$Pd(PPh_3)_4$ / THF
EP
Redox Polymer

9. The following scheme is designed to prepare a polymer attractive for electroluminescent (EL) devices. Identify the structure.

Br_2 / CH_2Cl_2; n-BuBr / K_2CO_3 / Acetone; 1. n-BuLi 2. DMF; t-BuOK / THF

Polymer

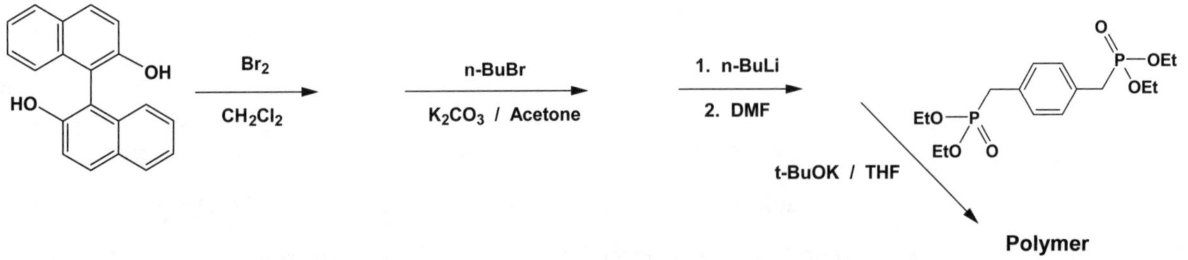

10. The following PPV analog has been synthesized via the Gilch route. Complete the reaction scheme.

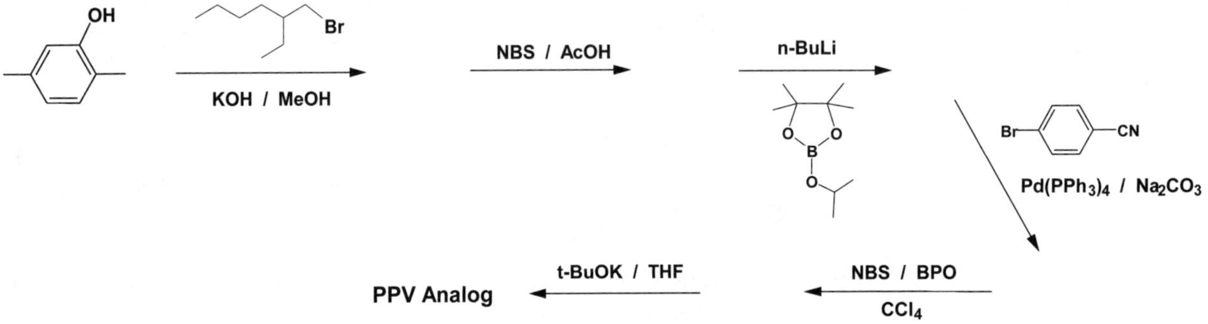

Br; KOH / MeOH; NBS / AcOH; n-BuLi; Br—CN; $Pd(PPh_3)_4$ / Na_2CO_3; NBS / BPO CCl_4; t-BuOK / THF

PPV Analog

11. Identify the structure of the target polymer, which contains alternating fluorene and divinylbenzene moieties and exhibits green electroluminescence.

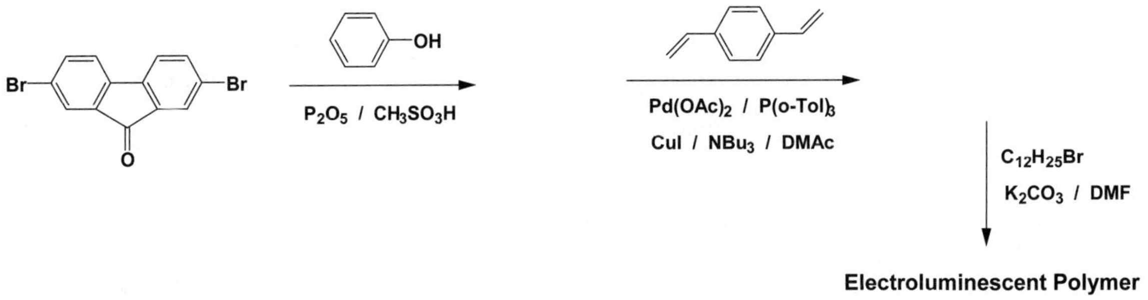

Br Br O; OH; P_2O_5 / CH_3SO_3H; $Pd(OAc)_2$ / P(o-Tol)$_3$; CuI / NBu_3 / DMAc; $C_{12}H_{25}Br$; K_2CO_3 / DMF

Electroluminescent Polymer

12. Light emission from the LEP in a PLED is produced via the recombination of electrons and holes injected through the electrodes. Applying an additional electron injection/transport layer between the emitter and cathode and/or a hole-transporting layer between the emitter and the anode has been used successfully to improve device efficiency and stability. Complete the following reaction scheme which incorporates this motivation.

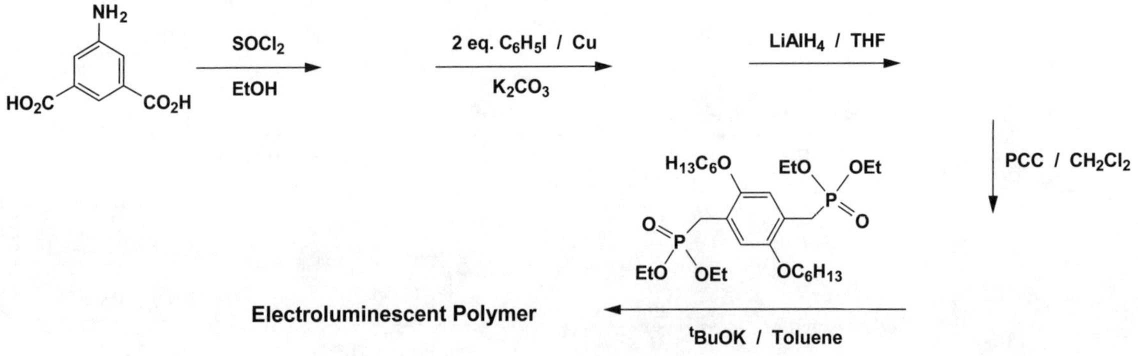

NH_2; HO_2C; CO_2H; $SOCl_2$ / EtOH; 2 eq. C_6H_5I / Cu; K_2CO_3; $LiAlH_4$ / THF; PCC / CH_2Cl_2; $H_{13}C_6O$; EtO; OEt; OC_6H_{13}; ^tBuOK / Toluene

Electroluminescent Polymer

13. The following nitrogen-bridged poly(ladder-type tetraphenylene), LTPP, possesses a lower electroluminescence onset voltage and is found to be more stable toward oxidative degradation compared with the all-carbon-bridged analog, which undergoes oxidative degradation over a period of time. Assign the structure to the polymer.

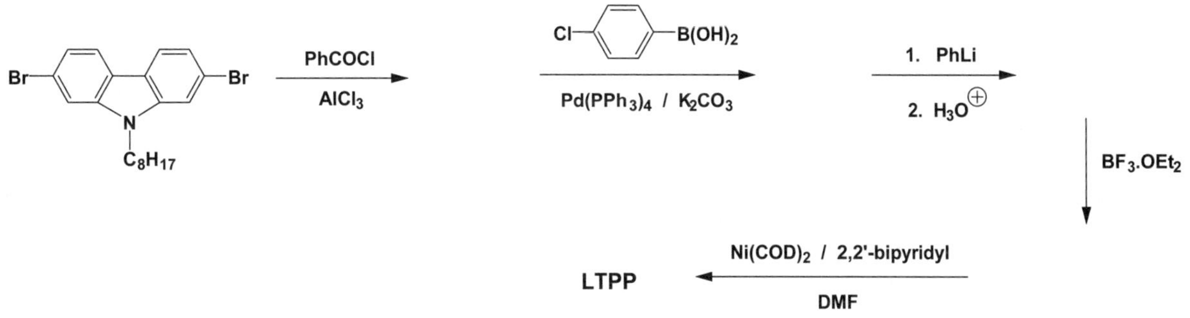

Br–(carbazole, N–C_8H_{17})–Br →[PhCOCl / $AlCl_3$] →[Cl–C_6H_4–$B(OH)_2$ / $Pd(PPh_3)_4$ / K_2CO_3] →[1. PhLi; 2. $H_3O^{\oplus}$] →[$BF_3.OEt_2$] →[$Ni(COD)_2$ / 2,2'-bipyridyl, DMF] LTPP

14. The following synthetic strategy is to prepare a spirobifluorene-based blue light emitting polymer, which exhibits extraordinary thermal and color stability. Identify the structure of the polymer.

2-Bromoaniline (Br, NH_2) →[$(HO)_2B$–C_6H_4–OMe / $Pd(PPh_3)_4$ / $NaHCO_3$, THF] →[1. $NaNO_2$ / HCl; 2. KI] →[1. ^nBuLi / Et_2O; 2. 2,7-dibromofluorenone (Br, Br, O); 3. $H_3O^{\oplus}$] →[AcOH / HCl] →[BBr_3 / CH_2Cl_2] →[$C_8H_{17}Br$ / K_2CO_3 / DMF] →[1. 1 eq. ^nBuLi; 2. $B(OMe)_3$; 3. Pinacol / CH_2Cl_2] →[$Pd(PPh_3)_4$ / $NaHCO_3$, THF] **Light Emitting Polymer**

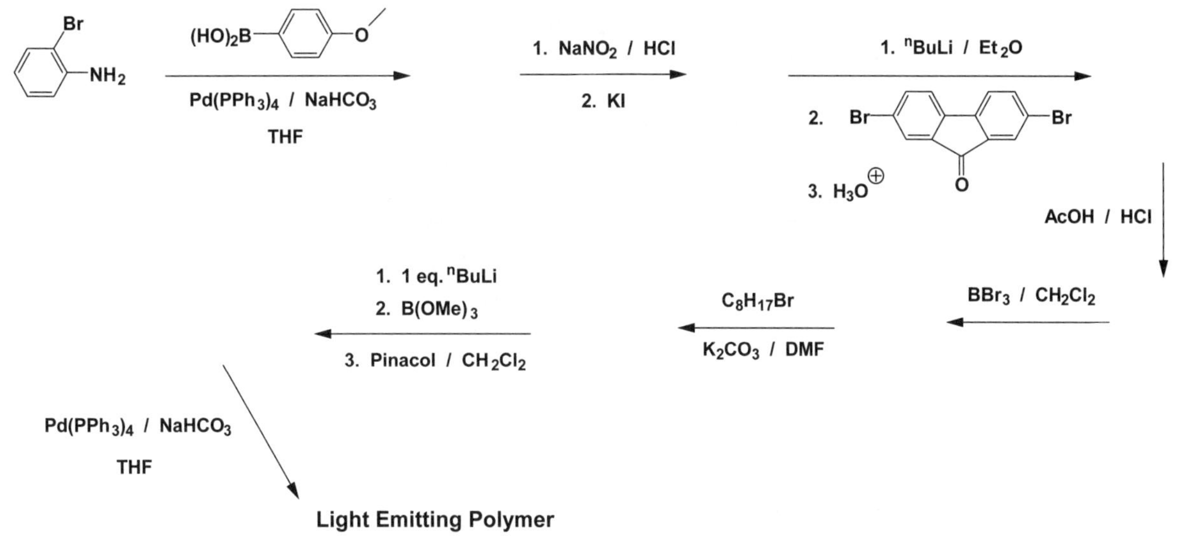

15. The following is an elegant synthetic strategy to prepare an organosoluble π-conjugated polymer with electroluminescent properties. Identify the structure of the polymer.

HO–C_6H_4–OH →[$C_8H_{17}Br$ / K_2CO_3 / DMF] →[NBS / DMF] →[dimethylphenylboronic acid ($B(OH)_2$) / $Pd(PPh_3)_4$ / $NaHCO_3$] →[NBS / BPO, CCl_4] →[^tBuOK / Dioxane] **Light Emitting Polymer**

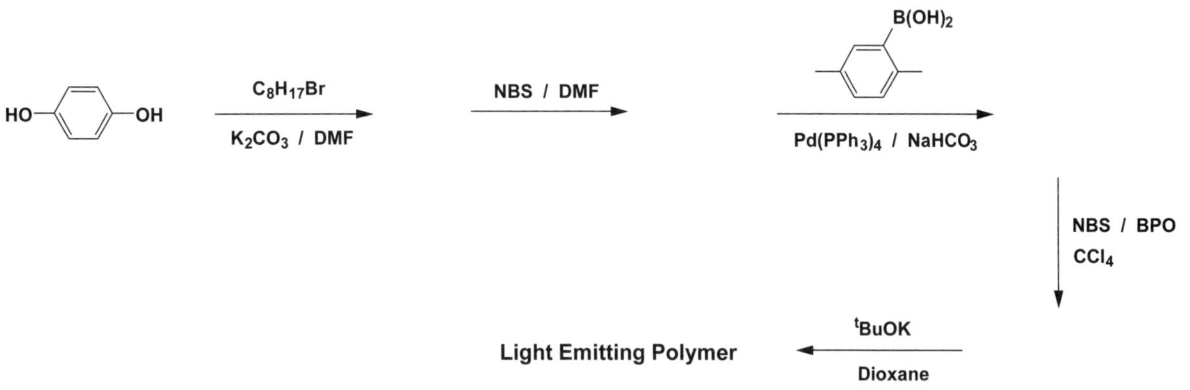

16. Shown below is the synthesis of two NLO-phore containing monomers which can be polymerized to obtain a second-order NLO-active polymer. Identify the structures of the monomers and the resulting polymer.

2 eq. 4-fluoronitrobenzene; NH_2 / Br; CsF / DMSO; PtS_2 / C, H_2 / DMF; $(CF_3CO)_2O$, NEt_3 / THF; 4-nitrostyrene (NO_2), $Pd(OAc)_2$ / $P(o\text{-}Tol)_3$, NEt_3 / DMF; K_2CO_3 / MeOH → **Monomer-1**

F / CHO; $HN(CH_2CH_2OH)_2$, K_2CO_3 / DMF; O_2N–C6H4–CH_2CO_2H, Py; CH_3SO_2Cl, NEt_3 / CH_2Cl_2; HO–C6H3(CO_2Me)(CO_2Me), K_2CO_3 / DMF; 1. NaOH 2. HCl; Ac_2O / AcOH, 125°C → **Monomer-2**

17. Upon electric field assisted poling, the following polymer exhibits large and extraordinarily stable second-order nonlinear susceptibilities, where the NLO-phores are part of the polymer backbone with their dipole moments oriented transversely to the polymer main chain. Identify the structure of the polymer.

H_2N–C6H3(CH_3)–NH_2; Ac_2O; HNO_3 / AcOH, 60°C; N(CH3)2–C6H4–CHO, Py; 1. Aq. HCl 2. NaOH; $ClOC{-}(CH_2)_8{-}COCl$, NMP → **NLO Polymer**

18. The following polymer is readily soluble in common organic solvents and exhibits large third-order NLO susceptibility. Identify the structure of the polymer.

9,10-dibromoanthracene (Br, Br); 1. 1 eq. nBuLi 2. Dry ice 3. HCl; $SOCl_2$ / $CHCl_3$; $C_6H_{13}OH$, Py; ≡–TMS, $Pd(PPh_3)_2Cl_2$, CuI / NEt_3; Bu_4NF / THF; WCl_6, Toluene → **Polymer**

19. The following polymer exhibits both greenish blue electroluminescence and liquid crystalline behavior (nematic phase) around 170-190°C. Identify the structure of the polymer.

Ph Ph
EtO_2C CO_2Et O
HO–C6H4–C6H4–OH → (1 eq. $C_7H_{15}Br$; K_2CO_3 / KI / MeCN) → (≡–$(CH_2)_3$–Cl; KOH / KI / MeCN) → (130°C) → ($LiAlH_4$ / THF) → ($SOCl_2$) → (^tBuOK) → Polymer

20. Slightly crosslinked liquid crystalline polymers that combine the properties of liquid crystalline phases (e.g., the self-organization of mesogens) and properties that provide stability of polymeric networks are known as liquid crystalline elastomers (**LCEs**). They are best prepared by a graft reaction, in which a crosslinking agent (**XLA**) and a mesogenic monomer (**MM**) are simultaneously attached to the highly flexible polysiloxane via a hydrosilylation reaction. Identify the structure of the LCE.

HO_2C–C6H4–OH → (=–CH_2Br; K_2CO_3 / KI / MeCN) → ($SOCl_2$) → ([CHOL]–OH (Cholesterol); NEt_3 / $CHCl_3$)

$HO(CH_2)_6OH$ → (2 eq. =–$(CH_2)_8$–CO_2H; H_2SO_4 (cat.)) → XLA

$SiMe_3$–[O–Si(Me)(H)]$_n$–O–$SiMe_3$; XLA (1/50 eq.); H_2PtCl_6 / THF → LCE

21. The following synthetic strategy involves ring-opening metathesis polymerization (ROMP) of a norbornene-based monomer bearing an alkoxy-substituted triphenylene to obtain a poly(norbornene), which exhibits an enantiotopic discotic hexagonal mesophase, a more ordered molecular organization than discotic columnar mesophase. Identify the structure of the discotic liquid crystalline polymer.

Catechol (OH, OH) → (2 eq. $C_{10}H_{21}Br$; K_2CO_3 / DMF) → (Br_2 / Fe) → (1. ^nBuLi 2. $B(OMe)_3$ 3. HCl) → (Br–C6H3–($OC_{10}H_{21}$)$_2$; $Pd(PPh_3)_4$) → (A; VOF_3, $BF_3.Et_2O$) → (norbornene–COCl; NEt_3 / $CHCl_3$) → ($Cl_2(PCy_3)_2Ru$=CHPh) → Discotic LCP

Catechol → (NaH; 1 eq. $C_{10}H_{21}Br$) → ($Br(CH_2)_{12}OH$; NaH) → A

22. High-resolution liquid crystal displays (LCDs), including full color addressed passive matrix super-twisted nematic (STN) LCDs and active matrix thin-film-transistor (TFT) LCDs, are extensively used in broadcasting, telecommunications and laptop/desktop computers. In the mass production of LCDs, polyimide alignment layers play a critical role, via mechanical rubbing, in controlling the bulk orientation of liquid crystals in a preferential direction. These layers are conveniently spin-coated or rotary-printed on indium tin-oxide (ITO) glass substrates with a thickness between 50 and 200 nm. It has been speculated that upon mechanical rubbing, the molecular alignment on the layer surface can differ substantially from the bulk. It is important to recognize that high pretilt alignment layers are essential to inhibit the occurrence of the twist nematic (TN) reverse-tilt disclination and the appearance of the STN two-dimensional striped distortion, in addition to reducing the operational voltage. The following polymer containing cyanobiphenyl mesogens has been designed and synthesized for achieving high pretilt angle alignment layers. Identify the structure of the polymer.

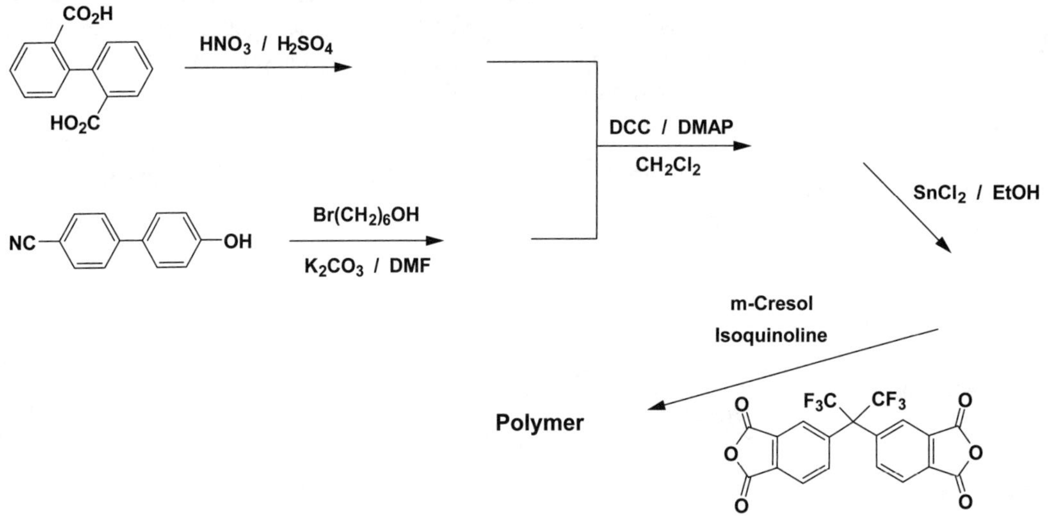

CO_2H / HO_2C (biphenyl dicarboxylic acid) —[HNO_3 / H_2SO_4]→

NC–biphenyl–OH —[$Br(CH_2)_6OH$; K_2CO_3 / DMF]→

—[DCC / DMAP; CH_2Cl_2]→ —[$SnCl_2$ / EtOH]→ —[m-Cresol; Isoquinoline; dianhydride with F_3C, CF_3]→ **Polymer**

23. Side-on fixed liquid crystal polymers (LCPs) represent a peculiar class of side-chain LCPs in which the mesogenic group is laterally attached to the polymer backbone. This kind of molecular architecture gives rise preferentially to the nematic phase due to hindered rotation around the long axes of the mesogenic moieties. Identify the structure of such a side-on fixed LCP.

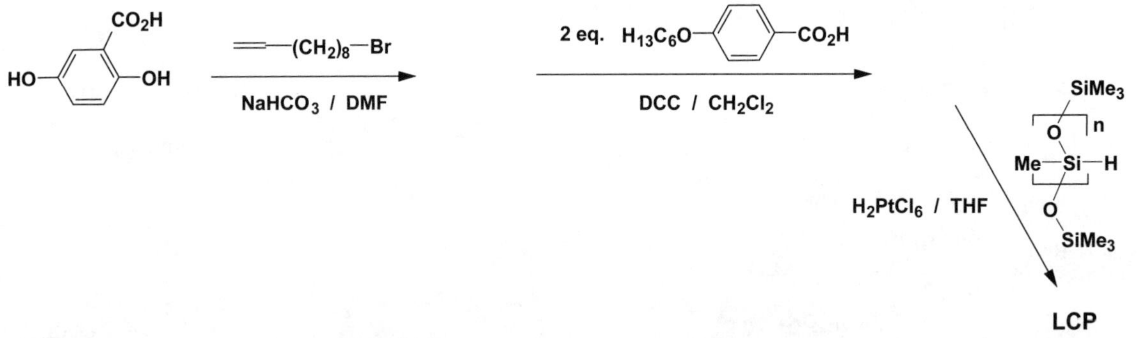

HO–(ring with CO_2H)–OH —[$=\!\!-(CH_2)_8$–Br; $NaHCO_3$ / DMF]→ —[2 eq. $H_{13}C_6O$–(phenyl)–CO_2H; DCC / CH_2Cl_2]→ —[H_2PtCl_6 / THF; $SiMe_3$–[O–Si(Me)(H)]$_n$–O–$SiMe_3$]→ **LCP**

24. The liquid crystalline polymer synthesized by the following scheme contains both horizontal and lateral rods in the main chain. Identify the structure.

HO–C₆H₄–CO_2Et —[$Br(CH_2)_{10}Br$ / K_2CO_3 / DMF]→ —[1. KOH / EtOH; 2. HCl]→ —[$SOCl_2$]→ —[Py / Dioxane]→ LCP

2,5-dihydroxy-1,4-benzoquinone —[EtO–C₆H₄–COCl / Py / THF]→ —[$Na_2S_2O_4$ / Dioxane]→

25. The following synthetic scheme used metathesis polymerization to prepare a new class of side-chain liquid crystalline polymers. Identify the structure of the polymer.

4-aminophenol (NH_2, OH) —[≡–CH_2Br / MeCN]→ —[Br–$(CH_2)_6$–O–C₆H₄–C₆H₄–CN / K_2CO_3 / MeCN]→ —[$MoCl_5$-$EtAlCl_2$ / THF]→ LCP

26. The following AB_2 monomer has been prepared to obtain a hyperbranched poly(ether ketone) containing biphenyl units. Identify the structure of the monomer.

5-nitroisophthaloyl chloride (NO_2, ClOC, COCl) —[fluorobenzene (F) / $AlCl_3$]→ —[$SnCl_2$ / HCl]→ —[1. $NaNO_2$ / H_2SO_4 / AcOH; 2. Aq. H_2SO_4 / △]→ —[$(CF_3SO_2)_2O$ / Py]→ —[MeO–C₆H₄–$B(OH)_2$ / $Pd(PPh_3)_4$ / K_2CO_3]→ —[Py.HCl]→ AB_2 Monomer

27. The following is a multi-step synthetic scheme for a dendronized polymer. Identify the structure of the polymer, including all intermediates.

Pyrogallol (HO, OH, OH) —[3 Eq. $C_{12}H_{25}Br$ / K_2CO_3 / DMF]→ —[HNO_3]→ —[NH_2NH_2 / Graphite]→ —[$^tBuNO_2$ / HBF_4]→ —[I_2 / KOAc]→ —[≡–TMS / NEt_3 / $PdCl_2(PPh_3)_2$ / CuI]→ —[K_2CO_3 / THF / MeOH]→ —[$[Rh(nbd)Cl]_2$ / NEt_3]→ Dendronized Polymer

Advanced Study Questions:

28. How can you distinguish a liquid crystalline polymer from a crystalline polymer by differential scanning calorimetry? Elaborate the answer by drawing their typical heating and cooling traces.

29. Why does poly(diethoxyphosphazene) exhibit high chain flexibility (T_g = -85°C) despite having conjugated double bonds in the main chain and pendent side groups?

30. Polyacetylene itself is non-luminescent. By contrast, di-substituted polyacetylenes with appropriate pendent groups, such as one shown below, are light-emitting, making them excellent candidates for PL and EL applications. They are best prepared in the presence of WCl_6 with $SnPh_4$ as a co-catalyst. Suggest a synthetic scheme for the monomer starting with commercially available compounds.

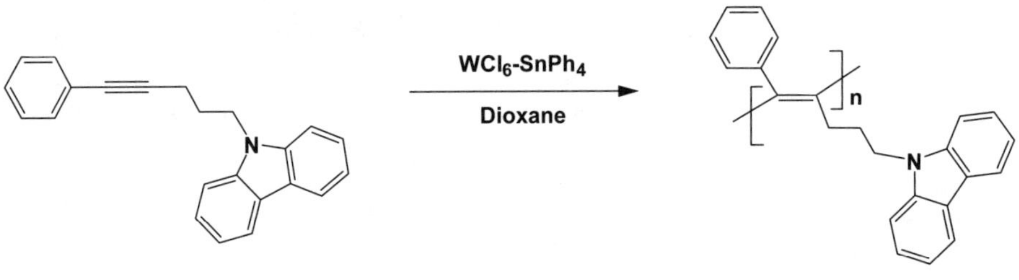

WCl_6-$SnPh_4$

Dioxane

31. Anthracene can be electrochemically polymerized in the presence of boron trifluoride diethyl etherate as an electrolyte to obtain polyanthracene films with conductivity ~0.1 S/cm. Spectroscopic studies indicate that the polymerization (coupling) occurs exclusively through 9 and 10 positions. Propose a mechanism for the electropolymerization.

32. While poly(p-phenylene) is insoluble and infusible, the following fully aromatic polymer is highly soluble in chloroform. Commencing from readily available starting materials, outline a synthetic strategy for this soluble polymer.

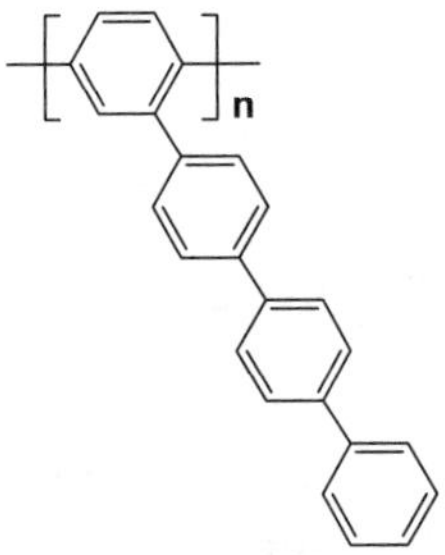

33. Starting from readily available commercial intermediates, outline a synthetic strategy for the following all aromatic PPV analogs.

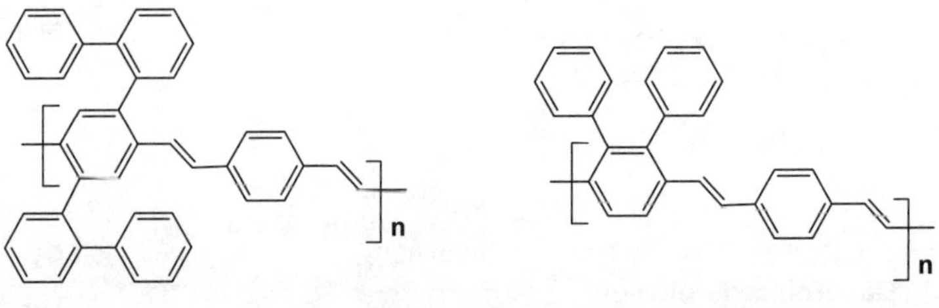

34. The following conjugated polymer electrolyte has a strong propensity to self-assemble into aggregates in solution and exhibits useful optical and electronic properties. Propose a convenient synthetic route to this polymer.

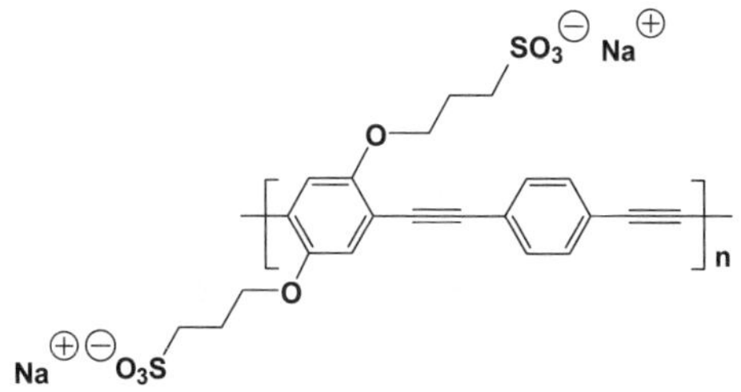

35. Polymers containing transition metals in the backbone have been the subject of recent research since these materials exhibit properties distinct from their individual organic and inorganic components. Suggest a plan for the synthesis of the following polymer.

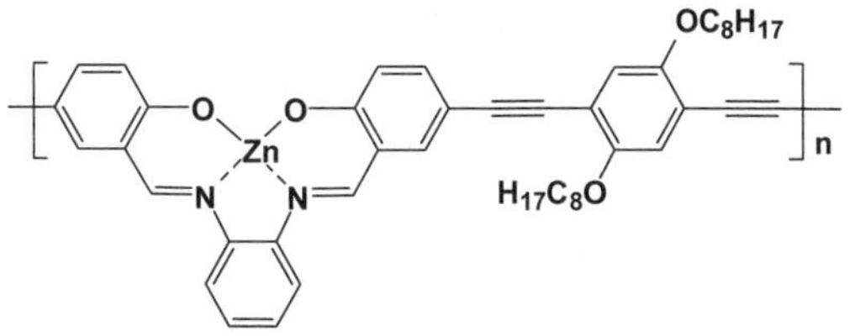

36. Starting from fluorene, synthesize the following polymer, which has a band gap of 2.8 eV, smaller than that of poly(2-(decyloxy)-1,4-phenylene), and emits blue light upon application of an electric field.

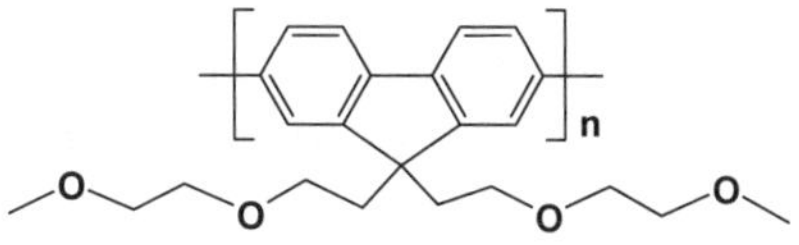

37. The following copolymer containing alternating fluorene and bithiophene moieties was synthesized to develop LEDs with green light emission. Suggest a synthetic strategy starting from fluorene and thiophene.

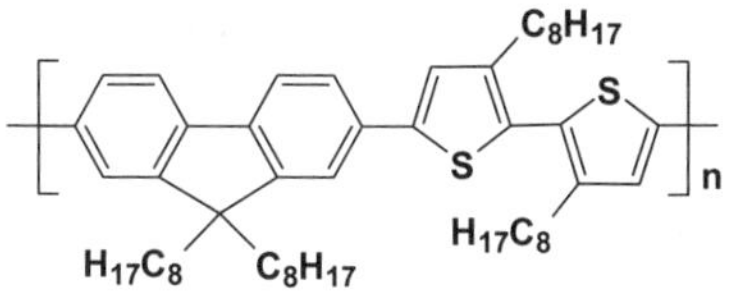

References for Chapter-5:

1. *Reproduced with kind permission of The Royal Society of Chemistry.* Source: Boas, U.; Christensen, J. B.; Heegaard, P. M. H., *J. Mater. Chem.,* **16**, 3785 (2006).
2. Shirakawa, H.; Ikeda, S., *Polym. J.*, **2**, 231 (1971).
3. Shirakawa, H.; Ito, T.; Ikeda, S., *Polym. J.*, **4**, 460 (1973).
4. Ito, T.; Shirakawa, H.; Ikeda, S., *J. Polym. Sci., Polym. Chem. Ed.*, **12**, 11 (1974).
5. Shirakawa, H.; Louis, E. J.; MacDiarmid, A. G.; Chiang, C. K.; Heeger, A. J., *J. Chem. Soc., Chem. Commun.*, 578, 1977.
6. Chiang, C. K.; Fincher, C. R.; Park, Y. W.; Heeger, A. J.; Shirakawa, H.; Louis, E. J.; Gau, S. C.; MacDiarmid, A. G., *Phys. Rev. Lett.,* **39**, 1098 (1977).
7. Patil, A. O.; Heeger, A. J.; Wudl, F., *Chem. Rev.,* **88**, 183 (1988).
8. Novak, P.; Muller, K.; Santhanam, K. S. V.; Haas, O., *Chem. Rev.*, **97**, 207 (1997).
9. Berresheim, A. J.; Muller, M.; Müllen, K., *Chem. Rev.*, **99**, 1747 (1999).
10. Roncali, J., *Chem. Rev.*, **97**, 173 (1997).
11. Coustel, N.; Foxonet, N.; Ribet, J. L.; Bernier, P.; Fischer, J. E., *Macromolecules,* **24**, 5867 (1991).
12. Shibahara, S.; Yamane, M.; Ishikawa, K.; Takezoe, H., *Macromolecules*, **31**, 3756 (1998).
13. Shirakawa, H.; Otaka, T.; Piao, G.; Akagi, K.; Kyotani, M., *Synth. Met.,* **117**, 1 (2001).
14. Edwards, J. H.; Feast, W. J., *Polymer*, **21**, 595 (1980).
15. Martens, J. H. F.; Pichler, K.; Marseglia, E. A.; Friend, R. H.; Cramail, H.; Feast, W. J., *Synth. Met.*, **55**, 443 (1993).
16. Scherman, O. A.; Grubbs, R. H., *Synth. Met.,* **124**, 431 (2001).
17. Scherman, O. A.; Rutenberg, I. M.; Grubbs, R. H., *J. Am. Chem. Soc.,* **125**, 8515 (2003).
18. Schuehler, D. E.; Williams, J. E.; Sponsler, M. B., *Macromolecules,* **37**, 6255 (2004).
19. Lam, J. W. Y.; Tang, B. Z., *Acc. Chem. Res.,* **38**, 745 (2005).
20. Okoshi, K.; Sakajiri, K.; Kumaki, J.; Yashima, E., *Macromolecules,* **38**, 4061 (2005).
21. Maeda, K.; Morino, K.; Okamoto, Y.; Sato, T.; Yashima, E., *J. Am. Chem. Soc.*, **126**, 4329 (2004).
22. Maeda, K.; Takeyama, Y.; Sakajiri, K.; Yashima, E., *J. Am. Chem. Soc.,* **126**, 16284 (2004).
23. Onouchi, H.; Hasegawa, T.; Kashiwagi, D.; Ishiguro, H.; Maeda, K.; Yashima, E., *Macromolecules,* **38**, 8625 (2005).
24. Koltzenburg, S.; Stelzer, F.; Nuyken, O., *Macromol. Chem. Phys.,* **200**, 821 (1999)
25. Tang, B. Z.; Poon, W. H.; Leung, S. M.; Leung, W. H.; Peng, H., *Macromolecules,* **30**, 2209 (1997).
26. Choi, S.-K.; Gal, Y.-S.; Jin, S.-H.; Kim, H. K., *Chem. Rev.,* **100**, 1645 (2000).
27. Wegner, G. Makromol. Chem. 154, 35 (1972).
28. Brandsma, L., *Preparative Acetylene Chemistry,* 2nd Edn., Elsevier, Amsterdam, 1988.
29. Lee, J.-H.; Curtis, M. D.; Kampf, J. W., *Macromolecules,* **33**, 2136 (2000).
30. Brandsma L.; Vasilevski, S. F.; Verkruijsse, H. D., *Application of Transition Metal Catalysts in Organic Synthesis,* Springer-Verlag: Berlin, Heidelberg, 1999; pp 49-105.

31. Negishi, E.-I.; Hata, M.; Xu, C., *Org. Lett.,* **2**, 3687 (2000).
32. Xu, R.; Gramlich, V.; Frauenrath, H., *J. Am. Chem. Soc.,* **128**, 5541 (2006).
33. Okada, S.; Peng, S.; Spevak, W.; Charych, D., *Acc. Chem. Res.,* **31**, 229 (1998).
34. Tamaoki, N.; Shimada, S.; Okada, Y.; Belaissaoui, A.; Kruk, G.; Yase, K.; Matsuda, H., *Langmuir,* **16**, 7545 (2000).
35. Ahn, D. J.; Chae, E.-H.; Lee, G. S.; Shim, H.-Y.; Chang, T.-E.; Ahn, K.-D.; Kim, J.-M., *J. Am. Chem. Soc.,* **125**, 8976 (2003).
36. Chang, J. Y.; Yeon, J. R.; Shin, Y. S.; Han, M. J.; Hong, S.-K., *Chem. Mater.,* **12**, 1076 (2000).
37. Chan, Y.-H.; Lin, J.-T.; Chen, I-W. P.; Chen, C.-h., *J. Phys. Chem. B.,* **109**, 19161 (2005).
38. Barentsen, H. M.; van Dijk, M.; Zuilhof, H.; Sudholter, E. J. R., *Macromolecules,* **33**, 766 (2000).
39. Ji, E-K.; Ahn, D. J.; Kim, J-M., *Bull. Korean Chem. Soc.,* **24**, 667 (2003).
40. Charych, D. H.; Nagy, J. O.; Spevak, W.; Bednarski, M. D., *Science*, **261**, 585 (1993).
41. Kim, J-M.; Ji, E-K.; Woo, S. M.; Lee, H.; Ahn, D. J., *Adv. Mater.*, **15**, 1118 (2003).
42. Kim, J.-M.; Lee, Y. B.; Yang, D. H.; Lee, J.-S.; Lee, G. S.; Ahn, D. J., *J. Am. Chem. Soc.,* **127**, 17580 (2005).
43. Huang, W-S.; Humphrey, B. D.; MacDiarmid, A. G., *J. Chem. Soc. Faraday. Trans-1,* **82**, 2385 (1986).
44. Genies, E. M.; Boyle, A.; Lapkowski, M.; Tsintavis, C., *Synth. Met.,* **36**, 139 (1990).
45. Shreepathi, S.; Holze, R., *Chem. Mater.,* **17**, 4078 (2005).
46. Majidi, M. R.; Kane-Maguire, L. A. P.; Wallace, G. G., *Polymer*, **36**, 3597 (1995).
47. Majidi, M. R.; Kane-Maguire, L. A. P.; Wallace, G. G., *Polymer,* **35**, 3113 (1994).
48. Yang, L.; Cao, W., *Chem. Mater.,* **18**, 297 (2006).
49. Li, W. G.; McCarthy, P. A.; Huang, J.; Yang, S. C.; Wang, H. L., *Macromolecules,* **35**, 9975 (2002).
50. Shoji, E.; Freund, M. S., *Langmuir,* **17**, 2918 (2001).
51. Deore, B. A.; Yu, I.; Freund, M. S., *J. Am. Chem. Soc.,* **126**, 52 (2004).
52. Deore, B. A.; Yu, I.; Aguiar, P. M.; Recksiedler, C.; Kroeker, S.; Freund, M. S., *Chem. Mater.,* **17**, 3803 (2005).
53. Deore, B. A.; Freund, M. S., *Chem. Mater.,* **17**, 2918 (2005).
54. De Jesus, M. C.; Fu, Y.; Weiss, R. A., *Polym. Eng. Sci.,* **37**, 1936 (1997).
55. Shenoy, S. L.; Cohen, D.; Erkey, C.; Weiss, R. A., *Ind. Eng. Chem. Res.,* **41**, 1484 (2002).
56. Zotti, G.; Zecchin, S.; Schiavon, G.; Vercelli, B.; Berlin, A.; Grimoldi, S., *Macromol. Chem. Phys.,* **205**, 2026 (2004).
57. Schottland, P.; Zong, K.; Gaupp, C. L.; Thompson, B. C.; Thomas, C. A.; Giurgiu, I.; Hickman, R.; Abboud, K. A.; Reynolds, J. R., *Macromolecules,* **33**, 7051 (2000).
58. Merz, A.; Schropp, R.; Dötterl, E., *Synthesis,* 795, 1995.
59. Liu, J.-H.; Chan, H.-W.; Wong, H. N. C., *J. Org. Chem.,* **65**, 3274 (2000).
60. Zong, K.; Reynolds, J. R., *J. Org. Chem.,* **66**, 6873 (2001).
61. Zotti, G.; Zecchin, S.; Schiavon, G.; Vercelli, B.; Berlin, A.; Grimoldi, S., *Macromol. Chem. Phys.,* **205**, 2026 (2004)
62. Zotti, G.; Zecchin, S.; Schiavon, G.; Vercelli, B.; Berlin, A.; Grimoldi, S., *Macromol. Chem. Phys.,* **205**, 2026 (2004).
63. Li, H.; Lambert, C.; Stahl, R. *Macromolecules,* **39**, 2049 (2006).
64. Jeppesen, J. O.; Takimiya, K.; Jensen, F.; Brimert, T.; Nielsen, K.; Thorup, N.; Becher, J., *J. Org. Chem.,* **65**, 5794 (2000).

65. Jeppesen, J. O.; Takimiya, K.; Jensen, F.; Brimert, T.; Nielsen, K.; Thorup, N.; Becher, J., *J. Org. Chem.,* **65**, 5794 (2000).
66. O'Connor, B. R.; Jones, F. N., *J. Org. Chem.,* **35**, 2002 (1970).
67. Easton, D. B. J.; Leaver, D., *J. Chem. Soc. Chem. Commun.,* 585 (1965).
68. Jeppesen, J. O.; Takimiya, Thorup, N.; Becher, J., *Synthesis,* 803 (1999).
69. Heywang, G.; Jonas, F., *Adv. Mater.,* **4**, 116 (1992).
70. Roncali, J., *Chem. Rev.,* **97**, 173 (1997).
71. Groenendaal, L.; Jonas, F.; Freitag, D.; Pielartzik, H.; Reynolds, J. R., *Adv. Mater.,* **12**, 481 (2000).
72. Wang, C.; Schindler, J. L.; Kannewurf, C. R.; Kanatzidis, M. G., *Chem. Mater.,* **7**, 58 (1995).
73. Reddinger, J. L.; Reynolds, J. R., *J. Org. Chem.,* **61**, 4833 (1996).
74. Blanchard, P.; Jousselme, B.; Frere, P.; Roncali, J., *J. Org. Chem.,* **67**, 3961 (2002).
75. Blanchard, P.; Cappon, A.; Levillain, E.; Nicolas, Y.; Frere, P.; Roncali, J., *Org. Lett.,* **4**, 607 (2002).
76. Turbiez, M.; Frere, P.; Allain, M.; Gallego-Planas, N.; Roncali, J., *Macromolecules,* **38**, 6806 (2005).
77. McQuade, D. T.; Pullen, A. E.; Swager, T. M., *Chem. Rev.,* **100**, 2537 (2000).
78. Bäuerle, P.; Scheib, S., *Adv. Mater.,* **5**, 848 (1993).
79. Marsella, M. J.; Swager, T. M., *J. Am. Chem. Soc.,* **115**, 12214 (1993).
80. Berresheim, A. J.; Muller, M.; Mullen, K., *Chem. Rev.,* **99**, 1747 (1999).
81. Yamamoto, T.; Morita, A.; Miyazaki, Y.; Maruyama, T.; Wakayama, H.; Zhou, Z. H.; Nakamura, Y.; Kanbara, T.; Sasaki, S.; Kubota, K., *Macromolecules,* **25**, 1214 (1992).
82. Percec, V.; Zhao, M.; Bae, J.-Y.; Hill, D. H., *Macromolecules,* **29**, 3727 (1996).
83. Vahlenkamp, T.; Wegner, G., *Macromol. Chem. Phys.,* **195**, 1933 (1994).
84. Schlüter, A. D., *J. Polym. Sci. Part-A: Polym. Chem.,* **39**, 1533 (2001).
85. Balanda, P. B.; Ramey, M. B.; Reynolds, J. R., *Macromolecules,* **32**, 3970 (1999).
86. Burroughes, J. H.; Bradley, D. D. C.; Brown, A. R.; Marks, R. N.; Mackay, K.; Friend, R. H.; Burns, P. L.; Holmes, A. B., *Nature,* **347**, 539 (1990).
87. Wessling, R. A., *J. Polym. Sci. Polym. Symp.,* **72**, 55 (1985).
88. Lenz, R. W.; Han, C. C.; Stenger-Smith, J.; Karasz, F. E., *J. Polym. Sci. Part-A: Polym. Chem.,* **26**, 3241 (1988).
89. Garay, R. O.; Baier, U.; Bubeck, C.; K. Müllen, K., *Adv. Mater.,* **5**, 561 (1993).
90. Marletta, A.; Goncalves, D.; Oliveira, O. N.; Faria, R. M.; Guimarães, F. E., *Adv. Mater.,* **12**, 69 (2000).
91. Burn, P. L.; Bradley, D. D. C.; Friend, R. H.; Halliday, D. A.; Holmes, A. B.; Jackson, R. W.; Kraft, A., *J. Chem. Soc. Perkin. Trans-1.,* 3225 (1992).
92. Palmaerts, A.; van Haren, M.; Lutsen, L.; Cleij, T. J.; Vanderzande, D., *Macromolecules,* **39**, 2438 (2006).
93. Henckens, A.; Colladet, K.; Fourier, S.; Cleij, T. J.; Lutsen, L.; Gelan, J.; Vanderzande, D., *Macromolecules,* **38**, 19 (200).
94. Henckens, A.; Duyssens, I.; Lutsen, L.; Vanderzande, D.; Cleij, T. J., *Polymer,* **47**, 123 (2006).
95. Peng, Z.; Zhang, J.; Xu, B., *Macromolecules,* **32**, 5162 (1999).
96. Krebs, F. C.; Jorgensen, M., *Macromolecules,* **36**, 4374 (2003).
97. Steuerman, D. W.; Star, A.; Narizzano, R.; Choi, H.; Ries, R. S.; Nicolini, C.; Stoddart, J. F.; Heath, J. R., *J. Phys. Chem. B.,* **106**, 3124 (2002).
98. Liang, Z.; Rackaitis, M.; Li, K.; Manias, E.; Wang, Q., *Chem. Mater.,* **15**, 2699 (2003).
99. Bao, Z.; Chen, Y.; Cai, R.; Yu, L., *Macromolecules,* **26**, 5281 (1993).
100. Wan, W. C.; Antoniadis, H.; Choong, V. E.; Razafitrimo, H.; Gao, Y.; Feld, W. A.; Hsieh, B. R., *Macromolecules,* **30**, 6567 (1997).

101. Hsieh, B. R.; Yu, Y.; Forsythe, E. W.; Schaaf, G. M.; Feld, W. A., *J. Am. Chem. Soc.,* **120**, 231 (1998).
102. Liu, H.; Wang, S.; Luo, Y.; Tang, W.; Yu, G.; Li, L.; Chen, C.; Liu, Y.; Xi, F., *J. Mater. Chem.,* **11**, 3063 (2001).
103. Luo, Y.-H.; Liu, H.-W.; Xi, F.; Li, L.; Jin, X.-G.; Han, C. C.; Chan, C.-M., *J. Am. Chem. Soc.,* **125**, 6447 (2003).
104. Bunz, U. H. F., *Chem. Rev.,* **100,** 1605 (2000).
105. Moroni, M.; Moigne, J. L., *Macromolecules,* **27**, 562 (1994).
106. Li, H.; Powell, D. R.; Hayashi, R. K.; West, R., *Macromolecules,* **31**, 52 (1998).
107. Weder, C.; Wrighton, M. S., *Macromolecules,* **29**, 5157 (1996).
108. Zhao, X.; Pinto, M. R.; Hardison, L. M.; Mwaura, J.; Muller, J.; Jiang, H.; Witker, D.; Kleiman, V. D.; Reynolds, J. R.; Schanze, K. S., *Macromolecules,* **39**, 6355 (2006).
109. Breitenkamp, R. B.; Tew, G. N., *Macromolecules,* **37**, 1163 (2004).
110. Kloppenburg, L.; Jones, D.; Bunz, U. H. F., *Macromolecules,* **32**, 4194 (1999).
111. Huang, W. Y.; Gao, W.; Kwei, T. K.; Okamoto, Y., *Macromolecules,* **34**, 1570 (2001).
112. Bunz, U. H. F.; Enkelmann, V.; Kloppenburg, L.; Jones, D.; Shimizu, K. D.; Claridge, J. B.; zur Loye, H.-C.; Lieser, G., *Chem. Mater.,* **11**, 1416 (1999).
113. Möbius, D., *Adv. Mater.,* **7**, 437 (1995).
114. Toal, S. J.; Trogler, W. C., *J. Mater. Chem.,* **16**, 2871 (2006).
115. Zhou, Q.; Swager, T. M., *J. Am. Chem. Soc.,* **117**, 12593 (1995).
116. Yang, J.-S.; Swager, T. M., *J. Am. Chem. Soc.,* **120**, 5321 (1998).
117. Yang, J.-S.; Swager, T. M., *J. Am. Chem. Soc.*, **120**, 11864 (1998).
118. Danilowicz, C.; Cortón, E.; Battaglini, F., *J. Electroanal. Chem.,* **445**, 89 (1998).
119. Sirkar, K.; Revzin, A.; Pishko, M. V., *Anal. Chem.,* **72**, 2930 (2000).
120. Calvo, E. J.; Etchenique, R.; Pietrasanta, L.; Wolosiuk, A.; Danilowicz, C., *Anal. Chem.,* **73**, 1161 (2001).
121. Abruna, H.D.; Denisevich, P.; Umana, M.; Meyer, T. J.; Murray, R. W., *J. Am. Chem. Soc.,* **103**, 1 (1981).
122. Wolf, M. O., *Adv. Mater.,* **13**, 545 (2001).
123. Zotti, G.; Schiavon, G.; Zecchin, S.; Berlin, A.; Pagani, G.; Canavesi, A., *Synth. Met.,* **76**, 255 (1996).
124. Ballarin, B.; Masiero, S.; Seeber, D.; Tonelli, D., *J. Electroanal. Chem.,* **449**, 173 (1998).
125. Crayston, J. A.; Iraqi, A. Morrison, J. J.; Walton, J. C., *Synth. Met.,* **84**, 441 (1997).
126. Xue, C.; Chen, Z.; Luo, F.-T.; Palaniappan, K.; Chesney, D. J.; Liu, J.; Chen, J.; Liu, H., *Biomacromolecules,* **6**, 1810 (2005).
127. Wang, J.; Keene, F. R., *J. Electroanal. Chem.,* **405**, 71 (1996).
128. Harbermüller, K.; Ramanavicius, A.; Laurinavicius, V.; Schuhmann, W. *Electroanalysis,* **12**, 1383 (2000).
129. Alfred T. Jeffries, Kenneth C. Moore, Debra M. Ondeyka, Arthur W. Springsteen, Denis W. H. MacDowell, *J. Org. Chem.,* **46**, 2885 (1981).
130. Zotti, G.; Zecchin, S.; Schiavon, G.; Berlin, A.; Pagani, G.; Canavesi, A., *Chem. Mater.,* **7**, 2309 (1995).
131. Reddinger, J. L.; Reynolds, J. R., *Macromolecules,* **30**, 673 (1997).
132. Reddinger, J. L.; Reynolds, J. R., *Chem. Mater.,* **10**, 3 (1998).
133. Pickup, P. G., *J. Mater. Chem.,* **9**, 1641 (1999).
134. Kingsborough, R. P.; Swager, T. M., *Adv. Mater.,* **10**, 1100 (1998).
135. Kingsborough, R. P.; Swager, T. M., *J. Am. Chem. Soc.,* **121**, 8825 (1999).
136. Zhu, Y.; Wolf, M. O., *Chem. Mater.,* **11**, 2995 (1999).
137. Hjelm, J.; Handel, R. W.; Hagfeldt, A.; Constable, E. C.; Housecroft, C. E.; Forster, R. J., *Inorg. Chem.,* **44**, 1073 (2005).

138. Hickner, M. A.; Ghassemi, H.; Kim, Y. S.; Einsla, B. R.; McGrath, J. E., *Chem. Rev.,* **104**, 4587 (2004).
139. Li, Q.; He, R.; Jensen, J. O.; Bjerrum, N. J., *Chem. Mater.,* **15**, 4896 (2003).
140. Di Vona, M. L.; Marani, D.; D'Ottavi, C.; Trombetta, M.; Traversa, E.; Beurroies, I.; Knauth, P.; Licoccia, S. Swier, S.; Gasa, J.; Shaw, M. T.; Weiss, R. A., *Ind. Eng. Chem. Res.,* **43**, 6948 (2004).
141. Kerres, J.; Tang, C.-M.; Graf, C., *Ind. Eng. Chem. Res.,* **43**, 4571 (2004).
142. Asano, N.; Miyatake, K.; Watanabe, M., *Chem. Mater.,* **16**, 2841 (2004).
143. Gosalawit, R.; Chirachanchai, S.; Shishatskiy, S,; Nunes, S. P., *J. Membrane Sci.,* **323**, 337 (2008).
144. Kerres, J.; Cui, W.; Reichle, S., *J. Polym. Sci. Part-A: Polym. Chem.,* **34**, 2421 (1996).
145. Chikashige, Y.; Chikyu, Y.; Miyatake, K.; Watanabe, M., *Macromolecules,* **38**, 7121 (2005).
146. Judeinstein, P.; Reichert, D.; deAzevedo, E. R.; Bonagamba, T. J., *Acta. Chim. Slov.,* **52**, 349 (2005).
147. Dias, F. B.; Plomp, L.; Veldhuis, J. B. J., J. Power Sources. 88, 169 (2000).
148. Meyer, W. H., *Adv. Mater.,* **10**, 439 (1998).
149. Brandell, D.; Liivat, A.; Aabloo, A.; Thomas, J. O., *Chem. Mater.,* **17**, 3673 (2005).
150. Gavelin, P.; Ljungbäck, R.; Jannasch, P.; Wesslén, B., *Electrochimica Acta.,* **46**, 1439 (2001).
151. Gavelin, P.; Jannasch, P.; Furo, I.; Pettersson, E.; Stilbs, P.; Topgaard, D.; Soderman, O., *Macromolecules,* **35**, 5097 (2002).
152. Jacobs, P.W.M.; Lorimer, J.W.; Russer, A.; Wasiucionek, M., *J. Power Resources,* **26** 483 (1989).
153. Blonsky, P. M.; Shriver, D. F.; Austin, P.; Allcock, H. R., *J. Am. Chem. Soc.,* **106**, 6854 (1984).
154. Allcock, H. R.; Bender, J. D.; Morford, R. V.; Berda, E. B., *Macromolecules,* **36**, 3563 (2003).
155. Matsumi, N.; Sugai, K.; Sakamoto, K.; Mizumo, T.; Ohno, H., *Macromolecules,* **38**, 4951 (2005).
156. Jannasch, P., *Macromolecules,* **33**, 8604 (2000).
157. Meador, M. A. B.; Cubon, V. A.; Scheiman, D. A.; Bennett, W. R., *Chem. Mater.,* **15**, 3018 (2003).
158. Rossi, N. A. A.; Zhang, Z.; Schneider, Y.; Morcom, K.; Lyons, L. J.; Wang, Q.; Amine, K.; West, R., *Chem. Mater.,* **18**, 1289 (2006).
159. Feiring, A. E.; Choi, S. K.; Doyle, M.; Wonchoba, E. R., *Macromolecules,* **33**, 9262 (2000).
160. Feiring, A. E.; Wonchoba, E. R., *J. Fluorine Chem.,* **105**, 129 (2000).
161. Mandal, B. K.; Walsh, C. J.; Sooksimuang, T.; Behroozi, S. J.; Kim, S.-g.; Kim, Y.-T.; Smotkin, E. S.; Filler, R.; Castro, C., *Chem. Mater.,* **12**, 6 (2000).
162. Matsumi, N.; Sugai, K.; Sakamoto, K.; Mizumo, T.; Ohno, H., *Macromolecules,* **38**, 4951 (2005).
163. Peng, Q.; Lu, Z.-Y.; Huang, Y.; Xie, M.-G.; Han, S.-H.; Peng, J.-B.; Cao, Y.; Huang, W., *Macromolecules,* **37**, 260 (2004).
164. Liu, M. S.; Luo, J.; Jen, A. K.-Y., *Chem. Mater.,* **15**, 3496 (2003).
165. Liu, M. S.; Jiang, X.; Herguth, P.; Jen, A. K-Y., *Chem. Mater.,* **13**, 3820 (2001).
166. Ranger, M.; Rondeau, D.; Leclerc, M., *Macromolecules,* **30**, 7686 (1997).
167. Mei, C.; Tu, G.; Zhou, Q.; Cheng, Y.; Xie, Z.; Ma, D.; Geng, Y.; Wang, L., *Polymer,* **47**, 4976 (2006).
168. Liu, B.; Yu, W.-L.; Lai, Y.-H.; Huang, W., *Macromolecules,* **33**, 8945 (2000).

169. Ego, C.; Marsitzky, D.; Becker, S.; Zhang, J.; Grimsdale, A. C.; Müllen, K.; MacKenzie, J. D.; Silva, C.; Friend, R. H., *J. Am. Chem. Soc.,* **125**, 437 (2003).
170. Ohshita, J.; Nodono, M.; Kai, H.; Watanabe, T.; Kunai, A.; Komaguchi, K.; Shiotani, M.; Adachi, A.; Okita, K.; Harima, Y.; Yamashita, K.; Ishikawa, M., *Organometallics,* **18**, 1453 (1999).
171. Yu, W-L.; Pei, J.; Cao, Y.; Huang, W.; Heeger, A. J., *Chem. Commun.,* 1837 (1999).
172. Vak, D.; Lim, B.; Lee, S.-H.; Kim, D.-Y., *Org. Lett.,* **7**, 4229 (2005).
173. Mishra, A. K.; Graf, M.; Grasse, F.; Jacob, J.; List, E. J. W.; Mullen, K., *Chem. Mater.,* **18**, 2879 (2006).
174. Chan, K. L.; McKiernan, M. J.; Towns, C. R.; Holmes, A. B., *J. Am. Chem. Soc.,* **127**, 7662 (2005).
175. Ahn, T.; Song, S.-Y.; Shim, H.-K., *Macromolecules,* **33**, 6764 (2000).
176. An, B.-K.; Kim, Y.-H.; Shin, D.-C.; Park, S. Y.; Yu, H.-S.; Kwon, S.-K., *Macromolecules,* **34**, 3993 (2001).
177. Taranekar, P.; Abdulbaki, M.; Krishnamoorti, R.; Phanichphant, S.; Waenkaew, P.; Patton, D.; Fulghum, T.; Advincula, R., *Macromolecules,* **39**, 3848 (2006).
178. Mikroyannidis, J. A.; Kazantzis, A. V., *J. Polym. Sci. Part A: Polym. Chem.,* **43**, 4486 (2005).
179. Jin, S.-H.; Kim, M.-Y.; Koo, D.-S.; Kim, Y.-I.; Park, S.-H.; Lee, K.; Gal, Y.-S., *Chem. Mater.,* **16**, 3299 (2004).
180. Dalton, L.; Harper, A.; Ren, A.; Wang, F.; Todorova, G.; Chen, J.; Zhang, C.; Lee, M., *Ind. Eng. Chem. Res.,* **38**, 8 (1999).
181. Luo, J.; Haller, M.; Li, H.; Tang, H.-Z.; Jen, A. K.-Y.; Jakka, K.; Chou, C.-H.; Shu, C.-F., *Macromolecules,* **37**, 248 (2004).
182. Kim, M. H.; Jin, J-H.; Lee, C. J.; Kim, N.; Park, K. H., *Bull. Korean Chem. Soc.,* **23**, 964 (2002).
183. Davey, M. H.; Lee, V. Y.; Wu, L.-M.; Moylan, C. R.; Volksen, W.; Knoesen, A.; Miller, R. D.; Marks, T. J., *Chem. Mater.,* **12**, 1679 (2000).
184. Leng, W.; Zhou, Y.; Xu, Q.; Liu, J., *Macromolecules,* **34**, 4774 (2001).
185. Liang, Z.; Yang, Z.; Sun, S.; Wu, B.; Dalton, L. R.; Garner, S. M.; Kalluri, S.; Chen, A.; Steier, W. H., *Chem. Mater.,* **8**, 2681 (1996).
186. Ahumada, O.; Weder, C.; Neuenschwander, P.; Suter, U. W.; Herminghaus, S., *Macromolecules,* **30**, 3256 (1997).
187. Jiang, H.; Kakkar, A. K., *Macromolecules,* **31**, 4170 (1998).
188. Cui, Y.; Qian, G.; Chen, L.; Wang, Z.; Gao, J.; Wang, M., *J. Phys. Chem. B.,* **110**, 4105 (2006).
189. Haller, M.; Luo, J.; Li, H.; Kim, T.-D.; Liao, Y.; Robinson, B. H.; Dalton, L. R.; Jen, A. K.-Y., *Macromolecules,* **37**, 688 (2004).
190. Chaumel, F.; Jiang, H.; Kakkar, A., *Chem. Mater.,* **13**, 3389 (2001).
191. Li, Z.; Zhao, Y.; Zhou, J.; Shen, Y., *Adv. Mater. Opt. Electron.,* **9**, 195 (1999).
192. Song, N.; Men, L.; Gao, J. P.; Bai, Y.; Beaudin, A. M. R.; Yu, G.; Wang, Z. Y., *Chem. Mater.,* **16**, 3708 (2004).
193. Bai, Y.; Song, N.; Gao, J. P.; Sun, X.; Wang, X.; Yu, G.; Wang, Z. Y., *J. Am. Chem. Soc.,* **127**, 2060 (2005).
194. Ma, H.; Chen, B.; Sassa, T.; Dalton, L. R.; Jen, A. K.-Y., *J. Am. Chem. Soc.,* **123**, 986 (2001).
195. Ma, H.; Wu, J.; Herguth, P.; Chen, B.; Jen, A. K.-Y., *Chem. Mater.,* **12**, 1187 (2000).
196. Kang, H.; Evmenenko, G.; Dutta, P.; Clays, K.; Song, K.; Marks, T. J., *J. Am. Chem. Soc.,* **128**, 6194 (2006).
197. Shi, Y.; Lin, W.; Olson, D. J.; Bechtel, J. H.; Zhang, H.; Steier, W. H.; Zhang, C.; Dalton, L. R., *Appl. Phys. Lett.,* **77**, 1 (2000).

198. Chen, D.; Fetterman, H. R.; Chen, A.; Steier, W. H.; Dalton, L. R.; Wang, W.; Shi, Y., *Appl. Phys. Lett.,* **70**, 3335 (1997).
199. Shi, Y.; Zhang, C.; Zhang, H.; Bechtel, J. H.; Dalton, L. R.; Robinson, B. H.; Steier, W. H., *Science,* **288**, 119 (2000).
200. Marder, S. R.; Cheng, L. T.; Tiemann, B. G.; Friedli, A. C.; Blanchard-Desce, M.; Perry, J. W.; Skindhoej, J., *Science*, **263**, 511 (1994).
201. Marder, S. R.; Perry, J. W.; Bourhill, G.; Gorman, C. B.; Tiemann, B. G.; Mansour, K., *Science*, **261**, 186 (1993).
202. Ermer, S.; Lovejoy, S. M.; Leung, D. S.; Warren, H.; Moylan, C. R.; Twieg, R. J., *Chem. Mater.,* **9**, 1437 (1997).
203. Zhang, C.; Dalton, L. R.; Oh, M.-C.; Zhang, H.; Steier, W. H., *Chem. Mater.,* **13**, 3043 (2001).
204. He, M.; Leslie, T.; Garner, S.; DeRosa, M.; Cites, J., *J. Phys. Chem. B,* **108**, 8731 (2004).
205. He, M.; Leslie, T. M.; Sinicropi, J. A.; Garner, S. M.; Reed, L. D., *Chem. Mater.,* **14**, 4669 (2002).
206. He, M.; Leslie, T. M.; Sinicropi, J. A., *Chem. Mater.,* **14**, 2393 (2002).
207. Breitung, E. M.; Shu, C.-F.; McMahon, R. J., *J. Am. Chem. Soc.,* **122**, 1154 (2000).
208. Cheng, L.T.; Tam, W.; Stevenson, S. H.; Meredith, G. R.; Rikken, G.; Marder, S. R., J. *Phys. Chem.,* **95**, 10631 (1991).
209. Luo, J.; Cheng, Y.-J.; Kim, T.-D.; Hau, S.; Jang, S.-H.; Shi, Z.; Zhou, X.-H.; Jen, A. K-Y., *Org. Lett.,* **8**, 1387 (2006).
210. Karim, A. S. M.; Nomura, R.; Kajii, H.; Hidayat, R.; Yoshino, K.; Masuda, T., *J. Polym. Sci. Part-A: Polym. Chem.,* **38**, 4717 (2000).
211. Hambir, S. A.; Wolfe, D.; Blanchard, G. J.; Baker, G. L., *J. Am. Chem. Soc.,* **119**, 7367 (1997).
212. Hales, J. M.; Zheng, S.; Barlow, S.; Marder, S. R.; Perry, J. W., *J. Am. Chem. Soc.,* **128**, 11362 (2006).
213. Reinitzer, F., *Monatsh. Chem.,* **9**, 421 (1888).
214. Elliott, A.; Ambrose, E., *J. Disc. Farad. Soc.,* **9**, 246 (1950).
215. Ogata, N.; Sanui, K.; Zhao, A-C.; Watanabe, M.; Hanaoka, T., *Polym. J.,* **20**, 529 (1988).
216. Heitz, W., *Makromol. Chem. Macromol. Symp.,* **47**, 111 (1991).
217. Bhowmik, P. K.; Han, H., *Polym. Prepr., (ACS, Div. Polym. Chem.),* **35**, 617 (1994).
218. Lenz, R. W., *Pure & Appl. Chem.,* **57**, 977 (1985).
219. Fu, K.; Nematsu, T.; Sone, M.; Itoh, T.; Hayakawa, T.; Ueda, M.; Tokita, M.; Watanabe, J., *Macromolecules,* **33**, 8367 (2000).
220. Percec, V.; Wang, C.-S.; Lee, M., *Polym. Bull.,* **26**, 15 (1991).
221. Lin, C.-H.; Hsu, C.-S., *Polym. Bull.,* **45**, 53 (2000).
222. Kouwer, P. H. J.; Jager, W. F.; Mijs, W. J.; Picken, S. J., *Macromolecules,* **34**, 7582 (2001).
223. Tokita, M.; Takahashi, T.; Hayashi, M.; Inomata, K.; Watanabe, J., *Macromolecules,* **29**, 1345 (1996).
224. Hu, Y. S.; Liu, R. Y. F.; Schiraldi, D. A.; Hiltner, A.; Baer, E., *Macromolecules,* **37**, 2128 (2004).
225. Krigbaum, W. R.; Watanabe, J.; Ishikawa, T., *Macromolecules,* **16**, 1271 (1983).
226. Okano, K.; Tsutsumi, O.; Shishido, A.; Ikeda, T., *J. Am. Chem. Soc.,* **128**, 15368 (2006).
227. Seo, S. H.; Kim, Y.-W.; Chang, J. Y., *Macromolecules,* **38**, 1525 (2005).
228. Percec, V.; Tomazo, D., *Adv. Mater.,* **4**, 548 (1992).
229. Percec, V.; Lee, M.; Jonsson, H., *J. Polym. Sci. Part-A: Polym. Chem.,* **29**, 327 (1991).

230. Lecommandoux, S.; Noirez, L.; Achard, M. F.; Hardouin, F., *Macromolecules,* **33**, 67 (2000).
231. Zhang, S.; Terentjev, E. M.; Donald, A. M., *J. Phys. Chem. B.,* **109**, 13195 (2005).
232. Brehmer, M.; Zentel, R., *Macromol. Chem. Phys.,* **195**, 1891 (1994).
233. Gebhard, E.; Zentel, R., *Macromol. Chem. Phys.,* **201**, 902 (2000).
234. Kouwer, P. H. J.; Jager, W. F.; Mijs, W. J.; Picken, S. J., *Macromolecules,* **33**, 4336 (2000).
235. Kouwer, P. H. J.; Jager, W. F.; Mijs, W. J.; Picken, S. J., *Macromolecules,* **35**, 4322 (2002).
236. Kouwer, P. H. J.; Jager, W. F.; Mijs, W. J.; Picken, S. J., *Macromolecules,* **34**, 7582 (2001).
237. Otmakhova, O. A.; Kuptsov, S. A.; Talroze, R. V.; Patten, T. E., *Macromolecules,* **36**, 3432 (2003).
238. Weck, M.; Mohr, B.; Maughon, B. R.; Grubbs, R. H., *Macromolecules,* **30**, 6430 (1997).
239. Deschenaux, R.; Kosztics, I.; Scholten, U.; Guillon, D.; Ibn-Elhaj, M., *J. Mater. Chem.,* **4**, 1351 (1994).
240. Singh, P.; Rausch, M. D.; Lenz, R. W., *Polym. Bull.,* **22**, 247 (1989).
241. Joo, S.-H.; Yun, Y.-K.; Jin, J.-I.; Kim, D.-C.; Zin, W.-C., *Macromolecules,* **33**, 6704 (2000).
242. Walba, D. M.; Keller, P.; Shao, R.; Clark, N. A.; Hillmyer, M.; Grubbs, R. H., *J. Am. Chem. Soc.,* **118**, 2740 (1996).
243. Allcock, H. R.; Kugel, R. L., *J. Am. Chem. Soc.,* **87**, 4216 (1965).
244. Allcock, H. R., *Angew Chem. Int. Ed. Engl.,* **16**, 147 (1977).
245. Blonsky, P. M.; Shriver, D. F.; Austin, P. E.; Allcock, H. R., *J. Am. Chem. Soc.,* **106**, 6854 (1984).
246. Neilson, R. H.; Wisian-Neilson, P., *Chem. Rev.,* **88**, 541 (1988).
247. Allcock, H. R.; Connolly, M. S.; Sisko, J. T.; Al-Shali, S., *Macromolecules,* **21**, 323 (1988).
248. Allcock, H. R.; Mang, M. N.; Dembek, A. A.; Wynne, K. J., *Macromolecules,* **22**, 4179 (1989).
249. Allcock, H. R., J. Inorg. *Organomet. Polym.,* **2**, 197 (1992).
250. Allcock, H. R.; Pucher, S. R.; Scopelianos, A. G., *Macromolecules,* **27**, 1071 (1994).
251. Singh, A.; Krogman, N. R.; Sethuraman, S.; Nair, L. S.; Sturgeon, J. L.; Brown, P. W.; Laurencin, C. T.; Allcock, H. R., *Biomacromolecules,* **7**, 914 (2006).
252. Allcock, H. R.; Singh, A.; Ambrosio, A. M. A.; Laredo, W. R., *Biomacromolecules,* **4**, 1646 (2003).
253. Lee, S. B.; Song, S.-C.; Jin, J.-I.; Sohn, Y. S., *Macromolecules,* **32**, 7820 (1999).
254. Tang, H.; Pintauro, P. N., *J. Appl. Polym. Sci.,* **79**, 49 (2000).
255. Guo, Q. H.; Pintauro, P. N.; Tang, H.; O'Connor, S., *J. Membr. Sci.,* **154**, 175 (1999).
256. Carter, R.; Evilia, R. F.; Pintauro, P. N., *J. Phys. Chem. B.,* **105**, 2351 (2001).
257. Allcock, H. R.; Fitzpatrick, R. J.; Salvati, L., *Chem. Mater.,* **3**, 1120 (1991).
258. Neilson, R. H.; Hani, R.; Wisian-Neilson, P.; Meister, J. J.; Roy, A. K.; Hagnauer, G. L., *Macromolecules,* **20**, 910 (1987).
259. Wisian-Neilson, P.; Islam, M. S.; Ganapathiappan, S.; Scott, D. L.; Raghuveer, K. S.; Ford, R. R., *Macromolecules,* **22**, 4382 (1989).
260. Wisian-Neilson, Ford, R. R., *Organometallics,* **6**, 2258 (1987).
261. West, R., *J. Organomet. Chem.,* **300**, 327 (1986).
262. Miller, R. D.; Michl, J., *Chem. Rev.,* **89**, 1359 (1989).
263. Aitken, C. T.; Harrod, J. F.; Samuel, E., *J. Am. Chem. Soc.,* **108**, 4059 (1986).
264. Tilley, T. D., *Acc. Chem. Res.,* **26**, 22 (1993).

265. Qui, H. Y.; Du, Z. D., *J. Polym. Sci. Part-A: Polym. Chem. Ed.,* **27**, 2849 (1989).
266. Qui, H. Y.; Du, Z. D., *J. Polym. Sci. Part-A: Polym. Chem. Ed.,* **27**, 2861 (1989).
267. Hsiao, Y.-L.; Waymouth, R. M., *J. Am. Chem. Soc.,* **116**, 9779 (1994).
268. Banovertz, J. P.; Hsiao, Y.-L.; Waymouth, R. M., *J. Am. Chem. Soc.,* **115**, 2540 (1993).
269. Toal, S. J.; Sohn, H.; Zakarov, L. N.; Kassel, W. S.; Golen, J. A.; Rheingold, A. L.; Trogler, W. C., *Organometallics,* **24**, 3081 (2005).
270. Sohn, H.; Huddleston, R. R.; Powell, D. R.; West, R.; Oka, K.; Yonghua, X., *J. Am. Chem. Soc.,* **121**, 2935 (1999).
271. Kim, B.-H.; Woo, H.-G., *Organometallics,* **21**, 2796 (2002).
272. Chen, J.; Xie, Z.; Lam, J. W. Y.; Law, C. C. W.; Tang, B. Z., *Macromolecules,* **36**, 1108 (2003).
273. Sohn, H.; Sailor, M. J.; Magde, D.; Trogler, W. C., *J. Am. Chem. Soc.,* **125**, 3821 (2003).
274. Nguyen, P.; Gomez-Elipe, P.; Manners, I., *Chem. Rev.,* **99**, 1515 (1999).
275. Rushkin, I. L.; Interrante, L. V., *Macromolecules,* **28**, 5160 (1995).
276. Kriner, W. A., *J. Polym. Sci. Part: A-1,* **4**, 444 (1966).
277. Pang, Y.; Ijadi-Maghsoodi, S.; Barton, T. J., *Macromolecules,* **26**, 5671 (1993).
278. Ijadi-Maghsoodi, S.; Pang, Y.; Barton, T. J., *J. Polym. Sci. Part-A: Polym. Chem.,* **28**, 955 (1990).
279. Wang, F.; Zhang, J.; Huang, J.; Yan, H.; Huang, F.; Du, L., *Polym. Bull.,* **56**, 19 (2006).
280. Manners, I., *Chem. Commun.,* 857 (1999).
281. Foucher, D. A.; Tang, B. Z.; Manners, I., *J. Am. Chem. Soc.,* **114**, 6246 (1992).
282. Pudelski, J. K.; Rulkens, R.; Foucher, D. A.; Lough, A. J.; MacDonald, P. M.; Manners, I., *Macromolecules,* **28**, 7301 (1995).
283. Cyr, P. W.; Rider, D. A.; Kulbaba, K.; Manners, I., *Macromolecules,* **37**, 3959 (2004).
284. Nguyen, P.; Stojcevic, G.; Kulbaba, K.; MacLachlan, M. J.; Liu, X.-H.; Lough, A. J.; Manners, I., *Macromolecules,* **31**, 5977 (1998).
285. Reneker, D. H.; Chun, I., *Nanotechnology,* **7**, 216 (1996).
286. Manners, I., *Adv. Organomet. Chem.,* **37**, 131 (1995).
287. Rulkens, R.; Resendes, R.; Verma, A.; Manners, I.; Murti, K.; Fossum, E.; Miller, P.; Matyjaszewski, K., *Macromolecules,* **30**, 8165 (1997).
288. Yim, H.; Foster, M. D.; Balaishis, D.; Manners, I., Langmuir, 14, 3921 (1998).
289. Nguyen, M. T.; Diaz, A. F.; Dement'ev, V. V.; Pannell, K. H., *Chem. Mater.,* **6**, 952 (1994).
290. Coult, R.; Fox, M. A.; Gill, W. R.; Herbertson, P. L.; MacBride, J. A. H.; Wade, K., *J. Orgmet. Chem.,* **462**, 19 (1993).
291. Müller, J.; Baše, K.; Magnera, T. F.; Michl, J., *J. Am. Chem. Soc.,* **114**, 9721 (1992).
292. Colquhoun, H. M.; Herbertson, P. L.; Wade, K.; Baxter, I.; Williams, D. J., *Macromolecules,* **31**, 1694 (1998).
293. Colquhoun, H. M.; Williams, D. J., *Acc. Chem. Res.,* **33**, 189 (2000).
294. Clegg, W.; Gill, W. R.; MacBride, J. A. H.; Wade, K., *Angew. Chem. Int. Ed. Engl.,* **32**, 1328 (1993).
295. Colquhoun, H. M.; Herbertson, P. L.; Wade, K., *J. Polym. Sci. Part-A: Polym. Chem.,* **34**, 2521 (1996).
296. Knollmueller, K. O.; Scott, R. N.; Kwasnik, H.; Sieckhaus, J. F., *J. Polym. Sci. Part A-1,* **9**, 1071 (1971).
297. Kolel-Veetil, M. K.; Beckham, H. W.; Keller, T. M., *Chem. Mater.,* **16**, 3162 (2004).
298. Henderson, L. J.; Keller, T. M., *Macromolecules*, **27**, 1660 (1994).

299. Sundar, R. A.; Keller, T. M., *J. Polym. Sci. Part-A:, Polym. Chem.,* **35**, 2387 (1997).
300. Kolel-Veetil, M. K.; Keller, T. M., *J. Polym. Sci. Part-A: Polym. Chem.,* **44**, 147 (2006).
301. Houser, E. J.; Keller, T. M., *J. Polym. Sci. Part-A: Polym. Chem.,* **36**, 1969 (1998).
302. Tomalia, D. A.; Naylor, A. M.; Goddard III, W. A., *Angew. Chem. Int. Ed.,* **29**, 138 (1990).
303. Moore, J. S., *Acc. Chem. Res.,* **30**, 402 (1997).
304. Fischer, M.; Vögtle, F., *Angew. Chem. Int. Ed.,* **38**, 884 (1999).
305. Klajnert, B.; Bryszewska, M., *Acta. Biochim. Polonica.,* **48**, 199 (2001).
306. Tomalia, D. A.; Fréchet, J. M. J., *J. Polym. Sci. Part-A: Polym. Chem.,* **40**, 2719 (2002).
307. Tomalia, D. A., *Prog. Polym. Sci.,* **30**, 294 (2005).
308. Crespo, L.; Sanclimens, G.; Pons, M.; Giralt, E.; Royo, M.; Albericio, F., *Chem. Rev.,* **105**, 1663 (2005).
309. Boas, U.; Christensen, J. B.; Heegaard, P. M. H., *J. Mater. Chem.,* **16**, 3785 (2006).
310. Fischer, M.; Vögtle, F., *Angew. Chem., Int. Edn.,* **38**, 884 (1999).
311. Wiesler, U.-M.; Berresheim, A. J.; Morgenroth, F.; Lieser, G.; Mullen, K., *Macromolecules,* **34**, 187 (2001).
312. Feng, X.-S.; Taton, D.; Chaikof, E. L.; Gnanou, Y., *J. Am. Chem. Soc.,* **127**, 10956 (2005).
313. Carnahan, M. A.; Grinstaff, M. W., *Macromolecules,* **34**, 7648 (2001).
314. Degoricija, L.; Carnahan, M. A.; Johnson, C. S.; Kim, T.; Grinstaff, M. W., *Macromolecules,* **39**, 8952 (2006).
315. Diallo, M. S.; Balogh, L.; Shafagati, A.; Johnson, J. H., Jr.; Goddard III, W. A.; Tomalia, D. A., *Environ. Sci. Technol.,* **33**, 820 (1999).
316. Tomalia, D. A.; Baker, H.; Dewald, J.; Hall, M.; Kallos, G.; Martin, S.; Roeck, J.; Ryder, J.; Smith, P., *Polymer J.,* **17**, 117 (1985).
317. Grayson, S. M.; Fréchet, J. M. J., *Chem. Rev.,* **101**, 3819 (2001).
318. Yamazaki, N.; Washio, I.; Shibasaki, Y.; Ueda, M., *Org. Lett.,* **8**, 2321 (2006).
319. Hawker, C. J.; Frechet, J. M. J., *J. Am. Chem. Soc.,* **112**, 7638 (1990).
320. Hecht, S.; Frechet, J. M. J., *J. Am. Chem. Soc.,* **121**, 4084 (1999).
321. Freeman, A. W.; Frechet, J. M. J., *Org. Lett.,* **1**, 685 (1999).
322. Higuchi, M.; Shiki, S.; Ariga, K.; Yamamoto, K., *J. Am. Chem. Soc.,* **123**, 4414 (2001).
323. Enoki, O.; Katoh, H.; Yamamoto, K., *Org. Lett.,* **8**, 569 (2006).
324. Takanashi, K.; Chiba, H.; Higuchi, M.; Yamamoto, K., *Org. Lett.,* **6**, 1709 (2004).
325. Imaoka, T.; Horiguchi, H.; Yamamoto, K., *J. Am. Chem. Soc.,* **125**, 340 (2003).
326. Yamamoto, K.; Imaoka, T., *Bull. Chem. Soc. Jpn.,* **79**, 511 (2006)
327. Onitsuka, K.; Kitajima, H.; Fujimoto, M.; Iuchi, A.; Takei, F.; Takahashi, S., *Chem. Commun.,* 2576 (2002).
328. Pollak, K. W.; Sanford, E. M.; Frechet, J. M. J., *Mater. Chem.,* **8**, 519 (1998).
329. Bhyrappa, P.; Young, J. K.; Moore, J. S.; Suslick, K. S., *J. Am. Chem. Soc.,* **118**, 5708 (1996).
330. Bharathi, P.; Patel, U.; Kawaguchi, T.; Pesak, D. J.; Moore, J. S., *Macromolecules,* **28**, 5955 (1995).
331. Moore, J. S., *Acc. Chem. Res.,* **30**, 402 (1997).
332. Deb, S. K.; Maddux, T. M.; Yu, L., *J. Am. Chem. Soc.,* **119**, 9079 (1997).
333. Washio, I.; Shibasaki, Y.; Ueda, M., *Macromolecules,* **38**, 2237 (2005).
334. Okazaki, M.; Washio, I.; Shibasaki, Y.; Ueda, M., *J. Am. Chem. Soc.,* **125**, 8120 (2003).
335. Washio, I.; Shibasaki, Y.; Ueda, M., *Org. Lett.,* **5**, 4159 (2003).
336. Morikawa, A.; Kakimoto, M.; Imai, Y., *Macromolecules,* **26**, 6324 (1993).

337. Morikawa, A.; Ono, K., *Macromolecules,* **32**, 1062 (1999).
338. Abramov, M. A.; Shukla, R.; Amabilino, D. B.; Dehaen, W., *J. Org. Chem.,* **67**, 1004 (2002).
339. Leu, C.-M.; Chang, Y.-T.; Shu, C.-F.; Teng, C.-F.; Shiea, J., *Macromolecules,* **33**, 2855 (2000).
340. Iyer, J.; Fleming, K.; Hammond, P. T., *Macromolecules,* **31**, 8757 (1998).
341. Fréchet, J. M. J.; Gitsov, I.; Monteil, T.; Rochat, S.; Sassi, J.-F.; Vergelati, C.; Yu, D., *Chem. Mater.,* **11**, 1267 (1999).
342. Chang, Y.; Kim, C., *J. Polym. Sci. Part-A: Polym. Chem.,* **39**, 918 (2001).
343. Tyan, L.; Nguyen, P.; Hammond, P. T., *Chem. Commun.,* 3489 (2006).
344. Jang, C.-J.; Ryu, J.-H.; Lee, J.-D.; Sohn, D.; Lee, M., *Chem. Mater.,* **16**, 4226 (2004). Namazi, H.; Adeli, M., *Polymer,* **46**, 10788 (2005).
345. Hawker, C. J.; Fréchet, J. M., *J. Am. Chem. Soc.,* **114**, 8405 (1992).
346. Hawker, C. J.; Wooley, K. L.; Fréchet, J. M. J., *Macromol. Symp.,* **11**, 77 (1994).
347. Aoi, K.; Itoh, K.; Okada, M., *Macromolecules,* **30**, 8072 (1997).
348. Trollsås, M; Claesson, H.; Atthoff, B.; Hedrick, J. L., *Angew. Chem. Int. Ed.,* **37**, 3132 (1998).
349. Trollsås, M; Atthoff, B.; Claesson, H.; Hedrick, J. L., *J. Polym. Sci. Part-A: Polym. Chem.,* **42**, 1174 (2004).
350. Pan, Y.; Ford, W. T., *Macromolecules,* **32**, 5468 (1999).
351. Pan, Y.; Ford, W. T., *J. Org. Chem.,* **64**, 8588 (1999).
352. Atanasov, V.; Sinigersky, V.; Klapper, M.; Mullen, K., *Macromolecules,* **38**, 1672 (2005).
353. Ihre, H.; Hult, A.; Soderlind, E., *J. Am. Chem. Soc.*, **118**, 6388 (1996).
354. Malkoch, M.; Malmström, E.; Hult, A., *Macromolecules,* **35**, 8307 (2002).
355. Schlüter, A. D.; Rabe, J. P., *Angew. Chem. Int. Ed.*, **39**, 864 (2000).
356. Zhang, A.; Shu, L.; Bo, Z.; Schlüter, A. D., *Macromol. Chem. Phys.,* **204**, 328 (2003).
357. Frauenrath, H., *Prog. Polym. Sci.,* **30**, 325 (2005).
358. Das, J.; Yoshida, M.; Fresco, Z. M.; Choi, T. L.; Fréchet, J. M. J.; Chakraborty, A. K., *J. Phys. Chem. B.,* **109**, 6535 (2005).
359. Welch, P. M.; Welch, C. F., *Nano Lett.,* **6**, 1922 (2006).
360. Freudenberger, R.; Claussen, W.; Schlüter, A. D.; Wallmeier, H., *Polymer,* **35**, 4496 (1994).
361. Rehahn, M.; Schlüter, A. D.; Wegner, G.; Feast, W. J., *Polymer,* **30**, 1060 (1989).
362. Karakaya, B.; Claussen, W.; Schaefer, A.; Lehmann, A.; Schlüter, A. D., *Acta Polym.,* **47**, 79 (1996).
363. Karakaya, B.; Claussen, W.; Gessler, K.; Saenger, W.; Schlüter, A. D., *J. Am. Chem. Soc.,* **119**, 3296 (1997).
364. Kolb, H. C.; Finn, M. G.; Sharpless, K. B., *Angew. Chem. Int. Edn.,* **40**, 2004 (2001).
365. Wu, P.; Feldman, A. K.; Nugent, A. K.; Hawker, C. J.; Scheel, A.; Voit, B.; Pyun, J.; Fréchet, J. M. J.; Sharpless, K. B.; Fokin, V. V., *Angew. Chem. Int. Edn.,* **43**, 3928 (2004).
366. Helms, B.; Mynar, J. L.; Hawker, C. J.; Fréchet, J. M. J., *J. Am. Chem. Soc.,* **126**, 15020 (2004).
367. Desai, A.; Atkinson, N.; Rivera-Jr., F.; Devonport, W.; Rees, I.; Branz, S. E.; Hawker, C. J., *J. Polym. Sci. Part-A, Polym. Chem.,* **38**, 1033 (2000).
368. Kim, K. T.; Han, J.; Ryu, C. Y.; Sun, F. C.; Sheiko, S. S.; Winnik, M. A.; Manners, I., *Macromolecules,* **39**, 7922 (2006).
369. Yin, R.; Zhu, Y.; Tomalia, D. A.; Ibuki, H., *J. Am. Chem. Soc.,* **120**, 2678 (1998).
370. Ouali, N.; Mery, S.; Skoulios, A.; Noirez., *Macromolecules,* **33**, 6185 (2000).
371. Kim, C.; Kang, S., *J. Polym. Sci. Part-A. Polym. Chem.,* **38**, 724 (2000).

372. Grayson, S. M.; Fréchet, J. M. J., *Macromolecules,* **34**, 6542 (2001).
373. Ihre, H.; Padilla de Jesús O. L.; Fréchet, J. M. J., *J. Am. Chem. Soc.,* **123**, 5908 (2001).
374. Yoshida, M.; Fresco, Z. M.; Ohnishi, S.; Fréchet, J. M. J., *Macromolecules,* **38**, 334 (2005).
375. Li, W.; Zhang, A.; Schlüter, A. D., *Macromolecules,* **41**, 43 (2008).
376. Cheng, C. X.; Tang, R. P.; Zhao, Y. L.; Xi, F., *J. Appl. Polym. Sci.,* **91**, 2733 (2004).
377. Nyström, A.; Hult, A., *J. Polym. Sci. Part-A. Polym. Chem.,* **43**, 3852 (2005).
378. Percec, V.; Heck, J.; Tomazos, D.; Falkenberg, F.; Blackwell, H.; Ungar, G., *J. Chem. Soc., Perkin Trans. 1,* 2799, 1993.
379. Malkoch, M.; Carlmark, A.; Woldegiorgis, A.; Hult, A.; Malmström, E. E., *Macromolecules,* **37**, 322 (2004).
380. Mynar, J. L.; Choi, T-L.; Yoshida, M.; Kim, V.; Hawker, C. J.; Fréchet, J. M. J., *Chem. Commun.,* 5169 (2005).
381. Bo., Z.; Schlüter, A. D., *Chem. Eur. J.,* **6**, 3235 (2000).
382. Chou, C-H.; Shu, C-F., *Macromolecules,* **35**, 9673 (2002).
383. Fu, Y.; Li, Y.; Li, J.; Yan, S.; Bo, Z., *Macromolecules,* **37**, 6395 (2004).
384. Schluter, A. D.; Wegner, G., *Acta Polym.,* **44**, 59 (1993).
385. Bao, Z.; Amundson, K. R.; Lovinger, A. J., *Macromolecules,* **31**, 8647 (1998).
386. Rajaram, S.; Choi, T.-L.; Rolandi, M.; Fréchet, J. M. J., *J. Am. Chem. Soc.,* **129**, 9619 (2007).
387. Nyström, A.; Malkoch, M.; Furó, I.; Nyström, D.; Unal, K.; Antoni, P.; Vamvounis, G.; Hawker, C.; Wooley, K.; Malmström, E.; Hult, A., *Macromolecules,* **39**, 7241 (2006).
388. Percec, V.; Schlüter, D.; Ronda, J. C.; Johansson, G.; Ungar, G.; Zhou, J. P., *Macromolecules,* **29**, 1464 (1996).
389. Ball, Z. T.; Sivula, K.; Fréchet, J. M. J., *Macromolecules,* **39**, 70 (2006).
390. Teertstra, S. J.; Gauthier, M., *Prog. Polym. Sci.,* **29**, 277 (2004).
391. Gauthier, M., *J. Polym. Sci. Part-A, Polym. Chem.*, **45**, 3803 (2007).
392. Njikang, G. N.; Cao, L.; Gauthier, M., J., *Macromol. Chem. Phys.,* **209**, 907 (2008).
393. Gauthier, M.; Möller, M., *Macromolecules,* **24**, 4548 (1991).
394. Hempenius, M. A.; Michelberger, W.; Möller, M., *Macromolecules,* **30**, 5602 (1997).
395. Kee, R. A.; Gauthier, M., *Am. Chem. Soc. Div. Polym. Chem. Prepr.,* **40**, 165 (1999).
396. Kee, R. A.; Gauthier, M., *Macromolecules,* **32**, 6478 (1999).
397. Li, J.; Gauthier, M.; Teertstra, S. J.; Xu, H.; Sheiko, S. S., *Macromolecules,* **37**, 795 (2004).
398. Kee, R. A.; Gauthier, M., *Macromolecules,* **35**, 6526 (2002).
399. Gauthier, M.; Li, J.; Dockendorff, J., *Macromolecules,* **36**, 2642 (2003).
400. Gauthier, M.; Tichagwa, L.; Downey, J. S.; Gao, S., *Macromolecules,* **29**, 519 (1996).
401. Eaton, P. E.; Cooper, G. F.; Johnson, R. C.; Möller, R. H., *J. Org. Chem.,* **37**, 1947 (1972).
402. Schappacher, M.; Deffieux, A., *Macromolecules,* **33**, 7371 (2000).
403. Bernard, J.; Schappacher, M.; Ammannati, E.; Kuhn, A.; Deffieux, A., *Macromolecules,* **35**, 8994 (2002).
404. Schappacher, M.; Deffieux, A.; Putaux, J-L.; Viville, P.; Lazzaroni, R., *Macromolecules,* **36**, 5776 (2003).
405. Schappacher, M.; Bernard, J.; Deffieux, A., *Macromol. Chem. Phys.,* **204**, 762 (2003).

406. Deffieux, A.; Schappacher, M., *Macromolecules,* **32**, 1797 (1999).
407. Bernard, J.; Schappacher, M.; Deffieux, A.; Viville, P.; Lazzaroni, R.; Charles, M. H.; Charreyre, M.-T.; Delair, T., *Bioconjugate Chem.,* **17**, 6 (2006).
408. Knauss, D. M.; Al-Muallem, H. A.; Huang, T.; Wu, D. T., *Macromolecules,* **33**, 3557 (2000).
409. Knauss, D. M.; Al-Muallem, H. A., *J. Polym. Sci. Part A: Polym. Chem.,* **38**, 4289 (2000).
410. Paulo, C.; Puskas, J. E., *Macromolecules,* **34**, 734 (2001).
411. Gao, C.; Yan, D., *Prog. Polym. Sci.,* **29**, 183 (2004).
412. Voit, B., *J. Polym. Sci. Part-A: Polym. Chem.,* **38**, 2505 (2000).
413. Flory, P. J., *J. Am. Chem. Soc.,* **74**, 2718 (1952).
414. Hao, J.; Jikei, M.; Kakimoto, M., *Macromolecules,* **35**, 5372 (2002).
415. Tabuani, D.; Monticelli, O.; Chincarini, A.; Bianchini, C.; Vizza, F.; Moneti, S.; Russo, S., *Macromolecules,* **36**, 4294 (2003).
416. Yang, G.; Jikei, M.; Kakimoto, M., *Macromolecules,* **32**, 2215 (1999).
417. Baek, J.-B.; Ferguson, J. B.; Tan, L.-S., *Macromolecules,* **36**, 4385 (2003).
418. Shu, C.-F.; Leu, C.-M., *Macromolecules,* **32**, 100 (1999).
419. Kwak, S.-Y.; Ahn, D. U., *Macromolecules*, **33**, 7557 (2000).
420. Hawker, C. J.; Chu, F., *Macromolecules*, **29**, 4370 (1996).
421. Jikei, M.; Hu, Z.; Kakimoto, M.; Imai, Y., *Macromolecules,* **29**, 1062 (1996).
422. Turner, S. R.; Walter, F.; Voit, B. I.; Mourey, T. H., *Macromolecules,* **27**, 1611 (1994).
423. Hawker, C. J.; Chu, F.; Pomery, P. J.; Hill, D. J. T., *Macromolecules*, **29**, 3831 (1996).
424. Thompson, D. S.; Markoski, L. J.; Moore, J. S., *Macromolecules,* **32**, 4764 (1999).
425. Yamanaka, K.; Jikei, M.; Kakimoto, M., *Macromolecules,* **33**, 6937 (2000).
426. Zheng, R.; Dong, H.; Peng, H.; Lam, J. W. Y.; Tang, B. Z., *Macromolecules,* **37**, 5196 (2004).
427. Xu, K.; Peng, H.; Sun, Q.; Dong, Y.; Salhi, F.; Luo, J.; Chen, J.; Huang, Y.; Zhang, D.; Xu, Z.; Tang, B. Z., *Macromolecules,* **35**, 5821 (2002).
428. Dong, H.; Zheng, R.; Lam, J. W. Y.; Haussler, M.; Qin, A.; Tang, B. Z., *Macromolecules,* **38,** 6382 (2005).
429. Shimizu, L. S., *Polym. Int.,* **56,** 444 (2007).
430. Weck, M., *Polym. Int.,* **56**, 453 (2007).
431. Bosman, A.W.; Brunsveld, L.; Folmer, B. J. B.; Sijbesma, R. P.; Meijer, E. W., *Macromol. Symp.,* **201**, 143 (2003).
432. Lehn, J. M., *Polym. Int.,* **51**, 825 (2002).
433. Brunsveld, L.; Folmer, B. J. B.; Meijer, E. W., Sijbesma, R. P., *Chem. Rev.,* **101**, 4071 (2001).
434. Schmuck, C.; Wienand, W., *Angew. Chem. Int. Ed.,* **23**, 40 (2001).
435. Sivakova, S.; Bohnsack, D. A.; Mackay, M. E.; Suwanmala, P.; Rowan, S. J., *J. Am. Chem. Soc.,* **127**, 18202 (2005).
436. Lortie, F.; Boileau, S.; Bouteiller, L.; Chassenieux, C.; Dem, B.; Ducouret, G.; Jalabert, M.; Lauprtre, F.; Terech, P., *Langmuir,* **18**, 7218 (2002).
437. Simic, V.; Bouteiller, L.; Jalabert, M., *J. Am. Chem. Soc.,* **125**, 13148 (2003).
438. Mayer, M. F.; Nakashima, S.; Zimmerman, S. C., *Org. Lett.,* **7**, 3005 (2005).
439. Jeong, Y.; Hanabusa, K.; Masunaga, H.; Akiba, I.; Miyoshi, K.; Sakurai, S.; Sakurai, K., *Langmuir,* **21**, 586 (2005).
440. Park, T.; Zimmerman, S. C., *J. Am. Chem. Soc.,* **128**, 13986 (2006).
441. Park, T.; Zimmerman, S. C.; Nakashima, S., *J. Am. Chem. Soc.,* **127**, 6520 (2005).
442. Yagai, S.; Higashi, M.; Karatsu, T.; Kitamura, A., *Chem. Mater.,* **17**, 4392 (2005).
443. Kunz, M. J.; Hayn, G.; Saf, R.; Binder, W. H., *J. Polym. Sci. Part-A, Polym. Chem.*, **42**, 661 (2004).

444. Jorgenson, W. L.; Pranata, J., *J. Am. Chem. Soc.,* **112**, 2008 (1990).
445. Pranata, J.; Wierschke, S. G.; Jorgenson, W. L., *J. Am. Chem. Soc.,* **113**, 2810 (1991).
446. Lehn, J. M., *Makromol. Chem. Makromol. Symp.,* **69**, 1 (1993).
447. Foquey, C.; Lehn, J. M.; Levelut, A. M., *Adv. Mater.,* **2**, 254 (1990).
448. Folmer, B. J. B.; Cavini, E.; Sijbesma, R. P.; Meijer, E. W., *Chem Commun.,* 1847 (1998).
449. Sijbesma, R. P.; Beijer, F. H.; Brunsveld, L.; Folmer, B. J. B.; Hirschberg, J. H. K. K.; Lange, R. F. M.; Lowe, J. K. L.; Meijer, E. W., *Science,* **278**, 1601 (1997).
450. Folmer, B. J. B.; Sijbesma, R. P.; Meijer, E. W., *Polym. Mater. Sci. Eng.,* **217**, 39 (1999).
451. Beijer, F. H.; Sijbesma, R. P.; Kooijman, H.; Spek, A. L.; Meijer, E. W., *J. Am. Chem. Soc.,* **120**, 6761 (1998).
452. Söntjens, S. H. M.; Sijbesma, R. P.; van Genderen, M. H. P.; Meijer, E. W., *J. Am. Chem. Soc.*, **122**, 7487 (2000).
453. Folmer, B. J. B.; Sijbesma, R. P.; Versteegen, R. M.; van der Rijt, J. A. J.; Meijer, E. W., *Adv. Mater.,* **12**, 874 (2000).
454. Schubert, U. S.; Eschbaumer, C., *Angew. Chem. Int. Ed.,* **41**, 2892 (2002).
455. Fustin, C-A.; Guillet, P.; Schubert, U. S.; Gohy, J-F., *Adv. Mater.,* **19**, 1665 (2007).
456. Hofmeier, H.; Hoogenboom, R.; Wouters, M. E. L.; Schubert, U. S., *J. Am. Chem. Soc.,* **127**, 2913 (2005).
457. Guerrero-Sanchez, C.; Lohmeijer, B. G. G.; Meier, M. A. R.; Schubert, U. S., *Macromolecules,* **38**, 10388 (2005).
458. Schubert, U. S.; Eschbaumer, C., *Macromol. Symp.,* **163**, 177 (2001).
459. Zhou, G.; Harruna, I. I., *Macromolecules,* **38**, 4114 (2005).
460. Gohy, J. F.; Lohmeijer, B. G. G.; Varshney, S. K.; Schubert, U. S., *Macromolecules,* **35**, 7427 (2002).
461. Gohy, J. F.; Lohmeijer, B. G. G.; Schubert, U. S., *Macromolecules,* **35**, 4560 (2002).
462. Hruska, Z.; Hurtrez, G.; Walter, S.; Riess, G., *Polymer,* **33**, 2447 (1992).
463. Constable, E. C., *Macromol. Symp.,* **98**, 503 (1995).
464. Constable, E. C.; Cargill Thompson, A. M. W., *J. Chem. Soc., Dalton Trans.,* 3467, 1992.
465. Storrier, G. D.; Colbran, S. B.; Craig, D. C., *J. Chem. Soc., Dalton Trans.,* 3011, 1992.
466. E. C. Constable, Cargill Thompson, A. M. W.; Tocher, D. A., *Macromol. Symp.,* **77**, 219 (1994).
467. Kelch, S.; Rehahn, M., *Macromolecules,* **32**, 5818 (1999).
468. El-Ghayoury, A.; Schenning, A. P. H. J.; Meijer, E. W., *J. Polym. Sci. A: Polym. Chem.,* **40**, 4020 (2002).
469. Yu, S-C.; Kwok, C-C.; Chan, W-K.; Che, C-M., *Adv. Mater,* **15**, 1643 (2003).
470. Froidevaux, P.; Harrowfield, J. M.; Sobolev, A. N., *Inorg. Chem.,* **39**, 4678 (2000).
471. Beck, J. B.; Rowan, S. J., *J. Am. Chem. Soc.,* **125**, 13922 (2003).
472. Boden, N.; Borner, R. C.; Bushby, R. J.; Cammidge, A. N.; Jesudason, M. V., *Liq. Cryst.,* **15**, 851 (1993).
473. Kumar, S.; Manickam, M., *Chem. Commun.,* 1615 (1997).
474. Kumar, S.; Varshney, S. K., *Synthesis*, 2, 305 (2001).
475. Cammidge, A. N., *Phil. Trans. R. Soc. A,* **364**, 2697 (2006).
476. Hoeben, F. J. M.; Jonkheijm, P.; Meijer, E. W.; Schenning, A. P. H., *Chem. Rev.,* **105**, 1491 (2005).
477. Herwig, P.; Kayser, C. W.; Müllen, K.; Spiess, H. W., *Adv. Mater.,* **8**, 510 (1996).
478. Fechtenkotter, A.; Tchebotareva, N.; Watson, M.; Müllen, K., *Tetrahedron,* **57**, 3769 (2001).

Appendix-I

Structures, Properties and Uses of Notable Commercial Polymers

Abbrev.	Polymer Name	Structure	Primary Properties and Uses
ABS	Acrylonitrile-butadiene-styrene copolymer	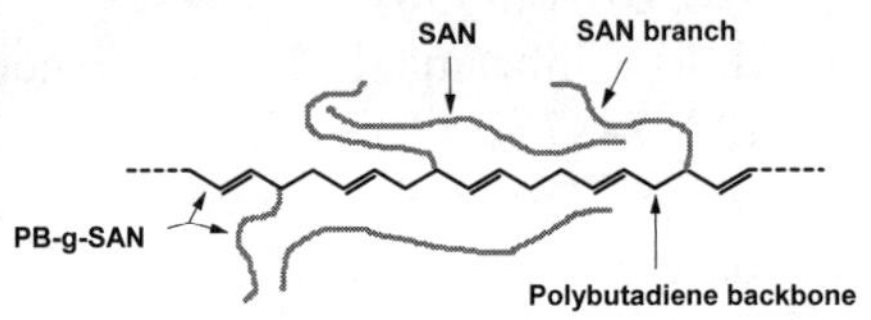	ABS is an ideal material wherever superlative surface quality, colorfastness and luster are required. ABS possesses outstanding impact strength and high mechanical strength, which makes it suitable for use in tough consumer and industrial products, including: appliances, automotive parts, pipe, business machines and telephone components.
COCs	Cycloolefin copolymers	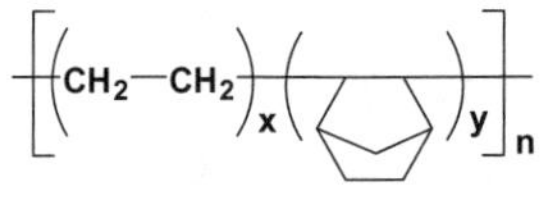	COCs possess some unique properties, such as high glass transition temperatures in combination with excellent transparency, low dielectric loss, low moisture absorption, high heat-deflection temperature and good chemical resistance for high-performance optical, medical, electrical, packaging and other applications, owing to their rigid cyclic monomer units. By adjusting norbornene content, COCs can be prepared with a T_g ranging from 90°C to 170°C.
COPs	Cycloolefin polymers	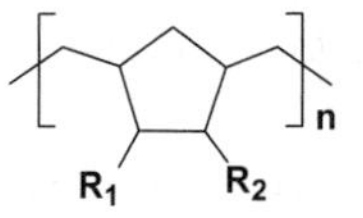 ($R_1 = R_2$ = H or alkyl)	COPs possess high transparency, low birefringence, chemical resistance, low moisture absorption, and thermal resistance equivalent to engineering plastics. Other beneficial characteristics include a tightly controlled refractive index (under four decimals) and exceptionally low level of residual metals and micro dusts. COPs are primarily used in high-precision optical parts (lenses, prisms), medical devices (vials, syringes) and electronic parts applications.
ECTFE	Ethylene-chlorotrifluoro ethylene copolymer	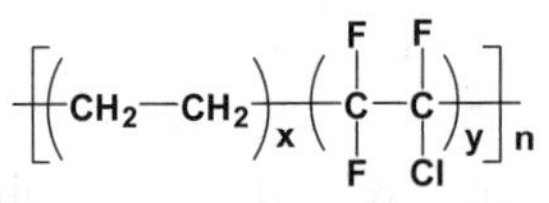	This is a tough fluoroplastic with properties similar to ETFE (*vide infra*). ECTFE film provides the highest, by far, abrasion resistance and the highest dielectric strength of any fluoropolymer film. ECTFE is melt-processable and withstands continuous exposure to extreme temperatures and maintains excellent mechanical properties across the entire range from cryogenic temperatures to 180°C. It has excellent electrical properties and chemical resistance, and has no known solvent at 120°C.
EP	Epoxy	(See p. 276)	Epoxies bond with nearly all materials, e.g., wood, metal, glass, and most importantly, they exhibit little or no shrinkage on cure. Aromatic amine cured epoxy composites exhibit better chemical, mechanical and thermal properties than composites cured with aliphatic and cycloaliphatic amines. Consequently, they are widely used in aerospace, PCB laminates and electronic encapsulations.

EPDM	Ethylene propylene diene monomer rubber		This is one of the most versatile, fastest growing and interesting synthetic rubbers. It possesses excellent resistance to heat, oxidation, ozone and weather aging, which provide continued value in demanding automotive, construction, sheet rubber for roofing and mechanical goods applications.
ETFE	Ethylene-tetrafluoroethylene copolymer	$-[(CH_2-CH_2)_x-(CF_2-CF_2)_y]_n-$	Unlike virgin PTFE and FEP, ETFE is a tough Teflon with a hardness similar to nylon. The improvement in stiffness is paid for by reduced chemical resistance and operating temperature.
FEP	Fluorinated ethylene-propylene copolymer	$-[(CF_2-CF_2)_x-(CF_2-CF(CF_3))_y]_n-$	FEP was developed by DuPont as a melt-processable Teflon, which, unlike virgin PTFE, can be processed by normal plastic methods. With the same benefits of PTFE, FEP has a lower maximum operating temperature (200°C).
HDPE	High density polyethylene	$-[CH_2-CH_2]_n-$	HDPE has virtually no branching, but possesses stronger intermolecular forces and tensile strength. The most common household uses are containers for milk and liquid laundry detergent.
HIPS	High impact polystyrene	PS; PS branch; PB-g-PS; Polybutadiene backbone (See p. 142)	HIPS is a blend of PS and a graft copolymer of butadiene and styrene, PB-*g*-PS. HIPS allows stress to be transferred from the polystyrene phase to the polybutadiene phase. Since polybutadiene is rubbery, it dissipates the energy which would otherwise cause the brittle polystyrene phase to break. This is why HIPS is tougher than regular polystyrene. HIPS is often specified for low strength structural applications when impact resistance, machinability, and low cost are required. It is frequently used in machining pre-production prototypes since it has excellent dimensional stability and is easy to fabricate, paint and glue. HIPS is translucent white and FDA compliant for use in food processing. Major uses of HIPS include, drinking tumblers, blender jars and covers, dishes, instrument panel lenses, and battery cases.
IR	Polyisoprene	Major Composition	Similar to polybutadiene (PB), IR with >98% *cis*-1,4 structure is produced by polymerization of isoprene (2-methyl-buta-1,3-diene) monomer in the presence of a Ziegler-Natta catalyst. IR is a synthetic substitute for natural Hevea rubber, and can have four possible chain unit geometric isomers: *cis*- and *trans*-1,4-polyisoprene, vinyl-1,2 and vinyl-3,4. The properties and processing of IR is similar to natural rubber, except for the strength, which is slightly lower due to a lower *cis*-1,4 content.
Kevlar®	Poly(*p*-phenylene terephthalamide)	$-[C_6H_4-NH-CO-C_6H_4-CO-NH]_n-$	Kevlar®, a DuPont product, is a type of aramid that consists of long polymeric chains with a parallel orientation. Kevlar derives its strength from intra-molecular hydrogen bonds and phenyl stacking interactions between aromatic moieties in neighboring strands. The strength of Kevlar fiber is five times that of steel, weight for weight. Kevlar is very heat resistant and decomposes above 400°C without melting. It is usually used in bulletproof vests, in extreme sports equipment, and for composite aircraft construction. It is also used as a replacement for steel cords in car tires, in fire suits and as an asbestos replacement.

LCPs	Liquid crystal polymers	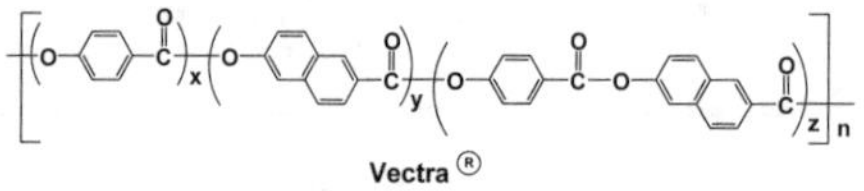 Vectra® 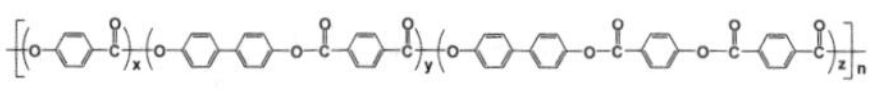 Xydar®	LCPs are wholly aromatic copolyesters (such as Vectra® and Xydar®) and possess excellent physical properties, high mechanical strength, high impact resistance, outstanding barrier properties, and low viscosity during processing. LCPs are virtually unaffected by most acids, bases, and solvents over a broad temperature range. LCP is a thermally stable thermoplastic, with an upper use temperature of more than 250°C and good inherent flame retardant properties. LCPs can be melt-spun into fibers with exceptional strength and rigidity, which attribute to its highly anisotropic orientation of polymer chains. Pound for pound, LCP fiber is five times stronger than steel and ten times stronger than aluminum. Consequently, LCP fibers are used in aerospace, ocean exploration and development, electronic support structures, the recreation and leisure industry, safety materials, industrial applications, ropes and cables, composites, and protective garments. The differences between LCP fiber and two other high-performance fibers, aramids and UHMWPE are as follows: LCP fiber is thermotropic, it is melt-spun, and it melts at a high temperature. Aramid fiber is lyotropic, it is solvent-spun, and it does not melt at high temperature. UHMWPE fiber is gel-spun, and it melts at a low temperature.
LDPE	Low density polyethylene	$\left[CH_2-CH_2\right]_n$ 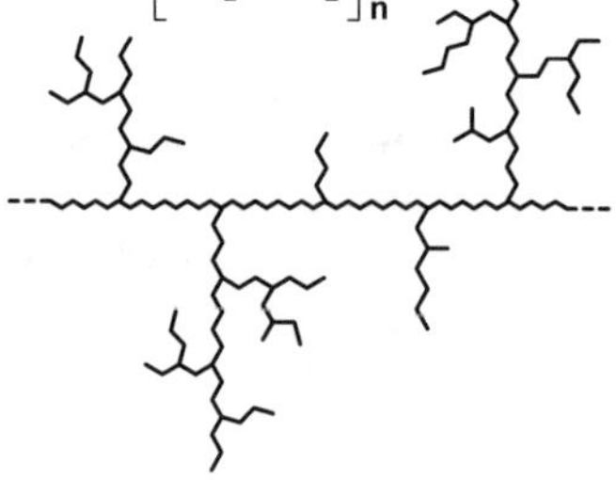	LDPE has many more and longer branches than LLDPE, with fewer intermolecular forces. This results in lower density and tensile strength, increased malleability and faster biodegradation. The most common household use of LDPE is in garment, grocery and shopping bags.
LLDPE	Linear low density polyethylene	$\left[CH_2-CH_2\right]_n$ 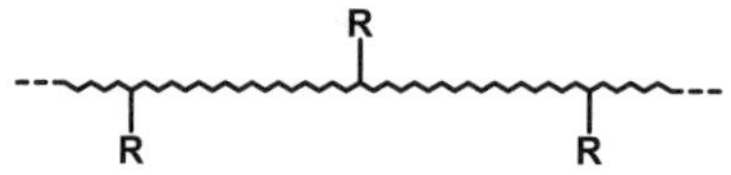 (R = butyl, hexyl or octyl)	LLDPE, a substantially linear polymer with significant numbers of short branches, is prepared by copolymerization of ethylene with an α-olefin (e.g., 1-butene, 1-hexene, or 1-octene) using Ziegler-Natta catalysts. Incorporation of an α-olefin unit into a polymer chain introduces a short-chain branch, but the chain structure is linear. Although the density of LLDPE is in the same range as LDPE, LLDPE has much improved impact strength, puncture resistance, and tear strength compared to LDPE. LLDPE combines the toughness of low-density polyethylene with the rigidity of high-density polyethylene and is used primarily in flexible tubing.
MF	Melamine formaldehyde	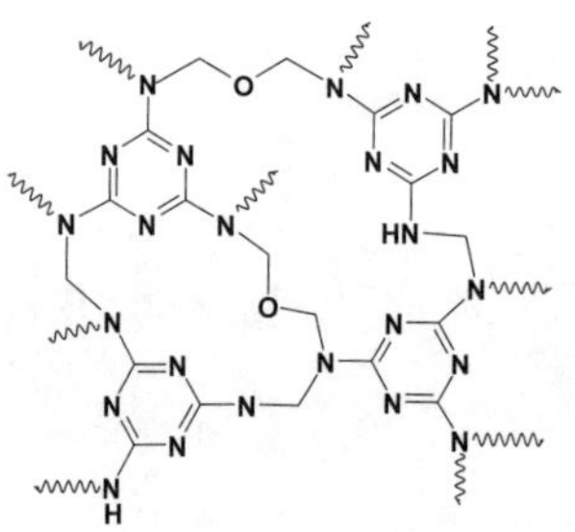	MF thermosets exhibit outstanding stability against hydrolysis, extreme hardness, excellent colorability and arc-resistant characteristics. MF polymers find extensive use in laminates and chemically resistant coatings, parquet flooring, and rigid electrical and decorative products, including popular colorful, rugged dinnerware.

Nomex®	Poly(*m*-phenylene isophthalamide)	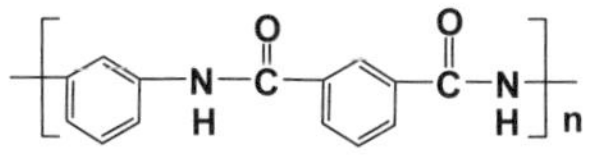	Nomex®, a DuPont product, is manufactured in both fiber and sheet forms and is used as a fabric wherever resistance from heat and flame is required. A Nomex hood is a common piece of firefighting equipment. It is placed on the head on top of a firefighters face mask which supplies air to him inside a smoke filled environment. The hood protects the portions of the head not covered by the helmet and face mask from the intense heat of the fire. Race car drivers commonly use a similar hood to protect them in the event that a fire engulfs their car. Nomex has been adapted to a wide variety of uses now, including machinery and circuitry for its insulation.
PAs	Polyamides (nylons)	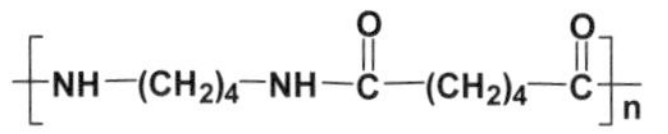 $-[NH-(CH_2)_4-NH-C(=O)-(CH_2)_4-C(=O)]_n-$ **Nylon-4,6 (PA46)** 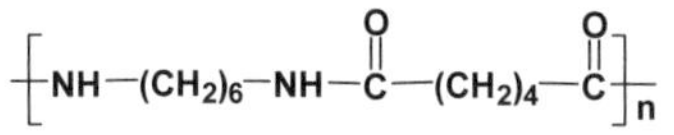 $-[NH-(CH_2)_6-NH-C(=O)-(CH_2)_4-C(=O)]_n-$ **Nylon-6,6 (PA66)** 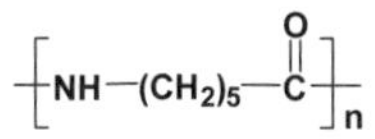 $-[NH-(CH_2)_5-C(=O)]_n-$ **Nylon-6 (PA6)**	Nylon represents the generic name for all synthetic fiber-forming polyamides. In general, nylons are strong, tough and resistant to abrasion, fatigue and impact. For example, nylon-6,6 is extensively used in fiber applications, such as carpeting, clothing, and tire cord. It also finds application as an engineering material in bearings and gears due to its good abrasion resistance and self-lubricating properties.
PAI	Poly(amide imide)	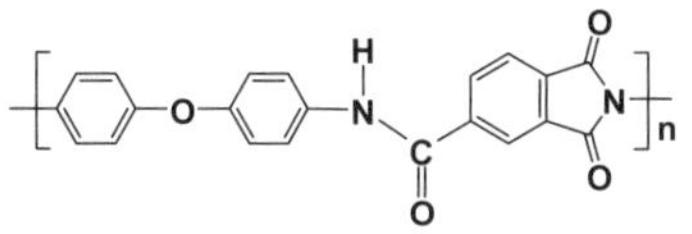 **Torlon®**	PAI (viz., Torlon®) provides exceptional strength at high temperatures and excellent resistance to chemical solvents. Torlon offers the advantages of a thermoset, in that once cured, it provides unstoppable performance in some of the most severe service environments. Like a thermoplastic, it can be processed by standard methods such as injection molding, extrusion and compression molding. Torlon is also very wear and friction resistant which makes it an ideal material for mechanical retention components, such as anti-decoupling springs and contact retention springs. The injection moldable material is non-conductive and operates at temperatures up to 250°C. Torlon is also a major player in coating applications, due to its outstanding surface adhesion to a multitude of materials, including metals and PTFE.
PAN	Polyacrylonitrile	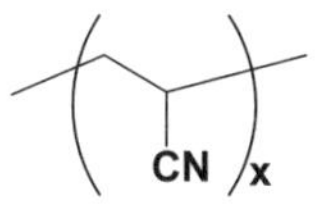 **PAN** 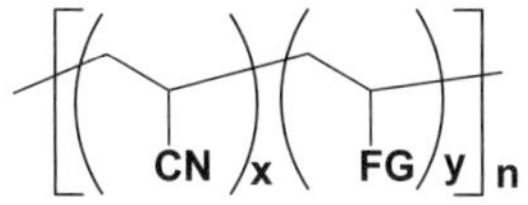 **Acrylic Fiber (FG = CO_2Me and/or OAc)**	More than half of acrylonitrile produced in the world is consumed for the production of acrylic fibers, while the major part of the other half is used for modacrylics, such as ABS and SAN copolymers. Commercial acrylic fibers, used primarily for the manufacture of apparel, including sweaters and sportswear, as well as home furnishings, viz., carpets, upholstery, and draperies, are produced by copolymerization of acrylonitrile (AN) with at least one other monomer. The co-monomers most employed are methyl acrylate (MA) and vinyl acetate (VAc).

PB	Polybutadiene	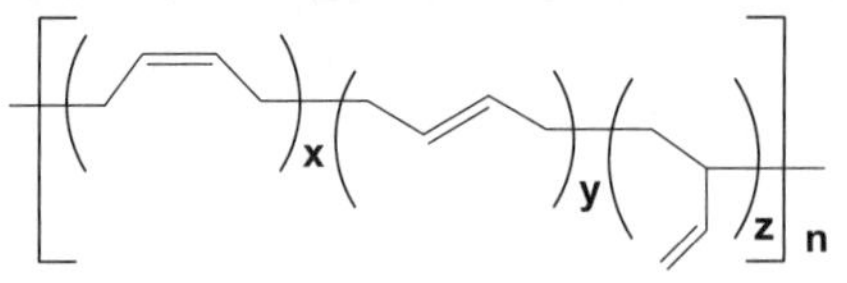	PB is a homopolymer of butadiene monomer and its rate of consumption is second to SBR. This very high *cis*-1,4 structure (>90%) and preferred geometry for applications in tires, is prepared by polymerization of butadiene using Ziegler-Natta catalysts.
PB-1	Polybutene-1	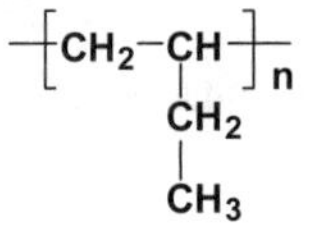 $-[CH_2-CH(CH_2CH_3)]_n-$	PB-1 is a semi-crystalline, highly isotactic thermoplastic, derived from polymerization of butene-1, utilizing a Ziegler-Natta type catalyst. Due to its inherent flexibility in combination with superior mechanical properties compared to other polyolefins, as well as excellent creep and burst pressure resistance, pipes produced from PB-1 have an ideal balance of performance properties to satisfy the demands of modern domestic and institutional heating and plumbing systems. PB-1 forms excellent blends with polypropylene. Incompatibility with polyethylene is used to make peelable PE based film seals. A major application area for PB-1 is seal-peel or easy-open packaging. Typical examples include carton liners (e.g., cereal packaging) and packs for pre-packed delicatessen products like cold meats, cheeses and smoked salmon. PB-1 offers the ability to customize sealing temperatures and seal strength while giving consistent, reliable processing and sealing performance on existing equipment. PB-1 can also be utilized in film modification to increase flexibility and softness without sacrificing clarity. For example, PB-1 is used to modify polypropylene fibers to enhance softness, flexibility and to provide a unique feel.
PBI	Polybenzimidazole	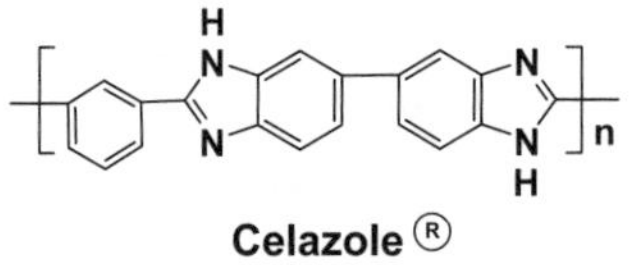 Celazole®	PBI offers one of the highest temperature resistant and best mechanical property retention of all unfilled thermoplastics. In 1983, Hoechst Celanese began commercial production of PBI fiber, Celazole®, which finds applications in firefighters' gear, industrial protective clothing, fire-blocking layers for aircraft seats, braided pump packings, and other high-performance products. It is a very appealing material to high-tech industries, such as semiconductor, aircraft and aerospace companies, because of their superior diverse properties, viz. (1) extremely high maximum allowable service temperature in air (310°C continuously, going up to 500°C for short periods of time), (2) excellent retention of mechanical strength, stiffness and creep resistance over a wide range of temperatures, (3) extremely low coefficient of linear thermal expansion up to 250°C, (4) excellent wear and frictional behavior, (5) inherent low flammability, (6) good electrical insulating and dielectric properties, (7) low outgassing in vacuum (dry material), (8) high ionic purity level, and (9) excellent resistance against high energy radiation.
PBO	Polybenzoxazole	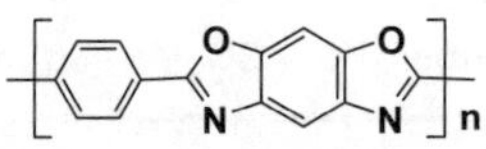 Zylon®	PBO is a new entrant to the high performance organic fibers market. The only product thus far, is Zylon® PBO fiber, which has the highest tensile strength (almost double that of Kevlar fiber) among high-performance fibers. Zylon is projected as the next generation super fiber as it possesses very high strength, 100°C higher decomposition temperature than Kevlar fiber, and the highest LOI (limiting oxygen index = 68) among organic super fibers. Its high modulus and LOI makes it an excellent

			candidate for composites reinforcement, thermal shields, safety and protective clothing, and ballistic applications.
PBT	Poly(butylene terephthalate)	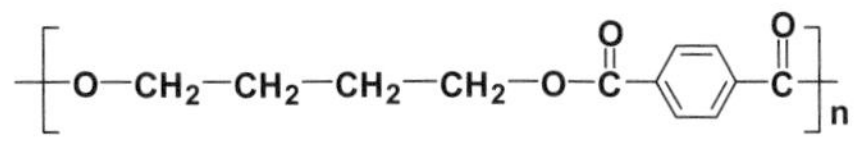	PBT is a semi-crystalline, white or off-white polyester similar in both composition and properties to PET. It has somewhat lower strength and stiffness than PET, is a little softer with higher impact strength and very similar chemical resistance and lower water absorption. As it crystallizes more rapidly than PET, it tends to be preferred for industrial scale molding. PBT is used for door and window hardware, automobile luggage racks and body panels, headlight reflectors, and fiber optic cables. It is being used to replace PVC for cable sheathing, due to a combination of environmental pressures and outstanding electrical properties across a wide range of temperatures. PBT is also replacing metals (in conjunction with PC as an alloy/blend) for automotive body panels.
PBZT	Polybenzthiazole	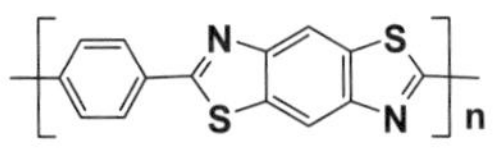	PBZT fiber, although not yet commercially available, has been established as a strong candidate for high-performance of nanostructured conducting fibers used in embedded sensors, electromagnetic shielding, and smart structures. Such fibers are fabricated by depositing silver nanoparticles *in-situ* into a polymer template structure, creating an interpenetrating silver network parallel to the fiber axis. Spatial control is achieved through precise fiber swelling and infiltration of the silver precursor and reduction agents. Silver infiltrated PBZT fibers exhibit electronic conductivities exceeding 10^4 S/cm. The Ag/PBZT composite fiber also maintains the high strength of the polymer. Tests have revealed an approximately 200-fold increase in strength and a 50% reduction in weight compared to the current aerospace signal wire cores.
PC	Polycarbonate	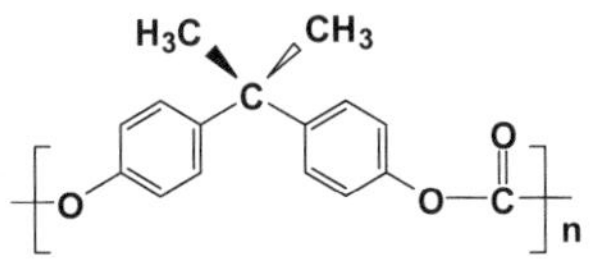	PC is one of the pioneering members of the family of engineering thermoplastics created to compete with die-cast metals. Transparency, scratch resistance, excellent toughness, thermal stability and a very high impact resistance make PC one of the most widely used engineering thermoplastics. It is believed that both the high impact strength and excellent amorphous character of PC are due to the presence of the V-shaped 2,2-diphenylpropane moiety which provides adequate free-volume. In addition, two flexible ether linkages on both sides of the 2,2-diphenylpropane moiety further facilitates dissipation of stress during impact. Thus, PC is ideal for parts requiring load-bearing capability or energy management. Compact discs, eyeglass lenses, shatterproof glass, electrical components, defroster and speaker grills, safety helmets and headlamp lenses are all typical applications of PC.
PCL	Polycaprolactone	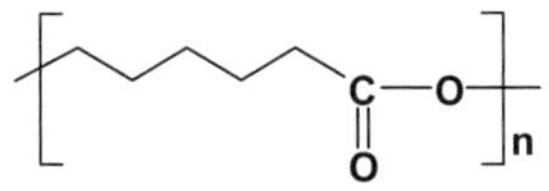	PCL is a biodegradable plastic. Because of its ease of degradation, the primary uses of PCL have been in biomedical applications and as an additive to bioplastics made from other polymers. For example, it can be added to starch to lower its cost and increase biodegradability or it can be added as a

			plasticizer to PVC to increase its impact resistance. PCL is a Food and Drug Administration (FDA) approved material that is used in the human body as, for example, a drug delivery device, suture, adhesion barrier and is being investigated as a scaffold for tissue repair via tissue engineering.
PCTFE	Poly(chlorotrifluoro ethylene)	$-[CF_2-CFCl]_n-$	This homopolymer is used extensively in pharmaceutical packaging and industrial applications for its chemical and moisture resistant properties. PCTFE film has a very high clarity, contains no plasticizers, is chemically resistant, and possess a very low coefficient of friction.
PDMS	Poly(dimethyl siloxane)	$-[O-Si(CH_3)_2]_n-$	Silicones (also called polysiloxanes) are an important class of synthetic polymers which do not have carbon in the polymer backbone, but are composed of alternating silicon and oxygen atoms. They possess very low glass transition temperatures, have very low surface energies, and form a hydrophobic surface that is resistant to water. The properties of silicones change markedly with variation of substituents on silicon. PDMS is one of the most important silicones with applications ranging from medical devices to elastomers, caulking, lubricating oils and heat resistant tiles. Silicone rubber keypads are widely used in the 'soft push-button' facilities found throughout our daily life, such as calculators, remote controllers, cellphones and cameras. Silicones are also used in shoe insoles because they are non-toxic, non-slippery stable materials with excellent shock absorbing and walking comfort features. Silicone rubber seals are employed in various applications for automobile parts, fuel pump seals, air conditioners, electric insulation packing and sealing.
PEEK	Poly(ether ether ketone)	$-[O-C_6H_4-O-C_6H_4-C(=O)-C_6H_4]_n-$	PEEK® is a semicrystalline thermoplastic which operates at extremely high temperatures, 250°C long term and 300°C short term. This makes it a high strength alternative to fluoropolymers. PEEK is an injection moldable material and can be reinforced with glass, mineral, and graphite fibers. PEEK has one of the lightest strength to weight ratios and exhibits outstanding resistance to aggressive chemicals. PEEK offers chemical and water resistance comparable to PPS, but can sustain higher temperatures.
PES	Poly(ethersulfone)	$-[O-C_6H_4-S(=O)_2-C_6H_4]_n-$	PES is a high-temperature engineering plastic- useful up to 180°C in general and some grades have continuous operating ratings as high as 200°C. It is resistant to most chemicals and may be extruded or injection molded to close tolerances. The properties are similar to those of nylons. Applications are as a replacement for glass for medical needs and food handling, circuit boards, general electrical components, and car parts requiring good mechanical properties and dimensional stability. PES offers unique properties- such as the ability to easily create porous filaments or flat sheet from stable solutions - that allow it to be used in micro and ultra filtration and reverse osmosis membranes. These membranes have applications ranging from artificial kidneys for blood purification to wastewater recovery as well as food and beverage processing. In

			addition, PES is used to create water purification membranes that filter harmful bacteria spores, such as cryptosporidium from municipal drinking water.
PET	Poly(ethylene terephthalate)	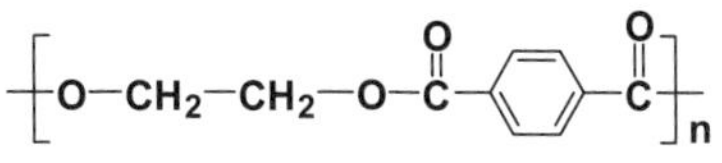 $-[O-CH_2-CH_2-O-C(=O)-C_6H_4-C(=O)]_n-$	PET has glass-like clarity, toughness and excellent gas-barrier properties which make it an outstanding choice for food packaging and storing biologicals. The three major packaging applications of PET are as containers (bottles, jars and tubs), semi-rigid sheet for thermoforming (trays and blisters) and thin oriented films (bags and snack food wrappers). Medical applications of PET include implantable sutures, surgical mesh, vascular grafts, sewing cuffs for heart valves and components for percutaneous access devices. PET is also used in fiber applications, such as in clothing (DuPont Dacron® polyester fiber) and home furnishings (carpets, curtains, draperies and pillowcases).
PFA	Perfluoroalkoxy-tetrafluoroethylene copolymer	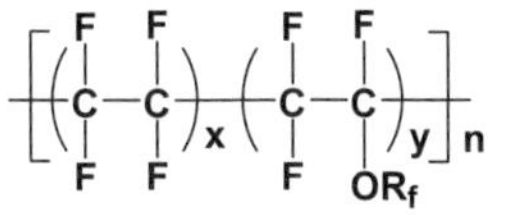 $-[(CF_2-CF_2)_x(CF_2-CF(OR_f))_y]_n-$ **(R_f = Fluoroalkyl, e.g., $-CF_2CF_2CF_3$)**	PFA is a special type of copolymer where the monomers are not added in the same ratio. PFA was developed by DuPont as a High Temperature Teflon with a maximum operation temperature of 260°C, while maintaining properties similar to those of other fluoropolymers. This added temperature resistance also adds a significant increase in cost. PFA is a melt-processable thermoplastic with chemical resistance similar to PTFE, but has much lower porosity and is translucent.
PIMs	Polyimides	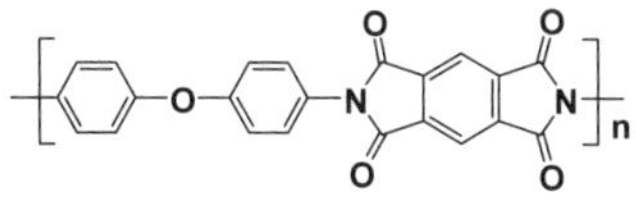 **Kapton 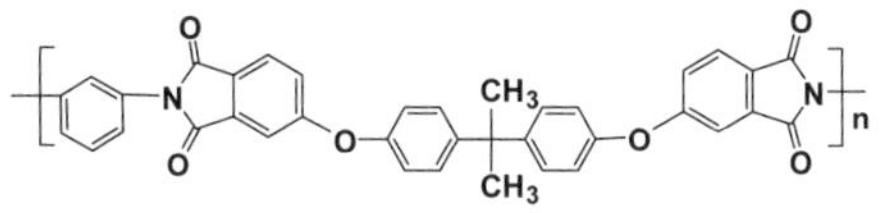 ®** **Ultem®** 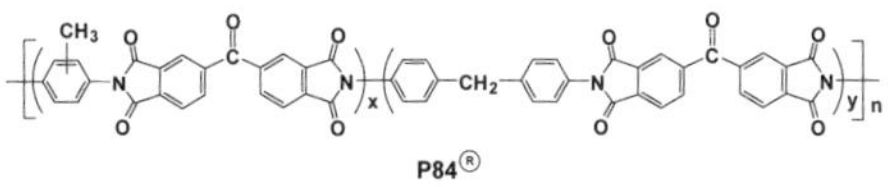 P84® 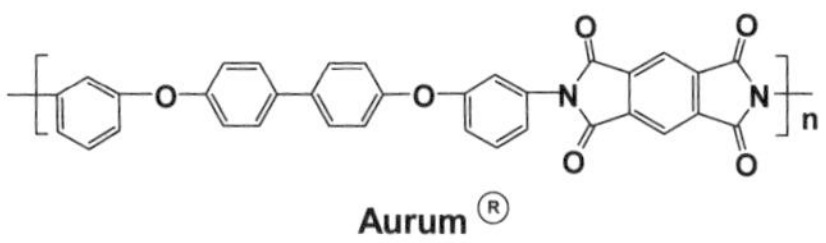 **Aurum ®**	The most common brand names for PEI include Kapton® (DuPont), Ultem® (General Electric), P84® (Degussa Corporation) and the newcomer, Aurum® (Mitsui Chemicals). Kapton is widely used in a wide variety of applications, such as substrates for flexible printed circuits, transformer and capacitor insulation and bar code labels. Kapton has more than 35 years of proven performance as the flexible material of choice in applications involving very high, 400°C, or very low, -265°C temperature extremes. Ultem is an amorphous thermoplastic available both in extruded bars as well as pellets for injection molding. Ultem can be filled with as high as 30 percent glass. Glass filled Ultem displays excellent property retention and resistance to environmental stress. Ultem can be further reinforced with conductive fibers, or plated, for EMI resistance. Ultem performs in operating environments up to 175°C long term and 200°C short term. P84 polyimide, unlike other polyimides which are prepared by condensation of dianhydrides and diamines, is obtained by reaction between an aromatic dianhydride and a mixture of aromatic diisocyanates (see Chapter 4). The polymer is non-melting, starts to carbonize at temperatures beyond 375°C, and has a glass transition temperature of 315°C. Despite the non-melting aromatic, halogen free structure, it is classified as non-flammable with a limiting oxygen index of 38%. P84 can be used at temperatures up to 260°C depending on the environment. P84 polyimide is stable against most common organic solvents like alcohols, ethers, halogenated hydrocarbons or ethers. P84 polyimide fiber, with a unique trilobal

			cross-section, provides outstanding surface-to-volume ratios, exceptional temperature resistance and good chemical resistance for fire-protective clothing, as well as for garment reinforcement. P84 filter bags provide a cost-effective solution for many industrial operations, including industrial coil-fired boilers, minerals processing, asphalt plants, cement production, soil remediation and waste incineration. However, because of the low modulus and the high elongation, P84 fiber is not destined for typical 'reinforcing' applications as *p*-aramid or carbon fibers. Due to its outstanding chemical and physical properties, P84 is employed in a variety of applications from use as filter media in high temperature applications, fire protective clothing, to sealing materials in spacecraft. Aurum, an easy melt processable and recyclable thermoplastic polyimide, is designed to withstand high-loads and high velocities at temperatures exceeding 250°C and can be injection-molded into complex shapes to tight and consistent tolerances using standard equipment. Aurum is utilized in a variety of other demanding applications, such as high PV automotive transmission thrust washers and oil seal rings, wear and friction components for business machinery, compressor valve seats, jet engine components, power tool parts, and high purity components for semiconductor handling and manufacturing equipment.
PKs	Aliphatic Polyketones	$-[CH_2-CH_2-C(=O)]_n-$ **ECO** $-[(CH_2-CH_2-C(=O))_x(CH_2-CH(CH_3)-C(=O))_y]_n-$ **EPCO**	This is a relatively new and unique family of aliphatic polymers derived from equal proportions of ethylene and carbon monoxide with an additional few percent of higher olefin (usually, propylene) for property and processibility adjustment. This family of semi-crystalline polymers exhibits many of the properties of engineering polymers, such as polyamides and polyacetals, with processing similar to polyolefins. Mechanical properties are characterized by preservation of high levels of stiffness, toughness, and strength over a broad temperature range. Tribological performance is very good, and in particular, PKs have a low coefficient of friction and a low wear factor against steel. They exhibit excellent chemical resistance. Major applications include gears and machine components.
PMMA	Poly(methyl methacrylate)	$-[CH_2-C(CH_3)(CO_2CH_3)]_n-$	PMMA is a rigid amorphous polymer with excellent clarity, used in shatterproof replacement for glass, including rear lights of cars. PMMA is commonly called Acrylic glass or simply Acrylic. The outstanding resistance to long-term exposure to sunlight and weathering is one of the most important characteristics of acrylic. Another major application is in the area of plastic optical fiber (POF) for digital home appliance interfaces, home networks, car networks and illumination. PMMA is used as a core material (refractive index = 1.49) with fluorinated acrylate (refractive index = 1.43) as clad material.

PMMI	Poly(N-methyl methacrylimide)	$\left[CH_2-C(H_3C)(-CH_2-)-C(CH_3)\right]_x\left[CH_2-C(CH_3)(CO_2CH_3)\right]_y$ (imide ring: $C(=O)-N(CH_3)-C(=O)$)	PMMI, also known as poly(N-methylglutarimide), a thermoplastic molding compound, is a modified PMMA and obtained by reacting PMMA with methylamine. The special molecular structure of PMMI offers a series of outstanding properties, such as high modulus of elasticity, low tendency to creep and thermal expansion, together with high chemical resistance, particularly toward alcohols. It also shows unsurpassed rigidity for an amorphous, non-reinforced thermoplastic, superior resistance to high temperatures and UV light, as well as transparency and excellent weather resistance. PMMI meets the stringent requirements regarding heat deflection temperature under load (150 - 170°C for PMMI depending on imidation vs. 109°C for PMMA), optical transparency (90% for PMMI vs. 93% for PMMA) and weather resistance that apply to the auto and lighting industries, for example, to road and signal lights, ship navigation lights and car headlamp lenses.
PMP	Poly(methyl pentene)	$\left[CH_2-CH(CH_2CH(CH_3)CH_3)\right]_n$	PMP possesses a structure similar to polypropylene, but it bears an isobutyl group instead of a methyl group attached to each monomer unit of the chain. PMP, despite being a semi-crystalline (~60% crystalline domains) polymer, exhibits very high optical transparency (90%), excellent chemical and electrical properties and the lowest density of all thermoplastics (0.84 g/cm^3), thus becoming a superior material for labware. PMP is transparent because, unlike other polyolefins, its crystalline and amorphous phases have the same index of refraction. Among all transparent plastics, PMP has the best resistance to distortion at high temperature. It compares well with acrylic for optical use, but has only 70% of its density. PMP withstands repeated molding, even at 150°C. It can also withstand intermittent exposure to temperatures as high as 175°C (soft soldering temperature) and is used for lamp covers (good heat resistance), medical and chemical ware, high-frequency electrical insulation, cables, microwave oven parts, and radar components.
POM	Polyoxymethylene	$\left[O-CH_2\right]_n$	POM, also known as Acetal, is a crystalline thermoplastic polymer first introduced to industry in 1956 as a replacement for die-cast metals. Acetals are extremely rigid without being brittle. They have high melting points, are very strong and possess good frictional properties and resistance to fatigue. Moisture has little to no effect on POM, and because of this, the dimensional stability of close tolerance fabricated items is excellent. POM is commonly used as a direct replacement for metals due to its stiffness, dimensional stability and corrosion resistance. POM, naturally opaque, can be reinforced with glass fibers for increased stiffness. Typical applications are water-pump parts, pipe fittings, shaver cartridges, zippers, washing machines, car instrument housings, bearings, and gears.
PP	Polypropylene	$\left[CH_2-CH(CH_3)\right]_n$	The tacticity of PP can have a dramatic effect on its physical properties. For example, the melting points of isotactic, syndiotactic, and atactic polypropylene are 175°C, 140°C, and 20°C, respectively. Atactic polypropylene is a

			soft rubbery polymer. It is formed as a waste product in the manufacture of *i*-PP and its uses are limited, for example, in road paint, in making roofing materials like 'roofing felt', and in some sealants and adhesives. *s*-PP has only recently been made on a large scale. A wide range of other potential uses - either on its own, or in mixtures with *i*-PP, is under investigation. It is somewhat softer than the isotactic polymer, but also tough and clear. It is stable to gamma radiation and will likely find applications, such as medical tubing and for medical bags and pouches. *i*-PP is strong and hard with excellent resistance to stress, cracking, and chemical reaction. The major applications of isotactic PP is in the area of non-woven industry, such as non-woven fabrics (cigarette and technical filters). Of the world's total non-woven production, *i*-PP is the most common non-woven fiber, accounting for about 60% of all fibers. Other applications include carpeting, automotive parts and toys.
PPA	Polyphthalamide	$\left[\left(NH-(CH_2)_6-NH-\overset{O}{\overset{\|}{C}}-(CH_2)_4-\overset{O}{\overset{\|}{C}}\right)_x\left(NH-(CH_2)_6-NH-\overset{O}{\overset{\|}{C}}-C_6H_4-\overset{O}{\overset{\|}{C}}\right)_y\right]_n$	PPA, also referred to as nylon-6,T or PA6T, is a semi-aromatic polyamide and is often called high-temperature nylon. As a member of the nylon family, it is derived from a diacid and a diamine. However, the diacid portion is believed to contains at least 55% terephthalic acid (TPA) or isophthalic acid (IPA) in order to obtain desired properties. The use of a small proportion of IPA comonomer is necessary to lower the T_m of PA6T from 370°C to 310°C while retaining a fast crystallization rate. Thus, PPA can be obtained in various grades by varying the composition of the monomers. TPA or IPA are aromatic components which serve to raise the T_m, T_g and generally improve chemical resistance vs. standard aliphatic nylon polymers. PPA possesses excellent mechanical properties (e.g., strength, stiffness, fatigue, creep resistance) over a broad temperature range. The exceptional dimensional stability and property retention of PPA over PA66 at higher temperatures are due largely to the higher T_g (125°C vs. 60°C) and T_m (310°C vs. 255°C). PPA features an excellent stiffness-to-cost ratio and a high strength-to-weight ratio, both of which are superior to PBT, PPS, PEI, PET and PA66. This combination of features provides PPA with the potential to reduce weight, cut costs, and deliver long service life for all types of automotive components, including parts for fuel, climate-control, transmission, braking, and engine systems.
PPCO	Propylene-ethylene copolymer	$\left[\left(CH_2-\underset{CH_3}{\underset{\|}{CH}}\right)_x\left(CH_2-CH_2\right)_y\right]_n$	PPCO is a linear random copolymer of propylene with a lower proportion of ethylene. It combines some of the advantages of both homopolymers. *i*-PP is harder and has a higher temperature resistance than HDPE but lower impact resistance and becomes brittle below 0°C. Hence, PPCO is preferred for all applications involving cold/winter conditions. PPCO exhibits better impact strength, maintained down to lower temperatures, than PP. For instance, PPCO has 10 times the impact strength of standard PP, even in cold temperatures and possesses an exceptionally high strength-to-weight ratio. The primary use of PPCO is in injection molding and thermoforming parts for automotive, appliances

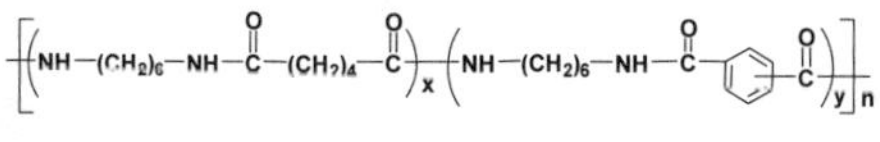

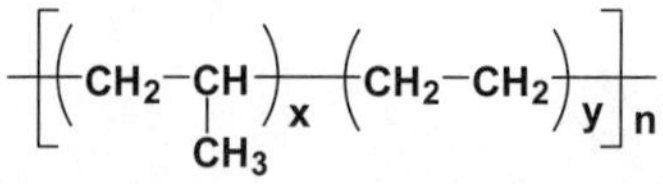

			and other durable applications.
PPO	Poly(phenylene oxide)	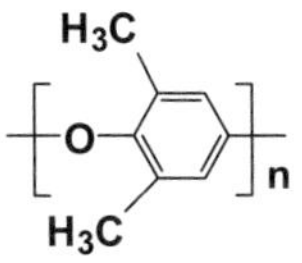	PPO is a rigid engineering plastic similar to polysulfone in its uses and exhibits high strength, excellent heat resistance, high T_g, and good dimensional stability. However, deficiencies such as natural brittleness, poor processibility and solvent resistance, prohibit its broader application. Most commercial products are a blend (or 'alloy') with polystyrene or high impact polystyrene (HIPS), which acts as a cost-effective extender. The alloy can be injection molded and has mechanical properties similar to those for nylon. It is used for automotive parts, domestic appliances, and parts requiring good dimensional stability.
PPS	Poly(phenylene sulfide)	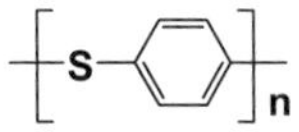	PPS is highly renowned today in the field of injection molding as a rapidly growing heat-resistant polymer with very stable dielectric and insulating properties, including high stiffness and good retention of mechanical properties at elevated temperatures. PPS generally shows excellent chemical properties and is almost insoluble in organic solvents up to 200°C. The polymer and the fiber are only affected by strong mineral acids like concentrated sulfuric and nitric acid or strong oxidizing environments. PPS melts at 285°C, provides a glass-transition temperature of 90°C, and the fibers can be used up to 200°C, depending on the environment. PPS products are available in neat grades for high purity and medium heat conditions. Impacts modified grades, with and without glass reinforcement, are available for high traffic and heavy handling applications. Glass reinforced grades go as high as 40% filled and provides extremely high strength to weight ratios with maximum heat resistance (>250°C). PPS exhibits inherent flame resistance which is described by the high limiting oxygen index of 40%. As with most aromatic polymers the UV resistance is poor. The major use for PPS is in electrical/electronic and automotive parts, and industrial hot gas and liquid process filtration processes.
PPSU	Poly(phenylene sulfone)	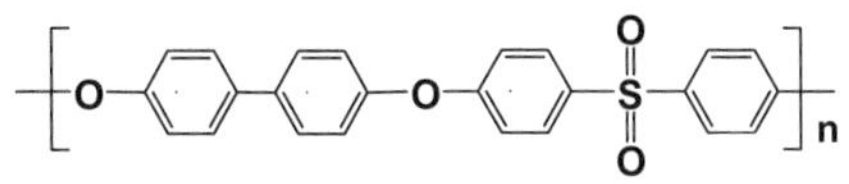	PPSU stands out as one of the best in medical applications requiring repeated sterilization or uncompromising toughness. With its high heat deflection temperature of 210°C, it can withstand continuous exposure to heat and still absorb tremendous impact without deflecting or breaking. Moreover, its chemical resistance surpasses that of most amorphous polymers. PPSU can be injection molded, vacuum formed or machined. Current applications include a wide assortment of medical trays and containers as well as surgical instruments, a binocular opthalmoscope and a bellow housing for anesthetics.
PS	Polystyrene	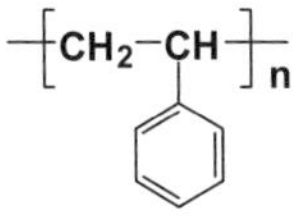	PS is transparent, rigid and non-toxic, with excellent dimensional stability and good chemical resistance to aqueous solutions. PS has a wide range of applications, such as in construction (thermal and sound insulation in walls, roofs and on floors), protective packaging for industrial, pharmaceutical and retail (excellent cushioning properties, heat resistance and limitless design possibilities),

			food packaging and transportation (shock resistant, non-toxic, odorless and does not attract insects or bacteria) and disposable laboratory products (glass-clear material).
PSF	Polysulfone	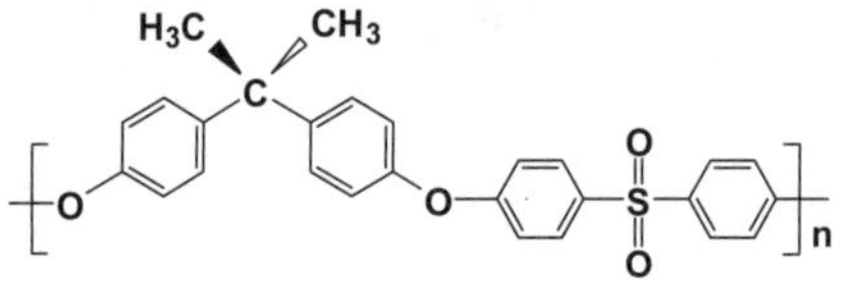	Like polycarbonate, PSF is clear, strong, non-toxic and extremely tough. PSF is resistant to acids, bases, aqueous solutions, aliphatic hydrocarbons and alcohols. PSF is composed of phenylene units linked by three different chemical groups-isopropylidene, ether and sulfone. Each of the three linkages imparts specific properties to the polymer, such as chemical resistance, temperature resistance and impact strength. PSF has properties similar to nylon, but these properties are retained up to 180°C compared with 120°C for nylon, which greatly expands the range of applications. Its optical clarity is good and its moisture absorption lower than that of nylon. Applications are as a replacement for glass for medical needs and chemistry equipment, circuit boards, electrical/electronic components and automotive parts.
PTFE	Poly(tetrafluoro ethylene)	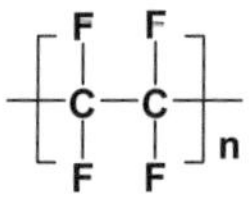	PTFE is better known by the trade name Teflon® (DuPont) and was the first fluorinated polyolefin developed. Unlike some other fluoropolymers, the carbon chain in Teflon is completely surrounded or wrapped by fluorine atoms so that nothing can get at it to react with it. Moreover, the carbon-fluorine bond is exceptionally strong, and the fluorine atoms shield the vulnerable carbon chain. This unusual structure gives Teflon its unique properties and makes it useful in the chemical and food industries to coat vessels and make them resistant to almost everything which might otherwise corrode them. Owing to the extremely low surface tensions of fluoroaliphatic compounds, PTFE possesses remarkable non-stick properties (extreme slipperiness)- which is the basis for its most familiar uses in non-stick kitchen and garden utensils. For the same reason, it can also be used in low-friction bearings. PTFE is not melt-processable because of the strength of the attractions between the chains, but can be processed by sintering of powders/paste through extrusion and compression molding. PTFE can be glass filled for increased strength and rigidity. PTFE possesses an outstanding working temperature range of –270°C to 260°C and is used in a broad range of applications, including gasketing, pump parts, electrical components, bearings, and anti-stick applications.
PUs	Polyurethanes	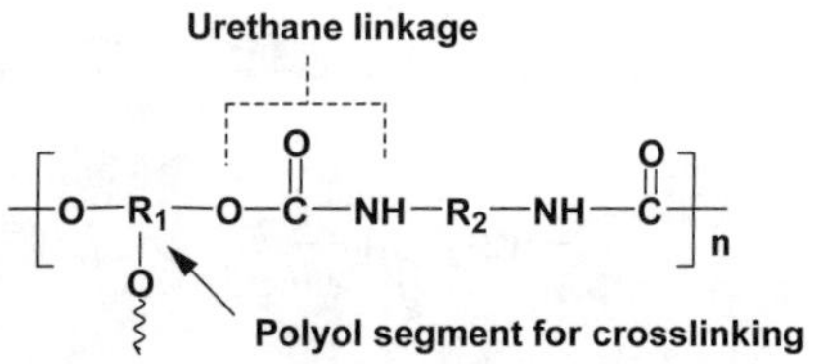 Urethane linkage Polyol segment for crosslinking	Polyurethanes belong to the class of thermosetting polymers and contain the characteristic urethane (-O-CO-NH-) group formed in the typical condensation polymerization between isocyanates with polyols. Polyurethanes are used extensively in the construction field. In housing, rigid foams are the best insulators for walls, floor and ceiling. Polyurethanes are also indispensable in the auto industry, because they offer improved comfort, safety and ecological energy conservation. Polyurethanes are now applied in an extremely wide variety of different physical forms in the automotive sector, such as heat-

			/sound-insulated roofing, comfortable seat cushioning, noise/vibration dampening flooring, sealants, instrument panels, door trims and dashboards. Flexible polyurethane foams are also widely used to produce seating cushion materials and futon bedding. In the kitchen, rigid polyurethane foams are used as insulators for refrigerators. Polyurethane elastomers or 'non-foams', which possess extremely good abrasion resistance and hardness, combined with good elasticity and resistance to greases, oils and solvents, are suitable for casting operations or sprayed as a protective or decorative coating.
PVA	Poly(vinyl alcohol)	$\left[CH_2-CH(OH) \right]_n$	Since vinyl alcohol does not exist because of its rapid tautomerization to acetaldehyde, PVA is manufactured by hydrolysis of PVAc via a base-catalyzed ester interchange with methanol, with elimination of methyl acetate. PVA has excellent film forming and adhesive properties as well as providing good resistance to oil, grease and many solvents. Major applications include use in textile warp sizing, and as a protective colloid for PVAc-based adhesive products.
PVAc	Poly(vinyl acetate)	$\left[CH_2-CH(OC(=O)CH_3) \right]_n$	Vinyl acetate monomer (VAM) is a key compound for the production of a variety of useful PVC substitutes. Approximately 80 percent of all VAM produced in the world is used to make PVAc and PVA. Major application of PVAc is in the area of adhesives.
PVC	Poly(vinyl chloride)	$\left[CH_2-CH(Cl) \right]_n$	PVC is usually plasticized with low or medium molecular weight materials, such as dioctyl phthalate, trioctyl phosphate, and poly(propylene glycol) esters. The properties can be finely tuned from rigid to soft and flexible by varying the plasticizer content from a few percent to more than 60%. PVC possesses excellent chemical resistance, good impact strength and crush resistance. PVC piping is the most widely used plastic piping material because it is environmentally friendly, possesses long service life, is easy to install and handle, and is corrosion resistant, cost effective and widely accepted by codes. Production of pipes and fittings, and windows and doors, consumes nearly 50% of PVC produced. Packaging, flooring, and cable and wire consume the majority of the remaining PVC. When blended with a high proportion of plasticizers, PVC becomes soft and pliable, providing the useful rubber-like flexible tubing to be found in every well-equipped laboratory.
PVDF	Poly(vinylidene fluoride)	$\left[CH_2-CF_2 \right]_n$	PVDF has the characteristic stability of fluoropolymers when exposed to harsh thermal, chemical, and ultraviolet environments, while the alternating CH_2 and CF_2 groups along the polymer chain provide a unique polarity that influences its solubility and electrical properties. PVDF is readily melt-processed by standard methods of extrusion, injection or compression molding. At elevated temperatures, PVDF can be dissolved in polar solvents, such as organic esters and amines. This selective solubility is advantageous in the preparation of corrosion-resistant coatings for chemical process equipment and long-life

			architectural finishes on building panels. PVDF components are used extensively in the high purity semiconductor market (low extractable values), pulp and paper industry (chemically resistant to halogens and acids), nuclear waste processing (radiation and hot acid applications), the general chemical processing industry (chemical and temperature applications), and water treatment membrane (industrial and potable water use). PVDF also meets specifications for the food and pharmaceutical processing industries and has also gained success in the battery sector as binders for cathodes and anodes in lithium-ion technology, and as battery separators in lithium-ion polymer technology. PVDF is known particularly for its creep resistance over a broad range of temperatures. It is widely used for gasketing and the lining of pipes and tanks.
PVK	Poly(vinyl carbazole)	$-\!\left[CH_2-CH(N\text{-carbazolyl})\right]_n\!-$	PVK is well-known for its photoconductivity. A PVK film containing 60 weight percent trinitrofluorenone (TNF) exhibits good results as a photoconductor. PVK has outstanding stability as an insulator in continuous high temperature use.
PVP	Poly(vinyl pyrrolidone)	$-\!\left[CH_2-CH(N\text{-pyrrolidone})\right]_n\!-$	PVP, a water soluble polymer, has excellent wetting and film-forming properties, which make PVP an attractive candidate for coatings and as a binder for many pharmaceutical tablets. Other uses include personal care products (such as shampoos and toothpastes), paints, adhesive in glue stick, and additive for batteries.
SAN	Styrene-acrylonitrile copolymer	$-\!\left[(CH_2-CH(C_6H_5))_x-(CH_2-CH(CN))_y\right]_n\!-$	SAN possesses superior thermal performance (up to 80°C) with a slightly higher T_g (105°C), higher impact strength, rigidity, and chemical resistance than polystyrene, but it is not quite as clear as polystyrene. Typical uses include automobile instrument panels and interior trim and housewares, such as water jugs and toothbrush handles, kitchen and picnic ware.
SBR	Styrene-butadiene rubber	$-\!\left[(CH_2-CH(C_6H_5))_x-(CH_2-CH{=}CH-CH_2)_y-(CH_2-CH(HC{=}CH_2))_z\right]_n\!-$	SBR, a random copolymer of styrene and butadiene monomers, is the most important synthetic rubber and represents more than half of all synthetic rubber production. SBR is predominantly used for the production of car and truck tires and tire retread compounds. A good amount of SBR latex also serves as substitutes for natural rubber latex.
SBS	Styrene-butadiene-styrene triblock copolymer	See thermoplastic elastomers below	
SIS	Styrene-isoprene-styrene triblock copolymer	See thermoplastic elastomers below	

TPEs	Thermoplastic elastomers	R–(CH$_2$–CH(Ph))$_x$–(CH$_2$–CH=CH–CH$_2$)$_y$–(CH$_2$–CH(Ph))$_x$–R **SBS** R–(CH$_2$–CH(Ph))$_x$–(CH$_2$–C(CH$_3$)=CH–CH$_2$)$_y$–(CH$_2$–CH(Ph))$_x$–R **SIS** **(R = H or initiator residue, see p. 170)**	TPEs, viz., SBS and SIS, possess unique properties which combine the mechanical and physical properties of rubber with the advantages of thermoplasticity and processability of plastics. In recent years, the use of TPEs as replacements for natural and synthetic rubber, as well as rigid thermoplastics and metals has increased significantly because of their versatile properties. In addition to direct displacement of competitive materials, TPEs are gaining many new applications in which they are over-molded onto rigid plastic or metal components to enhance ergonomic or 'soft-touch' features on a wide range of products, particularly consumer goods. There are four major types of TPEs: polyurethanes, polyester copolymers, styrene copolymers (e.g., styrene-butadiene-styrene and styrene-isoperene-styrene triblock copolymers), and the olefinics. Mechanical properties and dynamic properties (such as flex life) of the first two types are generally higher than those of the latter two. Thus, TPEs offer a wide range of applications, such as appliances, footwear, sporting goods, automotive, medical, toys and caps and plugs. The majority of shoe soles is now manufactured with TPE rather than vulcanized rubbers because of its ease of processing, performance and physical appearance.
UF	Urea formaldehyde		UF accounts for over 80% of total amine-formaldehyde polymer consumption because it is very cheap. Unfilled UF thermosets are transparent, but susceptible to hydrolysis, hence not suitable for applications involving higher relative humidity or increased moisture resistance. Major applications of UF polymers involve adhesives or binders for wooden materials (e.g., plywood and particle board) and expanded thermosets.
UHMWPE	Ultra high molecular weight polyethylene	–[CH$_2$–CH$_2$]$_n$–	UHMWPE possesses a structure similar to HDPE, and combines the traditional abrasion and cut resistance of metal alloys with the impact and corrosion resistance of synthetic polymers, making it ideal for fabricating heavy-duty industrial components. UHMWPE finds use in high modulus fibers for bulletproof vests. These fibers are 15 times stronger than steel and three times stronger than that of Kevlar®. Due to its low coefficient of friction and high resistance to wear, UHMWPE is used in industrial impact, wear, and sliding applications in both normal and corrosive environments. It is also employed in orthopedic implants, such as artificial hips and knees.

Appendix-II

Parameters Influencing T_g and T_m

I. Effect of Chain Flexing Groups

Polymer	Abbrev.	T_g (°C)	T_m (°C)	Comments/Contributing Feature
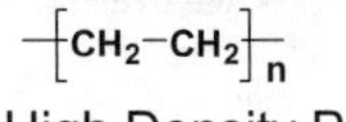 $-[CH_2-CH_2]_n-$ High Density Polyethylene	**HDPE**	-30	150	This set of polymers possesses the simplest structures, which impart high flexibility to the polymer backbone. The effect of an ether or methylene group is not prominent in polymers containing highly flexible backbone. Moreover, structural simplicity leads to greater tendency for crystallization (hence, higher T_m than expected) in these polymers.
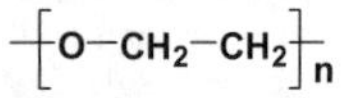 $-[O-CH_2-CH_2]_n-$ Poly(ethylene oxide)	**PEO**	-65	75	
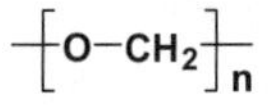 $-[O-CH_2]_n-$ Polyoxymethylene	**POM**	-30	180	
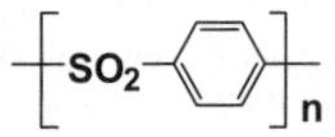 Poly(phenylene sulfone)	**$PPSO_2$**	---	Does not melt, decompose at 500	$PPSO_2$ backbone (which contains two strong chain stiffening moieties, *p*-phenylene and sulfone) is so stiff and rigid that it does not exhibit any T_g or T_m. The presence of ether linkages makes PES backbone angular structure at random directions, thus creating chain flexibility and amorphous character. Introduction of angular 2,2-diphenylpropane moiety between two ether linkages causes further increase in free volume and more randomness in PSF, thus T_g drops to a lower temperature.
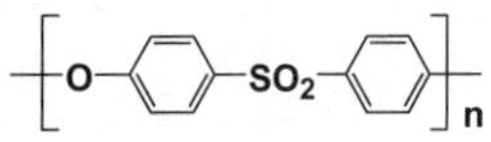 Poly(ether sulfone)	**PES**	225	Amorphous	
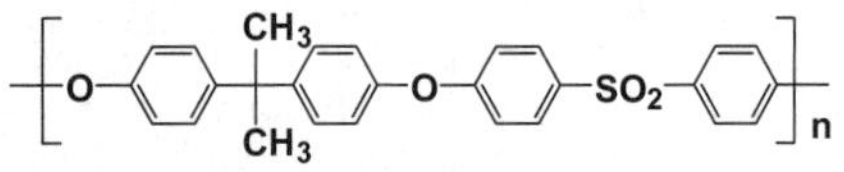 Polysulfone	**PSF**	190	Amorphous	
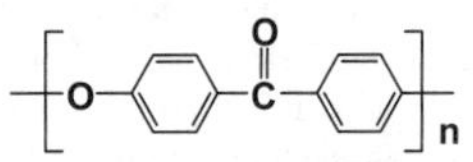 Poly(ether ketone)	**PEK**	155	365	Another set of polymers showing the effect of ether flexing group.
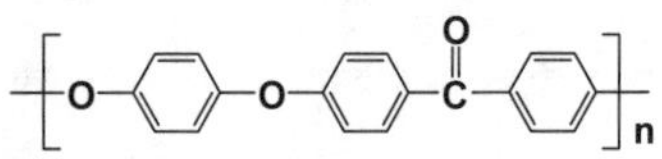 Poly(ether ether ketone)	**PEEK**	145	340	
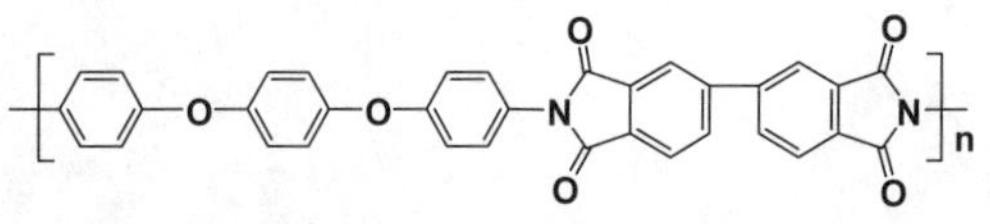 Poly(ether imide)-I	**PIM-I**	255	470	Another set of polymers showing the effect of ether flexing group.

Polymer	Abbrev.	T_g (°C)	T_m (°C)	Comments/Contributing Feature
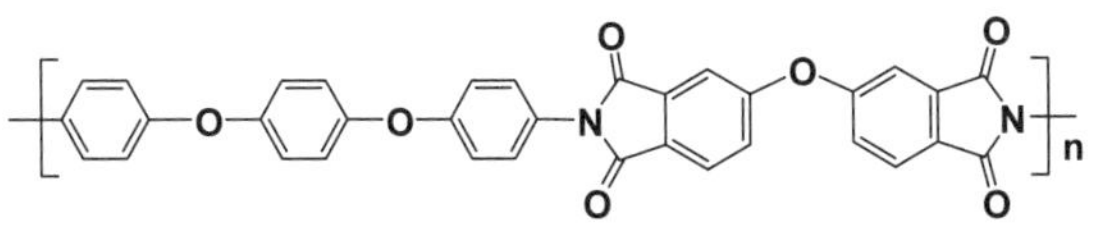 Poly(ether imide)-II	**PIM-II**	235	415	
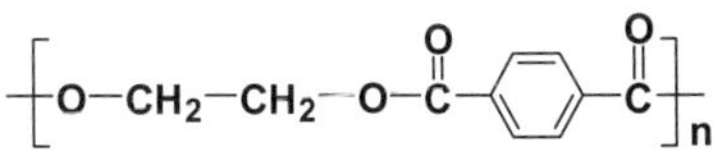 Poly(ethylene terephthalate)	**PET**	80	250	Polymers showing the effect of methylene flexing group.
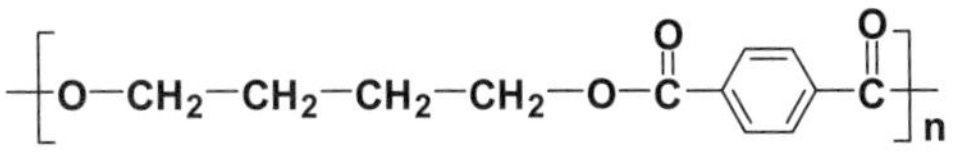 Poly(butylene terephthalate)	**PBT**	50	225	
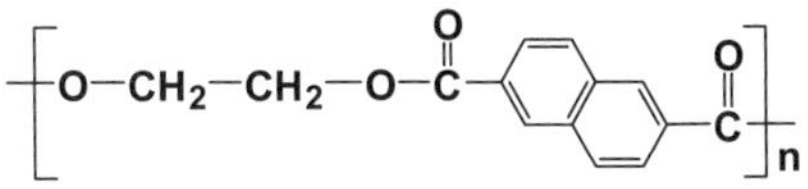 Poly(ethylene-2,6-naphthalenedicarboxylate)	**PEN**	125	270	
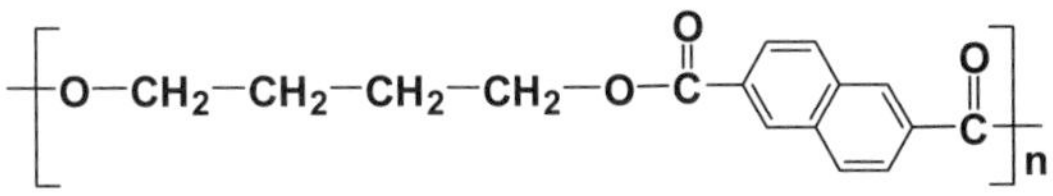 Poly(butylene-2,6-naphthalenedicarboxylate)	**PBN**	80	240	

II. Effect of Chain Stiffening Groups

Polymer	Abbrev.	T_g (°C)	T_m (°C)	Comments/Contributing Feature
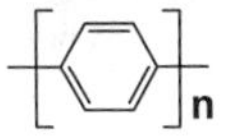 Poly(*p*-phenylene)	**PPP**	---	Does not melt, decompose above 600	PPP possesses extremely high chain stiffness due to the presence of continuous delocalized electron clouds (sp^2 carbons), which restrict free rotation of single bonds. PPX, which can be viewed as an alternating copolymer of *p*-phenylene and ethylene, is crystalline and melts at lower temperature. Thus, offers a very good example of the effect of *p*-phenylene moieties in a HDPE backbone.
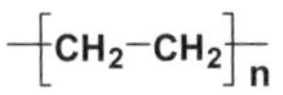 $-[CH_2-CH_2]_n-$ High Density Polyethylene	**HDPE**	-30	150	
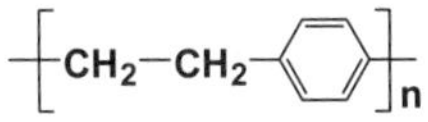 Poly(*p*-xylylene)	**PPX**	---	375	
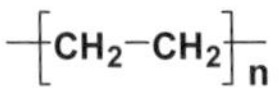 $-[CH_2-CH_2]_n-$ High Density Polyethylene	**HDPE**	-30	150	Another set of polymers demonstrates the effect of amide linkage, which is capable of forming strong intermolecular hydrogen bonds, in a polyethylene backbone.
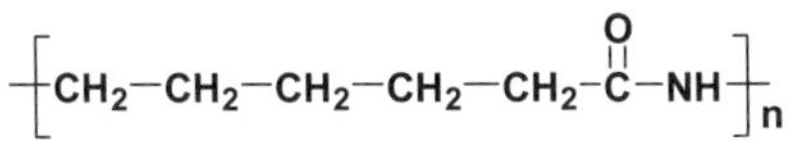 $-[CH_2-CH_2-CH_2-CH_2-CH_2-C(=O)-NH]_n-$ Polyamide 6	**Nylon 6 (PA6)**	50	225	

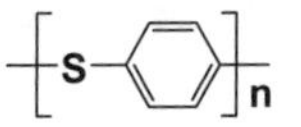 Poly(phenylene sulfide)	**PPS**	90	285	As mentioned earlier, $PPSO_2$ is very rigid. However, it's thioether version is flexible and melt processable. Of course, the thermal stability is somewhat sacrificed in PPS.
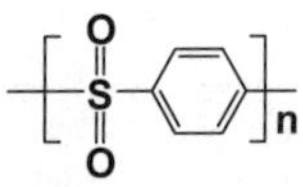 Poly(phenylene sulfone)	**$PPSO_2$**	---	Does not melt, decompose at 500	
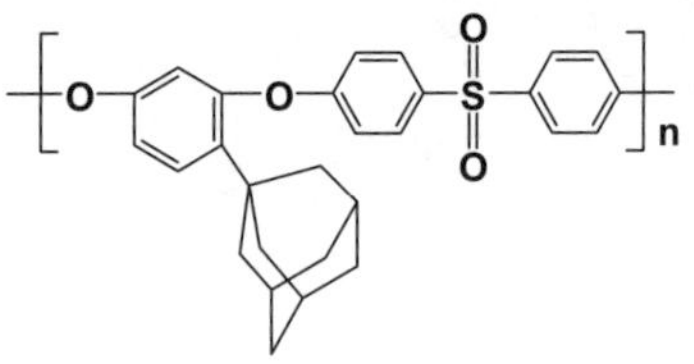 Adamantane PES	**PES-ADM**	260	Amorphous	These two examples show that the sulfone group has more chain-stiffening power than the keto group.
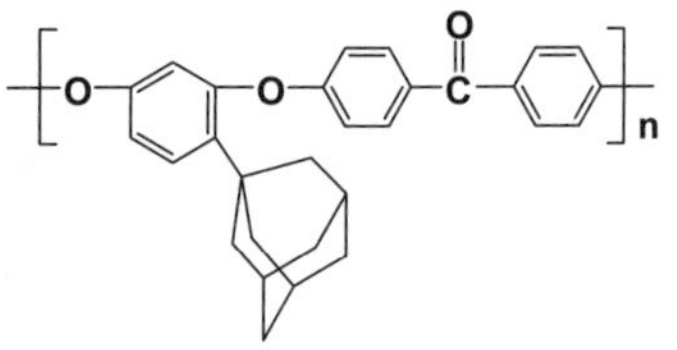 Adamantane PEEK	**PEEK-ADM**	225	Amorphous	
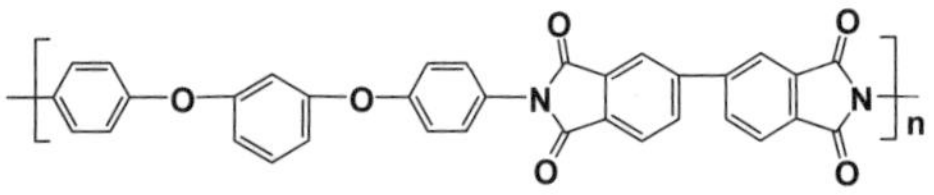 Poly(ether imide)-III	**PIM-III**	205	390	This set of polymers shows slight chain-stiffening effect due to the presence of carbonyl groups in a polymer backbone containing rigid phthalimide moieties.
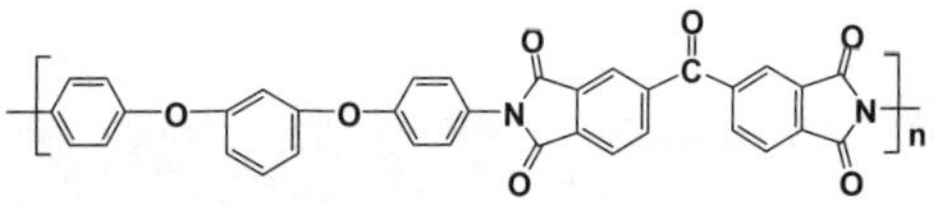 Poly(ether imide)-IV	**PIM-IV**	235	425	
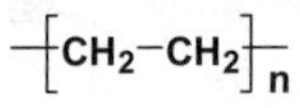 High Density Polyethylene	**HDPE**	-30	150	In this set of polymers, the presence of carbonyl (keto) groups in polyethylene backbone causes strong chain-stiffening. The polar carbonyl groups attract each other so strongly that while HDPE melts at a mere 150°C, the ECO does not melt until 255°C!
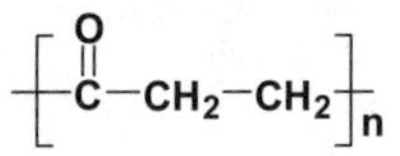 Polyketone (Ethylene carbon monoxide copolymer)	**ECO**	35	255	
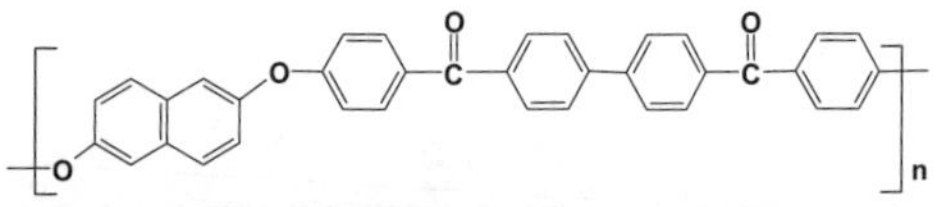 Poly(ether ether ketone)-I	**PEEK-I**	170	405	Linear rigid rod biphenyl group permits highly crystalline material.
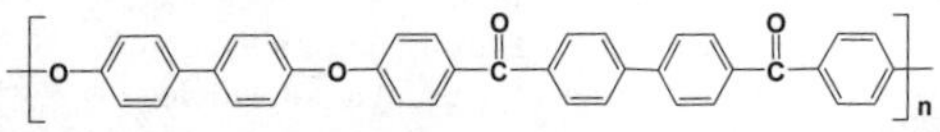 Poly(ether ether ketone)-II	**PEEK-II**	Crystalline	465	

III. Effect of Chain Symmetry

Polymer	Abbrev.	T_g (°C)	T_m (°C)	Comments/Contributing Feature
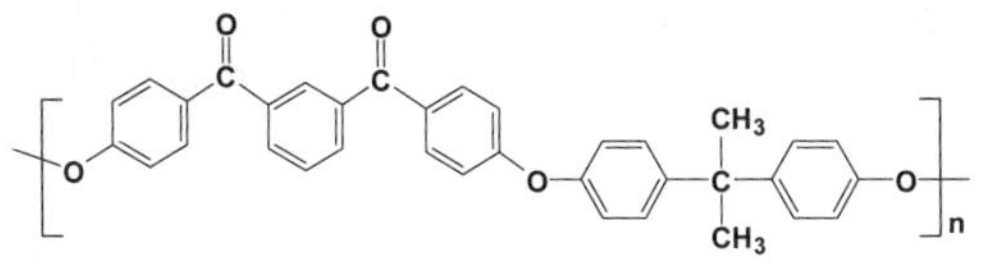 Poly(ether ether ketone)-III	PEEK-IIII	155	Amorphous	The *para* isomer has more symmetry than *meta* isomer.
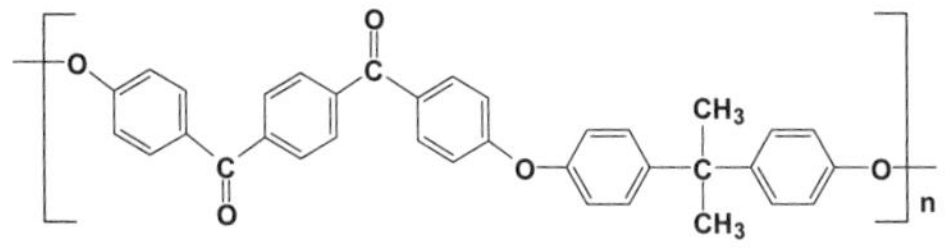 Poly(ether ether ketone)-IV	PEEK-IV	165	Amorphous	
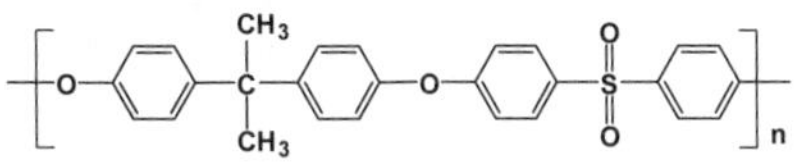 Polysulfone-I	PSF-I	185	Amorphous	Another two sets of isomers which demonstrate higher T_g for more symmetric *p*-isomer.
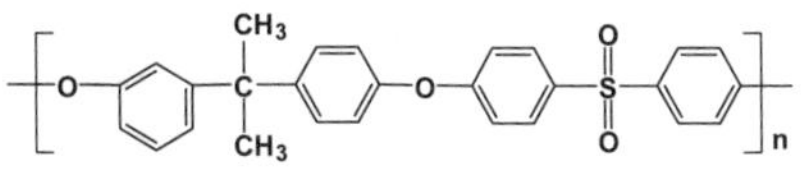 Polysulfone-II	PSF-II	155	Amorphous	
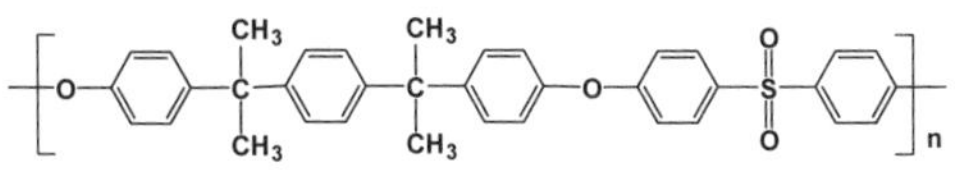 Polysulfone-III	PSF-III	190	Amorphous	
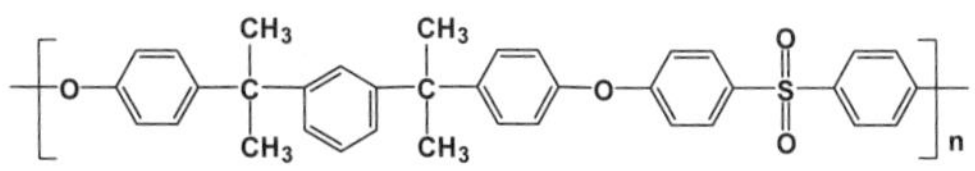 Polysulfone-IV	PSF-IV	140	Amorphous	
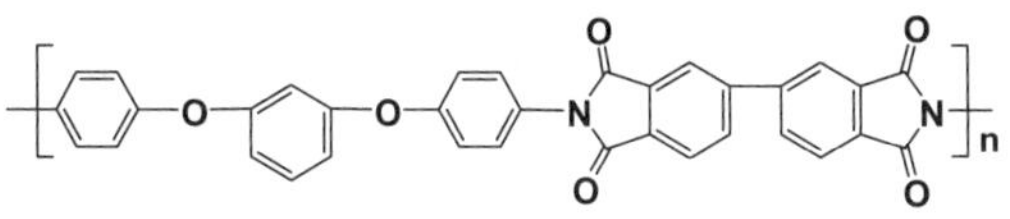 Polyimide-III	PIM-III	205	390	This set of polymers shows that chain symmetry is a dominant factor even in polymers containing rigid (phthalimide) moieties.
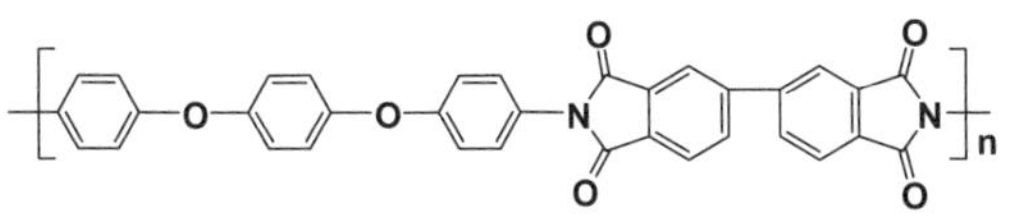 Polyimide-V	PIM-V	260	475	

IV. Effect of Pendent Groups

Polymer	Abbrev.	T_g (°C)	T_m (°C)	Comments/Contributing Feature
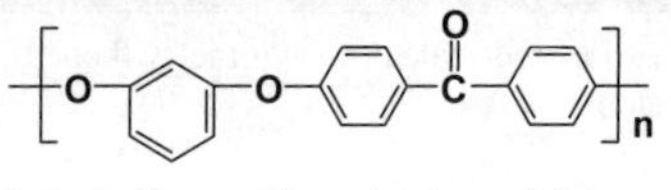 Poly(ether ether ketone)-V	**PEEK-V**	135	290	This set of examples shows how the attachment of very bulky adamantane (3-dimensional shape) groups can destroy high crystallinity of PEEK and concurrently increase the T_g of the polymer by restricting chain mobility.
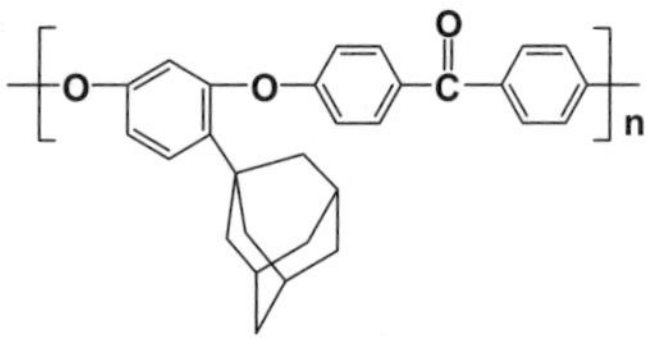 Adamantane PEEK	**PEEK-ADM**	225	Amorphous	
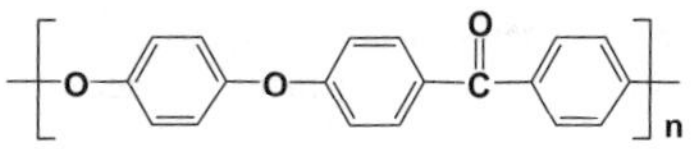 Poly(ether ether ketone)	**PEEK**	145	340	Another set of bulky groups containing PEEK derivatives, which possess high amorphous character and higher T_g than that of PEEK.
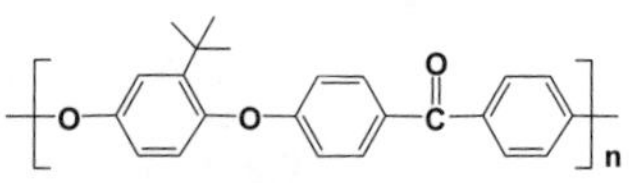 Poly(ether ether ketone)-VI	**PEEK-VI**	175	Amorphous	
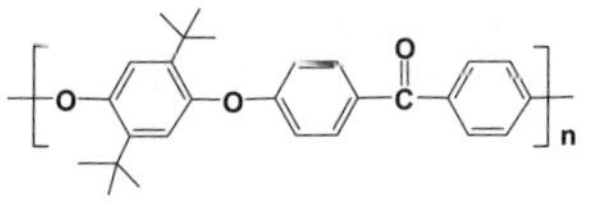 Poly(ether ether ketone)-VII	**PEEK-VII**	205	Amorphous	
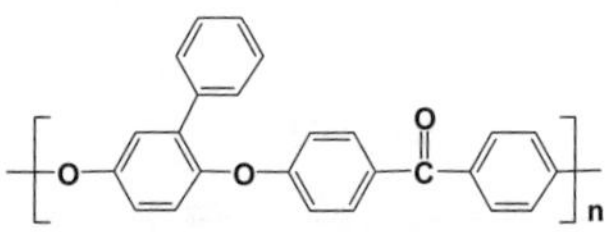 Poly(ether ether ketone)-VIII	**PEEK-VIII**	155	Amorphous	
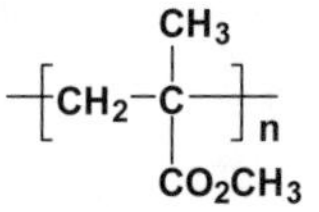 Poly(methyl methacrylate)	**PMMA**	105	Amorphous	In this set of polymers (PMMA through PHMA), free volume increases in dramatic fashion with the increase in length of the aliphatic chains. This explains why these polymers are highly amorphous. Chain stiffness does not play a major role as the increment in chain lengths occurs away from the main chain.
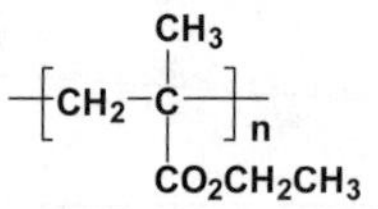 Poly(ethyl methacrylate)	**PEMA**	65	Amorphous	The trend, decrease in T_g with increase in aliphatic chain length, is lost when an aliphatic chain is replaced by a cycloalkane or an aromatic ring with the same number of carbon atoms, as observed in PCHMA and PPhMA. Both cyclohexyl and phenyl groups create less free volume compared to the n-hexyl group. In addition, they are bulky enough to hinder the motion of the main chain.
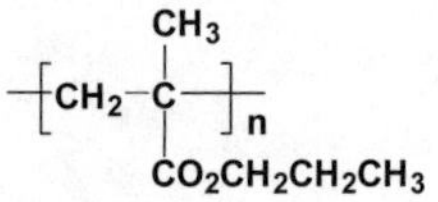 Poly(propyl methacrylate)	**PPMA**	40	Amorphous	The T_g drops again, when a flexible methylene group is introduced in PPhMA. For example, in PBzMA, the methylene group significantly enhances the mobility of the side chain, including pushing back the phenyl group from the main chain. Surprisingly, this polymer is semi-crystalline, which

$-[CH_2-C(CH_3)(CO_2CH_2CH_2CH_2CH_3)]_n-$ Poly(butyl methacrylate)	**PBMA**	20	Amorphous	presumably creates a favorable situation for interchain π-π stacking interactions of phenyl rings.
$-[CH_2-C(CH_3)(CO_2CH_2CH_2CH_2CH_2CH_2CH_3)]_n-$ Poly(hexyl methacrylate)	**PHMA**	-5	Amorphous	
$-[CH_2-C(CH_3)(CO_2C_6H_{11})]_n-$ Poly(cyclohexyl methacrylate)	**PCHMA**	104	Amorphous	
$-[CH_2-C(CH_3)(CO_2C_6H_5)]_n-$ Poly(phenyl methacrylate)	**PPhMA**	110	Amorphous	
$-[CH_2-C(CH_3)(CO_2CH_2C_6H_5)]_n-$ Poly(benzyl methacrylate)	**PBzMA**	55	200	
$-[CH_2-C(CH_3)(CO_2CH_2CH_2CH_3)]_n-$ Poly(propyl methacrylate)	**PPMA**	40	Amorphous	This set of examples compares the effect of branching in the pendent group. Although the branching is away from the main chain, the hindrance in chain mobility is detectable.
$-[CH_2-C(CH_3)(CO_2CH(CH_3)CH_3)]_n-$ Poly(isopropyl methacrylate)	**PIPMA**	81	Amorphous	
$-[CH_2-C(CH_3)(CO_2CH_2CH_2CH_2CH_3)]_n-$ Poly(butyl methacrylate)	**PBMA**	20	Amorphous	
$-[CH_2-C(CH_3)(CO_2CH_2CH(CH_3)CH_3)]_n-$ Poly(isobutyl methacrylate)	**PIBMA**	50	Amorphous	
$-[CH_2-CH(CH_2CH_2CH_2CH_3)]_n-$ Poly(1-hexene)	**PHE**	-50	Amorphous	

$-[CH_2-CH(CH_2CH(CH_3)CH_3)]_n-$ Poly(4-methyl-1-pentene)	**PMP**	35	240	

V. Effect of Intermolecular Forces

Polymer	Abbrev.	T_g (°C)	T_m (°C)	Comments/Contributing Feature
$-[CH_2-CH_2]_n-$ High Density Polyethylene	**HDPE**	-30	150	The presence of pendant hydroxyl groups leads to intermolecular hydrogen bonding and polar groups, such as chloro and nitrile, increase intermolecular dipolar intractions.
$-[CH_2-CH(OH)]_n-$ Poly(vinyl alcohol)	**PVOH**	85	220	
$-[CH_2-CH(Cl)]_n-$ Poly(vinyl chloride)	**PVC**	85	245	
$-[CH_2-CH(CN)]_n-$ Poly(acrylonitrile)	**PAN**	90	310	
$-[CF_2-CF_2]_n-$ Poly(tetrafluoroethylene)	**PTFE**	---	325	Strong intermolecular attractions and chain symmetry make PTFE highly crystalline with a very stiff backbone. The stiffness and thermal stability are markedly reduced in PVDF because of the replacement of one CF_2 group with a CH_2 in the monomer repeat unit.
$-[CH_2-CF_2]_n-$ Poly(vinylidene fluoride)	**PVDF**	-40	165	

Appendix-III

Key Similarities and Differences of Various Classes of Polymers

Thermoplastics	Thermosets	Fibers	Elastomers	Thermoplastic Elastomers
T_g well above room temperature (with few exceptions, e.g., PE)	No T_g	T_g well above room temperature	T_g well below room temperature	Multiple T_gs; at least one above and one below room temperature
Softens upon heating, solidifies upon cooling	Cures (solidifies) upon heating	Softens upon heating, solidifies upon cooling	Cures (rubbery) upon heating	Softens upon heating, solidifies upon cooling
High modulus (resistant to deformation) and low elongation	High modulus and no elongation	High modulus and low elongation	High modulus and large reversible elongation	High modulus and low elongation (almost reversible)
Covalent bonds along main chain (linear or branched)	Covalent bonds along main chain	Covalent bonds along main chain (linear and highly ordered)	Covalent bonds along main chain (linear)	Covalent bonds along main chain (linear)
Physical bonds between chains (dispersion forces)	Extensive covalent bonds between chains (highly crosslinked)	Physical bonds between chains (hydrogen bonding or dipole-dipole interactions)	Few covalent bonds between chains (lightly crosslinked)	Physical bonds between chains (dispersion forces)
Soluble in organic solvents	Insoluble in organic solvents (very little or no swelling)	Soluble in organic solvents	Insoluble in organic solvents (high degree of swelling)	Soluble in organic solvents
Convenient to recycle as same product	Not possible to recycle as same product	Theoretically recyclable, but practically inconvenient to recycle as same product due to difficulty in shorting	Cannot be recycled as same product	Convenient recycling as same product
Complex shapes can be fabricated by injection molding, extrusion and blow molding	Simple shapes can be obtained by compression or injection molding	Melt spinning through a spinneret of a fiber drawing tower	Variety of shapes by compression molding	Complex shapes can be fabricated by injection molding and extrusion
HDPE, PS, PMMA, PC	Phenolics, Epoxy, Unsaturated Polyester	Isotactic PP, Nylon 6,6, PET	PB, NR, Polyisoprene	SBS (styrene-butadiene-styrene) and SIS (styrene-isoprene-styrene) triblock copolymers

Appendix-IV

Types of Initiators

There are a variety of initiators differing in decomposition kinetics (half-life), type and energy of the generated radicals, nature of the decomposition products, and basic properties (physical form and solubility). Each parameter is very important in selecting an initiator for a particular polymerization process. For instance, the *half-life time*, $t_{1/2}$, of an initiator at any specified temperature is the time required at that temperature to decompose one half mole of the initiator's concentration. Because the efficiency of a free-radical initiator depends primarily on its rate of thermal decomposition, half-life data are essential for selecting the optimum initiator for specific time-temperature considerations. High energy free-radicals, such as phenyl radical, tend to abstract H from the polymer backbone leading to grafting, branching reactions or decomposition. Lower energy radicals, such as *t*-butyl radical, are more stable and preferentially attack the double bond of the monomer. Another parameter to consider for selection of an initiator is the nature of the decomposition products. These products may remain in the polymer, resulting in undesirable properties, such as poor organoleptic performances, yellowing and low weathering performances. Finally, physical properties, such as solubility, are also very important to consider as some polymerization requires monomer-soluble initiator and some water soluble. Thus, selection of the appropriate initiator is crucial for good control of the reaction and final properties of the polymer.

Initiators contain one or more labile bonds that cleave homolytically when sufficient energy is supplied to the molecule. The energy must be greater than the bond dissociation energy of the labile bond. The three important general processes for supplying the energy necessary to generate radicals from initiators are: thermal, electron transfer (redox) and photochemical. Below are some of the representatives from each class of initiators along with equations showing the formation of radical species.

I. Thermal Initiators:

There are two major classes of thermal initiators, peroxide and azo. Organic peroxides are essential to produce thermoplastic olefinic polymers (e.g., PVC, LDPE, PS and acrylics), to cure thermosetting polymers and to crosslink synthetic rubbers. They are also used to prepare controlled-rheology PP (CR-PP), which is produced by degrading normal PP in the presence of a peroxide to give a product with a high melt flow index (MFI), lower molecular weight, narrower molecular weight distribution and hence, easier and more consistent flow (see Chapter-2 for degradation mechanism). The most commonly used peroxides are benzoyl peroxide (BPO) and di-*t*-butyl peroxide (DTBP), which exhibit different decomposition kinetics and workable temperatures because of the structural variations close to the labile oxygen-oxygen bond.

For instance, BPO undergoes thermally induced homolysis of the peroxidic bonds to produce reactive oxy-radicals necessary to activate (initiation) vinyl monomers. The efficiency of an initiator is measured by the fraction of initiator radicals that produce growing polymer radical chains, i.e., are able to react with monomer. Typical initiator efficiencies fall in the range of 0.3 to 0.8. Besides adding to monomers, the oxy-radicals undergo several secondary reactions, viz., recombination with other radicals, such as another oxy-radical (i.e., reverse of decomposition) or a growing polymer radical chain, and/or partially decompose into non-initiating products (Figure A-1). Some of these secondary reactions are favored when the initiator molecule dissociates in a solvent "cage", which inhibits reaction with a monomer unless the radical diffuses out of the cage. For this *cage effect* or confinement of radical by solvent molecules, only a fraction of the original initiator concentration is effective in contributing to the polymerization process.

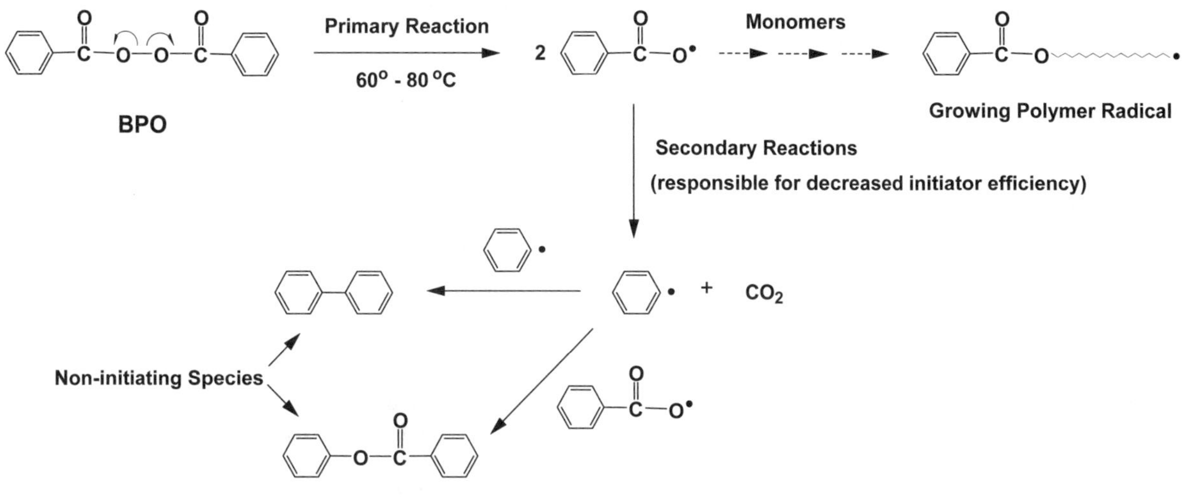

Figure A-1. Secondary reactions of BPO during vinyl polymerization, which lead to depletion of initiator.

DTBP, another widely used initiator, functions at higher temperatures by generating alkoxy radical pairs, which are suitable for vinyl monomer polymerizations (Figure A-2). DTBP is also useful for polymer crosslinking, grafting, and degradation because of β-scission of the alkoxy radical that occurs at higher temperatures to produce very reactive methyl radicals. The thermal decomposition rate of peroxides is a first order reaction. An increase in temperature of about 10°C results in a two to three fold increase in decomposition rate, which also depends on the solvent, mainly due to differences in polarity. For example, the one-hour half-life temperature of DTBP increases about 20 degrees when changing from chlorobenzene to aliphatic solvent.

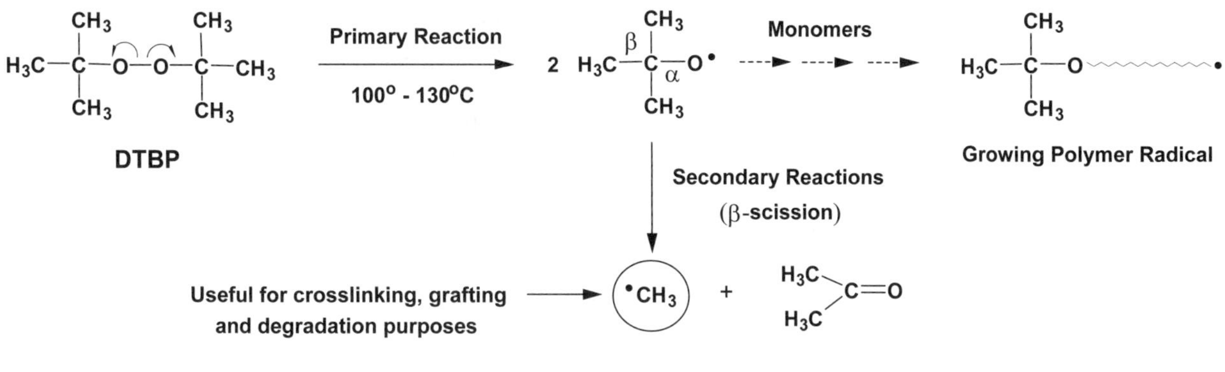

Figure A-2. Thermal homolysis reactions of DTBP.

By contrast, hydroperoxides, e.g., cumyl hydroperoxide (CHP), form alkoxy and hydroxyl radicals by thermally induced homolysis (Figure A-3). Since the oxygen-hydrogen bond in hydroperoxides is weak and susceptible to attack by higher energy radicals, secondary reactions become significant. Consequently, hydroperoxides have limited application as thermal initiators. However, their use is widespread at low temperature, where transition metal salts behave as activators (see redox initiators which follows).

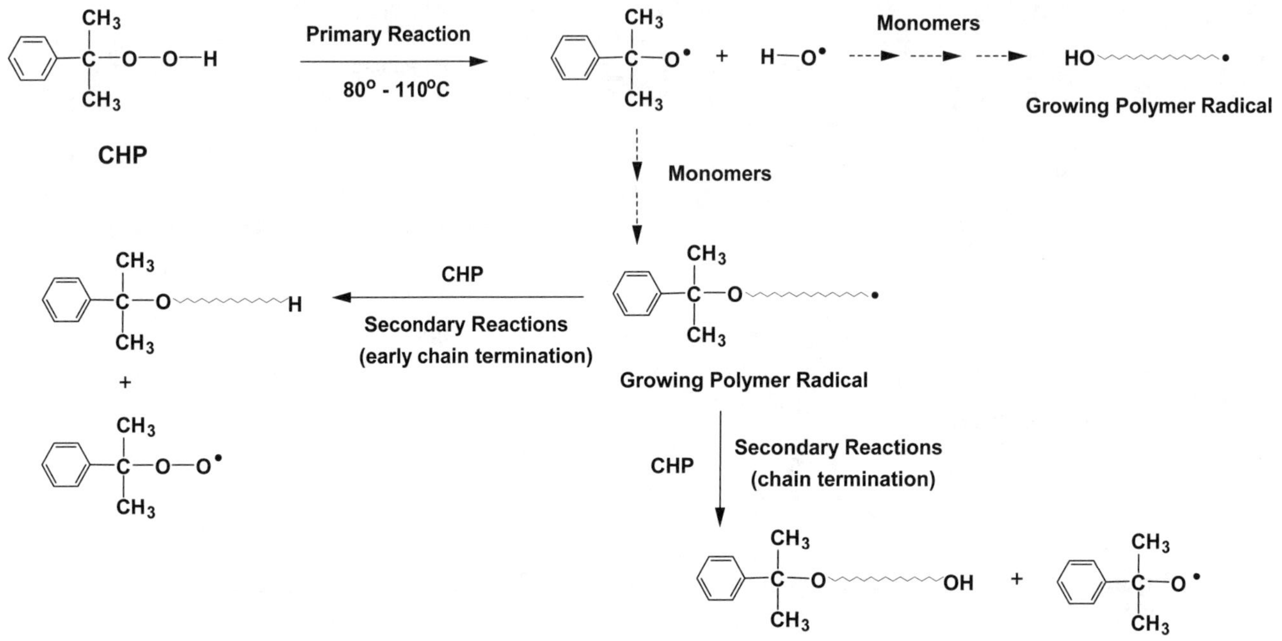

CHP

Primary Reaction

80° - 110°C

Monomers

Growing Polymer Radical

Monomers

CHP

Secondary Reactions
(early chain termination)

Growing Polymer Radical

CHP

Secondary Reactions
(chain termination)

Figure A-3. Major secondary reactions limit the use of CHP as a thermal initiator.

II. Azo Initiators:

Compared with peroxides, organic azo initiators generate carbon-centered radicals, which are usually less reactive with respect to hydrogen abstraction than the oxygen-centered radicals generated by peroxides. Consequently, branch grafting and preliminary chain termination are suppressed, and the efficiency of polymer chain growth increases. In contrast to peroxides, most commercial azo initiators are not affected much by solvents, acids or bases. The most used azo initiator is α,α'-azobis(isobutyronitrile), AIBN, especially for polymerization of a wide variety of monomers, such as styrene, vinyl chloride, vinylidene chloride, acrylonitrile, acrylates and methacrylates. The driving force for decomposition of azo initiators is the facile elimination of nitrogen and formation of the resonance-stabilized cyanopropyl radical (Figure A-4). Azo initiators are also susceptible to secondary reactions in the solvent cage to deplete initiator concentration.

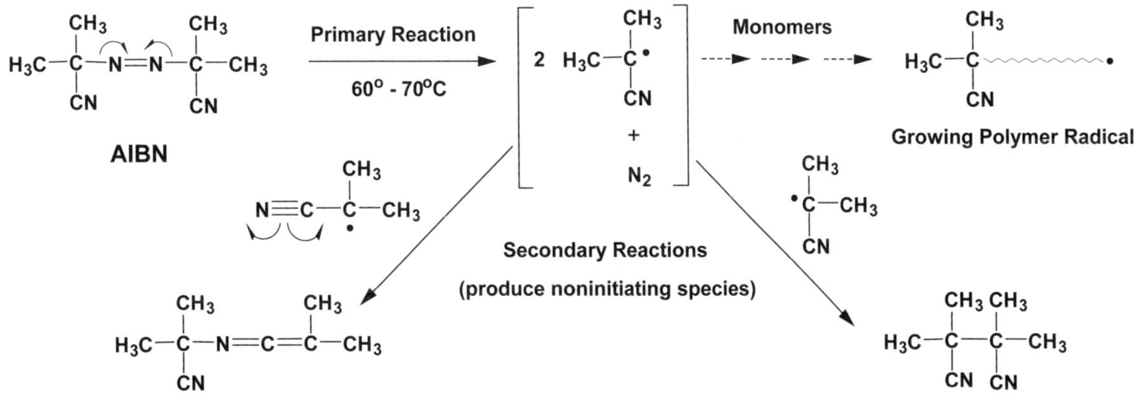

Figure A-4. Primary and secondary reactions of AIBN.

2,2'-Azobis(2-amidinopropane) (AAP) and 4,4'-Azobis(4-cyanovaleric acid) (ACVA) are two other notable azo initiators, which are water soluble, function at ~60°C and are used extensively for the production of industrially important water soluble polymers, such as polyacrylamide, poly (N-vinyl pyrrolidone) and polyacrylic acid (Figure A-5).

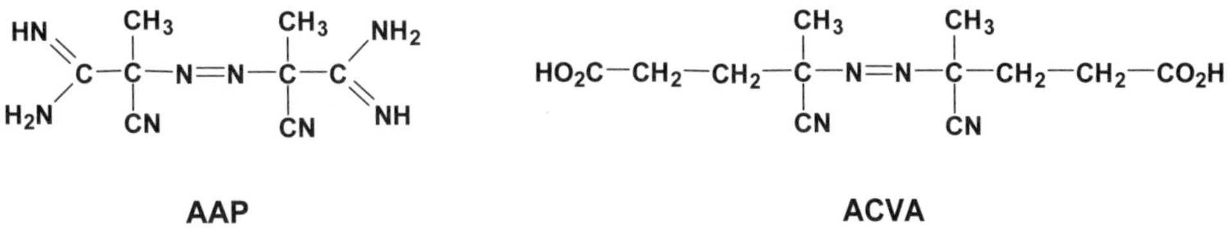

Figure A-5. Structures of two industrially important water soluble azo initiators.

III. Redox Initiators:

Besides the aforementioned water soluble azo initiators, redox initiation systems have provided an effective method of generating free-radicals under mild, aqueous conditions. Organic hydroperoxides, such as CHP, in the presence of transition metal salts, such as ferrous(II) sulfate, serve as one of the most used redox initiator systems. As shown in Figure A-6, the transition metal ion acts as an activator (which markedly lowers the activation temperature of CHP from 80°C to near room temperature) and facilitates a one-electron transfer (redox) process. Since the transition-metal ions can also destroy the generated radical to produce a noninitiating species in a secondary reaction, the optimum use levels of transition metal ions are very low.

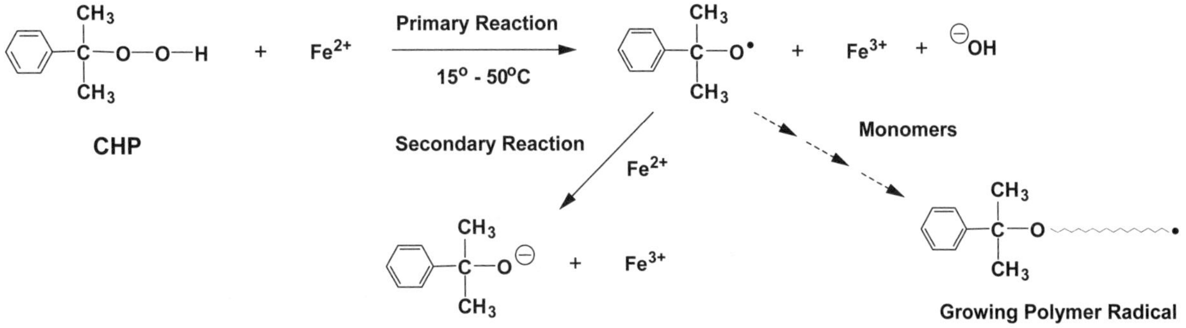

Figure A-6. Primary and secondary reactions of an organic hydroperoxide redox system.

Inorganic peroxide-redox systems, which also operate in aqueous media, are used for homo- and co-polymerization of vinyl monomers. As shown in Figure A-7, hydrogen peroxide (HPO)- ferrous(II) sulfate , and potassium peroxydisulfate, $K_2S_2O_8$, (or the corresponding sodium or ammonium salt), in combination with ferrous(II) sulfate or dodecyl mercaptan represent other important redox initiator systems to produce radicals in the aqueous phase.

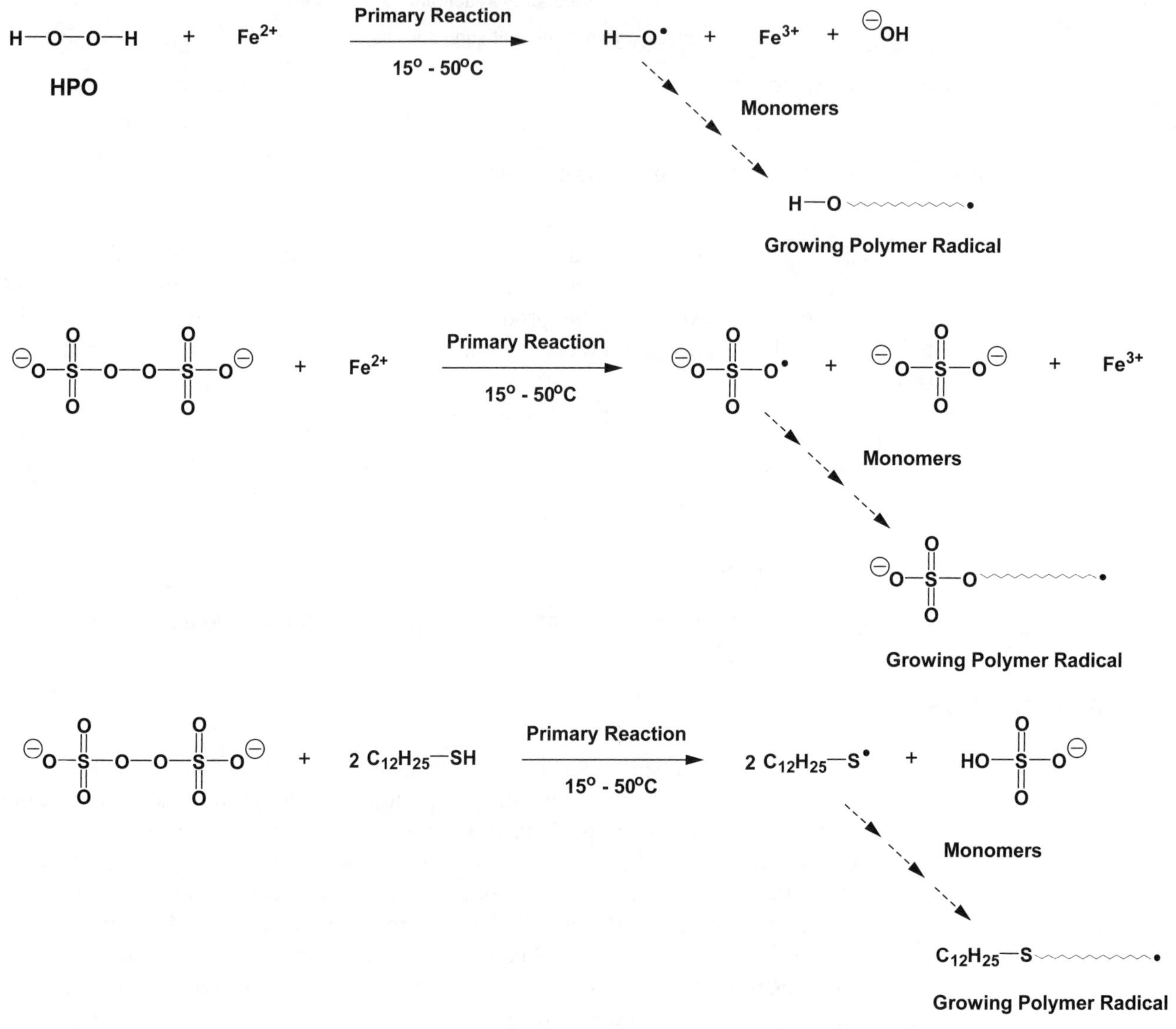

Figure A-7. Important inorganic peroxide redox systems.

A redox initiation system consisting of ammonium persulfate (APS) and *N,N,N′,N′*-tetramethylethylenediamine (TEMED), is also routinely used for preparation of acrylamide gels in gel electrophoresis. In this case, initiation is believed to occur via formation of a contact charge transfer complex (CCTC) and a cyclic transition state (CTS), yielding three active radical species (Figure A-8).

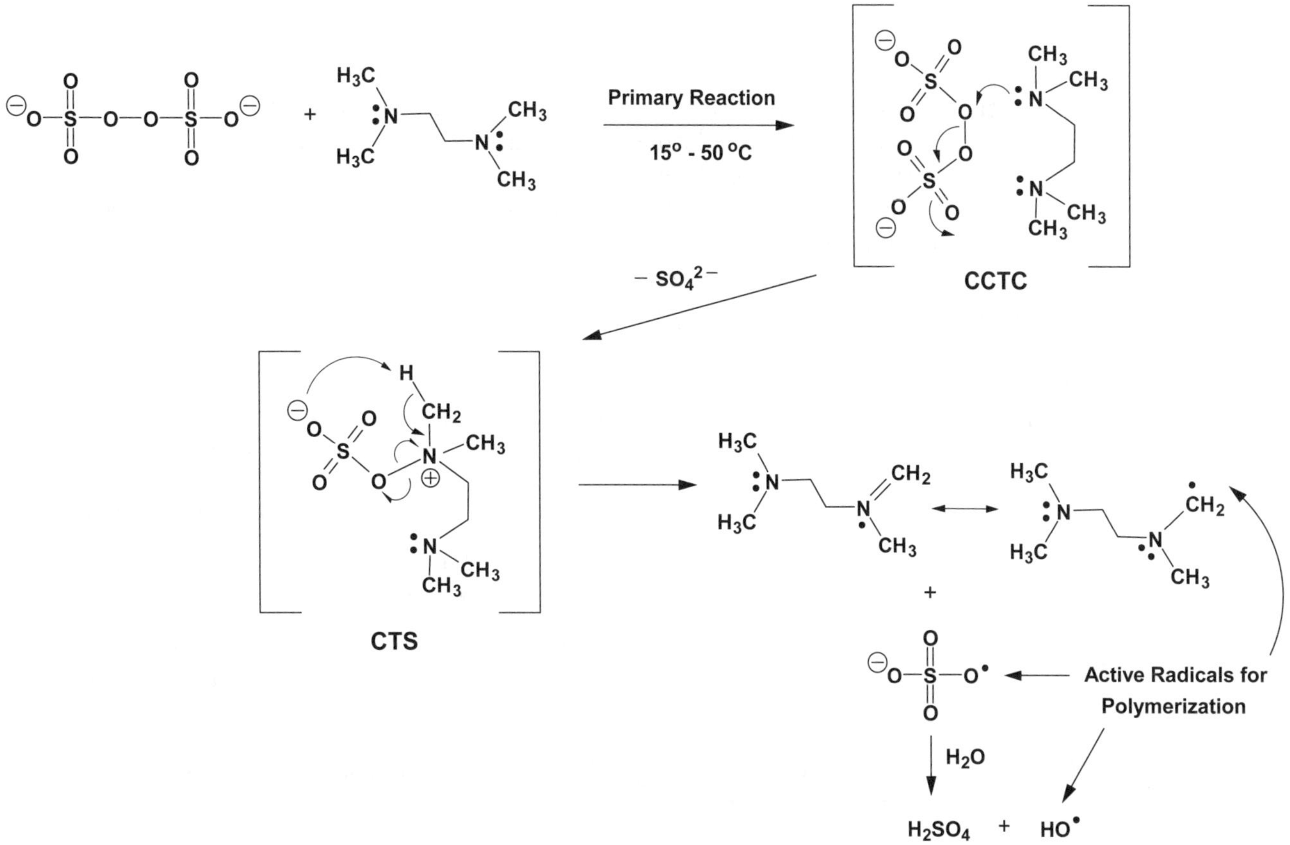

Figure A-8. Formation of active radicals in APS-TEMED redox system.

IV. Photoinitiators:

Photopolymerization is a very flexible process and can be used in various technological applications, such as photoresists in modern electronics. In this process, a film of monomer mixture is placed on the surface of a silicon wafer and a light is focused on the areas in which a polymer covering is desired. After polymerization has occurred, the unpolymerized material can be washed away, leaving the photopolymer intact. The polymer-covered areas on the silicon wafer permit selective operations (oxidation, etching, ion implantation, etc.), resulting in integrated circuit formation or printed circuit board construction. This technology has allowed billions of transistors to be placed on a single integrated circuit. Photoinitiators are also used in curing of unsaturated polyester for coatings on metal and wood surfaces (see Section 3.9.1. in Chapter-3).

In general, photoinitiators are used for ultraviolet light polymerizations. For photoinitiation to proceed efficiently, the absorption bands of the initiator must overlap with the emission spectrum of the source and there must be minimal competing absorption by the components of the formulation at the wavelengths corresponding to photoinitiator excitation. Photoinitiators for free-radical polymerization may be placed in two major classes: (1) those which undergo intramolecular bond cleavage (also called *unimolecular photoinitiators*) and (2) those which undergo intermolecular H-abstraction from a H-donor (also called *bimolecular photoinitiators*).

An important criterion for unimolecular photoinitiators is the presence of a bond with dissociation energy lower than the excitation energy of the reactive excited state, while sufficiently high to provide thermal stability. Benzoin ethers, such as benzoin methyl ether (BME), and benzil ketals, such as benzyl dimethyl ketal (BDK) represent two major classes of unimolecular photoinitiators. The benzoin ethers undergoes photo-cleavage exclusively to produce benzoyl and alkoxybenzyl radicals, which, depending on the structure of the monomers employed, are capable of initiating free radical polymerization, although at different rates (Figure A-9). In the case of BDK, in addition to the benzoyl radical, a methyl radical is produced through fragmentation of the α,α-dimethoxybenzyl radical.

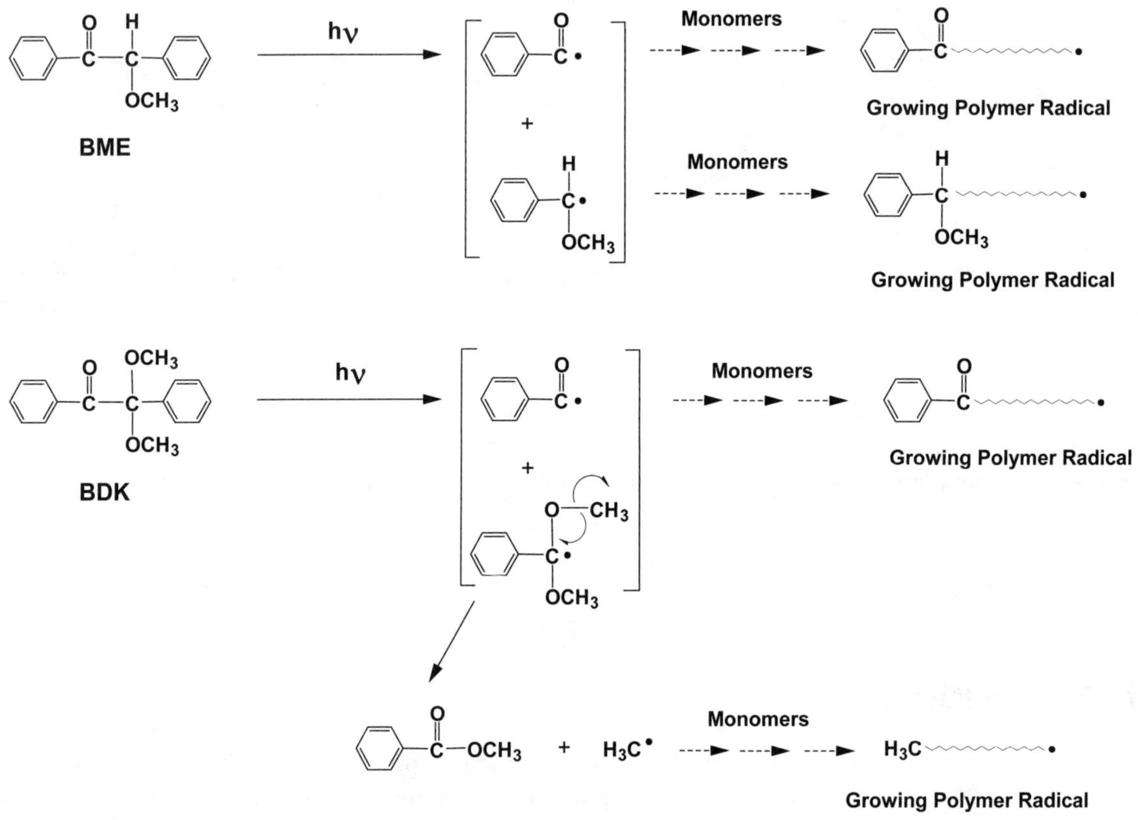

Figure A-9. Important unimolecular photoinitiators.

Bimolecular photoinitiators are so-called because two molecular species are needed to form the active radical: a photoinitiator that absorbs the light and a co-initiator that serves as a hydrogen or electron donor. Benzophenone (BPH) and its derivatives, e.g., Michler's ketone (MIK), and thioxanthone (TXN), are the most common photoinitiators, while alcohols (R_2CHOH), ethers (R_2CHOR) and *tert*-amines (R_2CHNR_2) that have an active hydrogen atom positioned α to an oxygen or nitrogen are popular donors. The mechanism of radical formation depends on the type of co-initiator. If an alcohol or ether is used, the photoinitiator proceeds through a triplet state (a diradical), which abstracts an alpha H atom from the alcohol or ether, resulting in the formation of two different initiating radicals (Figure A-10).

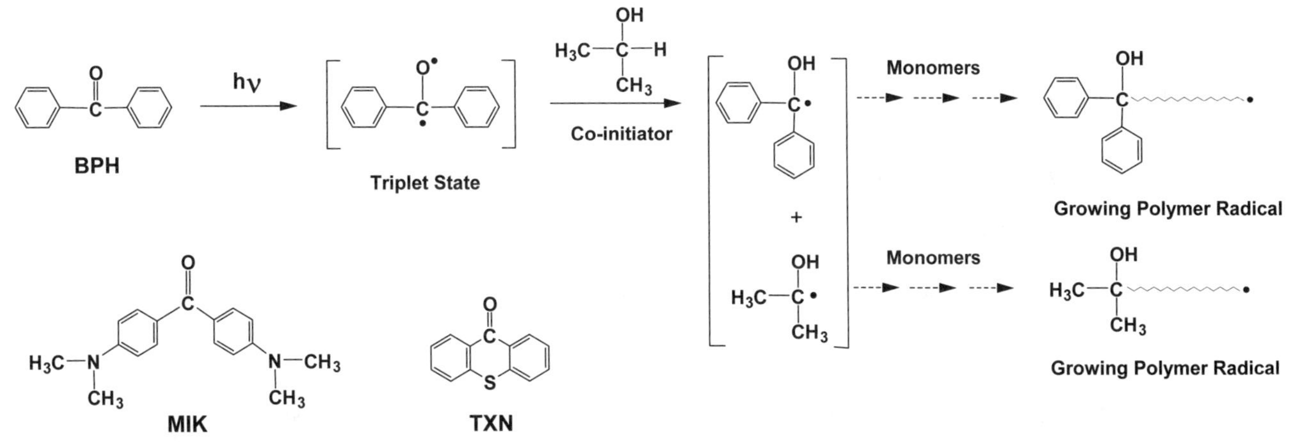

Figure A-10. Photoinitiation mechanism of BPH with alcohol or ether co-initiator.

When an amine H donor is used as a co-initiator, an electron transfer from an amine may precede the H transfer, as in triplet exciplex formation between benzophenone and amine (Figure A-11).

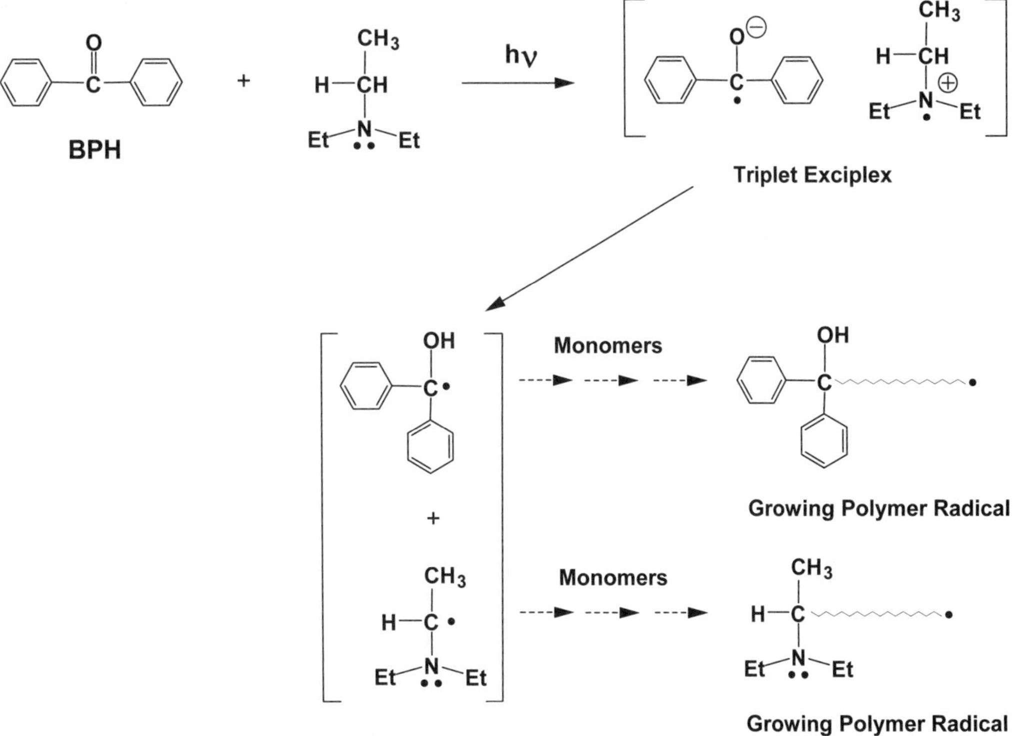

Figure A-11. Photoinitiation mechanism of BPH with amine co-initiator.

Appendix-V

Comparison of Important Physical and Mechanical Properties of Commercial Polymers[a]

Polymer	Density (g/cm^3)	Tensile Strength (MPa)	Tensile Modulus (Gpa)	Flexural Strength (Mpa)	Flexural Modulus (Gpa)	% Elongation	Izod Impact, Notched (J/cm)	HDT @1.8 Mpa (°C)
LDPE	0.92	18	0.28	15	0.7	800	1.1	45
LLDPE	0.94	25	0.47	17	0.7	600	4.8	48
HDPE	0.96	35	1.11	26	1.5	150	6.4	75
UHMWPE	0.94	57	2.2	43	2.4	350	No break	80
PP	0.90	43	2.4	40	1.5	400	0.7	92
PVC	1.40	47	2.5	72	2.6	100	4.3	84
PS	1.05	55	2.7	70	2.5	50	1.1	85
SBS TPE	1.02	35	1.8	49	0.5	700	1.2	67
PAN	1.06	57	2.8	73	2.4	10	4.5	82
PMMA	1.15	60	2.9	100	3.0	15	0.5	80
ABS	1.12	48	2.6	75	2.5	65	5.5	95
ABS + 30% Glass fiber	1.32	78	6.4	120	7.0	2	0.6	102
PPO	1.12	82	4.3	89	2.4	45	4.2	144
SAN	1.10	72	3.7	120	4.0	5	0.2	87
PMP	0.84	68	2.2	38	1.5	20	0.6	190
PMMI	1.21	87	4.3	85	3.3	5	3.9	140
PTFE	2.17	41	2.1	39	0.7	400	1.6	110
POM	1.38	62	2.8	85	2.5	75	5.7	115
POM + 30% Glass fiber	1.62	112	7.6	150	7.5	3	0.7	162
Nylon 6,6	1.14	78	2.9	91	2.6	250	7.8	154
PET	1.32	55	2.4	80	1.1	275	1.4	81
PC	1.20	66	2.1	97	2.7	125	5.5	115
PI	1.39	145	6.1	145	6.4	10	2.0	190
PI + 30% Glass fiber	1.55	172	10.5	255	11	2	0.8	205
PEEK	1.31	133	7.1	168	8.2	85	1.0	235
PPS	1.30	90	3.8	125	3.8	75	0.6	245
PSF	1.39	96	7.2	145	7.5	60	0.8	210
PAI	1.42	142	6.9	195	5.8	10	1.1	275
LCP	1.38	130	10.3	150	10.3	2.8	10.1	232

[a] See Appendix-I for abbreviation of polymers.

Appendix-VI

Electrical Properties of Commercial Polymers[a]

Polymer	Dielectric Constant	Dielectric Strength (kV/mm)	Electrical Resistivity (ohm-cm)
PTFE	2.1	62	1×10^{16} ohm-cm
FEP	2.1	50	1×10^{17} ohm-cm
PFA	2.1	57	1×10^{17} ohm-cm
PVDF	5.6	19	1×10^{15} ohm-cm
ETFE	2.4	64	1×10^{17} ohm-cm
LDPE	2.5	19	1×10^{16} ohm-cm
PP	2.2	83	1×10^{16} ohm-cm
PS	2.5	77	1×10^{16} ohm-cm
PMMA	3.6	38	1×10^{14} ohm-cm
PVC	3.3	18	1×10^{14} ohm-cm
Nylon 6,6	4.2	42	1×10^{14} ohm-cm
PC	3.0	22	1×10^{16} ohm-cm
ABS	3.1	24	1×10^{15} ohm-cm
ABS + 30% Glass filled	3.5	16	1×10^{15} ohm-cm

[a] See Appendix-I for abbreviation of polymers.

Appendix-VII

Physical and Optical Properties of Important Transparent Polymers[a]

Polymer	Trade Name	Density (g/cm^3)	Refractive Index	Visible Light Transmission[b] (%)	T_g (T_m) (°C)
PMMA	Plexiglas	1.15	1.49	92	105 (---)
COP	Zeonex	0.97	1.51	92	135 (---)
COC	Topas	1.02	1.53	92	90-170 (---)
PMMI	Pleximid	1.21	1.53	90	150-170 (---)
PC	Lexan	1.20	1.59	90	145 (---)
PS	Styron	1.05	1.59	90	100 (---)
PMP	TPX	0.84	1.46	90	35 (240)
Polyamide	Trogamid T	1.12	1.56	90	150 (---)
Polyamide	Trogamid CX	1.02	1.52	89	140 (250)
Cellulose acetate	Tenite	1.28	1.49	89	110 (---)
SAN	Tyril	1.10	1.56	87	105 (---)
PSF	Udel	1.39	1.63	84	190 (---)
ABS	Cycolac	1.12	1.52	79	105-115 (---)
PVC	Geon	1.40	1.50	76	85 (245)
Optical glass	---	---	1.52	99.5	---
Borosilicate (laboratory) glass	---	---	1.47	92	---

[a] See Appendix-I for abbreviation of polymers.

[b] Specimens 3mm thick; tested by ASTM D1003 procedures.

Appendix-VIII

Limiting Oxygen Indices of Selected Polymers[a]

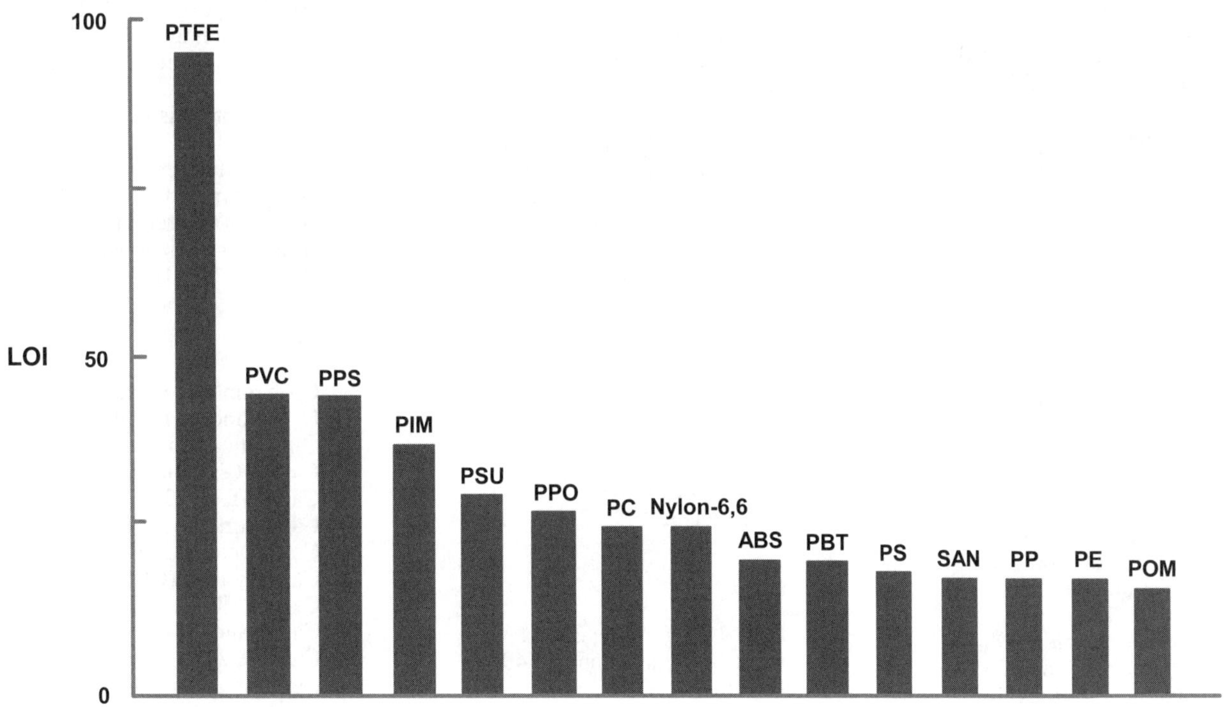

[a] See Appendix-I for abbreviation of polymers.

Index

A

B

C

D

E

F

G

H

I

K

L

M

N

O

P

Q

R

S

T

U

V

W

X

Y

Z